THE OXFORD ENCYCLOPEDIA OF
INDUSTRIAL, WORK, AND ORGANIZATIONAL PSYCHOLOGY

THE OXFORD ENCYCLOPEDIA OF
INDUSTRIAL, WORK, AND ORGANIZATIONAL PSYCHOLOGY

José M. Peiró

EDITOR IN CHIEF

VOLUME 2

OXFORD
UNIVERSITY PRESS

Oxford University Press is a department of the University of Oxford.
It furthers the University's objective of excellence in research, scholarship,
and education by publishing worldwide. Oxford is a registered trade mark of
Oxford University Press in the UK and in certain other countries.

Published in the United States of America by Oxford University Press
198 Madison Avenue, New York, NY 10016, United States of America.

© Oxford University Press 2024

All rights reserved. No part of this publication may be reproduced,
stored in a retrieval system, or transmitted, in any form or by any means,
without the prior permission in writing of Oxford University Press,
or as expressly permitted by law, by license or under terms agreed with
the appropriate reprographics rights organization. Inquiries concerning
reproduction outside the scope of the above should be sent to the
Rights Department, Oxford University Press, at the address above.

You must not circulate this work in any other form
and you must impose this same condition on any acquirer.

Library of Congress Cataloging-in-Publication Data
Names: Peiró, José M., editor.
Title: The Oxford Encyclopedia of Industrial, Work, and Organizational
Psychology / José M. Peiró, editor in chief.
Description: New York : Oxford University Press, 2024- |
Includes bibliographical references and index. | Contents: Vol 1—Vol 2
Identifiers: LCCN 2023037970 (print) | LCCN 2023037971 (ebook) |
ISBN 9780190641856 (set) | ISBN 9780190667689 (vol. 1 ; hardback) |
ISBN 9780190667832 (vol. 2 ; hardback) | ISBN 9780190866501 (ebk)
Subjects: LCSH: Work—Psychological aspects—Encyclopedias. |
Psychology, Industrial—Encyclopedias.
Classification: LCC BF481 .O943 2024 (print) | LCC BF481 (ebook) |
DDC 158.7—dc23/eng/20231218
LC record available at https://lccn.loc.gov/2023037970
LC ebook record available at https://lccn.loc.gov/2023037971

Sheridan Books, Inc., United States of America

About the
Oxford Research Encyclopedia of Psychology

The Oxford Encyclopedia of Industrial, Work, and Organizational Psychology is published as part of the *Oxford Research Encyclopedia of Psychology*, a dynamic and scholarly digital resource. This online collection of overview articles provides in-depth, foundational essays on both core and emerging topics in psychology. All articles are commissioned under the editorial leadership of international experts of the highest caliber and are vetted through rigorous peer review. A living reference work, the online publication is updatable and enriched with crosslinking and multimedia features. The essays are intended for scholars, practitioners, and university-level readers, including advanced undergraduates, graduate students, and researchers.

Oxford Research Encyclopedia of Psychology
Editor in Chief: Ingrid Johnsrude

Previously published in print from the *Oxford Research Encyclopedia of Psychology*:

The Oxford Encyclopedia of the History of Modern Psychology
Edited by Wade E. Pickren

The Oxford Encyclopedia of Sport, Exercise, and Performance Psychology
Edited by Edmund O. Acevedo

The Oxford Encyclopedia of Psychology and Aging
Edited by Bob G. Knight

Contents

List of Articles   ix

Preface (vol. 1)   xvii

THE OXFORD ENCYCLOPEDIA OF INDUSTRIAL, WORK, AND ORGANIZATIONAL PSYCHOLOGY

Directory of Contributors   1647

Index   1655

List of Articles

VOLUME 1

FOUNDATIONS AND HISTORY

1. History of Organizational Psychology   3
   HELIO CARPINTERO
2. Evidence-Based Decision-Making and Practice in Organizations   24
   ALESSANDRA CAPEZIO AND PATRICK L'ESPOIR DECOSTA
3. Ethics in Work and Organizational Psychology   49
   JOEL LEFKOWITZ

MAIN THEORIES AND APPROACHES

4. The Sociotechnical Approach to Work Organization   77
   DAVID E. GUEST
5. Action Regulation Theory   97
   HANNES ZACHER
6. Goal Setting Theory: Causal Relationships, Mediators, and Moderators   110
   GARY P. LATHAM

x • LIST OF ARTICLES

7. Self-Determination Theory and Its Relation to Organizations　121
ANJA H. OLAFSEN AND EDWARD L. DECI
8. Individual Differences in the Vitamin Model of Well-Being　140
PETER WARR
9. A Selective Review of Developments in Positive Studies of Work and Organizations　160
ARRAN CAZA
10. An Applied Approach to Psychology of Sustainability　172
ROBERT G. JONES
11. Humanitarian Work and Organizational Psychology　184
STUART C. CARR

RESEARCH METHODS

12. Mediator Variables　207
MATTHEW S. FRITZ AND HOUSTON F. LESTER
13. Moderator Variables　228
MATTHEW S. FRITZ AND ANN M. ARTHUR
14. Multilevel Modeling Methods　253
VICENTE GONZÁLEZ-ROMÁ AND ANA HERNÁNDEZ
15. Temporal Dynamics in Organizational Psychology　280
YANNICK GRIEP AND HANNES ZACHER
16. General Coding and Analysis in Qualitative Research　302
MICHAEL G. PRATT

THE ENVIRONMENT OF ORGANIZATIONS

17. Industrial and Organizational Psychology From a Global Perspective　329
MO WANG, CHENGQUAN HUANG, JUNHUI YANG, AND ZHEFAN HUANG
18. Cross-Cultural Issues in Industrial, Work, and Organizational Psychology　352
SHARON GLAZER AND CATHERINE KWANTES
19. The Group Dynamics of Interorganizational Collaboration　371
SANDRA SCHRUIJER

INDIVIDUALS IN ORGANIZATIONS

20. Judgment and Decision-Making Processes　391
RICHARD P. LARRICK AND M. ASHER LAWSON
21. Work Motivation　411
JAMES M. DIEFENDORFF, MEGAN E. KENWORTHY, FAITH C. LEE, AND
LINH K. NGUYEN
22. Employee Work Experiences, Feelings, and Morality　429
REMUS ILIES AND SHERRY AW
23. Emotions at Work　446
NEAL M. ASHKANASY AND AGATA BIALKOWSKI

LIST OF ARTICLES • xi

24. Person–Environment Fit From an Organizational Psychology Perspective   465
    TOMOKI SEKIGUCHI AND YUNYUE YANG
25. Political Skill at Work and in Careers   485
    IRIS KRANEFELD, GERHARD BLICKLE, AND JAMES A. MEURS
26. Dark Personalities in the Workplace   506
    BIRGIT SCHYNS, SUSANNE BRAUN, AND BARBARA WISSE

DIVERSITY IN ORGANIZATIONS

27. Diversity in the Workplace   529
    REGINE BENDL, ASTRID HAINZL, AND HEIKE MENSI-KLARBACH
28. Individual Differences at Work   550
    ADRIAN FURNHAM
29. Gender in Organizations   570
    KARYSSA COUREY, MAKAI RUFFIN, MIKKI HEBL, DILLON STEWART,
    MERIDITH TOWNSEND, LEILANI SEGED, JORDYN WILLIAMS,
    CEDRIC PATTERSON, SARA MEI, AND EDEN KING
30. Work and Organizational Issues Affecting Young Workers   594
    BELGIN OKAY-SOMERVILLE, EVA SELENKO, AND ROSALIND H. SEARLE
31. Aging Workforce Issues From a Multilevel Approach   613
    LALE M. YALDIZ, FRANCO FRACCAROLI, AND DONALD M. TRUXILLO
32. Ageism in the Workplace   633
    DAVID M. CADIZ, AMY C. PYTLOVANY, AND DONALD M. TRUXILLO
33. Sexual Orientation (LGBTQ+) Issues in Industrial and Organizational Psychology   648
    JENNICA WEBSTER AND RAYMOND TRAU
34. Disabilities at Work   667
    FRED ZIJLSTRA AND HENNY MULDERS

JOBS AND WORK SYSTEMS

35. Job and Work Design   683
    ANJA VAN DEN BROECK AND SHARON K. PARKER
36. Job Crafting   708
    FANGFANG ZHANG, SABREEN KAUR, AND SHARON K. PARKER
37. Human–Computer Interaction   728
    AMON RAPP
38. Telework and Remote Work   753
    MATTI VARTIAINEN
39. Informal Work   779
    MAHIMA SAXENA

INTERPERSONAL RELATIONSHIPS, GROUPS, AND TEAMS

40. Impression Management   797
    DAVID M. LONG

xii • LIST OF ARTICLES

41. Social Comparison in Organizations   813
ABRAHAM P. BUUNK

42. Team Dynamics and Processes in the Workplace   830
TIFFANY M. BISBEY AND EDUARDO SALAS

43. Virtual Teams and Digital Collaboration   860
CONNY H. ANTONI

44. Justice in Teams   879
VINCENTE MARTÍNEZ-TUR AND CAROLINA MOLINER

VOLUME 2

LEADERSHIP IN ORGANIZATIONS

45. Positive Leadership in Organizations   901
LUCAS MONZANI AND ROLF VAN DICK

46. The Psychology of Abusive Supervision   920
KATRINA A. GRAHAM, GAHYUN YOO, AND EMMA K. KRISTAL

47. Ethical Leadership   937
SUZANNE VAN GILS AND NIELS VAN QUAQUEBEKE

ORGANIZATIONAL PROCESSES

48. Organizational Behavior   955
NEAL M. ASHKANASY AND ALANA D. DORRIS

49. Communication in Organizations   977
RYAN S. BISEL AND KATHERINE ANN RUSH

50. Organizational Sensemaking   992
RAVI S. KUDESIA

51. Conflict Management   1025
PATRICIA ELGOIBAR, MARTIN EUWEMA, AND LOURDES MUNDUATE

52. Organizational Climate and Culture   1044
MARK G. EHRHART AND BENJAMIN SCHNEIDER

53. Organizational Justice   1063
DIRK D. STEINER

54. Corporate Social Responsibility: An Overview From an Organizational and
Psychological Perspective   1078
ANTE GLAVAS AND MISLAV RADIC

HUMAN RESOURCES PSYCHOLOGY

55. Human Resource Management and Organizational Psychology   1105
DAVID E. GUEST

56. Psychological Contracts and the Employment Relationship   1125
KERSTIN ISAKSSON

LIST OF ARTICLES • xiii

57. Personnel Selection   1140
JESÚS F. SALGADO

58. Job Insecurity   1160
NELE DE CUYPER AND HANS DE WITTE

59. Training From an Organizational Psychology Perspective   1177
KURT KRAIGER

60. Overqualification in the Workplace   1195
BERRIN ERDOGAN, TALYA N. BAUER, AND AYSEGUL KARAEMINOGULLARI

61. Careers and Career Development   1218
JOS AKKERMANS, DANIEL SPURK, AND NADYA FOUAD

62. Retirement   1251
MO WANG AND VALERIA ALTERMAN

ORGANIZATIONAL OUTPUTS AND OUTCOMES

63. Work Performance Management and Assessment   1273
ROSE MUELLER-HANSON

64. The Psychology of Work Engagement   1292
MICHAEL P. LEITER

65. Creativity at Work   1305
KRISTINA POTOČNIK AND NEIL ANDERSON

66. Counterproductive Work Behaviors   1319
ROSALIND H. SEARLE

OCCUPATIONAL HEALTH PSYCHOLOGY

67. Occupational Health Psychology   1339
SHARON CLARKE

68. Work and Family   1368
MACKENNA L. PERRY AND LESLIE B. HAMMER

69. Work, Stress, Coping, and Stress Management   1394
SHARON GLAZER AND CONG LIU

70. Bullying and Harassment in the Workplace   1426
STALE EINARSEN AND KARI WIK ÅGOTNES

71. Burnout in Organizations   1447
MICHAEL P. LEITER AND JO WINTLE

72. Organizational Dehumanization   1459
NOÉMIE BRISON, FLORENCE STINGLHAMBER, AND GAËTANE CAESENS

73. Safety at Work   1480
GUDELA GROTE

74. Quality of Working Life   1498
DAVID E. GUEST

75. Well-Being at Work   1515
MAŁGORZATA W. KOŻUSZNIK, AIDA SORIANO, AND JOSÉ M. PEIRÓ

ORGANIZATIONAL CHANGE

76. Organization Change 1553
GEORGE P. HUBER AND JEAN M. BARTUNEK
77. Generative Emergence: Research and Praxis for Social Innovation 1572
BENYAMIN LICHTENSTEIN
78. Organizational Interventions 1595
KARINA NIELSEN
79. Organization Development 1614
W. WARNER BURKE

Leadership in Organizations

POSITIVE LEADERSHIP IN ORGANIZATIONS

INTRODUCTION: WHAT IS POSITIVE LEADERSHIP?

The 21st century inaugurated a new way of understanding leadership (Dinh et al., 2014; Luthans & Avolio, 2003; Monzani, Ripoll, & Peiro, 2012). More precisely, the academic narrative on leadership moved beyond a purely dramaturgical view of leadership, where leaders are seen as charismatic heroes and followers as passive recipients of influence (Gardner & Avolio, 1998). As a result of such a narrative shift, myriad new leadership theories emerged.

Further, after such shift, the term *leadership* is frequently used to label an interactive process of reciprocal influence where social actors (leaders, followers, and other stakeholders) interact with each other and their context (Avolio & Gardner, 2005; Hannah, Balthazard, Waldman, Jennings, & Thatcher, 2013; Haslam, Reicher, & Platow, 2020; Hernandez, Eberly, Avolio, & Johnson, 2011; Meuser et al., 2016). Academia's shift away from leader-centric theories, models, and frameworks was partially driven by the general public's disappointment with how highly charismatic (yet also highly self-serving and narcissistic) leaders took part in and facilitated a series of scandals during the first decade of the 21st century. Such scandals peaked during the Wall Street Crash of 2008 and the devastating Great Recession that followed (Barling, Christie, & Turner, 2008; Gandz, Crossan, Seijts, & Stephenson, 2010; Price, 2003).

In this article, the adjective "positive" derives from the insights that positive psychology brought to the field of organizational behavior (Luthans & Youssef, 2007; Seligman & Csikszentmihalyi, 2014). Positive psychology is a domain of psychology that is theoretically anchored on classical Western and Eastern philosophical systems, and its primary aim is helping individuals to self-actualize, grow, and flourish (Snyder & Lopez, 2002). After more than 10 years since its inception, positive organizational scholarship is an established field of academic inquiry, and positive leadership is one of its major domains of interest (Luthans & Avolio, 2009).

One common characteristic of these new positive leadership theories, models, and frameworks is that most share a moral component grounded in one or more classical virtue ethics systems (Lemoine, Hartnell, & Leroy, 2019). Some examples include authentic leadership (Gardner, Avolio, Luthans, May, & Walumbwa, 2005), ethical leadership (Brown, Treviño, & Harrison, 2005), and servant leadership (Greenleaf, 1977; Liden, Wayne, Zhao, & Henderson, 2008). "Positive leadership" is extended to those leadership theories, models, and frameworks that aim to elevate followers, groups, and other organizational stakeholders and foster organizational excellence, veritable organizational performance, and sustainable processes and practices (Hernandez et al., 2011).

Positive leadership should matter for organizational stakeholders. For example, a line manager can increase the quality and quantity of solutions that engineers create by building and broadening psychological capital, meaning personal resources such as hope, optimism, resilience, and efficacy (Avey, Avolio, & Luthans, 2011). Similarly, project managers can elevate their team's functioning by clarifying the group's goals and processes (Hu & Liden, 2011), promoting a shared identity and "sense of us" (Steffens et al., 2014), and creating collective affective states (positive work climate; Woolley, Caza, & Levy, 2010). Similarly, at the upper echelons of a firm, positive leaders can use their authority to drive financial performance in a socially responsible way (De Hoogh & Den Hartog, 2008; Skubinn, Buengeler, & Schank, 2019). These are just some illustrations of the myriad outcomes that positive leadership has for followers, teams, organizations, and even society.

In order to understand positive leadership in organizations, an integrative effort is necessary (Meuser et al., 2016). Further, in order to provide a meaningful contribution to the leadership field so that it moves beyond the study of interpersonal influence, such integration should be horizontal (i.e., providing enough breath and coverage regarding research in positive leadership models) as well as vertical, meaning that it captures mechanisms that span across multiple levels of analysis (Yammarino, Dionne, Chun, & Dansereau, 2005). Thus, an integrative multilevel approach to theorizing on positive leadership in organizations would provide scholars with an account of how positive leaders extend their influence beyond a close collaborator (e.g., a follower), but also beyond teams and the organization. More importantly, it should capture those social forces and influences that facilitate or hinder leader(ship) emergence and development.

The article is structured as follows. First, instead of trying to cover the existing research on every positive leadership style (Zhao & Li, 2019), we abstract three core assumptions that generalize across positive leadership models. Then, we follow a suggestion by Hernandez et al. (2011) to explore the different sources (loci), transmission mechanisms, and recipients of positive leadership at multiple levels of analysis (see Figure 1; Skubinn et al., 2019; Yammarino et al., 2005). Finally, we discuss critiques to positive leadership, attempting to answer their concerns, and its implication for research and practice.

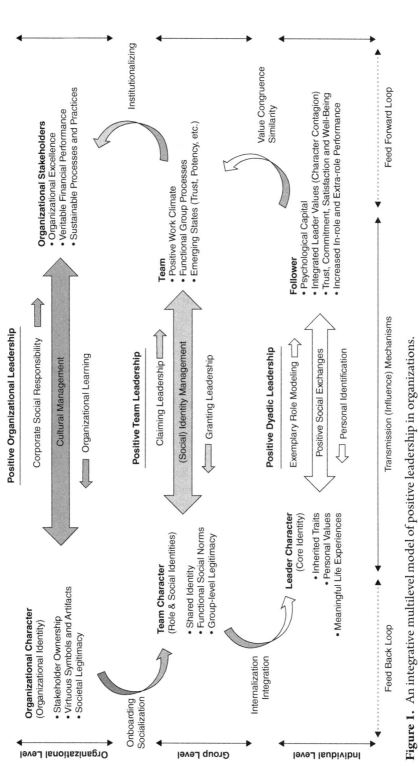

Figure 1. An integrative multilevel model of positive leadership in organizations.

Figure 1 can be interpreted as follows. First, the vertical axis captures levels of analysis (individual, group, and organization), whereas the horizontal axis captures the relations between leaders and different organizational actors. Second, reciprocal same-level effects are illustrated at the center of Figure 1, capturing the influence mechanisms between leaders and different organizational actors. Finally, cross-level mechanisms (either top-down or bottom-up) are illustrated following logic of "feed-forward" and "feed-back" loops according to Crossan, Lane, and White (1999). More precisely, the mechanisms by which leaders extend their influence into different organizational actors are operationalized as feed-forward loops (value congruence, similarity, institutionalizing) and the mechanisms by which the social context influences leaders (onboarding and socialization, integration, and internalization) are captured as feed-back loops.

CORE ASSUMPTIONS ACROSS POSITIVE LEADERSHIP THEORIES, MODELS, AND FRAMEWORKS

Three core assumptions seem to generalize across positive leadership theories, models, and frameworks. The first core assumption is that individuals internalize and organize their life experiences into a structure of the mind, which is called "The Self" by cognitive and humanistic psychologists (Ryan & Deci, 2002). The Self is "a knowledge structure that helps people organize and give meaning to memory and behavior" (van Knippenberg, van Knippenberg, De Cremer, & Hogg, 2004, p. 827). Thus, self-oriented cognitive processes and adaptive behavioral scripts (e.g., self-awareness and self-regulation, respectively) are core elements of mainstream positive leadership theories, such as authentic and servant leadership (Gardner et al., 2005; van Dierendonck, 2010).

The second overarching assumption is that humans are gregarious by nature. People seek to flourish and thrive by collaborating with others, rather than by exploiting others' weaknesses. This *homo socialis* perspective is at odds with the *homo economicus* view, which is a core assumption in behavioral economics that understands humans as mere "rational maximizers of individual profit" (Gintis & Helbing, 2015; Gluth & Fontanesi, 2016). The gregariousness assumption is a fundamental theoretical for relational approaches to positive leadership, such as the Social Identity Model of Leadership, (Hogg, 2001a) and Identity Leadership (Steffens et al., 2014; van Dick et al., 2018).

Similarly, a third overarching assumption refers to the nature of organizations. Most positive leadership theories understand organizations as something more than "shareholder profit-maximizing" entities (van Dierendonck, 2010). In other words, employees tend to expect more than a paycheck in exchange for their sustained commitment. Positive leadership styles such as transformational (Bass, 1985), responsible (Van Quaquebeke & Eckloff, 2010; Waldman & Siegel, 2008), and meaningful leadership (van Knippenberg, 2020) explicitly depict organizations as entities with purpose, such as being a valuable actor of the societies in which they operate.

LOCI, MECHANISMS, AND RECIPIENTS OF POSITIVE SELF-LEADERSHIP

The sources (loci) of positive self-leadership can be internal or external. The primary recipient of positive self-leadership is the leader. Self-awareness is the transmission mechanism for the internal sources of self-leadership, whereas internalization and integration are the two transmission mechanisms for external sources of positive self-leadership. Internalization refers to the process of transforming external regulations into internal regulations, whereas integration refers to the process of incorporating such regulations into one's sense of self (Deci, Eghrari, Patrick, & Leone, 1994).

The internal sources of positive self-leadership are genetically inherited traits (De Neve, Mikhaylov, Christakis, & Fowler, 2013; Zaccaro, 2007). Several meta-analyses show that intelligence (Antonakis, House, & Simonton, 2017; Lord, de Vader, & Alliger, 1986) and stable personality traits are predictors of transformational leadership (Bono & Judge, 2004; Judge, Piccolo, & Kosalka, 2009). Thus, by engaging in self-aware introspection, individuals can discover their dormant character strengths and start exercising them (Crossan et al., 2017). In turn, self-awareness enables individuals to voluntarily self-determine their behavior (Kernis, 2003; Kernis & Goldman, 2006). As stated in Henley's poem, positive self-leadership starts by becoming "the captain of one's soul" (i.e., displaying self-determined behaviors).

Being part of a group with functional social norms and experiencing meaningful life experiences (crucible moments; Byrne, Crossan, & Seijts, 2018) are the external sources of positive self-leadership. According to Self-Determination Theory (SDT), as individuals grow, they internalize any external behavioral regulation that contributes to fulfill three psychological needs. Further, such regulations are integrated into their selves by abstracting their context and recasting them as personal values (Hitlin, 2003). For example, the norms of the social context in which an individual operates might prescribe compassionately helping a stranger in need. Thus, if every time the opportunity of being compassionate appears said individual follows the social norm, such behavioral regulation will eventually be abstracted and integrated into the self as the character element of "compassion" and stored under the category of "humanity" (Crossan et al., 2017). Once integrated into the self, character elements such as "compassion" and dimensions such as "humanity" become the standards by which said individual will examine his or her behaviors, and consequently use such information to self-regulate his or her behavior (Ryan & Deci, 2002). The more self-aware individuals are about their character strengths, core values, and integrated regulations, the more their behavior will be self-determined (as opposed to being externally determined by someone else or a social structure).

Regarding the outcomes of positive self-leadership, SDT claims that self-determination is a source of both hedonic and eudaemonic happiness in general (Ryan & Deci, 2001). For those engaging in self-leadership when in a leadership role, constructive and self-determined behaviors predict eudemonic outcomes, such as subjective and physical well-being (Kaluza, Boer, Buengeler, & van Dick, 2020).

LOCI, MECHANISMS, AND RECIPIENTS OF POSITIVE DYADIC LEADERSHIP

As in any other dyadic relation, leaders and followers are simultaneously sources and recipients of positive dyadic leadership. However, its transmission mechanisms might vary depending on the level of analysis and temporal moment of the dyadic exchange. More precisely, at the dyadic level, the primary transmission mechanism is a positive social exchange between leader and follower (Ilies, Morgeson, & Nahrgang, 2005). Positive social exchanges refer to the high-quality exchanges explained by Leader-Member Exchange Theory (LMX; Graen & Uhl-Bien, 1995).

Leaders' exemplary role modeling and followers' identification are the two major transmission mechanisms of positive dyadic leadership. Exemplary role modeling is a mechanism by which leaders influence followers to achieve higher levels of self-determined behavior at earlier stages of the positive social exchange.[1] More precisely, by becoming behavioral exemplars, leaders invite followers to examine introspectively their character, their core values, and existing behavioral regulations (character contagion).

Followers can also be the source of positive dyadic leadership, by displaying behaviors such as "taking charge of work" (Xu, Loi, Cai, & Liden, 2019). "Taking charge of work" captures behaviors such as delivering work on time and proactively improving procedures. By displaying such behaviors, followers signal leaders that they are trustworthy, loyal, and professional. Thus, followers can use exemplary role modeling to elicit self-determined behaviors in their leaders.

As the positive social exchange matures, followers will likely start seeing their leaders as identification targets (and vice versa), triggering a personal identification process. Personal identification refers to "a process by which individuals realize cognitive overlap between the self and others over time in a relationship" (Humberd & Rouse, 2016, p. 427). Given that role modeling is accepted as a marker of identification (Gibson, 2004), leaders who act as exemplary models will elicit followers' personal identification, kick-starting in turn the internalization and integration processes by which individuals incorporate the positive characteristics, values, and behaviors of their relevant others at work (Avolio, Gardner, Walumbwa, Luthans, & May, 2004). Such identification, in turn, will validate leaders and signal that they attained legitimacy as exemplars in their followers' eyes.

Extant research shows that displaying leader self-determined behaviors like the behaviors prescribed by authentic (Walumbwa, Avolio, Gardner, Wernsing, & Peterson, 2008), transformational (Bass & Avolio, 1994), ethical (Brown et al., 2005), servant (Liden et al., 2008), and identity leadership (Steffens et al., 2014) predict LMX quality, at least when measured by followers' reports (Banks, McCauley, Gardner, & Guler, 2016; Eva, Robin, Sendjaya, van Dierendonck, & Liden, 2019; Hoch, Bommer, Dulebohn, & Wu, 2018; van Dick et al., 2018). In turn, LMX quality, as a type of positive social exchange, has been extensively reported as a predictor of follower outcomes, such as increased in-role and extra-role performance, constructive attitudes and psychological states (commitment, justice, psychological capital), reduced role conflict, turnover, and so forth (Dulebohn, Bommer, Liden, Brouer, & Ferris, 2012; Gerstner & Day, 1997; Ilies, Nahrgang, & Morgeson, 2007; Martin, Guillaume, Thomas, Lee, & Epitropaki, 2016; Rockstuhl, Dulebohn, Ang, & Shore, 2012; Schriesheim, Castro, & Cogliser, 1999). Indeed, Gottfredson and Aguinis (2017) in their "meta–meta"-analysis of 35 meta-analyses with more than 3,000 studies and one million participants confirms that LMX is the key mediator that translates all leadership behaviors (consideration, initiating structure, transformational) into performance and Organizational Citizenship Behaviors (OCB).

Finally, positive dyadic leadership has been linked to several followers' well-being criteria (hedonic, eudaemonic, and even physical well-being; for a comprehensive review, see Inceoglu, Thomas, Chu, Plans, & Gerbasi, 2018). For example, positive dyadic leadership elicits hedonic outcomes (e.g., job satisfaction and satisfaction with the leader) as well as eudaemonic outcomes, such as increased feelings of self-determination and self-esteem through the fulfillment of psychological needs (Ilies et al., 2005; Leroy, Anseel, Gardner, & Sels, 2015). Further, there is accumulating evidence on how positive leadership styles such as authentic (Banks et al., 2016), transformational (Hobman, Jackson, Jimmieson, & Martin, 2011), and identity leadership reduce followers' emotional exhaustion and burnout, either directly (Banks et al., 2016; van Dick et al., 2018) or through a decrease in frequency of deviant behaviors in their followers (e.g., workplace bullying; Escartín, Monzani, Leong, & Rodríguez-Carballeira, 2017).

LOCI, MECHANISMS, AND RECIPIENTS OF POSITIVE TEAM LEADERSHIP

The two sources (locus) of positive team leadership are a social group (team) and any person who provides direction to said social group (i.e., the team's leader(s)). The main recipient of positive team leadership is the workgroup. Our review identified two transmission mechanisms, as captured by the leader identity model and the (social) identity management model (DeRue & Ashford, 2010), with two (assuming and granting) and four subprocesses (identity prototypicality, entrepreneurship, advancement, impresarioship), respectively.

Positive dyadic leadership shapes positive team leadership because individuals tend to gravitate toward and "band with" other individuals who share similar characteristics and congruent values (McPherson, Smith-Lovin, & Cook, 2001). Thus, if a team leader has been adequately socialized into a virtuous organizational culture, that team leader can shape the collective character of the team for which they provide leadership. Alternatively, if the values comprised in their organization's culture are not virtuous, positive team leaders could draw from their personal values to shape the collective character of the team they lead. Yet, how can a group determine who will lead and who will follow when there is not a clear candidate leading the team?

The leader identity model of DeRue and Ashford (2010) provides a parsimonious explanation of how a group of individuals construct their leader and follower identities, respectively. These authors claim that leader and follower identities emerge from a two-phase, social construction process, consisting of the "claiming" and "granting" of leadership. This model aims to explain why some leaders might lack legitimacy, even when occupying a leadership position within a firm's hierarchy. In the first stage of the claiming-granting process, aspirational leaders claim the leadership of a social group. Then, the group decides whether to grant or decline leadership to said leader. Alternatively, a social group can grant their followership to a given individual, even if he or she didn't make a claim for informal leadership, and it is said individual who decides if he or she "will lead" or not. As the main outcome of this process, the role identities of the group members are actualized, validating leaders and followers' identities by the group. In turn, leaders gain group-level legitimacy. Yet, this model still does not explain how leaders can leverage the group's shared identity to elevate a group of individuals into an effective workgroup or team. Fortunately, recent advances in social identity approaches to leadership can cover such a conceptual gap in the model of DeRue and Ashford (2010).

The second transmission mechanism of positive team leadership can be best explained with a recent extension to the Social Identity Model of Leadership (Haslam et al., 2020; Steffens et al., 2014). The first subprocess of such identity leadership has been termed "prototypicality," and it refers to embodying the norms, beliefs, and behaviors of the workgroup ("being one of us"). In this regard, research based on the social identity model of leadership, which focuses on leader prototypicality, found that those who embody the characteristics of the shared mental representation of the social group are more likely to emerge as leaders (Hogg, 2001b; van Knippenberg & Hogg, 2003) and also are more effective (Barreto & Hogg, 2017). Such findings align with the claiming-granting process proposed by DeRue and Ashford (2010).

Identity leadership behaviors are a positive form of leadership because they elevate the functioning of a group of individuals by creating a collective awareness of their shared similarities, collective interests, and strengths as relative to the strengths of other groups. Despite the importance of leader prototypicality to elevate a group's functioning, leaders need to not only represent the groups they want to lead but also actively shape and manage the identities of those groups (van Dick et al., 2018). In short, Haslam et al. (2020) proposed three additional identity leadership dimensions. First, identity entrepreneurship captures those identity leadership behaviors aimed at shaping or actualizing the shared identity of the team ("crafting a sense of us"). Second, identity advancement refers to taking action to facilitate the attainment of group goals ("doing it for us"). Third, identity impresarioship refers to behaviors aimed at enhancing the standing of the group in front of other groups ("making us matter"), such as developing structures, events, and activities that give weight to the group existence and embed a shared understanding, coordination, and so forth (e.g., group processes and emerging states).

While research on identity leadership is still in its infancy, early findings suggest that identity leadership dimensions are associated with team members' self-esteem, perceived team support, and work engagement, with significant standardized coefficients ranging from $\beta = .27$ to $\beta = .53$. A study revealed that identity leadership also relates to outcomes that facilitate team functioning, such as team identification (van Dick et al., 2018). While there are yet little or no multilevel studies on identity leadership, based on prior findings, it seems plausible that identity leadership will predict a team's emerging states (e.g., positive work climate) and other outcomes that contribute to their overall team effectiveness (group potency, cohesion, etc.).

LOCI, MECHANISMS, AND RECIPIENTS OF POSITIVE ORGANIZATIONAL LEADERSHIP

Positive organizational leadership captures the effort of positive leaders to manage their organization's culture so that it remains anchored on virtuous, universal values (as opposed to toxic or non-virtuous values). Thus, the primary recipient of positive organizational leadership is an organization's culture, and its main outcomes concern organizational stakeholders and society at large. The two main transmission mechanisms of positive organizational leadership are organizational learning (Crossan et al., 1999) and corporate social responsibility (Aguinis, 2011). Whereas organizational learning is inward-looking (directed at organizational members), corporate social responsibility is outward-looking (directed at society).

An organization's culture might be virtuous or not, depending on what values and behaviors are promoted by leaders at the upper echelons of a firm and rewarded by the organization. One of the most well-accepted definitions of organizational culture is a pattern of basic assumptions that a given group has invented, discovered, or developed in learning to cope with its problems of external adaptation and internal integration, and which is that have worked well enough to be considered valid, and, therefore, to be taught to new members as the correct way to perceive, think and feel in relation to those problems. (Schein, 1984, p. 3)

Schein's definition of culture implies the notion of institutionalization as a cross-level process by which workgroups generalize and abstract their experiential insights and learnings. Once abstracted to the general principle level, such knowledge can be communicated to other members and applied into different situations (Crossan et al., 1999). Thus, in the same way that the Self is a repository of knowledge that hosts an individual's character, an organization's culture is the organizational-level repository that captures a firm's collective character.

Organizational character matters beyond its impact on organizational financial performance (Di Milia & Birdi, 2010; García-Morales, Jiménez-Barrionuevo, & Gutiérrez-Gutiérrez, 2012). The values and social norms incorporated into an organization's culture will trickle down into social norms by socialization processes such as newcomer onboarding (Bauer & Erdogan, 2011), and eventually internalize and integrate into organizational members' selves. Thus, ensuring that organization's culture is also anchored on virtuous universal values should be a priority for positive leaders. Surprisingly, despite the importance of organizational culture, there is little systematic research exploring how positive leaders contribute to shaping a virtuous culture (some noteworthy exceptions are Liden, Wayne, Liao, & Meuser, 2014; Sarros, Cooper, & Santora, 2008; Toor & Ofori, 2009; Wu, Kwan, Yim, Chiu, & He, 2015; Xenikou & Simosi, 2006).

Corporate social responsibility is a mechanism by which organizations can positively influence the broader context in which they operate. Corporate social responsibility can be conceptualized as "context-specific organizational actions and policies that take into account stakeholders' expectations and the triple bottom line of economic, social, and environmental performance" (Aguinis, 2011, p. 855; Wu et al., 2015).

In the same way that positive social exchanges enhance both leaders and followers, corporate social responsibility provides not only the social context but also societal legitimacy for the organization, but it also has been strongly related to veritable financial outcomes (Busch & Friede, 2018; Orlitzky, Schmidt, & Rynes, 2003) and sustainable business practices (Orlitzky, Siegel, & Waldman, 2011). Positive leadership behaviors such as those prescribed by ethical leadership and transformational leadership have been shown to predict corporate social responsibility initiatives, and in some studies, the existence of a constructive culture grounded on universal values mediated such relationship (Groves & LaRocca, 2011; Wu et al., 2015).

GLOBAL POSITIVE LEADERSHIP: LEADERSHIP PRINCIPLES ACROSS CULTURES

A major criticism to extant leadership research is that its mainstream theories are U.S.-centric (Hofstede, 1980). Thus, the behavioral prescriptions that apply to U.S. leaders might not necessarily apply to leaders in those societies who uphold substantially diverse cultural values.

POSITIVE LEADERSHIP IN ORGANIZATIONS

Such misfit is even greater for those regional alliances among emerging countries with diverse cultural values, such as the BRIC states (Brazil, Russia, India, and China; Kingah & Quiliconi, 2016). Prescribing a specific set of leader behaviors might then not be the best approach to foster global positive leadership, as what is acceptable in some cultures might not be acceptable in others. Thus, how would a positive leadership model then generalize to non-Western cultures?

Interestingly, cross-cultural psychological research found a common ground to theorize about positive global leadership. Despite the regional variations in cultural norms, certain values and principles seem to be universally endorsed (Peterson & Seligman, 2004; Schwartz, 1992). For example, there is a substantive overlap between the six cardinal virtues prescribed in Aristotelian and Confucian virtue ethics: mainly Courage, Temperance, Justice, Humanity, Integrity (understood as Truthfulness), and Prudence (understood as Practical Wisdom or Judgment) (see Crossan et al., 2017; Hackett & Wang, 2012). Similarly, the virtues of Humanity and Transcendence appear as underlying the cultural dimensions identified by the GLOBE study (Humane and Future orientation, respectively; House, Javidan, & Dorfman, 2001). We claim that these virtues are foundational for studies on positive global leadership.

Moving on to more specific positive leadership behaviors, another early finding of the GLOBE project was that the attributes describing transformational leadership tend to be culturally endorsed as indicators of outstanding leadership (Den Hartog et al., 1999). To a lesser extent, something similar occurred for both authentic and servant leadership behaviors (van Dierendonck et al., 2014; Walumbwa et al., 2008). Finally, a cross-cultural study involving more than 20 countries revealed that identity leadership generalizes across major cultural clusters and explains variance above and beyond other positive leadership styles (authentic, transformational, and LMX) on constructive follower outcomes at the individual level (trust, satisfaction, innovation).

Virtuous universal values are a critical component of the present model, as said universal values are the cultural source of constructive leadership principles, and thus, the hallmark of a virtuous organizational culture. The present model claims that through the cross-level mechanism of socialization, those behaviors rewarded and reinforced by a virtuous culture will eventually trickle down to social groups with the organization (e.g., teams). Further, virtuous social norms will be eventually integrated and internalized to their leader's self. The present model also acknowledges that both positive leaders and their followers are not mere passive recipients of contextual influence. Both leader and followers have individual and collective agency (and the moral duty) to resist the influence of either a toxic organizational culture or a national culture that rewards norms and behaviors that do not align with said universal values.

CRITIQUES TO POSITIVE LEADERSHIP

Despite the growing evidence suggesting that positive leadership matters for organizations and their stakeholders, this domain of positive organizational behavior is not without its detractors. There are three main criticisms. The first criticism is aimed at leadership research in general, and has been termed the "I like my leader" effect (Yammarino, Cheong, Kim, & Tsai, 2020), which seems a variation of the "romance of leadership" effect (Meindl, Ehrlich, &

Dukerich, 1985). The second criticism is the "old wine in new bottles" argument (Banks, Gooty, Ross, Williams, & Harrington, 2018; Banks et al., 2016). Finally, the third and hardest criticism depicts positive leadership as "naïve" and irrelevant for the study of organizational management.

The "I like my leader" effect refers to the notion that at the end of the day, what (positive) leaders do doesn't directly matter if their collaborators like them, "liking" being a general leadership factor, analog to how general cognitive ability is taken as a general factor underlying the different aspects of human intelligence (Yammarino et al., 2020). This idea is not new, given that nearly 40 years ago, Meindl et al. (1985) showed empirical evidence that the followers of charismatic leaders tend to distort their objective assessments and attributions of "what leaders do, what they are able to accomplish, and the general effects they have on our lives" (p. 76). Such distortions might explain why certain followers are willing to endorse leaders who are incompetent, narcissistic, and highly populist, even after being presented with undeniable evidence of their unethical behavior within a formal leadership role (Monzani, 2018).

The "I like my leader" effect also appears in other non-charismatic positive forms of leadership. For example, a recent study exploring the leader character of populist leaders of three Anglo-Saxon countries (e.g., Trump, Johnson, and Trudeau) reported that those voters who have a strong populist attitude tend to agree less with the idea that strength of character is essential to the role of a prime minister or president (Seijts & de Clercy, 2020). Not surprisingly, this effect was more substantial for Trump voters. Similarly, research on identity leadership revealed that followers are willing to omit breaches in procedural justice and the failure to attain goals of those leaders who are seen as representative of the groups they lead (Giessner & van Knippenberg, 2008; Ullrich & van Dick, 2009). While the "I like my boss" effect might be a real issue in the study of leadership, Yammarino et al. (2005; Yammarino et al., 2020) recommend that to prevent such a "halo effect," the study of (positive) leadership should abandon the still prevailing leader-centric focus and adopt a multilevel perspective. The model introduced in this article attempts to heed such call while still acknowledging that in the same way that positive leaders can influence followers, groups, and the organization, such social groups and structures can influence the positive leaders as well.

The second critique of the study of positive leadership regards its originality. More precisely, many critics claim that there are empirical and theoretical overlaps (Banks et al., 2018) across the different positive leadership models and their psychometric measures (e.g., the measures for the full range theory and the measures for authentic leadership), suggesting conceptual redundancy (Banks et al., 2016; Cooper et al., 2005; Hoch et al., 2018). Similarly, a network analysis of more than 66 leadership theories revealed that certain leadership models theoretically tend to "band together," forming "conceptual clusters" (Meuser et al., 2016); or in other words, there is a conceptual redundancy that spans across the myriad mainstream leadership styles, not just positive leadership.

To address such "old wine in new bottles" critique, we echo scholars' suggestion that leadership research should move toward a more holistic and integrative theorizing (Avolio, 2007) and use diverse measurement efforts (Palanski et al., 2019). Our review revealed that some leadership frameworks are moving toward such integration. For example, the work by Crossan et al. (2017) acknowledges that to be effective, leaders need to develop 11 dimensions of character and use them as guiding principles of leaders' behavior and decision-making processes. Similarly, the leader character-competence entanglement model (Sturm, Vera, & Crossan, 2017) acknowledges that neither leader character nor leader competencies alone are enough to ensure sustained leader effectiveness. However, as its name suggests, the leader character model (Crossan et al., 2017) is still highly leader-centric and could benefit from an extension to the group and organizational levels. This article attempts such extension by proposing group-level and organizational-level manifestations of character as well as suggesting cross-level processes that facilitate its emergence within social collectives that occur in contemporary organizations.

Finally, a more recent critique is that positive leadership is inherently "naïve." For example, Alvesson and Einola (2019) depict a positive leader as a "Disneyland-inspired good leader" (p. 383) that is "unhelpful in organizational practice" (p. 384). Not surprisingly, Alvesson and Einola (2019) recommend abandoning the study of positive leadership in favor of the struggle of ideals, focusing on followers and leaders' relations and the study of the self. Further, these authors call for investigations about cultures, social practices, and societal changes (p. 394). The perspective of this article regarding the critique by Alvesson and Einola (2019) is that while such criticism might be inspiring new research indeed, these and other critics of positive leadership still fail to provide a compelling alternative to the usual call for embracing social, historical, and structural determinisms in disfavor of any individual agency aimed at overcoming the oppressive systemic forces that lead to record levels of social inequality worldwide in the 21st century. Instead, the positive leadership model introduced in this article attempts to illustrate that it is still possible to develop a theoretically sound, multilevel model on positive leadership that extends above and beyond interpersonal influence and answers such calls without neglecting the agency that positive leaders have in shaping a better work environment where their followers, their teams, and even the organizations they lead can reach an optimal functioning level.

Whereas the conversation with such caustic critics of positive leadership is unlikely to be settled in this article, it is essential to signal readers that such critiques derive from incompatible core assumptions about human nature. Alvesson and Einola (2019) seem to assume, as do many other critics of positive leadership, that humans are mere *homo economicus*. That is, they are individuals whose behavior can be reduced to the alternating effect of "carrots" (rewards) and "sticks" (punishments) that minimizes deviations from established policies and procedures, regardless of whether such norms elevate or diminish them by alienating, and eventually dehumanizing, them. However, the model introduced in this article assumes that the true potential of human nature lies in its altruism, its gregariousness, and its agency over said determinisms. In other words, humans' behavior in organizations is driven by a larger sense of purpose than collecting and spending paychecks from the cradle to the grave.

IMPLICATIONS FOR RESEARCH AND PRACTICE

The model of positive leadership in organizations introduced in this article has two clear implications for research and practice. The first implication is regarding what confers the "positive" attribute to a leadership theory, framework, or model. For leadership to be positive, its assumptions and predictions must reflect a deep concern for humans working in contemporary organizations. Thus, leaders aspiring toward a humanistic management might consider refocusing their approaches so that the maximization of shareholder profit becomes subordinate to the welfare of their organizations' people. Future development efforts could use the present model as a roadmap to help leaders broaden their view on the human aspect of organizational life. To be regarded as such, positive leaders are accountable for (re)shaping a sustainable environment in their organizations so that their members find meaning, thrive, and flourish. Thus, the ultimate mandate of positive organizational leaders is "doing well by doing good."

The second implication of the present model is that positive leadership is a dynamic construct. Even the most virtuous and positive leader can eventually suffer a "character erosion" if he or she must operate continuously within an organization whose culture rewards toxic performance (i.e., "winning at any cost"), or that lacks the proper institutional checks and balances to limit the power of their leaders (Monzani, 2018; Sturm & Monzani, 2017). Similarly, the present model acknowledges leadership as a multi-actor, relational process. Thus, while "the bucket still stops at the top," workgroups and individual followers share some form of accountability in ensuring that their leaders do not abuse their authority. In other words, workgroups and even followers also have true power (and a true responsibility) to remove their "granting" of leadership to those leaders who abuse their power after "assuming the mantle." In this way, followers and workgroups can ensure their leaders' behavior remains positive and virtuous.

CONCLUDING REMARKS

The model presented in this article aims to help future leaders to embrace a more humanistic view of leadership in organizations. While we acknowledge the importance that leaders' behaviors have in eliciting positive outcomes for followers, workgroups, and their organizations, this article proposes a more integrative and democratic view of positive leadership. In other words, in the same way that "it takes a village to raise a child," it takes an organization to ensure that positive leadership in organizations is exercised and sustained.

A comedian once stated: "Our knowledge has made us cynical; our cleverness, hard and unkind; we think too much, and feel too little; more than machinery, we need humanity; more that cleverness, we need kindness and gentleness; without these qualities life will be violent, and all will be lost." The present work provides researchers and practitioners with a way to develop such qualities in the hope of promoting more humane leadership in organizations.

REFERENCES

Aguinis, H. (2011). Organizational responsibility: Doing good and doing well. In S. Zedeck (Ed.), *APA handbook of industrial and organizational psychology, volume 3: Maintaining, expanding, and contracting the organization* (pp. 855–879). Washington, DC: American Psychological Association.

Alvesson, M., & Einola, K. (2019). Warning for excessive positivity: Authentic leadership and other traps in leadership studies. *The Leadership Quarterly, 30*(4), 383–395. https://doi.org/10.1016/j.leaqua.2019.04.001

Antonakis, J., House, R. J., & Simonton, D. K. (2017). Can super smart leaders suffer from too much of a good thing? The curvilinear effect of intelligence on perceived leadership behavior. *Journal of Applied Psychology, 102*(7), 1003–1021. https://doi.org/10.1037/apl0000221

Avey, J. B., Avolio, B. J., & Luthans, F. (2011). Experimentally analyzing the impact of leader positivity on follower positivity and performance. *The Leadership Quarterly, 22*(2011), 282–294. https://doi.org/10.1016/j.leaqua.2011.02.004

Avolio, B. J. (2007). Promoting more integrative strategies for leadership theory-building. *American Psychologist, 62*(1), 25–33. https://doi.org/10.1037/0003-066X.62.1.25

Avolio, B. J., & Gardner, W. L. (2005). Authentic leadership development: Getting to the root of positive forms of leadership. *The Leadership Quarterly, 16*(3), 315–338. https://doi.org/10.1016/j.leaqua.2005.03.001

Avolio, B. J., Gardner, W. L., Walumbwa, F. O., Luthans, F., & May, D. R. (2004). Unlocking the mask: A look at the process by which authentic leaders impact follower attitudes and behaviors. *The Leadership Quarterly, 15*(6), 801–823. https://doi.org/10.1016/j.leaqua.2004.09.003

Banks, G. C., Gooty, J., Ross, R. L., Williams, C. E., & Harrington, N. T. (2018). Construct redundancy in leader behaviors: A review and agenda for the future. *The Leadership Quarterly, 29*(1), 236–251. https://doi.org/10.1016/j.leaqua.2017.12.005

Banks, G. C., McCauley, K. D., Gardner, W. L., & Guler, C. E. (2016). A meta-analytic review of authentic and transformational leadership: A test for redundancy. *The Leadership Quarterly, 27*(4), 634–652. https://doi.org/10.1016/j.leaqua.2016.02.006

Barling, J., Christie, A., & Turner, N. (2008). Pseudo-transformational leadership: Towards the development and test of a model. *Journal of Business Ethics, 81*(4), 851–861. https://doi.org/10.1007/s10551-007-9552-8

Barreto, N. B., & Hogg, M. A. (2017). Evaluation of and support for group prototypical leaders: A meta-analysis of twenty years of empirical research. *Social Influence, 12*(1), 41–55.

Bass, B. M. (1985). *Leadership and performance beyond expectations.* New York, NY: Free Press.

Bass, B. M., & Avolio, B. J. (Eds.). (1994). *Improving organizational effectiveness through transformational leadership.* Thousand Oaks, CA: SAGE.

Bauer, T. N., & Erdogan, B. (2011). Organizational socialization: The effective onboarding of new employees. In S. Zedeck (Ed.), *APA handbook of industrial and organizational psychology, volume 3: Maintaining, expanding, and contracting the organization* (pp. 51–64). Washington, DC: American Psychological Association. https://doi.org/10.1037/12171-002

Bono, J. E., & Judge, T. A. (2004). Personality and transformational and transactional leadership: A meta-analysis. *Journal of Applied Psychology, 89*(5), 901–910. https://doi.org/10.1037/0021-9010.89.5.901

Brown, M. E., Treviño, L. K., & Harrison, D. A. (2005). Ethical leadership: A social learning perspective for construct development and testing. *Organizational Behavior and Human Decision Processes, 97*(2), 117–134. https://doi.org/10.1016/j.obhdp.2005.03.002

Busch, T., & Friede, G. (2018). The robustness of the corporate social and financial performance relation: A second-order meta-analysis. *Corporate Social Responsibility and Environmental Management, 25*(4), 583–608. https://doi.org/10.1002/csr.1480

Byrne, A., Crossan, M. M., & Seijts, G. H. (2018). The development of leader character through crucible moments. *Journal of Management Education, 42*(2), 265–293. https://doi.org/10.1177/1052562917717292

Cooper, C. D., Scandura, T. A., & Schriesheim, C. A. (2005). Looking forward but learning from our past: Potential challenges to developing authentic leadership theory and authentic leaders. *The Leadership Quarterly, 16*(3), 475–493. https://doi.org/10.1016/j.leaqua.2005.03.008

Crossan, M. M., Byrne, A., Seijts, G. H., Reno, M., Monzani, L., & Gandz, J. (2017). Toward a framework of leader character in organizations. *Journal of Management Studies, 54*(7), 986–1018. https://doi.org/10.1111/joms.12254

Crossan, M. M., Lane, H. W., & White, R. E. (1999). An organizational learning framework: From intuition to institution. *Academy of Management Review, 24*(3), 522–537. https://doi.org/10.5465/amr.1999.2202135

De Hoogh, A. H. B., & Den Hartog, D. N. (2008). Ethical and despotic leadership, relationships with leader's social responsibility, top management team effectiveness and subordinates' optimism: A multimethod study. *The Leadership Quarterly, 19*(3), 297–311. https://doi.org/10.1016/j.leaqua.2008.03.002

De Neve, J.-E., Mikhaylov, S., Dawes, C. T., Christakis, N. A., & Fowler, J. H. (2013). Born to lead? A twin design and genetic association study of leadership role occupancy. *The Leadership Quarterly, 24*(1), 45–60. https://doi.org/10.1016/j.leaqua.2012.08.001

Deci, E. L., Eghrari, H., Patrick, B. C., & Leone, D. R. (1994). Facilitating internalization: The self-determination theory perspective. *Journal of Personality, 62*(1), 119–142.

Den Hartog, D. N., House, R. J., Hanges, P. J., Ruiz-Quintanilla, S. A., Dorfman, P. W., Abdalla, I. A., ... Zhou, J. (1999). Culture specific and cross-culturally generalizable implicit leadership theories: Are attributes of charismatic/transformational leadership universally endorsed? *The Leadership Quarterly, 10*(2), 219–256.

DeRue, D. S., & Ashford, S. J. (2010). Who will lead and who will follow? A social process of leadership identity construction in organizations. *The Academy of Management Review, 35*(4), 627–647. http://amr.aom.org/content/35/4/627.abstract

Di Milia, L., & Birdi, K. (2010). The relationship between multiple levels of learning practices and objective and subjective organizational financial performance. *Journal of Organizational Behavior, 31*(4), 481–498. https://doi.org/10.1002/job.623

Dinh, J. E., Lord, R. G., Gardner, W. L., Meuser, J. D., Liden, R. C., & Hu, J. (2014). Leadership theory and research in the new millennium: Current theoretical trends and changing perspectives. *The Leadership Quarterly, 25*(1), 36–62. https://doi.org/10.1016/j.leaqua.2013.11.005

Dulebohn, J. H., Bommer, W. H., Liden, R. C., Brouer, R. L., & Ferris, G. R. (2012). A meta-analysis of antecedents and consequences of leader-member exchange: Integrating the past with an eye toward the future. *Journal of Management, 38*(6), 1715–1759. https://doi.org/10.1177/0149206311415280

Escartín, J., Monzani, L., Leong, F., & Rodríguez-Carballeira, Á. (2017). A reduced form of the Workplace Bullying Scale—The EAPA-T-R: A useful instrument for daily diary and experience sampling studies. *Work & Stress: An International Journal of Work, Health & Organisations, 31*(1), 42–62. https://doi.org/10.1080/02678373.2017.1295113

Eva, N., Robin, M., Sendjaya, S., van Dierendonck, D., & Liden, R. C. (2019). Servant leadership: A systematic review and call for future research. *The Leadership Quarterly, 30*(1), 111–132. https://doi.org/10.1016/j.leaqua.2018.07.004

Gandz, J., Crossan, M. M., Seijts, G. H., & Stephenson, C. (2010). *Leadership on trial: A manifesto for leadership development.* London, ON, Canada: Richard Ivey School of Business.

García-Morales, V. J., Jiménez-Barrionuevo, M. M., & Gutiérrez-Gutiérrez, L. (2012). Transformational leadership influence on organizational performance through organizational learning and innovation. *Journal of Business Research, 65*(7), 1040–1050. https://doi.org/10.1016/j.jbusres.2011.03.005

Gardner, W. L., & Avolio, B. J. (1998). The charismatic relationship: A dramaturgical perspective. *The Academy of Management Review, 23*(1), 32–58. http://www.jstor.org/stable/259098

Gardner, W. L., Avolio, B. J., Luthans, F., May, D. R., & Walumbwa, F. O. (2005). "Can you see the real me?" A self-based model of authentic leader and follower development. *The Leadership Quarterly, 16*(3), 343–372. https://doi.org/10.1016/j.leaqua.2005.03.003

Gerstner, C. R., & Day, D. V. (1997). Meta-analytic review of leader–member exchange theory: Correlates and construct issues. *Journal of Applied Psychology, 82*(6), 827–844.

Gibson, D. E. (2004). Role models in career development: New directions for theory and research. *Journal of Vocational Behavior, 65*(1), 134–156. https://doi.org/10.1016/S0001-8791(03)00051-4

Giessner, S. R., & van Knippenberg, D. (2008). "License to fail": Goal definition, leader group prototypicality, and perceptions of leadership effectiveness after leader failure. *Organizational Behavior and Human Decision Processes, 105*(1), 14–35. https://doi.org/10.1016/j.obhdp.2007.04.002

Gintis, H., & Helbing, D. (2015). Homo socialis: An analytical core for sociological theory. *Review of Behavioral Economics, 2*(1–2), 1–59. https://doi.org/10.1561/105.00000016

Gluth, S., & Fontanesi, L. (2016). Wiring the altruistic brain. *Science, 351*(6277), 1028–1029. https://doi.org/10.1126/science.aaf4688

Gottfredson, R. K., & Aguinis, H. (2017). Leadership behaviors and follower performance: Deductive and inductive examination of theoretical rationales and underlying mechanisms. *Journal of Organizational Behavior, 38*(4), 558–591.

Graen, G. B., & Uhl-Bien, M. (1995). Relationship-based approach to leadership: Development of leader-member exchange (LMX) theory of leadership over 25 years: Applying a multi-level multi-domain perspective. *The Leadership Quarterly, 6*(2), 219–247. https://doi.org/10.1016/1048-9843(95)90036-5

Greenleaf, R. K. (1977). *Servant leadership: A journey into the nature of legitimate power and greatness.* New York, NY: Paulist Press.

Groves, K. S., & LaRocca, M. A. (2011). An empirical study of leader ethical values, transformational and transactional leadership, and follower attitudes toward corporate social responsibility. *Journal of Business Ethics, 103*(4), 511–528. https://doi.org/10.1007/s10551-011-0877-y

Hackett, R. D., & Wang, G. (2012). Virtues and leadership: An integrating conceptual framework founded in Aristotelian and Confucian perspectives on virtues. *Management Decision, 50*(5), 868–899. https://doi.org/10.1108/00251741211227564

Hannah, S. T., Balthazard, P. A., Waldman, D. A., Jennings, P. L., & Thatcher, R. W. (2013). The psychological and neurological bases of leader self-complexity and effects on adaptive decision-making. *Journal of Applied Psychology, 98*(3), 393–411. https://doi.org/10.1037/a0032257

Haslam, S. A., Reicher, S. D., & Platow, M. J. (2020). *The new psychology of leadership: Identity, influence and power* (2nd ed.). London, UK: Routledge.

Hernandez, M., Eberly, M. B., Avolio, B. J., & Johnson, M. D. (2011). The loci and mechanisms of leadership: Exploring a more comprehensive view of leadership theory. *The Leadership Quarterly, 22*(6), 1165–1185. https://doi.org/10.1016/j.leaqua.2011.09.009

Hitlin, S. (2003). Values as the core of personal identity: Drawing links between two theories of self. *Social Psychology Quarterly, 66*(2), 118–137. http://www.jstor.org/stable/1519843

Hobman, E. V., Jackson, C. J., Jimmieson, N. L., & Martin, R. (2011). The effects of transformational leadership behaviours on follower outcomes: An identity-based analysis. *European Journal of Work and Organizational Psychology, 20*(4), 553–580. https://doi.org/10.1080/1359432X.2010.490046

Hoch, J. E., Bommer, W. H., Dulebohn, J. H., & Wu, D. (2018). Do ethical, authentic, and servant leadership explain variance above and beyond transformational leadership? A meta-analysis. *Journal of Management, 44*(2), 501–529. https://doi.org/10.1177/0149206316665461

Hofstede, G. (1980). Motivation, leadership, and organization: Do American theories apply abroad? *Organizational Dynamics, 9*(1), 42–63. https://doi.org/10.1016/0090-2616(80)90013-3

Hogg, M. A. (2001a). A social identity theory of leadership. *Personality and Social Psychology Review, 5*(3), 184–200. https://doi.org/10.1207/S15327957PSPR0503_1

Hogg, M. A. (2001b). Social identification, group prototypicality, and emergent leadership. In M. A. Hogg & D. J. Terry (Eds.), *Social identity processes in organizational contexts* (pp. 197–212). Philadelphia, PA: Psychology Press.

House, R., Javidan, M., & Dorfman, P. (2001). Project GLOBE: An introduction. *Applied Psychology: An International Review, 50*(4), 489–505. https://doi.org/10.1111/1464-0597.00070

Hu, J., & Liden, R. C. (2011). Antecedents of team potency and team effectiveness: An examination of goal and process clarity and servant leadership. *Journal of Applied Psychology, 96*(4), 851–862. https://doi.org/10.1037/a0022465

Humberd, B. K., & Rouse, E. D. (2016). Seeing you in me and me in you: Personal identification in the phases of mentoring relationships. *Academy of Management Review, 41*, 435–455. https://doi.org/10.5465/amr.2013.0203

Ilies, R., Morgeson, F. P., & Nahrgang, J. D. (2005). Authentic leadership and eudaemonic well-being: Understanding leader-follower outcomes. *The Leadership Quarterly, 16*(3), 373–394. https://doi.org/10.1016/j.leaqua.2005.03.002

Ilies, R., Nahrgang, J. D., & Morgeson, F. P. (2007). Leader-member exchange and citizenship behaviors: A meta-analysis. *Journal of Applied Psychology, 92*(1), 269–277. https://doi.org/10.1037/0021-9010.92.1.269

Inceoglu, I., Thomas, G., Chu, C., Plans, D., & Gerbasi, A. (2018). Leadership behavior and employee well-being: An integrated review and a future research agenda. *The Leadership Quarterly, 29*(1), 179–202.

Judge, T. A., Piccolo, R. F., & Kosalka, T. (2009). The bright and dark sides of leader traits: A review and theoretical extension of the leader trait paradigm. *The Leadership Quarterly, 20*(6), 855–875. https://doi.org/10.1016/j.leaqua.2009.09.004

Kaluza, A. J., Boer, D., Buengeler, C., & van Dick, R. (2020). Leadership behaviour and leader self-reported well-being: A review, integration and meta-analytic examination. *Work and Stress: An International Journal of Work, Health & Organisations, 34*(1), 34–56. https://doi.org/10.1080/02678373.2019.1617369

Kernis, M. H. (2003). Toward a conceptualization of optimal self-esteem. *Psychological Inquiry, 14*(1), 1–26. https://doi.org/10.1207/S15327965PLI1401_01

Kernis, M. H., & Goldman, B. M. (2006). A multicomponent conceptualization of authenticity: Theory and research. In M. P. Zanna (Ed.), *Advances in experimental social psychology* (Vol. 38, pp. 283–357). San Diego, CA: Academic Press. https://doi.org/10.1016/S0065-2601(06)38006-9

Kingah, S., & Quiliconi, C. (Eds.). (2016). *Global and regional leadership of BRICS countries.* Cham, Switzerland: Springer. https://doi.org/10.1007/978-3-319-22972-0

Lemoine, G. J., Hartnell, C. A., & Leroy, H. (2019). Taking stock of moral approaches to leadership: An integrative review of ethical, authentic, and servant leadership. *Academy of Management Annals, 13*(1), 148–187. https://doi.org/10.5465/annals.2016.0121

Leroy, H., Anseel, F., Gardner, W. L., & Sels, L. (2015). Authentic leadership, authentic followership, basic need satisfaction, and work role performance: A cross-level study. *Journal of Management, 41*(6), 1677–1697. https://doi.org/10.1177/0149206312457822

Liden, R. C., Wayne, S. J., Liao, C., & Meuser, J. D. (2014). Servant leadership and serving culture: Influence on individual and unit performance. *Academy of Management Journal, 57*(5), 1434–1452. https://doi.org/10.5465/amj.2013.0034

Liden, R. C., Wayne, S. J., Zhao, H., & Henderson, D. J. (2008). Servant leadership: Development of a multidimensional measure and multi-level assessment. *The Leadership Quarterly, 19*(2), 161–177. https://doi.org/10.1016/j.leaqua.2008.01.006

Lord, R. G., de Vader, C. L., & Alliger, G. M. (1986). A meta-analysis of the relation between personality traits and leadership perceptions: An application of validity generalization procedures. *Journal of Applied Psychology, 71*(3), 402–410. https://doi.org/10.1037/0021-9010.71.3.402

Luthans, F., & Avolio, B. J. (2003). Authentic leadership development. In K. S. Cameron, J. E. Dutton, & R. E. Quinn (Eds.), *Positive organizational scholarship: Foundations of a new discipline* (pp. 241–258). San Francisco, CA: Berrett-Koehler.

Luthans, F., & Avolio, B. J. (2009). The "point" of positive organizational behavior. *Journal of Organizational Behavior, 30*(2), 291–307. https://doi.org/10.1002/job

Luthans, F., & Youssef, C. M. (2007). Emerging positive organizational behavior. *Journal of Management, 33*(3), 321–349. https://doi.org/10.1177/0149206307300814

Martin, R., Guillaume, Y., Thomas, G., Lee, A., & Epitropaki, O. (2016). Leader-member exchange (LMX) and performance: A meta-analytic review. *Personnel Psychology, 69*(1), 67–121. https://doi.org/10.1111/peps.12100

McPherson, M., Smith-Lovin, L., & Cook, J. M. (2001). Birds of a feather: Homophily in social networks. *Annual Review of Sociology, 27*, 415–444. http://www.jstor.org/stable/2678628

Meindl, J. R., Ehrlich, S. B., & Dukerich, J. M. (1985). The romance of leadership. *Administrative Science Quarterly, 30*(1), 78–102. https://doi.org/10.2307/2392813

Meuser, J. D., Gardner, W. L., Dinh, J. E., Hu, J., Liden, R. C., & Lord, R. G. (2016). A network analysis of leadership theory: The infancy of integration. *Journal of Management, 42*(5), 1374–1403. https://doi.org/10.1177/0149206316647099

Monzani, L. (2018). A model for positive leadership in Argentinean firms. In D. Cotter-Lockard (Ed.), *Authentic leadership and followership* (pp. 115–137). Cham, Switzerland: Palgrave Macmillan. https://doi.org/10.1007/978-3-319-65307-5_5

Monzani, L., Ripoll, P., & Peiro, J. M. (2012). Un nou enfocament en el lideratge del segle xxi [A new approach to leadership for the XXI century]. *Anuari de Psicologia, 14*(1), 31–41.

Orlitzky, M., Schmidt, F. L., & Rynes, S. L. (2003). Corporate social and financial performance: A meta-analysis. *Organization Studies, 24*(3), 403–441. https://doi.org/10.1177/0170840603024003910

Orlitzky, M., Siegel, D. S., & Waldman, D. A. (2011). Strategic corporate social responsibility and environmental sustainability. *Business & Society, 50*(1), 6–27. https://doi.org/10.1177/0007650310394323

Palanski, M., Newman, A., Leroy, H., Moore, C., Hannah, S., & Den Hartog, D. (2019). Quantitative research on leadership and business ethics: Examining the state of the field and an agenda for future research. *Journal of Business Ethics.* https://doi.org/10.1007/s10551-019-04267-9

Peterson, C., & Seligman, M. E. P. (2004). *Character strengths and virtues: A handbook and classification.* Washington, DC: American Psychological Association.

Price, T. L. (2003). The ethics of authentic transformational leadership. *The Leadership Quarterly, 14*(1), 67–81. https://doi.org/10.1016/S1048-9843(02)00187-X

Rockstuhl, T., Dulebohn, J. H., Ang, S., & Shore, L. M. (2012). Leader–member exchange (LMX) and culture: A meta-analysis of correlates of LMX across 23 countries. *Journal of Applied Psychology, 97*(6), 1097–1130. https://doi.org/10.1037/a0029978

Ryan, R. M., & Deci, E. L. (2001). On happiness and human potentials: A review of research on hedonic and eudaimonic well-being. *Annual Review of Psychology, 52*, 141–166. http://www.annualreviews.org/doi/abs/10.1146/annurev.psych.52.1.141

Ryan, R. M., & Deci, E. L. (2002). Overview of self-determination theory: An organismic-dialectical perspective. In E. L. Deci & R. M. Ryan (Eds.), *Handbook of self-determination research* (pp. 3–33). Rochester, NY: University of Rochester Press.

Sarros, J. C., Cooper, B. K., & Santora, J. C. (2008). Building a climate for innovation through transformational leadership and organizational culture. *Journal of Leadership & Organizational Studies, 15*(2), 145–158. https://doi.org/10.1177/1548051808324100

Schein, E. H. (1984). Coming to a new awareness of organizational culture. *Sloan Management Review, 25*(2), 3–14.

Schriesheim, C. A., Castro, S. L., & Cogliser, C. C. (1999). Leader-member exchange (LMX) research: A comprehensive review of theory, measurement, and data-analytic practices. *The Leadership Quarterly, 10*(1), 63–113. https://doi.org/10.1016/S1048-9843(99)80009-5

Schwartz, S. H. (1992). Universals in the content and structures of values: Theoretical advances and empirical tests in 20 countries. In M. P. Zanna (Ed.), *Advances in experimental social psychology* (Vol. 25, pp. 1–65). San Diego, CA: Academic Press.

Seijts, G. H., & de Clercy, C. (2020). How do populist voters rate their political leaders? Comparing citizen assessments in three jurisdictions. *Politics and Governance, 8*(1), 133–145. https://doi.org/10.17645/pag.v8i1.2540

Seligman, M. E. P., & Csikszentmihalyi, M. (2014). Positive psychology: An introduction. In M. Csikszentmihalyi (Eds.), *Flow and the foundations of positive psychology: The collected works of Mihaly Csikszentmihalyi* (pp. 279–298). Dordrecht, The Netherlands: Springer. https://doi.org/10.1007/978-94-017-9088-8_18

Skubinn, R., Buengeler, C., & Schank, C. (2019). Ethics in leadership: Carving out the ethical core in current leadership theories. In A. Sales (Ed.), *Corporate social responsibility and corporate change: Institutional and organizational perspectives* (pp. 97–116). Cham, Switzerland: Springer.

Snyder, C. R., & Lopez, S. J. (Eds.). (2002). *Handbook of positive psychology.* Oxford, UK: Oxford University Press.

Steffens, N. K., Haslam, S. A., Reicher, S. D., Platow, M. J., Fransen, K., Yang, J., ... Boen, F. (2014). Leadership as social identity management: Introducing the Identity Leadership Inventory (ILI) to assess and validate a four-dimensional model. *The Leadership Quarterly, 25*(5), 1001–1024. https://doi.org/10.1016/j.leaqua.2014.05.002

Sturm, R. E., & Monzani, L. (2017). Power and leadership. In J. Antonakis & D. V. Day (Eds.), *The nature of leadership* (3rd ed., pp. 272–299). Thousand Oaks, CA: SAGE.

Sturm, R. E., Vera, D., & Crossan, M. M. (2017). The entanglement of leader character and leader competence and its impact on performance. *The Leadership Quarterly, 28*(3), 349–366. https://doi.org/10.1016/j.leaqua.2016.11.007

Toor, S.-ur.-R., & Ofori, G. (2009). Ethical leadership: Examining the relationships with full range leadership model, employee outcomes, and organizational culture. *Journal of Business Ethics, 90*(4), 533–547. https://doi.org/10.1007/s10551-009-0059-3

Ullrich, J., Christ, O., & van Dick, R. (2009). Substitutes for procedural fairness: Prototypical leaders are endorsed whether they are fair or not. *Journal of Applied Psychology, 94*(1), 235–244. https://doi.org/10.1037/a0012936

van Dick, R., Lemoine, J. E., Steffens, N. K., Kerschreiter, R., Akfirat, S. A., Avanzi, L., ... Haslam, S. A. (2018). Identity leadership going global: Validation of the Identity Leadership Inventory across 20 countries. *Journal of Occupational and Organizational Psychology, 91*(4), 697–728. https://doi.org/10.1111/joop.12223

van Dierendonck, D. (2010). Servant leadership: A review and synthesis. *Journal of Management, 37*(4), 1228–1261. https://doi.org/10.1177/0149206310380462

van Dierendonck, D., Stam, D., Boersma, P., de Windt, N., & Alkema, J. (2014). Same difference? Exploring the differential mechanisms linking servant leadership and transformational leadership to follower outcomes. *The Leadership Quarterly, 25*(3), 544–562. https://doi.org/10.1016/j.leaqua.2013.11.014

van Knippenberg, D. (2020). Meaning-based leadership. *Organizational Psychology Review, 10*(1), 6–28. https://doi.org/10.1177/2041386619897618

van Knippenberg, D., & Hogg, M. A. (2003). A social identity model of leadership effectiveness in organizations. In R. M. Kramer & B. M. Staw (Eds.), *Research in organizational behavior* (Vol. 25, pp. 243–297). Oxford, UK: Elsevier.

van Knippenberg, D., van Knippenberg, B., De Cremer, D., & Hogg, M. A. (2004). Leadership, self, and identity: A review and research agenda. *The Leadership Quarterly, 15*(6), 825–856. https://doi.org/10.1016/j.leaqua.2004.09.002

van Quaquebeke, N., & Eckloff, T. (2010). Defining respectful leadership: What it is, how it can be measured, and another glimpse at what it is related to. *Journal of Business Ethics, 91*(3), 343–358. https://doi.org/10.1007/s10551-009-0087-z

Waldman, D. A., & Siegel, D. (2008). Defining the socially responsible leader. *The Leadership Quarterly, 19*(1), 117–131. https://doi.org/10.1016/j.leaqua.2007.12.008

Walumbwa, F. O., Avolio, B. J., Gardner, W. L., Wernsing, T. S., & Peterson, S. J. (2008). Authentic leadership: Development and validation of a theory-based measure. *Journal of Management, 34*(1), 89–126. https://doi.org/10.1177/0149206307308913

Woolley, L., Caza, A., & Levy, L. (2010). Authentic leadership and follower development: Psychological capital, positive work climate, and gender. *Journal of Leadership & Organizational Studies, 18*(4), 438–448. https://doi.org/10.1177/1548051810382013

Wu, L.-Z., Kwan, H., Yim, F., Chiu, R., & He, X. (2015). CEO ethical leadership and corporate social responsibility: A moderated mediation model. *Journal of Business Ethics, 130*(4), 819–831. https://doi.org/10.1007/s10551-014-2108-9

Xenikou, A., & Simosi, M. (2006). Organizational culture and transformational leadership as predictors of business unit performance. *Journal of Managerial Psychology, 21*(6), 566–579. https://doi.org/10.1108/02683940610684409

Xu, A. J., Loi, R., Cai, Z., & Liden, R. C. (2019). Reversing the lens: How followers influence leader–member exchange quality. *Journal of Occupational and Organizational Psychology, 92*(3), 475–497. https://doi.org/10.1111/joop.12268

Yammarino, F. J., Cheong, M., Kim, J., & Tsai, C.-Y. (2020). Is leadership more than "I like my boss"? In M. R. Buckley, A. R. Wheeler, J. E. Baur, & J. R. B. Halbesleben (Eds.), *Research in personnel and human resources management* (Vol. 38, pp. 1–56). Bingley, UK: Emerald Group.

Yammarino, F. J., Dionne, S. D., Chun, J. U., & Dansereau, F. (2005). Leadership and levels of analysis: A state-of-the-science review. *The Leadership Quarterly, 16*(6), 879–919. https://doi.org/10.1016/j.leaqua.2005.09.002

Zaccaro, S. J. (2007). Trait-based perspectives of leadership. *American Psychologist, 62*(1), 6–16. http://psycnet.apa.org/doi/10.1037/0003-066X.62.1.6

Zhao, H., & Li, C. (2019). A computerized approach to understanding leadership research. *The Leadership Quarterly, 30*(4), 396–416. https://doi.org/10.1016/j.leaqua.2019.06.001

NOTE

1. While authors like Ilies, Morgeson, and Nahrgang refer to growth-oriented exchanges as positive social exchanges, other authors such as Luthans and colleagues have used the term *exemplary role modeling.*

Lucas Monzani and Rolf Van Dick

THE PSYCHOLOGY OF ABUSIVE SUPERVISION

INTRODUCTION

Based on survey data collected by the Workplace Bullying Institute, it is projected that in the United States alone, tens of millions of employees are likely to have experienced mistreatment in the workplace (Namie, 2017). Supervisors are a common source of workplace bullying (Bowling & Beehr, 2006), and the term *abusive supervision* was coined by Bennett Tepper in 2000 to describe employees' perceptions of being treated with sustained hostility by supervisors. The good news is that experiences of abusive supervision remain relatively uncommon (Tepper et al., 2017) and the overwhelming majority of employees report experiencing little to no hostile behavior from their supervisors (Fischer et al., 2021). However, abusive supervision continues to be an important area of study for the minority of employees who do report receiving such mistreatment due to its profound effects on important psychological and behavioral outcomes.

The term *abusive supervision* captures employees' perceptions of a range of supervisors' rude and belittling behaviors. These behaviors can include direct insults, gossiping about employees behind their backs, and giving employees the silent treatment. Abusive supervision behaviors can generally be classified as actively hostile, such as putting an employee down in front of others, or more passive-aggressive, where the supervisor may not give credit to an employee for their work effort (Mitchell & Ambrose, 2007). While the term *abusive supervision* is predominantly used to describe leader mistreatment in the organizational psychology and management literatures (Tepper et al., 2017), abusive supervision has also been used fairly synonymously with the terms *supervisor social undermining* and *leader bullying* (Mackey et al., 2021). Ultimately, the number of negative outcomes stemming from abusive supervision are well documented: Abusive supervision is bad for employees, teams, organizations, and the leaders themselves (Mackey et al., 2017; Martinko et al., 2013; Tepper et al., 2017).

The following sections (a) discuss the role of perception in abusive supervision; (b) address reasons abusive supervision occurs; (c) review the effects of abusive supervision on employees, supervisors, and witnesses; (d) address potential benefits to abusive supervision; (e) discuss interventions that can be used to disrupt abusive supervision processes; and (f) review international differences.

THE ROLE OF PERCEPTION

There is some disagreement among abusive supervision researchers regarding the perceptual aspect of abusive supervision. In other words, is abusive behavior objectively occurring in most cases, or is the mistreatment in the mind of the employee? And to what extent do these distinctions matter? Put another way, there is debate around (a) the extent to which reports of abuse are affected significantly by employees' biases and (b) to what extent abusive supervision should be clearly discussed as perceptual in nature (Brees et al., 2016; Fischer et al., 2021; Harvey et al., 2014; Martinko et al., 2013; Tepper et al., 2017).[1]

In general, researchers agree that there are potential discrepancies between leader behaviors and employee perception, and they recognize that leader behavior is just one factor determining employees' perceptions of abuse. To highlight this issue, Tepper and colleagues (2017) discuss "tough love" leader behavior, which may or may not lead to employee perceptions of abusive supervision. For example, a leader who yells at a player in a sports context may not be perceived as abusive, but that same behavior would likely be considered abusive in a white-collar office environment. Additionally, an employee who feels badly about themself may be more likely than a confident employee to perceive certain behaviors as abusive (Martinko et al., 2013). In summary, the context in which the behavior occurs, as well as individual characteristics, can influence the extent to which a leader's behavior is interpreted as a reasonable form of "tough love" or instead unreasonable abuse. Thus, Tepper and colleagues agree with critics that perceptions are shaped by a variety of forces and that the same leader behavior may be perceived differently by various individuals.

Critics also argue that researchers too often frame their findings on abusive supervision as an objective behavior that is occurring rather than considering the perceptual nature of abuse (Brees et al., 2014; Martinko et al., 2013). In response, Tepper and colleagues (2017) contend that perception is embedded in the definition of abusive supervision. Ultimately, the debate largely involves how abusive supervision should be discussed in research and communicated to practitioners. Fischer et al. (2021) note that researchers "have often treated abusive supervision scores as markers of leader behavior" (p. 3).

An additional implication of this second debate involves how researchers *should* study abusive supervision, and the extent to which research can and should tease apart leader behaviors from perceptual influences. The survey measure commonly used in abusive supervision research (Tepper, 2000) asks employees to report how frequently their supervisor enacts 15 distinct behaviors (or five actively hostile behaviors using a shortened measure; Mitchell & Ambrose, 2007), rather than asking employees about their general, abstract perceptions of their leaders (Lemoine et al., 2019), though self-report measures inherently carry an element of subjective perceptions. Along these lines, there has been an increased attempt to isolate the role of perception from objective leader behaviors. For example, scenario-based experimental designs—where participants are asked to read or observe a scenario that presents specific leader behaviors—can add support to the notion that reports of abusive supervision do reflect offensive leader behavior (Korman et al., 2021; Taylor et al., 2019). Conversely, researchers have been able to isolate and measure the perceptual role of abusive supervision through experiments by examining how various individuals may view the same video of a leader's behavior differently (Brees et al., 2016). Thus, certain types of experimental designs have the potential to isolate perceptions and/or leader behavior when examining the effects of abusive supervision (Wang et al., 2019).

Additional methods have also attempted to consider the role of perception. In studies using survey measures, researchers have increasingly controlled for individual characteristics (such as low self-esteem) that are known to influence perceptions of abuse (Martinko et al., 2013). This may help reduce some of the role that perceptual biases play and more clearly capture the role of leader behavior, though other factors influencing perceptual processing cannot be ruled out. Researchers can also use multiple measures and assessments to triangulate the roles of perception and objective leader behavior (Fischer et al., 2021), and some studies have found high levels of agreement among team members regarding their supervisors' abusive behavior (e.g., Li et al., 2016). Arguably, there is value in emphasizing that abusive supervision consists of both a perceptual experience (as is inherent in the definition), even when these perceptions are shared among many people, as well as from a "reasonable person" standard of observable leader behavior. Ultimately, there are various opinions among researchers regarding the extent to which these two elements can and should be teased apart, as well as how they should be discussed.

ABUSIVE SUPERVISORS: HOW DO THEY GET THAT WAY?

Many leaders who are more likely to be abusive are not necessarily intending to behave with hostility, and they may also not be aware that they are perceived by their employees as abusive. However, in order to understand reasons supervisors may mistreat their employees, researchers commonly survey both employees and their supervisors to learn more about supervisor characteristics and other factors that are associated with employee-rated abusive supervision.

Past Experiences.   Not surprisingly, supervisors are more likely to behave abusively based on how they have been treated in the past. Social learning theory (Bandura, 1973) posits that individuals emulate behaviors that they have witnessed or experienced themselves. In other words, people role-model the behaviors and actions of others, particularly those of authority figures, and they learn how to behave through these interactions. For example, supervisors who grew up in a family where they were treated with hostility are more likely to be abusive in the workplace (Garcia et al., 2014; Kiewitz et al., 2012). Prior workplace experiences, including their own past workplace mistreatment or being treated unfairly, can potentially lead to posttraumatic stress (Vogel & Bolino, 2020) and even future abusive behavior (Huh & Lee, 2019). However, this association does not mean that all prior victims of abuse will go on to be abusers themselves.

Abusive leader behavior can also "trickle down" from top-level managers to lower-level supervisors in the organization (Aryee et al., 2007; Liu et al., 2012; Mawritz et al., 2012). The supervisors may be emulating the treatment they receive from their own bosses and/or enacting abusive behavior as an outlet for their own frustration with being treated with hostility (i.e., displaced aggression; Burton & Hoobler, 2006). Additionally, working in a hostile climate, where employees tend to behave with hostility, can lead to a greater likelihood of supervisors engaging in abuse (Mawritz, Dust, & Resick, 2014). Furthermore, when supervisors experience procedural injustice at work, whereby supervisors feel as though processes and procedures are not fair to them, they are also more likely to act abusively toward employees (Tepper et al., 2006). In general, working in an organizational climate that lacks justice and fairness is more likely to lead to hostile, aggressive behaviors among employees and supervisors (Priesemuth et al., 2013).

Another key reason leaders may enact abusive behavior is due to reciprocating mistreatment they have experienced from the employees. According to social exchange theory (Blau, 1964), supervisors may enact abusive mistreatment of their employees to "repay" their employees' disrespectful actions (Mitchell & Ambrose, 2007). However, while a social exchange theoretical argument implies that supervisors are consciously engaging in payback to "even the score," research suggests that engaging in abusive behaviors in reaction to hostile employees may not be fully conscious nor intentional. Employees who treat their supervisors with deviance (i.e., gossiping about the supervisor, insulting them, etc.) are potentially more likely to report abusive supervision not because the supervisors consciously intend to "get back" at them, but because the supervisors find these employees depleting and draining to deal with. Dealing with these deviant employees thus increases the likelihood that supervisors will respond with abusive actions in return (Lian, Ferris, et al., 2014; Mawritz et al., 2017).

Self-Regulation Failure.   In support of the idea that supervisors can behave aggressively when depleted, researchers have demonstrated that one of the primary reasons supervisors may be abusive is due to a failure to self-regulate their behavior (Vohs & Baumeister, 2004). As most people have probably experienced, when one is depleted of energy and cognitive resources (also called "ego depletion")—perhaps due to stress, having a bad day, or from feeling unwell—a person may be more likely to "snap" or make a rude comment to someone else, even though this action is not necessarily a deliberately conscious choice. Instead, behaviors that result from a failure to self-regulate one's reactions can be considered a somewhat automatic response. In addition to employee deviance, abusive supervision can result from ego depletion due to a number of stressors. Supervisors' cognitive resources can be taxed due to a lack of sleep (Barnes et al., 2015), experiencing conflict at home (Courtright et al., 2016), experiencing stress in the workplace (Burton et al., 2012), or having to "put on a front" during customer interactions (Yam et al., 2016), which can all increase the likelihood that supervisors will behave abusively.

Individual Differences. While a failure to self-regulate can be situationally dependent, individuals who are generally better able to demonstrate self-control are less likely to be abusive when depleted (Yam et al., 2016). Additionally, a number of stable traits and characteristics are more likely to make supervisors engage in abusive behaviors. For example, supervisors who score highly on one or more of the "Dark Triad" personality traits are more likely to be abusive. This means that supervisor Machiavellianism (i.e., a willingness to engage in unethical behavior and manipulate others to achieve one's goals; Wisse & Sleebos, 2016), narcissism (i.e., an inflated sense of self; Waldman et al., 2018), and psychopathy (i.e., a lack of empathy and display of antisocial behaviors; Mathieu & Babiak, 2016) can all be predictors of abusive behavior. Furthermore, supervisors' social dominance orientation (i.e., a belief that some groups should be dominant over others and the use of force is justified) has further been linked to abusive supervision (Graham et al., 2019; Hu & Liu, 2017). Other supervisor characteristics, such as being entitled (Eissa & Lester, 2021), are also positively related to reports of abuse.

Emotional and Cognitive Processes. Various emotional and cognitive processes impact whether supervisors will engage in hostile behavior toward employees. For example, when supervisors experience depression or negative emotional states (i.e., negative affect), employees are more likely to report mistreatment (Eissa et al., 2020; Pan & Lin, 2018; Tepper et al., 2006). Particular negative emotions such as supervisor anger (Mawritz, Folger, & Latham, 2014) are also associated with abusive supervision. Furthermore, moral cognitive processes can play a role in abusive supervision; when leaders morally disengage from their actions and ignore the ethical issues related to mistreating others, abusive supervision increases (Eissa & Lester, 2021; Qin et al., 2020).

Employee Factors. In addition to considering reasons why supervisors may behave abusively, researchers have also examined employee factors that may contribute to abuse. This research often draws from victim precipitation theory (Olweus, 1978), which argues that victims may be mistreated due to being perceived either as "weak" and submissive, or as annoying and provocative.

Certain employee attributes are more likely to lead to higher rates of abusive supervision. In particular, those with negative self-beliefs including low self-esteem, high neuroticism, or poor core self-evaluations (an integrative trait-like characteristic consisting of self-efficacy, self-esteem, locus of control, and low neuroticism) are more likely to report abusive supervision (Burton & Hoobler, 2006; Henle & Gross, 2014; Kiazad et al., 2010; Kluemper et al., 2019; Neves, 2014; Nevicka et al., 2018; Vogel & Mitchell, 2017; Wang et al., 2019; Wu & Hu, 2009; Yan et al., 2020). It is unclear to what extent these reports are due largely to perceptual biases (Brees et al., 2016) and/or because their behaviors resulting from their poor self-concepts display weaknesses or irritate supervisors, which may make these employees more likely to be targeted by hostile leader behaviors (Kluemper et al., 2019).

Certain employee workplace behaviors have also been found to be associated with increased abusive supervision. Low-performing employees may be targeted due to failing to meet performance expectations (Liang et al., 2016; Shen et al., 2021), particularly if supervisors perceive them as being outside their "scope of justice" and undeserving of ethical treatment (Tepper et al., 2011) or if supervisors make internal attributions (i.e., the employees are to blame) for poor performance (Lyubykh et al., 2022). Additionally, when supervisors assume that employees are failing to meet performance expectations for hostile reasons, this can increase rates of abusive supervision (Liang et al., 2016). Employees who engage in destructive, counterproductive performance behaviors such as deviance (e.g., insulting supervisors or gossiping about them behind their backs) are also more likely to report subsequently being abused (Camps et al., 2020; Lian, Ferris, et al., 2014; Mawritz et al., 2017).

Even high-performing employees can be targeted for abuse. This is more likely to occur when supervisors perceive the employees as a threat to the organizational hierarchy (Khan et al., 2018) or when supervisors are envious of employees and feel threatened by them (Yu et al., 2018). Additionally, when high-performing employees also behave rudely and undermine the supervisor, abusive supervision is more likely to result for supervisors who are focused on bottom-line outcomes such as profit (Mawritz et al., 2017).

The quality of the relationships between employees and supervisors can also impact abuse. For example, employees who have a poor leader-member exchange relationship with supervisors (i.e., the quality of the two-way interactions between the individuals) are more likely to report abusive supervision (Harris et al., 2011). Additionally, just as people experience more negative interactions with some others depending on their different beliefs or personalities, particular combinations of employee and supervisor individual characteristics can also increase conflict and ultimately impact the likelihood of abusive supervision (May et al., 2014). For example, when supervisors perceive their employees as having differing attitudes or values, or if they have other personality conflicts—such as both individuals having dominant tendencies—this is likely to lead to greater relationship conflict between the two individuals and result in subsequent abusive supervision (Graham et al., 2019; Tepper et al., 2011).

The use of victim precipitation arguments in workplace mistreatment research is not without its critics. Labeling the triggers of abuse as employee-driven can lead to victim blaming, which is one reason why the criminology literature, for example, has started to move away from this framing (Cortina et al., 2018). One approach researchers have taken is to avoid arguments that connote blame, and instead consider employee behaviors or characteristics as contributing to abusive supervision processes while still recommending that supervisors are held accountable for engaging in demeaning behaviors.

CONSEQUENCES OF ABUSIVE SUPERVISION

Effects on Employees.   Abuse can lead to detrimental psychological effects and counterproductive employee behaviors for a number of reasons. First, being mistreated can contribute to an employee's sense of powerlessness (Li et al., 2021). Employees working for abusive supervisors are also more likely to experience sleep deprivation and be emotionally exhausted (Han et al., 2017). Like supervisors who have difficulty self-regulating after being mistreated, employees can experience ego depletion and struggle with self-control after being abused by supervisors (Yuan et al., 2020) and experience emotions such as anger and fear (Simon et al., 2015). Not surprisingly, they are also more likely to experience work stress as a result of abusive supervision (Zhang et al., 2019).

Furthermore, experiences of abusive supervision can lead to employees becoming paranoid (Chan & McAllister, 2014; Lopes et al., 2019; Oh & Farh, 2017), fearful, and defensively silent (Kiewitz et al., 2016). Victims of abusive supervision are also more likely to experience reduced self-esteem (Vogel & Mitchell, 2017) and lower occupational self-efficacy (i.e., confidence in one's ability to perform job tasks; Lyubykh et al., 2022) and to believe that their peers respect them less as a result of the abuse (Schaubroeck et al., 2016).

Taken together, abusive supervision leads to many deleterious mental and physical health outcomes for employees (Carlson et al., 2012; Liang, Hanig, et al., 2018). Employees can ultimately experience heightened psychological distress (e.g., lower life satisfaction, greater depression, greater anxiety, greater emotional exhaustion) and negative states related to their jobs (e.g., lower job satisfaction and lower affective commitment) as a result of experiencing abusive supervision (Stempel & Rigotti, 2022; Tepper, 2000).

Unsurprisingly, the psychological effects of abusive supervision can lead to negative behavioral outcomes. Employees who experience abuse are more likely to engage in family conflict at home (Carlson et al., 2012; Hoobler & Brass, 2006; Hoobler & Hu, 2013; Wu et al., 2012), behave deviantly toward their organizations and supervisors (Lian, Brown, et al., 2014; Mitchell & Ambrose, 2007; Thau et al., 2009), engage in worsening reciprocal relational interactions with their supervisors (Simon et al., 2015), be less likely to engage in beneficial organizational citizenship behaviors (Zellars et al., 2002), perform worse at their jobs (Tepper, 2000), experience reduced creativity (Han et al., 2017), and engage in problem drinking (Bamberger & Bacharach, 2006), and ultimately are more likely to leave their organizations (Haar et al., 2016).

While the outcomes of abusive supervision are generally negative for employees, some fare better under conditions of abuse. For example, highly conscientious employees (i.e., those who are goal-oriented, organized, and dependable) appear to be better able to cope with abusive supervision and are less likely to engage in deviance than those with low conscientiousness after experiencing abusive supervision (Mawritz, Dust, & Resick, 2014). Experiencing positive emotions (i.e., positive affect) can also play a role in reducing the strain resulting from abusive supervision (Harvey et al., 2007).

How Supervisors React to Their Own Abusive Behavior. The effects of abusive supervision can also extend to the leaders themselves. For example, after engaging in abusive behaviors, supervisors can experience a diminished sense of self-worth, though those who have psychopathic tendencies are less likely to feel badly about themselves after behaving abusively (Priesemuth & Bigelow, 2020). Supervisors who mistreat employees can also feel an increased sense of power (Ju et al., 2019). Behaviorally, supervisors can react in a variety of ways after reflecting on their past abusive behavior. For example, when leaders talk about their past abusive behavior, they are more likely to feel hostile toward the employee they have previously mistreated and continue to engage in abusive actions (Chen, Qin, Johnson, et al., 2021). At the same time, some abusive supervisors may also experience feelings of guilt and recognition that their behaviors are unethical. As a result of their guilt, they can attempt to "make up" for their problematic behaviors by engaging in constructive leadership behaviors toward employees (Liao et al., 2018; Shum et al., 2020), even though these actions can sometimes be driven by image concerns (McClean et al., 2021).

Finally, leaders' abusive supervision can also have an impact on how they are perceived at work. In general, abusive supervisors are seen as less effective leaders (Johnson et al., 2012), particularly if they are female (due to female abusive leaders being seen as violating gender stereotypes; Kim et al., 2021). In summary, abusive supervision not only harms employees, but also has negative repercussions for the leaders themselves.

Beyond Employees and Supervisors: Effects on Witnesses. Witnesses to abusive supervisors, such as coworkers, can also experience adverse reactions to abusive supervision, even if they are not targeted by the leaders themselves. The deontic model of justice argues that witnesses can feel similarly to victims of mistreatment (Cropanzano et al., 2003). Witnesses may retaliate against the supervisor for mistreating their coworkers and engage in helping behavior toward the abused coworker (Mitchell et al., 2015; Priesemuth & Schminke, 2019). However, witnesses also can experience feelings of schadenfreude toward the targeted employees (Chen, Qin, Yam, & Wang, 2021; Qiao et al., 2021; Xu et al., 2020) and, in some cases, even contribute to further mistreatment toward the employee and "pile on" by excluding the abused employee when they believe the employee deserves the treatment (Bigelow, 2021; Mitchell et al., 2015). Witnesses to abuse, particularly pregnant working women, are also more likely to eventually leave their organization (Thompson et al., 2022).

At the team level, research has demonstrated that abusive supervision is often directed at groups of employees rather than just individuals (Farh & Chen, 2014; Priesemuth et al., 2014; Rousseau & Aubé, 2018). However, reports of abusive supervision can vary among individuals in the organization, which can be due to perceptual factors as well as the leader behaving differently toward various employees (Ambrose & Ganegoda, 2020; Ogunfowora, 2013). One factor that may lead to disparate abusive supervision reports involves leaders who are inconsistently abusive (Korman et al., 2021). Leaders often vary their behavior, and are rarely static in the types of interactions they have with employees (Matta et al., 2017). Duffy and colleagues (2002) considered when supervisors could behave in ways that could be both abusive and supportive, and they found that the negative outcomes were worse for employees when they experienced inconsistent mistreatment versus predictably consistent abusive supervision. Some abusive supervision research also explores how abuse continues over time (Kiewitz et al., 2016), and by examining these dynamic patterns of leadership, researchers can better understand the nuances of how abusive supervision forms as well as its impacts on employees (McClean et al., 2019).

Are There Any Benefits to Abuse? Can abusive supervision ever lead to positive outcomes? People may point to famous examples of effective leaders who were reported by some of their employees to be abusive, such as Steve Jobs of Apple or the well-known basketball coach Bobby Knight, as examples of abusive supervision being effective for high performance (Tepper et al., 2017). However, the few exceptions in research that highlight an "upside" to abusive supervision demonstrate limited potential benefits.

Some employees can engage in constructive, productive behaviors as a result of experiencing abuse. For example, individuals who have a high locus of control (i.e., a belief that they are in control of the outcomes in their lives) are more likely to attempt to problem-solve in the wake of being mistreated, such as asking for advice from others and trying to discuss the issue with the perpetrator (Mitchell & Ambrose, 2012). Additionally, when employees perceive abusive supervisors as caring about promoting high performance as a motive for their treatment (instead of hostile motives), employees are more likely to have an increase in task performance the next day (Liao et al., 2021). However, this effect is likely short-lived and does not help supervisors' performance goals in the long term, particularly since many employees are likely to assume supervisors are driven by hostility when they behave abusively (Liao et al., 2021).

One of the few potential long-term benefits of experiencing abusive supervision could be posttraumatic growth, where an individual is able to develop resilience and experience other growth benefits as a result of being mistreated (Vogel & Bolino, 2020). However, experiencing abuse can alternatively lead to posttraumatic stress and affect employees' careers detrimentally for years after the abuse occurs (Vogel & Bolino, 2020). Taken together, the body of research on abusive supervision suggests that short-term gains from hostile leader behavior and long-term benefits such as posttraumatic growth are likely to be experienced by only a minority of employees and ultimately offset by the harm resulting from abusive treatment. Thus, the research suggests that when abusive leaders achieve effective performance outcomes for their organizations, one can generally consider their success being *in spite of* rather than *because of* their abusive behavior, and only a minority of employees are more likely to be more motivated by abusive supervision than other forms of leadership. Additionally, the cost of abusive supervisors to organizations is high. When organizations retain high performers who treat others with hostility, the organizations often lose money in the long term due to higher turnover, time spent addressing the supervisors' behaviors, and other indirect effects of supervisor bullying behaviors (Sutton, 2007).

EFFECTIVE INTERVENTIONS

Organizational Interventions. One way for organizations to address abusive supervision is to reduce the likelihood of it occurring in the first place. One effective intervention is leadership training. For example, organizations can train supervisors to reinforce their positive support of subordinates in the workplace. Supervisors can engage in supportive behaviors with tactics such as benevolence, sincerity, fairness, and mindfulness, which can help leaders to enhance their perceived supervisor support and lower abusive supervision rates (Gonzalez-Morales et al., 2018). A second option involves sociotechnical interventions, which involve primarily changing objective work conditions with a focus on reducing or eliminating stressors. This intervention involves improving workplace conditions and can increase occupational health and safety for all employees (Kelloway & Barling, 2010).

Interventions can also focus on reducing the negative impacts of abusive supervision. One way to do this is to structure employees' jobs by giving them increased job autonomy (i.e., control over their work) and allow them to engage in job crafting to design their jobs, which can have positive impacts on employee job satisfaction, motivation, and organizational commitment. These techniques can be particularly advantageous for employees experiencing abusive supervision since providing them the opportunity to decide how to structure their work can reduce the extent to which they rely on their supervisor and help them regain feelings of control in the workplace (Tuan, 2019; Velez & Neves, 2016). Additionally, giving employees clear guidance on their job roles can reduce the likelihood of employees engaging in aggressive behavior after experiencing abuse (Priesemuth et al., 2022). Taken together, the research on interventions suggests that reducing ambiguity in employees' job roles while also giving them a sense of control over their work can help mitigate some of the negative effects of abusive supervision.

Individual Techniques and Coping.　Employees can also engage in behaviors that help mitigate the effects of abusive supervision in the workplace. Focusing on goals is one potentially advantageous approach. In particular, by having a high commitment to achieving their goals, employees can be more resilient to an abusive supervisor (Sungu et al., 2020). Employees can also disrupt continuing abuse by engaging in behaviors that alter the power imbalance present in the supervisor-employee relationship; by making themselves instrumental to the supervisors' goals, employees are less likely to continue to be mistreated (Wee et al., 2017). Combined with feeling positive emotions, if employees ingratiate themselves with their supervisor (i.e., behave in a friendly way), they are less likely to experience job tension due to abusive supervision (Harvey et al., 2007). Employees can also use upward maintenance tactics; by actively managing their relationship with supervisors, employees can minimize the harmful effects of abusive supervision and also make it less likely for abuse to occur in the first place (Tepper, 2007).

Research further demonstrates that social support, particularly support from one's coworkers, can be key in helping employees cope with abusive supervision (Duffy et al., 2002; Hobman et al., 2009; Rasheed et al., 2021). Retaliation toward abusive supervisors through deviant behaviors can also increase employee feelings of well-being due to restored perceptions of justice, though "getting back" at supervisors carries risk and may not be advisable (Liang et al., 2022). Another less risky and more ethical retaliation technique involves using a doll that represents the abusive supervisor: Using symbolic retaliation through the use of sticking pins in the doll can be cathartic for those who have experienced leader mistreatment (Liang, Brown, et al., 2018).

International Differences.　In the context of perceptions of abusive supervision, it is critical to consider cross-cultural differences since employees' perceptions of supervisory injustice are affected by culture (Shao et al., 2011). For instance, Confucian Asian cultures (i.e., Singapore, Taiwan, etc.) tend to consider abusive supervision more normative than Western cultures (i.e., the United States, Australia, etc.). As a result, employees in Western cultures may experience the negative effects of abusive supervision more strongly than those in Confucian Asian cultures (Vogel et al., 2015). As more companies operate in multinational environments and employ individuals from diverse cultural backgrounds, abusive supervisory behaviors and hostile work environments may be perceived differently, and the impacts on employees' workplace attitudes and well-being will also be varied (Kernan et al., 2011). Organizational leaders operating in a cross-cultural context can consider how various cultural orientations can impact how employees respond to abusive supervision. For example, those with higher power distance values (i.e., a belief that there should be differential power dynamics between supervisors and employees, which is more common in Eastern cultures) are less likely to experience negative outcomes of abusive supervision (Zhang & Liao, 2015). The findings suggest that employees in Western cultures, who tend to have lower power distance beliefs, may be more susceptible to the negative effects of abusive supervision.

However, limited research has compared findings from different countries to evaluate the perceptions of abusive supervision in cross-cultural settings (Mackey et al., 2017). The predominant location of research on abusive supervision has been the United States, with approximately 32% of published studies. The second most commonly studied location is China, with 25% of published studies on abusive supervision. The next most commonly studied location is the Philippines, with 4% of published studies (Fischer et al., 2021). Given the heavy reliance on U.S. samples, many abusive supervision findings may not be generalizable to other cultures (Tepper, 2007). Some barriers to studying abusive supervision in non-Western samples may be influenced by the prevalence of North American researchers studying the abusive supervision phenomena, as well as concerns about generalizability that are disproportionately raised during peer review when studies are conducted in a non-Western context (Avery et al., 2022).[2]

CONCLUSIONS

The abusive supervision literature captures a wide range of psychological processes related to leaders, employees, teams, and witnesses. Research has considered past leader experiences and personality traits that are more likely to lead to abusive supervision, as well as contextual factors and aspects of the supervisor-employee relationship that can increase hostile supervisory behavior. The evidence overwhelmingly demonstrates that abusive supervision leads to negative employee outcomes, though there are interventions that both organizations and employees can take to reduce the chances of abusive supervision occurring and having harmful effects on workplace outcomes. Research also continues to assess the perceptual biases and objective leader behaviors that contribute to reports of abusive supervision, as well as consider how abusive supervision can change and fluctuate over time. By incorporating various ways to measure and study abusive supervision, including using dynamic models of leader behavior and understanding the phenomenon across multiple cultures, researchers and practitioners can continue to gain insight into how to reduce the likelihood that employees experience abusive treatment in the workplace.

FURTHER READING

Peng, A., Mitchell, R., & Schaubroeck, J. M. (2019). Abusive supervision. In *Oxford Research Encyclopedia of business and management*. Oxford University Press.

REFERENCES

Ambrose, M. L., & Ganegoda, D. B. (2020). Abusive according to whom? Manager and subordinate perceptions of abusive supervision and supervisors' performance. *Journal of Organizational Behavior, 41*(8), 737–756.

Aryee, S., Chen, Z. X., Sun, L.-Y., & Debrah, Y. A. (2007). Antecedents and outcomes of abusive supervision: Test of a trickle-down model. *Journal of Applied Psychology, 92*(1), 191–201.

Avery, D. R., Darren, K. B., Dumas, T. L., George, E., Aparna, J., Loyd, D. L., van Knippenberg, D., Wang, M., & Xu, H. (2022). Racial biases in the publication process: Exploring expressions and solutions. *Journal of Management, 48*(1), 7–16.

Bamberger, P. A., & Bacharach, S. B. (2006). Abusive supervision and subordinate problem drinking: Taking resistance, stress and subordinate personality into account. *Human Relations, 59*(6), 723–752.

Bandura, A. (1973). *Aggression: A social learning analysis*. Prentice-Hall.

Barnes, C. M., Lucianetti, L., Bhave, D. P., & Christian, M. S. (2015). You wouldn't like me when I'm sleepy: Leaders' sleep, daily abusive supervision, and work unit engagement. *Academy of Management Journal, 58*(5), 1419–1437

Bigelow, B. (2021). Observer responses to workplace mistreatment: A competitive test of multiple theoretical perspectives. [Doctoral dissertation, University of Central Florida].

Blau, P. M. (1964). *Exchange and power in social life*. Transaction Publishers.

Bowling, N. A., & Beehr, T. A. (2006). Workplace harassment from the victim's perspective: A theoretical model and meta-analysis. *Journal of Applied Psychology, 91*(5), 998–1012.

Brees, J., Mackey, J., Martinko, M., & Harvey, P. (2014). The mediating role of perceptions of a abusive supervision in the relationship between personality and aggression. *Journal of Leadership & Organizational Studies, 21*(4), 403–413.

Brees, J., Martinko, M., & Harvey, P. (2016). Abusive supervision: Subordinate personality or supervisor behavior? *Journal of Managerial Psychology, 31*(2), 405–419.

Burton, J. P., & Hoobler, J. M. (2006). Subordinate self-esteem and abusive supervision. *Journal of Managerial Issues, 18*(3), 340–355.

Burton, J. P., Hoobler, J. M., & Scheuer, M. L. (2012). Supervisor workplace stress and abusive supervision: The buffering effect of exercise. *Journal of Business and Psychology, 27*(3), 271–279.

Camps, J., Stouten, J., Euwema, M., & De Cremer, D. (2020). Abusive supervision as a response to follower hostility: A moderated mediation model. *Journal of Business Ethics, 164*, 495–514.

Carlson, D., Ferguson, M., Hunter, E., & Whitten, D. (2012). Abusive supervision and work-family conflict: The path through emotional labor and burnout. *The Leadership Quarterly, 23*(5), 849–859.

Chan, M. E., & McAllister, D. J. (2014). Abusive supervision through the lens of employee state paranoia. *Academy of Management Review, 39*(1), 44–66.

Chen, C., Qin, X., Johnson, R. E., Huang, M., Yang, M., & Liu, S. (2021). Entering an upward spiral: Investigating how and when supervisors' talking about abuse leads to subsequent abusive supervision. *Journal of Organizational Behavior, 42*(3), 407–428.

Chen, C., Qin, X., Yam, K. C., & Wang, H. (2021). Empathy or schadenfreude? Exploring observers' differential responses to abusive supervision. *Journal of Business and Psychology, 36*, 1077–1094.

Cortina, L. M., Rabelo, V. C., & Holland, K. J. (2018). Beyond blaming the victim: Toward a more progressive understanding of workplace mistreatment. *Industrial and Organizational Psychology: Perspectives on Science and Practice, 11*(1), 81–100.

Courtright, S. H., Gardner, R. G., Smith, T. A., McCormick, B. W., & Colbert, A. E. (2016). My family made me do it: A cross-domain, self-regulatory perspective on antecedents to abusive supervision. *Academy of Management Journal, 59*(5), 1630–1652.

Cropanzano, R., Goldman, B., & Folger, R. (2003). Deontic justice: The role of moral principles in workplace fairness. *Journal of Organizational Behavior, 24*(8), 1019–1024.

Duffy, M. K., Ganster, D. C., & Pagon, M. (2002). Social undermining in the workplace. *Academy of Management Journal, 45*(2), 331–351.

Eissa, G., & Lester, S. W. (2021). A moral disengagement investigation of how and when supervisor psychological entitlement instigates abusive supervision. *Journal of Business Ethics, 169*, 1–20.

Eissa, G., Lester, S. W., & Gupta, R. (2020). Interpersonal deviance and abusive supervision: The mediating role of supervisor negative emotions and the moderating role of subordinate organizational citizenship behavior. *Journal of Business Ethics, 166*(3), 577–594.

Farh, C. I. C., & Chen, Z. (2014). Beyond the individual victim: Multilevel consequences of abusive supervision in teams. *Journal of Applied Psychology, 99*(6), 1074–095.

Fischer, T., Tian, A. W., Lee, A., & Hughes, D. J. (2021). Abusive supervision: A systematic review and fundamental rethink. *The Leadership Quarterly, 32*(6), 101054.

Garcia, P. R. J. M., Restubog, S. L. D., Kiewitz, C., Scott, K. L., & Tang, R. L. (2014). Roots run deep: Investigating psychological mechanisms between history of family aggression and abusive supervision. *Journal of Applied Psychology, 99*(5), 883–897.

Gonzalez-Morales, M. G., Kernan, M. C., Becker, T. E., & Eisenberger, R. (2018). Defeating abusive supervision: Training supervisors to support subordinates. *Journal of Occupational Health Psychology, 23*(2), 151–162.

Graham, K. A., Mawritz, M. B., Dust, S. B., Greenbaum, R. L., & Ziegert, J. C. (2019). Too many cooks in the kitchen: The effects of dominance incompatibility on relationship conflict and subsequent abusive supervision. *The Leadership Quarterly, 30*(3), 351–364.

Haar, J. M., de Fluiter, A., & Brougham, D. (2016). Abusive supervision and turnover intentions: The mediating role of perceived organisational support. *Journal of Management & Organization, 22*(2), 139–153.

Han, G. H., Harms, P. D., & Bai, Y. (2017). Nightmare bosses: The impact of abusive supervision on employees' sleep, emotions, and creativity. *Journal of Business Ethics, 145*(1), 21–31.

Harris, K. J., Harvey, P., & Kacmar, M. (2011). Abusive supervisory reactions to coworker relationship conflict. *The Leadership Quarterly, 22*(5), 1010–1023.

Harvey, P., Harris, K. J., Gillis, W. E., & Martinko, M. J. (2014). Abusive supervision and the entitled employee. *The Leadership Quarterly, 25*(2), 204–217.

Harvey, P., Soner, J., Hochwarter, W., & Kacmar, C. (2007). Coping with abusive supervision: The neutralizing effects of ingratiation and positive affect on negative employee outcomes. *The Leadership Quarterly, 18*(3), 264–280.

Henle, C. A., & Gross, M. A. (2014). What have I done to deserve this? Effects of employee personality and emotion on abusive supervision. *Journal of Business Ethics, 122*(3), 461–474.

Hobman, E. V., Restubog, S. L. D., Bordia, P., & Tang, R. L. (2009). Abusive supervision in advising relationships: Investigating the role of social support. *Applied Psychology: An International Review, 58*(2), 233–256.

Hoobler, J. M., & Brass, D. J. (2006). Abusive supervision and family undermining as displaced aggression. *Journal of Applied Psychology, 91*(5), 1125–1133.

Hoobler, J. M., & Hu, J. (2013). A model of injustice, abusive supervision, and negative affect. *The Leadership Quarterly, 24*(1), 256–269.

Hu, L., & Liu, Y. (2017). Abuse for status: A social dominance perspective of abusive supervision. *Human Resource Management Review, 27*(2), 328–337.

Huh, E., & Lee, E.-S. (2019). The roles of past workplace ostracism and current perceived power in predicting abusive supervision. *Academy of Management Proceedings, 2019*(1), 17814.

Johnson, R. E., Venus, M., Lanaj, K., Mao, C., & Chang, C.-H. (2012). Leader identity as an antecedent of the frequency and consistency of transformational, consideration, and abusive leadership behaviors. *Journal of Applied Psychology, 97*(6), 1262–1272.

Ju, D., Huang, M., Liu, D., Qin, X., Hu, Q., & Chen, C. (2019). Supervisory consequences of abusive supervision: An investigation of sense of power, managerial self-efficacy, and task-oriented leadership behavior. *Organizational Behavior and Human Decision Processes, 154,* 80–95.

Kelloway, E. K., & Barling, J. (2010). Leadership development as an intervention in occupational health psychology. *Work & Stress, 24*(3), 260–279.

Kernan, M. C., Watson, S., Fang Chen, F., & Gyu Kim, T. (2011). How cultural values affect the impact of abusive supervision on worker attitudes. *Cross Cultural Management: An International Journal, 18*(4), 464–484.

Khan, A. K., Moss, S., Quratulain, S., & Hameed, I. (2018). When and how subordinate performance leads to abusive supervision: A social dominance perspective. *Journal of Management, 44*(7), 2801–2826.

Kiazad, K., Restubog, S. L. D., Zagenczyk, T. J., Kiewitz, C., & Tang, R. L. (2010). In pursuit of power: The role of authoritarian leadership in the relationship between supervisors' Machiavellianism and the subordinates' perceptions. *Journal of Research in Personality, 44*(4), 512–519.

Kiewitz, C., Restubog, S. L., Zagencyz, T. J., Scott, K. D., Raymund, P., Garcia, J. M., & Tang, R. L. (2012). Sins of the parents: Self-control as a buffer between supervisors' previous experience of family undermining and subordinates' perceptions of abusive supervision. *The Leadership Quarterly, 23*(5), 869–882.

Kiewitz, C., Restubog, S. L. D., Shoss, M. K., Garcia, P. R. J. M., & Tang, R. L. (2016). Suffering in silence: Investigating the role of fear in the relationship between abusive supervision and defensive silence. *Journal of Applied Psychology, 101*(5), 731–742.

Kim, J. K., Harold, C. M., & Holtz, B. C. (2021). Evaluations of abusive supervisors: The moderating role of the abuser's gender. *Journal of Organizational Behavior, 43*(3), 465–482.

Kluemper, D. H., Mossholder, K. W., Ispas, D., Bing, M. N., Iliescu, D., & Ilie, A. (2019). When core self-evaluations influence employees' deviant reactions to abusive supervision: The moderating role of cognitive ability. *Journal of Business Ethics, 159*(2), 435–453.

Korman, B. A., Tröster, C., & Giessner, S. R. N. (2021). The consequences of incongruent abusive supervision: Anticipation of social exclusion, shame, and turnover intentions. *Journal of Leadership and Organizational Studies, 28*(3), 306–321.

Lemoine, G. J., Hartnell, C. A., & Leroy, H. (2019). Taking stock of moral approaches to leadership: An integrative review of ethical, authentic, and servant leadership. *Academy of Management Annals, 13*(1), 148–187.

Li., R., Chen, Z., Zhang, H., & Luo, J. (2021). How do authoritarian leadership and abusive supervision jointly thwart follower proactivity? A social control perspective. *Journal of Management, 47*(4), 930–956.

Li, Y., Wang, Z., Yang, L.-Q., & Liu, S. (2016). The crossover of psychological distress from leaders to subordinates in teams: The role of abusive supervision, psychological capital, and team performance. *Journal of Occupational Health Psychology, 21*(2), 142–153.

Lian, H., Brown, D. J., Ferris, D. L., Liang, L. H., Keeping, L. M., & Morrison, R. (2014). Abusive supervision and retaliation: A self-control framework. *Academy of Management Journal, 57*(1), 1513–1534.

Lian, H., Ferris, D. L., Morrison, R., & Brown, D. J. (2014). Blame it on the supervisor or the subordinate? Reciprocal relations between abusive supervision and organizational deviance. *Journal of Applied Psychology, 99*(4), 651–664.

Liang, L. H., Brown, D. J., Lian, H., Hanig, S., Ferris, D. L., & Keeping, L. M. (2018). Righting a wrong: Retaliation on a voodoo doll symbolizing an abusive supervisor restores justice. *The Leadership Quarterly, 29*(4), 443–456.

Liang, L. H., Coulombe, C., Brown, D. J., Lian, H., Hanig, S., Ferris, D. L., & Keeping, L. M. (2022). Can two wrongs make a right? The buffering effect of retaliation on subordinate well-being following abusive supervision. *Journal of Occupational Health Psychology, 27*(1), 37–52.

Liang, L. H., Hanig, S., Evans, R., Brown, D. J., & Lian, H. (2018). Why is your boss making you sick? A longitudinal investigation modeling time-lagged relations between abusive supervision and employee physical health. *Journal of Organizational Behavior, 39*(9), 1050–1065.

Liang, L. H., Lian, H., Brown, D. B., Ferris, D. L., Hanig, S., & Keeping, L. (2016). Why are abusive supervisors abusive? A dual-system of self-control model. *Academy of Management Journal, 59*(4), 1385–1406.

Liao, Z., Lee, H. W., Johnson, R. E., Song, Z., & Liu, Y. (2021). Seeing from a short-term perspective: When and why daily abusive supervisor behavior yields functional and dysfunctional consequences. *Journal of Applied Psychology, 106*(3), 377–398.

Liao, Z., Yam, K. C., Johnson, R. E., Liu, W., & Song, Z. (2018). Cleansing my abuse: A reparative response model of perpetrating abusive supervisor behavior. *Journal of Applied Psychology, 103*(9), 1039–1056.

Liu, D., Liao, H., & Loi, R. (2012). The dark side of leadership: A three-level investigation of the cascading effect of abusive supervision on employee creativity. *Academy of Management Journal, 55*(5), 1187–1212.

Lopes, B. C., Kamau, C., & Jaspal, R. (2019). Coping with perceived abusive supervision: The role of paranoia. *Journal of Leadership & Organizational Studies, 26*(2), 237–255.

Lyubykh, Z., Bozeman, J., Herschcovis, M. S., Turner, N., & Shan, V. (2022). Employee performance and abusive supervision: The role of supervisor over-attributions. *Journal of Organizational Behavior, 32*(1), 125–145.

Mackey, J. D., Ellen, P. E., McAllister, C. P., & Alexander, K. C. (2021). The dark side of leadership: A systematic literature review and meta-analysis of destructive leadership research. *Journal of Business Research, 132*, 705–718.

Mackey, J. D., Frieder, R. E., Brees, J. R., & Martinko, M. J. (2017). Abusive supervision: A meta-analysis and empirical review. *Journal of Management, 43*(6), 1940–1965.

Martinko, M. J., Harvey, P., Brees, J. R., & Mackey, J. (2013). A review of abusive supervision research. *Journal of Organizational Behavior, 34*(S1), 120–137.

Martinko, M. J., Mackey, J. D., Moss, S. E., Harvey, P., McAllister, C. P., & Brees, J. R. (2018). An exploration of the role of subordinate affect in leader evaluations. *Journal of Applied Psychology, 103*(7), 738–752.

Mathieu, C., & Babiak, P. (2016). Corporate psychopathy and abusive supervision: Their influence on employees' job satisfaction and turnover intentions. *Personality and Individual Differences, 91*, 102–106.

Matta, F. K., Scott, B. A., Colquitt, J. A., Koopman, J., & Passantino, L. (2017). Is consistently unfair better than sporadically fair? An investigation of justice variability and stress. *Academy of Management Journal, 60*(2), 154–180.

Mawritz, M. B., Dust, S. B., & Resick, C. J. (2014). Hostile climate, abusive supervision, and employee coping: Does conscientiousness matter? *Journal of Applied Psychology, 99*(4), 737–747.

Mawritz, M. B., Folger, R., & Latham, G. P. (2014). Supervisors' exceedingly difficult goals and abusive supervision: The mediating effects of hindrance stress, anger, and anxiety. *Journal of Organizational Behavior, 35*(3), 358–372.

Mawritz, M. B., Greenbaum, R. L., Butts, M. M., & Graham, K. A. (2017). I just can't control myself: A self-regulation perspective on the abuse of deviant employees. *Academy of Management Journal, 60*(4), 1482–1503.

Mawritz, M. B., Mayer, D. M., Hoobler, H. M., Wayne, S. J., & Marinova, S. V. (2012). A trickledown model of abusive supervision. *Personnel Psychology, 65*(2), 325–357.

May, D., Wesche, J. S., Heinitz, K., & Kerschreiter, R. (2014). Coping with destructive leadership: Putting forward an integrated theoretical framework for the interaction process between leaders and followers. *Journal of Psychology, 222*(4), 203–213.

McClean, S. T., Barnes, C. M., Courtright, S. H., & Johnson, R. E. (2019). Resetting the clock on dynamic leader behaviors: A conceptual integration and agenda for future research. *Academy of Management Annals, 13*, 479–508.

McClean, S. T., Courtright, S. H., Yim, J., & Smith, T. A. (2021). Making nice or faking nice? Exploring supervisors' two-faced response to their past abusive behavior. *Personnel Psychology, 74*(4), 693–719.

Mitchell, M. S., & Ambrose, M. L. (2007). Abusive supervision and workplace deviance and the moderating effects of negative reciprocity beliefs. *Journal of Applied Psychology, 92*(4), 1159–1168.

Mitchell, M. S., & Ambrose, M. L. (2012). Employees' behavioral reactions to supervisor aggression: An examination of individual and situational factors. *Journal of Applied Psychology, 97*(6), 1148–1170.

Mitchell, M. S., Vogel, R. M., & Folger, R. (2015). Third parties' reactions to the abusive supervision of coworkers. *Journal of Applied Psychology, 100*(4), 1040–1055.

Namie, G. (2017). *U.S. Workplace Bullying Survey.* Workplace Bullying Institute. https://workplacebullying .org/download/2017-wbi/

Neves, P. (2014). Taking it out on survivors: Submissive employees, downsizing, and abusive supervision. *Journal of Occupational and Organizational Psychology, 87*(3), 507–534.

Nevicka, B., De Hoogh, A. H., Den Hartog, D. N., & Belschak, F. D. (2018). Narcissistic leaders and their victims: Followers low on self-esteem and low on core self-evaluations suffer most. *Frontiers in Psychology, 9,* 422.

Ogunfowora, B. (2013). When the abuse is unevenly distributed: The effects of abusive supervision variability on work attitudes and behaviors. *Journal of Organizational Behavior, 34*(8), 1105–1123.

Oh, K. J., & Farh, C. (2017). An emotional process theory of how subordinates appraise, experience, and respond to abusive supervision over time. *Academy of Management Review, 42*(2), 207–232.

Olweus, D. (1978). *Aggression in the schools: Bullies and whipping boys.* Hemisphere.

Pan, S.-Y., & Lin, K. J. (2018). Who suffers when supervisors are unhappy? The roles of leader-member exchange and abusive supervision. *Journal of Business Ethics, 151*(3), 799–811.

Priesemuth, M., & Bigelow, B. (2020). It hurts me too! (or not?): Exploring the negative implications for abusive bosses. *Journal of Applied Psychology, 105*(4), 410–421.

Priesemuth, M., & Schminke, M. (2019). Helping thy neighbor: Prosocial reactions to observed abusive supervision in the workplace. *Journal of Management, 45*(3), 1225–1251.

Priesemuth, M., Arnaud, A., & Schminke, M. (2013). Bad behavior is groups: The impact overall justice climate and functional dependence on counterproductive work behavior in work units. *Group & Organization Management, 38*(2), 230–257.

Priesemuth, M., Schminke, M., Ambrose, M. L., & Folger, R. (2014). Abusive supervision climate: A multiple-mediation model of its impact on group outcomes. *Academy of Management Journal, 57*(5), 1513–1534.

Priesemuth, M., Schminke, M., Bigelow, B., & Mitchell, M. (2022). A light at the end of the tunnel: How the right workplace structure can help disrupt the negative impact of abusive supervision. *Human Performance, 35*(2), 71–93.

Qiao, Y., Zhang, Z., & Jia, M. (2021). Their pain, our pleasure: How and when peer abusive supervision leads to third parties' schadenfreude and work engagement. *Journal of Business Ethics, 169*(4), 695–711.

Qin, X., Dust, S. B., DiRenzo, M. S., & Wang, S. (2020). Negative creativity in leader-follower relations: A daily investigation of leaders' creative mindset, moral disengagement, and abusive supervision. *Journal of Business and Psychology, 35*(5), 665–682.

Rasheed, M. I., Weng, Q., Umrani, W. A., & Moin, M. F. (2021). Abusive supervision and career adaptability: The role of self-efficacy and coworker support. *Human Performance, 34*(4), 239–256.

Rousseau, V., & Aubé, C. (2018). When leaders stifle innovation in work teams: The role of abusive supervision. *Journal of Business Ethics, 151*(3), 651–664.

Schaubroeck, J. M., Peng, A. C., & Hannah, S. T. (2016). The role of peer respect in linking abusive supervision to follower outcomes: Dual moderation of group potency. *Journal of Applied Psychology, 101*(2), 267–278.

Shao, R., Rupp, D. E., Skarlicki, D. P., & Jones, K. S. (2011). Employee justice across cultures. *Journal of Management, 39*(1), 263–301.

Shen, W., Liang, L. H., Brown, D. J., Ni, D., & Zheng, X. (2021). Subordinate poor performance as a stressor on leader well-being: The mediating role of abusive supervision and the moderating role of motives for abuse. *Journal of Occupational Health Psychology, 26*(6), 491–506.

Shum, C., Ausar, K., & Tu, M.-H. (2020). When do abusive leaders experience guilt? *International Journal of Contemporary Hospitality and Management, 32,* 2239–2256.

Simon, L. S., Hurst, C., Kelley, K., & Judge, T. A. (2015). Understanding cycles of abuse: A multimotive approach. *Journal of Applied Psychology, 100*(6), 1798–1810.

Stempel, C. R., & Rigotti, T. (2022). Threatening the self: The conditional indirect effect of abusive supervision on well-being. *Scandinavian Journal of Work and Organizational Psychology, 7*(1), 3.

Sungu, L. J., Hu, E., & Weng, Q. (Derek). (2020). Goal commitment buffers the negative effects of perceived abusive supervision. *The Journal of Psychology: Interdisciplinary and Applied, 154*(4), 273–291.

Sutton, R. I. (2007). *The no asshole rule: Building a civilized workplace and surviving one that isn't.* Business Plus.

Taylor, S. G., Griffith, M. D., Vadera, A. K., Folger, R., & Letwin, C. R. (2019). Breaking the cycle of abusive supervision: How disidentification and moral identity help the trickle-down change course. *Journal of Applied Psychology, 104*(1), 164–182.

Tepper, B. J. (2000). Consequences of abusive supervision. *Academy of Management Journal, 43*(2), 178–190.

Tepper, B. J. (2007). Abusive supervision in work organizations: Review, synthesis, and research agenda. *Journal of Management, 33*(3), 261–289.

Tepper, B. J., Duffy, M. K., Henle, C. A., & Lambert, L. S. (2006). Procedural injustice, victim precipitation, and abusive supervision. *Personnel Psychology, 59*(1), 101–123.

Tepper, B. J., Moss, S. E., & Duffy, M. K. (2011). Predictors of abusive supervision: Supervisor perceptions of deep-level dissimilarity, relationship conflict, and subordinate performance. *Academy of Management Journal, 54*(2), 279–294.

Tepper, B. J., Simon, L. S., & Park, H. M. (2017). Abusive supervision. *Annual Review of Organizational Psychology and Organizational Behavior, 4*(1), 23–52.

Thau, S., Bennett, R. J., Mitchell, M. S., & Marrs, M. B. (2009). How management style moderates the relationship between abusive supervision and workplace deviance: An uncertainty management theory perspective. *Organizational Behavior and Human Decision Processes, 108*(1), 79–92.

Thompson, M. J., Carlson, D. S., Hackney, K., & Vogel, R. M. (2022). Vicarious abusive supervision and turnover in expectant working mothers: Does financial dependency trigger emotional disconnect? *Journal of Organizational Behavior, 43*(3), 448–464.

Tuan, T. L. (2019). Discretionary HR practices and employee well-being: The roles of job crafting and abusive supervision. *Personnel Review, 49*(1), 43–66.

Velez, M. J., & Neves, P. (2016). Abusive supervision, psychosomatic symptoms, and deviance: Can job autonomy make a difference? *Journal of Occupational Health Psychology, 21*(3), 322–333.

Vogel, R. M., & Bolino, M. C. (2020). Recurring nightmares and silver linings: Understanding how past abusive supervision may lead to posttraumatic stress and posttraumatic growth. *Academy of Management Review, 45*(3), 549–569.

Vogel, R. M., & Mitchell, M. S. (2017). The motivational effects of diminished self-esteem for employees who experience abusive supervision. *Journal of Management, 43*(7), 2218–2251.

Vogel, R. M., Mitchell, M. S., Tepper, B. J., Restubog, S. L. D., Hu, C., Hua, W., & Huang, J. C. (2015). A cross-cultural examination of subordinates' perceptions of and reactions to abusive supervision. *Journal of Organizational Behavior, 36*(5), 720–745.

Vohs, K. D., & Baumeister, R. F. (2004). Understanding self-regulation. In R. F. Baumeister & K. D. Vohs (Eds.), *Handbook of self-regulation* (pp. 1–12). Guilford Press.

Waldman, D. A., Wang, D., Hannah, S. T., Owens, B. P., & Balthazard, P. A. (2018). Psychological and neurological predictors of abusive supervision. *Personnel Psychology, 71*(3), 399–421.

Wang, G., Van Iddekinge, C. H., Zhang, L., & Bishoff, J. (2019). Meta-analytic and primary investigations of the role of followers in ratings of leadership behavior in organizations. *Journal of Applied Psychology, 104*(1), 70–106.

Wee, E. X. M., Liao, H., Liu, D., & Liu, J. (2017). Moving from abuse to reconciliation: A power-dependence perspective on when and how a follower can break the spiral of abuse. *Academy of Management Journal*, 60(6), 2352–2380.

Wisse, B., & Sleebos, E. (2016, September). When the dark ones gain power: Perceived position power strengthens the effect of supervisor machiavellianism on abusive supervision in work teams. *Personality and Individual Differences*, 99, 122–126.

Wu, L., Kwong Kwan, H., Liu, J., & Resick, C. J. (2012). Work-to-family spillover effects of abusive supervision. *Journal of Managerial Psychology*, 27(7), 714–731.

Wu, T., & Hu, C. (2009). Abusive supervision and employee emotional exhaustion: Dispositional antecedents and boundaries. *Group Organization Management*, 34(2), 143–169.

Xu, E., Huang, X., Jia, R., Xu, J., Liu, W., Graham, L., & Snape, E. (2020). The "evil pleasure": Abusive supervision and third-party observers' malicious reactions towards victims. *Organization Science*, 5(31), 1115–1137.

Yam, K. C., Fehr, R., Keng-Highberger, F. T., Klotz, A. C., & Reynolds, S. J. (2016). Out of control: A self-control perspective on the link between surface acting and abusive supervision. *Journal of Applied Psychology*, 101(2), 292–301.

Yan, X., Wang, Z., Su, J., & Luo, Z. (2020). Relationship between core self-evaluations and team identification: The perception of abusive supervision and work engagement. *Current Psychology*, 39(1), 121–127.

Yu, L., Duffy, M. K., & Tepper, B. J. (2018). Consequences of downward envy: A model of self-esteem threat, abusive supervision, and supervisory leader self-improvement. *Academy of Management Journal*, 61(6), 2296–2318.

Yuan, X., Xu, Y., & Li, Y. (2020). Resource depletion perspective on the link between abusive supervision and safety behaviors. *Journal of Business Ethics*, 162(1), 213–228.

Zellars, K. L., Tepper, B. J., & Duffy, M. K. (2002). Abusive supervision and subordinates' organizational citizenship behavior. *Journal of Applied Psychology*, 87(6), 1068–1076.

Zhang, Y., & Liao, Z. (2015). Consequences of abusive supervision: A meta-analytic review. *Asia Pacific Journal of Management*, 32, 959–987.

Zhang, Y., Liu, X., Xu, S., Yang, L.-Q., & Bednall, T. C. (2019). Why abusive supervision impacts employee OCB and CWB: A meta-analytic review of competing mediating mechanisms. *Journal of Management*, 45(6), 2474–2497.

NOTES

1. The consideration of perception and leader behaviors and the explanatory power of each is part of a larger discussion in the leadership literature and a source of criticism regarding how leadership in the workplace is measured and discussed (Martinko et al., 2018; Wang et al., 2019). Thus, the following issues are not limited to the abusive supervision literature.

2. This concern is applicable to the larger organizational psychology and management literatures and is not limited to research on abusive supervision (Avery et al., 2022).

Katrina A. Graham, Gahyun Yoo, and Emma K. Kristal

ETHICAL LEADERSHIP

INTRODUCTION

Since the 1960s, the *how* of leadership has mostly fallen into one of two categories: person-orientation or task-orientation (Bowers & Seashore, 1966; Hollander, 1979; Schriesheim &

Bird, 1979; Stogdill, 1950). The subsequent question was, To *what end* are these two basic leadership styles used? On this point, recent research has squarely focused on *change* as the core objective of leadership (Derue et al., 2011; Yukl, 2012; Yukl et al., 2002). The question that logically follows is, Within which (normative) boundaries? It is this question that is central to the bulk of research on ethical leadership.

Although the question of ethics in leadership is age old and has been deeply discussed by philosophers, the concept is relatively new in the literature on organizational behavior and psychology. Research on ethical leadership surged following a range of corporate scandals in the early 2000s—with Enron being a landmark—as it became clear that the literature lacked explanations for unethical leadership behavior. Moral components had already been identified as an important part of follower-focused leadership (the earliest references to ethical leadership as a style in itself derive from Burns' [1978] work on transforming leadership, as well as discussions of the ethical dimensions of transformational leadership [e.g., Bass & Steidlmeier, 1999] or charismatic leadership [Conger et al., 2000]). However, the field still lacked systematic research into the domain of ethical leadership at that time. It was then that the literature gained one of the most cited definitions of ethical leadership—as "the demonstration of normatively appropriate conduct through personal actions and interpersonal relationships, and the promotion of such conduct to followers through two-way communication, reinforcement, and decision-making" (Brown et al., 2005, p. 120). This research piece put ethical leadership on the map.

Since the publication of Brown and colleagues' initial studies, the number of articles specifically focusing on ethical leadership has increased substantially. As a result, recent meta-analyses have discussed the incremental effect of ethical leadership and its related constructs. These studies have specifically focused on ethics as a primary quality of the leadership style and contrasted it with leadership constructs, such as transformational leadership, that merely contain morality as one of their components. The findings show either small effects or effects that are limited to specifically ethical outcomes (Hoch et al., 2018; Ng & Feldman, 2015). Indeed, despite the volume of research on ethical leadership and the consensus on its importance, the domain does not come without challenges. This article discusses the current findings and issues with this line of research. As done in the literature overall, the discussion interchangeably uses the terms *ethical*—relating to behavior that is in accordance with established external rules and codes of conduct—and *moral*—relating to individual moral rules that guide awareness, judgment, and decisions about integrity and conduct in the situation (cf. Kohlberg, 1981; Treviño et al., 2006). Most of the ethical leadership styles have components relating to the code of conduct in organizations as well as components relating to personal integrity.

OPERATIONALIZATION AND DIMENSIONALITY OF ETHICAL LEADERSHIP

Researchers have published a variety of scales that measure ethical leadership. In early versions, ethical leadership was operationalized as moral managers who discussed business ethics with employees and disciplined those who violated moral standards (Treviño et al., 2000). More recent attempts have envisioned leaders as moral persons who adhere to moral standards both privately and publicly (Treviño et al., 2003). Although this theorizing conceptualizes ethical leadership as two dimensional—that is, moral person and moral manager—the 10-item Ethical Leadership Scale mostly treats ethical leadership as a one-dimensional concept

(Treviño et al., 2000). To the authors' knowledge, no published study has empirically differentiated the characteristics of moral managers from moral persons. Others have extended the concept of ethical leadership to include multiple dimensions, such as the 35-item Ethical Leadership at Work Questionnaire that distinguishes seven dimensions: fairness, integrity, ethical guidance, people orientation, power sharing, role clarification, and concern for sustainability (Kalshoven et al., 2011). Likewise, Yukl and colleagues (2013) developed a one-dimensional, 15-item measure that aims to produce less overlap with supportive and empowering leadership behaviors. Specifically, they set out to minimize the conceptual overlap between leader-member exchange (Graen & Uhl-Bien, 1995) and ethical leadership—and thereby distinguish ethical leadership from task- and change-oriented leadership.

However, most of these scales reflect a hodgepodge of desirable leader behaviors, attitudes, and relational outcomes. Because these measures tap into so many elements at once, it is difficult to meaningfully advance research on the concept of ethical leadership. Moreover, because the operationalizations largely focus on follower perceptions rather than concrete behavior, they lack the clarity to serve for sound assessment (Fischer et al., 2020). In addition, the items are often normatively charged in a way that does not reflect the plurality of ethics. Indeed, one can argue that the current operationalizations may be better coined "moral leadership" because they prescribe leadership styles that depend on the leaders' personal adherence to certain ethical concepts that are rooted in a Western, usually utilitarian, perspective. The assessment of ethical leadership depends mostly on whether their observable behavior is normatively appropriate (Brown et al., 2005) because reliable insight into personal motives driving the behavior is difficult to obtain. This is not only a very simplistic notion of what it means to be ethical but also a gross reduction of "normative appropriateness," which occupies a central role in the definition of ethical leadership.

The concept also faces methodological criticisms, both as part of the general skepticism toward the heavy reliance on survey studies in leadership research (Fischer et al., 2020) and as a critique of the study of ethical leadership (Banks et al., 2021; Palanski et al., 2021). These critiques highlight that the measurement of ethical leadership is conflated with its outcomes, underlying motives in terms of leader virtues or values, or confirmation of norms (Banks et al., 2021). Thus, there are promising avenues for future research in terms of studying the actual behaviors of ethical leaders, adopting experimental approaches that address endogeneity concerns (Antonakis et al., 2010), and more strongly connecting the concept to its context via ethical theory.

ANTECEDENTS OF ETHICAL LEADERSHIP

When trying to explain ethical leadership, researchers have focused on either external factors, such as organizational culture or climate (Kish-Gephart et al., 2010; Treviño & Youngblood, 1990), or internal factors that mostly relate to leaders' moral personality characteristics (Den Hartog, 2015) or cognitive moral development. The latter generally derive from Kohlberg's (1981) conceptualization of moral maturity and development (Jordan et al., 2013; Schminke et al., 2005). Relatedly, the past decade has seen growing attention on leaders' moral character as a factor that can predict moral decision-making (Hannah et al., 2011) and specifically moral leadership (Hannah & Avolio, 2010; Wright & Quick, 2011).

Research on external factors has started from the question of whether unethical behavior in organizations stems from a "bad apple" that spoils the barrel (Treviño & Youngblood, 1990).

Studies show that top-ranked ethical leaders do create an ethical climate that then positively influences the ethical leadership of middle- or lower-level managers (Dickson et al., 2001; Mayer et al., 2009; Neubert et al., 2009). Considering organizations as a whole, researchers have found that ethical climates exert positive effects, especially if the climate is based less on egoism and more on benevolence or principle (Martin & Cullen, 2006; Victor & Cullen, 1988). Likewise, research on organizational ethical culture has found mixed but mostly positive effects for the presence of ethical codes of conduct in organizations (Kish-Gephart et al., 2010), as well as that ethical leaders can reinforce said codes (Treviño & Youngblood, 1990; Treviño et al., 2000). Finally, ethical leaders can be an important component of the organization's ethical infrastructure (Tenbrunsel et al., 2003). Specifically, top managers have substantial influence on the structuring of incentive systems, as well as an important role in modeling ethical decision-making and setting priorities in the organizational context (Park et al., 2022). The structure of incentive systems can, in turn, reduce employees' focus on the ethical aspects of organizational decisions (Gino & Mogilner, 2014; Park et al., 2022; Tenbrunsel & Messick, 1999). Relatedly, ethical leaders can play an important role in sanctioning and surveilling unethical behavior (Tenbrunsel et al., 2003), and they may substantially influence employees' thinking process to help them refrain from unethical behavior (Manara et al., 2020).

One of the most researched internal antecedents of ethical leadership is leader moral identity—the extent to which moral values are central to the person's identity. The centrality of moral values—such as honesty, fairness, care, and compassion—is both an internalized characteristic and a matter of external symbolization and self-expression toward others (Aquino & Reed, 2002). Research has investigated leader moral identity as a predictor of both ethical leadership in itself (Grover, 2014; Mayer et al., 2012) and followers' moral identity centrality (Gerpott et al., 2017), as well as its interaction with follower moral identity. For instance, when there is better fit between leader and follower ethical leadership, those followers with higher ratings of moral identity rate their leader as more ethical (Giessner et al., 2015). Moreover, when both leader and follower score high on moral identity, their congruence can effectively predict higher (perceived) ethical leadership and fewer negative sentiments from the leader toward the follower (Qin et al., 2018).

Other studies related to leader and follower moral cognitions have found similar interaction effects. For example, studies have found positive effects of leader courage and honesty/humility on follower ethical behavior (Ete et al., 2020; Palanski et al., 2015). As an extension of this argument, studies have also found an interaction between leader and follower moral *disengagement*, namely that the negative relationship between leader moral disengagement and follower perceptions of ethical leadership was especially pronounced for followers low in moral disengagement (Bonner et al., 2016). Correspondingly, followers high in moral attentiveness also showed increased scrutinizing of perceived ethical leadership, reacting more strongly when ethical leadership was low (van Gils et al., 2015).

UNDERLYING MECHANISMS: SOCIAL LEARNING, SOCIAL EXCHANGE, AND IDENTIFICATION

Scholars theorize that ethical leaders influence their followers through a variety of mechanisms. Early studies drew on social learning theory (Bandura, 1977; Brown & Treviño, 2013) to suggest that ethical leaders are role models for their followers. By modeling ethical behavior in their personal interactions, ethical leaders become persons to look up to (Jordan et al., 2013; Weaver et al., 2005). Moreover, by reprimanding employees who violate ethical codes, ethical leaders encourage their followers to learn from the feedback provided to others. In addition to social learning, ethical leaders and their followers also engage in a social exchange (Blau, 1964) whereby followers feel inclined to reciprocate the leaders' moral behavior with their own (Brown et al., 2005; Peng & Kim, 2020). Similarly, ethical leadership has also been directly linked to the exchange quality in leader–follower relationships, as expressed by the notion of leader–member exchange (LMX) (Giessner et al., 2015; Peng & Kim, 2020). Social exchange, sometimes operationalized as LMX, and social learning are often tested in combination, with a recent meta-analysis showing LMX to be the stronger mediator in the effect of ethical leadership on performance (Peng & Kim, 2020).

In addition to the previously mentioned mechanisms, various researchers have discussed how ethical leaders influence the organization's norms and climate (Schminke et al., 2005) and thereby provide a basis for employee identification with not just the leader but also the organization as a whole (Bedi et al., 2016; Zhu et al., 2015). Together, both aspects are supposed to increase followers' ethical behavior by encouraging them to emulate the norms of their leaders/organizations. Recent meta-analyses correspondingly found effects on employee identification, self-efficacy, as well as employee's willingness to speak up (Bedi et al., 2016). A meta-analysis comparing the strength of different mediators for specific outcomes found ethical culture to be the strongest mediator in the negative relationship between ethical leadership and counterproductive work behavior (Peng & Kim, 2020). However, most of the underlying data are correlational in nature, and hence any parallelism or sequential order implied in the mediation analyses stands on somewhat shaky ground. Although most of these studies show positive effects of ethical leadership, research has also reported potential negative behaviors resulting from ethical leadership, such as employees engaging in unethical behavior when they perceive it as helpful for the company (Miao et al., 2013). This highlights another largely unexplored mechanism of ethical leadership: that people weigh the cost and effort needed to conduct business ethically against the financial interests of the company—which could be considered an ethical consideration in and of itself (i.e., doing it for the group).

ETHICAL LEADERSHIP EFFECTS ON ORGANIZATIONAL CITIZENSHIP BEHAVIORS, COUNTERPRODUCTIVE WORK BEHAVIOR, AND OTHER OUTCOMES

The definition of ethical leadership heavily relies on leaders' behavioral outcomes (in terms of displaying moral management) and being a moral person (Brown et al., 2005). As a consequence, ethical leadership and leaders' ethical decision-making are near tautological; however, very few studies have researched whether moral leaders truly make ethical decisions (for an exception, see Hannah & Avolio, 2010). Instead, research has predominantly focused on how ethical leadership influences followers' (moral) behavior. Ethical leadership has been associated with a wide range of employee behaviors—most notably those in the ethical domain because they can potentially speak to the more unique normative effect of ethical leadership (for recent meta-analyses, see Bedi et al., 2016; Hoch et al., 2018; Peng & Kim, 2020). Initial studies, for instance, found positive relationships between ethical leadership and followers' organizational citizenship behaviors (OCB; Mayer et al., 2009), which include voluntary extra-role behaviors that are not directly rewarded but aid the organization, such as taking over other employees' shifts (Organ, 1988). As mentioned previously, this relationship is often explained through social learning and exchange processes (Mayer et al., 2009), ethical culture or climate, and follower identification (Peng & Kim, 2020).

A second outcome of interest is counterproductive work behavior (Bedi et al., 2016; Peng & Kim, 2020), which is basically the opposite of ethical behavior at work. Researchers have investigated how ethical leadership relates to decreases in various harmful work behaviors, such as organizational deviance (defined as voluntary behavior that violates organizational norms and harms the organization; Avey et al., 2011; Brown & Treviño, 2006; van Gils et al., 2015), interpersonal deviance (deviant behavior directed at other persons in the organization; Kuenzi et al., 2019; Mo & Shi, 2017), incivility (Taylor & Pattie, 2014; Walsh et al., 2018), and corruption (Manara et al., 2020).

A third line of research focuses on how ethical leadership (or variants of it) shapes the relationship between leader and follower. In particular, scholars argue that perceived integrity should foster more trust within followers (Craig & Gustafson, 1998; Palanski & Yammarino, 2009; van den Akker et al., 2009) and ultimately allow the relationship to evolve from being purely transactional to high quality (Craig & Gustafson, 1998; Yukl et al., 2013) Some recent studies on leader–follower relationships and ethics have considered how changes in ethical leadership within the same leader have corresponding changes in follower outcomes such as pride, contempt, and turnover intentions (Ng et al., 2021). Such results also corroborate the field's causal assumptions about ethical leadership.

Various researchers have also investigated the positive relationships between ethical leadership and employee performance (e.g., Piccolo et al., 2010), although they are less central to the core ethical argument. These studies support the notion that there is a clear instrumental basis for enacting ethical leadership from a business standpoint: For instance, ethical leadership has been found to improve employee well-being (Kalshoven & Boon, 2012) and reduce stress and burnout (Avey et al., 2012; Vullinghs et al., 2020). However, meta-analytical results raise some doubts about whether ethical leadership explains more variance on such general organizational outcomes in addition to other leadership styles. In many cases, the effects are either small (Bedi et al., 2016; Peng & Kim, 2020) or restricted to specific ethical outcomes (Hoch et al., 2018).

RELATED MORAL LEADERSHIP TYPES AND DISTINCTIONS

In parallel with ethical leadership, several other streams of research have developed notions of leadership with moral components (Lemoine et al., 2019). First, the literature on authentic leadership emphasizes leaders' display of their authentic self as part of an internalized moral perspective (Avolio et al., 2004; Luthans & Avolio, 2003). Compared to ethical leadership, authentic leadership is strongly focused on leaders' self-awareness, balanced processing, and relational transparency. Meanwhile, the separate literature on servant leadership has focused heavily on leaders who prioritize followers and help them grow (Greenleaf, 1970). Conceptualizations of servant leadership predominantly revolve around the creation of value for multiple stakeholders simultaneously (Lemoine et al., 2019). Of course, these concepts overlap with ethical leadership in terms of being concerned for followers, showing oneself as a consistent moral person, and behaving morally in general. But ethical leadership is distinguished by its focus on the discussion and reinforcement of ethical codes of conduct in organizations (Bedi et al., 2016; Lemoine et al., 2019). Critical assessment of those concepts shows high intercorrelations among the concepts (Bedi et al., 2016) but also incremental validity over traditional leadership styles, such as transformational leadership, when investigated in the context of specific moral outcomes (Hoch et al., 2018).

Another stream of related research has evolved around the concept of respect in leader–follower relationships. This research on so-called respectful leadership centers on the dignity of the follower (Van Quaquebeke & Eckloff, 2010; Van Quaquebeke et al., 2009). According to the philosopher Immanuel Kant (Kant, 1987), respect should be core to any ethical consideration between human beings (Van Quaquebeke et al., 2007). As such, this research stream is more focused than the ethical leadership literature and therefore naturally covers a narrower territory in terms of mechanisms and outcomes. However, some studies have shown that respectful leadership has comparable effects to ethical leadership (Gerpott et al., 2019; van Gils et al., 2018; Van Quaquebeke & Eckloff, 2010).

As previously noted, moral leadership theories have been criticized for taking a largely context-free perspective on morality and moral theories (Fehr et al., 2015), as well as limiting their consideration of cultural perspectives (Buchtel et al., 2015; Eisenbeiss, 2012). Few studies have addressed this concern: The notable exceptions have tried to connect ethical leadership to moral foundations theory (Fehr et al., 2015) or build on relational models theory (Rai & Fiske, 2012). The latter argues that what is considered ethical leader behavior can depend on the relationship between leaders and their followers (Giessner & Van Quaquebeke, 2010; Keck et al., 2020). Such considerations about the moral core of ethical leadership are even more important in light of arguments by Greenbaum and colleagues (2015), who have questioned the idea that leadership always contains a moral component and instead suggest that leaders frequently practice amoral leadership.

ETHICAL VERSUS UNETHICAL LEADERSHIP

Interestingly, the research streams on ethical and unethical leadership have developed somewhat separately. One reason for this is the theoretical argument that the absence of ethical leadership does not imply the presence of unethical or abusive behavior. However, there are several problems with this stance. First, if effects are interpreted linearly without the establishment of a clear "neutral" control condition, then it is difficult to identify the driver of said effects. In other words, does it matter more to actually be ethical or to simply not be unethical? Second, the absence of a neutral condition entails that we do not really know how to interpret low scores on certain ethical leadership scales. Are the effects of low ethical leadership on follower behavior simply due to the *absence* of ethical leadership, or do they reflect the *presence* of unethical leadership? In fairness, the question of whether the absence of a good relationship is a sign of a bad relationship generally riddles much of psychological research (for a discussion of this question in the context of leader–member exchange, see Gottfredson et al., 2020). Together, these challenges make it difficult to formulate concrete advice and practical implications based on extant survey studies or experimental studies that lack a neutral control.

On the other end of the ethical spectrum, there is an extensive literature on the different types of negative and unethical leadership. Although the term *unethical leadership* mainly appears in theoretical work (Brown & Mitchell, 2010), there have been attempts to assess the effects of negative leadership styles—such as abusive, destructive, undermining, narcissistic, and tyrannical leadership behaviors—that threaten or undermine the dignity of other people, and specifically the employees entrusted to the leader (Tepper, 2000, 2007). Abusive supervision—the most cited construct in that domain—is defined as "subordinates' perceptions of the extent to which supervisors engage in the sustained display of hostile verbal and nonverbal behaviors, excluding physical contact" (Tepper, 2000, p. 178). A full discussion of this literature is beyond the scope of this article, but overall, abusive supervision has been found to negatively affect OCB and increase counterproductive work behavior or stress. Scholars have also tested some similar underlying mechanisms, such as social learning and exchange (for recent meta-analyses, see Schyns & Schilling, 2013; Zhang et al., 2019). In addition, unethical leadership has been associated with psychological mechanisms that cognitively distance the perpetrator from the unethical behavior, such as moral disengagement (cf. Bandura, 1999; Detert et al., 2008). Moral disengagement has been identified in leaders who show unethical leadership (Bonner et al., 2016) and in employees when they imitate their leaders' unethical behavior (Fehr et al., 2020). Moreover, studies have found that ethical leaders reduce moral disengagement in their employees, thus suggesting that ethical leadership matters morally (Moore et al., 2019).

EMPIRICAL COMPLEXITY AND RESEARCH QUESTIONS

As highlighted previously, much of the research on ethical leadership has presented a simplified picture of its effects. This mainly derives from (predominantly cross-sectional) studies focusing on linear relationships between ethical leadership and its outcomes and also on explorations of underlying mechanisms and boundary effects in terms of moderators. Fortunately, the past decade has produced increasingly robust research models for investigating ethical leadership and its effects. These newer explorations show that ethical leadership can benefit many people but does not necessarily yield positive outcomes for all employees. For example, a recent study investigating the three-way interaction between ethical leadership (Wang et al., 2021), identification with the leader, and moral identity showed that the ethical leader's identification as a role model only occurs when the leader shows ethical leadership, the follower scores high on moral identity, and the follower identifies with the leader. The researchers also found that ethical leadership may evoke unethical behavior if followers are missing one of the two identity components (Wang et al., 2021).

Other studies—exploring the nonlinear relationships between ethical leadership and follower outcomes—reveal that ethical leadership can suffer from being "too much of a good thing." For instance, followers show lower levels of OCB when ethical leadership is either low or very high (Stouten et al., 2013). Curvilinear effects have also been found for the relationship between ethical leadership and unethical pro-organizational behavior, which was higher at moderate levels of ethical leadership than at high or low levels (Miao et al., 2013). Thus, whether ethical leadership benefits employees depends on the optimal level of ethical leadership in interaction with the employees' moral traits.

In addition to expanding model complexity, an increasing number of studies have taken a multilevel approach to ethical leadership by investigating its effects in samples of followers nested in teams (Palanski & Yammarino, 2009; Schaubroeck et al., 2012). These studies address so-called trickle-down effects of ethical leadership (Mayer et al., 2009) and clarify the influence that higher level managers' ethical leadership exerts on lower level managers and employees.

CURRENT DIRECTIONS

After two decades of rapidly developing research, ethical leadership has become a firmly established concept in the domain of organizational behavior—and its critiques have grown in tandem. These critiques relate to both the broadness of operationalization and the conflatedness of the subject with its outcomes and underlying motives (Banks et al., 2021), as discussed previously. In addition, researchers in the domain of ethical leadership are increasingly aware that relying on follower perspectives assessed in surveys limits the understanding of organizational dynamics. Increasingly, studies call for a richer focus on what (ethical) leaders actually do and more strongly connecting the concept to its context via ethical theory. In response, newer studies investigate ethical leader behaviors through interview techniques (Haar et al., 2019), experimental intervention studies, and other methods tapping directly into leader behaviors, such as video coding (Hemshorn de Sanchez et al., 2022). Others have called for the use of archival or big data (Palanski et al., 2021). Moreover, current studies in the domain of ethical leadership show that researchers are aware of the need to adapt the research to address current societal issues, such as ethical leadership in the context of burnout (Vullinghs et al., 2020), or the function of leadership in a remote working setting (Carsten et al., 2021).

Undoubtedly, ethics in leadership is an important topic that deserves attention. As such, scholars need to hone their theorizing and operationalization. It is only then that the field can be expected to generate research insights that are truly practice relevant.

REFERENCES

Antonakis, J., Bendahan, S., Jacquart, P., & Lalive, R. (2010). On making causal claims: A review and recommendations. *Leadership Quarterly, 21*(6), 1086–1120. https://doi.org/10.1016/j.leaqua.2010.10.010

Aquino, K. F., & Reed, A., II. (2002). The self-importance of moral identity. *Journal of Personality and Social Psychology, 83*(6), 1423–1440. https://doi.org/10.1037/0022-3514.83.6.1423

Avey, J. B., Palanski, M., & Walumbwa, F. O. (2011). When leadership goes unnoticed: The moderating role of follower self-esteem on the relationship between ethical leadership and follower behavior. *Journal of Business Ethics, 98*(4), 573–582. https://doi.org/10.1007/s10551-010-0610-2

Avey, J. B., Wernsing, T. S., & Palanski, M. (2012). Exploring the process of ethical leadership: The mediating role of employee voice and psychological ownership. *Journal of Business Ethics, 107*(1), 21–34. https://doi.org/10.1007/s10551-012-1298-2

Avolio, B. J., Gardner, W. L., Walumbwa, F. O., Luthans, F., & May, D. R. (2004). Unlocking the mask: A look at the process by which authentic leaders impact follower attitudes and behaviors. *Leadership Quarterly, 15*(6), 801–823. https://www.sciencedirect.com/science/article/pii/S1048984304000876

Bandura, A. (1977). *Social learning theory*. Prentice Hall.

Bandura, A. (1999). Moral disengagement in the perpetration of inhumanities. *Personality and Social Psychology Review, 3*(3), 193–209. https://doi.org/10.1207/s15327957pspr0303_3

Banks, G. C., Fischer, T., Gooty, J., & Stock, G. (2021). Ethical leadership: Mapping the terrain for concept cleanup and a future research agenda. *Leadership Quarterly, 32*(2), 101471. https://doi.org/10.1016/j.leaqua.2020.101471

Bass, B. M., & Steidlmeier, P. (1999). Ethics, character, and authentic transformational leadership behavior. *Leadership Quarterly, 10*(2), 181–217.

Bedi, A., Alpaslan, C. M., & Green, S. (2016). A meta-analytic review of ethical leadership outcomes and moderators. *Journal of Business Ethics, 139*(3), 517–536. https://doi.org/10.1007/s10551-015-2625-1

Blau, P. (1964). *Exchange and power in social life*. Wiley.

Bonner, J. M., Greenbaum, R. L., & Mayer, D. M. (2016). My boss is morally disengaged: The role of ethical leadership in explaining the interactive effect of supervisor and employee moral disengagement on employee behaviors. *Journal of Business Ethics, 137*(4), 731–742. https://doi.org/10.1007/s10551-014-2366-6

Bowers, D. G., & Seashore, S. E. (1966). Predicting organizational effectiveness with a four-factor theory of leadership. *Administrative Science Quarterly, 11*(2), 238. https://doi.org/10.2307/2391247

Brown, M. E., & Mitchell, M. S. (2010). Ethical and unethical leadership: Exploring new avenues for future research. *Business Ethics Quarterly, 20*(4), 583–616. https://doi.org/10.5840/beq201020439

Brown, M. E., & Treviño, L. K. (2006). Ethical leadership: A review and future directions. *Leadership Quarterly, 17*(6), 595–616. https://doi.org/10.1016/j.leaqua.2006.10.004

Brown, M. E., & Treviño, L. K. (2013, July 21). Do role models matter? An investigation of role modeling as an antecedent of perceived ethical leadership. *Journal of Business Ethics, 122*, 587–598. https://doi.org/10.1007/s10551-013-1769-0

Brown, M. E., Treviño, L. K., & Harrison, D. A. (2005). Ethical leadership: A social learning perspective for construct development and testing. *Organizational Behavior and Human Decision Processes, 97*(2), 117–134. https://doi.org/10.1016/j.obhdp.2005.03.002

Buchtel, E. E., Guan, Y., Peng, Q., Su, Y., Sang, B., Chen, S. X., & Bond, M. H. (2015). Immorality East and West: Are immoral behaviors especially harmful, or especially uncivilized? *Personality and Social Psychology Bulletin, 41*(10), 1382–1394. https://doi.org/10.1177/0146167215595606

Burns, J. (1978). *Leadership*. Harper & Row.

Carsten, M., Goswami, A., Shepard, A., & Donnelly, L. I. (2021). Followership at a distance: Follower adjustment to distal leadership during COVID-19 [Special issue]. *Applied Psychology*. https://doi.org/10.1111/apps.12337

Conger, J. A., Kanungo, R. N., & Menon, S. T. (2000). Charismatic leadership and follower effects. *Journal of Organizational Behavior, 21*(7), 747–767. https://doi.org/10.1002/1099-1379(200011)21:7%3C747::AID-JOB46%3E3.0.CO;2-J

Craig, S. B., & Gustafson, S. B. (1998). Perceived Leader Integrity Scale: An instrument for assessing employee perceptions of leader integrity. *Leadership Quarterly, 9*(2), 127–145. https://doi.org/10.1016/S1048-9843(98)90001-7

Den Hartog, D. N. (2015). Ethical leadership. *Annual Review of Organizational Psychology and Organizational Behavior, 22*(1), 409–434. https://doi.org/10.1097/HNP.0b013e318263f2da

Derue, D. S., Nahrgang, J. D., Wellman, N., & Humphrey, S. E. (2011). Trait and behavioral theories of leadership: An integration and meta-analytic test of their relative validity. *Personnel Psychology, 64*(1), 7–52. https://doi.org/10.1111/j.1744-6570.2010.01201.x

Detert, J. R., Treviño, L. K., & Sweitzer, V. V. L. (2008). Moral disengagement in ethical decision making: A study of antecedents and outcomes. *Journal of Applied Psychology, 93*(2), 374–391. https://doi.org/10.1037/0021-9010.93.2.374

Dickson, M. W., Smith, D. B., Grojean, M. W., & Ehrhart, M. (2001). An organizational climate regarding ethics: The outcome of leader values and the practices that reflect them. *Leadership Quarterly, 12*(2), 197–217.

Eisenbeiss, S. A. (2012). Re-thinking ethical leadership: An interdisciplinary integrative approach. *Leadership Quarterly, 23*(5), 791–808. https://doi.org/10.1016/j.leaqua.2012.03.001

Ete, Z., Sosik, J. J., Cheong, M., Chun, J. U., Zhu, W., Arenas, F. J., & Scherer, J. A. (2020). Leader honesty/humility and subordinate organizational citizenship behavior: A case of too-much-of-a-good-thing? *Journal of Managerial Psychology, 35*(5), 391–404. https://doi.org/10.1108/JMP-10-2019-0557

Fehr, R., Fulmer, A., & Keng-Highberger, F. T. (2020). How do employees react to leaders' unethical behavior? The role of moral disengagement. *Personnel Psychology, 73*(1), 73–93. https://doi.org/10.1111/PEPS.12366

Fehr, R., Yam, K. C., & Dang, C. (2015). Moralized leadership: The construction and consequences of ethical leader perceptions. *Academy of Management Review, 40*(2), 182–209. https://doi.org/10.5465/amr.2013.0358

Fischer, T., Hambrick, D. C., Sajons, G. B., & Van Quaquebeke, N. (2020). Beyond the ritualized use of questionnaires: Toward a science of actual behaviors and psychological states. *Leadership Quarterly, 31*(4), 101449. https://doi.org/10.1016/s1048-9843(20)30076-x

Gerpott, F. H., Fasbender, U., & Burmeister, A. (2019). Respectful leadership and followers' knowledge sharing: A social mindfulness lens. *Human Relations, 73*(6), 789–810. https://doi.org/10.1177/0018726719844813

Gerpott, F. H., van Quaquebeke, N., Schlamp, S., & Voelpel, S. C. (2017). An identity perspective on ethical leadership to explain organizational citizenship behavior: The interplay of follower moral identity and leader group prototypicality. *Journal of Business Ethics, 156*, 1063–1078. https://doi.org/10.1007/s10551-017-3625-0

Giessner, S. R., & Van Quaquebeke, N. (2010). Using a relational models perspective to understand normatively appropriate conduct in ethical leadership. *Journal of Business Ethics, 95*, 43–55. https://doi.org/10.1007/s10551-011-0790-4

Giessner, S. R., Van Quaquebeke, N., van Gils, S., van Knippenberg, D., & Kollée, J. A. J. M. (2015). In the moral eye of the beholder: The interactive effects of leader and follower moral identity on perceptions of ethical leadership and LMX quality. *Frontiers in Psychology, 6*, 1126. https://doi.org/10.3389/fpsyg.2015.01126

Gino, F., & Mogilner, C. (2014). Time, money, and morality. *Psychological Science, 25*(2), 414–421. https://doi.org/10.1177/0956797613506438

Gottfredson, R. K., Wright, S. L., & Heaphy, E. D. (2020). A critique of the leader–member exchange construct: Back to square one. *Leadership Quarterly, 31*(6), 101385. https://doi.org/10.1016/j.leaqua.2020.101385

Graen, G. B., & Uhl-Bien, M. (1995). Relationship-based approach to leadership: Development of leader–member exchange (LMX) theory of leadership over 25 years: Applying a multi-level multi-domain perspective. *Leadership Quarterly, 6*(2), 219–247

Greenbaum, R. L., Quade, M. J., & Bonner, J. (2015). Why do leaders practice amoral management? A conceptual investigation of the impediments to ethical leadership. *Organizational Psychology Review, 5*(1), 26–49. https://doi.org/10.1177/2041386614533587

Greenleaf, R. (1970). *The servant as leader*. Robert Greanleaf Center.

Grover, S. L. (2014). Moral identity as a lens for interpreting honesty of indirect leaders. *Journal of Change Management, 14*(1), 48–65. http://dx.doi.org/10.1080/14697017.2013.790836

Haar, J., Roche, M., & Brougham, D. (2019). Indigenous insights into ethical leadership: A study of Māori leaders. *Journal of Business Ethics, 160*(3), 621–640. https://doi.org/10.1007/s10551-018-3869-3

Hannah, S. T., & Avolio, B. J. (2010). Moral potency: Building the capacity for character-based leadership. *Consulting Psychology Journal, 62*(4), 291–310. https://doi.org/10.1037/a0022283

Hannah, S. T., Avolio, B. J., & May, D. R. (2011). Moral maturation and moral conation: A capacity approach to explaining moral thought and action. *Academy of Management Review, 36*(4), 663–685. https://journals.aom.org/doi/10.5465/amr.2010.0128

Hemshorn de Sanchez, C. S., Gerpott, F. H., & Lehmann-Willenbrock, N. (2022). A review and future agenda for behavioral research on leader–follower interactions at different temporal scopes. *Journal of Organizational Behavior, 43*(2), 342–368. https://doi.org/10.1002/JOB.2583

Hoch, J. E., Bommer, W. H., Dulebohn, J. H., & Wu, D. (2018). Do ethical, authentic, and servant leadership explain variance above and beyond transformational leadership? A meta-analysis. *Journal of Management, 44*(2), 501–529. https://doi.org/10.1177/0149206316665461

Hollander, E. P. (1979). The impact of Ralph M. Stogdill and the Ohio State Leadership Studies on a transactional approach to leadership. *Journal of Management, 5*(2), 157–165. https://doi.org/10.1177/014920637900500206

Jordan, J., Brown, M. E., Treviño, L. K., & Finkelstein, S. (2013). Someone to look up to: Executive-follower ethical reasoning and perceptions of ethical leadership. *Journal of Management, 39*(3), 660–683. https://doi.org/10.1177/0149206311398136

Kalshoven, K., & Boon, C. T. (2012). Ethical leadership, employee well-being, and helping: The moderating role of human resource management. *Journal of Personnel Psychology, 11*(1), 60–68. https://doi.org/10.1027/1866-5888/a000056

Kalshoven, K., Den Hartog, D. N., & De Hoogh, A. H. B. (2011). Ethical Leadership at Work Questionnaire (ELW): Development and validation of a multidimensional measure. *Leadership Quarterly, 22*(1), 51–69. https://doi.org/10.1016/j.leaqua.2010.12.007

Kant, I. (1987). *Critique of judgment.* Hackett Publishing.

Keck, N., Giessner, S. R., Van Quaquebeke, N., & Kruijff, E. (2020). When do followers perceive their leaders as ethical? A relational models perspective of normatively appropriate conduct. *Journal of Business Ethics, 164*(3), 477–493. https://doi.org/10.1007/s10551-018-4055-3

Kish-Gephart, J. J., Harrison, D. A., & Treviño, L. K. (2010). Bad apples, bad cases, and bad barrels: Meta-analytic evidence about sources of unethical decisions at work. *Journal of Applied Psychology, 95*(1), 1–31.

Kohlberg, L. (1981). *Essays on moral development, Vol. I: The philosophy of moral development.* Harper & Row.

Kuenzi, M., Brown, M. E., Mayer, D. M., & Priesemuth, M. (2019). Supervisor–subordinate (dis)agreement on ethical leadership: An investigation of its antecedents and relationship to organizational deviance. *Business Ethics Quarterly, 29*(1), 25–53. https://doi.org/10.1017/beq.2018.14

Lemoine, G. J., Hartnell, C. A., & Leroy, H. (2019). Taking stock of moral approaches to leadership: An integrative review of ethical, authentic, and servant leadership. *Academy of Management Annals, 13*(1), 148–187. https://doi.org/10.5465/annals.2016.0121

Luthans, F., & Avolio, B. (2003). Authentic leadership development. In R. E. Quinn, J. E. Dutton, & K. S. Cameron (Eds.), *Positive organizational scholarship: Foundations of a new discipline* (pp. 241–257). Berret-Koehler.

Manara, M. U., van Gils, S., Nübold, A., & Zijlstra, F. R. H. (2020). Corruption, fast or slow? Ethical leadership interacts with Machiavellianism to influence intuitive thinking and corruption. *Frontiers in Psychology, 11*, 3119. https://www.ncbi.nlm.nih.gov/pmc/articles/PMC7693446/

Martin, K. D., & Cullen, J. B. (2006). Continuities and extensions of ethical climate theory: A meta-analytic review. *Journal of Business Ethics, 69*(2), 175–194. https://doi.org/10.1007/s10551-006-9084-7

Mayer, D. M., Aquino, K. F., Greenbaum, R. L., & Kuenzi, M. (2012). Who displays ethical leadership and why does it matter? An examination of antecedents and consequences of ethical leadership. *Academy of Management Journal, 55*(1), 151–171. https://doi.org/10.5465/amj.2008.0276

Mayer, D. M., Kuenzi, M., Greenbaum, R. L., Bardes, M., & Salvador, R. (2009). How low does ethical leadership flow? Test of a trickle-down model. *Organizational Behavior and Human Decision Processes, 108*(1), 1–13. https://doi.org/10.1016/j.obhdp.2008.04.002

Miao, Q., Newman, A., Yu, J., & Xu, L. (2013). The relationship between ethical leadership and unethical pro-organizational behavior: Linear or curvilinear effects? *Journal of Business Ethics, 116*(3), 641–653. https://doi.org/10.1007/s10551-012-1504-2

Mo, S., & Shi, J. (2017). Linking ethical leadership to employee burnout, workplace deviance and performance: Testing the mediating roles of trust in leader and surface acting. *Journal of Business Ethics, 144*(2), 293–303. https://doi.org/10.1007/s10551-015-2821-z

Moore, C., Mayer, D. M., Chiang, F. F. T., Crossley, C., Karlesky, M. J., & Birtch, T. A. (2019). Leaders matter morally: The role of ethical leadership in shaping employee moral cognition and misconduct. *Journal of Applied Psychology, 104*(1), 123–145. https://doi.org/10.1037/apl0000341

Neubert, M., Carlson, D., Kacmar, K. M., Roberts, J., & Chonko, L. (2009). The virtuous influence of ethical leadership behavior: Evidence from the field. *Journal of Business Ethics, 90*(2), 157–170. https://doi.org/10.1007/s10551-009-0037-9

Ng, T. W. H., & Feldman, D. C. (2015). Ethical leadership: Meta-analytic evidence of criterion-related and incremental validity. *Journal of Applied Psychology, 100*(3), 948–965. https://doi.org/10.1037/a0038246

Ng, T. W. H., Wang, M., Hsu, D. Y., & Su, C. (2021). Changes in perceptions of ethical leadership: Effects on associative and dissociative outcomes. *Journal of Applied Psychology, 106*(1), 92–121. https://doi.org/10.1037/apl0000496

Organ, D. W. (1988). *Organizational citizenship behavior: The good soldier syndrome.* Lexington Books/DC Heath and Com.

Palanski, M., Cullen, K. L., Gentry, W. A., & Nichols, C. M. (2015). Virtuous leadership: Exploring the effects of leader courage and behavioral integrity on leader performance and image. *Journal of Business Ethics, 132*(2), 297–310. https://doi.org/10.1007/s10551-014-2317-2

Palanski, M., Newman, A., Leroy, H., Moore, C., Hannah, S., & Den Hartog, D. (2021). Quantitative research on leadership and business ethics: Examining the state of the field and an agenda for future research. *Journal of Business Ethics, 168*(1), 109–119. https://doi.org/10.1007/s10551-019-04267-9

Palanski, M., & Yammarino, F. J. (2009). Integrity and leadership: A multi-level conceptual framework. *Leadership Quarterly, 20*(3), 405–420. https://doi.org/10.1016/j.leaqua.2009.03.008

Park, T.-Y., Park, S., & Barry, B. (2022). Incentive effects on ethics. *Academy of Management Annals, 16*(1), 297–333. https://journals.aom.org/doi/abs/10.5465/annals.2020.0251?journalCode=annals

Peng, A. C., & Kim, D. (2020). A meta-analytic test of the differential pathways linking ethical leadership to normative conduct. *Journal of Organizational Behavior, 41*(4), 348–368. https://doi.org/10.1002/job.2427

Piccolo, R. F., Greenbaum, R. L., Den Hartog, D. N., & Folger, R. (2010). The relationship between ethical leadership and core job characteristics. *Journal of Organizational Behavior, 31*, 259–278. https://doi.org/10.1002/job.627

Qin, X., Huang, M., Hu, Q., Schminke, M., & Ju, D. (2018). Ethical leadership, but toward whom? How moral identity congruence shapes the ethical treatment of employees. *Human Relations, 71*(8), 1120–1149. https://doi.org/10.1177/0018726717734905

Rai, T. S., & Fiske, A. P. (2012). Moral psychology is relationship regulation: Moral motives for unity, hierarchy, equality, and proportionality. *Psychological Review, 23*, 189–193. https://doi.org/10.1037/a0021867

Schaubroeck, J. M., Hannah, S. T., Avolio, B. J., Kozlowski, S. W., Lord, R. G., Treviño, L. K., Dimotakis, N., & Peng, A. C. (2012). Embedding ethical leadership within and across organization levels. *Academy of Management Journal, 55*(5), 1053–1078. https://doi.org/10.5465/amj.2011.0064

Schminke, M., Ambrose, M. L., & Neubaum, D. O. (2005). The effect of leader moral development on ethical climate and employee attitudes. *Organizational Behavior and Human Decision Processes*, 97(2), 135–151. https://doi.org/10.1016/j.obhdp.2005.03.006

Schriesheim, C. A., & Bird, B. J. (1979). Contributions of the Ohio State Studies to the field of leadership. *Journal of Management*, 5(2), 135–145. https://doi.org/10.1177/014920637900500204

Schyns, B., & Schilling, J. (2013). How bad are the effects of bad leaders? A meta-analysis of destructive leadership and its outcomes. *Leadership Quarterly*, 24(1), 138–158. https://doi.org/10.1016/J.LEAQUA.2012.09.001

Stogdill, R. (1950). Leadership, membership and organization. *Psychological Bulletin*, 47(1), 1–14. https://psycnet.apa.org/journals/bul/47/1/1/

Stouten, J., van Dijke, M., Mayer, D. M., De Cremer, D., & Euwema, M. C. (2013). Can a leader be seen as too ethical? The curvilinear effects of ethical leadership. *Leadership Quarterly*, 24(5), 680–695. https://doi.org/10.1016/j.leaqua.2013.05.002

Taylor, S. G., & Pattie, M. W. (2014). When does ethical leadership affect workplace incivility? The moderating role of follower personality. *Business Ethics Quarterly*, 24(4), 595–616. https://doi.org/10.5840/BEQ201492618

Tenbrunsel, A. E., & Messick, D. M. (1999). Sanctioning systems, decision frames, and cooperation. *Administrative Science Quarterly*, 44(4), 684–707. https://doi.org/10.2307/2667052

Tenbrunsel, A. E., Smith-Crowe, K., & Umphress, E. E. (2003, September). Building houses on rocks: The role of the ethical infrastructure in organizations. *Social Justice Research*, 16, 285–307. https://doi.org/10.1023/A:1025992813613

Tepper, B. J. (2000). Consequences of abusive supervision. *Academy of Management Journal*, 43(2), 178–190. https://doi.org/10.2307/1556375

Tepper, B. J. (2007). Abusive supervision in work organizations: Review, synthesis, and research agenda. *Journal of Management*, 33(3), 261–289. https://doi.org/10.1177/0149206307300812

Treviño, L. K., Brown, M. E., & Hartman, L. P. (2003). A qualitative investigation of perceived executive ethical leadership: Perceptions from inside and outside the executive suite. *Human Relations*, 56(1), 5–37. https://doi.org/10.1177/0018726703056001448

Treviño, L. K., Hartman, L. P., & Brown, M. E. (2000). Moral person and moral manager: How executives develop a reputation for ethical leadership. *California Management Review*, 42(4), 128–142.

Treviño, L. K., Weaver, G. R., & Reynolds, S. J. (2006). Behavioral ethics in organizations: A review. *Journal of Management*, 32(6), 951–990. https://doi.org/10.1177/0149206306294258

Treviño, L. K., & Youngblood, S. A. (1990). Bad apples in bad barrels: A causal analysis of ethical decision-making behavior. *Journal of Applied Psychology*, 75(4), 378–385. https://doi.org/10.1037/0021-9010.75.4.378

van den Akker, L., Heres, L., Lasthuizen, K., & Six, F. (2009). Ethical leadership and trust: It's all about meeting expectations. *International Journal of Leadership Studies*, 5(2), 102–122.

van Gils, S., Van Quaquebeke, N., Borkowski, J., & van Knippenberg, D. (2018). Respectful leadership: Reducing performance challenges posed by leader role incongruence and gender dissimilarity. *Human Relations*, 71(12), 1590–1610. https://doi.org/10.1177/0018726718754992

van Gils, S., Van Quaquebeke, N., van Knippenberg, D., van Dijke, M., & De Cremer, D. (2015). Ethical leadership and follower organizational deviance: The moderating role of follower moral attentiveness. *Leadership Quarterly*, 26(2), 190–203. https://doi.org/10.1016/j.leaqua.2014.08.005

Van Quaquebeke, N., & Eckloff, T. (2010). Defining respectful leadership: What it is, how it can be measured, and another glimpse at what it is related to. *Journal of Business Ethics*, 91(3), 343–358. https://doi.org/10.1007/s10551-009-0087-z

Van Quaquebeke, N., Henrich, D. C., & Eckloff, T. (2007). It's not tolerance I'm asking for, it's respect! A conceptual framework to differentiate between tolerance, acceptance and (two types of) respect. *Gruppendynamik Und Organisationsberatung, 38*(2), 185–200.

Van Quaquebeke, N., Zenker, S., & Eckloff, T. (2009). Find out how much it means to me! The importance of interpersonal respect in work values compared to perceived organizational practices. *Journal of Business Ethics, 89*(3), 423–431. https://doi.org/10.1007/s10551-008-0008-6

Victor, B., & Cullen, J. B. (1988). The organizational bases of ethical work climates. *Administrative Science Quarterly, 33*(1), 101–125. https://doi.org/10.2307/2392857

Vullinghs, J. T., De Hoogh, A. H. B., Den Hartog, D. N., & Boon, C. (2020). Ethical and passive leadership and their joint relationships with burnout via role clarity and role overload. *Journal of Business Ethics, 165*(4), 719–733. https://doi.org/10.1007/s10551-018-4084-y

Walsh, B. M., Lee, J., Jensen, J. M., McGonagle, A. K., & Samnani, A. K. (2018). Positive leader behaviors and workplace incivility: The mediating role of perceived norms for respect. *Journal of Business and Psychology, 33*(4), 495–508. https://link.springer.com/article/10.1007/s10869-017-9505-x

Wang, Z., Xing, L., Xu, H., & Hannah, S. T. (2021). Not all followers socially learn from ethical leaders: The roles of followers' moral identity and leader identification in the ethical leadership process. *Journal of Business Ethics, 170*(3), 449–469. https://doi.org/10.1007/s10551-019-04353-y

Weaver, G. R., Treviño, L. K., & Agle, B. (2005). "Somebody I look up to:" Ethical role models in organizations. *Organizational Dynamics, 34*(4), 313–330. https://doi.org/10.1016/j.orgdyn.2005.08.001

Wright, T. A., & Quick, J. C. (2011). The role of character in ethical leadership research. *Leadership Quarterly, 22*(5), 975–978. https://doi.org/10.1016/j.leaqua.2011.07.015

Yukl, G. (2012). Effective leadership behavior: What we know and what questions need more attention. *Academy of Management Perspectives, 26*(4), 66–85. https://doi.org/10.5465/amp.2012.0088

Yukl, G., Gordon, A., & Taber, T. (2002). A hierarchical taxonomy of leadership behavior: Integrating a half century of behavior research. *Journal of Leadership & Organizational Studies, 9*(1), 15–32. https://doi.org/10.1177/107179190200900102

Yukl, G., Mahsud, R., Hassan, S., & Prussia, G. E. (2013). An improved measure of ethical leadership. *Journal of Leadership and Organizational Studies, 20*(1), 38–48. https://doi.org/10.1177/1548051811429352

Zhang, Y., Liu, X., Xu, S., Yang, L. Q., & Bednall, T. C. (2019). Why abusive supervision impacts employee OCB and CWB: A meta-analytic review of competing mediating mechanisms. *Journal of Management, 45*(6), 2474–2497. https://doi.org/10.1177/0149206318823935

Zhu, W., He, H., Treviño, L. K., Chao, M. M., & Wang, W. (2015). Ethical leadership and follower voice and performance: The role of follower identifications and entity morality beliefs. *Leadership Quarterly, 26*(5), 702–718. https://doi.org/10.1016/j.leaqua.2015.01.004

Suzanne van Gils and Niels Van Quaquebeke

Organizational Processes

ORGANIZATIONAL BEHAVIOR

INTRODUCTION

Organizational behavior (OB) is the study of how people behave in organizational work environments. More specifically, Robbins, Judge, Millett, and Boyle (2014, p. 8) describe it as "a field of study that investigates the impact that individual groups and structure have on behavior within organizations, for the purposes of applying such knowledge towards improving an organization's effectiveness." The OB field looks at the specific context of the work environment in terms of human attitudes, cognition, and behavior, and it embodies contributions from psychology, social psychology, sociology, and anthropology. The field is also rapidly evolving because of the demands of today's fast-paced world, where technology has given rise to work-from-home employees, globalization, and an ageing workforce. Thus, while managers and OB researchers seek to help employees find a work-life balance and improve ethical behavior (Ardichivili, Mitchell, & Jondle, 2009), customer service, and people skills (see, e.g., Brady & Cronin, 2001), they must simultaneously deal with issues such as workforce diversity, work-life balance, and cultural differences.

The most widely accepted model of OB consists of three interrelated levels: (1) *micro* (the individual level), (2) *meso* (the group level), and (3) *macro* (the organizational level). The behavioral sciences that make up the OB field contribute an element to each of these levels. In particular, OB deals with the interactions that take place among the three levels and, in turn, addresses how to improve performance of the organization as a whole.

In order to study OB and apply it to the workplace, it is first necessary to understand its end goal. In particular, if the goal is organizational effectiveness, then these questions arise: What can be done to make an organization more effective? And what determines organizational effectiveness? To answer these questions, dependent variables that include attitudes and behaviors such as productivity, job satisfaction, job performance, turnover intentions, withdrawal, motivation, and workplace deviance are introduced. Moreover, each level—micro, meso, and macro—has implications for guiding managers in their efforts to create a healthier work climate to enable increased organizational performance that includes higher sales, profits, and return on investment (ROE).

THE MICRO (INDIVIDUAL) LEVEL OF ANALYSIS

The micro or individual level of analysis has its roots in social and organizational psychology. In this article, six central topics are identified and discussed: (1) diversity; (2) attitudes and job satisfaction; (3) personality and values; (4) emotions and moods; (5) perception and individual decision-making; and (6) motivation.

Diversity. An obvious but oft-forgotten element at the individual level of OB is the diverse workforce. It is easy to recognize how different each employee is in terms of personal characteristics like age, skin color, nationality, ethnicity, and gender. Other, less biological characteristics include tenure, religion, sexual orientation, and gender identity. In the Australian context, while the Commonwealth Disability Discrimination Act of 1992 helped to increase participation of people with disabilities working in organizations, discrimination and exclusion still continue to inhibit equality (Feather & Boeckmann, 2007). In Western societies like Australia and the United States, however, antidiscrimination legislation is now addressing issues associated with an ageing workforce.

In terms of gender, there continues to be significant discrimination against female employees. Males have traditionally had much higher participation in the workforce, with only a significant increase in the female workforce beginning in the mid-1980s. Additionally, according to Ostroff and Atwater's (2003) study of engineering managers, female managers earn a significantly lower salary than their male counterparts, especially when they are supervising mostly other females.

Job Satisfaction and Job Engagement. Job satisfaction is an attitudinal variable that comes about when an employee evaluates all the components of her or his job, which include affective, cognitive, and behavioral aspects (Weiss, 2002). Increased job satisfaction is associated with increased job performance, organizational citizenship behaviors (OCBs), and reduced turnover intentions (Wilkin, 2012). Moreover, traditional workers nowadays are frequently replaced by contingent workers in order to reduce costs and work in a nonsystematic manner. According to Wilkin's (2012) findings, however, contingent workers as a group are less satisfied with their jobs than permanent employees are.

Job engagement concerns the degree of involvement that an employee experiences on the job (Kahn, 1990). It describes the degree to which an employee identifies with their job and considers their performance in that job important; it also determines that employee's level of participation within their workplace. Britt, Dickinson, Greene-Shortridge, and McKibbin (2007) describe the two extremes of job satisfaction and employee engagement: a feeling of responsibility and commitment to superior job performance versus a feeling of disengagement leading to the employee wanting to withdraw or disconnect from work. The first scenario is also related to organizational commitment, the level of identification an employee has with an organization and its goals. Employees with high organizational commitment, job satisfaction, and employee engagement tend to perceive that their organization values their contribution and contributes to their well-being.

Personality. Personality represents a person's enduring traits. The key here is the concept of *enduring*. The most widely adopted model of personality is the so-called Big Five (Costa & McCrae, 1992): extraversion, agreeableness, conscientiousness, emotional stability, and openness. Employees high in conscientiousness tend to have higher levels of job knowledge, probably because they invest more into learning about their role. Those higher in emotional stability tend to have higher levels of job satisfaction and lower levels of stress, most likely because of their positive and opportunistic outlooks. Agreeableness, similarly, is associated with being better liked and may lead to higher employee performance and decreased levels of deviant behavior.

Although the personality traits in the Big Five have been shown to relate to organizational behavior, organizational performance, and career success (Judge, Higgins, Thoresen, & Barrick, 2006), other personality traits are also relevant to the field. Examples include positive self-evaluation, self-monitoring (the degree to which an individual is aware of comparisons with others), Machiavellianism (the degree to which a person is practical, maintains emotional distance, and believes the end will justify the means), narcissism (having a grandiose sense of self-importance and entitlement), risk-taking, proactive personality, and type A personality. In particular, those who like themselves and are grounded in their belief that they are capable human beings are more likely to perform better because they have fewer self-doubts that may impede goal achievements. Individuals high in Machiavellianism may need a certain environment in order to succeed, such as a job that requires negotiation skills and offers significant rewards, although their inclination to engage in political behavior can sometimes limit their potential. Employees who are high on narcissism may wreak organizational havoc by manipulating subordinates and harming the overall business because of their over-inflated perceptions of self. Higher levels of self-monitoring often lead to better performance but they may cause lower commitment to the organization. Risk-taking can be positive or negative; it may be great for someone who thrives on rapid decision-making, but it may prove stressful for someone who likes to weigh pros and cons carefully before making decisions. Type A individuals may achieve high performance but may risk doing so in a way that causes stress and conflict. Proactive personality, on the other hand, is usually associated with positive organizational performance.

Employee Values. Personal value systems are behind each employee's attitudes and personality. Each employee enters an organization with an already established set of beliefs about what should be and what should not be. Today, researchers realize that personality and values are linked to organizations and organizational behavior. Years ago, only personality's relation to organizations was of concern, but now managers are more interested in an employee's flexibility to adapt to organizational change and to remain high in organizational commitment. Holland's (1973) theory of personality-job fit describes six personality types (realistic, investigative, social, conventional, enterprising, and artistic) and theorizes that job satisfaction and turnover are determined by how well a person matches her or his personality to a job. In addition to person-job (P-J) fit, researchers have also argued for person-organization (P-O) fit, whereby employees desire to be a part of and are selected by an organization that matches their values. The Big Five would suggest, for example, that extraverted employees would desire to be in team environments; agreeable people would align well with supportive organizational cultures rather than more aggressive ones; and people high on openness would fit better in organizations that emphasize creativity and innovation (Anderson, Spataro, & Flynn, 2008).

Individual Differences, Affect, and Emotion.   Personality predisposes people to have certain moods (feelings that tend to be less intense but longer lasting than emotions) and emotions (intense feelings directed at someone or something). In particular, personalities with extraversion and emotional stability partially determine an individual predisposition to experience emotion more or less intensely.

Affect is also related as describing the positive and negative feelings that people experience (Ashkanasy, 2003). Moreover, emotions, mood, and affect interrelate; a bad mood, for instance, can lead individuals to experience a negative emotion. Emotions are action-oriented while moods tend to be more cognitive. This is because emotions are caused by a specific event that might only last a few seconds, while moods are general and can last for hours or even days. One of the sources of emotions is personality. Dispositional or trait affects correlate, on the one hand, with personality and are what make an individual more likely to respond to a situation in a predictable way (Watson & Tellegen, 1985). Moreover, like personality, affective traits have proven to be stable over time and across settings (Diener, Larsen, Levine, & Emmons, 1985; Watson, 1988; Watson & Tellegen, 1985; Watson & Walker, 1996). State affect, on the other hand, is similar to mood and represents how an individual feels in the moment.

THE ROLE OF AFFECT IN ORGANIZATIONAL BEHAVIOR

For many years, affect and emotions were ignored in the field of OB despite being fundamental factors underlying employee behavior (Ashforth & Humphrey, 1995). OB researchers traditionally focused on solely decreasing the effects of strong negative emotions that were seen to impede individual, group, and organizational-level productivity. More recent theories of OB focus, however, on affect, which is seen to have positive, as well as negative, effects on behavior, described by Barsade, Brief, and Spataro (2003, p. 3) as the "affective revolution." In particular, scholars now understand that emotions can be measured objectively and be observed through nonverbal displays such as facial expression and gestures, verbal displays, fMRI, and hormone levels (Ashkanasy, 2003; Rashotte, 2002).

Fritz, Sonnentag, Spector, and McInroe (2010) focus on the importance of stress recovery in affective experiences. In fact, an individual employee's affective state is critical to OB, and today more attention is being focused on discrete affective states. Emotions like fear and sadness may be related to counterproductive work behaviors (Judge et al., 2006). Stress recovery is another factor that is essential for more positive moods leading to positive organizational outcomes. In a study, Fritz et al. (2010) looked at levels of psychological detachment of employees on weekends away from the workplace and how it was associated with higher well-being and affect.

EMOTIONAL INTELLIGENCE AND EMOTIONAL LABOR

Ashkanasy and Daus (2002) suggest that emotional intelligence is distinct but positively related to other types of intelligence like IQ. It is defined by Mayer and Salovey (1997) as the ability to perceive, assimilate, understand, and manage emotion in the self and others. As such, it is an individual difference and develops over a lifetime, but it can be improved with training. Boyatzis and McKee (2005) describe emotional intelligence further as a form of adaptive resilience, insofar as employees high in emotional intelligence tend to engage in positive coping mechanisms and take a generally positive outlook toward challenging work situations.

Emotional labor occurs when an employee expresses her or his emotions in a way that is consistent with an organization's display rules, and usually means that the employee engages in either surface or deep acting (Hochschild, 1983). This is because the emotions an employee is expressing as part of their role at work may be different from the emotions they are actually feeling (Ozcelik, 2013). Emotional labor has implications for an employee's mental and physical health and well-being. Moreover, because of the discrepancy between felt emotions (how an employee actually feels) and displayed emotions or surface acting (what the organization requires the employee to emotionally display), surface acting has been linked to negative organizational outcomes such as heightened emotional exhaustion and reduced commitment (Erickson & Wharton, 1997; Brotheridge & Grandey, 2002; Grandey, 2003; Groth, Hennig-Thurau, & Walsh, 2009).

AFFECT AND ORGANIZATIONAL DECISION-MAKING

Ashkanasy and Ashton-James (2008) make the case that the moods and emotions managers experience in response to positive or negative workplace situations affect outcomes and behavior not only at the individual level, but also in terms of strategic decision-making processes at the organizational level. These authors focus on affective events theory (Weiss & Cropanzano, 1996), which holds that organizational events trigger affective responses in organizational members, which in turn affect organizational attitudes, cognition, and behavior.

Perceptions and Behavior.   Like personality, emotions, moods, and attitudes, perceptions also influence employees' behaviors in the workplace. Perception is the way in which people organize and interpret sensory cues in order to give meaning to their surroundings. It can be influenced by time, work setting, social setting, other contextual factors such as time of day, time of year, temperature, a target's clothing or appearance, as well as personal trait dispositions, attitudes, and value systems. In fact, a person's behavior is based on her or his perception of reality—not necessarily the same as actual reality. Perception greatly influences individual decision-making because individuals base their behaviors on their perceptions of reality. In this regard, attribution theory (Martinko, 1995) outlines how individuals judge others and is our attempt to conclude whether a person's behavior is internally or externally caused.

Decision-Making and the Role of Perception.   Decision-making occurs as a reaction to a problem when the individual perceives there to be discrepancy between the current state of affairs and the state s/he desires. As such, decisions are the choices individuals make from a set of alternative courses of action. Each individual interprets information in her or his own way and decides which information is relevant to weigh pros and cons of each decision and its alternatives to come to her or his perception of the best outcome. In other words, each of our unique perceptual processes influences the final outcome (Janis & Mann, 1977).

Common Biases in Decision-Making.   Although there is no perfect model for approaching decision-making, there are nonetheless many biases that individuals can make themselves aware of in order to maximize their outcomes. First, *overconfidence* bias is an inclination to overestimate the correctness of a decision. Those most likely to commit this error tend to be people with weak intellectual and interpersonal abilities. *Anchoring* bias occurs when individuals focus on the first information they receive, failing to adjust for information received subsequently. Marketers tend to use anchors in order to make impressions on clients quickly and project their brand names. *Confirmation* bias occurs when individuals only use facts that support their decisions while discounting all contrary views. Lastly, *availability* bias occurs when individuals base their judgments on information readily available. For example, a manager might rate an employee on a performance appraisal based on behavior in the past few days, rather than the past six months or year.

Errors in Decision-Making.   Other errors in decision-making include *hindsight bias* and *escalation of commitment*. Hindsight bias is a tendency to believe, incorrectly, after an outcome of an event has already happened, that the decision-maker would have accurately predicted that same outcome. Furthermore, this bias, despite its prevalence, is especially insidious because it inhibits the ability to learn from the past and take responsibility for mistakes. Escalation of commitment is an inclination to continue with a chosen course of action instead of listening to negative feedback regarding that choice. When individuals feel responsible for their actions and those consequences, they escalate commitment probably because they have invested so much into making that particular decision. One solution to escalating commitment is to seek a source of clear, less distorted feedback (Staw, 1981).

Motivation.   The last but certainly not least important individual level topic is motivation. Like each of the topics discussed so far, a worker's motivation is also influenced by individual differences and situational context. Motivation can be defined as the processes that explain a person's intensity, direction, and persistence toward reaching a goal. Work motivation has often been viewed as the set of energetic forces that determine the form, direction, intensity, and duration of behavior (Latham & Pinder, 2005). Motivation can be further described as the persistence toward a goal. In fact many non-academics would probably describe it as the extent to which a person wants and tries to do well at a particular task (Mitchell, 1982).

Early theories of motivation began with Maslow's (1943) hierarchy of needs theory, which holds that each person has five needs in hierarchical order: physiological, safety, social, esteem, and self-actualization. These constitute the "lower-order" needs, while social and esteem needs are "higher-order" needs. Self-esteem for instance underlies motivation from the time of childhood. Another early theory is McGregor's (1960) X-Y theory of motivation: Theory X is the concept whereby individuals must be pushed to work; and theory Y is positive, embodying the assumption that employees naturally like work and responsibility and can exercise self-direction.

Herzberg subsequently proposed the "two-factor theory" that attitude toward work can determine whether an employee succeeds or fails. Herzberg (1966) relates intrinsic factors, like advancement in a job, recognition, praise, and responsibility to increased job satisfaction, while extrinsic factors like the organizational climate, relationship with supervisor, and salary relate to job dissatisfaction. In other words, the hygiene factors are associated with the work context while the motivators are associated with the intrinsic factors associated with job motivation.

CONTEMPORARY THEORIES OF MOTIVATION

Although traditional theories of motivation still appear in OB textbooks, there is unfortunately little empirical data to support their validity. More contemporary theories of motivation, with more acceptable research validity, include *self-determination theory*, which holds that people prefer to have control over their actions. If a task an individual enjoyed now feels like a chore, then this will undermine motivation. Higher self-determined motivation (or intrinsically determined motivation) is correlated with increased well-being, job satisfaction, commitment, and decreased burnout and turnover intent. In this regard, Fernet, Gagne, and Austin (2010) found that work motivation relates to reactions to interpersonal relationships at work and organizational burnout. Thus, by supporting work self-determination, managers can help facilitate adaptive employee organizational behaviors while decreasing turnover intention (Richer, Blanchard, & Vallerand, 2002).

Core self-evaluation (CSE) theory is a relatively new concept that relates to self-confidence in general, such that people with higher CSE tend to be more committed to goals (Bono & Colbert, 2005). These core self-evaluations also extend to interpersonal relationships, as well as employee creativity. Employees with higher CSE are more likely to trust coworkers, which may also contribute to increased motivation for goal attainment (Johnson, Kristof-Brown, van Vianen, de Pater, & Klein, 2003). In general, employees with positive CSE tend to be more intrinsically motivated, thus additionally playing a role in increasing employee creativity (Judge, Bono, Erez, & Locke, 2005). Finally, according to research by Amabile (1996), intrinsic motivation or self-determined goal attainment is critical in facilitating employee creativity.

GOAL-SETTING AND CONSERVATION OF RESOURCES

While self-determination theory and CSE focus on the reward system behind motivation and employee work behaviors, Locke and Latham's (1990) *goal-setting theory* specifically addresses the impact that goal specificity, challenge, and feedback has on motivation and performance. These authors posit that our performance is increased when specific and difficult goals are set, rather than ambiguous and general goals. Goal-setting seems to be an important motivational tool, but it is important that the employee has had a chance to take part in the goal-setting process so they are more likely to attain their goals and perform highly.

Related to goal-setting is Hobfoll's (1989) *conservation of resources* (COR) theory, which holds that people have a basic motivation to obtain, maintain, and protect what they value (i.e., their resources). Additionally there is a global application of goal-setting theory for each of the motivation theories. Not enough research has been conducted regarding the value of goal-setting in global contexts, however, and because of this, goal-setting is not recommended without consideration of cultural and work-related differences (Konopaske & Ivancevich, 2004).

SELF-EFFICACY AND MOTIVATION

Other motivational theories include self-efficacy theory, and reinforcement, equity, and expectancy theories. *Self-efficacy* or *social cognitive* or *learning theory* is an individual's belief that s/he can perform a task (Bandura, 1977). This theory complements goal-setting theory in that self-efficacy is higher when a manager assigns a difficult task because employees attribute the manager's behavior to him or her thinking that the employee is capable; the employee in turn feels more confident and capable.

Reinforcement theory (Skinner, 1938) counters goal-setting theory insofar as it is a behaviorist approach rather than cognitive and is based in the notion that reinforcement conditions behavior, or in other words focuses on external causes rather than the value an individual attributes to goals. Furthermore, this theory instead emphasizes the behavior itself rather than what precedes the behavior. Additionally, managers may use operant conditioning, a part of behaviorism, to reinforce people to act in a desired way.

Social-learning theory (Bandura, 1977) extends operant conditioning and also acknowledges the influence of observational learning and perception, and the fact that people can learn and retain information by paying attention, observing, and modeling the desired behavior.

Equity theory (Adams, 1963) looks at how employees compare themselves to others and how that affects their motivation and in turn their organizational behaviors. Employees who perceive inequity for instance, will either change how much effort they are putting in (their inputs), change or distort their perceptions (either of self or others in relation to work), change their outcomes, turnover, or choose a different referent (acknowledge performance in relation to another employee but find someone else they can be better than).

Last but not least, Vroom's (1964) *expectancy theory* holds that individuals are motivated by the extent to which they can see that their effort is likely to result in valued outcomes. This theory has received strong support in empirical research (see Van Erde & Thierry, 1996, for meta-analytic results). Like each of the preceding theories, expectancy theory has important implications that managers should consider. For instance, managers should communicate with employees to determine their preferences to know what rewards to offer subordinates to elicit motivation. Managers can also make sure to identify and communicate clearly the level of performance they desire from an employee, as well as to establish attainable goals with the employee and to be very clear and precise about how and when performance will be rewarded (Konopaske & Ivancevich, 2004).

THE MESO (GROUP) LEVEL OF ANALYSIS

The second level of OB research also emerges from social and organizational psychology and relates to groups or teams. Topics covered so far include individual differences: diversity, personality and emotions, values and attitudes, motivation, and decision-making. Thus, in this section, attention turns to how individuals come together to form groups and teams, and begins laying the foundation for understanding the dynamics of group and team behavior. Topics at this level also include communication, leadership, power and politics, and conflict.

A group consists of two or more individuals who come together to achieve a similar goal. Groups can be formal or informal. A formal group on the one hand is assigned by the organization's management and is a component of the organization's structure. An informal group on the other hand is not determined by the organization and often forms in response to a need for social contact. Teams are formal groups that come together to meet a specific group goal.

Although groups are thought to go through five stages of development (Tuckman, 1965: forming, storming, norming, performing, and adjourning) and to transition to effectiveness at the halfway mark (Gersick, 1988), group effectiveness is in fact far more complex. For example, two types of conformity to group norms are possible: compliance (just going along with the group's norms but not accepting them) and personal acceptance (when group members' individual beliefs match group norms). Behavior in groups then falls into required behavior usually defined by the formal group and emergent behavior that grows out of interactions among group members (Champoux, 2011).

GROUP DECISION-MAKING

Although many of the decisions made in organizations occur in groups and teams, such decisions are not necessarily optimal. Groups may have more complex knowledge and increased perspectives than individuals but may suffer from conformity pressures or domination by one or two members. Group decision-making has the potential to be affected by groupthink or group shift. In *groupthink*, group pressures to conform to the group norms deter the group from thinking of alternative courses of action (Janis & Mann, 1977). In the past, researchers attempted to explain the effects of group discussion on decision-making through the following approaches: group decision rules, interpersonal comparisons, and informational influence. Myers and Lamm (1976), however, present a conceptual schema comprised of interpersonal comparisons and informational influence approaches that focus on attitude development in a more social context. They found that their research is consistent with the group polarization hypothesis: The initial majority predicts the consensus outcome 90% of the time. The term *group polarization* was founded in Serge Moscovici and his colleagues' literature (e.g., Moscovici & Zavalloni, 1969). *Polarization* refers to an increase in the extremity of the *average* response of the subject population.

In other words, the Myer and Lamm (1976) schema is based on the idea that four elements feed into one another: social motivation, cognitive foundation, attitude change, and action commitment. *Social motivation* (comparing self with others in order to be perceived favorably) feeds into *cognitive foundation*, which in turn feeds into *attitude change* and *action commitment*. Managers of organizations can help reduce the negative phenomena and increase the likelihood of functional groups by encouraging brainstorming or openly looking at alternatives in the process of decision-making such as the nominal group technique (which involves restricting interpersonal communication in order to encourage free thinking and proceeding to a decision in a formal and systematic fashion such as voting).

ELEMENTS OF TEAM PERFORMANCE

OB researchers typically focus on team performance and especially the factors that make teams most effective. Researchers (e.g., see De Dreu & Van Vianen, 2001) have organized the critical components of effective teams into three main categories: context, composition, and process. *Context* refers to the team's physical and psychological environment, and in particular the factors that enable a climate of trust. *Composition* refers to the means whereby the abilities of each individual member can best be most effectively marshaled. *Process* is maximized when members have a common goal or are able to reflect and adjust the team plan (for reflexivity, see West, 1996).

Communication. In order to build high-performing work teams, communication is critical, especially if team conflict is to be minimized. Communication serves four main functions: control, motivation, emotional expression, and information (Scott & Mitchell, 1976). The communication process involves the transfer of meaning from a sender to a receiver through formal channels established by an organization and informal channels, created spontaneously and emerging out of individual choice. Communication can flow downward from managers to subordinates, upward from subordinates to managers, or between members of the same group. Meaning can be transferred from one person to another orally, through writing, or nonverbally through facial expressions and body movement. In fact, body movement and body language may complicate verbal communication and add ambiguity to the situation as does physical distance between team members.

High-performance teams tend to have some of the following characteristics: interpersonal trust, psychological and physical safety, openness to challenges and ideas, an ability to listen to other points of view, and an ability to share knowledge readily to reduce task ambiguity (Castka, Bamber, Sharp, & Belohoubek, 2001). Although the development of communication competence is essential for a work team to become high-performing, that communication competence is also influenced by gender, personality, ability, and emotional intelligence of the members. Ironically, it is the self-reliant team members who are often able to develop this communication competence. Although capable of working autonomously, self-reliant team members know when to ask for support from others and act interdependently.

Emotions also play a part in communicating a message or attitude to other team members. Emotional contagion, for instance, is a fascinating effect of emotions on nonverbal communication, and it is the subconscious process of sharing another person's emotions by mimicking that team member's nonverbal behavior (Hatfield, Cacioppo, & Rapson, 1993). Importantly, positive communication, expressions, and support of team members distinguished high-performing teams from low-performing ones (Bakker & Schaufeli, 2008).

Team Conflict. Because of member interdependence, teams are inclined to more conflict than individual workers. In particular, diversity in individual differences leads to conflict (Thomas, 1992; Wall & Callister, 1995; see also Cohen & Bailey, 1997). Jehn (1997) identifies three types of conflict: task, relationship, and process. *Process* conflict concerns how task accomplishment should proceed and who is responsible for what; *task* conflict focuses on the actual content and goals of the work (Robbins et al., 2014); and *relationship* conflict is based on differences in interpersonal relationships. While conflict, and especially task conflict, does have some positive benefits such as greater innovation (Tjosvold, 1997), it can also lead to lowered team performance and decreased job satisfaction, or even turnover. De Dreu and Van Vianen (2001) found that team conflict can result in one of three responses: (1) collaborating with others to find an acceptable solution; (2) contending and pushing one member's perspective on others; or (3) avoiding and ignoring the problem.

Team Effectiveness and Relationship Conflict. Team effectiveness can suffer in particular from relationship conflict, which may threaten team members' personal identities and self-esteem (Pelled, 1995). In this regard, Murnighan and Conlon (1991) studied members of British string quartets and found that the most successful teams avoided relationship conflict while collaborating to resolve task conflicts. This may be because relationship conflict distracts team members from the task, reducing team performance and functioning. As noted earlier, positive affect is associated with collaboration, cooperation, and problem resolution, while negative affect tends to be associated with competitive behaviors, especially during conflict (Rhoades, Arnold, & Jay, 2001).

Team Climate and Emotionality. Emotional climate is now recognized as important to team processes (Ashkanasy & Härtel, 2014), and team climate in general has important implications for how individuals behave individually and collectively to effect organizational outcomes. This idea is consistent with Druskat and Wolff's (2001) notion that team emotional-intelligence climate can help a team manage both types of conflict (task and relationship). In Jehn's (1997) study, she found that emotion was most often negative during team conflict, and this had a negative effect on performance and satisfaction regardless of the type of conflict team members were experiencing. High emotionality, as Jehn calls it, causes team members to lose sight of the work task and focus instead on the negative affect. Jehn noted, however, that absence of group conflict might also may block innovative ideas and stifle creativity (Jehn, 1997).

Power and Politics. Power and organizational politics can trigger employee conflict, thus affecting employee well-being, job satisfaction, and performance, in turn affecting team and organizational productivity (Vigoda, 2000). Because power is a function of dependency, it can often lead to unethical behavior and thus become a source of conflict. Types of power include formal and personal power. Formal power embodies coercive, reward, and legitimate power. Coercive power depends on fear. Reward power is the opposite and occurs when an individual complies because s/he receives positive benefits from acting in accordance with the person in power. In formal groups and organizations, the most easily accessed form of power is legitimate because this form comes to be from one's position in the organizational hierarchy (Raven, 1993). Power tactics represent the means by which those in a position of power translate their power base (formal or personal) into specific actions.

The nine influence tactics that managers use according to Yukl and Tracey (1992) are (1) rational persuasion, (2) inspirational appeal, (3) consultation, (4) ingratiation, (5) exchange, (6) personal appeal, (7) coalition, (8) legitimating, and (9) pressure. Of these tactics, inspirational appeal, consultation, and rational persuasion were among the strategies most effective in influencing task commitment. In this study, there was also a correlation found between a manager's rational persuasion and a subordinate rating her effectively. Perhaps this is because persuasion requires some level of expertise, although more research is needed to verify which methods are most successful. Moreover, resource dependence theory dominates much theorizing about power and organizational politics. In fact, it is one of the central themes of Pfeffer and Salancik's (1973) treatise on the external control of organizations. First, the theory emphasizes the importance of the organizational environment in understanding the context of how decisions of power are made (see also Pfeffer & Leblebici, 1973). Resource dependence theory is based on the premise that some organizations have more power than others, occasioned by specifics regarding their interdependence. Pfeffer and Salancik further propose that external interdependence and internal organizational processes are related and that this relationship is mediated by power.

Organizational Politics. Political skill is the ability to use power tactics to influence others to enhance an individual's personal objectives. In addition, a politically skilled person is able to influence another person without being detected (one reason why he or she is effective). Persons exerting political skill leave a sense of trust and sincerity with the people they interact with. An individual possessing a high level of political skill must understand the organizational culture they are exerting influence within in order to make an impression on his or her target. While some researchers suggest political behavior is a critical way to understand behavior that occurs in organizations, others simply see it as a necessary evil of work life (Champoux, 2011). Political behavior focuses on using power to reach a result and can be viewed as unofficial and unsanctioned behavior (Mintzberg, 1985). Unlike other organizational processes, political behavior involves both power and influence (Mayes & Allen, 1977). Moreover, because political behavior involves the use of power to influence others, it can often result in conflict.

Organizational Politics, Power, and Ethics. In concluding this section on power and politics, it is also appropriate to address the dark side, where organizational members who are persuasive and powerful enough might become prone to abuse standards of equity and justice and thereby engage in unethical behavior. An employee who takes advantage of her position of power may use deception, lying, or intimidation to advance her own interests (Champoux, 2011). When exploring interpersonal injustice, it is important to consider the intent of the perpetrator, as well as the effect of the perpetrator's treatment from the victim's point of view. Umphress, Simmons, Folger, Ren, and Bobocel (2013) found in this regard that not only does injustice perceived by the self or coworkers influence attitudes and behavior within organizations, but injustice also influences observer reactions both inside and outside of the organization.

Leadership. Leadership plays an integrative part in understanding group behavior, because the leader is engaged in directing individuals toward attitudes and behaviors, hopefully also in the direction of those group members' goals. Although there is no set of universal leadership traits, extraversion from the Big Five personality framework has been shown in meta-analytic studies to be positively correlated with transformational, while neuroticism appears to be negatively correlated (Bono & Judge, 2004). There are also various perspectives to leadership, including the *competency* perspective, which addresses the personality traits of leaders; the *behavioral* perspective, which addresses leader behaviors, specifically task versus people-oriented leadership; and the *contingency* perspective, which is based on the idea that leadership involves an interaction of personal traits and situational factors. Fiedler's (1967) contingency, for example, suggests that leader effectiveness depends on the person's natural fit to the situation and the leader's score on a "least preferred coworker" scale.

More recently identified styles of leadership include transformational leadership (Bass, Avolio, & Atwater, 1996), charismatic leadership (Conger & Kanungo, 1988), and authentic leadership (Luthans & Avolio, 2003). In a nutshell, transformational leaders inspire followers to act based on the good of the organization; charismatic leaders project a vision and convey a new set of values; and authentic leaders convey trust and genuine sentiment.

Leader-member exchange theory (LMX; see Graen & Uhl-Bien, 1995) assumes that leadership emerges from exchange relationships between a leader and her or his followers. More recently, Tse, Troth, and Ashkanasy (2015) expanded on LMX to include social processes (e.g., emotional intelligence, emotional labor, and discrete emotions), arguing that affect plays a large part in the leader-member relationship.

Leadership Development. An emerging new topic in leadership concerns leadership development, which embodies the readiness of leadership aspirants to change (Hannah & Avolio, 2010). In this regard, the learning literature suggests that intrinsic motivation is necessary in order to engage in development (see Hidi & Harackiewicz, 2000), but also that the individual needs to be goal-oriented and have developmental efficacy or self-confidence that s/he can successfully perform in leadership contexts.

Ashkanasy, Dasborough, and Ascough (2009) argue further that developing the affective side of leaders is important. In this case, because emotions are so pervasive within organizations, it is important that leaders learn how to manage them in order to improve team performance and interactions with employees that affect attitudes and behavior at almost every organizational level.

Abusive Leadership. Leaders, or those in positions of power, are particularly more likely to run into ethical issues, and only more recently have organizational behavior researchers considered the ethical implications of leadership. As Gallagher, Mazur, and Ashkanasy (2015) describe, since 2009, organizations have been under increasing pressure to cut costs or "do more with less," and this sometimes can lead to abusive supervision, whereby employee job demands exceed employee resources, and supervisors engage in bullying, undermining, victimization, or personal attacks on subordinates (Tepper, 2000).

Supervisors who are very high or low in emotional intelligence may be more likely to experience stress associated with a very demanding high-performance organizational culture. These supervisors may be more likely to try to meet the high demands and pressures through manipulative behaviors (Kilduff, Chiaburu, & Menges, 2010). This has serious implications for employee well-being and the organization as a whole. Abusive supervision detracts from the ability for those under attack to perform effectively, and targets often come to doubt their own ability to perform (Tepper, 2000).

THE MACRO (ORGANIZATIONAL) LEVEL OF ANALYSIS

The final level of OB derives from research traditions across three disciplines: organizational psychology, organizational sociology, and organizational anthropology. Moreover, just as teams and groups are more than the sum of their individual team members, organizations are also more than the sum of the teams or groups residing within them. As such, structure, climate, and culture play key roles in shaping and being shaped by employee attitudes and behaviors, and they ultimately determine organizational performance and productivity.

Organizational Structure. Organizational structure is a sociological phenomenon that determines the way tasks are formally divided and coordinated within an organization. In this regard, jobs are often grouped by the similarity of functions performed, the product or service produced, or the geographical location. Often, the number of forms of departmentalization will depend on the size of the organization, with larger organizations having more forms of departmentalization than others. Organizations are also organized by the chain of command or the hierarchy of authority that determines the span of control, or how many employees a manager can efficiently and effectively lead. With efforts to reduce costs since the global financial crisis of 2009, organizations have tended to adopt a wider, flatter span of control, where more employees report to one supervisor.

Organizational structure also concerns the level of centralization or decentralization, the degree to which decision-making is focused at a single point within an organization. Formalization is also the degree to which jobs are organized in an organization. These levels are determined by the organization and also vary greatly across the world. For example, Finnish organizations tend to be more decentralized than their Australian counterparts and, as a consequence, are more innovative (Leiponen & Helfat, 2011).

Mintzberg (1979) was the first to set out a taxonomy of organizational structure. Within his model, the most common organizational design is the simple structure characterized by a low level of departmentalization, a wide span of control, and centralized authority. Other organizational types emerge in larger organizations, which tend to be bureaucratic and more routinized. Rules are formalized, tasks are grouped into departments, authority is centralized, and the chain of command involves narrow spans of control and decision-making. An alternative is the matrix structure, often found in hospitals, universities, and government agencies. This form of organization combines functional and product departmentalization where employees answer to two bosses: functional department managers and product managers.

New design options include the *virtual organization* and the *boundaryless organization*, an organization that has no chain of command and limitless spans of control. Structures differ based on whether the organization seeks to use an innovation strategy, imitation strategy, or cost-minimization strategy (Galunic & Eisenhardt, 1994). Organizational structure can have a significant effect on employee attitudes and behavior. Evidence generally shows that work specialization leads to higher employee productivity but also lower job satisfaction (Porter & Lawler, 1965). Gagné and Deci emphasize that autonomous work motivation (i.e., intrinsic motivation and integrated extrinsic motivation) is promoted in work climates that are interesting, challenging, and allow choice. Parker, Wall, and Jackson (1997) specifically relate job enlargement to autonomous motivation. Job enlargement was first discussed by management theorists like Lawler and Hall (1970), who believed that jobs should be enlarged to improve the intrinsic motivation of workers. Today, most of the job-design literature is built around the issue of work specialization (job enlargement and enrichment). In Parker, Wall, and Jackson's study, they observed that horizontally enlarging jobs through team-based assembly cells led to greater understanding and acceptance of the company's vision and more engagement in new work roles. In sum, by structuring work to allow more autonomy among employees and identification among individual work groups, employees stand to gain more internal autonomous motivation leading to improved work outcomes (van Knippenberg & van Schie, 2000).

The Physical Environment of Work.   Ashkanasy, Ayoko, and Jehn (2014) extend the topic of organizational structure to discuss, from a psychological perspective, how the physical work environment shapes employee attitudes, behaviors, and organizational outcomes. Elsbach (2003) pointed out that the space within which employees conduct their work is critical to employees' levels of performance and productivity. In their study, Ashkanasy and his colleagues looked at the underlying processes influencing how the physical environment determines employee attitudes and behaviors, in turn affecting productivity levels. They base their model on affective events theory (Weiss & Cropanzano, 1996), which holds that particular "affective" events in the work environment are likely to be the immediate cause of employee behavior and performance in organizations (see also Ashkanasy & Humphrey, 2011). Specifically, Ashkanasy and colleagues (2014) looked at how this theory holds in extremely crowded open-plan office designs and how employees in these offices are more likely to experience negative affect, conflict, and territoriality, negatively impacting attitudes, behaviors, and work performance.

Organizational Climate and Culture.   Although organizational structure and the physical environment are important determinants of employee attitudes and behaviors, organizational culture and climate lie at the heart of organizational interactions (Ashkanasy & Jackson, 2001). Organizational culture derives from an anthropological research tradition, while organizational climate is based on organizational psychology.

A central presumption of culture is that, as Smircich (1983) noted, organizational behavior is not a function of what goes on inside individual employees' heads, but *between* employees, as evidenced in daily organizational communication and language. As such, organizational culture allows one organization to distinguish itself from another, while conveying a sense of identity for its members.

Organizational Climate and Its Relation to Organizational Culture. Organizational culture creates organizational climate or employees' shared perceptions about their organization and work environment. Organizational climate has been found to facilitate and/or inhibit displays of certain behaviors in one study (Smith-Crowe, Burke, & Landis, 2003), and overall, organizational climate is often viewed as a surface-level indicator of the functioning of the employee/organizational environment relationship (Ryan, Horvath, Ployhart, Schmitt, & Slade, 2000). For instance, a more restrictive climate may inhibit individual decision-making in contrast to a more supportive climate in which the organization may intervene at the individual level and in which the ability/job performance relationship is supported (James, Demaree, Mulaik, & Ladd, 1992). In a study focused on safety climate, Smith-Crowe and colleagues found that organizational climate is essential in determining whether training will transfer to employee performance, and this is most likely because organizational climate moderates the knowledge/performance relationship. Gibbs and Cooper (2010) also found that a supportive organizational climate is positively related to employee performance. They specifically looked at PsyCap, the higher-order construct of psychological capital first proposed by Luthans and Youssef (2004).

ORGANIZATIONAL CHANGE

The final topic covered in this article is organizational change. Organizational culture and climate can both be negatively impacted by organizational change and, in turn, negatively affect employee well-being, attitudes, and performance, reflecting onto organizational performance. Often, there is great resistance to change, and the success rate of organizational change initiatives averages at less than 30% (Al-Haddad & Kotnour, 2015). In order to overcome this resistance, it is important that managers plan ahead for changes and emphasize education and communication about them. As organizations becoming increasingly globalized, change has become the norm, and this will continue into the future.

Additionally, as organizations become increasingly globalized, organizational changes often involve mergers that have important organizational implications. In this regard, Kavanagh and Ashkanasy (2006) found that, for a merger to be successful, there needs to be alignment between the individual values and organizational cultures of merging partners. Managers during a merger situation need to be especially cognizant of how this organizational change affects the company's original organizational culture.

Organizational development (OD), a collection of planned change interventions, may be the way to improve organizational performance and increase employee well-being. OD focuses on employees respecting one another, trust and support, equal power, confrontation of problems, and participation of everyone affected by the organizational change (Lines, 2004).

Moreover, when an organization already has an established climate and culture that support change and innovation, an organization may have less trouble adapting to the change.

Organizational change research encompasses almost all aspects of organizational behavior. Individuals and employees are motivated to achieve success and be perceived as successful. In this regard, each of the individual differences—personality, affect, past experiences, values, and perceptions—plays into whether individuals can transcend obstacles and deal with the barriers encountered along the journey toward achievement. Teams are similarly motivated to be successful in a collective sense and to prove that they contribute to the organization as a whole. In addition to individual differences, team members deal with bringing all those individual differences together, which can wreak havoc on team communication and cause further obstacles in terms of power differences and conflicts in regard to decision-making processes. Last, at the organizational level of organizational behavior, it is important to account for all of these micro- and meso-level differences, and to address the complexity of economic pressures, increasing globalization, and global and transnational organizations to the mix. This is at the top level of sophistication because, as emphasized before, just as groups equal much more than the sum of individual members, organizations are much more than the sum of their teams. The organizational structure, the formal organization, the organizational culture, and climate and organizational rules all impact whether an organization can perform effectively. Organizational behavior, through its complex study of human behavior at its very conception, offers much-needed practical implications for managers in understanding people at work.

REFERENCES

Adams, J. S. (1963). Towards an understanding of inequity. *Journal of Abnormal and Social Psychology, 67,* 422–436.

Al-Haddad, S., & Kotnour, T. (2015). Integrating the organizational change literature: A model for successful change. *Journal of Organizational Change Management, 28,* 234–262.

Amabile, T. M. (1996). *Creativity in context: Update to the social psychology of creativity.* Boulder, CO: Westview Press.

Anderson, C., Spataro, S. E., & Flynn, F. J. (2008). Personality and organizational culture as determinants of influence. *Journal of Applied Psychology, 93,* 702–710.

Ardichivili, A., Mitchell, J. A., & Jondle, D. (2009). Characteristics of ethical business cultures. *Journal of Business Ethics, 85,* 445–451.

Ashforth, B. E., & Humphrey, R. H. (1995). Emotion in the workplace: A reappraisal. *Human Relations, 48,* 97–125.

Ashkanasy, N. M. (2003). Emotions in organizations: A multilevel perspective. In F. Danserau & F. J. Yammarino (Eds.), *Research in multilevel issues* (Vol. 2, pp. 9–54). Oxford: Elsevier.

Ashkanasy, N. M., & Ashton-James, C. E. (2008). Affective events theory: A strategic perspective. In W. J. Zerbe, C. E. J. Härtel, & N. M. Ashkanasy (Eds.), *Research on emotion in organizations* (Vol. 4, pp. 1–34). Bingley, U.K.: Emerald Group.

Ashkanasy, N. M., Ayoko, O. B., & Jehn, K. A. (2014). Understanding the physical environment of work and employee behavior: An affective events perspective. *Journal of Organizational Behavior, 35,* 1169–1184.

Ashkanasy, N. M., & Dasborough, M. T. (2003). Emotional awareness and emotional intelligence in leadership teaching. *Journal of Education in Business, 79,* 18–22.

972 • ORGANIZATIONAL BEHAVIOR

Ashkanasy, N. M., Dasborough, M. T., & Ascough, K. W. (2009). Developing leaders: Teaching about emotional intelligence and training in emotional skills. In S. J. Armstrong & C. V. Fukami (Eds.), *The Sage handbook of management learning, education and development* (pp. 161–185). London: SAGE.

Ashkanasy, N. M., & Daus, C. S. (2002). Emotion in the workplace: The new challenge for managers. *Academy of Management Executive, 16,* 76–86.

Ashkanasy, N. M., & Härtel, C. E. J. (2014). Emotional climate and culture: The good, the bad, and the ugly. In B. Schneider & K. Barbera (Eds.), *The Oxford handbook of organizational culture and climate* (pp. 136–152). New York: Oxford University Press.

Ashkanasy, N. M., & Humphrey, R. H. (2011). Current research on emotion in organizations. *Emotion Review, 3,* 214–224.

Ashkanasy, N. M., & Jackson, C. R. A. (2001). Organizational culture and climate. In N. Anderson, D. S. Ones, H. K. Sinangil, & C. Viswesvaran (Eds.), *Handbook of work and organizational psychology* (pp. 398–415). London: SAGE.

Bakker, A. B., & Schaufeli, W. B. (2008). Positive organizational behavior: Engaged employees in flourishing organizations. *Journal of Organizational Behavior, 29,* 147–154.

Bandura, A. (1977). *Social learning theory.* Alexandria, VA: Prentice Hall.

Barsade, S. G., Brief, A. P., & Spataro, S. E. (2003). The affective revolution in organizational behavior: The emergence of a paradigm. In J. Greenberg (Ed.), *Organizational behavior: The state of the science* (pp. 3–50). Mahwah, NJ: Lawrence Erlbaum.

Bass, B. M., Avolio, B. J., & Atwater, L. E. (1996). The transformational and transactional leadership of men and women. *Applied Psychology: An International Review, 45,* 5–34.

Bono, J. E., & Colbert, A. E. (2005). Understanding responses to multi-source feedback: The role of core self-evaluations. *Personnel Psychology, 58,* 171–203.

Bono, J. E., & Judge, T. A. (2004). Personality and transformational and transactional leadership: A meta-analysis. *Journal of Applied Psychology, 89,* 901–910.

Boyatzis, R. E., & McKee, A. (2005). *Resonant leadership: Renewing yourself and connecting with others through mindfulness, hope, and compassion.* Cambridge, MA: Harvard University Press.

Brady, M. K., & Cronin, J. J., Jr. (2001). Customer orientation: Effects on customer service perceptions and outcome behaviors. *Journal of Service Research, 3,* 241–251.

Britt, T. W., Dickinson, J. M., Greene-Shortridge, T. M., & McKibbin, E. S. (2007). Self-engagement at work. In D. L. Nelson & C. L Cooper (Eds.), *Positive organizational behavior* (pp. 143–158). Thousand Oaks, CA: SAGE.

Brotheridge, C., & Grandey, A. (2002). Emotional labor and burnout: Comparing two perspectives of "people work." *Journal of Vocational Behavior, 60,* 17–39.

Castka, P., Bamber, C. J., Sharp, J. M., & Belohoubek, P. (2001). Factors affecting successful implementation of high performance teams. *Team Performance Management: An International Journal, 7(7/8),* 123–134.

Champoux, J. E. (2011). *Organizational behavior: Integrating individuals, groups and organizations* (4th ed.). New York: Routledge.

Cohen, S. G., & Bailey, D. E. (1997). What makes teams work? Group effectiveness research from the shop floor to the executive suite. *Journal of Management, 23,* 239–290.

Conger, J. A., & Kanungo, R. N. (1988). *Charismatic leadership. The elusive factor in organizational effectiveness.* San Francisco: Jossey-Bass.

Costa, P. T., Jr., & McCrae, R. R. (1992). *Revised NEO personality inventory (NEO-PI-R) and NEO five-factor inventory (NEO-FFI) manual.* Odessa, FL: Psychological Assessment Resources.

De Dreu, C. K. W., & Van Vianen, A. E. M. (2001). Managing relationship conflict and the effectiveness of organizational teams. *Journal of Organizational Behavior, 22,* 309–3278.

Diener, E., Larsen, R. J., Levine, S., Emmons, R. (1985). Intensity and frequency: Dimensions underlying positive and negative affect. *Journal of Personality and Social Psychology, 28*, 1253–1265.

Druskat, V. U., & Wolff, S. B. (2001). Building the emotional intelligence of groups. *Harvard Business Review, 79*, 81–90.

Elsbach, K. D. (2003). Relating physical environment to self-categorizations: Identity threat and affirmation in a non-territorial office space. *Administrative Science Quarterly, 48*, 622–654.

Erickson, R. J., & Wharton, A. S. (1997). Inauthenticity and depression: Assessing the consequences of interactive service work. *Work and Occupations, 24*, 188–213.

Feather, N. T., & Boeckmann, R. J. (2007). Beliefs about gender discrimination in the workplace in the context of affirmative action: Effects of gender and ambivalent attitudes in an Australian sample. *Sex Roles, 57*, 31–42.

Fernet, C., Gagne, M., & Austin, S. (2010). When does quality of relationships with coworkers predict burnout over time? The moderating role of work motivation. *Journal of Organizational Behavior, 31*, 1163–1180.

Fiedler, F. E. (1967). *A theory of leadership effectiveness.* New York: McGraw-Hill.

Fritz, C., Sonnentag, S., Spector, P. E., & McInroe, J. (2010). The weekend matters: Relationships between stress recovery and affective experiences. *Journal of Organizational Behavior, 31*, 1137–1162.

Galunic, D. C., & Eisenhardt, K. M. (1994). Renewing the strategy-structure-performance paradigm. In B. M. Staw & L. L. Cummings (Eds.), *Research in organizational behavior* (Vol. 16, pp. 215–255). Greenwich, CT: JAI Press.

Gallagher, E. C., Mazur, A. K., & Ashkanasy, N. M. (2015). Rallying the troops or beating the horses? How project-related demands can lead to either high performance or abusive supervision. *Project Management Journal, 46*(3), 10–24.

Gersick, C. J. G. (1988). Time and transition in work teams: Toward a new model of group development. *Academy of Management Journal, 31*, 9–41.

Gibbs, P. C., & Cooper, C. L. (2010). Fostering a positive organizational culture and climate in an economic downturn. In N. M. Ashkanasy, C. P. M. Wilderom, & M. F. Peterson, *The handbook of organizational culture and climate* (2d ed., pp. 119–137). Thousand Oaks, CA: SAGE.

Graen, G. B., & Uhl-Bien, M. (1995). Development of LMX theory of leadership over 25 years: Applying a multi-level, multi-domain perspective. *Leadership Quarterly, 6*, 219–247.

Grandey, A. (2003). When the show must go on: Surface and deep acting as predictors of emotional exhaustion and service delivery. *Academy of Management Journal, 46*, 86–96.

Groth, M., Hennig-Thurau, T., & Walsh, G. (2009). Customer reactions to emotional labor: The roles of employee acting strategies and customer detection accuracy. *Academy of Management Journal, 52*, 958–974.

Hannah, S. T., & Avolio, B. J. (2010). Ready or not: How do we accelerate the developmental readiness of leaders? *Journal of Organizational Behavior, 31*, 1181–1187.

Hatfield, E., Cacioppo, J. T., & Rapson, R. L. (1993). Emotional contagion: Current directions. *Psychological Science, 2*, 96–99.

Herzberg, F. (1966). *Work and the nature of man.* Cleveland, OH: World Publishing.

Hidi, S., & Harackiewicz, J. M. (2000). Motivating the academically unmotivated: A critical issue for the 21st century. *Review of Educational Research, 70*, 151–179.

Hobfoll, S. E. (1989). Conservation of resources: A new attempt at conceptualizing stress. *American Psychologist, 44*, 513–524.

Hochschild, A. R. (1983). *The managed heart: Commercialization of human feeling.* Berkeley: University of California Press.

Holland, J. (1973). *Making vocational choices: A theory of careers.* Englewood Cliffs, NJ: Prentice-Hall.

James, L. R., Demaree, R. G., Mulaik, S. A., & Ladd, R. T. (1992). Validity generalization in the context of situational models. *Journal of Applied Psychology, 77*, 3–14.

Janis, I. L., & Mann, L. (1977). *Decision making: A psychological analysis of conflict, choice, and commitment.* New York: Free Press.

Jehn, K. A. (1997). A qualitative analysis of conflict types and dimensions in organizational groups. *Administrative Science Quarterly, 42*, 538–566.

Johnson, E. C., Kristof-Brown, A. L, van Vianen, A. E. M., de Pater, I. E., & Klein, M. R. (2003). Expatriate social ties: Personality antecedents and consequences for adjustment. *International Journal of Selection and Assessment, 11*, 277–288.

Judge, T. A., Bono, J. E., Erez, A., & Locke, E. A. (2005). Core self-evaluations and job and life satisfaction: The role of self-concordance and goal attainment. *Journal of Applied Psychology, 90*, 257–268.

Judge, T. A., Higgins, C. A., Thoresen, C. J., & Barrick, M. R. (2006). The Big Five personality traits, general mental ability, and career success across the life span. *Personnel Psychology, 52*, 621–652.

Judge, T. A., Ilies, R., & Scott, B. A. (2006). Work-family conflict and emotions: Effects at work and home. *Personnel Psychology, 59*, 779–814.

Kahn, W. A. (1990). Psychological conditions of personal engagement and disengagement at work. *Academy of Management Journal, 33*, 692–724.

Kavanagh, M. H., & Ashkanasy, N. M. (2006). The impact of leadership and change management strategy on organizational culture and individual acceptance of change during a merger. *British Journal of Management, 17*, S81–S103.

Kilduff, M., Chiaburu, D. S., & Menges, J. I. (2010). Strategic use of emotional intelligence in organizational settings: Exploring the dark side. *Research in Organizational Behavior, 30*, 129–152.

Konopaske, R., & Ivancevich, J. M. (2004). *Global management and organizational behavior: Text, readings, cases, and exercises.* New York: McGraw-Hill.

Latham, G. P., & Pinder, C. C. (2005). Work motivation theory and research at the dawn of the twenty-first century. *Annual Review of Psychology, 56*, 485–516.

Lawler, E. E., & Hall, D. T. (1970). Relationship of job characteristics to job involvement, satisfaction, and intrinsic motivation. *Journal of Applied psychology, 54*, 305–312.

Leiponen, A., & Helfat, C. E. (2011). Location, decentralization, and knowledge sources for innovation. *Organization Science, 22*, 641–658.

Lines, R. (2004). Influence of participation in strategic change: Resistance, organizational commitment and change goal achievement. *Journal of Change Management, 4*(3), 193–215.

Locke, E. A., & Latham, G. P. (1990). *A theory of goal setting and task performance.* Englewood Cliffs, NJ: Prentice-Hall.

Luthans, F., & Avolio, B. J. (2003). Authentic leadership development. In K. S. Cameron, J. E. Dutton, & R. E. Quinn (Eds.), *Positive organizational scholarship: Foundations of a new discipline* (pp. 241–261). San Francisco: Barrett-Koehler.

Luthans, F., & Youssef, C. M. (2004). Human, social, and now positive psychological capital management. *Organizational Dynamics, 33*, 143–160.

Martinko, M. J. (1995). The nature and function of attribution theory within the organizational sciences. In. M. J. Martinko (Ed.), *Advances in attribution theory: An organizational perspective* (pp. 7–14). Delray Beach, FL: St. Lucie Press.

Maslow, A. H. (1943). A theory of human motivation. *Psychological Review, 50*, 370–396.

Mayer, J. D., & Salovey, P. (1997). What is emotional intelligence? In P. Salovey & D. J. Sluyter (Eds.), *Emotional development and emotional intelligence: Educational implications* (pp. 3–31). New York: Basic Books.

Mayes, B. T., & Allen, R. W. (1977). Toward a definition of organizational politics. *Academy of Management Journal, 2*, 635–644.

McGregor, D. (1960). *The human side of enterprise*. New York: McGraw-Hill.

Mintzberg, H. (1979). *The structuring of organizations: A synthesis of the research*. Englewood Cliffs, NJ: Prentice-Hall.

Mintzberg, H. (1985). The organization as a political arena. *Journal of Management Studies, 22*, 133–154.

Mitchell, T. R. (1982). Motivation: New directions for theory, research, and practice. *Academy of Management Review, 7*, 80–88.

Moscovici, S., & Zavalloni, M. (1969). The group as a polarizer of attitudes. *Journal of Personality and Social Psychology, 12*, 125–135.

Murnighan, J. K., & Conlon, D. E. (1991). The dynamics of intense workgroups: A study of British string quartets. *Administrative Science Quarterly, 36*, 165–186.

Myers, D. G., & Lamm, H. (1976). The group polarization phenomenon. *Psychological Bulletin, 83*, 602–627.

Ostroff, C., & Atwater, L. E. (2003). Does whom you work with matter? Effects of referent group and age composition on managers' compensation. *Journal of Applied Psychology, 88*, 725–740.

Ozcelik, H. (2013). An empirical analysis of surface acting in intra-organizational relationships. *Journal of Organizational Behavior, 34*, 291–309.

Parker, S. K., Wall, T. D., & Jackson, P. R. (1997). "That's not my job": Developing flexible employee work orientations. *Academy of Management Journal, 40*, 899–929.

Pelled, L. H. (1995). Demographic diversity, conflict, and work group outcomes: An intervening process theory. *Organization Science, 7*, 615–631.

Pfeffer, J., & Leblebici, H. (1973). Executive recruitment and the development of interfirm organizations. *Administrative Science Quarterly, 18*, 449–461.

Pfeffer, J., & Salancik, G. R. (1973). *The external control of organizations: A resource dependence perspective*. Palo Alto, CA: Stanford University Press.

Porter, L. W., & Lawler, E. E. (1965). Properties of organization structure in relation to job attitudes and job behavior. *Psychological Bulletin, 64*, 23–51.

Rashotte, L. S. (2002). What does that smile mean? The meaning of nonverbal behaviors in social interaction. *Social Psychology Quarterly, 65*, 92–102.

Raven, B. H. (1993). The bases of power: Origins and recent developments. *Journal of Social Issues, 49*, 227–251.

Rhoades, J. A., Arnold, J., & Jay, C. (2001). The role of affective traits and affective states in disputants' motivation and behavior during episodes of organizational conflict. *Journal of Organizational Behavior, 22*, 329–345.

Richer, S., Blanchard, C., & Vallerand, R. J. (2002). A motivational model of work turnover. *Journal of Applied Social Psychology, 32*, 2089–2113.

Robbins, S. P., Judge, T. A., Millett, B., & Boyle, M. (2014). *Organisational behaviour* (7th ed.). French's Forest, NSW, Australia: Pearson Education.

Ryan, A. M., Horvath, M., Ployhart, R. E., Schmitt, N., & Slade, L. A. (2000). Hypothesizing differential item functioning in global employee opinion surveys. *Personnel Psychology, 53*, 531–562.

Scott, W. G., & Mitchell, T. R. (1976). *Organization theory: A structural and behavioral analysis*. Homewood, IL: Irwin.

Skinner, B. F. (1938). *The behavior of organisms: An experimental analysis*. New York: Appleton-Century-Crofts.

Smircich, L. (1983). Concepts of culture and organizational analysis. *Administrative science quarterly, 28*, 339–358.

Smith-Crowe, K., Burke, M. J., & Landis, R. S. (2003). Organizational climate as a moderator of safety knowledge-safety performance relationships. *Journal of Organizational Behavior, 24*, 861–876.

Staw, B. M. (1981). The escalation of commitment to a course of action. *Academy of Management Review, 6,* 577–587.

Tepper, B. J. (2000). Consequences of abusive supervision. *Academy of Management Journal, 43,* 178–190.

Thomas, K. W. (1992). Conflict and negotiation processes in organizations. In M. D. Dunnette, & L. M. Hough (Eds.), *Handbook of industrial and organizational psychology* (2d ed., Vol. 3, pp. 652–717). Mountain View, CA: Consulting Psychologist Press.

Tjosvold, D. (1997). Networking by professionals to manage change: Dentists' cooperation and competition to develop their business. *Journal of Organizational Behavior, 18,* 745–752.

Tse, H. M. M., Troth, A. M., & Ashkanasy, N. M. (2015). Leader-member exchange and emotion in organizations. In B. Erdogan & T. N. Bauer (Eds.), *The Oxford handbook of leader-member exchange* (pp. 209–225). New York: Oxford University Press.

Tuckman, B. (1965). Developmental sequence in small groups. *Psychological Bulletin, 63,* 384–399.

Umphress, E. E., Simmons, A. L., Folger, R., Ren, R., & Bobocel, R. (2013). Observer reactions to interpersonal injustice: The roles of perpetrator intent and victim perception. *Journal of Organizational Behavior, 34,* 327–349.

Van Erde, W., & Thierry, H. (1996). Vroom's expectancy models and work-related criteria: A meta-analysis. *Journal of Applied Psychology, 81,* 576–588.

Van Knippenberg, D., & Van Schie, E. L. S. (2000). Foci and correlates of organizational identification. *Journal of Occupational and Organizational Psychology, 73,* 137–147.

Vigoda, E. (2000). Organizational politics, job attitudes, and work outcomes: Exploration and implications for the public sector. *Journal of Vocational Behavior, 57,* 326–347.

Vroom, V. H. (1964). *Work and motivation.* New York: Wiley.

Wall, J., & Callister, R. (1995). Conflict and its management. *Journal of Management, 21,* 515–558.

Wallach, M. A., Kogan, N., & Bem D. J. (1964). Diffusion of responsibility and level of risk taking in groups. *Journal of Abnormal Social Psychology, 68,* 263–274.

Watson, D. (1988). The vicissitudes of mood measurement: Effects of varying descriptors, time frames, and response formats on measures of positive and negative affect. *Journal of Personality and Social Psychology, 55,* 128–141.

Watson, D., & Tellegen, A. (1985). Toward a consensual structure of mood. *Psychological Bulletin, 98,* 219–235.

Watson, D., & Walker, L. M. (1996). The long-term stability and predictive validity of trait measures of affect. *Journal of Personality and Social Psychology, 70,* 567–577.

Weiss, H. M. (2002). Deconstructing job satisfaction: Separating evaluations, beliefs and affective experiences. *Human Resource Management Review, 12,* 173–194.

Weiss, H. M., & Cropanzano, R. (1996). Affective events theory: A theoretical discussion of the structure, causes and consequences of affective experiences at work. In B. M. Staw & L. L. Cummings (Eds.), *Research in organizational behavior* (Vol. 18, pp. 1–74). Westport, CT: JAI Press.

West, M. (1996). Reflexivity and work group effectiveness: A conceptual integration. In M. A. West (Ed.), *The handbook of work group psychology* (pp. 555–579). Chichester, U.K.: Wiley.

Wilkin, C. L. (2012). I can't get no job satisfaction: Meta-analysis comparing permanent and contingent workers. *Journal of Organizational Behavior, 34,* 47–64.

Yukl, G., & Tracey, J. B. (1992). Consequences of influence tactics used with subordinates, peers, and the boss. *Journal of Applied Psychology, 77,* 525–535.

Neal M. Ashkanasy and Alana D. Dorris

COMMUNICATION IN ORGANIZATIONS

CONDUIT VERSUS CONSTITUTIVE PERSPECTIVE OF COMMUNICATION IN ORGANIZATIONS

Modern organizational communication scholarship tends to avoid "transmission" or "conduit" perspectives of communicating in organizations. In a transmission perspective, communication is relegated to a byproduct, variable, or mere secondary interest to organizing processes (Axley, 1984). The transmission view of organizational communication positions communication as occurring "within" the container of the organization; messages are encoded and sent via media to receivers who decode those messages with greater or lesser degrees of accuracy. Here, communication is assumed to be organizational if it occurs within the structure of the organization. Organizational communication problems are assumed to involve inadequate information transfer—whether the right information gets to the right person at the right time. Yet, Eisenberg (1984) critiqued this perspective by exploring members' use of strategic ambiguity in ordinary organizational communication, such as with mission statements. Mission statements are often worded in abstract and equivocal terms, but they also have the positive function of unifying diverse interests under a single—albeit ambiguous—goal. In other words, message clarity cannot be the only function or even the only positive function of organizational communication, since strategic ambiguity is so widespread and useful. The notion of strategic ambiguity in organizational communication suggests that communication is not only about transmitting facts.

Contrary to a transmissional view, modern organizational communication scholarship tends to take a constitutive view of communicating in organizations (Boivins et al., 2017). In a constitutive view, communication is the location of the organization's ontology (Taylor & Van Every, 1999); communication calls organizations into being and makes organizations what they are (Bisel, 2010). From this view, improving communication is a chief means of improving the organization; in contrast, it can be assumed that operationally dysfunctional or unethical organizing is, at least partially, the product of dysfunctional communication patterns (Bisel, 2018). The constitutive perspective was labeled communication constitutes organizing (CCO) theory. Currently, organizational scholars tend to work in three main traditions of CCO theory: the four flows model, the Montréal school, and the Niklas Luhmann school (for more details, see Schoeneborn et al., 2014).

For instance, the four flows model explains how organizations are constituted in communication processes. McPhee and Zaug (2000) explained that activity coordination (i.e., working with others), self-structuring (i.e., dividing labor, rights, and responsibilities), membership negotiation (i.e., managing the inclusion and exclusion of members), and institutional positioning (i.e., generating perceptions of legitimacy among stakeholders in the organizational field) are forms of meaning-making that constitute organization. The authors argue that the process is not reducible to a single communication flow type, but that the communicative constitution of organization occurs where at least two or more of the flows intermingle and overlap across time and space. Later critiques to the four flows model sought to correct what might be seen as excessive social constructionism in the constitutive perspective broadly and the four flows model specifically. Currently, organizational communication scholars are proposing addendums to address this potential shortcoming and to explain how material realities interact with and are already present within constitutive communication forces (Bruscella & Bisel, 2018). Thus, most modern studies of organizational communication situate research findings within the larger constitutive perspective.

DOWNWARD COMMUNICATION IN ORGANIZATIONS

Downward communication refers to those messages primarily sent from organizational management and leadership to members who have less decision-making authority within an organization's formalized hierarchy (e.g., frontline employees). Research demonstrates that management philosophies and managers' taken-for-granted assumptions about human nature often manifest in particular ways in their downward communication patterns, as described in McGregor's (1957) theory X/Y. For example, organizational leaders who can be described as adhering to a classical management philosophy (Taylor, 1923) value top-down directive-giving and the coherent efficiency those kinds of messages can provide; however, the classical management philosophy may also result in managements' reluctance to engage in participatory decision-making with employees and the ignoring of critical upward feedback, including innovative ideas. Elsewhere, organizational leaders who can be described as adhering to a human resource management philosophy value employees' creative input but may be reluctant to issue top-down mandates that can encourage rapid coordinated action. Importantly, managerial philosophies and taken-for-granted assumptions can be contradictory and result in paradoxical downward communication patterns (e.g., soliciting advice from frontline employees while disregarding dissent). Thus, in a sense, downward communication patterns both reflect and reproduce the cultural communication assumptions of organizational management and other members.

Productivity. The influence of downward communication on employee productivity is multifaceted and complex. Despite colloquial sayings to the contrary (e.g., "We had a failure to communicate!"), the relationship between the frequency of communication and employee productivity is complicated. The quality of downward communication must be considered as much as its quantity in order to understand likely outcomes. On one hand, downward communication that socializes employees into their job responsibilities with accuracy and specificity can improve productivity by providing clear guidance on which tasks to accomplish and the preferred methods of accomplishing them. In this way, role clarity (or ambiguity) is a key outcome of downward communication that can influence employee productivity (Kramer, 2010). On the other hand, abusive supervision, managerial bullying behaviors, and organizational injustices perpetrated by management can adversely affect employee productivity, even leading to employee slowdowns, resistance, pilfering, and sabotage (Conrad, 2011). In sum, understanding the quality of downward communication is key to understanding likely outcomes for the organization.

Research explores the role of downward communication in shaping employees' motivation. Here the focus often involves identifying how certain forms of downward communication can shape employees' beliefs about the meaningfulness of their work. A body of research suggests that downward communication designed to enhance employees' contact with beneficiaries of their work outputs is particularly potent in enhancing employee productivity (Grant, 2007). While not traditionally associated with downward communication per se, the idea is that management can frame the meaningfulness of work by proxy by designing job descriptions and functions so that employees have opportunities to interact with beneficiaries. Similarly, management can collect and remind employees of situations in which their work outputs benefited customers, clients, patients, students, and community members. The net result of these downward communication efforts is the bolstering of key intrinsic motivation associated with meaningfulness of work and purpose, which tends to increase persistence behaviors and productivity.

Job Satisfaction. Similarly, the quality of downward communication is highly predictive of employee job and work satisfaction. Unsurprisingly, fair and kind treatment by management is strongly associated with employees' job satisfaction (Pincus, 1986). Downward communication is a significant force in constituting the quality of supervisor–subordinate relationships. When downward communication is perceived by employees to be affirming, just, pleasant, and predictable, the supervisor–subordinate relationship is likely to be perceived as satisfying. The subsequent influence of that relational satisfaction on broader forms of job satisfaction is obvious. More specifically, a pattern of person-centered communication in downward communication is strongly associated with employee job satisfaction (Fix & Sias, 2006). Person-centered communication involves dialogue that invites the other to perspective-take, consider alternatives within the present situation carefully, and then implement decision-making as an autonomous, responsible agent. In contrast, position-centered communication is characterized by directives that neglect perspective-taking and reduce the sense that one is autonomous in his or her choices. Position-centered communication relies on status differences and power arrangements at the expense of reinforcing relational partnerships. In sum, person-centered downward communication is associated with strong job and supervisory satisfaction.

Turnover. Downward communication can influence employee turnover. Voluntary exit by employees can be costly for organizational resources and weaken the organization's ability to circulate insights and lessons among new and veteran coworkers. Where poor-quality or abusive downward communication harms employees' job satisfaction, affective and continuance commitments to the organization tend to wane (Allen, 1992). Job dissatisfaction that is produced by poor-quality downward communication tends to lead to turnover intentions or voluntary exit. Furthermore, work on the erosion model of employee turnover suggests other possible relationships between downward communication and turnover. The model suggests that downward communication—which is characterized by social support (i.e., the perception one is being cared for by the group) and that stimulates greater network centrality for employees (i.e., being relationally interconnected with other organizational members)—reduces employee turnover (Feeley et al., 2010). Conversely, studies reveal that supervisors can also engage in surreptitious downward communication strategies designed to encourage unwanted employees to quit voluntarily, which may shield the manager and organization from unpleasant termination conversations and related financial costs associated with terminations (e.g., unemployment and wrongful termination lawsuits; Cox & Kramer, 1995). In sum, downward communication can predict both organizational turnover and continuance commitment.

Leader–Member Exchange (LMX). Downward supervisor-to-subordinate communication often occurs within the context of a role-negotiation and relational-development process. In contrast to theories that presumed leaders' communication could be characterized by a single average leadership style (ALS), the leader–member exchange (LMX) theory proposed that leaders use at least two common styles of downward communication with members, depending on the quality of relationships they develop with members over time. The LMX theory has a long history and is supported by ample empirical evidence (Graen & Uhl-Bien, 1995). The theory proposes that over time leaders develop differentiated relationships with members such that a few members are eventually treated as in-group members and all others are treated as out-group members. Role negotiation begins when the leader–member relationship is initiated. During "role-making," the leader communicates the role and its responsibilities; then the leader tests the member by observing the quality of the members' role performances. During "role-taking," members negotiate the boundaries of their role by performing responsibilities and making adaptations and adjustments. Eventually, the relational dyad (i.e., leader and member) settles into "role routinization" in which in-group relationships are marked by strong mutual influence, trust, and respect, while out-group relationships are not. According to the theory, a few in-group members will be treated as "trusted lieutenants" while all others will be treated as "hired hands." High-quality LMX (i.e., in-group) relationships are characterized by advice-seeking and giving, reciprocal and deepening self-disclosures, social and career support, as well as a mixture of task and relational messages. Conversely, low-quality LMX (i.e., out-group) relationships are characterized by a lack of advice-seeking by the supervisor, superficial and rare self-disclosures, little social and career support, as well as task-focused communication to the exclusion of relationally focused messages (Kelley & Bisel, 2014).

High-quality LMX relationships have many benefits for both organizations (e.g., better employee performance, more organizational citizenship behaviors by employees, lower turnover) and members (e.g., empowerment, career progress). Yet, some critics worry that demographic dissimilarity with a leader will make it less likely for members to achieve in-group status and enjoy its benefits. Such a pattern could partially explain the race and gender-based inequity in career advancement apparent in many organizations and institutions (Randolph-Seng et al., 2016). The leadership-making model was proposed to address this concern while maximizing the potential benefits of high LMX relationships—termed "LMX partnerships" (Graen & Uhl-Bien, 1995). Within the leadership-making model, leaders are urged to engage in downward communication designed to develop high-quality exchange relationships with all members such that over time, leaders and members build trust, respect, and mutual influence. Additionally, leaders are urged to engage in strategic partnership building via relational bids, which are small and gradual opportunities to engage in richer exchanges. For example, a leader may ask the advice of a new employee regarding an organizational agenda item of small to moderate significance. The relational bid creates an opportunity for the two to develop a richer working relationship over time, especially if reciprocated incrementally and with appropriate frequency and intensity. Thus, LMX theory explores how leader–member relationships are both a context for and the product of downward communication.

Framing and Sense-Giving. Leadership framing provides a conceptual framework for exploring the implications of downward communication for organizations, institutions, and societies. Fairhurst's (2010) notion of leadership framing contrasts with transmissional views of communicating in organizations (see "Conduit Versus Constitutive Perspective of Communication in Organization") and explores how leaders shape members' attributions of events and circumstances which, in turn, determine members' decisions and actions. Note that "framing" is used in various contexts in the social and behavioral sciences in divergent ways (cf. Entman, 2004). Here, a frame is a taken-for-granted assumption about how organizational reality should or does work. Framing refers to attempts to shape how others believe organizational reality should or does work. Thus, the phrase "leadership framing" is used to designate leaders' downward communication attempts to influence employees' attributions involving organizational events. The leadership framing literature avoids excessive social constructionism by acknowledging material realities, but also suggests most material realities have a quality of uncertainty, ambiguity, or undecidability, which makes them open to a range of interpretations, including contested interpretations. For example, missed sales goals can be framed as divergently as avoidable (e.g., lagging the competition) or unavoidable (e.g., the result of new and excessive government regulations). The key idea is that leaders can influence organizational members' attributions of events and, in doing so, influence likely consequences and outcomes of members' actions.

The organizational framing literature borrows from message design logic theory (O'Keefe, 1988). The theory proposes that individuals hold beliefs about the goal(s) of communication, which are apparent in their communication habits and practices. The theory categorizes communicators as expressive, conventional, and rhetorical/strategic. Expressives assume language is a medium for expressing one's thoughts. Conventionals assume communication is a cooperative game played by widely shared rules. Rhetorical/strategics assume communication can shape and reshape the self and situations. The concept of leadership framing aligns well with this schema; leaders hold beliefs about the goals of communication, which are apparent in their communication habits.

Scholars recommend leaders should develop rhetorical/strategic mind-sets toward their downward communication (Fairhurst & Sarr, 1996). Specifically, leaders who build diverse repertoires of poetic language forms can enhance their capacity to shape followers' mental models and attributions. Metaphor, story, contrast, jargon, and spin are common poetic language forms that help leaders succeed in influencing members' beliefs about how organizational reality should or does work. Prescriptive implications of the leadership framing concept suggest that leaders can improve their rhetorical sensitivity and execution through priming. To prime for framing, leaders can attend to and collect poignant poetic language forms (e.g., metaphors, stories, aphorism), anticipate organizational situations that will benefit from the management of meaning, and practice playing with meaning (Barge & Fairhurst, 2008).

Sense-giving and leadership framing are virtually synonymous concepts. Sense-giving refers to attempts to shape others' sense-making—the meaning individuals attribute to events (Maitlis & Lawrence, 2007). Sense-giving tends to be used when the scholarly focus is on whether or how organizational leaderships' communication influences members' beliefs about organizational reality (e.g., during planned changes or crisis situations). While the two labels describe a similar idea, the term *sense-giving* tends to be used in the management literature and where sense-making theory is a chief concern of the authors. Both terms are used in communication literature.

Corrective Feedback.   Scholarship on feedback in organizations was largely inspired by systems theory and cybernetics (Farace et al., 1977). From this vantage point, feedback as a mechanism explains whether and how individuals, teams, and organizations adapt (or fail to adapt) to their environments. When feedback is missing, inadequate, or ignored, it can trigger a series of events that link, amplify, and recur, thereby making individuals, teams, and organizations increasingly less adapted to and fit for the challenges of the environment. It is therefore not a surprise that strategies for providing downward corrective feedback are a perennial concern for executives, managers, and supervisors. Indeed, research demonstrated that managers tend to avoid, delay, or distort their delivery of downward corrective feedback because of the social costs associated with giving it. The communication pattern is termed "the mum effect" and refers to individuals' reluctance to provide negative feedback to one another for fear of damaging identities and relationships. The mum effect in downward corrective feedback-giving can be problematic for the health of organizations when underperformance remains unaddressed by management for long periods of time (Yariv, 2006).

Business communication specialists offer some direction. First, when dealing with minor operational annoyances and underperformance (as opposed to ethical lapses), managers are encouraged to engage in soft starts that seek to provide corrective feedback gently while also raising subordinates' awareness that their performance is not meeting expectations (e.g., "Do me a favor and. . ." or "The expectation is that everyone will. . ."). Soft starts are helpful in that they maintain relational trust and individual dignity while also encouraging improvement for the sake of the organizational system. In cases where soft starts have been attempted and yet proven ineffective in addressing underperformance, the "EAGR" approach is recommended. The EAGR approach involves four steps that can unfold over time and are designed to be repeated, if needed. First, the manager explains where the subordinate's performance is not meeting expectations, with an emphasis on facts and observations (i.e., Explain). Second, the manager asks how the subordinate intends to remedy this situation in order to meet expectations (i.e., Ask). Third, the manager and subordinate agree to a timeframe for expectations to be met (i.e., Get a commitment to a timeframe). Fourth, and finally, the manager revisits the corrective conversation with the subordinate to either praise and express gratitude or to begin the process again, with the added force of mentioning the subordinate's own previous development plan (i.e., Revisit). These conversations can be recorded in written form and serve as documentation for personnel decisions. Like soft starts, the EAGR approach to downward corrective feedback fits situations involving relatively minor operational annoyances, but not severe ethical lapses (Kramer & Bisel, 2017).

UPWARD COMMUNICATION IN ORGANIZATIONS

Upward communication refers to those messages primarily sent from organizational members who have comparably less decision-making authority to those who hold more authority.

Communicating upwardly in organizations involves interacting in the context of asymmetrical power arrangements that disadvantage the speaker. Unsurprisingly, a silencing power of power is widely and easily observable in many laboratory and field settings (Morrison, 2014). The silencing power of power is relevant to the study of organizations for many reasons. Among those reasons is the idea that silenced or muted upward communication about critical issues can hinder organizational learning and adaptation regarding both operational troubles (Bisel et al., 2012) and ethical malfeasance (Bisel, 2018). Free-flowing dissent can serve a protective function against these troubling organizational issues. Admittedly, though, not all upward communication involves important information about operations and ethics. Yet, when important information is hindered from moving freely up the chain of command, small and resolvable problems can be left unaddressed. Problems left unaddressed, in turn, can become large and intractable, threatening members, stakeholders, organizations, and even societies. Additionally, when new ideas and fresh debates can flow freely within a workplace, it can facilitate a culture of innovation and creativity.

Organizational Silence.   Organizational silence refers to a communication phenomenon that occurs in organizations in which problems are known by members but are not discussed collectively with key decision-makers. Scholarship indicates that organizational silence is common (Morrison, 2014). Theorizing by Chris Argyris (1994) explained organizational silence is primarily motivated by fear of retribution. Members fear exposing decision-makers' errors and thereby triggering decision-makers' embarrassment. Organizational members fear embarrassing power holders who might use their power to sanction members or engage in retributive penalties. To avoid that possibility, members remain silent or avoid discussing critical information. Additionally, over time, organizational members come to create and play by learned social rules in which the "undiscussability" of certain issues itself is rendered undiscussable.

Distortion.   In addition to silence, upward communication in organizations can also be described in terms of distortion. Distortion refers to the ways messages are modified among interlocutors, which have the consequence of being vague or misleading (Fulk & Mani, 1986). While the term *distortion* is used infrequently in contemporary organizational communication scholarship, derivative concepts are common. Chief among them is equivocation in which members use polite and euphemistic language instead of harsh truth-telling. The concept of distortion is important in that it suggests communicators have more options for talking with power holders about critical information than either silence or outright dissent. In fact, communication scholarship in diverse settings attests to the widespread use of equivocation. Communicators use equivocation to manage everyday tensions between the need to avoid threatening relational partners' face while also avoiding accusations of being deceptive (Bavelas et al., 1990). Here, equivocation provides communicators a compromise between potentially hurtful truth-telling and potentially hurtful deception—both of which could hurt employees' desire to manage impressions with power holders.

Equivocation can be strategic but can also become so culturally normative that it is used without much forethought. Because equivocation tends to soften otherwise harsh truth-telling, it can result in widespread misperceptions about the nature or severity of issues.

Equivocation is common in upward communication because of employees' fear of retribution from management. When excessive equivocation permeates the organizational communication norms of a team or workplace, management can misperceive the nature or severity of issues that employees are reluctant to discuss candidly. Weick and Sutcliffe (2007) warn managers of the "fallacy of centrality" in which a power holder assumes that if troubles were present within the social system, he or she would know. Silence and distortions in organizational communication mean that power holders' information environments can diverge from reality—an outcome of power that is allegorized in Hans Christian Andersen's (1837) children's tale, *The Emperor's New Clothes*.

Upward Dissent.   Organizational dissent occurs when employees voice their disagreements with managements' policies or decisions. Dissent can be voiced upwardly to management, laterally to workplace peers, or displaced outside the organization to friends and family. A large body of research by Jeffrey Kassing (2011) and colleagues has provided many insights into dissent in organizations. Dissenters tend to be confident individuals with strong communication skills and established positive working relationships with their supervisor. Extensive research categorized organizational dissent into five strategies: solution presentation (i.e., providing solutions to address issues); direct factual appeal (i.e., supporting dissent with objective information); repetition (i.e., reminding others of the dissent); circumvention (i.e., dissenting to a target even higher in the chain of command); and threatening resignation (i.e., giving an ultimatum to exit if dissent is not taken seriously). Studies demonstrated that employees tend to view solution presentation and direct factual appeals to be the most communicatively competent and skillful of the dissent strategies. However, circumvention and threatening resignation are increasingly likely where supervisors are perceived as too inactive, incompetent, or unethical. Research indicates that upward ethical dissent is especially challenging to discuss frankly and candidly (Bisel, 2018). Dissent voiced within an organization is often labeled "boat rocking" in order to differentiate it from "whistle blowing," which occurs when dissent is voiced to external agencies such as law enforcement or the media. At times, boat rocking is met with managers' inaction or dismissiveness, which can, in turn, lead employees to engage in whistle blowing.

LATERAL COMMUNICATION IN ORGANIZATIONS AND WORKPLACE RELATIONSHIPS

Peer relationships are a crucial aspect of the workplace, as coworkers are important sources of information, friendship, social support, belonging, feedback, and coaching (Kram & Isabella, 1985). Lateral communication in organizations is important given that coworker interactions shape employees' work environment, well-being, and job satisfaction. However, an organizational communication perspective shifts the focus from culture and satisfaction to meaning-making and interaction, as communication scholars are primarily interested in how people attribute meaning to events and the ways those attributions shape thought, decision, action, choice, and experience. For this reason, modern consideration of horizontal workplace interactions focuses more on how lateral communication is a meaning-making context for employee sense-making.

Sense-Making and Grapevine Communication.

Lateral communication functions as an important sense-making mechanism in organizational life, shaping employee attitudes, decisions, behaviors, and perceptions. Sense-making is the ongoing process by which people attribute meaning to events through talk (Weick, 1995; Weick et al., 2005). Weick (1995) posits that most sense-making is effortless and beneath conscious awareness until ambiguity and uncertainty interrupt the ease with which people interpret their world. The process of sense-making is made more difficult by confusing, troubling, or uncertain situations. Organizational events that generate anxiety for employees will slow their sense-making. In slowing sense-making, the process of meaning-making becomes more observable—at least, temporarily. Coworkers, motivated by a desire to regain a sense of psychosocial calm, seek out one another in order to talk about events and search for a meaning to attribute to them. Members will prefer event labels and attributions that help them achieve a sense of individual and shared identity affirmation (Weick et al., 2005).

Given that this meaning-making process occurs through interaction, lateral communication with coworkers is an integral source of sense-making for employees. The office grapevine, which describes informal communication in the workplace, is a primary context for peer-to-peer talk about organizational life (Burke & Wise, 2003). Employees often perceive these lateral, casual, spontaneous grapevines to be more reliable than downward, formal communication from supervisors. "Office buzz" in the grapevine tends to increase when ambiguity arises in organizational life (Burke & Wise, 2003). The prevalence of office buzz during ambiguous situations demonstrates that coworkers talk to each other to make sense of uncertainty, likely more often than they talk to their supervisors.

Kram and Isabella's (1985) continuum of peer relationships offers a helpful framework for understanding how employees may rely on one another to interpret organizational change, stress, scandal, and other environmental disruptions. Their categorization of workplace peer relationships ranges from information peers (i.e., characterized by information exchange, low self-disclosure, and low trust), collegial peers (i.e., characterized by information exchange and moderate self-disclosure, trust, and self-expression), and special peers (i.e., characterized by close friendship, high trust, and high support). Organizational members may turn to information peers to obtain information necessary for sense-making. However, employees rely on collegial and special peers to make sense of more personal matters in the workplace, as the lateral communication in these relationships is defined by higher levels of interpersonal bonds, trust, and support (Kram & Isabella, 1985). Through these friendships, employees may engage in higher levels of self-disclosure to attribute meaning collectively to events, revealing personal feelings and ideas in the meaning-making process rather than merely engaging in an information exchange. In each of these relationships, lateral communication with coworkers functions as a crucial element of the meaning-making process in organizations.

Troublesome Others to Close Friendships.

Though positive workplace relationships are associated with numerous benefits, such as emotional and instrumental support, innovation, flourishing, and identity development, workplace peer relationships can also lead to negative outcomes, such as bullying, relational conflict, distraction, and exclusion (Pillemer & Rothbard, 2018; Sias, 2004, 2008). Fritz (2002) offered a classification of troublesome peers in the workplace, naming the intrusive unprofessional (i.e., intrudes on others' business, displays poor attitude, and acts rudely), the incompetent renegade (i.e., resists directions, demonstrates incompetence, distracts coworkers), the abrasive harasser (i.e., sexually harasses, criticizes, exhibits rudeness), the backstabbing self-promoter (i.e., acts in self-advancing ways, criticizes others), and the harmless busybody (i.e., tends to intrude on others' business but otherwise has no negative attributions) as five primary negative categorizations of coworkers. These "troublesome others" differ greatly from special peers, whom Kram and Isabella (1985) characterized as the best friends of the workplace. The range of coworker relationships that exists in organizational life is an influential context for employee sense-making. The lateral communication that occurs in these relationships determines how employees attribute meaning to events as they make sense of organizational reality together.

NETWORK PERSPECTIVES

Thinking about organizational communication through the lens of hierarchical relationships (i.e., downward, upward, lateral) remains a reasonable strategy; however, alternatives exist. For example, around the beginning of the 21st century, scholarship conducted from a network perspective gained in popularity in organizational communication. Network perspectives emphasize the exploration of workplace communication dynamics through the study of actual patterns of information sending and receiving. For example, network analysts could investigate the frequency and flow of messages within and between work teams using specialized software, which produces visual representations of interactional patterns. Web-like diagrams can then be used to identify team members who serve as critical links between teams or who are isolated from the conversations of the workplace. Many, many innovative insights have been garnered from network perspectives. Sophisticated applications of the network perspective have provided insights into workplace topics as diverse as expertise performance and recognition (Treem, 2016), high-stakes team coordination (Pilny et al., 2020), and collective leadership (Contractor et al., 2012).

NEW TECHNOLOGIES

Telecommuting and Work. New information and communication technologies (ICTs) are increasingly widespread and being integrated into many aspects of modern work life. ICTs are therefore creating new opportunities and challenges, advantages, and disadvantages. Likewise, the prevalence of telework, telecommuting, and distributed work is increasing (Nicklin et al., 2016; Wilhoit Larson, 2020). Telework is an arrangement in which organizational members partially or fully complete their responsibilities outside the boundaries of an organization's physical site while maintaining a virtual presence through various information and communication technologies (ICT; Nicklin et al., 2016). Telework arrangements vary widely in terms of schedule, format, location, autonomy, synchrony, and purpose. Though telework may lead to increased productivity, work–life balance, autonomy, and flexibility, some organizations are tentative to promote telework because of the lack of control, accountability, collaboration, and interaction that ICTs entail (Nicklin et al., 2016). In addition, some scholars are skeptical about who is advantaged by telework arrangements, as explained by the connectivity paradox (Fonner & Roloff, 2012). The connectivity paradox suggests that teleworkers' virtual connection to others facilitates remote work, while diminishing the benefits of telework by enabling constant interruptions—from both home and work sources. As teleworkers experience these disruptions, their stress increases and they may be inhibited from completing tasks effectively (Leonardi et al., 2010). Thus, the potential advantages and disadvantages of telework arrangements are paradoxically complex.

Though traditional organizing occurs in physical spaces through face-to-face relationships, telework enables organizations to develop virtually across any number of physical locations, often asynchronously. The prevalence of virtual connections in telecommuting makes it difficult to define the physical boundaries of an organization. However, according to communication constitutes organizing (CCO) theory, insofar as two flows of organizing occur simultaneously (e.g., activity coordination, institutional positioning, self-structuring, and membership negotiation), an organization exists (McPhee & Zaug, 2000; Wilhoit Larson, 2020). Though CCO research emphasizes the four flows of organizing, a CCO perspective does not ignore the role of space completely, as CCO scholars have argued that spaces and organizations mutually constitute each other (Wilhoit, 2018).

Telework is of interest to organizational communication scholars because where employees work greatly shapes their interactions with one another and, in turn, the organization itself. Wilhoit Larson (2020) differentiates between an organizational workspace (i.e., anywhere that organizational activities or work are accomplished) and an organizational space (any space attributed to the organization). Based on these definitions, she argues that any space where employees work becomes, at minimum, a partial and temporary organizational space. Thus, telework and telecommuting become virtual organizational spaces where the downward, upward, and lateral communication in the workplace occur.

Downward. Downward communication in telework contexts involves supervisors' virtual interactions with subordinates. One of the more significant disadvantages of telecommuting arrangements is supervisors' fear of losing the ability to observe and evaluate employees' work practices (Nicklin et al., 2016). Given that management may struggle with performance management and monitoring, work coordination, and scheduling across virtual platforms, downward communication may become more formal and task-related rather than informal and relational. However, because employees value person-centered downward communication in the workplace (Fix & Sias, 2006), it is critical that supervisors prioritize relational communication with teleworkers, particularly because of the reduced opportunity for informal conversation and relationship building. Given the importance of the quality of downward communication in the workplace for employee productivity and satisfaction, it is also important that managers continue to clarify employee role responsibilities and frame work as meaningful, even virtually. Telework may also impact mentoring opportunities and interactions between supervisors and subordinates. Mentoring enables employees to learn and develop professionally and is facilitated by conversations related both to work and to life outside of work (Cooper & Kurland, 2002). However, supervisors have reported feeling inhibited in their mentoring by the reduced number of opportunities to develop telecommuters, particularly because they were unable to observe employees extensively (Cooper & Kurland, 2002). However, virtual mentoring can still occur in telework contexts, often through formal communication, such as email.

Upward. Upward communication in virtual organizations may function differently than in face-to-face contexts, as employees must negotiate silence, distortion, and dissent through more formalized online media rather than through face-to-face interactions. Media richness theory explains that media are either rich (e.g., face to face) or lean (e.g., texting) in their ability to convey nonverbal cues (Daft & Lengel, 1984). Because teleworkers use a variety of rich and lean media to interact with supervisors, they must consider the sensitivity of topics while negotiating which technology medium is best suited for various conversations (Hastings & Payne, 2013). Emails, for example, reduce feedback such that the message sender is unable to self-correct, repair, and filter the message once the email is sent (Hastings & Payne, 2013). Employees who dissent over email sense heightened monitoring and a loss of message control and therefore seek to maintain appropriateness in their communication, which may change the nature of their message (Hastings & Payne, 2013).

Given that dissenters consider climate dimensions (e.g., relationship with supervisor or organization, manager's willingness to receive feedback) when choosing how to voice feedback (Kassing, 2008), telecommuters may especially consider the virtual nature of their environment when engaging in upward communication. The distance and isolation that virtual contexts often imply may even discourage employees from voicing upward corrective feedback at all, thus increasing silence in the organization. However, though telecommuters may feel that they have fewer opportunities to voice concerns and feedback to supervisors, employees may also perceive that upward corrective feedback through online communication is less face-threatening than face to face, thus heightening the prevalence of upward communication in virtual contexts.

Lateral. Lateral communication in telework contexts is key to consider, as the most commonly cited employee concern related to telecommuting is a fear of isolation (Crandall & Gao, 2005; Nicklin et al., 2016). Professional isolation occurs when employees miss opportunities for significant organizational rewards (e.g., informal learning, interpersonal networking, and mentoring) because they are teleworking (Cooper & Kurland, 2002). To prevent such isolation, employees should form and maintain relationships with strategic people, specifically people who are connected to more extensive networks in the organization which will meet further task and relational needs even virtually (Jarrahi & Thompson, 2017).

Coworking relationships afford a certain level of belongingness in organizational life, often fostering job satisfaction, well-being, and organizational commitment (Kurland & Bailey, 1999). However, telework arrangements may limit lateral communications and force them to become more formal and task related in nature. Particularly at risk in teleworking is informal lateral communication, which typically takes place through spontaneous conversations during breaks, in between meetings, or through other daily interactions (Nicklin et al., 2016). However, given that telecommuting restricts spontaneous, casual interactions, the bonding that develops collegial and special peer coworking relationships may be thwarted or slowed, as well as questions that provoke knowledge exchange between information peers (Kram & Isabella, 1985). Employees miss opportunities for humor, gossip, and other relational communication, and the lack of these interactions may reduce their perceptions of belongingness and relatedness, both of which are critical for job satisfaction (Cooper &

Kurland, 2002; Nicklin et al., 2016). Thus, telework may inhibit the development of traditional coworking relationships by limiting informal communication and interaction.

CONCLUSION

A communication-based perspective of organizing posits that communication constitutes organizations. Thus, communication does not merely occur within the organization, but *is* the organization. Downward, upward, and lateral communication are critical avenues of sensemaking and feedback as leaders and followers organize. Through downward communication, leaders develop relationships with followers, attribute meaning to events through framing, and offer corrective feedback to subordinates. Through upward communication, subordinates convey feedback to managers; however, upward communication is often defined by silence, distortion, and dissent rather than candid feedback. Instead, employees often establish avenues of lateral communication with their coworkers to make sense of their perceptions and experiences in the organization. Employees develop grapevines through which they obtain information and with whom they form varying levels of relationships. In the early 21st century, telework arrangements have affected communication in organizations in both positive and negative ways, potentially isolating employees by removing opportunities for informal interactions in the workplace but also enabling productivity through temporary, partial sites of work. The qualities of downward, upward, and lateral communication make organizations what they are.

FURTHER READING

Jablin, F. M., & Putnam, L. L. (Eds.). (2004). *The new handbook of organizational communication: Advances in theory, research, and methods*. SAGE.

Keyton, J. (2017). Communication in organizations. *Annual Review of Organizational Psychology and Organizational Behavior, 4*, 501–526.

Kramer, M. W., & Bisel, R. S. (2017). *Organizational communication: A lifespan approach*. Oxford University Press.

Salem, P. J., & Timmerman, C. E. (Eds.). (2018). Forty years of organizational communication. In *Transformative practice and research in organizational communication* (pp. 1–28). IGI Global. https://doi.org/10.4018/978-1-5225-2823-4

REFERENCES

Allen, M. W. (1992). Communication and organizational commitment: Perceived organizational support as a mediating factor. *Communication Quarterly, 40*(4), 357–367. https://doi.org/10.1080/01463379209369852

Andersen, H. C. (1837). *The emperor's new clothes*. C. A. Reitzel.

Argyris, C. (1994). Good communication that blocks learning. *Harvard Business Review, 72*(4), 77–85.

Axley, S. R. (1984). Managerial and organizational communication in terms of the conduit metaphor. *Academy of Management Review, 9*(3), 428–437.

Barge, J. K., & Fairhurst, G. T. (2008). Living leadership: A systemic constructionist approach. *Leadership, 4*(3), 227–251. https://doi.org/10.1177/1742715008092360

Bavelas, J. B., Black, A., Chovil, N., & Mullett, J. (1990). Truths, lies, and equivocations: The effects of conflicting goals on discourse. *Journal of Language and Social Psychology, 9*(1–2), 135–161.

Bisel, R. S. (2010). A communicative ontology of organization? A description, history, and critique of CCO theories for organization science. *Management Communication Quarterly, 24*(1), 124–131. https://doi.org/10.1177/0893318909351582

Bisel, R. S. (2018). *Organizational moral learning: A communication approach.* Routledge.

Bisel, R. S., Messersmith, A. S., & Kelley, K. M. (2012). Supervisor-subordinate communication: Hierarchical mum effect meets organizational learning. *Journal of Business Communication, 49*, 128–147. https://doi.org/10.1177/0021943612436972

Boivin, G., Brummans, B. H., & Barker, J. R. (2017). The institutionalization of CCO scholarship: Trends from 2000 to 2015. *Management Communication Quarterly, 31*(3), 331–355. https://doi.org/10.1177/0893318916687396

Bruscella, J. S., & Bisel, R. S. (2018). Four flows theory and materiality: ISIL's use of material resources in its communicative constitution. *Communication Monographs, 85*(3), 331–356. https://doi.org/10.1080/03637751.2017.1420907

Burke, L. A., & Wise, J. M. (2003). The effective care, handling and pruning of the office grapevine. *Business Horizons, 46*(3), 71–76.

Conrad, C. (2011). *Organizational rhetoric: Strategies of resistance and domination.* Polity Press.

Contractor, N. S., DeChurch, L. A., Carson, J., Carter, D. R., & Keegan, B. (2012). The topology of collective leadership. *The Leadership Quarterly, 23*(6), 994–1011. https://doi.org/10.1016/j.leaqua.2012.10.010

Cooper, C. D., & Kurland, N. B. (2002). Telecommuting, professional isolation, and employee development in public and private organizations. *Journal of Organizational Behavior, 23*(4), 511–532. https://doi.org/10.1002/job.145

Cox, S. A., & Kramer, M. W. (1995). Communication during employee dismissals: Social exchange principles and group influences on employee exit. *Management Communication Quarterly, 9*(2), 156–190.

Crandall, W., & Gao, L. (2005). An update on telecommuting: Review and prospects for emerging issues. *S.A.M. Advanced Management Journal, 70*(3), 30.

Daft, R. L., & Lengel, R. H. (1984). Information richness: A new approach to managerial behavior and organizational design. In L. L. Cummings, & B. Staw (Eds.), *Research in organizational behavior* (Vol. 6, pp. 191–233). JAI Press.

Eisenberg, E. M. (1984). Ambiguity as strategy in organizational communication. *Communication Monographs, 51*(3), 227–242.

Entman, R. M. (2004). *Projections of power: Framing news, public opinion, and US foreign policy.* University of Chicago Press.

Fairhurst, G., & Sarr, R. (1996). *The art of framing.* Jossey-Bass.

Fairhurst, G. T. (2010). *The power of framing: Creating the language of leadership.* Wiley.

Farace, R. V., Monge, P. R., & Russell, H. M. (1977). *Communicating and organizing* (Vol. 1077). Addison-Wesley.

Feeley, T. H., Moon, S. I., Kozey, R. S., & Slowe, A. S. (2010). An erosion model of employee turnover based on network centrality. *Journal of Applied Communication Research, 38*(2), 167–188. https://doi.org/10.1080/00909881003639544

Fix, B., & Sias, P. M. (2006). Person-centered communication, leader-member exchange, and employee job satisfaction. *Communication Research Reports, 23*(1), 35–44. https://doi.org/10.1080/17464090500535855

Fonner, K. L., & Roloff, M. E. (2012). Testing the connectivity paradox: Linking teleworkers' communication media use to social presence, stress from interruptions, and organizational identification. *Communication Monographs, 79*(2), 205–231. https://doi.org/10.1080/03637751.2012.673000

Fritz, J. M. (2002). How do I dislike thee? Let me count the ways. *Management Communication Quarterly, 15*, 410–438.

Fulk, J., & Mani, S. (1986). Distortion of communication in hierarchical relationships. *Annals of the International Communication Association, 9*(1), 483–510.

Graen, G. B., & Uhl-Bien, M. (1995). Development of leader-member exchange (LMX) theory of leadership over 25 years: Applying a multi-level multi-domain perspective. *Leadership Quarterly, 6*(2), 219–247.

Grant, A. M. (2007). Relational job design and the motivation to make a prosocial difference. *Academy of Management Review, 32*(2), 393–417.

Hastings, S. O., & Payne, H. J. (2013). Expressions of dissent in email. *Journal of Business Communication, 50*(3), 309–331. https://doi.org/10.1177/0021943613487071

Jarrahi, M. H., & Thomson, L. (2017). The interplay between information practices and information context: The case of mobile knowledge workers. *Journal of the Association for Information Science and Technology, 68*, 1073–1089. https://asistdl.onlinelibrary.wiley.com/doi/abs/10.1002/asi.23773

Kassing, J. W. (2008). Consider this: A comparison of factors contributing to employees' expressions of dissent. *Communication Quarterly, 56*, 342–355. https://doi.org/10.1080/01463370802240825

Kassing, J. W. (2011). *Dissent in organizations*. Polity Press.

Kelley, K. M., & Bisel, R. S. (2014). Leaders' narrative sense-making during LMX role negotiations: Explaining how leaders make sense of who to trust and when. *Leadership Quarterly, 25*(3), 433–448. https://doi.org/10.1016/j.leaqua.2013.10.011

Kram, K. E., & Isabella, L. A. (1985). Mentoring alternatives: The role of peer relationships in career development. *Academy of Management Journal, 28*(1), 110–132.

Kramer, M. W. (2010). *Organizational socialization: Joining and leaving organizations*. Polity Press.

Kramer, M. W., & Bisel, R. S. (2017). *Organizational communication: A lifespan approach*. Oxford University Press.

Kurland, N. B., & Bailey, D. E. (1999). Telework: The advantages and challenges of working here, there, anywhere, and anytime. *Organizational Dynamics, 28*, 53–67.

Leonardi, P. M., Treem, J. W., & Jackson, M. H. (2010). The connectivity paradox: Using technology to both decrease and increase perceptions of distance in distributed work arrangements. *Journal of Applied Communication Research, 38*(1), 85–105. https://doi.org/10.1080/00909880903483599

Maitlis, S., & Lawrence, T. B. (2007). Triggers and enablers of sense-giving in organizations. *Academy of Management Journal, 50*, 57–84.

McGregor, D. M. (1957). The human side of the enterprise. Reprinted in J. M. Shafritz, J. S. Ott, & Y. S. Jang (Eds.), *Classics in organizational theory* (2005, 6th ed., pp. 179–184). Wadsworth.

McPhee, R. D., & Zaug, P. (2000). The communicative constitution of organizations: A framework for explanation. *Electronic Journal of Communication, 10*(1–2). http://www.cios.org/EJCPUBLIC/010/1/01017.html

Morrison, E. W. (2014). Employee voice and silence. *Annual Review of Organizational Psychology and Organizational Behavior, 1*(1), 173–197. https://doi.org/10.1146/annurev-orgpsych-031413-091328

Nicklin, J. M., Cerasoli, C. P., & Dydyn, K. L. (2016). Telecommuting: What? Why? When? and how? In J. Lee (Ed.), *The impact of ICT on work* (pp. 41–70). Springer, Singapore. https://www.researchgate.net/publication/297921651_Telecommuting_What_Why_When_and_How

O'Keefe, B. J. (1988). The logic of message design: Individual differences in reasoning about communication. *Communication Monographs, 55*(1), 80–103.

Pillemer, J., & Rothbard, N. P. (2018). Friends without benefits: Understanding the dark sides of workplace friendship. *Academy of Management Review, 43*(4), 635–660. https://doi.org/10.5465/amr.2016.0309

Pilny, A., Dobosh, M., Yahja, A., Poole, M. S., Campbell, A., Ruge-Jones, L., & Proulx, J. (2020). Team coordination in uncertain environments: The role of processual communication networks. *Human Communication Research, 46*(4), 385–411. https://doi.org/10.1093/hcr/hqz020

Pincus, J. D. (1986). Communication satisfaction, job satisfaction, and job performance. *Human Communication Research, 12*(3), 395–419.

Randolph-Seng, B., Cogliser, C. C., Randolph, A. F., Scandura, T. A., Miller, C. D., & Smith-Genthôs, R. (2016). Diversity in leadership: Race in leader-member exchanges. *Leadership & Organization Development Journal, 37*, 750–772. https://doi.org/10.1108/LODJ-10-2014-0201

Schoeneborn, D., Blaschke, S., Cooren, F., McPhee, R. D., Seidl, D., & Taylor, J. R. (2014). The three schools of CCO thinking: Interactive dialogue and systematic comparison. *Management Communication Quarterly, 28*(2), 285–316. https://doi.org/10.1177/0893318914527000

Sias, P. M. (2004). Disengaging from workplace relationships. *Human Communication Research, 30*(4), 589–602.

Sias, P. M. (2008). *Organizing relationships: Traditional and emerging perspectives on workplace relationships.* SAGE.

Taylor, F. W. (1923). *The principles of scientific management.* Harper & Brothers.

Taylor, J. R., & Van Every, E. J. (1999). *The emergent organization: Communication as its site and surface.* Routledge.

Treem, J. W. (2016). How organizations communicate expertise without experts: Practices and performances of knowledge-intensive firms. *Management Communication Quarterly, 30*(4), 503–531. https://doi.org/10.1177/0893318916635750

Treem, J. W. (2012). Communicating expertise: Knowledge performances in professional-service firms. *Communication Monographs, 79*(1), 23–47. https://doi.org/10.1080/03637751.2011.646487

Weick, K. E. (1995). *Sensemaking in organizations.* SAGE.

Weick, K. E., & Sutcliffe, K. M. (2007). *Managing the unexpected: Resilient performance in an age of uncertainty.* Wiley.

Weick, K. E., Sutcliffe, K. M., & Obstfeld, D. (2005). Organizing and the process of sensemaking. *Organization Science, 16*(4), 409–421. https://doi.org/10.1287/orsc.1050.0133

Wilhoit, E. D. (2018). Space, place, and the communicative constitution of organizations: A constitutive model of organizational space. *Communication Theory, 28*(3), 311–331. https://doi.org/10.1093/ct/qty007

Wilhoit Larson, E. D. (2020). Where is an organization? How workspaces are appropriated to become (partial and temporary) organizational spaces. *Management Communication Quarterly, 34*(3), 299–327. https://doi.org/10.1177/0893318920933590

Yariv, E. (2006). "Mum effect": Principals' reluctance to submit negative feedback. *Journal of Managerial Psychology, 21*, 533–546. https://doi.org/10.1108/02683940610684382

Ryan S. Bisel and Katherine Ann Rush

ORGANIZATIONAL SENSEMAKING

INTRODUCTION TO SENSEMAKING

Sensemaking in Action: The Chicago Board Options Exchange. It is often easiest to understand sensemaking with an example of how it unfolds in action. For this reason, we begin with an example (see MacKenzie & Millo, 2003):

There are few organizational environments as tumultuous as that of financial derivatives trading. In 1973, the economists Black and Scholes tried to understand how options were priced in the newly instituted Chicago Board Options Exchange. They developed a formula that priced options (i.e., the ability to purchase a particular commodity at a specific price) based on a handful of parameters like its spot price or time to maturity. In the first months of trading, the formula failed to predict option prices, with typical deviations as large as 30% to 40%. Yet, over time, the formula became accurate to within the low single digits, leading its creators to receive Nobel Prizes. Interestingly enough, however, the formula became accurate only because market participants acted *as if* it was accurate. Traders used values derived from the formula to inform their bids, the formula became integrated into trading regulations, and assumed in technological infrastructure. The Black–Scholes formula began by modeling options prices. It ended up modeling options prices in response to its modeling of option prices.

This case has much to tell us about sensemaking. In fact, it describes three pertinent features of the sensemaking perspective: (1) organizations operate in environments characterized by chaos and flux, (2) people develop plausible and tentative interpretations of their environments by noticing and bracketing out certain pieces of information, and (3) by acting on the basis of these interpretations, people actually make their environments more orderly and better understood (Weick, Sutcliffe, & Obstfeld, 2005). As our story indicates, from the initial chaos of prices and bids in options trading, Black and Scholes extracted certain plausible parameters and compiled them into a tentative formula, broader social utilization of this formula changed prices and bidding behavior, and the world of options trading became more orderly as a result.

Sensemaking: A Perspective and a Process.   Perhaps the critical point underlying sensemaking research is that action and knowledge are recursively entangled. It is difficult to act without knowing the context in which action is to occur. And yet, it is difficult to know much about any context without first acting on it. This insight is not always obvious because when the events we face are familiar—as they typically are—our existing knowledge structures most often prove adequate. We can form a reasonable interpretation of what an event means and how we should respond to it. At times, however, we are faced with equivocal events. Equivocal events contain elements of shock and surprise: They defy straightforward applications of our existing knowledge structures.

In order to understand what such events mean and how we should respond to them, we engage in a process of *sensemaking*. Sensemaking models how people adjust their knowledge structures as they notice and interpret an equivocal event and coordinate a response to clarify what the event means (Holt & Cornelissen, 2014; Maitlis & Christianson, 2014; Sandberg & Tsoukas, 2015; Weick et al., 2005). It is for this reason that sensemaking is so important to organizational scholarship: If "organization" is a pattern of interlocking group behaviors, then sensemaking is the pattern formation process (Weick, 1979). And if equivocal events disrupt these patterns of interlocking group behaviors, then organization can only be restored through sensemaking. If sensemaking fails, organized groups can rapidly disintegrate into disorganized individuals who lack the capacity for action (Weick, 1993b). In this view, organization only navigates the chaotic flux of perpetual change by the sense that it makes (Tsoukas & Chia, 2002). Thus, sensemaking functions not only as a *process* that organizational members engage in when responding to equivocal events, but also as a *perspective* on what organization is and how it is accomplished. Stated differently, sensemaking is both a method and object of inquiry in organizational contexts (Blatt, Christianson, Sutcliffe, & Rosenthal, 2006).

ARTICLE OVERVIEW

The purpose of this article is thus to provide an accessible introduction to sensemaking as it relates to organizations. It begins by contextualizing the sensemaking perspective within its historical milieu and delimiting its boundaries relative to rational decision-making and cognitive psychology perspectives. It then describes the sensemaking process by reviewing the types of events that trigger sensemaking, how actors notice and bracket information from such events, the means by which they interpret that information, the immediate products resulting from this interpretive process, the proximal and distal consequences of enacting interpretations, and the contextual factors that influence this overall sensemaking process. Taken as a whole, this article should provide a solid conceptual foundation for readers interested in the role that sensemaking plays in the field of organizational psychology.

SENSEMAKING AS PERSPECTIVE

Reductionist Approach to Organizations.   How is it that individuals organize and act collectively? It is worthwhile to begin by considering two very different schools of thought, both of which purport to answer this question. In reviewing the behavioral strategy literature, Powell, Lovallo, and Fox (2011) distinguish between the "reductionist" school on one end and the "contextualist" school on the other. The reductionist approach "relies on positivist, realist, and objectivist philosophies of science and favors quantitative hypothesis testing using methods such as mathematical modelling, simulation, and laboratory decision experiments" (Powell et al., 2011, p. 1371).

This approach models individuals as decision-makers who face an objectively defined reality, are given ex ante options for how they can act, and choose actions based on a forward-looking process that maximizes their expected value (e.g., Edwards, 1954; Von Neumann & Morgenstern, 1947). It thus best describes an idealized hypothetical individual who makes decisions about a world that he or she knows with clarity. When work in this reductionist paradigm embraces more realistic psychological assumptions, it focuses on how actual human rationality is "bounded" in its ability to process all the available information and calculate the objectively best course of action. It therefore highlights the resulting "cognitive biases" that inhibit rational decision-making (Kahneman, 2003). It also prescribes ways for managers to improve their rationality while capitalizing on the irrationality of others (cf. Raiffa, 1982).

Contextualist Approach to Organizations.   In contrast, the contextualist school—in which the sensemaking perspective plays a central role—describes a world in which "subjective beliefs, shared ideologies, and cognitive frames matter more than explicit ex ante decisions, which seldom correspond with what people or firms actually do" (Powell et al., 2011, p. 1373). In doing so, this school suggests that organizational environments are not objectively defined, but are socially constructed. People are not passively given all available options for how they can act, but must actively search for or even improvise them. And when searching for options, people draw on past memories more than they imagine future outcomes. Through these memories, they generate plausible interpretations that enable tentative action rather than pursuing maximal accuracy and absolute certainty.

This approach clearly appreciates a central insight offered by cognitive psychology: people use their beliefs to interpret their circumstances (Fiske & Taylor, 1991). Yet, it also goes beyond this work in several ways (cf. Gilliland & Day, 1999). The first way is by noting the key role that people play in sculpting the very circumstances they later need to interpret. The second way is modeling how order at the higher level of a group can emerge even when the individual members that constitute the group lack a full mental understanding of it. The third way is how people's sense of identity is tightly interwoven into the emergence and continuation of this higher-level order. And the fourth way is that plausibility rather than accuracy is the criterion. Indeed, if we undertake action to express our identity and sculpt our circumstances, we do not need perfectly accurate knowledge about our current situation before we can act meaningfully or produce order at the higher level.

As a result, sensemaking is not about cognitive biases (the extent to which a person's knowledge reflects "reality") or even shared cognition (the extent to which multiple people's knowledge structures align or not). It is about *collective cognition*: how people come to think together, forming higher order patterns of interpretation and action that are fundamentally irreducible down to any one individual (Daft & Weick, 1984; Elsbach, Barr, & Hargadon, 2005; Sandelands & Stablein, 1987; Weick & Roberts, 1993). Given these defining characteristics, researchers within the contextualist school typically "conduct empirical work 'in context,' favoring qualitative and interpretive methods such as ethnography and textual analysis and rejecting positivism and quantitative hypothesis testing" (Powell et al., 2011, p. 1373).

Building Blocks of the Sensemaking Perspective. Historically, the reductionist and decision-making approach ascended to prominence in organizational scholarship before the contextualist and sensemaking approach did. Throughout the 1950s and into the early 1960s, rationality assumptions were dominant in the field. By the late 1960s, however, there was both an appetite for a new way of thinking about human behavior and the conceptual building blocks to construct such a way of thinking. This appetite existed due to growing dissatisfaction with stimulus–response models of human behavior and increasing interest in existentialism. It called for greater emphasis on the active role that people play in sculpting their lives. The building blocks of the sensemaking perspective were also developed by this time and ready for assembly into a coherent perspective. These building blocks include the following:

- As groups of people act, they take their collective patterns of action and interpretation for granted, seeing these patterns as part of a reality that exists independently of them and which would continue even without their participation in it (Berger & Luckmann, 1966).
- People apply these taken-for-granted understandings to navigate their everyday activities. In doing so, people ask others to account for behavior that challenges their taken-for-granted understandings (Garfinkel, 1967).

- Producing such "accounts" of behavior requires people to step outside the flow of their ongoing experience and retrospectively interpret their past behavior (Schutz, 1967).
- People form these interpretations by rationalizing their past behavior, such that they reduce the unpleasant experience of cognitive dissonance (Festinger, 1957).

Formative Historical Context. These disparate ideas were first assembled into a coherent sensemaking perspective on organizations by Karl Weick in his 1969 text, *The Social Psychology of Organizing*. Weick (2003) later described the historical context in the late 1960s where these ideas, so radically distinct from the dominant rational decision perspectives, first emerged:

> These ideas coincided with a growing societal realization that administrators in Washington were trying to justify committing more resources to a war in Vietnam that the United States was clearly losing. One could not escape the feeling that rationality had a demonstrable retrospective core, that people looked forward with anxiety and put the best face on it after the fact, and that the vaunted prospective skills of McNamara's "whiz kids" in the Pentagon were a chimera. It was easy to put words to this mess. People create their own fate. Organizations enact their own environments. The point seemed obvious. (p. 186)

Here we can see that, far from being some arcane academic exercise, sensemaking came about precisely to explain messy and complicated real-world phenomena. Yet, at the time, these insights remained somewhat underappreciated. Rather, the 1970s saw the rise in three highly influential theories of organization: transaction cost economics (Williamson, 1975), population ecology (Hannan & Freeman, 1977), and resource dependence (Pfeffer & Salancik, 1978). As Kaplan (2011) rightfully noted, each of these theories "privileged position and situation" in objective terms—bypassing insights that managers interpret their positions and enact situations (p. 667). It was only when Weick substantially extended *The Social Psychology of Organizing* into what became the seminal second edition in 1979 that scholars took note. And these ideas, derived from Vietnam-era concerns, remain relevant even today. Indeed, *The Social Psychology of Organizing* continues to be well-cited for precisely the idea that sensemaking is a retrospective process by which organizations help create the very environments that perplex them (Anderson, 2006). These ideas have also influenced practitioners through their integral role in Peters and Waterman's (1982) bestselling management book, *In Search of Excellence* (see Colville, Waterman, & Weick, 1999).

Consequences of Taking a Sensemaking Perspective. To understand the continued interest in the sensemaking perspective, we must consider the consequences for scholars who embrace it. When compared to its "reductionist" counterpart, the sensemaking perspective performs an important rhetorical function: it induces a figure-ground reversal between rationality and human behavior. Decision-making theories begin with rationality as their theoretical grounding, and thus assess human behavior in light of it. From this perspective, they find human behavior to be boundedly rational. The sensemaking perspective, however, begins with, and is grounded in, lived human behavior. By examining rationality in light of human behavior, it finds that rationality lacks explanatory power. In other words, while decision-making characterizes humans as "boundedly rational," sensemaking characterizes rationality as a "boundedly relevant" way to explain human behavior. As such, sensemaking offers a rather distinct perspective on what organizations are, how they function, and how they should be studied.

This perspective has generative potential for organizational scholars precisely because it differs from commonly shared assumptions in the field. Namely, we typically theorize about "entities" connected by box and arrow diagrams (Whetten, 1989). The sensemaking perspective emphasizes how theoretical entities—like people, identities, interpretations, and environments—are not distinct from each other. Rather, they can only be defined in relation to each other. This emphasizes how processes unfold over time and encourages us to study relations rather than entities (cf. Bradbury & Lichtenstein, 2000; Langley, 2007). The sensemaking perspective thus "acts as a lens that...focuses our attention on agency because action is viewed as part of people's efforts to make sense; on equivocality because sensemaking is triggered by people's need to understand an equivocal flow of experience; and on relationships as sensemaking is social" (Blatt et al., 2006, p. 898). Indeed, in his analysis of a friendly fire accident in Iraq, Snook (2000) compares a sensemaking perspective to that of decision-making. Adopting a sensemaking perspective, he suggests, enables scholars to maintain a richer understanding of how events come to be, portraying even terrible tragedies "as 'good people struggling to make sense,' rather than as 'bad ones making poor decisions'" (pp. 206–207).

A Sensemaking Perspective on Environments.   To understand the sensemaking perspective on organizations, we must first consider the nature of the environment in which organizations exist. We can begin with a helpful distinction between certainty, risk, and uncertainty. Certainty describes environments where actions "lead invariably to a specific outcome," risk describes when actions lead to many possible outcomes that occur "with a known probability," and uncertainty describes when these possible outcomes occur with "completely unknown" probabilities (Luce & Raiffa, 1957, p. 13). To clarify, if you see that it is clearly raining outside, you are operating under conditions of certainty. This makes your decision to carry an umbrella unproblematic. More interesting is when you see looming clouds and must weigh the convenience of avoiding wet clothes in the case of rain with the inconvenience of needlessly holding an umbrella in the case of no rain. Here, the best advice is to move from a situation of uncertainty to one of risk: instead of estimating a subjective probability of rain, you can consult the official weather forecast to find the objective probability.

These environmental conditions of certainty, risk, and uncertainty are mutually exclusive. However, they are not exhaustive because of their implicit assumptions. Namely, they assume that more information inherently brings more clarity to environments. To make good decisions, organizations should therefore gather enough information to derive probabilities for outcomes that are as objective as possible (Galbraith, 1973; Thompson, 1967). To unsettle these implicit assumptions, sensemaking scholars make further distinctions about environmental conditions that foreground different properties of information. Namely, they distinguish ambiguity and equivocality from uncertainty (Weick, 1995, pp. 91–100). Whereas uncertainty can be remedied by more information, ambiguity and equivocality cannot. The latter two conditions capture how any one piece of information can support many possible meanings. As such, gathering more information can actually make action harder rather than easier, as the number of possible meanings multiply as the amount of information increases. People must therefore reduce the possible meanings of existing information instead of adding more information (Weick, 1979).

Ambiguity and equivocality differ in one important regard. Ambiguity implies that there is some "true" state of the environment out there to be discovered. Equivocality suggests instead that the state of the environment must be invented: by focusing on certain pieces of information and acting on the basis of certain interpretations of that information, organizations help invent their environments. Now, organizations certainly vary in the degree to which their members treat environments as ambiguous or equivocal (Daft & Weick, 1984; Weick & Daft, 1983). But in either case, their members reduce the number of possible meanings through interpretation: the information they receive does not inherently bring clarity. And objective probabilities seldom exist because organizations influence the outcomes they seek to predict. Sensemaking scholars have elaborated the nature of uncertainty, ambiguity, and equivocality in several helpful ways (see Milliken, 1987; Smircich & Stubbart, 1985; Sutcliffe, 2001). For example, these distinctions shed light on important questions including how to balance knowledge and action (Colville, Brown, & Pye, 2012), respond to ethical issues (Sonenshein, 2007; Thiel, Bagdasarov, Harkrider, Johnson, & Mumford, 2012), and routinize processes (Becker & Knudsen, 2005).

A Sensemaking Perspective on Organizations. As sensemaking scholars emphasize how people interpret and sculpt their environments, some describe sensemaking as supporting an "interpretive" view of organizations rather than a "computational" view that is predicated on gathering and processing more information (Lant & Shapira, 2000). This brings us from a view of the environment to a view of the organization. Within a sensemaking perspective, it is often less helpful to talk about "organizations" than it is to talk about "organizing" (Gioia, 2006; Weick, 1969). Talking about an organization as though it was a single actor (e.g., "the company launched a new product" or "the government went to war") is misleading. It minimizes the presence of multiple conflicting rationalities that exist among different groups within a single organization. It also gives the illusion of stability to what is actually an ongoing process that is always subject to disruption and therefore always in need of re-accomplishment. An organization is merely a snapshot at a single point in time of the consequences of an ongoing organizing process. Thus, taking organizing as the focus of research helps sensitize scholars to group-level processes that enable people to coordinate patterns of interlocking behaviors and respond to other groups with alternate rationalities.

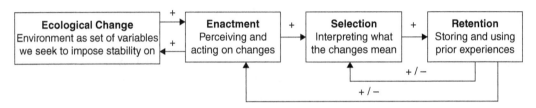

Figure 1. Organizing as enactment-selection-retention.

The organizing process occurs when changes in their environment prompt groups of organizational members to enter cycles of enactment, selection, and retention (Weick, 1979; Weick et al., 2005). This enactment-selection-retention process explicitly adopts the variation-selection-retention model described in natural selection and evolution, but as applied to social systems like organizations (Campbell, 1970). Because enactment-selection-retention collectively define what "organizing" means and how "organization" comes about, each of the three stages merits attention and explanation (see Figure 1):

- *Enactment* refers to the ways in which organizational members do not merely *react* to their environments, but help to *en*act it much in the same way that legislators enact laws. Enactment occurs both through perception and behavior. Perceptually, organizational members notice only limited portions of their environment. They notice information that is puzzling or problematic and then bracket that information so they can interpret what it means. Once they have a plausible interpretation at hand, enactment occurs again through behavior. Through behaviors taken through speech or with the body, organizational members act out their interpretations, thereby embedding their interpretations into their environment. Enactment thus reminds us how organizations "construct, rearrange, single out, and demolish many of the 'objective' features of their surroundings" as they engage with it through perception and behavior (Weick, 1979, p. 164).
- *Selection* refers to the interpretive process, in which organizational members work to determine what the bracketed information means. It is an equivocality reduction process: reducing the number of possible meanings allowed by the information until it becomes actionable. In essence, selection imposes knowledge structures that configure the bracketed pieces of information in different arrangements: making some variables more or less central and relating these variables in new ways. Selection is thus "both a cognitive process and a political process as organizational members struggle with the definition of the situation and the resulting choices consistent with the definition" (Ocasio, 2000, p. 51). As we will see, various cognitive, discursive, and embodied means of interpretation can be used for selection. Either way, selection produces a plausible understanding of what the environment means that can serve as a guide for enactment.
- *Retention* is a social process by which the selected interpretations become integrated into the group's identity, interwoven into its narrative of the environment, and used as a reference to guide subsequent enactment and selection. Whereas selection describes how interpretations influence the information currently being processed, retention describes how current interpretations influence subsequent behavior. Importantly, for organizing to work, retained understandings must be not only believed, but also doubted (signified respectively by the + and – feedback loops in Figure 1). Belief means that we notice the same type of information we previously noted, interpret that information in similar ways, and enact that interpretation in similar ways. With unmitigated belief, however, the accumulation of retained experience will pose increasing constraints on organizing. Thus, we must infuse doubt into organizing by noticing new information, questioning our entrenched interpretations, or acting out our old interpretations in new ways.

Taken together, organizing can thus be seen as a process whereby groups of individuals reduce the equivocality in their environment through a series of interlocking behaviors; through these behaviors, the group notices and brackets information from the environment, applies knowledge structures to interpret that information, and then acts out their interpretations in ways that develop the group's knowledge and bring order to its environment (Weick, 1979).

Although early work emphasized organizing and characterized "organization" as a term that adds more confusion than it does clarity (Weick, 1969), more recent perspectives see room for both terms—if properly understood. Namely, when people organize, they enact their retained interpretations to navigate moment-to-moment changes in their environment. As such, we can think of "organization" in two ways (see Tsoukas & Chia, 2002). Organization can refer to the retained interpretations that characterize groups of people: their beliefs, identities, etc. It can also refer to the moment-to-moment patterns of actions that apply these interpretations to the current environment. In neither case is the organization a place where people work. It is a result of people's attempts to stabilize understandings of their environment (see Walsh & Ungson, 1991). In Wiley's (1988) terminology, this directs us to the intersubjective and generically subjective levels of analysis. As opposed to the private interpretations of single individuals (intrasubjective level) or interpretations that exist with little need for personal involvement like mathematics (extrasubjective level), the intersubjective and generically subjective levels are socially negotiated. At the *intersubjective* level, fragile interpretations emerge from social interactions among specific people. At the *generically subjective* level, interpretations remain stable regardless of the people involved. The organizational form is unique in that it foregrounds the "bridging operations" between these two levels (Weick, 1995, p. 75). Organizations must enable the innovation and vivid understandings that occur within groups at the intersubjective level. But they must also value the managerial control and ability to hire and fire people without losing substantial operational knowledge that is entailed by generic subjectivity.

As such, this sensemaking perspective on organizations is uniquely versatile. It can describe small groups, large corporations, or even entire options trading markets. Although some find the idea of producing objective knowledge about subjectivity to be "paradoxical" (Allard-Poesi, 2005) or guilty of "ontological oscillation" (Burrell & Morgan, 1979, p. 266), such challenges may be less incisive than they seem at first. As Weick (1995) noted, "People who study sensemaking oscillate ontologically because that is what helps them understand the actions of people in everyday life who could care less about ontology" (p. 35). People who interact within organizational forms necessarily treat the generically subjective as objective—until challenges, contradictions, and breakdowns in meaning require innovative new intersubjective understandings. This oscillation is not a flaw of sensemaking research, but a crucial feature.

SENSEMAKING AS PROCESS

Properties of the Sensemaking Process. As organizational scholarship grew increasingly interested in cognition throughout the 1980s and early 1990s (Kaplan, 2011; Walsh, 1995), a body of work began exploring the sensemaking process in organizational contexts (e.g., Louis, 1980; Porac, Thomas & Baden-Fuller, 1989; Starbuck & Milliken, 1988; Thomas, Clark, & Gioia, 1993). And as the 1990s progressed, scholars—especially in Europe—turned toward language and discourse (see Alvesson & Karreman, 2000; Czarniawska, 1998). As Maitlis and Christianson suggest (2014), an impetus behind the growth of sensemaking research in the 1990s was Weick's (1995) *Sensemaking in Organizations*. This book documented the state of the research at this important transitional time, while also providing some structure and direction (see Manning, 1997).

In it, Weick identified seven properties of the sensemaking process. Although the literature proliferated and the theorizing has matured since this text, these seven properties remain influential in guiding how scholars understand the sensemaking process (cf. Helms Mills, Thurlow, & Mills, 2010). For this reason, we consider each of the seven sensemaking properties briefly as an informative introduction to the sensemaking process. After, we will delve deeper into the nuances of sensemaking as they exist in the current literature.

Sensemaking is:

(1) *Grounded in identity construction* because in responding to equivocal events, individuals and groups must determine who they are now in relation to a suddenly strange environment and who they will become as they start trying to change the environment.
(2) *Retrospective in nature* because disruptions prompt individuals to turn their attention to information from the past in order to interpret how the current disruption came about.
(3) *Based on enacting sensible environments* because a key output of sensemaking is an enacted environment that is more orderly than the equivocal environment that triggered sensemaking in the first place.
(4) *Social* in that interpretations are negotiated and enacted through social interactions.
(5) *An ongoing process* because sense is never made in perpetuity, but is always subject to disruption and therefore in need of re-accomplishment.
(6) *Focused on cues extracted from the environment* because informational cues containing equivocality provide the raw material for interpretation.
(7) *Driven by plausibility* rather than accuracy because sensemaking helps people reach only enough clarity to coordinate action, not to maximize expected outcomes with certainty.

Sensemaking Within the Context of Organizing. These seven properties can help guide our growing understanding of the sensemaking process. As a first step, we can relate sensemaking back to the overall project of organizing. Sensemaking captures the way organizing proceeds when the environment suddenly becomes more equivocal or ambiguous. Thus, whereas organizing is a process that is always operative, sensemaking is typically described in terms of particular episodes triggered by unexpected events that infuse equivocality into the environment (Sandberg & Tsoukas, 2015).

Without denying that the many small, routine events that demand little attention and characterize much of organizational life also require interpretation and influence action (Gioia & Mehra, 1996), sensemaking typically describes the process by which interpretation and action are shaped by rarer and more unexpected events. As such, we can consider sensemaking to be a special case of organizing: organizing in response to the unexpected. The value in making this distinction is that organizing operates in a somewhat different manner when members are faced with unexpected events and equivocal inputs. The stakes of organizing in these cases are also certainly higher, lending a certain salience and intrigue to sensemaking episodes.

Thus, it is valuable to note how sensemaking occurs through the same enactment-selection-retention process as does organizing more generally. We can therefore link the organizing process with each of the aforementioned seven sensemaking principles from (1) to (7).

- Enactment describes the perceptual process of noticing and bracketing information from the environment (6: focused on cues) and the behavioral process by which acting on the basis of interpretations helps shape the world and bring order to it (3: enacting sensible environments).
- Selection describes how people draw on the past to interpret bracketed information (2: retrospective in nature) and seek to find workable interpretations rather than completely accurate ones (7: driven by plausibility).
- Retention describes how the outputs of interpretation are stored in ways that affect individual and collective identities (1: grounded in identity), and how these outputs are negotiated through interactions with others (4: social) as they are applied continuously to the environment as its equivocality levels constantly fluctuate (5: ongoing).

Many have characterized this relationship between sensemaking and organizing in similar ways. For example, Sandberg and Tsoukas (2015) explain:

organizing is a process in which individuals interactively undertake action (enactment), the results of which they subsequently confront as their "environment," which they then seek to make sense of by retrospectively chopping their lived experiences into meaningful chunks, labeling them, and connecting them (i.e., selection). This sense made is retained in their minds in the form of cognitive 'cause maps,' indicating what is crucial for carrying out their tasks and how they are interconnected (retention). Through sustained interaction, individuals interlock their behaviors over time, and, in so doing, they deal with residual equivocality, which they seek to remove through negotiating a consensus about their common task and how it ought to be handled. Thus, a group of individuals become organized when their cause maps converge (Weick, 1979). In other words, sensemaking is homologous to organizing: The latter is achieved to the extent that the former is accomplished.
(p. 8)

Similarly, others suggest that "people organize to make sense of equivocal inputs and enact this sense back into the world to make that world more orderly" (Weick et al., 2005, p. 410). Alternatively, "to make sense is to organize, and sensemaking refers to processes of organizing using the technology of language . . . to identify, regularize and routinize memories into plausible explanations" (Brown, Stacey, & Nandhakumar, 2008, p. 1055). With this key relation in place, we can turn to sensemaking in greater detail by reviewing its components.

Triggers of Sensemaking. In differentiating sensemaking from organizing in general, the initial question arises: What types of events prompt sensemaking in the first place? By definition, these are events that contain higher degrees of equivocality. However, it is also worthwhile to consider broader taxonomies of such events that occur in organizations (e.g., Maitlis & Christianson, 2014; Sandberg & Tsoukas, 2015). Triggering events can vary in how equivocal and thus disruptive they are (mild to extreme), where they originate (inside or outside the organization), and the degree to which they are planned or unexpected. For example, events can be completely unexpected and occur for reasons largely external to the organization, as when the roof of a railroad museum collapsed due to inclement weather, prompting the museum to reassess its strategy (Christianson, Farkas, Sutcliffe, & Weick, 2009). In other cases, triggering events stem from broader social phenomena, such as when university administrators faced demographic trends of diminishing numbers of 18–22 year olds enrolling in college (Milliken, 1990).

At other times, triggering events can stem more directly from feedback to organizational behavior. This occurs when employees of a retail store notice disappointed or apathetic customer reactions to their change initiative (Sonenshein, 2009) or when customers adapt an organization's technology product in new and unexpected ways (Griffith, 1999). Sensemaking is also triggered by the collapse of organizations, and plays an important role in guiding how employees respond to the news (Walsh & Bartunek, 2011). Indeed, sensemaking can be triggered by events entirely due to past organizational behaviors and interpretations. For example, a group of firefighters assumed they were facing a routine fire that would be contained by 10 o'clock the following morning, only to face an entirely different type of fire (Weick, 1993b). For them, the triggering event came entirely from their expectations, not the fire itself, which could have been handled if they faced it with a different set of interpretations.

Sensemaking can also be triggered more intentionally in organizations (see Barnett & Pratt, 2000). For instance, art initiatives in organizations can be intentionally utilized to this end (Barry & Meisiek, 2010). Perhaps the most common intentional sensemaking trigger stems from the actions of other people. For example, Pratt (2000b) described how, in the process of being socialized into a multilevel marketing organization, individuals underwent a "sensebreaking" process that disrupted how they understood their current identity. This, in turn, allowed for the organization to more deeply influence individuals as they subsequently made sense through socialization into the organization. Similarly, a large body of work focuses on the process of sensegiving (e.g., Fiss & Zajac, 2006; Gioia & Chittipeddi, 1991; Hill & Levenhagen, 1995; Maitlis & Lawrence, 2007). Sensegiving describes "the process of attempting to influence the sensemaking and meaning construction of others toward a preferred redefinition of organizational reality" (Gioia & Chittipeddi, 1991, p. 442). Leaders often engage in sensegiving during periods of strategic planned change or crises to ensure that organizing does not unravel, but instead progresses toward their envisioned outcome (e.g., Christianson et al., 2009).

Noticing and Bracketing. When existing patterns of organizing adequately control the equivocality levels in the environment, individuals find themselves immersed in a flowing stream of experience (Schutz, 1967). Sensemaking begins when information cues from the environment disrupt this flow, requiring individuals to interpret the nature and meaning of this information. When sensemaking scholars talk about "noticing and bracketing," they are describing how information can prompt individuals to step out of the ongoing flow. Foundational research identified characteristics of informational cues that are more likely be noticed within the flow of experience. For example, as social psychology research has noted, information is more likely to be noticed when it is novel, intense, and unpleasant (Fiske &

Taylor, 1991). It is important to note, however, that not all information that is novel, intense, or unpleasant is also relevant to organizing. Information gains relevance to organizing based on how it compares against expectations (Weick, 1995).

Organizing implies certain retained expectations about the environment, and information that confronts those expectations is most likely to be bracketed for interpretive work. For this reason, noticed information becomes bracketed based on its relevance to organizing. Information is bracketed for interpretation when it makes the meaning of their environment unclear, indicates that current actions are failing, or enables no obvious set of behavioral responses (e.g., Ashforth & Fried, 1988; Kiesler & Sproull, 1982; Starbuck & Milliken, 1988; Weiss & Ilgen, 1986). These ideas about bracketing align with managerial problem-solving approaches that see problems not as defined inherently, but as constructed based on context and expectations (Smith, 1988). Therefore, while novel and intense information is especially likely to be noticed, novel and intense information that makes the environment more equivocal will not only be noticed, but will also be bracketed for interpretive work—thus sparking the sensemaking process.

Interpretive Processes: Cognitive Means.   Once information is noticed and bracketed for interpretation, how precisely does the interpretive process occur? As the sensemaking literature has developed, scholarly interest has shifted sequentially from cognitive to discursive to embodied means of interpretation. Early work in sensemaking focused on cognitive means of sensemaking such as frames, cause maps, and schemata (e.g., Bartunek, 1984; Bougon, Weick, & Binkhorst, 1977; Starbuck & Milliken, 1988; Weick, 1969). These generally synonymous terms refer to relatively stable knowledge structures that individuals can apply to interpret ongoing events (Walsh, 1995). Doing so imposes "a structure of assumptions, rules, and boundaries that guide sensemaking and over time become embedded and taken-for-granted" (Lüscher & Lewis, 2008, p. 222).

This work focused on how informational cues that individuals notice and bracket from the environment and cognitive frames retained in their memory jointly enable interpretation. As Weick (1995) describes, "Frames tend to be past moments of socialization and cues tend to be present moments of experience. If a person can construct a relation between these two moments, meaning is created. This means that the content of sensemaking is to be found in the frames and categories that summarize past experience, in the cues and labels that snare specifics of present experience, and in the ways these two settings of experience are connected" (p. 111). A similar, but distinct concept to frames is the script, which is a "cognitive structure that specifies a typical sequence of occurrences in a given situation, such as an employment interview or formal meeting" (Ashforth & Fried, 1988, p. 306). Unlike frames, which clarify the present moment of experience, scripts also set expectations that guide how actions should proceed over time (Gioia, 1986; Weber & Glynn, 2006).

Although these knowledge structures can be shared across organizational members to varying degrees, their character is mostly cognitive and individual. They primarily reside passively in the mind of individuals, rather than actively in socially vocalized speech or physical body movements (for a review of frames both within and beyond sensemaking, see Cornelissen & Werner, 2014). It is certainly true that cognitive means of sensemaking have become somewhat less prevalent than the subsequent discursive and embodied approaches, which we will soon explore. Nonetheless, cognitive means of interpretation should not be discounted. For instance, the data-frame theory of sensemaking describes expert behavior with remarkable precision (Klein, Moon, & Hoffman, 2006a, 2006b; Klein, Phillips, Rall, & Peluso, 2007; Klein, Wiggins, & Dominguez, 2010). Contrary to decision-making models, this naturalistic approach notes how experts do not typically evaluate multiple options. Instead, experts draw on diagnostic cues in the environment to invoke a single best-fitting frame, which they then mentally simulate in order to assess fit between the cues and frame. This process describes, for instance, how fireground commanders quickly recognize the appropriate routines to handle a particular fire. In this way, cognitive means of sensemaking can still be profitably investigated within particular contexts.

Although not discussed as frequently in the sensemaking literature, another such context concerns formulas like the Black–Scholes formula mentioned earlier (MacKenzie & Millo, 2003). Formulas, algorithms, and formal models are also tools of interpretation (cf. Boland, 1984; Gephart, 1997). After all, formulas specify what variables we should extract from the environment, how these variables relate to each other, and what outcomes are meaningful. Such formulas are likely to become especially important as they underlie "the Internet of things," whereby aspects of our everyday life are increasingly quantified, networked, and optimized. Formulas also matter because of what they exclude. For example, in advocating for considering stakeholders in addition to shareholders, Freeman (1994) argued that most formulas quantifying organizational success exclude ethical consequences on third parties.

Interpretive Processes: Discursive Means.   The discussion of shareholders and stakeholders attunes us to another important means of interpretation: language. Indeed, sensemaking research in the 1990s and beyond increasingly shifted away from cognition and toward language. Weick (1995) provided an early example of the power of language and verbal labels in interpretation: battered child syndrome. Pediatricians had long puzzled over children whose observed injuries were discrepant from their reported medical histories. Only after creating the label "battered child syndrome" could they interpret this odd phenomenon: The observed injuries differed from reported medical histories precisely because the parents of the children were both inflicting the injuries and misreporting their medical histories (Westrum, 1982). In this way, verbal labels provide an important means of interpretation (Weick et al., 2005). Similarly, it becomes easier to advocate for strategies that benefit "stakeholders" rather than mere "shareholders" once we have a label to describe the otherwise diffuse grouping of people impacted by organizational practices.

In addition to labels, a good deal of discursive interpretive work also occurs through metaphors (e.g., Cornelissen, 2005; Cornelissen, Holt, & Zundel, 2011; Gioia, 1986; Patriotta & Brown, 2011). Perhaps one reason metaphors are especially useful for sensemaking is that they are "incomplete statements of one thing—in terms of another" (Hill & Levenhagen, 1995, p. 1062). As a result, they help reduce equivocality to a limited degree, but still allow for paradox, incongruity, and contradiction. This makes them especially useful as means to foreground some pieces of information over others and connect novel aspects of ongoing events to existing knowledge structures in creative ways. Yet, metaphors do not merely serve to link ongoing events to knowledge structures. They also serve to socially justify certain actions over others

(Cornelissen, 2012). For example, by invoking the metaphor of a "learning curve," a hospital interpreted their poor performance in ways that legitimized it (Weick & Sutcliffe, 2003).

Building from the simpler discursive tools of labels and metaphors, interpretation also occurs through more complex accounts and narratives. Accounts and narratives differ from cognitive means of interpretation (frames, schemata, cause maps) most crucially in that they are fundamentally discursive: based in language (e.g., labels, metaphors). Therefore, by focusing on accounts and narratives, we are made to notice how events are translated into language, how that language selection is socially negotiated, and how organization is thus talked into existence. Instead of residing passively in mental knowledge structures, accounts and narratives live socially in acts of speech. This has the added benefit of making them more observable, including through secondary sources. In contrast, cognitive means of interpretation are most reliably elicited through interviews (e.g., Bougon et al., 1977; Weber & Manning, 2001).

An account is a "situation that is comprehended explicitly in words and serves as a springboard to action" (Taylor & Van Every, 2000, p. 40). As "discursive constructions of reality," accounts "provide members with ordered representations of previously unordered external cues... [that] describe or explain the world and thus make it meaningful" (Maitlis, 2005, p. 23). The underlying idea of "accounting for" behavior stems from ethnomethodology (Garfinkel, 1967; Heritage, 1984). On the other hand, narratives stem from a wide multiplicity of scholarly traditions (e.g., Bakhtin, 1981; Ricœur, 1984). Narratives are "a discursive construction that actors use as a tool to shape their own understanding (sensemaking), as a tool to influence others' understandings (sensegiving), and as an outcome of the collective construction of meaning" (Sonenshein, 2010, p. 480). The crucial distinction between narratives and accounts are that narratives are explicitly temporal: Narratives make sense by describing how events have proceeded over time to produce the triggering event. Narratives thus have at least three components: "an original state of affairs, an action or an event, and the consequent state of affairs" (Czarniawska, 1998, p. 2). Given this temporal component, narratives can serve to support both stability and change in organizations (Vaara, Sonenshein, & Boje, 2016).

From poststructuralist and postmodernist perspectives, narratives differ from stories in a key way. Narratives need not have "coherent storylines, shared meaning, and common values" but can entertain multiple, even contradictory meanings (Cunliffe, Luhman, & Boje, 2004, p. 264). Further, some of these meanings are favored while others are suppressed. This brings questions of power and privilege into the picture. Indeed, asking how some meanings gain favor over others can help link sensemaking with more critical approaches (Brown, 2000; Helms Mills et al., 2010; Mumby, 1987). It is evident that powerful individuals play an important role in shaping narratives. This role is well exemplified in how a central bank's chairman listened to several competing narratives about economic recovery in a meeting and decided which of these narratives would actually be enacted publicly (Abolafia, 2010). It is also evident in the way that leaders narrate their own personal stories in ways intended to grant them social legitimacy (Maclean, Harvey, & Chia, 2012). Similarly, but at a higher level of analysis, organizations that foster a strong "official narrative" invariably relegate other narratives to a secondary position—as exemplified by analyses of the Walt Disney company (e.g., Boje, 1995; Van Maanen, 1991).

Taken as a whole, discursive means of interpretation therefore add important value beyond cognitive means (Cooren, 2000; Taylor & Van Every, 2000). Discursive interpretations are neither an intrasubjective matter of an individual's cognition, nor are they necessarily an extra-subjective matter of taken-for-granted reality. Rather, they highlight how groups first establish their intersubjective understandings and then make these understandings generic over time through discourse (e.g., Schall, 1983). Sensemaking research has accordingly explored these discursive processes in a variety of contexts: fire fighters, intensive care units, blue-collar work, hostage situations, and monetary policy groups (e.g., Abolafia, 2010; Albolino, Cook, & O'Connor, 2007; Baran & Scott, 2010; Mills, 2002; Quinn & Worline, 2008).

This raises a further question: How should discourse best proceed if it is to facilitate sense-making? Some highlight specific techniques, which balance members voicing their ideas, needs, and attitudes as well as respectfully questioning the ideas of others (Blatt et al., 2006; Wright & Manning, 2004; Wright, Manning, Farmer, & Gilbreath, 2000). As we will shortly see, although not focused entirely on discourse, the ideas of mindfulness and "heedful interrelating" (Weick & Roberts, 1993) also provide valuable insights into how groups form intersubjectivity (e.g., Bijlsma-Frankema, de Jong, & van de Bunt, 2008; Jordan & Daniel, 2010; Stephens & Lyddy, 2016). Others highlight the types of situations under which discursive means of inter-pretation are most likely to flourish (Browning & Boudès, 2005; Rouleau & Balogun, 2011). Nonetheless, we should not assume that any single technique or situation will fit all possible sensemaking contexts. For instance, depending on the context, there is certainly room for stra-tegically ambiguous communications, using language that is intentionally decoupled from actual business practices, using language to revise understandings of prior events rather than changing practices, or formalizing language into written contracts and rules (Eisenberg, 1984; Fiss & Zajac, 2006; Gioia, Corley, & Fabbri, 2002; Vlaar, Van den Bosch, & Volberda, 2006).

From a discursive perspective, organizations can thus be seen as a "storytelling system" (see Boje, 1991) or even a "text" (Westwood & Linstead, 2001). Yet, such perspectives are open to a critique, namely, that "organizations may emerge through conversation, but they do not emerge for the sake of conversation" (Engeström, 1999, p. 170). Sensemaking intends to answer the latter question: modeling not just how organizations emerge, but also why. Thus, while some describe sensemaking and discourse as equal members of interpretive organiza-tional research (Morgan, Frost, & Pondy, 1983), sensemaking scholars typically disagree. They note how sensemaking differs from interpretation: Sensemaking emphasizes how orga-nizations do not merely interpret their environments, but instead help create them through perception and action (Sutcliffe, 2014; Weick, 1995). Thus, discourse has a subsidiary place within sensemaking: It is an important means of interpretation, but cannot be considered aside from the information that people notice and the actions they take on their environment (cf. Taylor & Robichaud, 2004). And it is only in understanding how environments are en-acted that we can start to understand why organizations emerge.

Interpretive Processes: Embodied Means. Thus, even this discursive perspective has its limits. Through it, we may inadvertently start to "portray sensemaking as more cerebral, more passive, more abstract than it typically is ... [because sensemaking] starts with immedi-ate actions, local context, and concrete cues" (Weick et al., 2005, p. 412). Indeed, there can be a tendency to forget immediate actions in favor of the more cerebral use of language over time. And, as noted, discourse research has not always made the connection between language, action, and environments (Taylor & Robichaud, 2004). For instance, although the technique is not frequently used in sensemaking research, agent-based models can serve as a helpful reminder about the power of action (cf. Gavetti & Levinthal, 2000; Gavetti & Warglien, 2015; Rudolph, Morrison, & Carroll, 2009; Rudolph & Repenning, 2002). In such models, we see that organization can emerge from individuals with remarkably simple interpretations (see Nowak & Vallacher, 2007). Physical action can be a means of interpretation given the central importance of retrospect: We make sense by looking back on what we have done. It is through physical action that we often identify our interpretations. And, as institutional theory perspectives highlight (Weber & Glynn, 2006), even seemingly unthinking and mundane actions also carry interpretive weight. Our rooting in a larger "lifeworld" provides such everyday actions with taken-for-granted meanings (Wright & Manning, 2004).

An important aspect of physical action is the role of the body. Indeed, the literature on sensemaking is puzzlingly rather mute on the role of the physical senses as an interpretive tool (Maitlis & Sonenshein, 2010; Sandberg & Tsoukas, 2015). This trend is reversing, as work continues to explore how sensemaking occurs in and through the body (Cornelissen, Mantere, & Vaara, 2014; Cunliffe & Coupland, 2012; Harquail & King, 2010). For example, physiological states, gestures, and body posture are inextricably interwoven into the verbal narratives that individuals use to interpret events (Cunliffe & Coupland, 2012). Our interpretations are encoded in our movements—and shared with others through our embodied actions (Whiteman & Cooper, 2011). What is less fully appreciated is that embodied emotional states are not merely influences on interpretation, but are interpretations themselves (see Myers, 2007). An embodied state contains a map of what the event is, who the relevant social actors are, and what generally might be done to address the event (see Averill, 1983). In this way, embodied action and emotion not only influence interpretation, but are a means by which interpretation occurs. Furthermore, an embodied approach dovetails nicely with phenomenological approaches to sensemaking and organizing (Chia & Holt, 2006; Guiette & Vandenbempt, 2016; Yanow & Tsoukas, 2009). Such approaches, which draw most heavily from Heidegger (Dreyfus, 1991), help us attend to the actual firsthand embodied experience of breakdowns in meaning and recovery from them.

Immediate Products of Interpretation. What exactly is produced by interpretation? We may use frames, narratives, or gestures during the selection process, but what exactly do they produce? As Elsbach, Barr, and Hargadon (2005) argued, scholars have historically given inadequate attention to the temporary outcomes of the interpretive process. Instead, much of the scholarly attention highlights the more stable knowledge structures that are retained as the result of enactment. Yet, the momentary and fleeting understandings that stem from selection are the key drivers of enactment. Weick and colleagues (2005) describe these interpretive products as answers to two questions: "What's the story here?" and "Now what should I do?" (p. 410). In other words, individuals and groups first draw on retrospective processes to understand what the disruptive event means and then use this understanding to turn an eye more prospectively toward action in the present moment.

Similarly, Elsbach and colleagues (2005) delimited four products of the interpretive process as identified in the literature. Considering these interpretive products is valuable because they provide some structure to the transient but influential products that come from selection and guide enactment. These four interpretive products describe the following:

(1) *Our understanding of the problem at hand.* This interpretive product answers the question, "what's the story here?" whereas the remaining three answer "now what should I do?" Problem understandings concern the variables of interest that we bracket from ongoing events and the relations we propose among them. For example, a workgroup geographically dispersed into two separate locations formed two separate understandings of their joint task, thereby forestalling their ability to decide on an action moving forward (Cramton, 2001). Until a group comes to a plausible shared understanding of "the story," the second question of "what to do next" becomes fundamentally unworkable.

(2) *The attractiveness of various options.* Option attractiveness refers to the value people associate with a particular path forward. For example, two sets of research teams developing cochlear ear implants responded to different cues from institutional forces like government agencies and business partners. As a result, they differentially valued the attractiveness of starting with a simpler initial model and adding complexity relative to beginning with a more complex initial model (Garud & Rappa, 1994). The cues available to them and the way those cues were interpreted guided the attractiveness of various options for enactment.

(3) *The features about ourselves we perceive as being distinctive.* These perceptions capture the elements of our identity such as our skills, traits, or expertise that are especially salient in the current situation. For example, in a crucial moment after a fire grew uncontainable, several firefighters failed to drop their heavy tools and run from the fire (Weick, 1993b). Within the context of their interpreted environment, it was unfathomable to drop the very tools that constituted their distinct identity as firefighters. To drop their tools would be to enact a rather different identity. This shows how interpretations influence identity, and thus the kinds of behaviors that are available for enactment.

(4) *Our receptivity to a collectivist mindset.* The interpretive process can open individuals up to greater degrees of a collectivist mindset in which knowledge is pooled and integrated. For example, in trying to interpret what a particular business opportunity means, some firms generate cultures that increase a collectivist mindset. This mindset taps more broadly into organizational memory to ultimately influence the way these business opportunities are interpreted (Sutton & Hargadon, 1996). Based on how we interpret our situations, we may be more or less open to these collective modes of thinking.

Proximal Consequences of Enactment.   Together, these four interpretive products set the stage for enactment. In enactment, interpretation leads to some type of action, be it verbal or embodied. For this reason, we must "designate binding action as the object of sensemaking" (Weick, 1993a, p. 17). In other words, cognitive, discursive, or embodied interpretations only shape reality through action that binds. By enacting an interpretation, we produce two important and related consequences. First, we grow more committed to the interpretations we enact. And, second, we produce new changes in the environment that either bring the environment closer in line with the interpretation or violate the expectations embedded in our interpretations, and thus trigger a new round of sensemaking.

In regard to the first consequence, enacted interpretations are especially commitment producing when they are the result of a volitional choice that is public and hard to reverse (Salancik, 1977; Weick, 1993a). In regard to the second consequence, a key question becomes: How will groups respond to violations of their enacted interpretations? At times, groups are able to "query an initial frame and…mobilize instead an alternative frame from background knowledge or make novel associations as a way of structuring expectations and make inferences" (Cornelissen et al., 2014, p. 703). This phenomenon is sometimes referred to as "adaptive sensemaking" (Cornelissen et al., 2014; Strike & Rerup, 2015; Weick et al., 2005). Adaptive sensemaking shows how violations produced by enactment can prompt groups to rethink their commitment to an interpretation. Adaptive sensemaking is evident in the example of a railroad museum facing a roof collapse (Christianson et al., 2009). After the roof collapsed, the museum changed how they framed their organization from one of a historical repository to an attraction, thereby enabling new strategic initiatives and greater involvement from the community.

In many cases, however, commitment to continued enactment outweighs considerations of alternatives. Such "staunch commitment to a particular set of meanings" can be especially problematic in crisis situations because it "creates substantial blind spots that impede adaptation" (Maitlis & Sonenshein, 2010, p. 562). We can see this effect in firefighters who perished after enacting a "10 o'clock fire" label—that the fire will be contained by 10 a.m. the following morning—despite evidence to the contrary (Weick, 1993b). Similarly, with high shared levels of nervousness and fear, an anti-terrorist police force committed to enact their interpretation of an innocent citizen as a terrorist (Cornelissen et al., 2014). Although there were opportunities for doubt and reflection, their strong commitment led them to ultimately kill the wrong person.

These groups remained committed to enacting their interpretation despite violations of their interpretations. In some cases, however, the violations of expectations may arrive too late to reverse the course of enactment. For example, consider the fatal actions of NASA in launching the Challenger and Columbia shuttles. Employees frequently used labels like "acceptable risk" or metaphors like "in-family" to "waive" security concerns (Dunbar & Garud, 2009; Vaughan, 1996). In the process, employees grew committed to the environment as they enacted it. Only in retrospect—after these shuttles exploded in a harsh violation of their enacted environment—were these cues interpreted in alternative ways.

In sum, we can see that there is "a delicate tradeoff between dangerous action which produces understanding and safe inaction which produces confusion" (Weick, 1988, p. 305). The tradeoff is that enactment helps us understand past events, but also creates new future events. Thus, there is value in considering what enables some groups to skillfully notice, bracket, and interpret information, and to manage the delicate tradeoff as they enact their interpretations.

Mindful Organizing as Effective Sensemaking.   Indeed, as these examples reveal, not all groups are equally effective at sensemaking (e.g., Blatt et al., 2006; Winch & Maytorena, 2009). Some of the most important differences can be captured through the idea of *mindfulness*: the ability of groups to sustain attention toward and interpret ongoing events in a manner that captures enough discriminatory detail to act with speed and flexibility (Levinthal & Rerup, 2006; Weick & Sutcliffe, 2006, 2015; Weick, Sutcliffe, & Obstfeld, 1999). Mindfulness has an important basis in the attentional and interpretive capabilities of individual members, including those described by meditative practices (Kudesia & Nyima, 2015; Reb & Atkins, 2015; Weick & Putnam, 2006). However, it can also be nurtured by more enduring mechanisms such as human resource policies, leader modeling, and organizational climate (Ray, Baker, & Plowman, 2011; Vogus & Sutcliffe, 2012; Vogus & Welbourne, 2003). As shown in Figure 2, mindful organizing describes five processes that make sensemaking more adaptive.

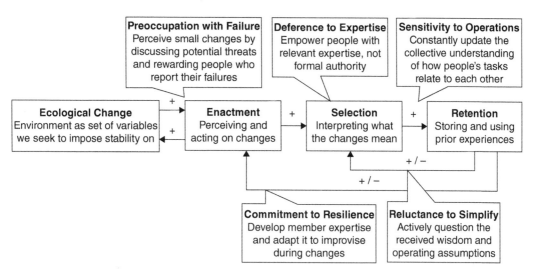

Figure 2. Processes of mindful organizing.

Groups that organize mindfully do a better job of anticipating potential disruptive events. This is because they constantly update their shared understanding of real-time events by pooling information and expertise across all members instead of relying on assumptions derived from past experience. As such, they are better able to notice and respond to minor disruptions in their environment before these disruptions cascade into full-blown crises. In this way, mindfulness captures a "quality of organizational attention" that prevents the normalizing away of important information and thereby enables more effective sensemaking (Weick & Sutcliffe, 2006). Mindfulness also shapes how groups respond to violations of their expectations (Levinthal & Rerup, 2006; Rerup & Levinthal, 2013; Weick & Sutcliffe, 2015). Groups that organize mindfully respond to these violations by adopting a resilient mindset that flexibly adapts past knowledge and by empowering the group members who have relevant expertise, rather than members with the most formal power. Mindfulness can therefore hedge the tendency to enact interpretations in an unthinking manner (Fiol & O'Connor, 2003). It helps groups anticipate triggering events and contain these events when they arise through skillful enactment. This is one reason why mindful organizing is especially prevalent in high-reliability organizations, where sensemaking failures can prompt disasters (Weick & Sutcliffe, 2015). Nonetheless, mindful organizing is relevant across a number of organizational contexts, including investment banks (Michel, 2007), management and design consultants (Hargadon & Bechky, 2006), information technology (Swanson & Ramiller, 2004), and others (see Sutcliffe, Vogus, & Dane, 2016).

Distal Consequences of Enactment. Why might an organization care to support mindful organizing? What are the big picture benefits of sensemaking? The answer is that enactment produces important distal consequences in terms of how an organization changes, learns, and negotiates its identity (for a comprehensive review, see Maitlis & Christianson, 2014). This is evident in how a railroad museum not only responded to the crisis of its roof collapsing, but turned this roof collapse into an opportunity to develop a new and more effective business strategy (Christianson et al., 2009). It is evident in how Air Force pilots who faced and effectively made sense of dangerous circumstances shared their stories with other pilots, prompting vicarious learning throughout the organization (Catino & Patriotta, 2013). It is evident in how sensemaking after an organization collapsed prompted members to pool their resources and found a new organization (Walsh & Bartunek, 2011). And a number of quantitative studies have also explored how various aspects of the sensemaking process influence overall firm financial performance (e.g., Daft, Sormunen, & Parks, 1988; Osborne, Stubbart, & Ramaprasad, 2001; Thomas et al., 1993).

Enactment, however, does not simply influence single organizations, but entire industries. For example, consider Porac, Thomas, and Baden-Fuller's (1989) seminal analysis of the Scottish knitwear industry. They found that managers across knitwear firms had shared cognitive frames in how they categorized various subsets of textiles. Given these shared frames, most managers interpreted only other Scottish knitwear firms as their real competitors. They enacted these interpretations through the strategies and pricing, their supplier and distributor relationships, and so forth. Despite other companies producing similar goods at similar prices, these managers essentially enacted a "cognitive oligopoly" that shaped the behavior of an entire market. In this way, enactment completes the sensemaking process. Enactment produces an environment that may appear objectively true, and existing independent of our own actions (see Kaplan, 2011). However, our environment is really constructed through our actions and the actions of those with whom we are interlocked.

Contextual Influences on Sensemaking. As the Scottish knitwear example illustrates, the sensemaking process links individuals, groups, organizations, and broader institutional forces into interlocking patterns of mutual action and understanding. Sensemaking simultaneously operates at the level of ongoing environmental changes, social interactions within an organization, and the broader institutional context (e.g., Jensen, Kjærgaard, & Svejvig, 2009; Jeong & Brower, 2008). It also draws on cultural values that help define what properties make accounts sensible and to whom one should be accountable (e.g., Malsch, Tremblay, & Gendron, 2012; O'Leary & Chia, 2007). Nonetheless, much of the relevant research focuses on single levels without exploring cross-level processes (for a notable exception, see Stigliani & Ravasi, 2012). It is therefore helpful to outline some of the contextual, multiparty, and cross-level phenomena that affect sensemaking. For instance, individuals certainly have strong moral intuitions—but collective factors like social pressures and interaction partners shape how individuals define, communicate, and act upon ethical issues (Sonenshein, 2007). In this way, collectives can influence how individuals make sense of their environments in a top-down manner. The reverse process also occurs. For example, Strike and Rerup (2015) found that trusted outside advisors can attenuate the tendency toward commitment by inserting doubt into the sensemaking process. Such doubt is crucial for adaptive sensemaking. This shows how individuals can also influence how collectives make sense. In considering the degree to which individuals can influence collective sensemaking, we must note how social positions grant various forms of economic, social, and cultural capital that shape how people construct issues (Ibarra & Andrews, 1993; Lockett, Currie, Finn, Martin, & Waring, 2014; Westley, 1990).

When we consider multiple parties, this inevitably brings up questions of power, politics, and influence. For instance, Maitlis (2005) explored how sensemaking occurs across multiple parties in more complex organizational settings. She found that leaders influenced the degree to which sensemaking was controlled. Leaders controlled sensemaking processes by scheduling meetings, forming committees, and planning events. Importantly, they also controlled which organizational members had access to these sensemaking channels. In this way, leaders had greater ability to engage in sensegiving and they typically did so in less public forums. On the other hand, stakeholders influenced the degree to which sensemaking was animated. Active and involved stakeholders induced more sharing of information, reporting to board members, and so on. This prompted greater and more constant communication of issues and interpretations within the organization. In this way, multiple parties within organizations influence sensemaking (Fiss & Zajac, 2006). They can also prevent effective sensemaking. For instance, Dunbar and Garud (2009) found that two groups at NASA developed different patterns of interpretation, focusing respectively on safety issues and scheduling issues. As a result, they were unable to effectively interpret and act on a cue of foam shedding on the Columbia space shuttle, resulting in disaster as it re-entered Earth's atmosphere. This case clearly highlights how the transition from group-level intersubjectivity to organization-level generic subjectivity is fraught with danger.

Similarly, there is also value in considering *second-order sensemaking* (Sandberg & Tsoukas, 2015). Second-order sensemaking refers to how outside groups subsequently make sense of another group's sensemaking process. A famous case is the Rogers Commission, which investigated the sensemaking process that led to the Challenger launch decision (cf. Vaughan, 1996). Such public inquiries extract cues from the original sensemaking episode and often seek to find fault or blame. For example, if an individual reports being emotional during sensemaking in crisis, this can later be interpreted during second-order sensemaking as a lack of professionalism (Gephart, 1993). It is important to remember that this second-order sensemaking process is not simply "finding facts" and "uncovering the truth." Second-order sensemaking often occurs as part of a broader strategy of "depoliticizing disaster events," "legitimating the actions and interests of dominant groups," and reducing post-disaster anxiety "by elaborating fantasies of omnipotence and control" (Brown, 2000, p. 45; see also Boudès & Laroche, 2009; Brown, 2004). However, it is certainly possible that sensemaking about crises can foster greater preparedness for similar future crises as well (Nathan, 2004).

Finally, we can also consider how sensemaking at the group and organizational level connect with the broader social forces described by institutional theory (see Jennings & Greenwood, 2003; Weick, 2003). On one hand, the interpretive tools most readily available to organizational members necessarily reflect the institutions in which they participate (Weber & Glynn, 2006). This means that individuals in organizations draw on institutional resources like identities (e.g., union member), expectations (e.g., loyalty), and frames (e.g., going on strike) in making sense. In fact, given how thoroughly we internalize our institutional realities, it may even be hard to make sense outside of the resources they offer. At the very least, local context can cognitively prime individuals to draw on institutional resources and socially prompt others to push behavior in line with these resources. On the other hand, sensemaking processes can also help us understand these forces as well (Ocasio, Loewenstein, & Nigam,

2015; Porac, Ventresca, & Mishina, 2005). For instance, sensemaking analyses have shed light on institutions as diverse as religion (Pratt, 2000a), globalization (Fiss & Hirsch, 2005), policing (Maguire & Katz, 2002), markets (Abolafia & Kilduff, 1988), and health care (Nigam & Ocasio, 2010). In this way, a wealth of contextual factors across multiple types of social agents and levels of analysis influence the sensemaking process.

CONCLUSIONS AND FUTURE DIRECTIONS

In sum, we can see that sensemaking offers both a general perspective on organizations and describes a specific process by which people collectively organize their world. It challenges us to complicate ourselves such that we are comfortable with retrospect, enactment, feedback loops, human agency, multiple conflicting narratives, plausible interpretations, emergent order, and process. Nonetheless, we still have much to learn (cf. Miner, 2005). Some avenues include developing richer conceptualizations of how embodiment and emotions sculpt the sensemaking process and how sensemaking occurs across individual, group, organization, and institutional levels. Questions of how much sensemaking operates through prospective, future-oriented thinking in addition to the established retrospective processes also remain open and worth exploring (Gephart, Topal, & Zhang, 2010; Gioia, Thomas, Clark, & Chittipeddi, 1994; MacKay, 2009; Stigliani & Ravasi, 2012; Wright, 2005). New technologies including social media likely change how sensemaking occurs by distributing interpretations across wider groups (Boland, Tenkasi, & Te'eni, 1994). They also offer opportunities to collect valuable data on discursive means of sensemaking (Gephart, 2004; Herrmann, 2007). To this end, there is also value in expanding methodological and research design considerations. For instance, alternate methodological approaches such as action research (Allard-Poesi, 2005; Lüscher & Lewis, 2008) and agent-based modeling (Gavetti & Warglien, 2015; Rudolph et al., 2009) may prove valuable. We can also better tie sensemaking to the actual practice of social science and management. In this way, sensemaking can become not only a topic to research, but more closely integrated into the process of social science research itself (Cornelissen, 2006; Weick, 1993c, 2007). Managers can similarly understand and apply a sensemaking perspective to their own work in fruitful ways (Parry, 2003).

Finally, although sensemaking may help us understand how humans *do* behave descriptively, it cannot make claims regarding how humans prescriptively *should* behave. A sensemaking perspective reminds us that it is not merely the facts of history that matter, but how those facts are interpreted. The "logical conclusion" of this reminder is potentially discouraging: that "the organizational world will tend ever more relentlessly toward a postmodern world where image dominates substance—and in particular a world in which images of change supplant substantive change" (Gioia et al., 2002, p. 632). Therefore, we must realize that the descriptive validity of sensemaking as a perspective does not mean it cannot have a potentially harmful influence in practice. This calls our attention to the need to participate responsibly in the sensemaking process. To make sense with and through organizations, we must be willing to not only reinterpret the past, but also help author the future through mindful action. Such mindful action requires not only commitment to our values and beliefs, but also the courage to doubt.

ACKNOWLEDGMENTS

This research was supported by the Future Resilient Systems project at the Singapore-ETH Centre, which is funded by the National Research Foundation of Singapore under its Campus for Research Excellence and Technological Enterprise program (FI 370074011).

REFERENCES

Abolafia, M. Y. (2010). Narrative construction as sensemaking: How a central bank thinks. *Organization Studies, 31*(3), 349–367. http://dx.doi.org/10.1177/0170840609357380

Abolafia, M. Y., & Kilduff, M. (1988). Enacting market crisis: The social construction of a speculative bubble. *Administrative Science Quarterly, 33*(2), 177–193. https://dx.doi.org/10.2307/2393054

Albolino, S., Cook, R., & O'Connor, M. (2007). Sensemaking, safety, and cooperative work in the intensive care unit. *Cognition, Technology & Work, 9*(3), 131–137. https://dx.doi.org/10.1007/s10111-006-0057-5

Allard-Poesi, F. (2005). The paradox of sensemaking in organizational analysis. *Organization, 12*(2), 169–196. https://dx.doi.org/10.1177/1350508405051187

Alvesson, M., & Karreman, D. (2000). Varieties of discourse: On the study of organizations through discourse analysis. *Human Relations, 53*(9), 1125–1149. https://dx.doi.org/10.1177/0018726700539002

Anderson, M. H. (2006). How can we know what we think until we see what we said?: A citation and citation context analysis of Karl Weick's *The social psychology of organizing. Organization Studies, 27*(11), 1675–1692. https://dx.doi.org/10.1177/0170840606068346

Ashforth, B. E., & Fried, Y. (1988). The mindlessness of organizational behaviors. *Human Relations, 41*(4), 305–329. https://dx.doi.org/10.1177/001872678804100403

Averill, J. R. (1983). Studies on anger and aggression: Implications for theories. *American Psychologist, 38*(11), 1145. https://dx.doi.org/10.1037/0003-066X.38.11.1145%20of%20emotion

Bakhtin, M. M. (1981). *The dialogic imagination: Four essays.* Austin: University of Texas Press.

Baran, B. E., & Scott, C. W. (2010). Organizing ambiguity: A grounded theory of leadership and sensemaking within dangerous contexts. *Military Psychology, 22*(Suppl. 1), S42–S69. https://dx.doi.org/10.1080/08995601003644262

Barnett, C. K., & Pratt, M. G. (2000). From threat-rigidity to flexibility—Toward a learning model of autogenic crisis in organizations. *Journal of Organizational Change Management, 13*(1), 74–88. https://dx.doi.org/10.1108/09534810010310258

Barry, D., & Meisiek, S. (2010). Seeing more and seeing differently: Sensemaking, mindfulness, and the workarts. *Organization Studies, 31*(11), 1505–1530. https://dx.doi.org/10.1177/0170840610380802

Bartunek, J. M. (1984). Changing interpretive schemes and organizational restructuring: The example of a religious order. *Administrative Science Quarterly, 29*(3), 355–372. https://dx.doi.org/10.2307/2393029

Becker, M. C., & Knudsen, T. (2005). The role of routines in reducing pervasive uncertainty. *Journal of Business Research, 58*(6), 746–757. https://dx.doi.org/10.1016/j.jbusres.2003.10.003

Berger, P. L., & Luckmann, T. (1966). *The social construction of reality.* New York: Penguin.

Bijlsma-Frankema, K., de Jong, B., & van de Bunt, G. (2008). Heed, a missing link between trust, monitoring and performance in knowledge intensive teams. *The International Journal of Human Resource Management, 19*(1), 19–40. https://dx.doi.org/10.1080/09585190701763800

Blatt, R., Christianson, M. K., Sutcliffe, K. M., & Rosenthal, M. M. (2006). A sensemaking lens on reliability. *Journal of Organizational Behavior, 27*(7), 897–917. https://dx.doi.org/10.1002/job.392

Boje, D. M. (1991). The storytelling organization: A study of story performance in an office-supply firm. *Administrative Science Quarterly, 36*(1), 106. https://dx.doi.org/10.2307/2393432

Boje, D. M. (1995). Stories of the storytelling organization: A postmodern analysis of Disney as "Tamara-Land". *Academy of Management Journal, 38*(4), 997–1035. https://dx.doi.org/10.2307/256618

Boland, R. J. (1984). Sense-making of accounting data as a technique of organizational diagnosis. *Management Science, 30*(7), 868–882. https://dx.doi.org/10.1287/mnsc.30.7.868

Boland, R. J., Tenkasi, R. V., & Te'eni, D. (1994). Designing information technology to support distributed cognition. *Organization Science, 5*(3), 456–475. https://dx.doi.org/10.1287/orsc.5.3.456

Boudès, T., & Laroche, H. (2009). Taking off the heat: Narrative sensemaking in post-crisis inquiry reports. *Organization Studies, 30*(4), 377–396. https://dx.doi.org/10.1177/0170840608101141

Bougon, M., Weick, K. E., & Binkhorst, D. (1977). Cognition in organizations: An analysis of the Utrecht Jazz Orchestra. *Administrative Science Quarterly, 22*(4), 606–639. https://dx.doi.org/10.2307/2392403

Bradbury, H., & Lichtenstein, B. M. B. (2000). Relationality in organizational research: Exploring the space between. *Organization Science, 11*(5), 551–564.

Brown, A. D. (2000). Making sense of inquiry sensemaking. *Journal of Management Studies, 37*(1), 45–75. https://dx.doi.org/10.1111/1467-6486.00172

Brown, A. D. (2004). Authoritative sensemaking in a public inquiry report. *Organization Studies, 25*(1), 95–112. https://dx.doi.org/10.1177/0170840604038182

Brown, A. D., Stacey, P., & Nandhakumar, J. (2008). Making sense of sensemaking narratives. *Human Relations, 61*(8), 1035–1062. https://dx.doi.org/10.1177/0018726708094858

Browning, L., & Boudès, T. (2005). The use of narrative to understand and respond to complexity: A comparative analysis of the Cynefin and Weickian models. *E:CO, 7*(3–4), 32–39.

Burrell, G., & Morgan, G. (1979). *Sociological paradigms and organizational analysis: Elements of the sociology of corporate life.* London: Heinemann.

Campbell, D. T. (1970). Natural selection as an epistemological model. In M. Sherif & C. W. Sherif (Eds.), *A handbook of method in cultural anthropology* (pp. 51–85). Garden City, NY: Natural History Press.

Catino, M., & Patriotta, G. (2013). Learning from errors: Cognition, emotions and safety culture in the Italian Air Force. *Organization Studies, 34*(4), 437–467. https://dx.doi.org/10.1177/01708406 12467156

Chia, R., & Holt, R. (2006). Strategy as practical coping: A Heideggerian perspective. *Organization Studies, 27*(5), 635–655. https://dx.doi.org/10.1177/0170840606064102

Christianson, M. K., Farkas, M. T., Sutcliffe, K. M., & Weick, K. E. (2009). Learning through rare events: Significant interruptions at the Baltimore & Ohio Railroad Museum. *Organization Science, 20*(5), 846–860. https://dx.doi.org/10.1287/orsc.1080.0389

Colville, I. D., Brown, A. D., & Pye, A. (2012). Simplexity: Sensemaking, organizing and storytelling for our time. *Human Relations, 65*(1), 5–15. https://dx.doi.org/10.1177/0018726711425617

Colville, I. D., Waterman, R. H., & Weick, K. E. (1999). Organizing and the search for excellence: Making sense of the times in theory and practice. *Organization, 6*(1), 129–148.

Cooren, F. (2000). *The organizing property of communication.* Amsterdam: John Benjamins.

Cornelissen, J. P. (2005). Beyond compare: Metaphor in organization theory. *Academy of Management Review, 30*(4), 751–764. https://dx.doi.org/10.5465/AMR.2005.18378876

Cornelissen, J. P. (2006). Making sense of theory construction: Metaphor and disciplined imagination. *Organization Studies, 27*(11), 1579–1597. https://dx.doi.org/10.1177/0170840606068333

Cornelissen, J. P. (2012). Sensemaking under pressure: The influence of professional roles and social accountability on the creation of sense. *Organization Science, 23*(1), 118–137. https://dx.doi.org/10.1287 /orsc.1100.0640

Cornelissen, J. P., Holt, R., & Zundel, M. (2011). The role of analogy and metaphor in the framing and legitimization of strategic change. *Organization Studies, 32*(12), 1701–1716. https://dx.doi.org/10.1177 /0170840611425729

Cornelissen, J. P., Mantere, S., & Vaara, E. (2014). The contraction of meaning: The combined effect of communication, emotions, and materiality on sensemaking in the Stockwell shooting. *Journal of Management Studies, 51*(5), 699–736. https://dx.doi.org/10.1111/joms.12073

Cornelissen, J. P., & Werner, M. D. (2014). Putting framing in perspective: A review of framing and frame analysis across the management and organizational literature. *Academy of Management Annals, 8*(1), 181–235. https://dx.doi.org/10.1080/19416520.2014.875669

Cramton, C. D. (2001). The mutual knowledge problem and its consequences for dispersed collaboration. *Organization Science, 12*(3), 346–371. https://dx.doi.org/10.1287/orsc.12.3.346.10098

Cunliffe, A. L., & Coupland, C. (2012). From hero to villain to hero: Making experience sensible through embodied narrative sensemaking. *Human Relations, 65*(1), 63–88. https://dx.doi.org/10.1177/0018726711424321

Cunliffe, A. L., Luhman, J. T., & Boje, D. M. (2004). Narrative temporality: Implications for organizational research. *Organization Studies, 25*(2), 261–286. https://dx.doi.org/10.1177/0170840604040038

Czarniawska, B. (1998). *A narrative approach in organization studies.* Thousand Oaks, CA: SAGE.

Daft, R. L., Sormunen, J., & Parks, D. (1988). Chief executive scanning, environmental characteristics, and company performance: An empirical study. *Strategic Management Journal, 9*(2), 123–139. https://dx.doi.org/10.1002/smj.4250090204

Daft, R. L., & Weick, K. E. (1984). Toward a model of organizations as interpretation systems. *Academy of Management Review, 9*(2), 284–295. https://dx.doi.org/10.5465/AMR.1984.4277657

Dreyfus, H. L. (1991). *Being-in-the-world: A commentary on Heidegger's being and time, division I.* Cambridge, MA: MIT Press.

Dunbar, R. L. M., & Garud, R. (2009). Distributed knowledge and indeterminate meaning: The case of the Columbia shuttle flight. *Organization Studies, 30*(4), 397–421. https://dx.doi.org/10.1177/0170840608101142

Edwards, W. (1954). The theory of decision-making. *Psychological Bulletin, 51*(4), 380–417. https://dx.doi.org/10.1037/h0053870

Eisenberg, E. M. (1984). Ambiguity as strategy in organizational communication. *Communication Monographs, 51*(3), 227–242. https://dx.doi.org/10.1080/03637758409390197

Elsbach, K. D., Barr, P. S., & Hargadon, A. B. (2005). Identifying situated cognition in organizations. *Organization Science, 16*(4), 422–433. https://dx.doi.org/10.1287/orsc.1050.0138

Engeström, Y. (1999). Communication, discourse and activity. *Communication Review, 3*(1–2), 165–185. https://dx.doi.org/10.1080/10714429909368577

Festinger, L. (1957). *A theory of cognitive dissonance.* Stanford, CA: Stanford University Press.

Fiol, C. M., & O'Connor, E. J. (2003). Waking up! Mindfulness in the face of bandwagons. *Academy of Management Review, 28*(1), 54–70. https://dx.doi.org/10.5465/AMR.2003.8925227

Fiske, S. T., & Taylor, S. E. (1991). *Social cognition* (2d ed.). New York: McGraw-Hill.

Fiss, P. C., & Hirsch, P. M. (2005). The discourse of globalization: Framing and sensemaking of an emerging concept. *American Sociological Review, 70*(1), 29–52. https://dx.doi.org/10.1177/000312240507000103

Fiss, P. C., & Zajac, E. J. (2006). The symbolic management of strategic change: Sensegiving via framing and decoupling. *Academy of Management Journal, 49*(6), 1173–1193. https://dx.doi.org/10.5465/AMJ.2006.23478255

Freeman, R. E. (1994). The politics of stakeholder theory: Some future directions. *Business Ethics Quarterly, 4*(4), 409–421. https://dx.doi.org/10.2307/3857340

Galbraith, J. R. (1973). *Designing complex organizations.* Reading, MA: Addison-Wesley.

Garfinkel, H. (1967). *Studies in ethnomethodology.* Englewood Cliffs, NJ: Prentice-Hall.

Garud, R., & Rappa, M. A. (1994). A socio-cognitive model of technology evolution: The case of cochlear implants. *Organization Science, 5*(3), 344–362. https://dx.doi.org/10.1287/orsc.5.3.344

Gavetti, G., & Levinthal, D. A. (2000). Looking forward and looking backward: Cognitive and experiential search. *Administrative Science Quarterly, 45*(1), 113. https://dx.doi.org/10.2307/2666981

Gavetti, G., & Warglien, M. (2015). A model of collective interpretation. *Organization Science, 26*(5), 1263–1283. https://dx.doi.org/10.1287/orsc.2015.0987

Gephart, R. P. (1993). The textual approach: Risk and blame in disaster sensemaking. *Academy of Management Journal, 36*(6), 1465–1514.

Gephart, R. P. (1997). Hazardous measures: An interpretive textual analysis of quantitative sensemaking during crises. *Journal of Organizational Behavior, 18*(S1), 583–622. https://dx.doi.org/10.1002/(SICI)1099-1379(199711)18:1+%3C583::AID-JOB908%3E3.0.CO;2-T

Gephart, R. P. (2004). Sensemaking and new media at work. *American Behavioral Scientist, 48*(4), 479–495. https://dx.doi.org/10.1177/0002764204270283

Gephart, R. P., Topal, C., & Zhang, Z. (2010). Future-oriented sensemaking: Temporalities and institutional legitimation. In T. Hernes & S. Maitlis (Eds.), *Process, sensemaking, and organizing* (pp. 275–312). Oxford: Oxford University Press.

Gilliland, S. W., & Day, D. V. (1999). Business management. In F. T. Durso (Ed.), *Handbook of applied cognition* (pp. 315–342). Chichester, U.K.: Wiley.

Gioia, D. A. (1986). Symbols, scripts, and sensemaking: Creating meaning in the organizational experience. In H. P. Sims & D. A. Gioia (Eds.), *The thinking organization* (pp. 49–74). San Francisco: Jossey-Bass.

Gioia, D. A. (2006). On Weick: An appreciation. *Organization Studies, 27*(11), 1709–1721. https://dx.doi.org/10.1177/0170840606068349

Gioia, D. A., & Chittipeddi, K. (1991). Sensemaking and sensegiving in strategic change initiation. *Strategic Management Journal, 12*(6), 433–448. https://dx.doi.org/10.1002/smj.4250120604

Gioia, D. A., Corley, K. G., & Fabbri, T. (2002). Revising the past (while thinking in the future perfect tense). *Journal of Organizational Change Management, 15*(6), 622–634. https://dx.doi.org/10.1108/09534810210449532

Gioia, D. A., & Mehra, A. (1996). Book review: Sensemaking in organizations. *Academy of Management Review, 21*(4), 1226–1230. https://dx.doi.org/10.2307/259169

Gioia, D. A., Thomas, J. B., Clark, S. M., & Chittipeddi, K. (1994). Symbolism and strategic change in academia: The dynamics of sensemaking and influence. *Organization Science, 5*(3), 363–383.

Griffith, T. L. (1999). Technology features as triggers for sensemaking. *Academy of Management Review, 24*(3), 472–488. https://dx.doi.org/10.5465/AMR.1999.2202132

Guiette, A., & Vandenbempt, K. (2016). Learning in times of dynamic complexity through balancing phenomenal qualities of sensemaking. *Management Learning, 47*(1), 83–99. https://dx.doi.org/10.1177/1350507615592112

Hannan, M. T., & Freeman, J. (1977). The population ecology of organizations. *American Journal of Sociology, 82*(5), 929–964. https://dx.doi.org/10.1086/226424

Hargadon, A. B., & Bechky, B. A. (2006). When collections of creatives become creative collectives: A field study of problem solving at work. *Organization Science, 17*(4), 484–500. https://dx.doi.org/10.1287/orsc.1060.0200

Harquail, C. V., & King, A. W. (2010). Construing organizational identity: The role of embodied cognition. *Organization Studies, 31*(12), 1619–1648. https://dx.doi.org/10.1177/0170840610376143

Helms Mills, J., Thurlow, A., & Mills, A. J. (2010). Making sense of sensemaking: The critical sensemaking approach. *Qualitative Research in Organizations and Management: An International Journal, 5*(2), 182–195. https://dx.doi.org/10.1108/17465641011068857

Heritage, J. (1984). *Garfinkel and ethnomethodology.* Cambridge, U.K.: Polity.

Herrmann, A. F. (2007). Stockholders in cyberspace: Weick's sensemaking online. *Journal of Business Communication, 44*(1), 13–35. https://dx.doi.org/10.1177/0021943606295778

Hill, R. C., & Levenhagen, M. (1995). Metaphors and mental models: Sensemaking and sensegiving in innovative and entrepreneurial activities. *Journal of Management, 21*(6), 1057–1074. https://dx.doi.org/10.1177/014920639502100603

Holt, R., & Cornelissen, J. P. (2014). Sensemaking revisited. *Management Learning, 45*(5), 525–539. https://dx.doi.org/10.1177/1350507613486422

Ibarra, H., & Andrews, S. B. (1993). Power, social influence, and sense making: Effects of network centrality and proximity on employee perceptions. *Administrative Science Quarterly, 38*(2), 277. https://dx.doi.org/10.2307/2393414

Jennings, P. D., & Greenwood, R. (2003). Constructing the iron cage: Institutional theory and enactment. In R. Westwood & S. Clegg (Eds.), *Debating organization: Point-counterpoint in organization studies* (pp. 195–207). Malden, MA: Wiley-Blackwell.

Jensen, T. B., Kjærgaard, A., & Svejvig, P. (2009). Using institutional theory with sensemaking theory: A case study of information system implementation in healthcare. *Journal of Information Technology, 24*(4), 343–353. https://dx.doi.org/10.1057/jit.2009.11

Jeong, H.-S., & Brower, R. S. (2008). Extending the present understanding of organizational sensemaking: Three stages and three contexts. *Administration & Society, 40*(3), 223–252. https://dx.doi.org/10.1177/0095399707313446

Jordan, M. E., & Daniel, S. R. (2010). Heedful interrelating in the academic discourse of collaborative groups. *The Journal of Classroom Interaction, 45*(2), 4–19.

Kahneman, D. (2003). A perspective on judgment and choice: Mapping bounded rationality. *American Psychologist, 58*(9), 697–720. https://dx.doi.org/10.1037/0003-066X.58.9.697

Kaplan, S. (2011). Research in cognition and strategy: Reflections on two decades of progress and a look to the future. *Journal of Management Studies, 48*(3), 665–695. https://dx.doi.org/10.1111/j.1467-6486.2010.00983.x

Kiesler, S., & Sproull, L. (1982). Managerial response to changing environments: Perspectives on problem sensing from social cognition. *Administrative Science Quarterly, 27*(4), 548–570. https://dx.doi.org/10.2307/2392530

Klein, G., Moon, B., & Hoffman, R. R. (2006a). Making sense of sensemaking 1: Alternative perspectives. *IEEE Intelligent Systems, 21*(4), 70–73. https://dx.doi.org/10.1109/MIS.2006.75

Klein, G., Moon, B., & Hoffman, R. R. (2006b). Making sense of sensemaking 2: A macrocognitive model. *IEEE Intelligent Systems, 21*(5), 88–92. https://dx.doi.org/10.1109/MIS.2006.100

Klein, G., Phillips, J. K., Rall, E. L., & Peluso, D. A. (2007). A data-frame theory of sensemaking. In R. Hoffman (Ed.), *Expertise out of context* (pp. 113–155). New York: Lawrence Erlbaum Associates.

Klein, G., Wiggins, S., & Dominguez, C. O. (2010). Team sensemaking. *Theoretical Issues in Ergonomics Science, 11*(4), 304–320. https://dx.doi.org/10.1080/14639221003729177

Kudesia, R. S., & Nyima, V. T. (2015). Mindfulness contextualized: An integration of Buddhist and neuropsychological approaches to cognition. *Mindfulness, 6*(4), 910–925. https://dx.doi.org/10.1007/s12671-014-0337-8

Langley, A. (2007). Process thinking in strategic organization. *Strategic Organization, 5*(3), 271–282. https://dx.doi.org/10.1177/1476127007079965

Lant, T. K., & Shapira, Z. (2000). *Organizational cognition: Computation and interpretation.* Mahwah, NJ: Lawrence Erlbaum Associates.

Levinthal, D. A., & Rerup, C. (2006). Crossing an apparent chasm: Bridging mindful and less-mindful perspectives on organizational learning. *Organization Science, 17*(4), 502–513. https://dx.doi.org/10.1287/orsc.1060.0197

Lockett, A., Currie, G., Finn, R., Martin, G., & Waring, J. (2014). The influence of social position on sensemaking about organizational change. *Academy of Management Journal, 57*(4), 1102–1129. https://dx.doi.org/10.5465/amj.2011.0055

Louis, M. R. (1980). Surprise and sense making: What newcomers experience in entering unfamiliar organizational settings. *Administrative Science Quarterly, 25*(2), 226. https://dx.doi.org/10.2307/2392453

Luce, R. D., & Raiffa, H. (1957). *Games and decisions: Introduction and critical survey.* New York: Wiley.

Lüscher, L. S., & Lewis, M. W. (2008). Organizational change and managerial sensemaking: Working through paradox. *Academy of Management Journal, 51*(2), 221–240. https://dx.doi.org/10.5465/AMJ.2008.31767217

MacKay, R. B. (2009). Strategic foresight: Counterfactual and prospective sensemaking in enacted environments. In L. Costanzo & R. MacKay (Eds.), *Handbook of research on strategy and foresight* (pp. 90–112). Northampton, MA: Edward Elgar.

MacKenzie, D., & Millo, Y. (2003). Negotiating a market, performing theory: The historical sociology of a financial derivatives exchange. *American Journal of Sociology, 109*, 107–145. https://dx.doi.org/10.1086/374404

Maclean, M., Harvey, C., & Chia, R. (2012). Sensemaking, storytelling and the legitimization of elite business careers. *Human Relations, 65*(1), 17–40. https://dx.doi.org/10.1177/0018726711425616

Maguire, E. R., & Katz, C. M. (2002). Community policing, loose coupling, and sensemaking in American police agencies. *Justice Quarterly, 19*(3), 503–536. https://dx.doi.org/10.1080/07418820200095331

Maitlis, S. (2005). The social processes of organizational sensemaking. *Academy of Management Journal, 48*(1), 21–49. https://dx.doi.org/10.5465/AMJ.2005.15993111

Maitlis, S., & Christianson, M. (2014). Sensemaking in organizations: Taking stock and moving forward. *Academy of Management Annals, 8*(1), 57–125. https://dx.doi.org/10.1080/19416520.2014.873177

Maitlis, S., & Lawrence, T. B. (2007). Triggers and enablers of sensegiving in organizations. *Academy of Management Journal, 50*(1), 57–84. https://dx.doi.org/10.5465/AMJ.2007.24160971

Maitlis, S., & Sonenshein, S. (2010). Sensemaking in crisis and change: Inspiration and insights from Weick (1988). *Journal of Management Studies, 47*(3), 551–580. https://dx.doi.org/10.1111/j.1467-6486.2010.00908.x

Malsch, B., Tremblay, M.-S., & Gendron, Y. (2012). Sense-making in compensation committees: A cultural theory perspective. *Organization Studies, 33*(3), 389–421. https://dx.doi.org/10.1177/0170840611433993

Manning, P. K. (1997). Organizations as sense-making contexts. *Theory, Culture & Society, 14*(2), 139–150. https://dx.doi.org/10.1177/026327697014002012

Michel, A. A. (2007). A distributed cognition perspective on newcomers' change processes: The management of cognitive uncertainty in two investment banks. *Administrative Science Quarterly, 52*(4), 507–557. https://dx.doi.org/10.2189/asqu.52.4.507

Milliken, F. J. (1987). Three types of perceived uncertainty about the environment: State, effect, and response uncertainty. *Academy of Management Review, 12*(1), 133–143. https://dx.doi.org/10.5465/AMR.1987.4306502

Milliken, F. J. (1990). Perceiving and interpreting environmental change: An examination of college administrators' interpretation of changing demographics. *Academy of Management Journal, 33*(1), 42–63. https://dx.doi.org/10.2307/256351

Mills, C. (2002). The hidden dimension of blue-collar sensemaking about workplace communication. *Journal of Business Communication, 39*(3), 288–313. https://dx.doi.org/10.1177/002194360203900301

Miner, J. B. (2005). Organizing and sensemaking. In *Organizational behavior 2: Essential theories of process and structure* (pp. 90–108). Armonk, NY: M. E. Sharpe.

Morgan, G., Frost, P. J., & Pondy, L. R. (1983). Organizational symbolism. In L. R. Pondy, P. J. Frost, G. Morgan, & T. C. Dandridge (Eds.), *Organizational symbolism* (pp. 3–35). Greenwich, CT: JAI Press.

Mumby, D. K. (1987). The political function of narrative in organizations. *Communications Monographs, 54*(2), 113–127. https://dx.doi.org/10.1080/03637758709390221

Myers, P. (2007). Sexed up intelligence or irresponsible reporting? The interplay of virtual communication and emotion in dispute sensemaking. *Human Relations, 60*(4), 609–636. https://dx.doi.org/10.1177/0018726707078352

Nathan, M. L. (2004). How past becomes prologue: A sensemaking interpretation of the hindsight-foresight relationship given the circumstances of crisis. *Futures, 36*(2), 181–199. https://dx.doi.org/10.1016/S0016-3287(03)00149-6

Nigam, A., & Ocasio, W. (2010). Event attention, environmental sensemaking, and change in institutional logics: An inductive analysis of the effects of public attention to Clinton's health care reform initiative. *Organization Science, 21*(4), 823–841. https://dx.doi.org/10.1287/orsc.1090.0490

Nowak, A., & Vallacher, R. R. (2007). Dynamical social psychology: Finding order in the flow of human experience. In A. W. Kruglanski & E. T. Higgins (Eds.), *Social psychology: Handbook of basic principles* (2d ed., pp. 734–758). New York: Guilford.

Ocasio, W. (2000). How do organizations think? In T. K. Lant & Z. Shapira (Eds.), *Organizational cognition: Computation and interpretation* (pp. 39–60). Mahwah, NJ: Lawrence Erlbaum Associates.

Ocasio, W., Loewenstein, J., & Nigam, A. (2015). How streams of communication reproduce and change institutional logics: The role of categories. *Academy of Management Review, 40*(1), 28–48. https://dx.doi.org/10.5465/amr.2013.0274

O'Leary, M., & Chia, R. (2007). Epistemes and structures of sensemaking in organizational life. *Journal of Management Inquiry, 16*(4), 392–406. https://dx.doi.org/10.1177/1056492607310976

Osborne, J. D., Stubbart, C. I., & Ramaprasad, A. (2001). Strategic groups and competitive enactment: A study of dynamic relationships between mental models and performance. *Strategic Management Journal, 22*(5), 435–454. https://dx.doi.org/10.1002/smj.166

Parry, J. (2003). Making sense of executive sensemaking: A phenomenological case study with methodological criticism. *Journal of Health Organization and Management, 17*(4), 240–263. https://dx.doi.org/10.1108/14777260310494771

Patriotta, G., & Brown, A. D. (2011). Sensemaking, metaphors and performance evaluation. *Scandinavian Journal of Management, 27*(1), 34–43. https://dx.doi.org/10.1016/j.scaman.2010.12.002

Peters, T. J., & Waterman, R. H. (1982). *In search of excellence: Lessons from America's best-run companies.* New York: Harper & Row.

Pfeffer, J., & Salancik, G. R. (1978). *The external control of organizations: A resource dependence perspective.* New York: Harper & Row.

Porac, J. F., Thomas, H., & Baden-Fuller, C. (1989). Competitive groups as cognitive communities: The case of Scottish knitwear manufacturers. *Journal of Management Studies, 26*(4), 397–416. https://dx.doi.org/10.1111/j.1467-6486.1989.tb00736.x

Porac, J. F., Ventresca, M. J., & Mishina, Y. (2005). Interorganizational cognition and interpretation. In J. A. C. Baum (Ed.), *The Blackwell companion to organizations* (pp. 579–598). Oxford: Blackwell.

Powell, T. C., Lovallo, D., & Fox, C. R. (2011). Behavioral strategy. *Strategic Management Journal, 32*(13), 1369–1386. https://dx.doi.org/10.1002/smj.968

Pratt, M. G. (2000a). Building an ideological fortress: The role of spirituality, encapsulation and sensemaking. *Studies in Cultures, Organizations and Societies, 6*(1), 35–69. https://dx.doi.org/10.1080/10245280008523537

Pratt, M. G. (2000b). The good, the bad, and the ambivalent: Managing identification among Amway distributors. *Administrative Science Quarterly, 45*(3), 456–493. https://dx.doi.org/10.2307/2667106

Quinn, R. W., & Worline, M. C. (2008). Enabling courageous collective action: Conversations from United Airlines Flight 93. *Organization Science, 19*(4), 497–516. https://dx.doi.org/10.1287/orsc.1070.0331

Raiffa, H. (1982). *The art and science of negotiation.* Cambridge, MA: Belknap.

Ray, J. L., Baker, L. T., & Plowman, D. A. (2011). Organizational mindfulness in business schools. *Academy of Management Learning & Education, 10*(2), 188–203. https://dx.doi.org/10.5465/AMLE.2011.62798929

Reb, J., & Atkins, P. W. B. (2015). *Mindfulness in organizations: Foundations, research, and applications.* Cambridge, U.K.: Cambridge University Press.

Rerup, C., & Levinthal, D. A. (2013). Situating the concept of organizational mindfulness: The multiple dimensions of organizational learning. In G. Becke (Ed.), *Mindful change in times of permanent reorganization: Organizational, institutional and sustainability perspectives* (pp. 33–48). New York: Springer.

Ricœur, P. (1984). *Time and narrative* (3 vols.). (K. McLaughlin & D. Pellauer, Trans.). Chicago: University of Chicago Press.

Rouleau, L., & Balogun, J. (2011). Middle managers, strategic sensemaking, and discursive competence. *Journal of Management Studies, 48*(5), 953–983. https://dx.doi.org/10.1111/j.1467-6486.2010.00941.x

Rudolph, J. W., Morrison, J. B., & Carroll, J. S. (2009). The dynamics of action-oriented problem solving: Linking interpretation and choice. *Academy of Management Review, 34*(4), 733–756. https://dx.doi.org/10.5465/AMR.2009.44886170

Rudolph, J. W., & Repenning, N. P. (2002). Disaster dynamics: Understanding the role of quantity in organizational collapse. *Administrative Science Quarterly, 47*(1), 1–30. https://dx.doi.org/10.2307/3094889

Salancik, G. R. (1977). Commitment and the control of organizational behavior and belief. In B. M. Staw & G. R. Salancik (Eds.), *New directions in organizational behavior* (pp. 2–54). Chicago: St. Clair.

Sandberg, J., & Tsoukas, H. (2015). Making sense of the sensemaking perspective: Its constituents, limitations, and opportunities for further development. *Journal of Organizational Behavior, 36*(S1), S6–S32. https://dx.doi.org/10.1002/job.1937

Sandelands, L. E., & Stablein, R. E. (1987). The concept of organizational mind. In N. DiTomaso & S. Bachrach (Eds.), *Research in the sociology of organizations* (Vol. 5, pp. 135–161). Greenwich, CT: JAI Press.

Schall, M. S. (1983). A communication-rules approach to organizational culture. *Administrative Science Quarterly, 28*(4), 557–581. https://dx.doi.org/10.2307/2393009

Schutz, A. (1967). *The phenomenology of the social world.* Evanston, IL: Northwestern University Press.

Smircich, L., & Stubbart, C. (1985). Strategic management in an enacted world. *Academy of Management Review, 10*(4), 724–736. https://dx.doi.org/10.5465/AMR.1985.4279096

Smith, G. F. (1988). Towards a heuristic theory of problem structuring. *Management Science, 34*(12), 1489–1506. https://dx.doi.org/10.1287/mnsc.34.12.1489

Snook, S. (2000). *Friendly fire: The accidental shootdown of US Black Hawks over Northern Iraq.* Princeton, NJ: Princeton University Press.

Sonenshein, S. (2007). The role of construction, intuition, and justification in responding to ethical issues at work: The sensemaking-intuition model. *Academy of Management Review, 32*(4), 1022–1040. https://dx.doi.org/10.5465/AMR.2007.26585677

Sonenshein, S. (2009). Emergence of ethical issues during strategic change implementation. *Organization Science, 20*(1), 223–239. https://dx.doi.org/10.1287/orsc.1080.0364

Sonenshein, S. (2010). We're changing—or are we? Untangling the role of progressive, regressive, and stability narratives during strategic change implementation. *Academy of Management Journal, 53*(3), 477–512. https://dx.doi.org/10.5465/AMJ.2010.51467638

Starbuck, W. H., & Milliken, F. J. (1988). Executives' perceptual filters: What they notice and how they make sense. *The Executive Effect: Concepts and Methods for Studying Top Managers, 35,* 65.

Stephens, J. P., & Lyddy, C. J. (2016). Operationalizing heedful interrelating: How attending, responding, and feeling comprise coordinating and predict performance in self-managing teams. *Frontiers in Psychology, 7*(362), 1–17. https://dx.doi.org/10.3389/fpsyg.2016.00362

Stigliani, I., & Ravasi, D. (2012). Organizing thoughts and connecting brains: Material practices and the transition from individual to group-level prospective sensemaking. *Academy of Management Journal*, 55(5), 1232–1259. https://dx.doi.org/10.5465/amj.2010.0890

Strike, V., & Rerup, C. (2015). Mediated sensemaking. *Academy of Management Journal*, 59(3), 880–905. https://dx.doi.org/10.5465/amj.2012.0665

Sutcliffe, K. M. (2001). Organizational environments and organizational information processing. In F. M. Jablin & L. L. Putnam (Eds.), *The new handbook of organizational communication: Advances in theory, research, and methods* (pp. 197–230). Thousand Oaks, CA: SAGE.

Sutcliffe, K. M. (2014). Sensemaking. In M. Augier & D. J. Teece (Eds.), *The Palgrave encyclopedia of strategic management* (pp. 1–4). Basingstoke: Palgrave Macmillan. Retrieved from http://link.springer.com/referenceworkentry/10.1057/978-1-349-94848-2_371-1.

Sutcliffe, K. M., Vogus, T. J., & Dane, E. (2016). Mindfulness in organizations. *Annual Review of Organizational Psychology and Organizational Behavior*, 3(1), 55–81. https://dx.doi.org/10.1146/annurev-orgpsych-041015-062531

Sutton, R. I., & Hargadon, A. (1996). Brainstorming groups in context: Effectiveness in a product design firm. *Administrative Science Quarterly*, 41(4), 685–718. https://dx.doi.org/10.2307/2393872

Swanson, E. B., & Ramiller, N. C. (2004). Innovating mindfully with information technology. *MIS Quarterly*, 28(4), 553–583.

Taylor, J. R., & Robichaud, D. (2004). Finding the organization in the communication: Discourse as action and sensemaking. *Organization*, 11(3), 395–413. https://dx.doi.org/10.1177/1350508404041999

Taylor, J. R., & Van Every, E. J. (2000). *The emergent organization: Communication as its site and surface.* Mahwah, NJ: Lawrence Erlbaum Associates.

Thiel, C. E., Bagdasarov, Z., Harkrider, L., Johnson, J. F., & Mumford, M. D. (2012). Leader ethical decision-making in organizations: Strategies for sensemaking. *Journal of Business Ethics*, 107(1), 49–64. https://dx.doi.org/10.1007/s10551-012-1299-1

Thomas, J. B., Clark, S. M., & Gioia, D. A. (1993). Strategic sensemaking and organizational performance: Linkages among scanning, interpretation, action, and outcomes. *Academy of Management Journal*, 36(2), 239–270. https://dx.doi.org/10.2307/256522

Thompson, J. D. (1967). *Organizations in action: Social science bases of administrative theory.* New York: McGraw-Hill.

Tsoukas, H., & Chia, R. (2002). On organizational becoming: Rethinking organizational change. *Organization Science*, 13(5), 567–582. https://dx.doi.org/10.1287/orsc.13.5.567.7810

Vaara, E., Sonenshein, S., & Boje, D. M. (2016). Narratives as sources of stability and change in organizations: Approaches and directions for future research. *Academy of Management Annals*, 10(1), 495–560. https://dx.doi.org/10.1080/19416520.2016.1120963

Van Maanen, J. (1991). The smile factory: Work at Disneyland. In P. J. Frost (Ed.), *Reframing organizational culture* (pp. 59–76). Newbury Park, CA: SAGE.

Vaughan, D. (1996). *The Challenger launch decision: Risky technology, culture, and deviance at NASA.* Chicago: University of Chicago Press.

Vlaar, P. W. L., Van den Bosch, F. A. J., & Volberda, H. W. (2006). Coping with problems of understanding in interorganizational relationships: Using formalization as a means to make sense. *Organization Studies*, 27(11), 1617–1638. https://dx.doi.org/10.1177/0170840606068338

Vogus, T. J., & Sutcliffe, K. M. (2012). Organizational mindfulness and mindful organizing: A reconciliation and path forward. *Academy of Management Learning & Education*, 11(4), 722–735. https://dx.doi.org/10.5465/amle.2011.0002C

Vogus, T. J., & Welbourne, T. M. (2003). Structuring for high reliability: HR practices and mindful processes in reliability-seeking organizations. *Journal of Organizational Behavior*, 24(7), 877–903. https://dx.doi.org/10.1002/job.221

Von Neumann, J., & Morgenstern, O. (1947). *Theory of games and economic behavior*. Princeton, NJ: Princeton University Press.

Walsh, I. J., & Bartunek, J. M. (2011). Cheating the fates: Organizational foundings in the wake of demise. *Academy of Management Journal, 54*(5), 1017–1044. https://dx.doi.org/10.5465/amj.2008.0658

Walsh, J. P. (1995). Managerial and organizational cognition: Notes from a trip down memory lane. *Organization Science, 6*(3), 280–321. https://dx.doi.org/10.1287/orsc.6.3.280

Walsh, J. P., & Ungson, G. R. (1991). Organizational memory. *Academy of Management Review, 16*(1), 57–91. https://dx.doi.org/10.2307/258607

Weber, K., & Glynn, M. A. (2006). Making sense with institutions: Context, thought and action in Karl Weick's theory. *Organization Studies, 27*(11), 1639–1660. https://dx.doi.org/10.1177/0170840606068343

Weber, P. S., & Manning, M. R. (2001). Cause maps, sensemaking, and planned organizational change. *Journal of Applied Behavioral Science, 37*(2), 227–251. https://dx.doi.org/10.1177/0021886301372006

Weick, K. E. (1969). *The social psychology of organizing*. Reading, MA: Addison-Wesley.

Weick, K. E. (1979). *The social psychology of organizing* (2d ed.). Reading, MA: Addison-Wesley.

Weick, K. E. (1988). Enacted sensemaking in crisis situations. *Journal of Management Studies, 25*(4), 305–317. https://dx.doi.org/10.1111/j.1467-6486.1988.tb00039.x

Weick, K. E. (1993a). Sensemaking in organizations: Small structures with large consequences. In J. K. Murnighan (Ed.), *Social psychology in organizations: Advances in theory and research* (pp. 10–37). Englewood Cliffs, NJ: Prentice-Hall.

Weick, K. E. (1993b). The collapse of sensemaking in organizations: The Mann Gulch disaster. *Administrative Science Quarterly, 38*(4), 628–652. https://dx.doi.org/10.2307/2393339

Weick, K. E. (1993c). Turning context into text: An academic life as data. In A. G. Bedeian (Ed.), *Management laureates: A collection of autobiographical essays* (pp. 285–323). Greenwich, CT: JAI Press.

Weick, K. E. (1995). *Sensemaking in organizations*. Thousand Oaks, CA: SAGE.

Weick, K. E. (2003). Enacting an environment: The infrastructure of organizing. In R. Westwood & S. Clegg (Eds.), *Debating organization: Point-counterpoint in organization studies* (pp. 184–194). Malden, MA: Wiley-Blackwell.

Weick, K. E. (2007). The experience of theorizing: Sensemaking as topic and resource. In K. G. Smith & M. A. Hitt (Eds.), *Great minds in management: The process of theory development* (pp. 394–406). Oxford: Oxford University Press.

Weick, K. E., & Daft, R. L. (1983). The effectiveness of organizational interpretation systems. In K. S. Cameron & D. A. Whetten (Eds.), *Organizational effectiveness: A comparison of multiple models* (pp. 71–93). New York: Academic Press.

Weick, K. E., & Putnam, T. (2006). Organizing for mindfulness: Eastern wisdom and Western knowledge. *Journal of Management Inquiry, 15*(3), 275–287. https://dx.doi.org/10.1177/1056492606291202

Weick, K. E., & Roberts, K. H. (1993). Collective mind in organizations: Heedful interrelating on flight decks. *Administrative Science Quarterly, 38*(3), 357–381. https://dx.doi.org/10.2307/2393372

Weick, K. E., & Sutcliffe, K. M. (2003). Hospitals as cultures of entrapment: A re-analysis of the Bristol Royal Infirmary. *California Management Review, 45*(2), 73–84. https://dx.doi.org/10.2307/41166166

Weick, K. E., & Sutcliffe, K. M. (2006). Mindfulness and the quality of organizational attention. *Organization Science, 17*(4), 514–524. https://dx.doi.org/10.1287/orsc.1060.0196

Weick, K. E., & Sutcliffe, K. M. (2015). *Managing the unexpected: Sustained performance in a complex world* (3d ed.). Hoboken, NJ: John Wiley.

Weick, K. E., Sutcliffe, K. M., & Obstfeld, D. (1999). Organizing for high reliability: Processes of collective mindfulness. In R. I. Sutton & B. M. Staw (Eds.), *Research in organizational behavior* (Vol. 21, pp. 81–123). Stanford, CA: JAI Press.

Weick, K. E., Sutcliffe, K. M., & Obstfeld, D. (2005). Organizing and the process of sensemaking. *Organization Science, 16*(4), 409–421.

Weiss, H. M., & Ilgen, D. R. (1986). Routinized behavior in organizations. *Journal of Behavioral Economics, 14*(1), 57–67. https://dx.doi.org/10.1016/0090-5720(85)90005-1

Westley, F. R. (1990). Middle managers and strategy: Microdynamics of inclusion. *Strategic Management Journal, 11*(5), 337–351. https://dx.doi.org/10.1002/smj.4250110502

Westrum, R. (1982). Social intelligence about hidden events: Its significance for scientific research and social policy. *Science Communication, 3*(3), 381–400. https://dx.doi.org/10.1177/107554708200300306

Westwood, R. I., & Linstead, S. (2001). *The language of organization.* London: SAGE.

Whetten, D. A. (1989). What constitutes a theoretical contribution? *Academy of Management Review, 14*(4), 490–495. https://dx.doi.org/10.5465/AMR.1989.4308371

Whiteman, G., & Cooper, W. H. (2011). Ecological sensemaking. *Academy of Management Journal, 54*(5), 889–911. https://dx./doi.org/10.5465/amj.2008.0843

Wiley, N. (1988). The micro-macro problem in social theory. *Sociological Theory, 6*(2), 254. https://dx.doi.org/10.2307/202119

Williamson, O. E. (1975). *Markets and hierarchies, analysis and antitrust implications: A study in the economics of internal organization.* New York: Free Press.

Winch, G. M., & Maytorena, E. (2009). Making good sense: Assessing the quality of risky decision-making. *Organization Studies, 30*(2–3), 181–203. https://dx.doi.org/10.1177/0170840608101476

Wright, A. (2005). The role of scenarios as prospective sensemaking devices. *Management Decision, 43*(1), 86–101. https://dx.doi.org/10.1108/00251740510572506

Wright, C. R., & Manning, M. R. (2004). Resourceful sensemaking in an administrative group. *Journal of Management Studies, 41*(4), 623–643. https://dx.doi.org/10.1111/j.1467-6486.2004.00447.x

Wright, C. R., Manning, M. R., Farmer, B., & Gilbreath, B. (2000). Resourceful sensemaking in product development teams. *Organization Studies, 21*(4), 807–825. https://dx.doi.org/10.1177/0170840600214006

Yanow, D., & Tsoukas, H. (2009). What is reflection-in-action? A phenomenological account. *Journal of Management Studies, 46*(8), 1339–1364. https://dx.doi.org/10.1111/j.1467-6486.2009.00859.x

Ravi S. Kudesia

CONFLICT MANAGEMENT

DEFINITION OF CONFLICT

Conflicts are part of nature, and certainly part of human relations. People experience conflict with other persons, in teams or in groups, as well as between larger entities, departments, organizations, communities, and countries. Conflicts appear at home, at work, and in our spare-time activities with friends, with people we love and with people we hate, as well as with our superiors and with our subordinates and coworkers. Parties need to accept conflicts as part of life dynamics and learn to deal with them effectively and efficiently. Conflict management refers to the way we manage incompatible actions with others, where *others* can be a person or a group.

Conflict is a component of interpersonal interactions; it is neither inevitable nor intrinsically bad, but it is commonplace (Coleman, Deutsch, & Marcus, 2014; Schellenberg, 1996). In the 20th century, Lewin (1935) concluded that an intrinsic state of tension motivates group members to move toward the accomplishment of their desired common goals. Later on, Parker Follett (1941) explored the constructive side of conflict and defined conflict as the appearance of difference, difference of opinions, or difference of interests. Deutsch (1949) developed this line of thought and analyzed the relation between the way group members believe their goals are related and their interactions and relationships.

A common definition of conflict argues that there is a conflict between two (or more) parties (individuals or groups) if at least one of them is offended, or feels bothered by the other (Van de Vliert, 1997; Wall & Callister, 1995). Traditionally, conflict has been defined as opposing interests involving scarce resources and goal divergence and frustration (Pondy, 1967). However, Deutsch (1973) defined conflict as incompatible activities: one person's actions interfere, obstruct, or in some way get in the way of another's action. Tjosvold, Wan, and Tang (2016) proposed that defining conflict as incompatible actions is a much stronger foundation than defining conflict as opposing interests, because conflicts also can occur when people have common goals (i.e., they may disagree about the best means to achieve their common goals). The key contribution of Deutsch's (1973) proposal is that incompatible activities occur in both compatible and incompatible goal contexts. Whether the protagonists believe their goals are cooperative or competitive very much affects their expectations, interaction, and outcomes as they approach conflict (Tjosvold et al., 2016).

Characteristics of Conflict. Euwema and Giebels (2017) highlighted some key elements of conflict.

1. Conflict implies dependence and interdependence. Parties rely to some extent on the other parties to realize their goals (Kaufman, Elgoibar, & Borbely, 2016). This interdependence can be positive (a cooperative context), negative (a competitive context), or mixed. Positive interdependence is strongly related to cooperative conflict behaviors, while negative interdependence triggers competitive behaviors (Johnson & Johnson, 2005). Interdependence also reflects the power difference between parties. A short-term contractor on a low-paid job usually is much more dependent on the employer than vice versa. Many conflicts, however, can be seen as "mixed motive" situations.

2. Conflicts are mostly mixed motive situations because parties have simultaneous motives to cooperate and motives to compete. Parties are, on the one hand, dependent on each other to realize their goal, and, on the other hand, they are at the same time competitors. For example, two colleagues on a team are cooperating for the same team result; however, there is competition for the role as project leader. In a soccer team, the players have a team goal of working together to win, but they can be competing to be the top scorer. The mixed motive structure is very important to understand conflict dynamics. When conflicts arise, the competitive aspects become more salient, and the cooperative structure often is perceived less by parties. Interventions to solve conflict, therefore, are often related to these perceptions and the underlying structures.

3. Conflict is a psychological experience. Conflict is by definition a personal and subjective experience, as each individual can perceive and manage the same conflict in a different manner. Conflict doesn't necessarily have an objective basis (Van de Vliert, 1997). It depends on the perception of the specific situation, and the perception is by definition subjective and personal.

4. Conflict concerns cognitive and affective tension. When someone perceives blocked goals and disagreements, he or she can also, although not necessarily, feel fear or anger.

Many authors consider that conflict is emotionally charged (Nair, 2007; Pondy, 1967; Sinaceur, Adam, Van Kleef, & Galinky, 2013), although the emotion doesn't need to be labeled necessarily as a negative emotion. Some people actually enjoy conflict. Emotional experiences in conflict are also scripted by cultural, historical, and personal influences (Lindner, 2014).

5. Conflict can be unidirectional. One party can feel frustrated or thwarted by the other while the second party is hardly aware of, and doesn't perceive the same reality of, the conflict.
6. Conflict is a process. Conflict is a dynamic process that does not appear suddenly, but takes some time to develop and passes through several stages (Spaho, 2013). Conflict is the process resulting from the tension in interpersonal interactions or between team members because of real or perceived differences (De Dreu & Weingart, 2003; Thomas, 1992; Wall & Callister, 1995).

Type of Conflict: Task, Process, and Relationship Conflict. Early conflict and organizational research concluded that conflict interferes with team performance and reduces satisfaction due to an increase in tension and distraction from the objective (Brown, 1983; Hackman & Morris, 1975; Pondy, 1967; Wall & Callister, 1995). Jehn (1995) differentiated between task and relational conflict, and later also included process conflict (De Wit, Greer, & Jehn, 2012). Task conflict refers to different opinions on content (Jehn & Mannix, 2001). Examples of task conflict are conflict about distribution of resources, about procedures and policies, and judgment and interpretation of facts (De Dreu & Weingart, 2003). Process conflict refers to how tasks should be accomplished (Jehn, Greer, Levine, & Szulanski, 2008). Examples are disagreements about logistic and delegation issues (Jehn et al., 2008). Finally, relationship conflict refers to "interpersonal incompatibility" (Jehn, 1995, p. 257). Examples of relationship conflict are conflict about personal taste, political preferences, values, and interpersonal style (De Dreu & Weingart, 2003). All three types of conflict—task, process, and personal (relational) conflicts—are usually disruptive, especially personal conflict, which is highly disruptive (De Dreu & Weingart, 2003; Jehn, 1995, 1997). A review and meta-analysis by De Wit et al. (2012) showed that, under specific conditions, task conflict can be productive for teams. Moreover, conflict can wreck a team's efforts to share information and reach a consensus (Amason & Schweiger, 1994). Therefore, research supporting the benefit of task and relationship conflict is not conclusive and each situation varies. What seems to be clear is that managing conflict efficiently to avoid escalation is a priority for teams.

CONFLICT BEHAVIOR, CONFLICT MANAGEMENT, AND CONFLICT RESOLUTION

Conflict behavior, conflict management, and conflict resolution are different layers of a conflict process and therefore should be distinguished. Conflict behavior is any behavioral response to the experience of frustration, while conflict management is the deliberate action to deal with conflictive situations, both to prevent or to escalate them. Also, conflict management is differentiated from conflict resolution, which is specific action aimed to end a conflict.

Conflict Behavior. Conflict behavior is the behavioral response to the experience of conflict (Van de Vliert et al., 1995). Conflict behavior is defined as one party's reaction to the perception that one's own and the other party's current aspiration cannot be achieved simultaneously (Deutsch, 1973; Pruitt, 1981; Rubin, Pruitt, & Kim, 1994). It is both what people experiencing conflict intend to do, as well as what they actually do (De Dreu, Evers, Beersma, Kluwer, & Nauta, 2001; Van de Vliert, 1997). In conflict situations people often respond primarily, following their emotions, more or less conscientiously.

Many factors affect how people respond to the experience of conflict. Social psychology shows the processes are largely unconscious (Wilson, 2004). For example, how people respond to intimidating behavior by their supervisor might be primarily influenced by the context and individual perception, as well as previous relations with persons in authority, including parents and teachers (Gelfand & Brett, 2004; Van Kleef & Cote, 2007). These natural behavioral responses are also referred to as "conflict styles." They are rooted in our personality and can differ in context. Some people will naturally respond by being friendly and accommodating, where others will start arguing or fighting (Barbuto, Phipps, & Xu, 2010; Kilmann & Thomas, 1977; Van Kleef & Cote, 2007).

Conflict behavior becomes more effective once we are more aware of our natural tendencies and are also able not to act upon them, and instead to show flexibility in behavioral approaches. This is where conflict behavior becomes conflict management. Therefore, one can be a naturally highly accommodating person who will spontaneously give in to others who make demands, but one will be more effective after learning to assess the situation at hand and to carefully decide on a response, which might be quite different from the natural or spontaneous reaction.

Dual-Concern Model. The dual-concern model holds that the way in which parties handle conflicts can de described and is determined by two concerns: concern for self (own interests) and concern for others (relational interests) (Blake & Mouton, 1964; Pruitt & Rubin, 1986; Rahim, 1983; Thomas, 1992; Van de Vliert, 1999) (see Figure 1). Usually, the two concerns define five different conflict behaviors: forcing, avoiding, accommodating, compromising, and problem solving or integrating. These behaviors are studied at the level of general personal conflict styles, closely connected to personality, as well as at the level of strategies and tactics (Euwema & Giebels, 2017).

The different conflict styles have been studied intensively, with three approaches: a normative approach, wherein integrating (also known as problem solving) is seen as the preferred behavior for conflict resolution; a contingency approach, exploring conditions under which each of the behaviors is most appropriate; and a conglomerate approach, focusing on a combination of the behaviors (see "Conglomerate Conflict Behavior").

Forcing.   In forcing, one party aims to achieve his or her goal by imposing a solution onto the other party. Concern for one's own interests and own vision is what matters. There is little attention and care for the interests and needs of the other party, or the relationship with the other (Euwema & Giebels, 2017). This style is appropriate when the outcome is important for one party but trivial to the opponent, or when fast decision-making is necessary. It becomes inappropriate when issues are complex, when both parties are equally powerful, when the

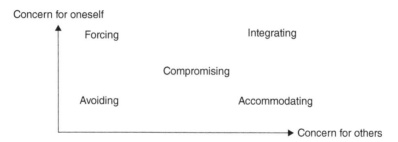

Figure 1. Dual-concern model.
Source: Blake & Mouton, 1964; Pruitt & Rubin, 1986.

outcome is not worth the effort for one party, or when there is enough time to make a collective decision. Moreover, forcing decisions can seriously damage a relationship and contribute to bullying in the workplace (Baillien, Bollen, Euwema, & De Witte, 2014); however, normative forcing, which is referring to rules and imposing them, can be effective (De Dreu, 2005). Note that some alternative terms that have been used for forcing in the literature are *competitive*, *contending*, or *adversarial behavior*.

Avoiding. With avoiding, one party aims to stay out of any confrontation with the other. This behavior prevents efforts to yield, to negotiate constructively, or to compete for one's own gains. The conflict issue receives little attention, usually because the avoiding party thinks he or she won't gain from entering into the conflict (Euwema & Giebels, 2017; Van de Vliert, 1997). Avoiding may be used when the benefits of resolving the conflict are not worth confronting the other party, especially when the problem is trivial or minor; when no good solutions are available for now; or when time is needed (Van Erp et al., 2011). An important motive for avoiding also is to prevent loss of face and to maintain the relationship. This is particularly true in collectivistic cultures, particularly in Asian societies (Oetzel et al., 2001). Avoiding is inappropriate when the issues are important to a party, when the parties cannot wait, or when immediate action is required (Rahim, 2002). Rubin, Pruitt, and Kim (1994) distinguished between long-term avoidance, which is a permanent move to leave the conflict, and short-term avoidance, defined as temporary inaction.

Accommodating. Accommodating is giving in or going along with the ideas, wishes, and needs of the other party. Accommodating usually is the result of a low concern for one's own conflictive interests combined with a high concern for the interests and needs of the other party. Giving in often is related to a strong need for harmony and a sensitivity to the needs of the other. Accommodation is useful when a party is not familiar with the issues involved in the conflict, when the opponent is right, when the issue is much more important to the other party, and in order to build or maintain a long-term relationship, in exchange for future consideration when needed. Giving in also can be an educational strategy, giving space to the other to find out what the effect will be. Accommodating is less appropriate when the issue is of great concern, when accommodation creates frustration, or when accommodation reinforces dynamics of exploitation (Spaho, 2013). Note that an alternative term for this concept that can be found in the literature is *yielding*.

1030 • CONFLICT MANAGEMENT

Compromising. Compromising involves searching for a middle ground, with an eye on both one's own interest and the interest of the other. The premise is that both parties must find a middle ground where everyone receives equal consideration, meaning that each party makes some concession (Van de Vliert, 1997). Compromising is appropriate when a balance of forces exists and the goals of parties are mutually exclusive (Buddhodev, 2011). Compromise leads to a democratic solution. However, compromise may also prevent arriving at a creative solution to the problem and a limited effort to increase resources before distributing them (Spaho, 2013).

Problem Solving or Integrating. Problem solving is a win–win strategy aimed at "optimizing rather than satisfying the parties" (Van de Vliert, 1997, p. 36). Great value is attached to one's own interests and vision, but also a lot of attention is given to the needs, ideas, and interests of the other. One looks for open and creative solutions that meet both interests. Problem solving or integrating is useful in dealing with complex issues, and it allows both parties to share skills, information, and other resources to redefine the problem and formulate alternative solutions. It is, however, inappropriate when the task is simple or trivial, and when there is no time. Also, it is more difficult to develop when the other party does not have experience in problem solving or when the parties are unconcerned about the outcomes (Pruitt & Rubin, 1986). Note that some alternative terms that can be found in the literature for this concept are *cooperation* and *collaboration*.

The dual-concern model is used as a contingency model, describing which conflict behaviors are used best under what conditions (Van de Vliert et al., 1997), and also as a normative model, promoting integrating behaviors as the most effective style, particularly when it comes to joined outcomes and long-term effectiveness. Forcing, in contrast, is often described as a noncooperative behavior, with risk of escalated and unilateral outcomes (Blake & Mouton, 1964; Burke, 1970; Deutsch, 1973; Fisher & Ury, 1981; Pruitt & Rubin, 1986; Rahim, 2010; Thomas, 1992). As a result, authors define forcing and integrating as two opposed behavioral approaches (Tjosvold, Morishima, & Belsheim, 1999). Following this model, many scholars during the 1970s and 1980s proposed that individuals use a single behavior in conflict, or that the behaviors should be seen as independent. Therefore, the antecedents and effects of different conflict behaviors are often analyzed separately (Tjosvold, 1997; Volkema & Bergmann, 2001). However, parties usually try to achieve personal outcomes, and try to reach mutual agreements by combining several behaviors in a conflict episode (Van de Vliert, 1997). This is the basic assumption of the conglomerate conflict behavior (CCB) theory (Van de Vliert, Euwema, & Huismans, 1995), which established that conflict behaviors are used in a compatible manner, sequentially or simultaneously.

Conglomerate Conflict Behavior (CCB). In the dual-concern model, a contrast is made between forcing (contending with an adversary in a direct way) and integrating (reconciling the parties' basic interests) as two opposed behavioral approaches (Tjosvold et al., 1999). However, the CCB framework assumes that individual reactions to conflict typically are complex and consist of multiple components of behavior (Van de Vliert, 1997; Van de Vliert et al., 1995). The CCB theory covers the idea that behavioral components may occur simultaneously or sequentially and that the combination drives toward effectiveness (Euwema & Van Emmerik, 2007; Medina & Benitez, 2011). The theory has been supported in studies analyzing conflict management effectiveness in different contexts, such as in managerial behavior (Munduate, Ganaza, Peiro, & Euwema, 1999), in military peacekeeping (Euwema & Van Emmerik, 2007), and by worker representatives in organizations (Elgoibar, 2013).

The main reason that people combine different behaviors is because conflicts are often mixed-motive situations (Euwema, Van de Vliert, & Bakker, 2003; Euwema & Van Emmerik, 2007; Walton & McKersie, 1965). Mixed-motive situations are described as situations that pose a conflict between securing immediate benefits through competition, and pursuing benefits for oneself and others through cooperation with other people (Komorita & Parks, 1995; Sheldon & Fishbach, 2011). Therefore, a person's behavior in a conflict episode is viewed as a combination of some of the five forms of conflict behaviors. An example of sequential complex behavior is to first put the demands clearly (forcing), followed by integrating (searching for mutual gains, and expanding the pie), and finally compromising, where distributive issues are dealt with in a fair way. An example of serial complexity can be found in multi-issue conflict, when for some issues conflict can be avoided, while for high priorities, demands are put on the table in a forcing way. Another CCB pattern is the conglomeration of accommodating and forcing. This pattern is sometimes referred to as "logrolling" (Van de Vliert, 1997, p. 35), and it is a classic part of integrative strategies, to maximize the outcomes for both parties. Logrolling behavior consists of accommodating the high-concern issues of the other party and forcing one's own high-concern issues. This approach is usually helpful in multi-issue trade negotiations; however, it requires openness of both parties to acknowledging key interests.

How to Explore Your Tendency in Conflict. The most famous and popular conflict behavior questionnaires are:

- MODE (Management of Differences Exercise). MODE, developed in 1974 by Thomas and Killman, presents 30 choices between two options representing different conflict styles.
- ROCI (Rahim's Organizational Conflict Inventory). The ROCI is a list of 28 items that measures the five styles of conflict behavior described.
- Dutch Test of Conflict Handling. This list of 20 items measures the degree of preference for the five styles (Van de Vliert & Euwema, 1994; De Dreu et al., 2001, 2005). It has been validated internationally.

Conflict Management. Conflict management is deliberate action to deal with conflictive situations, either to prevent or to escalate them. Unlike conflict behavior, conflict management encompasses cognitive responses to conflict situations, which can vary from highly competitive to highly cooperative. Conflict management does not necessarily involve avoidance, reduction, or termination of conflict. It involves designing effective strategies to minimize the dysfunctions of conflict and to enhance the constructive functions of conflict in order to improve team and organizational effectiveness (Rahim, 2002).

Conflicts are not necessarily destructive (De Dreu & Gelfand, 2008; Euwema, Munduate, Elgoibar, Pender, & Garcia, 2015), and research has shown that constructive conflict management is possible (Coleman, Deutsch, & Marcus, 2014). The benefits of conflict are much more likely to arise when conflicts are discussed openly, and when discussion skillfully promotes new ideas and generates creative insights and agreements (Coleman et al., 2014; De Dreu & Gelfand, 2008; Euwema et al., 2015; Tjosvold, Won, & Chen, 2014). To make a constructive experience from conflict, conflict needs to be managed effectively.

Deutsch's classic theory of competition and cooperation describes the antecedents and consequences of parties' cooperative or competitive orientations and allows insights into what can give rise to constructive or destructive conflict processes (Deutsch, 1973, 2002). The core of the theory is the perceived interdependence of the parties, so that the extent that protagonists believe that their goals are cooperative (positively related) or competitive (negatively related) affects their interaction and thus the outcomes. Positive interdependence promotes openness, cooperative relations, and integrative problem solving. Perceived negative interdependence, on the other hand, induces more distance and less openness, and promotes competitive behavior, resulting in distributive bargaining or win–lose outcomes (Tjosvold et al., 2014).

Whether the protagonists believe their goals are cooperative or competitive very much affects their expectations, interactions, and outcomes. If parties perceive that they can reach their goals only if the other party also reaches their goals, the goal interdependence is positively perceived and therefore parties will have higher concern for the other's goals and manage the conflict cooperatively (De Dreu et al., 2001; Tjosvold et al., 2014). On the contrary, if one party perceives that they can reach their goals only if the other party fails to obtain their goals, the interdependence becomes negatively perceived and the approach to conflict becomes competitive (Tjosvold et al., 2014). Goals can also be independent; in that case, conflict can be avoided (the parties don't need to obstruct each other's goals to be successful). Therefore, how parties perceive their goals' interdependence affects how they negotiate conflict and whether the conflict is constructively or destructively managed (Alper et al., 2000; Deutsch, 1973; Johnson & Johnson, 1989; Tjosvold, 2008).

Successfully managing conflict cooperatively requires intellectual, emotional, and relational capabilities in order to share information, to contribute to value creation, and to discuss differences constructively (Fisher & Ury, 1981; Tjosvold et al., 2014). In contrast, a competitive-destructive process leads to material losses and dissatisfaction, worsening relations between parties, and negative psychological effects on at least one party—the loser of a win–lose context (Deutsch, 2014).

Deutsch's theory proposes that emphasizing cooperative goals in conflict by demonstrating a commitment to pursue mutually beneficial solutions creates high-quality resolutions and relationships, while focusing on competitive interests by pursuing one's own goals at the expense of the other's escalates conflict, resulting in imposed solutions and suspicious relationships (Tjosvold et al., 2014).

In summary, Deutsch's theory states that the context in which the conflict process is expressed drives parties toward either a cooperative or a competitive orientation in conflicts (Alper et al., 2000; Deutsch, 2006; Johnson & Johnson, 1989). In other words, a cooperative context is related to a cooperative conflict pattern, and a competitive context is related to a competitive conflict pattern. When parties have a cooperative orientation toward conflict, parties discuss their differences with the objective of clarifying them and attempting to find a solution that is satisfactory to both parties—both parties win (Carnevale & Pruitt, 1992). On the contrary, in competition, there is usually a winner and a loser (Carnevale & Pruitt, 1992) (see Table 1). In the CCB model, the patterns can include cooperative (i.e., integrating) and competitive (i.e. forcing) behavior; however, the cooperative pattern will be dominated by integrating while the competitive pattern will be dominated by forcing (Elgoibar, 2013).

Table 1. Characteristics of Cooperative and Competitive Climates

Cooperative climate	Competitive climate
• Effective communication is exhibited. • Friendliness, helpfulness, and lessened obstructiveness. • Feeling of agreement with the ideas of others and a sense of basic similarities in beliefs and values, as well as confidence in one's own ideas and in the value that other members attach to those ideas. • Recognizing and respecting the other by being responsive to the other's needs. • Willingness to enhance the other's power (e.g., knowledge, skills, and resources). • Defining conflicting interests as a mutual problem to be solved by collaborative effort.	• Communication is impaired as the conflicting parties seek to gain advantage by misleading the other (e.g., false promises, disinformation). • Obstructiveness and lack of helpfulness lead to mutual negative attitudes and suspicion of one another's intentions. • The repeated experience of disagreement and critical rejection of ideas reduces confidence in oneself as well as the other. • The conflicting parties seek to enhance their own power and to reduce the power of the other. • The competitive orientation stimulates the view that the solution of a conflict only can be imposed by one side on the other.

Source: Coleman, Deutsch, and Marcus (2014).

How to Manage Conflicts Constructively. The Need for Trust is commonly defined as a belief or expectation about others' benevolent motives during a social interaction (Holmes & Rempel, 1989; Rousseau et al., 1998). Mutual trust is one important antecedent as well as a consequence of cooperation in conflicts (Deutsch, 1983; Ferrin, Bligh, & Kohles, 2008). As Nahapiet and Ghoshal pointed out, "Trust lubricates cooperation, and cooperation itself breeds trust" (1998, p. 255). There is ample evidence that constructive conflict and trust are tightly and positively related (Hempel, Zhang, & Tjosvold, 2009; Bijlsma & Koopman, 2003; Lewicki, Tonlinson, & Gillespie, 2006).

Successful constructive conflict management requires maximal gathering and exchange of information in order to identify problems and areas of mutual concern, to search for alternatives, to assess their implications, and to achieve openness about preferences in selecting optimal solutions (Bacon & Blyton, 2007; Johnson & Johnson, 1989; Tjosvold, 1999). Trust gives parties the confidence to be open with each other, knowing that the shared information won't be used against them (Zaheer & Zaheer, 2006). Various studies revealed that trust leads to constructive conglomerate behaviors and to more integrative outcomes in interpersonal and intergroup conflicts (Lewicki, Elgoibar, & Euwema, 2016; Lewicki, McAllister, & Bies, 1998; Ross & LaCroix, 1996).

How can trust be promoted? Developing trust is challenging (Gunia, Brett, & Nandkeolyar, 2014; Hempel et al., 2009). Numerous scholars have noted that trust is easier to destroy than to create (Hempel et al., 2009; Meyerson et al., 1996). There are two main reasons for this assertion. First, trust-breaking events are often more visible and noticeable than positive trust-building actions (Kramer, 1999). Second, trust-breaking events are judged to have a higher impact on trust judgments than positive events (Slovic, 1993). Furthermore, Slovic (1993) concluded that trust-breaking events are more credible than sources of good news. Thus, the general belief is that trust is easier to destroy than it is to build, and trust rebuilding may take even longer than it took to create the original level of trust (Lewicki et al., 2016).

However, there is room for optimism, and different strategies have been shown to promote trust. As held in social exchange theory (Blau, 1964), risk-taking by one party in supporting the other party has been found to signal trust to the other party (Serva et al., 2005). Yet, fears of exploitation make trust in conflict management and negotiation scarce. Therefore, the use of trust-promoting strategies depends on the specific situation, and parties need practical guidance on how and when to manage conflict constructively by means of promoting mutual trust.

How does the possibility of trust development between parties depend on the conflict context? Based on this practical question, some strategies for trust development have been proposed (Fisher & Ury, 1981; Fulmer & Gelfand, 2012; Gunia, Brett, & Nandkeolyar, 2012; Lewicki et al., 2016). In relationships where trust is likely, the following strategies can help: assume trustworthiness, prioritize your interests and give away a little information about them, engage in reciprocity (concessions), highlight similarities and spend time together, get to know your counterpart personally and try to be likable, behave consistently and predictably, and paraphrase your counterpart's positions. In relationships where trust seems possible: emphasize common goals; focus on the subject, not on the people; look to the future and find a shared vision; mix questions and answers about interests and priorities—the fundamental elements of information sharing—with making and justifying offers; take a break; suggest another approach; call in a mediator; and forgive the other party's mistakes. In relationships where trust is not possible, more cautious strategies can help: make multi-issue offers; think holistically about your counterpart's interests; engage in reciprocity (concessions); express sympathy, apologize, or compliment your counterpart; and look for preference patterns in your counterpart's offers and responses.

Constructive Controversy. *Constructive controversy* is defined as the open-minded discussion of conflicting perspectives for mutual benefit, which occurs when protagonists express their opposing ideas that obstruct resolving the issues, at least temporarily (Tjosvold et al., 2014). Indicators of constructive controversy include listening carefully to each other's opinion, trying to understand each other's concerns, and using opposing views to understand the problem better. These skills are considered vitally important for developing and implementing cooperative problem-solving processes successfully and effectively.

Deutsch (2014) stated that there haven't been many systematic discussions of the skills involved in constructive solutions to conflict, and he proposed three main types of skills for constructive conflict management:

1. Rapport-building skills are involved in establishing effective relationships between parties (such as breaking the ice; reducing fears, tensions, and suspicion; overcoming resistance to negotiation; and fostering realistic hope and optimism).

2. Cooperative conflict-resolution skills are concerned with developing and maintaining a cooperative conflict resolution process among the parties involved (such as identifying the type of conflict in which the parties are involved; reframing the issues so that conflict is perceived as a mutual problem to be resolved cooperatively; active listening and responsive communication; distinguishing between effective relationships between parties and positions; encouraging, supporting, and enhancing the parties; being alert to cultural differences and the possibilities of misunderstanding arising from them; and controlling anger).
3. Group process and decision-making skills are involved in developing a creative and productive process (such as monitoring progress toward group goals; eliciting, clarifying, coordinating, summarizing, and integrating the contributions of the various participants; and maintaining group cohesion).

Tjosvold et al. (2014) and Johnson et al. (2014) also elaborate on the skills needed for facilitating open-minded discussions and constructive controversy. They developed four mutually reinforcing strategies for managing conflict constructively:

1. Developing and expressing one's own view. Parties need to know what each of the others wants and believes, and expressing one's own needs, feelings, and ideas is essential to gaining that knowledge. By strengthening expression of their own positions, both parties can learn to investigate their position, present the best case they can for it, defend it vigorously, and try at the same time to refute opposing views. However, expressing one's own position needs to be supplemented with an open-minded approach to the other's position.
2. Questioning and understanding others' views. Listening and understanding opposing views, as well as defending one's own views, makes discussing conflicts more challenging but also more rewarding; therefore, the parties can point out weaknesses in each other's arguments to encourage better development and expression of positions by finding more evidence and strengthening their reasoning.
3. Integrating and creating solutions. The creation of new alternatives lays the foundation for genuine agreements about a solution that both parties can accept and implement. However, protagonists may have to engage in repeated discussion to reach an agreement, or indeed they may be unable to create a solution that is mutually acceptable, and then they can both learn to become less adamant, to exchange views directly, and to show that they are trying to understand and integrate each other's ideas so that all may benefit.
4. Agreeing to and implementing solutions. Parties can learn to seek the best reasoned judgment, instead of focusing on "winning"; to criticize ideas, not people; to listen and understand everyone's position, even if they do not agree with it; to differentiate positions before trying to integrate them; and to change their minds when logically persuaded to do so.

Conflict Resolution. Conflict resolution processes are aimed at ending a conflict. So, while conflict management can also include escalation, conflict resolution searches for a way of ending the conflict. The difference between resolution and management of conflict is more than semantic (Robbins, 1978). Conflict resolution means reduction, elimination, or termination of conflict.

To find a resolution, parties have to bring an extra piece of information, relate the information they have differently, or transform the issue, change the rules, change the actors or the structure, or bring in a third party (Vayrynen, 1991). The most popular conflict resolution processes are: negotiation, mediation, conflict coaching, and arbitration (Rahim, 2002). Conflict resolution can also be accomplished by ruling by authorities. Integration of the different techniques sequentially or simultaneously has been shown to support optimal conflict resolution (Jones, 2016).

Negotiation. Negotiation is a process in which the parties attempt to jointly create an agreement that resolves a conflict between them (Lewicki & Tomlinson, 2014). Walton and McKersie (1965) were the first to identify the two polar yet interdependent strategies known as distributive and integrative negotiation. Distributive negotiation means that activities are instrumental to the attainment of one party's goals when they are in basic conflict with those of the other party. Integrative negotiation means that parties' activities are oriented to find common or complementary interests and to solve problems confronting both parties. Other scholars also focused on the opposite tactical requirements of the two strategies, using a variety of terms, such as *contending* versus *cooperating* (Pruitt, 1981), *claiming value* versus *creating value* (Lax & Sebenius, 1987), and the difference between *positions* and *interests* (Fisher & Ury, 1981).

If a distributive strategy is pursued too vigorously, a negotiator may gain a greater share of gains, but of a smaller set of joint gains, or, worse, may generate an outcome in which both parties lose. However, if a negotiator pursues an integrative negotiation in a single-minded manner—being totally cooperative and giving freely accurate and credible information about his/her interests—he or she can be taken advantage of by the other party (Walton & McKersie, 1965). The different proposals that have been formulated to cope with these central dilemmas in negotiation are mainly based on a back-and-forth communication process between the parties, which is linked to the negotiators' interpersonal skills (Brett, Shapiro, & Lytle, 1998; Fisher & Ury, 1981; Rubin et al., 1994).

Mediation. Mediation is the process by which a third party facilitates constructive communication among disputants, including decision-making, problem solving, and negotiation, in order to reach a mutually acceptable agreement (Bollen, Munduate, & Euwema, 2016; Goldman, Cropanzano, Stein, & Benson, 2008; Moore, 2014). Using mediation in conflict resolution has been proven to prevent the negative consequences of conflict in the workplace (Bollen & Euwema, 2010; Bollen et al., 2016), in collective bargaining (Martinez-Pecino et al., 2008), in inter- and intragroup relations (Jones, 2016), and in interpersonal relations (Herrman, 2006). However, mediation is not a magic bullet and works better in conflicts that are moderate rather than extreme, when parties are motivated to resolve the conflict, and when parties have equal power, among other characteristics (Kressel, 2014).

Conflict Coaching. Conflict coaching is a new and rapidly growing process in the public as well as private sector (Brinkert, 2016). In this process, a conflict coach works with a party to accomplish three goals (Jones & Brinkert, 2008): (a) analysis and coherent understanding of the conflict, (b) identification of a future preferred direction, and (c) skills development to implement the preferred strategy. Therefore, a conflict coach is defined as a conflict expert who respects the other party's self-determination and aims to promote the well-being of the parties involved. Giebels and Janssen (2005) found that, when outside help was called in, parties in conflict experienced fewer negative consequences in terms of individual well-being than people who did not ask for third-party help.

Sometimes, the leader of a team can act as conflict coach. A study by Romer and colleagues (2012) showed that a workplace leader's problem-solving approach to conflicts increased employees' perception of justice and their sense that they had a voice in their workplace, as well as reduced employees' stress (De Reuver & Van Woerkom, 2010; Romer et al., 2012). In contrast, the direct expression of power in the form of forcing behavior can harm employees' well-being (Peterson & Harvey, 2009). A forcing leader may become an additional party to the conflict (i.e., employees may turn against their leader; Romer et al., 2012).

Conflict coaching and mediation are different processes. First, in conflict coaching, only one party is involved in the process, while in mediation, the mediator helps all the parties in conflict to engage in constructive interaction. Second, conflict coaching focuses on direct skills instructions to the party (i.e., negotiation skills). In that, conflict coaching is also a leadership development tool (Romer et al., 2012). There is a growing tendency to integrate conflict coaching and workplace mediation, particularly in preparation for conflict resolution, because the coach can help the coached party to investigate options and weigh the advantages of the different options (Jones, 2016).

Arbitration. Arbitration is an institutionalized procedure in which a third party provides a final and binding or voluntary decision (Lewicki, Saunders, & Barry, 2014; Mohr & Spekman, 1994). Arbitration allows the parties to have control over the process, but not over the outcomes. Therefore, arbitration differs from negotiation, mediation, and conflict coaching, in which the parties decide the agreement themselves (Posthuma & Dworkin, 2000; Lewicki et al., 2014). In arbitration, the third party listens to the parties and decides the outcome. This procedure is used mainly in conflicts between organizations, in commercial disputes, and in collective labor conflicts (Beechey, 2000; Elkouri & Elkouri, 1995).

Decision-Making by Authorities. The strategies of negotiation, mediation, conflict coaching, and arbitration have in common that the parties together decide about the conflict process, even when they agree to accept an arbitration. This is different from how authorities resolve conflict. Decision-making by authorities varies from parents' intervening in children's fights to rulings by teachers, police officers, managers, complaint officers, ombudsmen, and judges. Here, often one party complains and the authority acts to intervene and end the conflict. This strategy is good for ending physical violence and misuse of power. However, the authorities' decisive power is limited, and therefore in most situations authorities are strongly urged to first explore the potential for conflict resolution and reconciliation among the parties involved. The authority can act as an escalator for the process, or as a facilitator, and only in cases of immediate threat can intervene or rule as a last resort. Authorities who employ this strategy can improve the learning skills of the parties and can impose upon the parties an acceptance of responsibility, both for the conflict and for the ways to end it.

CONCLUSION

It is important to emphasize the natural and positive aspects of conflict management. Conflict occurs in all areas of organizations and private lives and its management is vital for their effectiveness. Through conflict, conventional thinking is challenged, threats and opportunities are identified, and new solutions are forged (Tjosvold et al., 2014). Therefore, when conflict occurs, it shouldn't be avoided but should be managed constructively.

FURTHER READING

Coleman, P., Deutsch, M., & Marcus, E. (2014). *The handbook of conflict resolution. Theory and practice* (3d ed.). San Francisco: John Wiley & Sons.

De Dreu, C.K.W., Evers, A., Beersma, B., Kluwer, E., & Nauta, A. (2001). A theory-based measure of conflict management strategies in the workplace. *Journal of Organizational Behavior, 22*(6), 645–668.

Elgoibar, P., Euwema, M., & Munduate, L. (2016). *Trust building and constructive conflict management in industrial relations.* Springer International.

Lewicki, R. J., McAllister, D. J., & Bies, R. J. (1998). Trust and distrust: New relationship and realities. *Academy of Management Review, 23*, 438–458.

Pruitt, D. G. & Rubin, J. Z. (1986). *Social conflict: Escalation, stalemate, and settlement.* New York: McGraw Hill.

Van de Vliert, E., Euwema, M.C., & Huismans, S.E. (1995). Managing conflict with a subordinate or a superior: Effectiveness of conglomerated behavior. *Journal of Applied Psychology, 80*(2), 271–281.

Wall, J. A., & Callister, R. R. (1995). Conflict and its management. *Journal of Management, 21*, 515–558.

REFERENCES

Alper, S., Tjosvold, D., & Law, K. S. (2000). Conflict management, efficacy, and performance in organizational teams. *Personnel Psychology, 53*, 625–642.

Amason, A. C., & Schweiger, D. M. (1994). Resolving the paradox of conflict: Strategic decision making and organizational performance. *International Journal of Conflict Management, 5*, 239–253.

Bacon, N., & Blyton, P. (2007). Conflict for mutual gains. *Journal of Management Studies, 44*(5), 814–834.

Baillien, E., Bollen, K., Euwema, M., & De Witte, H. (2014). Conflicts and conflict management styles as precursors of workplace bullying: A two-wave longitudinal study. *European Journal of Work and Organizational Psychology, 23*(4), 511–524.

Barbuto, J. E., Phipps, K. A., & Xu, Y. (2010). Testing relationships between personality, conflict styles and effectiveness. *International Journal of Conflict Management, 21*(4), 434–447.

Beechey, J. (2000) International commercial arbitration: A process under review and change. *Dispute Resolution Journal, 55*(3), 32–36.

Bijlsma, K., & Koopman, P. (2003) Introduction: Trust within organizations. *Personnel Review, 32*(5), 543–555.

Blake, R. R., & Mouton, J. S. (1964). *The managerial GRID.* Houston: Gulf.

Blau, E. M. (1964). *Exchange and power in social life.* New York: Wiley.

Bollen, K., Euwema, M., & Müller, P. (2010). Why are subordinates less satisfied with mediation? The role of uncertainty. *Negotiation Journal, 26*(4), 417–433.

Bollen, K., & Euwema, M. (2013). Workplace mediation: An underdeveloped research area. *Negotiation Journal, 29*, 329–353.

Bollen, K., Munduate, L., & Euwema, M. (2016). *Advancing workplace mediation: Integrating theory and practice.* Springer International.

Brett, J. M., Shapiro, D. L., & Lytle, A. L. (1998). Breaking the bonds of reciprocity in negotiations. *Academy of Management Journal, 41*(4), 410–424.

Brinkert, R. (2016). An appreciative approach to conflict: Mediation and conflict coaching. In K. Bollen, M. Euwema, & L. Munduate (Eds.), *Advancing workplace mediation: Integrating theory and practice*. Springer International.

Brown, L. D. (1983). *Managing conflict at organizational interfaces*. Reading, MA: Addison-Wesley.

Buddhodev, S. A. (2011). Conflict management: Making life easier. *The IUP Journal of Soft Skills, 5*(4), 31–43.

Burke, R. J. (1970). Methods of resolving superior-subordinate conflict: The constructive use of subordinate differences and disagreements. *Organizational Behavior and Human Performance, 5*, 393–411.

Carnevale, P. J., & Pruitt, D. G. (1992). Negotiation and mediation. *Annual Review of Psychology, 43*, 531–582.

Coleman, P., Deutsch, M., & Marcus, E. (2014). *The handbook of conflict resolution. Theory and practice* (3d ed.). San Francisco: John Wiley & Sons.

De Dreu, C. K. (2005). Conflict and conflict management. *Wiley Encyclopedia of Management, 11*, 1–4.

De Dreu, C. K., & Gelfand, M. J. (2008). *Conflict in the workplace: Sources, functions, and dynamics across multiple levels of analysis*. New York: Lawrence Erlbaum Associates.

De Dreu, C. K. W., Evers, A., Beersma, B., Kluwer, E., & Nauta, A. (2001). A theory-based measure of conflict management strategies in the workplace. *Journal of Organizational Behavior, 22*(6), 645–668.

De Dreu, C. K. W., & Weingart, L. R. (2003). Task versus relationship conflict, team performance, and team member satisfaction: A meta-analysis. *Journal of Applied Psychology, 88*(4), 741–749.

De Reuver, R., & Van Woerkom, M. (2010). Can conflict management be an antidote to subordinate absenteeism? *Journal of Managerial Psychology, 25*(5), 479–494.

De Wit, F. R., Greer, L. L., & Jehn, K. A. (2012). The paradox of intragroup conflict: A meta-analysis. *Journal of Applied Psychology, 97*(2), 360–390.

Deutsch, M. (1949). A theory of cooperation and competition. *Human Relations, 2*, 129–151.

Deutsch, M. (1973). *The resolution of conflict*. New Haven, CT: Yale University Press.

Deutsch, M. (1983). Conflict resolution: Theory and practice. *Political Psychology, 4*, 43–453.

Deutsch, M. (2002). Social psychology's contributions to the study of conflict resolution. *Negotiation Journal, 18*(4), 307–320.

Deutsch, M. (2006). Cooperation and competition. In M. Deutsch, P. Coleman, & E. Marcus (Eds.), *The handbook of conflict resolution*, 23–42. San Francisco: John Wiley & Sons.

Deutsch, M. (2014). Cooperation, competition and conflict. In P. Coleman, M. Deutsch, & E. Marcus (Eds.), *The handbook of conflict resolution: Theory and practice*, 3–28 (3d ed.). San Francisco: Jossey Bass.

Elgoibar, P. (2013). *Worker representatives' conflict behavior in Europe with a focus on Spain* (PhD diss., University of Leuven, Belgium, and University of Seville, Spain).

Elgoibar, P., Euwema, M., & Munduate, L. (2016). *Trust building and constructive conflict management in industrial relations*. Springer International.

Elkouri, F., & Elkouri, E. A. (1995). *How arbitration works*. ABA: Section of Labour and Employment Law.

Euwema, M., & Giebels, E. (2017). *Conflictmanagement en mediation*. Groningen, The Netherlands: Noordhoff Uitgevers.

Euwema, M., Munduate, L., Elgoibar, P., Garcia, A., & Pender, E. (2015). *Promoting social dialogue in European organizations: Human resources management and constructive conflict behavior*. Dordrecht, The Netherlands: Springer Verlag.

Euwema, M. C., & Van Emmerik, I. J. H. (2007). Intercultural competencies and conglomerated conflict behavior in intercultural conflicts. *International Journal of Intercultural Relations, 31*, 427–441.

Euwema, M. C., Van de Vliert, E., & Bakker, A. B. (2003). Substantive and relational effectiveness of organizational conflict behavior. *International Journal of Conflict Management, 14*(2), 119–139.

Ferrin, D. L., Bligh, M. C., & Kohles, J. C. (2008). It takes two to tango: An interdependence analysis of the spiraling of perceived trustworthiness and cooperation in interpersonal and intergroup relationships. *Organizational Behavior and Human Decision Processes, 107,* 161–178.

Fisher, R., & Ury, W. L. (1981). *Getting to yes: Negotiating agreements without giving in.* New York: Penguin Books.

Follett, M. P. (1941). Constructive conflict. In H. C. Metcalf & L. Urwick (Eds.), *Dynamic administration: The collected papers of Mary Parker Follett* (pp. 30–49). New York: Harper & Row. (Originally published in 1926.)

Fulmer, C. A., & Gelfand, M. J. (2012). At what level (and in whom) we trust? Trust across multiple organizational levels. *Journal of Management, 38*(4), 1167–1230.

Gelfand, M. J., & Brett (2004). *The handbook of negotiation and culture.* Stanford, CA: Stanford University Press.

Giebels, E., & Janssen, O. (2005). Conflict stress and reduced well-being at work: The buffering effect of third-party help. *European Journal of Work and Organizational Psychology, 14*(2), 137–155.

Goldman, B. M., Cropanzano, R., Stein, J. H., Shapiro, D. L., Thatcher, S., & Ko, J. (2008). The role of ideology in mediated disputes at work: A justice perspective. *International Journal of Conflict Management, 19*(3), 210–233.

Gunia, B., Brett, J., & Nandkeolyar, A. K. (2012). In global negotiations, it's all about trust. *Harvard Business Review,* December.

Gunia, B., Brett, J., & Nandkeolyar, A. K. (2014). Trust me, I'm a negotiator. Diagnosing trust to negotiate effectively, globally. *Organizational Dynamics, 43*(1), 27–36.

Hackman, J. R., & Morris, C. G. (1975). Group tasks, group interaction process, and group performance effectiveness: A review and proposed integration. In L. Berkowitz (Ed.), *Advances in experimental social psychology* (Vol. 8). New York: Academic Press. https://scholar.harvard.edu/rhackman/publications/group-tasks-group-interaction-process-and-group-performance-effectiveness-revi

Hempel, P., Zhang, Z., & Tjosvold, D. (2009). Conflict management between and within teams for trusting relationships and performance in China. *Journal of Organizational Behavior, 30,* 41–65.

Herrmann, M. S. (2006). *Blackwell handbook of mediation: Bridging theory, research, and practice.* Malden, MA: Blackwell Publishing.

Holmes, J. G., & Rempel, J. K. (1989). Trust in close relationships. In C. Hendrick (Ed.), *Review of personality and social psychology* (Vol. 10, pp. 187–220). Thousand Oaks, CA: SAGE.

Jehn, K. (1995). A multimethod examination of the benefits and detriments of intragroup conflict. *Administrative Science Quarterly, 40*(2), 256–282.

Jehn, K. (1997). A qualitative analysis of conflict types and dimensions in organizational groups. *Administrative Science Quarterly, 42,* 530–557.

Jehn, K., & Chatman, J. A. (2000). The influence of proportional and perceptual conflict composition on team performance. *International Journal of Conflict Management, 11*(1), 56–73.

Jehn, K. A., Greer, L., Levine, S., & Szulanski, G. (2008). The effects of conflict types, dimensions, and emergent states on group outcomes. *Group Decision and Negotiation, 17,* 465–495.

Jehn, K. A., & Mannix, E. A. (2001). The dynamic nature of conflict: A longitudinal study of intragroup conflict and group performance. *Academy of Management Journal, 44*(2), 238–251.

Johnson, D. V., Johnson, R. T., & Tjosvold, D. (2014). Constructive controversy: The value of intellectual opposition. In P. Coleman, M. Deutsch, & E. Marcus (Eds.), *The handbook of conflict resolution: Theory and practice* (3d ed.). San Francisco: John Wiley & Sons.

Johnson, D. W., & Johnson, R. (2005). New developments in social interdependence theory. *Genetic, Social, and General Psychology Monographs, 131*(4), 285–358.

Johnson, D. W., & Johnson, R. T. (1989). *Cooperation and competition: Theory and research.* Edina, MN: Interaction Book Company.

Jones, T. S. (2016). Mediation and conflict coaching in organizational dispute systems. In K. Bollen, M. Euwema, & L. Munduate (Eds.), *Advancing workplace mediation: Integrating theory and practice.* Springer International.

Jones, T. S., & Brinkert, R. (2008). *Conflict coaching: Conflict management strategies and skills for the individual.* Thousand Oaks, CA: Sage.

Kaufman, S., Elgoibar, P., & Borbely, A. (2016). *Context matters: Negotiators' interdependence in public, labor and business disputes.* International Association of Conflict Management Conference, New York, June 26–29, 2016.

Kilmann, R. H., & Thomas, K. W. (1977). Developing a forced-choice measure of conflict-handling behavior: The "mode" instrument. *Educational and Psychological Measurement, 37*(2), 309–325.

Komorita, S. S., & Parks, C. D. (1995). Interpersonal relations: Mixed-motive interaction. *Annual Review of Psychology, 46*(1), 183–207.

Kramer, R. M., & Tyler, T. R. (1996). *Trust in organizations: Frontiers of theory and research.* Thousand Oaks, CA: SAGE.

Kramer, R. M. (1999). Trust and distrust in organizations: Emerging perspectives, enduring questions. *Annual Review of Psychology, 50,* 569–598.

Kressel, K. (2006). Mediation revised. In M. Deutsch, P. T. Coleman, & E. C. Marcus (Eds.), *The handbook of conflict resolution: Theory and practice.* San Francisco: Jossey-Bass.

Kressel, K. (2014). The mediation of conflict: Context, cognition and practice. In P. Coleman, M. Deutsch, & E. C. Marcus (Eds.), *The handbook of conflict resolution: Theory and practice* (3d ed., pp. 817–848). San Francisco: Jossey Bass.

Lax, D., & Sebenius, J. (1987). *The manager as negotiator: Bargaining for cooperative and competitive gain.* New York: Free Press.

Lewicki, R., Elgoibar, P., & Euwema, M. (2016). The tree of trust: Building and repairing trust in organizations. In P. Elgoibar, M. Euwema, & L. Munduate (Eds.), *Trust building and constructive conflict management in industrial relations.* The Netherlands: Springer Verlag.

Lewicki, R. J., McAllister, D. J., & Bies, R. J. (1998). Trust and distrust: New relationship and realities. *Academy of Management Review, 23,* 438–458.

Lewicki, R. J., Saunders, D. M., & Barry, B. (2014). *Essentials of negotiation.* New York: McGraw Hill.

Lewicki, R. J., & Tomlinson, E. (2014). Trust, trust development and trust repair. In M. Deutsch, P. Coleman, & E. Marcus (Eds.), *The handbook of conflict resolution: Theory and practice* (3d ed., pp. 104–136). San Francisco: Jossey-Bass.

Lewicki, R. J., Tomlinson, E. C., & Gillespie, N. (2006). Models of interpersonal trust development: Theoretical approaches, empirical evidence, and future directions. *Journal of Management, 32*(6), 991–1022.

Lewin, K. (1935). *A dynamic theory of personality.* New York: McGraw Hill.

Lindner, E. G. (2014). Emotion and conflict: Why it is important to understand how emotions affect conflict and how conflict affects emotions. In P. Coleman, M. Deutsch, & E. Marcus (Eds.), *The handbook of conflict resolution: Theory and practice* (3d ed., pp. 283–309). San Francisco: Jossey-Bass.

Lytle, A. L., Brett, J. M., & Shapiro, D. L. (1999). The strategic use of interests, rights, and power to resolve disputes. *Negotiation Journal, 15,* 31–51.

Martinez-Pecino, R., Munduate, L., Medina, F., & Euwema, M. (2008). Effectiveness of mediation strategies in collective bargaining: Evidence from Spain. *Industrial Relations, 47*(3), 480–495.

Medina, F. J., & Benitez, M. (2011). Effective behaviors to de-escalate organizational conflicts. *Spanish Journal of Psychology, 14*(2), 789–797.

Meyerson, D., Weick, K. E., & Kramer, R. M. (1996). Swift trust and temporary groups. In R. Kramer & T. Tyler (Eds.), *Trust in organizations*. Thousand Oaks, CA: SAGE.

Mohr, J., & Spekman, R. (1994). Characteristics of partnership success: Partnership attributes, communication behavior, and conflict resolution techniques. *Strategic Management Journal, 15*(2), 135–152.

Moore, C. W. (2014). *The mediation process: Practical strategies for resolving conflict*. San Francisco: Jossey Bass.

Munduate, L., Ganaza, J., Peiro, J. M., & Euwema, M. (1999). Patterns of styles in conflict management and effectiveness. *International Journal of Conflict Management, 10*(1), 5–24.

Nahapiet, J., & Goshal, S. (1998). Social capital, intellectual capital, and the organizational advantage. *The Academy of Management Review, 23*(2), 242–266.

Nair, N. (2007). Towards understanding the role of emotions in conflict: A review and future directions. *International Journal of Conflict Management, 19*(4), 359–381.

Oetzel, J., Ting-Toomey, S., Masumoto, T., Yokochi, Y., Pan, X., Takai, J., & Wilcox, R. (2001). Face and facework in conflict: A cross-cultural comparison of China, Germany, Japan, and the United States. *Communication Monographs, 68*(3), 235–258.

Peterson, R. S., & Harvey, S. (2009). Leadership and conflict: Using power to manage in groups for better rather than worse. In D. Tjosvold & B. Wisse (Eds.), *Power and interdependence in organizations* (pp. 281–298). Cambridge, U.K.: Cambridge University Press.

Pondy, L. R. (1967). Organizational conflict: Concepts and models. *Administrative Science Quarterly, 12*, 296–320.

Posthuma, R. A., & Dworkin, J. B. (2000). A behavioral theory of arbitrator acceptability. *International Journal of Conflict Management, 11*(3), 249–266.

Pruitt, D. G. (1981). *Negotiation behavior*. New York: Academic Press.

Pruitt, D. G., & Rubin, J. Z. (1986). *Social conflict: Escalation, stalemate, and settlement*. New York: McGraw Hill.

Rahim, M. A. (1983). *Rahim organizational conflict inventories*. Palo Alto, CA: Consulting Psychologists Press.

Rahim, M. A. (2002). Towards a theory of managing organizational conflict. *The International Journal of Conflict Management, 13*(3), 206–235.

Rahim, M.A. (2010). *Managing conflict in organizations*. 4th ed. New Jersey: Transaction Publishers.

Robbins, S. P. (1978). "Conflict management" and "conflict resolution" are not synonymous terms. *California Management Review, 21*(2), 67–75.

Römer, M., Rispens, S., Giebels, E., & Euwema, M. (2012). A helping hand? The moderating role of leaders' conflict management behavior on the conflict-stress relationship of employees. *Negotiation Journal, 28*(3), 253–277.

Ross, W., & LaCroix, J. (1996). Multiple meanings of trust in negotiation theory and research: A literature review and integrative model. *International Journal of Conflict Management, 7*(4), 314–360.

Rousseau, D. M., Sitkin, S. B., Burt, R. S., & Camerer, C. (1998). Not so different after all: A cross discipline view of trust. *Academy of Management Review, 23*(3), 393–404.

Rubin, J. Z., Pruitt, & Kim (1994). Models of conflict management. *Journal of Social Issues, 50*, 33–45.

Schellenberg, J. A. (1996). *Conflict resolution: Theory, research, and practice*. Albany, NY: State University of New York Press.

Serva, M. A., Fuller, M. A., & Mayer, R. C. (2005). The reciprocal nature of trust: A longitudinal study of interacting teams. *Journal of Organizational Behavior, 26*, 625–648.

Sheldon, O. J., & Fishbach, A. (2011). Resisting the temptation to compete: Self-control promotes cooperation in mixed-motive interactions. *Journal of Experimental Social Psychology, 47*, 403–410.

Sinaceur, M., Adam, H., Van Kleef, G. A., & Galinsky, A. D. (2013). The advantages of being unpredictable: How emotional inconsistency extracts concessions in negotiation. *Journal of Experimental Social Psychology, 49*, 498–508.

Slovic, P. (1993). Perceived risk, trust, and democracy. *Risk Analysis, 13*, 675–682.

Spaho, K. (2013). Organizational communication and conflict management. *Journal of Contemporary Management Issues, 18*(1), 103–118.

Thomas, K. W. (1992). Conflict and conflict management: Reflections and update. *Journal of Organizational Behavior, 13*(3), 265–274.

Thomas, K. W., & Kilmann, R. H. (1974). *Thomas-Kilmann conflict mode instrument.* Mountain View, CA: Xicom.

Tjosvold, D. (1997). Conflict within interdependence: Its value for productivity and individuality. In C. K. W. De Dreu & E. Van de Vliert (Eds.), *Using conflict in organizations* (pp. 23–37). London: SAGE.

Tjosvold, D. (1998). Cooperative and competitive goal approach to conflict: Accomplishments and challenges. *Applied Psychology: An International Review, 47*(3), 285–342.

Tjosvold, D., Morishima, M., & Belsheim, J. A. (1999). Complaint handling in the shop floor: Cooperative relationship and open-minded strategies. *International Journal of Conflict Management, 10*, 45–68.

Tjosvold, D. (2008). The conflict-positive organization: It depends upon us. *Journal of Organizational Behavior, 29*(1), 19–28.

Tjosvold, D., Wong, A. S. H., & Chen, N. Y. F. (2014). Constructively managing conflicts in organizations. *Annual Review of Organizational Psychology and Organizational Behaviour, 1*, 545–568.

Tjosvold, D., Wan, P., & Tang, M. L. (2016). Trust and managing conflict: Partners in developing organizations. In P. Elgoibar, M. Euwema, & L. Munduate (Eds.), *Building trust and conflict management in organizations.* The Netherlands: Springer Verlag.

Van de Vliert, E. (1997). *Complex interpersonal conflict behavior: Theoretical frontiers.* Hove, U.K.: Psychology Press.

Van de Vliert, E., & Euwema, M. C. (1994). Agreeableness and activeness as components of conflict behaviors. *Journal of Personality and Social Psychology, 66*(4), 674–687.

Van de Vliert, E., Euwema, M. C., & Huismans, S. E. (1995). Managing conflict with a subordinate or a superior: Effectiveness of conglomerated behavior. *Journal of Applied Psychology, 80*(2), 271–281.

Van de Vliert, E., Nauta, A., Euwema, M. C., & Janssen, O. (1997). The effectiveness of mixing problem solving and forcing. In C. K. W. De Dreu & E. Van de Vliert (Eds.), *Using conflict in organizations* (pp. 38–52). London: SAGE.

Van de Vliert, E., Nauta, A., Giebels, E., & Janssen, O. (1999). Constructive conflict at work. *Journal of Organizational Behavior, 20*, 475–491.

Van Erp, K. J., Giebels, E., van der Zee, K. I., & van Duijn, M. A. (2011). Let it be: Expatriate couples' adjustment and the upside of avoiding conflicts. *Anxiety, Stress & Coping, 24*(5), 539–560.

Van Kleef, G. A., & Cote, S. (2007). Expressing anger in conflict: When it helps and when it hurts. *Journal of Applied Psychology, 92*(6), 1557–1569.

Vayrynen, R. (1991). *New directions in conflict theory.* London: SAGE.

Volkema, R. J., & Bergmann, T. J. (2001). Conflict styles as indicators of behavioral patterns in interpersonal conflicts. *The Journal of Social Psychology, 135*(1), 5–15.

Wall, J. A., & Callister, R. R. (1995). Conflict and its management. *Journal of Management, 21*, 515–558.

Walton, R. E., & McKersie, R. B. (1965). *A behavioral theory of labor negotiations: An analysis of a social interaction system.* Ithaca, NY: Cornell University Press.

Wilson, T. D. (2004). *Strangers to ourselves. Discovering the adaptive unconscious.* Cambridge, MA: Belknap.

Zaheer, S., & Zaheer, A. (2006). Trust across borders. *Journal of International Business Studies, 37*(1), 21–29.

Patricia Elgoibar, Martin Euwema, and Lourdes Munduate

ORGANIZATIONAL CLIMATE AND CULTURE

INTRODUCTION

Insights from the literatures on both organizational climate and organizational culture are needed to gain a full understanding of how organizational environments come to be, how they influence important organizational outcomes, and how they can be changed. An introduction to organizational climate and organizational culture is provided along with an overview of their similarities, differences, and ways the two can be profitably integrated in future research and practice.

ORGANIZATIONAL CLIMATE

Organizational climate has been defined as "the shared meaning organizational members attach to the events, policies, practices, and procedures they experience and the behaviors they see being rewarded, supported, and expected" (Ehrhart, Schneider, & Macey, 2014, p. 69). Although the concept was discussed and at times studied in various ways prior to the late 1960s, empirical research on organizational climate began in earnest at that time. The 1970s was a time of clarification for research in this area, as critics questioned the utility of the construct and supporters clarified its definition and measurement. For instance, critics questioned whether it was distinct from individual-level attitudes (e.g., Guion, 1973), whether it was different from other unit-level constructs (e.g., James & Jones, 1974), whether it should be measured as a perception (e.g., Payne & Pugh, 1976), and why its relationship with outcomes was not more consistent (e.g., Hellriegel & Slocum, 1974). The resolution of these issues set the foundation for climate research for the decades to follow. One central clarification came from James and Jones (1974), who distinguished between psychological climate (climate at the individual level of analysis) and organizational climate (climate at the organizational or subunit level of analysis). Most contemporary climate research addresses organizational climate, viewing climate as a property of the unit that is clearly distinct from individual perceptions. Another important clarification that emerged was Schneider's (1975) differentiation of molar climate, or the generic environment in the organization, and focused climate, or those facets of the environment that are most relevant for a specific criterion of interest. Research on molar climate tends to address a broad number of dimensions intended to capture the many ways that employees might experience their work environments. In contrast, Schneider (1975) emphasized the value of a focused approach, arguing that if researchers focused on the most relevant aspects of the environment for a particular outcome, then the predictive validity of those climate measures should be stronger. Subsequent research on service climate (e.g., Schneider, Parkington, & Buxton, 1980) and safety climate (e.g., Zohar, 1980) supported this assertion. In fact, the idea of focused climates has been widely adopted such that researchers have distinguished types of focused climates, with some focused on the organization's strategic goals (e.g., safety, service) and others focused on internal processes (e.g., fairness, innovation; Ehrhart et al., 2014).

Another important issue that emerged from the critiques of climate in the 1970s was how to properly measure climate at the organization or subunit level. If organizational climate is grounded in shared perceptions, then it is necessary to demonstrate that individuals agree sufficiently in their perceptions such that the mean of their ratings is a valid representation of the unit's climate. Addressing these issues positioned climate research and researchers as a major influence on multilevel research design, measurement, and analysis (Klein & Kozlowski, 2000). From a measurement perspective, the wording of survey items became an important issue; if the goal is to have employees describe the organizational environment, then the items must be asked in a way to encourage description (instead of evaluation) and to have respondents report on what happens in the overall unit of interest (rather than their personal perspective or opinion). This approach is consistent with the "referent-shift" aspect of the referent-shift consensus model described by Chan (1998). The consensus or agreement part of that model reflects one of the other key issues addressed in climate research: how to demonstrate that there is consensus among raters within the unit of interest. Beginning with the work of James and his colleagues (James, 1982; James, Demaree, & Wolf, 1984), researchers have made significant advances on the topics of aggregate interrater agreement and reliability (Bliese, 2000; LeBreton & Senter, 2008). An in-depth discussion of these issues is beyond the scope here. However, the important takeaway is that researchers now have the tools to demonstrate that there is adequate agreement among respondents and that the relative proportion of between unit variance to within unit variance is high enough to support the aggregation of individual climate perceptions to the unit level. An important implication of these measurement and design issues is that climate can be studied both between organizations and at multiple levels within an organizational hierarchy (Powell & Butterfield, 1978; Schneider, 1975) as long as the researcher provides theoretical and analytical support for the level of interest and documents sufficient consensus at the level of analysis of interest.

Although much progress was made in clarifying the concept of climate throughout the 1970s and into the 1980s, research in the area waned, perhaps because of the rise in interest in the related concept of organizational culture. Nevertheless, a resurgence of research on climate occurred beginning in the late 1990s (Kuenzi & Schminke, 2009), and the popularity of the construct continues to be strong. Most of the contemporary literature on climate can be categorized as focused climate research at the unit or organizational level, and the foundation of this literature is the continued strength of the findings for climate's relationship with outcomes across levels of analysis. For instance, service climate has been shown to be related to a variety of service-related outcomes across levels of analysis, including customer satisfaction, financial outcomes, service behavior, and customer loyalty (e.g., Hong, Liao, Hu, & Jiang, 2013; Liao & Chuang, 2004; Schneider, Ehrhart, Mayer, Saltz, & Niles-Jolly, 2005; Schneider, Macey, Lee, & Young, 2009; Schneider, White, & Paul, 1998; Way, Sturman, & Raab, 2010). Safety climate has been shown to be associated with safety behavior, accidents, and injuries (Beus, Payne, Bergman, & Arthur, 2010; Christian, Bradley, Wallace, & Burke, 2009; Hofmann & Stetzer, 1996; Zohar, 1980, 2000). Justice climate has been shown to be related to team performance, turnover, absenteeism, citizenship behavior, and job attitudes (Colquitt, Noe, & Jackson, 2002; Ehrhart, 2004; Liao & Rupp, 2005; Naumann & Bennett, 2000; Simons & Roberson, 2003; Whitman, Caleo, Carpenter, Horner, & Bernerth, 2012). And as a final example, ethical climate has been associated with fewer unethical behaviors (such as lying or organizational deviance; Martin & Cullen, 2006; Peterson, 2002), more ethical behaviors (such as ethical management and whistle-blowing; Deshpande, George, &

Joseph, 2000; Rothwell & Baldwin, 2007), and more positive employee attitudes (such as satisfaction and commitment; Martin & Cullen, 2006; Treviño, Butterfield, & McCabe, 1998). This list is merely a sampling; the focused climate construct has been applied to many more organizational processes and strategic outcomes with consistently strong findings for its predictive validity (see Ehrhart et al., 2014; Kuenzi & Schminke, 2009, for detailed reviews). Just as the number of focused climates that researchers have studied is substantial, so also is the number of focused climates that could potentially be created in organizations. The climate literature has not directly addressed the choices that organizations or leaders make in the climates they establish, and thus precisely how to choose the "best" set of focused climates on which to focus has not received attention to our knowledge. However, the Gestalt psychology tradition behind much climate research (Schneider, 1975) suggests that every possible facet of climate need not be assessed. So, we can state that if companies simultaneously address a set of process issues (e.g., fairness, ethics, inclusion) that collectively such emphases will send a message to employees that the organization cares about people. In addition, if a company simultaneously emphasized a climate for service and a climate for innovation, these would not necessarily send conflicting messages about where the company believes important effort and attention is required. The issue of multiple focused climates provides an interesting area for future research as well as a basis for an integration of research on climate and strategy.

As support has grown for the relationship between focused climates and outcomes, researchers have integrated more nuance and complexity into their research designs. One area that has received growing interest is the topic of climate strength. Although researchers typically must demonstrate that there is adequate agreement within groups to justify aggregation, research on climate strength addresses the extent to which there is agreement as a variable in and of itself. The typical approach to studying climate strength is to treat it as a moderator of the relationship between climate and outcomes. The theory behind this approach is that relatively greater consensus in climate reports provides a more reliable indicator and will thus be more strongly related to outcomes of interest. Research findings on this proposed moderated relationship have been mixed, with some studies finding support (e.g., Colquitt et al., 2002; Drach-Zahavy & Somech, 2013; González-Romá, Peiró, & Tordera, 2002; Schneider, Salvaggio, & Subirats, 2002) and others not (e.g., Dawson, González-Romá, Davis, & West, 2008; Lindell & Brandt, 2000; Rafferty & Jimmieson, 2010; Sowinski, Fortmann, & Lezotte, 2008). Even when climate strength has not had moderating effects, however, it has still shown some direct positive effects on outcomes like store profitability, turnover, team-level stress, and well-being (Rafferty & Jimmieson, 2010; Sowinski et al., 2008). Additional research on climate strength has provided some insight into why some climates may be stronger or weaker than others. Factors such as leadership, social interaction, group cohesiveness, group size, average tenure, and team diversity have all been identified as antecedents of climate strength (Beus, Bergman, & Payne, 2010; Colquitt et al., 2002; González-Romá et al., 2002; Luria, 2008; Naumann & Bennett, 2000; Roberson, 2006; Zohar & Luria, 2004).

Researchers have also shown interest in other possible boundary conditions of the relationships between climate and outcomes. The goal of much of this research is to uncover the factors that strengthen or weaken the effects of climate. In the service climate literature, for example, a series of studies has shown that its effects are stronger when the level of customer contact is high, when the product is less tangible, when service employees are more interdependent, and when the internal service levels (the service provided to front-line workers from other units within the organization) are high (Dietz, Pugh, & Wiley, 2004; Ehrhart, Witt, Schneider, & Perry, 2011; Mayer, Ehrhart, & Schneider, 2009). Another example of research on climate's boundary condition is in the safety literature, where higher levels of a safety climate are associated with fewer back injuries and medication errors for nurses, but only when patient complexity is high (Hofmann & Mark, 2006). From the justice literature, there is some evidence to suggest that the effects of justice climate on individual-level outcomes are stronger when group power distance is low or when the individual's justice orientation is high (Liao & Rupp, 2005; Yang, Mossholder, & Peng, 2007). In addition, recent research suggests that one climate may influence the outcomes of another climate. For instance, diversity climate has the strongest relationships with customer satisfaction when service climate and minority representation are both high (McKay, Avery, Liao, & Morris, 2011), and high levels of procedural justice climate can buffer the negative effects of a low distributive justice climate (Spell & Arnold, 2007).

Additional research on moderation effects has focused on climate as the moderator. For individual-level relationships, the thinking is that the environment (as indicated by the climate) plays a role in the extent to which individual differences manifest themselves behaviorally. Along these lines, research has shown that customer orientation is more strongly related to service behavior when service climate levels are high, the idea being that there are more opportunities for individuals with a high customer orientation to provide high-quality customer service when they are in a climate that supports such high-quality customer service (Grizzle, Zablah, Brown, Mowen, & Lee, 2009). Another way of thinking about climate as a moderator is that it can compensate for low levels of important individual differences in employee behavior. For instance, research has shown that individual-level customer orientation and job autonomy are important predictors of customer-focused voice behaviors when service climate levels are low, but when service climate levels are high, employees tend to perform such voice behaviors no matter their customer orientation or autonomy (Lam & Mayer, 2014). Climate is also studied as a moderator of the effects of unit-level constructs. In some of this research, the idea is that the environment must be right for certain variables to be maximally effective. So, for instance, process innovation will result in improved firm performance, but only when the climate for initiative and the climate for psychological safety are high (Baer & Frese, 2003). Along the same lines, safety training will have a greater impact on reducing accidents when safety climate levels are high (Burke, Chan-Serafin, Salvador, Smith, & Sarpy, 2008). The diversity climate literature has shown that the presence of a positive diversity climate can result in a positive relationship between racial or ethnic heterogeneity and unit performance versus a negative relationship when diversity climate levels are low (Gonzalez & DeNisi, 2009), and it can reduce or eliminate racial differences in sales performance (McKay, Avery, & Morris, 2008). Thus, research indicates that focused climates can play a particularly critical role in establishing the context for the effectiveness of organizational processes and functioning.

As climate research has increased in its complexity, another direction it has taken is to clarify the mechanisms through which various constructs internal to the organization are related to organizational effectiveness. This category of research includes research on antecedents of climate, on climate as a mediator of the effects of other variables, and mediators of climate's effects on organizational outcomes. All of this research provides insights into either climate as a mechanism for how other variables are related to effectiveness or the processes through which climate has its effects on outcomes. With regard to the latter, perhaps the most studied variable has been leadership, with roots going back to the earliest climate research by Lewin, Lippitt, and White (1939) on how the democratic versus autocratic style of the leader impacted the social climate of the group. Leadership is one of the primary antecedents of climate, and climate appears to be one of the main mechanisms through which leaders have an influence on the units they lead. Research on leadership and climate has examined leader individual differences such as goal orientation (Dragoni, 2005), core self-evaluations (Salvaggio et al., 2007), and personality (Mayer, Nishii, Schneider, & Goldstein, 2007), negative leader behaviors such as undermining (Frazier & Bowler, 2015), general leadership styles such as transformational leadership (Zohar, 2002; Zohar & Tenne-Gazit, 2008) and servant leadership (Ehrhart, 2004; Walumbwa, Hartnell, & Oke, 2010), and strategically focused leadership behaviors such as service leadership (Jiang, Chuang, & Chiao, 2015; Schneider et al., 2005) and safety leadership (Barling, Loughlin, & Kelloway, 2002). Beyond leadership, researchers have examined a number of "foundation issues" (Schneider et al., 1998) that are viewed as being necessary but not sufficient for the development of a focused climate. These foundation issues have included organizational resources (Salanova, Agut, & Peiró, 2005), organizational rewards (Wallace, Popp, & Mondore, 2006), human resource practices (Hong et al., 2013), high performance work systems (Jiang et al., 2015), and a general concern for employees (Towler, Lezotte, & Burke, 2011). These foundation issues would seem to create a generally positive work environment for employees, which is the primary focus of research on molar climate. Thus, the literatures on molar climates and focused climates can be integrated by viewing the molar climates, which might emerge from simultaneously focusing on multiple process climates, as supporting employee morale, and then a strategic climate as indicating the target for employees' efforts toward specific strategic organizational goals. In other words, the positive molar climate makes employees more receptive to what the organization is attempting to accomplish through its strategic climate(s). The strategic focus of the climate then can increase employees' motivation, effort, and engagement toward the accomplishment of the organization's strategic goals, as well as increase employees' strategically focused behaviors and performance (Abdelhadi & Drach-Zahavy, 2012; Greenslade & Jimmieson, 2011; Jiang et al., 2015; Neal & Griffin, 2006; Schneider et al., 2005). It is employees acting in ways consistent with the climate in their unit that ultimately produces the outcomes of interest, such as customer satisfaction, reduced accident rates, and financial performance (as in models presented by Ehrhart & Raver, 2014; Ostroff, Kinicki, & Muhammad, 2012).

Finally, there are a few trends in recent climate research that are likely to persist in the future. One is the study of how multiple climates operate simultaneously in work units. Recent research has explored how both diversity climate and service climate interact in predicting customer satisfaction (McKay et al., 2011) and how safety climate, service climate, and productivity climate simultaneously influence the relationship between safety versus production conflict and safety behavior (Jiang & Probst, 2015). Related to this research is how climate operates simultaneously at multiple levels of the organization, and how the alignment across levels is critical for organizational effectiveness (Zohar & Luria, 2005). Another trend is to examine configurations or profiles of climate dimensions (Schulte, Ostroff, Shmulyian, &

Kinicki, 2009), an idea that has also been applied to climate strength by examining patterns of (dis)agreement in work units (González-Romá & Hernández, 2014). A final trend is the development of interventions specifically to improve the climate of work units. This trend has been particularly prevalent in the safety literature (Kines et al., 2010; Naveh & Katz-Navon, 2015; Zohar & Polachek, 2014), although interventions have been developed in other areas as well, including how leaders can develop a climate for the implementation of evidence-based practices in mental health organizations (Aarons, Ehrhart, Farahnak, & Hurlburt, 2015). The focus on leadership in these interventions highlights the critical role leaders seem to play in developing and changing organizational climate, and the inclusion of leadership at multiple levels in some of them (e.g., Aarons et al., 2015; Naveh & Katz-Navon, 2015) again highlights the importance of the alignment of leadership across levels to develop positive, strong molar, process, and strategic climates. Nevertheless, more research is needed on how climates emerge and are created, and specifically on the role of leadership and culture in their creation.

ORGANIZATIONAL CULTURE

Organizational culture has been defined as "a pattern of shared basic assumptions learned by [an organization] as it solved its problems of external adaptation and internal integration, which has worked well enough to be considered valid and, therefore, to be taught to new members as the correct way to perceive, think, and feel in relation to those problems" (Schein, 2010, p. 18). Organizational culture is closely aligned with the values and beliefs that manifest themselves in almost all aspects of organizational life, and which ultimately make the organization unique. Most scholars point to Pettigrew's (1979) article analyzing the culture of a British private boarding school as the starting point of contemporary research on organizational culture. Although the concept of culture had been applied to organizations before that point, Pettigrew's article legitimized academic research on the topic (Alvesson & Berg, 1992) and coincided with a rise in interest in organizational behavior by both academics and practitioners. In fact, it could be argued that practitioner interest in organizational culture is what pushed academics to explore the concept in more depth, as books on the topic gained strong popularity in the business world (e.g., Deal & Kennedy, 1982; Ouchi, 1981; Pascale & Athos, 1982; Peters & Waterman, 1982). Throughout the 1980s and 1990s, in particular, the concept of organizational culture and its emphasis on the expressive and symbolic aspects of organizational life received extensive attention, eventually becoming a cornerstone topic in the literature on organizational behavior and management (Alvesson, 2011).

With the popularity of organizational culture came a variety of perspectives on how it should be conceptualized and studied. Although there are many ways of categorizing and organizing these different approaches (which have been addressed in depth elsewhere; see Alvesson, 1993, 2002; Giorgi, Lockwood, & Glynn, 2015; Martin & Frost, 1996; Ott, 1989; Trice & Beyer, 1993), one broad but useful distinction is between cultures as something organizations *have* and something organizations *are* (Smircich, 1983). When culture is conceptualized as something organizations *have*, it is treated as an organizational variable to be studied side-by-side with other organizational variables, with the goal of understanding how it relates to organizational effectiveness, typically with a management audience in mind. When culture is conceptualized as something organizations *are*, it is viewed as a root metaphor with the goal of understanding the symbolic meaning behind the day-to-day experiences of organizational life, with a particular interest in understanding those experiences from the perspective of organizational members. These two perspectives for studying and understanding organizational culture tend to be related to the methods used for studying organizational culture. Because those who view organizations as *having* cultures tend to be interested in predicting organizational outcomes and making comparisons across organizations, the tendency is to use quantitative methods, particularly surveys, to measure culture. Because those who view culture as something organizations *are* tend to be interested in understanding the insider's perspective and in the deeper layers of organizational culture that organizational members may not even be fully aware of, the propensity is to use qualitative methods that can provide rich, in-depth accounts of organizational life. Although this description is fairly broad and groups a wide variety of perspectives and methods into two general categories, overlooking a number of important distinctions in culture research, it is a useful starting point for understanding how culture is studied.

One area of commonality in these perspectives is that culture has deep elements that capture the core assumptions and basic values that are pervasive across the organization. These deeper elements are then manifested in outer, more observable elements, which constitute a variety of cultural forms such as language, stories, rituals, ceremonies, traditions, behavioral norms, dress, the physical arrangement of the space, and many more. These outer elements are more obvious and easier to access by outsiders; however, their meaning may not be as obvious without a full understanding of the deeper cultural layers. The most widely cited framework of the levels of culture comes from the work of Schein (2010). He labeled the deepest layers of culture as underlying assumptions, noting that they make up the essence of organizational culture, guiding how organizational members think and behave, even if they are outside of workers' conscious experiences. The intermediate layer of culture identified by Schein was espoused values. Espoused values constitute what organizational members and particularly management say is most important to them; however, they may be more aspirational than reality, and potentially biased to give a positive impression to outsiders about the organization. Finally, Schein labeled the outermost layer of culture as the artifacts; as noted previously, these elements may provide a starting point for understanding culture, but more digging is needed to understand the "true" culture, especially because the same cultural artifacts can have very different meanings across organizations. Although other authors have included additional layers such as patterns of behavior and behavioral norms (Rousseau, 1990; Sathe, 1985), values-in-use (Ott, 1989), enacted content themes (Siehl & Martin, 1990), and strategic beliefs (Lundberg, 1990), the most important takeaway is that culture is deep and manifests itself throughout the organization in a variety of ways. Those manifestation processes are dynamic, and do not go only from the deeper to outer layers; changes in the outer layers may also influence the deeper levels (Hatch, 1993).

One major question that has been addressed in the organizational culture literature is its source. Perhaps the most cited source is the founder. As Schein (1983, 2010) has discussed in depth, the founder's ideas and decisions when first establishing the organization are infused with his or her values, assumptions, and beliefs. One of the ways the founder has a major influence on the culture that develops is through the people he or she brings into the organization. As outlined in Schneider's (1987) attraction-selection-attrition (ASA) model, the individuals the founder hires to work with him or her and who are retained over time will tend to be those who share the personality, values, and beliefs of the founder. Furthermore, new workers who are attracted to the organization will tend to also have commonalities with those currently in the organization. As the ASA cycle continues over time, the organization's culture will tend to be consistent with the original founder's values, perpetuating his or her influence over time. The founder is not the only influence on an organization's culture, however. Schein (2010) also discussed the role of the collective learning of the organization's members; the organization's success acts as a reinforcement and the members of the organization will tend to continue those behaviors that have been successful in the past, sometimes even after the environment has changed and those behaviors no longer result in the same success. The organization is also a product of its environment. For instance, organizations within the same industry tend to mimic each other and work within the same sets of constraints and with the same external parties (e.g., government bodies, customers, etc.; Ott, 1989). Certain industries tend to also be made up of workers from certain professions, and professions tend to have their own cultures that can influence the organization's culture (Holland, 1997; Louis, 1985; Trice & Beyer, 1993; Van Maanen & Barley, 1984). The organization's culture is also embedded in a national culture, and although there is variability within any national culture in the nature of organizations and their cultures, research indicates that between 21% and 47% of the variance in organizational culture may be due to national culture (Brodbeck, Hanges, Dickson, Gupta, & Dorfman, 2004).

How organizational culture is perpetuated over time is the focus of the literature on socialization. Socialization is a critical variable in the organizational culture literature, so much so that Schein (2010) included how culture is taught to new members in the very definition of culture. It is critical because organizational culture must be passed on to new members to be perpetuated over time, and if it is not perpetuated, then its effects will be minimized. Thus, the literature on socialization is quite developed and has addressed a number of facets of the socialization process. One of the types of information that new employees learn during socialization involves the larger organization within which they will function (Ostroff & Kozlowski, 1992), including such cultural information as the language and terminology employees use, the internal politics of the organization, the organization's goals and values, and the history of how the organization was founded and how it developed over time (Chao, O'Leary-Kelly, Wolf, Klein, & Gardner, 1994). Newcomers learn this information from a variety of sources, including organizational literature, formal socialization programs, mentors, supervisors, and coworkers, ordered here from those over which the organization has the most control to those over which it has the least (Cooper-Thomas & Anderson, 2006). Along this continuum, the cultural information becomes richer, and there are more opportunities for employees to learn where the espoused values of the organization may contradict employees' actual experiences. How organizations use formal approaches to socialization has been another focus of research, with two broad categories of socialization tactics (Jones, 1986): those that are less formal and that are customized to the individual (individualized tactics) and those that are more formal and structured for groups of employees (institutionalized tactics). Although the more individualized tactics may be more flexible and may promote more innovation (Jones, 1986), institutionalized tactics tend to produce more positive outcomes for employees (Bauer, Bodner, Erdogan, Truxillo, & Tucker, 2007). Finally, as employees are formally or informally socialized, they go through a number of phases in the process of becoming full members of the organization, along the lines of the literature on rites of passage (Trice & Beyer, 1993). One socialization model includes four stages of socialization (Ashforth, Sluss, & Harrison, 2007): anticipation (including the information new employees learn and the expectations they form before entry), encounter (new employees' entry into the organization and the comparison between the actual experiences and their expectations), adjustment (when new employees learn more about the organization and figure out how things work), and stabilization (when employees have made the transition from an outsider to an insider).

Especially for practitioners and researchers viewing culture as something an organization has, the importance of the concept of organizational culture rests in its relationship with organizational effectiveness. There are multiple reasons for expecting a link between organizational culture and effectiveness, including the tendency for a strong culture to align employees around the organization's goals and values, culture's informal influence and control of employees that reinforce the performance of desired behaviors, and the humanistic orientation of most of the culture literature emphasizing employee participation and well-being, which increases employee commitment and motivation (Denison & Mishra, 1995; Kotter & Heskett, 1992). Sackmann's (2011) review of the relationship between culture and performance found general support for the existence of this relationship. Hartnell, Ou, and Kinicki's (2011) meta-analysis of 94 independent samples was also supportive of culture dimensions predicting a variety of organizational outcomes, including employee attitudes, operational performance, and financial performance. Moreover, recent research on the causal sequence of culture and performance found consistent support for culture predicting performance rather than the other way around (Boyce, Nieminen, Gillespie, Ryan, & Denison, 2015). Although there is evidence for the culture-performance relationship, there are also those that question whether the search for a direct link between culture and performance makes sense in light of the complexity of the organizational culture construct, including its many forms and multiple layers (Alvesson, 2002; Saffold, 1988; Siehl & Martin, 1990). Others have pointed out the need to take into account the situation and how the link between cultural components and effectiveness is likely to vary depending on the organization's external environment (Kotter & Heskett, 1992; Sørensen, 2002). Despite these criticisms and the general lack of theory guiding research in this area (Wilderom, Glunk, & Maslowski, 2000), most culture researchers agree that the construct has important implications for organizational effectiveness, whatever form the exact relationships may take.

Although much of the literature discusses organizational culture as if it was uniform across the organization, that is not always the case; there can be (and perhaps typically are) subcultures that also exist throughout the organization, and some cultures are generally weaker or stronger than others. These differences are highlighted in Martin's (1992, 2002) organizational culture framework that includes three perspectives on the uniformity of culture in organizations: (1) integration (a focus on cultural elements that are shared across the organization), (2) differentiation (the acknowledgement of subcultures within the organization that may be inconsistent with each other or in conflict), and (3) fragmentation (in which ambiguity, tension, and paradox are the primary focus). Most of the literature on organizational culture tends to take an integration perspective, but the other two perspectives shed light on important aspects of organizational culture as well. The differentiation perspective emphasizes subcultures, which can come in many shapes and forms, and exist for a variety of reasons. Subcultures can come to exist within divisions or departments, or be based on occupation or profession, skill requirements for jobs, management level, products sold, or union membership (Gregory, 1983; Hopkins, Hopkins, & Mallette, 2005; Martin & Siehl, 1983; Morgan & Ogbonna, 2008; Trice & Beyer, 1993; Van Maanen, 1991; Van Maanen & Barley, 1985). Martin and Siehl (1983) described three general types of subcultures: (1) enhancing subcultures in which a certain group within the organization identifies with and represents the culture to a stronger degree than is found elsewhere in the organization; (2) an orthogonal subculture that shares in the general organizational culture but also has a separate set of values that are not in conflict with the overall values in the culture; and (3) a countercultural subculture that is in direct opposition to the overall or dominant culture. Closely related to the fragmentation perspective is the idea of culture strength, in that the weaker the culture, the more it will be characterized by ambiguity. The strength of the culture has been discussed in a variety of ways, including the extent the cultural values are shared throughout the organization, how deeply members hold the values and beliefs of the culture, how long the culture has existed within the organization, the extent to which the deeper-level assumptions and values are manifested broadly across organizational artifacts, and the range of beliefs or behaviors that are targeted by the organization's culture (Chatman, Caldwell, O'Reilly, & Doerr, 2014; Louis, 1985; Mannix, Thatcher, & Jehn, 2001; Payne, 2000, 2001; Saffold, 1988). There is evidence to suggest that a strong culture is associated with higher organizational effectiveness (Denison, 1990; Gordon & DiTomaso, 1992; Kotter & Heskett, 1992), although others have found such effects can vary depending on environmental factors (Lee & Yu, 2004; Sørensen, 2002). Still others have suggested that a strong culture will have consistent relationships with effectiveness when the content of the culture emphasizes flexibility and adaptability (Chatman et al., 2014; Flynn & Chatman, 2001; Kotter & Heskett, 1992). The common theme across these perspectives is that there is not always agreement about organizational culture, and it is important to account for potential subcultures or the possibility of weak cultures.

Finally, the issue of change is prevalent throughout the culture literature, whether it be in terms of how to change a culture or the implications of culture for other types of change. The topic of organizational change has received extensive attention (Burke, 2011; Cummings & Worley, 2014; Kotter, 2012), so the focus here will be on those issues most commonly discussed in the organizational culture literature. Cultures exist to provide order and to remove ambiguity and uncertainty; as a result, they are very resistant to change (Deal & Kennedy, 1982; Ogbonna & Harris, 2014; Ott, 1989; Schein, 2010; Trice & Beyer, 1993). In fact, one of the major critiques of the early practitioner literature on culture was that it characterized culture change as overly simple and straightforward (Martin, 1985). This is not to say that cultures do not change; the issue is more whether organizational leaders and consultants can plan for and initiate that change, or whether it is caused by a variety of uncontrollable forces and is, thus, unpredictable (Alvesson & Sveningsson, 2008). It may be the case that culture can be changed at some times more easily than others; for instance, leaders may be more able to change culture at certain points in the organization's life cycle or when the organization is experiencing a crisis (Louis, 1985; Lundberg, 1985; Schein, 2010; Siehl, 1985). It may be more useful to think about how cultural elements can be leveraged to bring about positive change in an organization, and to avoid attempting to change less desirable aspects of the culture unless they are in direct opposition to necessary changes to be made (Schein, 2010). Even then, it would probably be most effective to focus culture change efforts as narrowly as possible, always remembering that cultures exist for reasons of history and prior success so they will be durable over time and be difficult to change.

INTEGRATION AND CONCLUSION

Although both organizational climate and organizational culture address the psychosocial organizational environment, the two constructs have existed on relatively parallel tracks for the last several decades, with little integration between the two. Building on earlier work by Denison (1996), Ehrhart, Schneider, and Macey (2014) highlighted a number of similarities and differences between the two constructs to emphasize what they have in common and to clarify their unique aspects. With regard to commonalities, both constructs provide a macro perspective of organizational context and both are primarily focused on the context rather than the idiosyncratic experiences of individuals. In addition, both place considerable emphasis on the shared experiences of employees, the role of meaning, the role of leadership, issues of strength or alignment, and the implications of the context for organizational effectiveness. Although they have many similarities, there are also some critical differences. For instance, they come from different theoretical and methodological traditions; the concept of culture is rooted in anthropology where qualitative methods have traditionally been favored over quantitative, whereas climate is rooted in psychology with an emphasis on surveys and quantitative analysis. Organizational culture is a broader construct that encompasses much of employees' experiences at work, whereas climate is more narrowly defined in terms of employees' shared perceptions of the organization's policies, practices, procedures, and reward systems. The deeper layers of culture are potentially outside of the day-to-day awareness of employees, whereas climate is based on employees' reports of what is happening around them at work. Although both culture and climate are difficult to change, the deepest assumptions and core values of culture are more difficult to change than climate. Finally, climate research has moved in the direction of being studied with a particular strategic or process focus, whereas culture research tends to take a broader perspective attempting to be more all-encompassing and less focused.

These differences in research on organizational climate and culture are important because they suggest the strengths of each literature and how integrative approaches that take advantage of this complementarity could provide additional insights beyond what can currently be found in either literature alone. Several recent efforts have attempted to demonstrate how the two constructs may work together to yield a better understanding of organizational environments and their outcomes. For instance, Schneider, Ehrhart, and Macey (2011) proposed the "climcult framework" in which positive, humanistic values create a culture of well-being, which forms a foundation for strategically oriented climates and the achievement of the organization's strategic goals. At the same time, a positive culture for employees helps make the organization an attractive place to work, and attracting and retaining talent also contribute to organizational effectiveness. In another model, Ostroff, Kinicki, and Muhammad (2012) depicted organizational culture as influencing climate through the structures and processes that are put into place as organizations grow and develop. The alignment of culture, structure, practices, and climate shapes the collective attitudes and behavior of employees, which then lead to the attainment of important organizational outcomes. Finally, Zohar and Hofmann (2012) aligned organizational climate with the concept of enacted values. In their model, climate perceptions of strategic climates represent employee perceptions of what the actual values and priorities are in the organization. These can be contrasted with the espoused values, and gaps between the two provide insight into the core assumptions and values that make up the deep layers of culture.

The study of organizational climate and culture has provided deep insights into the role of the organizational environment for employees and organizational effectiveness. Although much has been learned, there is still work to be done. Learning from the culture literature, climate researchers can include a broader variety of variables in their research, focus more on issues of socialization and change, and add qualitative methods to complement their quantitative designs. Learning from the climate literature, culture researchers can develop more of a strategic focus in their conceptualization and study of culture, include more complex models with mediators and moderators of the relationship between culture and effectiveness, and focus more attention on how culture research is relevant for organizational leaders. Ultimately, the usefulness of the two constructs is derived from the insights they provide about how organizations come to be and how they can be changed. First founders and then leaders implement policies and procedures to meet their goals, thereby creating strategic climates within their organizations. Their actions reflect their own values, and those values become enacted in the behaviors displayed in the organization that literally operationalize the core values that are the organization's culture. At the same time, the climates that are created reinforce behavior, and as certain behaviors become normative across organizational members, it becomes taken for granted that they represent the appropriate and proper way to behave. Insights from both literatures are needed to fully understand these processes, and thus, the integration of ideas and approaches from both lines of research will result in a richer, deeper understanding of the psychosocial organizational environment for leaders, practitioners, and researchers.

ACKNOWLEDGMENTS

We greatly appreciate the feedback from Dan Denision on an earlier draft of this article. His comments were very helpful to us in framing the potential integration of climate and culture and their use.

REFERENCES

Aarons, G. A., Ehrhart, M. G., Farahnak, L. R., & Hurlburt, M. S. (2015). Leadership and organizational change for implementation (LOCI): A randomized mixed method pilot study of a leadership and organization development intervention for evidence-based practice implementation. *Implementation Science*, *10*, 11.

Abdelhadi, N., & Drach-Zahavy, A. (2012). Promoting patient care: Work engagement as a mediator between ward service climate and patient-centred care. *Journal of Advanced Nursing*, *68*(6), 1276–1287.

Alvesson, M. (1993). *Cultural perspectives on organizations*. Cambridge, U.K.: Cambridge University Press.

Alvesson M. (2002). *Understanding organizational culture*. London: SAGE.

Alvesson, M. (2011). Organizational culture: Meaning, discourse, and identity. In N. M. Ashkanasy, C. P. M. Wilderom, & M. F. Peterson (Eds.), *Handbook of organizational culture and climate* (2d ed., pp. 11–28). Thousand Oaks, CA: SAGE.

Alvesson, M., & Berg, P. O. (1992). *Corporate culture and organizational symbolism*. New York: de Gruyter.

Alvesson, M., & Sveningsson, S. (2008). *Changing organizational culture: Cultural change work in progress*. New York: Routledge.

Ashforth, B. E., Sluss, D. M., & Harrison, S. H. (2007). Socialization in organizational contexts. In G. P. Hodgkinson & J. K. Ford (Eds.), *International review of industrial and organizational psychology* (Vol. 22, pp. 1–70). Chichester, U.K.: Wiley.

Baer, M., & Frese, M. (2003). Innovation is not enough: Climates for initiative and psychological safety, process innovations, and firm performance. *Journal of Organizational Behavior, 24*, 45–68.

Barling, J., Loughlin, C., & Kelloway, E. K. (2002). Development and test of a model linking safety-specific transformational leadership and occupational safety. *Journal of Applied Psychology, 87*, 488–496.

Bauer, T. N., Bodner, T., Erdogan, B., Truxillo, D. M., & Tucker, J. S. (2007). Newcomer adjustment during organizational socialization: A meta-analytic review of antecedents, outcomes, and methods. *Journal of Applied Psychology, 92*, 707–721.

Beus, J. M., Bergman, M. E., & Payne, S. C. (2010). The influence of organizational tenure on safety climate strength: A first look. *Accident Analysis and Prevention, 42*, 1431–1437.

Beus, J. M., Payne, S. C., Bergman, M. E., & Arthur, W., Jr. (2010). Safety climate and injuries: An examination of theoretical and empirical relationships. *Journal of Applied Psychology, 95*, 713–727.

Bliese, P. D. (2000). Within-group agreement, non-independence, and reliability: Implications for data aggregation and analyses. In K. J. Klein & S. W. J. Kozlowski (Eds.), *Multilevel theory, research and methods in organizations: Foundations, extensions, and new directions* (pp. 349–381). San Francisco: Jossey-Bass.

Boyce, A. S., Nieminen, L. R., Gillespie, M. A., Ryan, A. M., & Denison, D. R. (2015). Which comes first, organizational culture or performance? A longitudinal study of causal priority with automobile dealerships. *Journal of Organizational Behavior, 36*(3), 339–359.

Brodbeck, F. C., Hanges, P. J., Dickson, M., Gupta, V., & Dorfman, P. (2004). Societal culture and industrial sector influences on organizational culture. In R. J. House, P. J. Hanges, M. Javidan, P. W. Dorfman, & V. Gupta (Eds.), *Culture, leadership, and organizations: The GLOBE study of 62 societies* (pp. 654–668). Thousand Oaks, CA: SAGE.

Burke, M. J., Chan-Serafin, S., Salvador, R., Smith, A., & Sarpy, S. A. (2008). The role of national culture and organizational climate in safety training effectiveness. *European Journal of Work and Organizational Psychology, 17*, 133–152.

Burke, W. W. (2011). *Organization change: Theory and practice* (3d ed.). Thousand Oaks, CA: SAGE.

Chan, D. (1998). Functional relations among constructs in the same content domain at different levels of analysis: A typology of composition models. *Journal of Applied Psychology, 83*, 234–246.

Chao, G. T., O'Leary-Kelly, A. M., Wolf, S., Klein, H. J., & Gardner, P. D. (1994). Organizational socialization: Its content and consequences. *Journal of Applied Psychology, 79*(5), 730–743.

Chatman, J. A., Caldwell, D. F., O'Reilly, C. A., & Doerr, B. (2014). Parsing organizational culture: How the norm for adaptability influences the relationship between culture consensus and financial performance in high-technology firms. *Journal of Organizational Behavior, 35*(6), 785–808.

Christian, M. S., Bradley, J. C., Wallace, J. C., & Burke, M. J. (2009). Workplace safety: A meta-analysis of the roles of person and situation factors. *Journal of Applied Psychology, 94*, 1103–1127.

Colquitt, J. A., Noe, R. A., & Jackson, C. L. (2002). Justice in teams: Antecedents and consequences of procedural justice climate. *Personnel Psychology, 58*, 83–109.

Cooper-Thomas, H. D., & Anderson, N. (2006). Organizational socialization: A new theoretical model and recommendations for future research and HRM practices in organizations. *Journal of Managerial Psychology, 21*(5), 492–516.

Cummings, T., & Worley, C. (2014). *Organization development and change* (10th ed.). Stamford, CT: Cengage Learning.

Dawson, J. F., González-Romá, V., Davis, A., & West, M. A. (2008). Organizational climate and climate strength in UK hospitals. *European Journal of Work and Organizational Psychology, 17,* 89–111.

Deal, T. E., & Kennedy, A. A. (1982). *Corporate cultures: The rites and rituals of corporate life.* Reading, MA: Addison-Wesley.

Denison, D. R. (1990). *Corporate culture and organizational effectiveness.* New York: Wiley.

Denison, D. R. (1996). What *is* the difference between organizational culture and organizational climate? A native's point of view on a decade of paradigm wars. *Academy of Management Review, 21,* 619–654.

Denison, D. R., & Mishra, A. K. (1995). Toward a theory of organizational culture and effectiveness. *Organization Science, 6,* 204–223.

Deshpande, S. P., George, E., & Joseph, J. (2000). Ethical climates and managerial success in Russian organizations. *Journal of Business Ethics, 23*(2), 211–217.

Dietz, J., Pugh, S. D., & Wiley, J. W. (2004). Service climate effects on customer attitudes: An examination of boundary conditions. *Academy of Management Journal, 47,* 81–92.

Drach-Zahavy, A., & Somech, A. (2013). Linking task and goal interdependence to quality service: The role of the service climate. *Journal of Service Management, 24*(2), 151–169.

Dragoni, L. (2005). Understanding the emergence of state goal orientation in organizational work groups: The role of leadership and multi-level climate perceptions. *Journal of Applied Psychology, 90,* 1084–1095.

Ehrhart, K. H., Witt, L. A., Schneider, B., & Perry, S. J. (2011). Service employees give as they get: Internal service as a moderator of the service climate–service outcomes link. *Journal of Applied Psychology, 96*(2), 423–431.

Ehrhart, M. G. (2004). Leadership and procedural justice climate as antecedents of unit-level organizational citizenship behavior. *Personnel Psychology, 57,* 61–94.

Ehrhart, M. G., & Raver, J. L. (2014). The effects of organizational climate and culture on productive and counterproductive behavior. In B. Schneider & K. Barbera (Eds.), *The Oxford handbook of organizational climate and culture* (pp. 153–176). New York: Oxford University Press.

Ehrhart, M. G., Schneider, B., & Macey, W. H. (2014). *Organizational climate and culture: An introduction to theory, research, and practice.* New York: Routledge.

Flynn, F. J., & Chatman, J. A. (2001). Strong cultures and innovation: Oxymoron or opportunity? In C. L. Cooper, S. Cartwright, & P. C. Earley (Eds.), *The international handbook of organizational culture and climate* (pp. 263–287). New York: Wiley.

Frazier, M. L., & Bowler, W. M. (2015). Voice climate, supervisor undermining, and work outcomes: A group-level examination. *Journal of Management, 41*(3), 841–863.

Giorgi, S., Lockwood, C., & Glynn, M. A. (2015). The many faces of culture: Making sense of 30 years of research on culture in organization studies. *Academy of Management Annals, 9*(1), 1–54.

Gonzalez, J. A., & DeNisi, A. S. (2009). Cross-level effects of demography and diversity climate on organizational attachment and firm effectiveness. *Journal of Organizational Behavior, 30,* 21–40.

González-Romá, V., & Hernández, A. (2014). Climate uniformity: Its influence on team communication quality, task conflict, and team performance. *Journal of Applied Psychology, 99*(6), 1042–1058.

González- Romá, V., Peiró, J. M., & Tordera, N. (2002). An examination of the antecedents and moderator influences of climate strength. *Journal of Applied Psychology, 87,* 465–473.

Gordon, G., & DiTomaso, N. (1992). Predicting corporate performance from organizational culture. *Journal of Management Studies, 29,* 783–798.

Greenslade, J. H., & Jimmieson, N. L. (2011). Organizational factors impacting on patient satisfaction: A cross sectional examination of service climate and linkages to nurses' effort and performance. *International Journal of Nursing Studies, 48*(10), 1188–1198.

Gregory, K. (1983). Native-view paradigms: Multiple culture and culture conflicts in organizations. *Administrative Science Quarterly, 28*, 359–376.

Grizzle, J. W., Zablah, A. R., Brown, T. J., Mowen, J. C., & Lee, J. M. (2009). Employee customer orientation in context: How the environment moderates the influence of customer orientation on performance outcomes. *Journal of Applied Psychology, 94*(5), 1227–1242.

Guion, R. M. (1973). A note on organizational climate. *Organizational Behavior and Human Performance, 9*, 120–125.

Hartnell, C. A., Ou, A. Y., & Kinicki, A. (2011). Organizational culture and organizational effectiveness: A meta-analytic investigation of the competing values framework's theoretical suppositions. *Journal of Applied Psychology, 96*, 677–694.

Hatch, M. J. (1993). The dynamics of organizational culture. *Academy of Management Review, 18*, 657–693.

Hellriegel, D., & Slocum, J. W., Jr. (1974). Organizational climate: Measures, research, and contingencies. *Academy of Management Journal, 17*, 255–280.

Hofmann, D., & Stetzer, A. (1996). A cross-level investigation of factors influencing unsafe behaviors and accidents. *Personnel Psychology, 49*, 307–339.

Hofmann, D. A., & Mark, B. (2006). An investigation of the relationship between safety climate and medication errors as well as other nurse and patient outcomes. *Personnel Psychology, 59*, 847–869.

Holland, J. L. (1997). *Making vocational choices* (3d ed.). Odessa, FL: PAR.

Hong, Y., Liao, H., Hu, J., & Jiang, K. (2013). Missing link in the service profit chain: A meta-analytic review of the antecedents, consequences, and moderators of service climate. *Journal of Applied Psychology, 98*, 237–267.

Hopkins, W. E., Hopkins, S. A., & Mallette, P. (2005). *Aligning organizational subcultures for competitive advantage: A strategic change approach.* New York: Basic Books.

James, L. R. (1982). Aggregation bias in estimates of perceptual agreement. *Journal of Applied Psychology, 67*, 219–229.

James, L. R., Demaree, R. G., & Wolf, G. (1984). Estimating within-group interrater reliability with and without response bias. *Journal of Applied Psychology, 69*, 85–98.

James, L. R., & Jones, A. P. (1974). Organizational climate: A review of theory and research. *Psychological Bulletin, 81*, 1096–1112.

Jiang, K., Chuang, C., & Chiao, Y. (2015). Developing collective customer knowledge and service climate: The interaction between service-oriented high-performance work systems and service leadership. *Journal of Applied Psychology, 100*(4), 1089–1106.

Jiang, L., & Probst, T. M. (2015). The relationship between safety–production conflict and employee safety outcomes: Testing the impact of multiple organizational climates. *Work & Stress, 29*(2), 171–189.

Jones, G. R. (1986). Socialization tactics, self-efficacy, and newcomers' adjustments to organizations. *Academy of Management Journal, 29*, 262–279.

Kines, P., Andersen, L. P., Spangenberg, S., Mikkelsen, K. L., Dyreborg, J., & Zohar, D. (2010). Improving construction site safety through leader-based verbal safety communication. *Journal of Safety Research, 41*(5), 399–406.

Klein, K. J., & Kozlowski, S. W. J. (Eds.). (2000). *Multilevel theory, research and methods in organizations: Foundations, extensions, and new directions.* San Francisco: Jossey-Bass.

Kotter, J. (2012). *Leading change* (Rev. ed.). Boston: Harvard Business School Press.

Kotter, J. P., & Heskett, J. L. (1992). *Corporate culture and performance.* New York: Free Press.

Kuenzi, M., & Schminke, M. (2009). Assembling fragments into a lens: A review, critique, and proposed research agenda for the organizational work climate literature. *Journal of Management, 35*, 634–717.

Lam, C. F., & Mayer, D. M. (2014). When do employees speak up for their customers? A model of voice in a customer service context. *Personnel Psychology, 67*(3), 637–666.

LeBreton, J. M., & Senter, J. L. (2008). Answers to twenty questions about interrater reliability and interrater agreement. *Organizational Research Methods, 11*, 815–852.

Lee, S. K. J., & Yu, K. (2004). Corporate culture and organizational performance. *Journal of Managerial Psychology, 19*, 340–359.

Lewin, K., Lippitt, R., & White, R. K. (1939). Patterns of aggressive behavior in experimentally created "social climates." *Journal of Social Psychology, 10*, 271–299.

Liao, H., & Chuang, A. (2004). A multilevel investigation of factors influencing employee service performance and customer outcomes. *Academy of Management Journal, 47*, 41–58.

Liao, H., & Rupp, D. E. (2005). The impact of justice climate and justice orientation on work outcomes: A cross-level multifoci framework. *Journal of Applied Psychology, 90*, 242–256.

Lindell, M., & Brandt, C. (2000). Climate quality and climate consensus as mediators of the relationship between organizational antecedents and outcomes. *Journal of Applied Psychology, 85*, 331–348.

Louis, M. R. (1985). An investigator's guide to workplace culture. In P. J. Frost, L. F. Moore, M. R. Louis, C. C. Lundberg, & J. Martin (Eds.), *Organizational culture* (pp. 73–93). Beverly Hills, CA: SAGE.

Lundberg, C. (1985). On the feasibility of cultural intervention in organizations. In P. J. Frost, L. F. Moore, M. R. Louis, C. C. Lundberg, & J. Martin (Eds.), *Organizational culture* (pp. 169–185). Beverly Hills, CA: SAGE.

Lundberg, C. C. (1990). Surfacing organisational culture. *Journal of Managerial Psychology, 5*(4), 19–26.

Luria G. (2008). Climate strength—How leaders form consensus. *Leadership Quarterly, 19*, 42–53.

Mannix, E. A., Thatcher, S., & Jehn, K. A. (2001). Does culture always flow downstream? Linking group consensus and organizational culture. In C. L. Cooper, S. Cartwright, & P. C. Earley (Eds.), *The international handbook of organizational culture and climate* (pp. 289–306). New York: Wiley.

Martin, J. (1985). Can organizational culture be managed? In P. J. Frost, L. F. Moore, M. R. Louis, C. C. Lundberg, & J. Martin (Eds.), *Organizational culture* (pp. 95–98). Beverly Hills, CA: SAGE.

Martin, J. (1992). *Cultures in organizations: Three perspectives.* New York: Oxford University Press.

Martin, J. (2002). *Organizational culture: Mapping the terrain.* Thousand Oaks, CA: SAGE.

Martin, J., & Frost, P. (1996). The organizational culture war games: A struggle for intellectual dominance. In S. R. Clegg, C. Hardy, & W. R. Nord (Eds.), *Handbook of organizational studies* (pp. 599–621). Thousand Oaks, CA: SAGE.

Martin, J., & Siehl, C. J. (1983). Organizational culture and counterculture: An uneasy symbiosis. *Organizational Dynamics, 12*, 52–64.

Martin, K. D., & Cullen, J. B. (2006). Continuities and extensions of ethical climate theory: A meta-analytic review. *Journal of Business Ethics, 69*(2), 175–194.

Mayer, D. M., Ehrhart, M. G., & Schneider, B. (2009). Service attribute boundary conditions of the service climate–customer satisfaction link. *Academy of Management Journal, 52*, 1034–1050.

Mayer, D. M., Nishii, L. H., Schneider, B., & Goldstein, H. W. (2007). The precursors and products of fair climates: Group leader antecedents and employee attitudinal consequences. *Personnel Psychology, 60*, 929–963.

McKay, P. F., Avery, D. R., Liao, H., & Morris, M. A. (2011). Does diversity climate lead to customer satisfaction? It depends on the service climate and business unit demography. *Organization Science, 22*, 788–803.

McKay, P. F., Avery, D. R., & Morris, M. A. (2008). Mean racial-ethnic differences in employee sales performance: The moderating role of diversity climate. *Personnel Psychology, 61*, 349–374.

Morgan, P. I., & Ogbonna, E. (2008). Subcultural dynamics in transformation: A multi-perspective study of healthcare professionals. *Human Relations, 61*(1), 39–65.

Naumann, S. E., & Bennett, N. (2000). A case for procedural justice climate: Development and test of a multilevel model. *Academy of Management Journal, 43,* 881–889.

Naveh, E., & Katz-Navon, T. (2015). A longitudinal study of an intervention to improve road safety climate: Climate as an organizational boundary spanner. *Journal of Applied Psychology, 100,* 216–226.

Neal, A., & Griffin, M. A. (2006). A study of the lagged relationships among safety climate, safety motivation, safety behavior, and accidents at the individual and group levels. *Journal of Applied Psychology, 91,* 946–953.

Ogbonna, E., & Harris, L. C. (2014). Organizational cultural perpetuation: A case study of an English premier league football club. *British Journal of Management, 25*(4), 667–686.

Ostroff, C., Kinicki, A. J., & Muhammad, R. S. (2012). Organizational culture and climate. In N. W. Schmitt & S. Highhouse (Eds.), *Handbook of psychology, Vol. 12: Industrial and organizational psychology* (2d ed., pp. 643–676). Hoboken, NJ: Wiley.

Ostroff, C., & Kozlowski, S. W. J. (1992). Organizational socialization as a learning process: The role of information acquisition. *Personnel Psychology, 45*(4), 849–874.

Ott, J. S. (1989). *The organizational culture perspective.* Pacific Grove, CA: Brooks-Cole.

Ouchi, W. G. (1981). *Theory Z: How American business can meet the Japanese challenge.* Reading, MA: Addison-Wesley.

Pascale, R., & Athos, A. (1982). *The art of Japanese management.* London: Penguin.

Payne, R. L. (2000). Climate and culture: How close can they get? In N. M. Ashkanasy, C. P. M. Wilderom, & M. F. Peterson (Eds.), *Handbook of organizational culture and climate* (pp. 163–176). Thousand Oaks, CA: SAGE.

Payne, R. L. (2001). A three dimensional framework for analyzing and assessing culture/climate and its relevance for cultural change. In C. L. Cooper, S. Cartwright, & P. C. Earley (Eds.), *The international handbook of organizational culture and climate* (pp. 107–122). New York: Wiley.

Payne, R. L., & Pugh, D. S. (1976). Organizational structure and climate. In M. D. Dunnette (Ed.), *Handbook of industrial and organizational psychology* (pp. 1125–1173). Chicago: Rand McNally.

Peters, T. J., & Waterman, R. H., Jr. (1982). *In search of excellence.* New York: Harper & Row.

Peterson, D. K. (2002). Deviant workplace behavior and the organization's ethical climate. *Journal of Business and Psychology, 17,* 47–61.

Pettigrew, A. M. (1979). On studying organizational cultures. *Administrative Science Quarterly, 24,* 570–581.

Powell, G. N., & Butterfield, D. A. (1978). The case for subsystem climates in organizations. *Academy of Management Review, 3*(1), 151–157.

Rafferty, A. E., & Jimmieson, N. L. (2010). Team change climate: A group-level analysis of the relationships among change information and change participation, role stressors, and well-being. *European Journal of Work and Organizational Psychology, 19,* 551–586.

Roberson, Q. M. (2006). Justice in teams: The effects of interdependence and identification on referent choice and justice climate strength. *Social Justice Research, 19,* 323–344.

Rothwell, G. R., & Baldwin, J. N. (2007). Ethical climate theory, whistle-blowing, and the code of silence in police agencies in the state of Georgia. *Journal of Business Ethics, 70*(4), 341–361.

Rousseau, D. M. (1990). Assessing organizational culture: The case for multiple methods. In B. Schneider (Ed.), *Organizational climate and culture* (pp. 153–192). San Francisco: Jossey-Bass.

Sackmann, S. A. (2011). Culture and performance. In N. M. Ashkanasy, C. P. M. Wilderom, & M. F. Peterson (Eds.), *Handbook of organizational culture and climate* (2d ed., pp. 188–224). Thousand Oaks, CA: SAGE.

Saffold, G. S. (1988). Culture traits, strength, and organizational performance: Moving beyond "strong" culture. *Academy of Management Review, 13*, 546–558.

Salanova, M., Agut, S., & Peiró, J. M. (2005). Linking organizational resources and work engagement to employee performance and customer loyalty: The mediation of service climate. *Journal of Applied Psychology, 90*, 1217–1227.

Salvaggio, A. N., Schneider, B., Nishii, L. H., Mayer, D. M., Ramesh, A., & Lyon, J. S. (2007). Manager personality, manager service quality orientation, and service climate: Test of a model. *Journal of Applied Psychology, 92*, 1741–1750.

Sathe, V. (1985). *Culture and related corporate realities*. Homewood, IL: Irwin.

Schein, E. H. (1983). The role of the founder in creating organizational culture. *Organizational Dynamics, 12*(1), 13–28.

Schein, E. H. (2010). *Organizational culture and leadership* (4th ed.). San Francisco: Jossey-Bass.

Schneider, B. (1975). Organizational climates: An essay. *Personnel Psychology, 28*, 447–479.

Schneider, B. (1987). The people make the place. *Personnel Psychology, 40*, 437–453.

Schneider, B., Ehrhart, M. G., & Macey, W. A. (2011). Perspectives on organizational climate and culture. In S. Zedeck (Ed.), *APA handbook of industrial and organizational psychology: Vol. 1. Building and developing the organization* (pp. 373–414). Washington, DC: American Psychological Association.

Schneider, B., Ehrhart, M. G., Mayer, D. M., Saltz, J. L., & Niles-Jolly, K. (2005). Understanding organization-customer links in service settings. *Academy of Management Journal, 48*, 1017–1032.

Schneider, B., Macey, W. H., Lee, W., & Young, S. A. (2009). Organizational service climate drivers of the American Customer Satisfaction Index (ACSI) and financial and market performance. *Journal of Service Research, 12*, 3–14.

Schneider, B., Parkington, J. P., & Buxton, V. M. (1980). Employee and customer perceptions of service in banks. *Administrative Science Quarterly, 25*, 252–267.

Schneider, B., Salvaggio, A. N., & Subirats, M. (2002). Climate strength: A new direction for climate research. *Journal of Applied Psychology, 87*, 220–229.

Schneider, B., White, S. S., & Paul, M. C. (1998). Linking service climate and customer perceptions of service quality: Test of a causal model. *Journal of Applied Psychology, 83*, 150–163.

Schulte, M., Ostroff, C., Shmulyian, S., & Kinicki, A. (2009). Organizational climate configurations: Relationships to collective attitudes, customer satisfaction, and financial performance. *Journal of Applied Psychology, 94*, 618–634.

Siehl, C. (1985). After the founder: An opportunity to manage culture. In P. J. Frost, L. F. Moore, M. R. Louis, C. C. Lundberg, & J. Martin (Eds.), *Organizational culture* (pp. 125–140). Beverly Hills, CA: SAGE.

Siehl, C., & Martin, J. (1990). Organizational culture: A key to financial performance? In B. Schneider (Ed.), *Organizational climate and culture* (pp. 241–281). San Francisco: Jossey-Bass.

Simons, T., & Roberson, Q. (2003). Why managers should care about fairness: The effects of aggregate justice perceptions on organizational outcomes. *Journal of Applied Psychology, 88*, 432–443.

Smircich, L. (1983). Concepts of culture and organizational analysis. *Administrative Science Quarterly, 28*, 339–358.

Sørensen, J. B. (2002). The strength of corporate culture and the reliability of firm performance. *Administrative Science Quarterly, 47*, 70–91.

Sowinski, D. R., Fortmann, K. A., & Lezotte, D. V. (2008). Climate for service and the moderating effects of climate strength on customer satisfaction, voluntary turnover, and profitability. *European Journal of Work and Organizational Psychology, 17*, 73–88.

Spell, C. S., & Arnold, T. J. (2007). A multi-level analysis of organizational justice climate, structure, and employee mental health. *Journal of Management, 33*, 724–751.

Towler, A., Lezotte, D. V., & Burke, M. J. (2011). The service climate–firm performance chain: The role of customer retention. *Human Resource Management, 50*(3), 391–406.

Treviño, L. K., Butterfield, K. D., & McCabe, D. L. (1998). The ethical context in organizations: Influences on employee attitudes and behaviors. *Business Ethics Quarterly, 8,* 447–476.

Trice, H. M., & Beyer, J. M. (1993). *The cultures of work organizations.* Englewood Cliffs, NJ: Prentice-Hall.

Van Maanen, J. (1991). The smile factory: Work at Disneyland. In P. Frost, L. Moore, M. R. Louis, C. C. Lundberg, & J. Martin (Eds.), *Reframing organizational culture* (pp. 58–76). Newbury Park, CA: SAGE.

Van Maanen, J., & Barley, S. R. (1984). Occupational communities: Cultural control in organizations. In L. L. Cummings & B. M. Staw (Eds.), *Research in organizational behavior* (Vol. 6, pp. 287–365). Greenwich, CT: JAI Press.

Van Maanen, J., & Barley, S. R. (1985). Cultural organization: Fragments of a theory. In P. J. Frost, L. F. Moore, M. R. Louis, C. C. Lundberg, & J. Martin (Eds.), *Organizational culture* (pp. 31–54). Beverly Hills, CA: SAGE.

Wallace, J. C., Popp, E., & Mondore, S. (2006). Safety climate as a mediator between foundation climates and occupational accidents: A group-level investigation. *Journal of Applied Psychology, 91,* 681–688.

Walumbwa, F. O., Hartnell, C. A., & Oke, A. (2010). Servant leadership, procedural justice climate, service climate, employee attitudes, and organizational citizenship behavior: A cross-level investigation. *Journal of Applied Psychology, 95,* 517–529.

Way, S. A., Sturman, M. C., & Raab, C. (2010). What matters more? Contrasting the effects of job satisfaction and service climate on hotel food and beverage managers' job performance. *Cornell Hotel Quarterly, 51,* 379–397.

Whitman, D. S., Caleo, S., Carpenter, N. C., Horner, M. T., & Bernerth, J. B. (2012). Fairness at the collective level: A meta-analytic examination of the consequences and boundary conditions of organizational justice climate. *Journal of Applied Psychology, 97,* 776–791.

Wilderom, C. P. M., Glunk, U., & Maslowski, R. (2000). Organizational culture as a predictor of organizational performance. In N. M. Ashkanasy, C. P. M. Wilderom, & M. F. Peterson (Eds.), *Handbook of organizational culture and climate* (pp. 193–209). Thousand Oaks, CA: SAGE.

Yang, J., Mossholder, K. W., & Peng, T. K. (2007). Procedural justice climate and group power distance: An examination of cross-level interaction effects. *Journal of Applied Psychology, 92*(3), 681–692.

Zohar, D. (1980). Safety climate in industrial organizations: Theoretical and applied implications. *Journal of Applied Psychology, 65,* 96–102.

Zohar, D. (2000). A group level model of safety climate: Testing the effect of group climate on microaccidents in manufacturing jobs. *Journal of Applied Psychology, 85,* 587–596.

Zohar, D. (2002). The effects of leadership dimensions, safety climate, and assigned priorities on minor injuries in work groups. *Journal of Organizational Behavior, 23*(1), 75–92.

Zohar, D., & Hofmann, D. H. (2012). Organizational culture and climate. In S. W. J. Kozlowski (Ed.), *The Oxford handbook of industrial and organizational psychology* (pp. 643–666). Oxford: Oxford University Press.

Zohar, D., & Luria, G. (2004). Climate as social-cognitive construction of supervisory safety practices: Scripts as proxy of behavior patterns. *Journal of Applied Psychology, 89,* 322–333.

Zohar, D., & Luria, G. (2005). A multi-level model of safety climate: Cross-level relationships between organization and group-level climates. *Journal of Applied Psychology, 90,* 616–628.

Zohar, D., & Polachek, T. (2014). Discourse-based intervention for modifying supervisory communication as leverage for safety climate and performance improvement: A randomized field study. *Journal of Applied Psychology, 99*(1), 113–124.

Zohar, D., & Tenne-Gazit, O. (2008). Transformational leadership and group interaction as climate antecedents: A social network analysis. *Journal of Applied Psychology, 93,* 744–757.

Mark G. Ehrhart and Benjamin Schneider

ORGANIZATIONAL JUSTICE

The importance of people's perceptions of fairness in the workplace is clearly established in the literature in work and organizational psychology as well as in organizational behavior, where organizational justice occupies a dominant position. Indeed, responding to events by asserting that the treatment one has received is "unfair" is recognized as a basic human reaction occurring even in infancy (McAuliffe, Blake, Steinbeis, & Warneken, 2017; Weir, 2014) as well as across the lifespan and in all spheres of life. Organizational justice, or the study of fairness judgments and reactions and their consequences in the organizations where people work, is the focus of this article. The term was proposed by Greenberg (1987) to integrate the various components of fairness perceptions studied in relation to organizational life that had been developed at the time of his publication. In the following paragraphs, a review of the research defining the different dimensions of organizational justice including the antecedents and consequences of employees' perceptions of justice or fairness is presented. Then, the processes by which fairness perceptions are formed and affect outcomes are explored. Finally, some perspectives to be developed in future research are proposed.

FAIRNESS JUDGMENTS

Questions of fairness typically arise following particular events, such as the communication of a decision, or interactions with people. Frequently, decisions concern the distribution of limited resources, and certain individuals have the authority to make such decisions. In work settings, salaries and other forms of compensation are a resource that often comes to mind in thinking about fairness. But resources are much more vast than those that are tied directly to monetary rewards; decisions about various developmental opportunities, working conditions, recognition, or task assignments are other kinds of resources that people receive, or not, and their allocation may give rise to varying perceptions about their fairness. The resources distributed can thus be material or immaterial and still produce strong reactions when the distributions are considered to be unfair.

Throughout history, various scholars from many disciplines have addressed the question of what is fair. The Greek philosopher Socrates wrote about the equitable (or fair) distribution of rewards (see Cropanzano, Stein, & Nadisic, 2011, for a summary of Socrates' perspectives). Labor law defines what is legal, or illegal, in how employers treat their employees. The psychological approach, presented here, takes a subjective angle in analyzing fairness. In this perspective, people's perceptions of their treatment are examined. That is why the literature on organizational justice uses terms like *justice judgments*, *reactions*, or *perceptions* when seeking to understand what is considered to be fair (or unfair) treatment at work. If a worker thinks (perceives) that the way the organization has treated her is unfair, the consequences for the worker and for her organization generally result from her perceptions and not from what her boss or some other person outside the situation thinks.

ORGANIZATIONAL JUSTICE PRINCIPLES

In organizational life, various justice principles or norms have been proposed and studied since the 1960s (for more complete treatments of the history of these concepts, see Colquitt,

Greenberg, & Zapata-Phelan, 2005, or Rupp, Shapiro, Folger, Skarlicki, & Shao, 2017). The dominant perspective for studying organizational justice today focuses on the respect or violation of these principles in making and communicating decisions that leads people to react concerning the fairness of their treatment. Respecting the principles is associated with judgments of fair treatment; violating them gives rise to judgments of unfairness. The judgments or perceptions of being treated fairly or not, in turn, lead to other reactions and behaviors by employees (Colquitt & Zipay, 2015). Since the 1980s, the justice principles have been grouped into three (or four, depending on whether interpersonal justice is subdivided or not) categories; each of these is explored in a specific section hereafter. It is important to emphasize at this point that these categories are the result of the chronology in which various principles or norms of justice emerged in the organizational justice literature, and not the result of an overarching systematic consideration of what constitutes the domain of organizational justice (cf. Rupp et al., 2017). This limitation in the conceptualization of justice constructs is explored throughout the article.

Distributive Justice. Distributive justice is the initial category or dimension studied in the history of research on organizational justice. Most generally, it addresses people's fairness reactions regarding the rewards, compensation, or other outcomes that they receive—things that are distributed to them in work contexts. The primary principle used to understand fairness perceptions of outcome distributions is based on equity theory (Adams, 1965). This principle has its theoretical roots in concepts from relative deprivation theory, social comparison theory, or cognitive dissonance (for reviews, see Colquitt et al., 2005, and Rupp et al., 2017). Adams formalized the notion of equity by proposing that an actor constructs a mental ratio of his or her outcomes relative to his or her inputs. The more one contributes (inputs) to a situation, the more one expects to be compensated (outputs). Further, in order to evaluate whether the actor's outcomes are appropriate for his or her inputs, the actor also constructs a ratio for an "other" and then compares the other's ratio to the ratio constructed for him- or herself. An equitable situation is defined as resulting when one's own ratio of outcomes to inputs is equivalent to that of the comparison other. If the ratios are not equivalent, the situation is bothersome to the actor because this means that either he or she is over- or underpaid relative to the comparison other. Equity theory supposes that the actor will be motivated to reduce the discomfort of these inequitable situations, and the actor can do this by many possible avenues. Increasing or decreasing one's inputs so that they are proportional to the outcomes received are some behavioral strategies that can be adopted. The actor may also use cognitive strategies and simply change the perceptions of his or her inputs or outcomes. The actor can even change the comparison other that resulted in the perception of inequitable rewards.

Many interesting studies on the mechanisms of equity theory have been conducted in laboratory studies where the inputs and outcomes, as well as the other person to whom actors should compare themselves, were obvious and clear to research participants (see, for example Adams & Jacobsen, 1964, and van den Bos, 2001). In a laboratory, for example, two research participants can be seated at the same table, perform the same task, and yet be paid differently (for example, see van den Bos, Peters, Bobocel, & Jan, 2006). Studying their reactions or subsequent behaviors permits interpretations based on the different conditions introduced experimentally. Greenberg (1988) conducted a field experiment that also showed results consistent with those of the more basic, laboratory research. His experiment involved the outcomes of office space characteristics (e.g., prestige, size) and the inputs of job performance. During office renovation, insurance underwriters were randomly assigned to temporary offices that represented better, worse, or equivalent outcomes relative to their ongoing work situations. Thus, the workers were induced to compare their new temporary situation to their own typical office space. The changes were associated with subsequent increases in performance for the employees whose temporary office space was more prestigious (their outcomes improved) and decreases in performance for those whose office space was less prestigious (their outcomes decreased). Workers assigned to equivalent offices, thus constituting a control group, showed no change in performance during the period of the temporary assignment.

Although the equity principle is the dominant one for examining distributive justice evaluations in the organizational justice literature, there has been some attention to other principles that can influence how we evaluate what is fair in certain situations. Distributing resources equally among people, without consideration for their contributions to the situation, has been identified as particularly relevant for perceptions of fairness when group harmony is important (Bierhoff, Buck, & Klein, 1986; Deutsch, 1985, 1986; Gergen, Morse, & Gergen, 1980), such as in cases where individuals work as a team. The application of this principle requires that all people concerned by the distribution of outcomes receive exactly the same amount or the same decision, irrespective of their inputs. In yet other situations, taking into account the specific needs of individuals can be the principle that people consider to be fair in determining outcomes to be distributed. This principle indicates that more resources should be distributed to individuals having the greatest needs (Lerner, 1977; Schwinger, 1986). These other principles have been much less studied in the organizational justice literature (see Rupp et al., 2017), and rarely have been studied together (for an exception, see Steiner, Trahan, Haptonstahl, & Fointiat, 2006). By and large, in economic contexts like working life, the equity principle is considered to be fair both by the decision-makers who distribute outcomes and by the individuals who receive them. Indeed, much of the early research adopted the perspective of the decision-maker to study how they would distribute rewards to a group of individuals; this type of study focuses on what has been called the proactive aspect of justice (Greenberg, 1987). Later research and the great majority of studies conducted since the 1980s have examined how people react to the distributions they receive; this is the reactive approach to justice (Greenberg, 1987).

Despite the history of research on distributive justice, certain questions have received little attention, according to Rupp et al. (2017), who suggest attending more to social comparison processes and the differences in response to under- versus over-reward.

Procedural Justice. Thibaut and Walker (1975) and Leventhal (1976, 1980) studied the procedures or processes used to make decisions, beyond considerations of the decisions themselves. Thibaut and Walker examined the principle of "voice" during the decision-making process. Their research was initially conducted in the context of jury trials, and then it was extended to other areas of application. Their studies found that when people concerned by a decision had the opportunity to voice their point of view during the decision-making process, these people not only viewed the process or procedures as more fair than when this opportunity was absent, but also evaluated the decision (or outcome) as more fair, whether it was favorable or unfavorable to them. They considered that having voice gave protagonists a degree of control, be it directly by participating in the decision or only by participating in the process leading to it. The impact of a fair process (voice) on the evaluation of the outcome or decision itself became known as the fair process effect, and this effect was found to be robust in numerous contexts. Today, the fair process effect is considered more globally as the numerous positive benefits that result from using fair processes (van den Bos, 2005).

Leventhal (1976, 1980) defined six other characteristics of procedures that are generally considered to be fair when applied during decision-making. Leventhal's propositions were based on his own decision-making experiences and speculating about what criteria were likely to be important during the decision process. Although they were not developed through a comprehensive, theoretical approach, Leventhal's procedural justice principles are widely cited today and are the bases for many research studies. The principles are:

1. Consistency: applying the same procedures to everyone.
2. Bias-suppression: avoiding self-interest or personal biases.
3. Accuracy: basing decisions on correct and appropriate information.
4. Correctability: including the possibility of modifying a decision or correcting an error (i.e., an appeal process).
5. Representativeness: taking into consideration the concerns of various subgroups affected by the decision.
6. Ethicality: basing decisions on fundamental moral and ethical values.

While researchers have examined or measured perceptions of voice and the Leventhal criteria since the late 1970s, they have also sometimes proposed various other procedural justice principles. Rupp et al. (2017) summarized the situation by indicating that not enough attention has been accorded to defining and validating what the procedural criteria are and the factors contributing to their relative importance according to particular situations. Furthermore, although procedural justice is supposed to reduce the negative impact of unfavorable outcomes, the boundary conditions for observing such an effect are not sufficiently acknowledged. For example, research on violations of moral convictions (moral mandates; Skitka, 2002) or personal and social identities (Mayer, Greenbaum, Kuezi, & Shteynberg, 2009) indicates that such violations limit the attenuating impact of procedural fairness on judgments of outcome fairness.

The "dark side" of justice is also a rather neglected question in the literature, with researchers typically placing a high value on respecting organizational justice principles across all contexts. In applying organizational justice concepts to personnel selection, Gilliland (1993) proposed and then supported empirically (Gilliland, 1994) that perceiving the hiring process as fair is beneficial to self-perceptions (self-esteem or self-efficacy) of those selected and is detrimental to those of rejected candidates. Other research has arrived at similar conclusions (e.g., Brockner & Wiesenfeld, 2005; Ployhart, Ryan, & Bennett, 1999) in various types of applications. Given the typically positive consequences associated with applying fair procedures, Brockner and Wiesenfeld (2005) indicated that these negative effects give rise to a managerial dilemma when unfavorable decisions are a possibility. These authors maintain that applying fair procedures is important, and they propose using other strategies to reduce the negative impacts on self-perceptions for those receiving negative decisions.

Interactional Justice.   Given that procedures and decisions are implemented by authority figures, the interpersonal and relational considerations of how authorities interact with the group were included in some early conceptualizations of procedural justice where interactional justice was often construed as a form of procedural justice (e.g., Folger & Bies, 1989; Greenberg, Bies, & Eskew, 1991; Tyler & Bies, 1990; cf. Colquitt et al., 2005), despite interactional justice's being conceptualized by Bies and Moag (1986) as a specific form of justice (for a review, see Bies, 2005). Initially, interactional justice subsumed interpersonal and informational considerations, which were later separated into two specific dimensions of organizational justice in a four-dimensional perspective in accordance with a taxonomy presented by Greenberg (1993) and subsequent empirical work (e.g., Colquitt, 2001; Colquitt, Conlon, Wesson, Porter, & Ng, 2001). The interpersonal dimension focuses on the social sensitivity exhibited by an authority in communicating decisions and is characterized by treating concerned parties with dignity and respect. Informational justice describes the content of the message communicated and is more favorable when it is rich in relevant explanations and justifications.

More recently, interactional justice has been suggested to have three principal foundations (Bies, 2015; Rupp et al., 2017). The first focuses on the *information* communicated regarding a decision or event, and this information exchange involves both the role of the decision-maker and the content of the communication. Rupp et al. (2017) indicated that the responsibility of the decision-maker, the principles behind the decisions made, and other aspects of the content of the information have been insufficiently explored. An example of this type of research is found in the meta-analysis by Shaw, Wild, and Colquitt (2003), which examined information in terms of excuses or justifications for negative decisions. Considering more thoroughly and independently the role of the decision-maker's responsibility for the treatment and the content of the information that justifies the treatment could clarify our understanding of these separate influences and provide more relevant lines of action to produce desired outcomes.

Interactional justice's second foundation englobes the normative criteria influencing perceptions of justice, and they are now conceptualized by Bies (2015) as relating to the principles of respect for truth and human dignity. Violations of these principles cover a wide range of uncivil behaviors ranging from defamatory to abusive remarks or behaviors. The third foundation expands the agents of justice beyond the authority figure (e.g., decision-maker) to include reactions we might have during interactions with coworkers, customers, or other individuals who affect our working lives.

In addition to the need for greater conceptual development of the principles that underlie interactional justice, more theoretical and empirical development of the role of social comparison in how people are treated on the interactional dimension is needed. Further, theoretical and empirical explorations of the possibility that people desire both equal and unique treatment (cf. Bies, 2015) would advance our understanding of this aspect of organizational justice.

Dimensionality of Organizational Justice.   Whereas many studies show the relevance of studying organizational justice by taking into account four distinct dimensions—distributive, procedural, interpersonal, and informational (Colquitt, 2001; Colquitt et al., 2001, 2013)—frequently, research groups interpersonal and informational justice together in a single dimension of interactional justice (e.g., Ambrose & Schminke, 2009b). Each of the four dimensions brings a unique perspective to understanding when people think they are treated fairly, but there is also agreement that a general, overall, or global perception of justice tends to characterize the way people evaluate the fairness they experience. Ambrose and Schminke (2009b) developed a short measure of overall justice and supported a model where this overall perception mediated the relationship between the three more specific dimensions of justice (interpersonal and informational were grouped together) and some of the typically observed outcome variables in justice studies (job satisfaction, commitment, and turnover intentions).

Rupp et al. (2017) noted that the Colquitt (2001) measure of the four dimensions of justice has dominated research in the field since its publication, and this despite Colquitt himself arguing for different forms of justice measures as early as 2005 (e.g., Colquitt & Shaw, 2005; see also Colquitt, Long, Rodell, Halvorsen, & Ganepola, 2015). As Rupp et al. pointed out, the dimensions of justice studied today are those that emerged successively over the history of the study of organizational justice. Researchers have not systematically sought to define the entire domain of what constitutes the experience of justice or injustice, and this gap merits attention.

PROACTIVE JUSTICE AND MODERATORS OF JUSTICE PERCEPTIONS

The four dimensions of organizational justice have mostly been studied from a reactive perspective, focusing on how employees react to or perceive different forms of treatment they receive. On the other hand, proactive justice (cf. Greenberg, 1987), which examines how people make decisions in an effort to be fair, has largely been neglected, despite early research on distributive justice examining how decision-makers allocated rewards (Jouglard & Steiner, 2015). Ambrose and Schminke (2009a) developed a framework to study factors influencing actors' fair behaviors through a process starting with their justice awareness and continuing through to enacting justice behaviors. They proposed that individual differences or situational factors could intervene at different points in this process. Among the individual differences, they explored such characteristics as equity sensitivity, justice orientation, values, and personality traits (these are also developed in the next section, "Consequences of Justice Perceptions"). For situational factors, organizational structure, uncertainty, and culture were considered. Similarly, Jouglard and Steiner (2015) examined individual and contextual factors as they relate to fair leadership, defined as leader behaviors aimed at enacting justice principles.

Sillito-Walker (2015) conducted research that illustrates the role of individual factors in influencing managerial fair behavior. She presented theoretical propositions and their empirical tests linking managerial personality to implementing distributive, procedural, and interactional justice behaviors. Her results found honesty-humility, agreeableness, conscientiousness, and openness to experience related to self-reports of justice behaviors. A series of studies conducted by Huang et al. (2017) included both proactive and reactive approaches and found that the employee personality traits of agreeableness and conscientiousness were associated with supervisor evaluations of employee efforts and likability, which in turn influenced supervisors' adherence to justice principles. In turn, employee perceptions of (reactions to) their supervisors' adherence to justice principles did indeed result from the supervisors' actions.

Concerning situational factors, Schminke, Ambrose, and Cropanzano (2000) examined organizational structure and found that two aspects of centralization, participation in decision-making and hierarchy of authority, related (positively and negatively, respectively) to perceived procedural justice, whereas organizational size related negatively to perceived interactional justice. In an expanded study, Schminke, Cropanzano, and Rupp (2002) replicated these findings and also found that the centralization aspects and formalization (of rule and policies) related to distributive justice perceptions. Further, stronger reliance on the hierarchy of authority interacted with employees' level in the organization, with lower-level employees being particularly sensitive to this aspect of organizational structure in reporting their justice perceptions. Finally, lower-level employees also reported lower interactional justice with increasing organizational size. A study conducted in Turkey found formalization to be related to perceived distributive, procedural, and interactional justice, but centralization in terms of authority hierarchy was not, suggesting that cultural factors may moderate these relations (Özşahin & Yürür, 2018).

CONSEQUENCES OF JUSTICE PERCEPTIONS

In the organizational psychology and management literatures, an important body of work has accumulated indicating the importance of justice perceptions for a large array of individual and organizational outcomes. Various meta-analyses have summarized these results (Cohen-Charash & Spector, 2001; Colquitt et al., 2001, 2013; Robbins, Ford, & Tetrick, 2012; Whitman, Caleo, Carpenter, Horner, & Bernerth, 2012). The outcomes include employee attitudes and evaluations of their organization and its leaders; behaviors like turnover, retaliation, and counterproductive acts; job performance and organizational citizenship behaviors; and variables representing health, stress, and affect. Depending on the outcome examined, the bivariate correlations between at least one organizational justice dimension and the outcome have typically ranged from moderate (i.e., $r = 0.30$) to quite strong (correlations in the 0.60s); combining several organizational justice dimensions to predict an outcome has resulted in explaining more than 40% of the outcome's variance for some of the variables. The magnitude of these effects is consistent across the meta-analyses cited here, with stronger effects typically observed for attitudinal behaviors and more modest ones for behavioral outcomes. The consistent robustness of these results has contributed to the continued interest in studying organizational justice across several decades.

The health-related consequences of unfair treatment have received growing attention (for a review, see Steiner, 2017), following some early studies showing links to anxiety, stress, and insomnia (e.g., Greenberg, 2006; Tepper, 2001; Vermunt & Steensma, 2005). Robbins et al. (2012) proposed a model illustrating the causal linkages between unfair treatment and health problems. In it, unfair treatment is conceived as producing stress and other psychological conditions (negative emotions, anxiety, depression), which impact health behavior and then health problems. Indeed, their meta-analysis found moderate to strong relations between justice perceptions and psychological health-related variables (burnout, stress, negative affect, mental health) and weak to moderate relations with physical health. Research also indicates that unfair treatment is one of the factors that can contribute to the development of musculoskeletal disorders (Manville, El Akremi, Niezborala, & Mignonac, 2016).

Moderators of the relationship between justice perceptions and various consequences have also been examined. Greater uncertainty of individuals, for example, tends to strengthen reactions to unfairness (see the section "Why People Care About Fair Treatment" for greater consideration of this variable; Lind & van den Bos, 2002; van den Bos, 2001; van den Bos & Lind, 2002), and some authors have considered low self-esteem to indicate such uncertainty (e.g., DeCremer & Sedikides, 2005). Colquitt, Scott, Judge, and Shaw (2006) explored various personality traits as moderators based on an analysis of traits that should render individuals more sensitive to justice concerns, more likely to ruminate about them, or more likely to react to them. Their analysis led them to study propensity to trust, risk aversion, and trait morality; they also compared the moderating impact of these variables to that of equity sensitivity and the Big Five personality factors (Digman, 1990). The results of their laboratory study indicated that propensity to trust, risk aversion, and trait morality did indeed act as moderators of the relationship between justice and behavioral consequences in terms of task performance and counterproductive behavior; equity sensitivity and the Big Five were not significant moderators (except for an interaction between conscientiousness and procedural justice for counterproductive behavior). Justice orientation, defined as "the extent to which individuals internalize justice as a moral virtue" (Liao & Rupp, 2005, p. 244) has also been found to moderate relations between justice events or perceptions and outcome variables (Liao & Rupp, 2005; Sasaki & Hayashi, 2014).

THE PROCESSES THAT LINK JUSTICE TO OUTCOMES

After finding relatively strong relations between the justice dimensions and various outcomes, research turned to examining the psychological mechanisms that could explain these relations. Besides the idea that specific justice dimension perceptions give rise to an overall justice perception that in turn is linked to outcomes (Ambrose & Schminke, 2009b), various other processes have been explored. Individual versus collective identity is one such process that has fruitfully investigated how justice affects certain outcomes. This perspective theorizes that fair treatment contributes to a more collective or interdependent identity, such as identifying with one's employing organization, whereas unfair treatment leads employees to focus more on themselves, thus on an individual identity. In field (Blader & Tyler, 2009) or laboratory (Johnson & Lord, 2010) settings, empirical support in line with these theoretical positions has resulted. Specifically, when one's identity is collective, one is more likely to support the group or the organization with commitment and performance, for example, because such efforts support part of one's self. On the other hand, when one's identity is more individual, the group or organization is not part of this identity. The person thus becomes more self-oriented in attitudes and behaviors and may be inclined to direct counterproductive behaviors toward the group or agent responsible for the unfair treatment.

Colquitt et al. (2013) explored meta-analytically other mechanisms that can explain the links between specific justice dimension perceptions and positive and negative work outcomes. These authors proposed and confirmed empirically the mediating roles of social exchange quality and affect (positive and negative) as mechanisms resulting from justice perceptions and producing various outcomes. Their results showed that social exchange quality (the quality of the relationship between employees and their managers) and positive affect mediated the relations between favorable justice perceptions and the positive outcomes of job performance and organizational citizenship behaviors, whereas negative affect mediated the relations between unfavorable justice perceptions and counterproductive work behavior.

Matta, Sabey, Scott, Lin, and Koopman (2020) introduced an interesting perspective implicating considerations of proactive justice from the employee's (reactive) point of view. They examined attributions subordinates make for their supervisor's fair behavior, and found that when employees attribute the supervisor's actions to establishing fairness or to creating an emotionally positive environment, trust in the supervisor or positive affect results, respectively, which in turn relates to subsequent organizational citizenship behaviors. Attributions to supervisors' self-serving motives or to trying to effect compliance did not have such beneficial effects.

SOURCES OF (UN)FAIR TREATMENT

Many perspectives on organizational justice theorize that the role of an authority is central to concerns about fair treatment (van den Bos & Lind, 2002). But work contexts often involve interactions with coworkers, peers, subordinates, or even customers who may be perceived as having some degree of control or power (cf. Wessel & Steiner, 2015) over rewards and the criteria for distributing them. Whereas justice researchers initially focused on the role of authorities in their relations with subordinates, they have expanded their focus to examinations of treatment by one's peers or subordinates and other parties with whom one interacts at work. The actors of justice therefore become explicit in this multifocal perspective (Lavelle, Rupp, Manegold, & Thornton, 2015; Marques, Patient, & Cojuharenco, 2017). Thus, when people feel they are treated unfairly, they seek to identify the source of the unfair treatment, and their reactions in terms of social exchange processes and their ensuing consequences are targeted toward the unfair source (Lavelle et al., 2015). As reviewed by Lavelle et al. (2015), including considerations of the various sources of fair (or unfair) treatment has beneficially completed our understanding of how justice principles function and their consequences for employees and organizations. Martinez-Tur and Moliner (2017) have also applied multifocal considerations to work teams.

WHY PEOPLE CARE ABOUT FAIR TREATMENT

Over the history of organizational justice research, theoretical and empirical treatments have examined the question of why justice concerns are so important to people, as evidenced in particular by strong negative reactions to unfair treatment. In a thoughtful review of this question in 2002, Cropanzano and Rupp explored the major positions present in the literature at the time. The dominant perspectives were: the self-interest or instrumental model (cf. Tyler, 1994; Walster, Walster, & Berscheid, 1978), the relational or group-value model (Lind & Tyler, 1988), and the deontic model (Folger, 1994, 1998, 2001). The first of these suggests that people are attached to various forms of justice because they believe that in the long term, they will obtain the outcomes that they deserve. Thus, fair procedures are thought to contribute to obtaining equitable rewards. The second perspective, the relational or group-value model, focuses on identity-related issues, and its promoters believe that the various facets of justice communicate to people the value they have in the group or organization. In other words, authorities can use rewards, consider people's individual perspectives through voice, and apply respectful interpersonal treatment to indicate that group members are valued, or not. The deontic approach insists on justice as a basic value that humans consider important. This approach helps to explain why third parties who observe unfair treatment to others, and who are not directly concerned with the treatment themselves, sometimes react strongly to the observed unfair treatment. Cropanzano and Rupp (2002) concluded that the three approaches are compatible in that, at different times and for different circumstances, each can explain our attachment to fairness.

In relation or in parallel to the three major approaches just described, an important body of research has addressed how justice helps to reduce uncertainty that people experience in response to authorities or group membership (e.g., Colquitt & Zipay, 2015; De Cremer et al., 2010; De Cremer & Sedikides, 2005; Lind & van den Bos, 2002; van den Bos, 2001; van den Bos & Lind, 2002). The empirical research supporting these theoretical positions indicates that when people are more uncertain, they react more strongly to unfair treatment. Furthermore, the application of various justice principles by authorities helps reduce uncertainty and facilitates the experience of value in a group, in coherence with the group-value model. More recent research in the field has incorporated experience sampling over several days, allowing for exploration of changes in justice perceptions over time. Matta, Scott, Guo, and Matusik (2020) argued that variability in the applications of interpersonal justice can also be a source of uncertainty, with negative consequences on the experiences of employees. Their research effectively integrates uncertainty management and group-oriented concepts for a more complete treatment of justice judgments and shows that variability in applying interpersonal justice is a boundary condition limiting the strength of the relationship between justice perceptions and group identity and subsequent cooperative behavior.

A third general approach for understanding the importance of fair treatment comes from research on primates and children or infants, which finds that these populations react negatively to some variants of inequitable treatment, suggesting that some reactions to unfairness are inherent to basic human (or even primate) functioning (for a review, see McAuliffe et al., 2017). Consistent with this idea is research incorporating neuropsychological approaches using fMRI scanning, which also finds that some processing of inequitable treatment is "relatively automatic and intuitive" (Tabibnia, Satpute, & Lieberman, 2008, p. 345).

WHERE WE ARE GOING

Theory and research in organizational justice have reached a certain maturity, but as the critical review by Rupp et al. (2017) argued, there remain many unexplored questions and areas where progress is still needed. Many of these are mentioned throughout this article, but some others merit attention in this concluding section.

In addition to a great variety of applications of justice principles to different domains of organizational life, the field continues to inspire new theoretical considerations on the way justice works to produce its diverse consequences. Further, the hypotheses resulting from these considerations are tested using many different, and often innovative, methodological approaches. The field also examines the question of what gives rise to being fair with others and incorporates multidisciplinary and alternative theoretical perspectives in exploring such questions in what Brockner and Carter (2015) called the fifth wave of organizational justice, where justice is viewed as a dependent variable.

As indicated throughout this article, despite enthusiasm about the efficiency of applying justice principles for achieving desirable outcomes, researchers are thoughtfully examining the boundary conditions limiting these effects in order to provide a better understanding of when justice works and when it doesn't. The role played by time has also been a strong trend since approximately 2010, as longitudinal and experience sampling designs have allowed demonstration of the important role played by the dynamic and changing nature of justice perceptions (see Hausknecht, Sturman, & Roberson, 2011; Holtz & Harold, 2009; Loi, Yang, & Diefendorff, 2009). In a similar vein, in applying construal-level theory, Rizvi and Bobocel (2015) have examined psychological distance, of which one factor is time, and how it influences mental representations of events, influencing both justice judgments of events and the consequences of the judgments.

Finally, the nature of work is undergoing profound mutations, notably due to the gig economy, collaboration in distant work teams composed of people from many nations, the automatization of decision-making processes, being connected and receiving communications via smartphone or personal computer 24/7, and teleworking, to cite just a few of the evolutionary factors influencing how people work (cf. Cascio & Montealegre, 2016), and all of these changes are likely to influence how people perceive fair treatment (cf. Rupp et al., 2017). They variously reduce direct interpersonal interactions among workers, limit the opportunities for social support, change the dynamics of social comparisons among workers, and introduce new and varied cultural lenses for interpreting work events. Incorporating these considerations into the understanding of justice perceptions, their causes, and their consequences may be the sixth wave of organizational justice.

REFERENCES

Adams, J. S. (1965). Inequity in social exchange. In L. Berkowitz (Ed.), *Advances in experimental social psychology* (Vol. 2, pp. 267–299). New York, NY: Academic Press.

Adams, J. S., & Jacobsen, P. R. (1964). Effects of wage inequities on work quality. *The Journal of Abnormal and Social Psychology, 69*(1), 19–25. http://dx.doi.org/10.1037/h0040241

Ambrose, M. L., & Schminke, M. (2009a). Assessing roadblocks to justice: A model of fair behavior in organizations. *Research in Personnel and Human Resources Management, 28*, 219–263.

Ambrose, M. L., & Schminke, M. (2009b). The role of overall justice judgments in organizational justice research: A test of mediation. *Journal of Applied Psychology, 94*, 491–500.

Bierhoff, H. W., Buck, E., & Klein, R. (1986). Social context and perceived justice. In H. W. Bierhoff, R. L. Cohen, & J. Greenberg (Eds.), *Justice in social relations* (pp. 165–185). New York, NY: Plenum Press.

Bies, R. J. (2005). Are procedural justice and interactional justice conceptually distinct? In J. Greenberg & J. A. Colquitt (Eds.), *Handbook of organizational justice* (pp. 85–112). Mahwah, NJ: Lawrence Erlbaum Associates.

Bies, R. J. (2015). Interactional justice: Looking backward, looking forward. In R. Cropanzano & M. Ambrose (Eds.), *Oxford handbook of psychology: Justice in work organizations* (pp. 89–107). New York, NY: Oxford University Press.

Bies, R., & Moag, J. (1986). Interactional justice: Communication criteria of fairness. In R. Lewicki, B. Sheppard, & M. Bazerman (Eds.), *Research on negotiation in organizations* (pp. 43–55). Greenwich, CT: JAI Press.

Blader, S., & Tyler, T. (2009). Testing and extending the group engagement model: Linkages between social identity, procedural justice, economic outcomes, and extrarole behavior. *Journal of Applied Psychology, 94,* 445–464.

Brockner, J., & Carter, A. (2015). Toward the fifth wave: Justice as a dependent variable. In S. W. Gilliland, D. D. Steiner, & D. Skarlicki (Eds.), *The social dynamics of organizational justice* (pp. 251–284). Charlotte, NC: Information Age Publishing.

Brockner, J., & Wiesenfeld, B. (2005). How, when, and why does outcome favorability interact with procedural fairness? In J. Greenberg & J. A. Colquitt (Eds.), *Handbook of organizational justice* (pp. 525–553). Mahwah, NJ: Lawrence Erlbaum Associates.

Cascio, W. F., & Montealegre, R. (2016). How technology is changing work and organizations. *Annual Review of Organizational Psychology and Organizational Behavior, 3,* 349–375. http://dx.doi.org/10.1146/annurev-orgpsych-041015-062352

Cohen-Charash, Y., & Spector, P. E. (2001). The role of justice in organizations: A meta-analysis. *Organizational Behavior and Human Decision Processes, 86,* 278–321.

Colquitt, J. A. (2001). On the dimensionality of organizational justice: A construct validation of a measure. *Journal of Applied Psychology, 86,* 386–400.

Colquitt, J. A., Conlon, D. E., Wesson, M. J., Porter, C. O. L. H., & Ng, K. Y. (2001). Justice at the millennium: A meta-analytic review of 25 years of organizational justice research. *Journal of Applied Psychology, 86,* 425–445.

Colquitt, J. A., Greenberg, J., & Zapata-Phelan, C. P. (2005). What is organizational justice? A historical overview. In J. Greenberg & J. A. Colquitt (Eds.), *Handbook of organizational justice* (pp. 3–56). Mahwah, NJ: Lawrence Erlbaum Associates.

Colquitt, J. A., Long, D. M., Rodell, J. B., & Halvorsen-Ganepola, M. D. K. (2015). Adding the "in" to justice: A qualitative and quantitative investigation of the differential effects of justice rule adherence and violation. *Journal of Applied Psychology, 100,* 278–297.

Colquitt, J. A., Scott, B. A., Judge, T. A., & Shaw, J. C. (2006). Justice and personality: Using integrative theories to derive moderators of justice effects. *Organizational Behavior and Human Decision Processes, 100*(1), 110–127. http://dx.doi.org/10.1016/j.obhdp.2005.09.001

Colquitt, J. A., Scott, B. A., Rodell, J. B., Long, D. M., Zapata, C. P., Conlon, D. E., & Wesson, M. J. (2013). Justice at the millennium, a decade later: A meta-analytic test of social exchange and affect-based perspectives. *Journal of Applied Psychology, 98*(2), 199–236. http://dx.doi.org/10.1037/a0031757

Colquitt, J. A., & Shaw, J. (2005). How should organizational justice be measured? In J. D. Colquitt & J. Greenberg (Eds.), *Handbook of organizational justice* (pp. 113–152). Mahwah, NJ: Lawrence Erlbaum Associates.

Colquitt, J. A., & Zipay, K. P. (2015). Justice, fairness, and employee reactions. *Annual Review of Organizational Psychology and Organizational Behavior, 2,* 75–99. http://dx.doi.org/10.1146/annurev-orgpsych-032414-111457

Cropanzano, R., & Rupp, D. E. (2002). Some reflections on the morality of organizational justice. In S. W. Gilliland, D. D. Steiner, & D. P. Skarlicki (Eds.), *Emerging perspectives on managing organizational justice* (pp. 225–278). Greenwich, CT: Information Age Publishers.

Cropanzano, R., Stein, J. H., & Nadisic, T. (2011). *Social justice and the experience of human emotion.* New York, NY: Taylor & Francis.

De Cremer, D., Brockner, J., Fishman, A., van Dijke, M., van Olffen, W., & Mayer, D. M. (2010). When do procedural fairness and outcome fairness interact to influence employees' work attitudes and behaviors?

The moderating effect of uncertainty. *Journal of Applied Psychology, 95*(2), 291–304. http://dx.doi.org/10.1037/a0017866

De Cremer, D., & Sedikides, C. (2005). Self-uncertainty and responsiveness to procedural justice. *Journal of Experimental Social Psychology, 41,* 157–173.

Deutsch, M. (1985). *Distributive justice.* New Haven, CT: Yale University Press.

Deutsch, M. (1986). Cooperation, conflict, and justice. In H. W. Bierhoff, R. L. Cohen, & J. Greenberg (Eds.), *Justice in social relations* (pp. 3–18). New York, NY: Plenum Press.

Digman, J. (1990). Personality structure: Emergence of the five-factor model. *Annual Review of Psychology, 41,* 417–440. https://doi.org/10.1146/annurev.ps.41.020190.002221

Folger, R. (1994). Workplace justice and employee worth. *Social Justice Research, 7,* 225–241.

Folger, R. (1998). Fairness as a moral virtue. In M. Schminke (Ed.), *Managerial ethics: Moral management of people and processes* (pp. 13–34). Mahwah, NJ: Lawrence Erlbaum Associates.

Folger, R. (2001). Fairness as deonance. In S. W. Gilliland, D. D. Steiner, & D. Skarlicki (Eds.), *Theoretical and cultural perspectives on organizational justice* (pp. 3–33). Greenwich, CT: Information Age Publishers.

Folger, R., & Bies, R. J. (1989). Managerial responsibilities and procedural justice. *Employee Responsibilities and Rights Journal, 2,* 79–89.

Gergen, K. J., Morse, S. J., & Gergen, M. M. (1980). Behavior exchange in cross-cultural perspective. In H. C. Triandis & R. W. Brislin (Eds.), *Handbook of cross-cultural psychology: Vol. 5. Social psychology* (pp. 121–154). Boston, MA: Allyn & Bacon.

Gilliland, S. W. (1993). The perceived fairness of selection systems: An organizational justice perspective. *Academy of Management Review, 18,* 694–734.

Gilliland, S. W. (1994). Effects of procedural and distributive justice on reactions to a selection system. *Journal of Applied Psychology, 79,* 691–701.

Greenberg, J. (1987). A taxonomy of organizational justice theories. *Academy of Management Review, 12,* 9–22.

Greenberg, J. (1988). Equity and workplace status: A field experiment. *Journal of Applied Psychology, 73,* 606–613.

Greenberg, J. (1993). The social side of fairness: Interpersonal and informational classes of organizational justice. In R. Cropanzano (Ed.), *Justice in the workplace: Approaching fairness in human resource management* (pp. 79–103). Hillsdale, NJ: Lawrence Erlbaum Associates.

Greenberg, J. (2006). Losing sleep over organizational injustice: Attenuating insomniac reactions to underpayment inequity with supervisory training in interactional justice. *Journal of Applied Psychology, 91,* 58–69.

Greenberg, J., Bies, R. J., & Eskew, D. E. (1991). Establishing fairness in the eye of the beholder: Managing impressions of organizational justice. In R. Giacalone & P. Rosenfeld (Eds.), *Applied impression management: How image making affects managerial decisions* (pp. 111–132). Newbury Park, CA: SAGE.

Hausknecht, J. P., Sturman, M. C., & Roberson, Q. M. (2011). Justice as a dynamic construct: Effects of individual trajectories on distal work outcomes. *Journal of Applied Psychology, 96,* 872–880.

Holtz, B., & Harold, C. (2009). Fair today, fair tomorrow? A longitudinal investigation of overall justice perceptions. *Journal of Applied Psychology, 94,* 1185–1199.

Huang, J. L., Cropanzano, R., Li, A., Shao, P., Zhang, X., & Li, Y. (2017). Employee conscientiousness, agreeableness, and supervisor justice rule compliance: A three-study investigation. *Journal of Applied Psychology, 112,* 1564–1589.

Johnson, R., & Lord, R. (2010). Implicit effects of justice on self-identity. *Journal of Applied Psychology, 95,* 681–695.

Jouglard, D., & Steiner, D. D. (2015). Fair leadership: A proactive approach to organizational justice. In S. W. Gilliland, D. D. Steiner, & D. Skarlicki (Eds.), *The social dynamics of organizational justice* (pp. 177–200). Charlotte, NC: Information Age Publishing.

Lavelle, J., Rupp, D. E., Manegold, J., & Thornton, M. A. (2015). Multifoci justice and target similarity: Emerging research and extensions. In R. S. Cropanzano & M. L. Ambrose (Eds.), *The Oxford handbook of justice in the workplace* (pp. 165–186). New York, NY: Oxford University Press.

Lerner, M. J. (1977). The justice motive: Some hypotheses as to its origins and forms. *Journal of Personality, 45*, 1–52.

Leventhal, G. S. (1976). Fairness in social relationships. In J. W. Thibaut, J. T. Spence, & R. C. Carson (Eds.), *Contemporary topics in social psychology* (pp. 211–239). Morristown, NJ: General Learning Press.

Leventhal, G. S. (1980). What should be done with equity theory? New approaches to the study of fairness in social relationships. In K. Gergen, M. Greenberg, & R. Willis (Eds.), *Social exchange: Advances in theory and research* (pp. 27–55). New York, NY: Plenum.

Liao, H., & Rupp, D. E. (2005). The impact of justice climate and justice orientation on work outcomes: A cross-level multifoci framework. *Journal of Applied Psychology, 90*, 242–256. http://dx.doi.org/10.1037/0021-9010.90.2.242

Lind, E. A., & Tyler, T. R. (1988). *The social psychology of procedural justice.* New York, NY: Plenum.

Lind, E. A., & van den Bos, K. (2002). When fairness works: Toward a general theory of uncertainty management. *Research in Organizational Behavior, 24*, 181–223. http://dx.doi.org/10.1016/S0191-3085(02)24006-X

Loi, R., Yang, J., & Diefendorff, J. (2009). Four-factor justice and daily job satisfaction: A multilevel investigation. *Journal of Applied Psychology, 94*, 770–781.

Manville, C., El Akremi, A., Niezborala, M., & Mignonac, K. (2016). Injustice hurts, literally: The role of sleep and emotional exhaustion in the relationship between organizational justice and musculoskeletal disorders. *Human Relations, 69*(6), 1315–1339.

Marques, T., Patient, D., & Cojuharenco, I. (2017). The "who" of organizational justice. In C. Moliner, R. Cropanzano, & V. Martínez-Tur (Eds.), *Organizational justice: International perspectives and conceptual advances* (pp. 58–83). London, UK: Routledge.

Martínez-Tur, V., & Moliner, C. (2017). Justice in teams. *Oxford research encyclopedia of psychology.* New York, NY: Oxford University Press. https://oxfordre.com/psychology/view/10.1093/acrefore/9780190236557.001.0001/acrefore-9780190236557-e-16

Matta, F. K., Sabey, T. B., Scott, B. A., Lin, S.-H. (J.), & Koopman, J. (2020). Not all fairness is created equal: A study of employee attributions of supervisor justice motives. *Journal of Applied Psychology, 105*(3), 274–293. http://dx.doi.org/10.1037/apl0000440

Matta, F. K., Scott, B. A., Guo, Z. (A.), & Matusik, J. G. (2020). Exchanging one uncertainty for another: Justice variability negates the benefits of justice. *Journal of Applied Psychology, 105*(1), 97–110. http://dx.doi.org/10.1037/apl0000425

Mayer, D. M., Greenbaum, R. L., Kuezi, M., & Shteynberg, G. (2009). When do fair procedures not matter? A test of the identity violation effect. *Journal of Applied Psychology, 94*, 142–161.

McAuliffe, K., Blake, P. R., Steinbeis, N., & Warneken, F. (2017). The developmental foundations of human fairness. *Nature Human Behavior, 1*, 0042. http://dx.doi.org/10.1038/s41562-016-0042

Özşahin, M., & Yürür, S. (2018). The effect of organizational structure on organizational justice perceptions of employees. *International Journal of Organizational Leadership, 7*, 440–453.

Ployhart, R. E., Ryan, A. M., & Bennett, M. (1999). Explanations for selection decisions: Applicants' reactions to informational and sensitivity features of explanations. *Journal of Applied Psychology, 84*, 87–106.

Rizvi, S., & Bobocel, R. (2015). Using the concept of distance to broaden the horizons of organizational justice. In S. W. Gilliland, D. D. Steiner, & D. Skarlicki (Eds.), *The social dynamics of organizational justice* (pp. 37–60). Charlotte, NC: Information Age Publishing.

Robbins, J. M., Ford, M. T., & Tetrick, L. E. (2012). Perceived unfairness and employee health: A meta-analytic integration. *Journal of Applied Psychology, 97*(2), 235–272.

Rupp, D. E., Shapiro, D. L., Folger, R., Skarlicki, D. S., & Shao, R. (2017). A critical analysis of the conceptualization and measurement of organizational justice: Is it time for reassessment? *Academy of Management Annals, 11*, 915–959.

Sasaki, H., & Hayashi, Y. (2014). Justice orientation as a moderator of the framing effect on procedural justice perception. *The Journal of Social Psychology, 154*(3), 251–263. https://doi.org/10.1080/00224545.2014.888329

Schminke, M., Ambrose, M. L., & Cropanzano, R. S. (2000). The effect of organizational structure on perceptions of procedural fairness. *Journal of Applied Psychology, 85*, 294–304.

Schminke, M., Cropanzano, R. S., & Rupp, D. E. (2002). Organization structure and fairness perceptions: The moderating effects of organizational level. *Organizational Behavior and Human Decision Processes 89*, 881–905.

Schwinger, T. (1986). The need principle of distributive justice. In H. W. Bierhoff, R. L. Cohen, & J. Greenberg (Eds.), *Justice in social relations* (pp. 211–225). New York, NY: Plenum Press.

Shaw, J. C., Wild, E., & Colquitt, J. A. (2003). To justify or excuse? A meta-analytic review of the effects of explanations. *Journal of Applied Psychology, 88*(3), 444–458.

Sillito Walker, S. D. (2015). Maintaining justice: The effect of managerial personality and trait activation on procedural, interpersonal, and informational fairness. In S. W. Gilliland, D. D. Steiner, & D. Skarlicki (Eds.), *The social dynamics of organizational justice* (pp. 143–175). Charlotte, NC: Information Age Publishing.

Skitka, L. J. (2002). Do the means always justify the ends, or do the ends sometimes justify the means? A value model of justice reasoning. *Personality and Social Psychology Review, 28*, 588–597.

Steiner, D. D. (2017). Organizational justice for understanding employee health and well-being. In C. Moliner, R. Cropanzano, & V. Martínez-Tur (Eds.), *Organizational justice: International perspectives and conceptual advances* (pp. 160–180). London, UK: Routledge.

Steiner, D. D., Trahan, W. A., Haptonstahl, D. E., & Fointiat, V. (2006). The justice of equity, equality, and need in reward distributions: A comparison of French and American respondents. *Revue Internationale de Psychologie Sociale/International Review of Social Psychology, 19*, 49–74.

Tabibnia, G., Satpute, A. B., & Lieberman, M. D. (2008). The sunny side of fairness: Preference for fairness activates reward circuitry (and disregarding unfairness activates self-control circuitry). *Psychological Science, 19*, 339–347.

Tepper, B. J. (2001). Health consequences of organizational injustice: Tests of main and interactive effects. *Organizational Behavior and Human Decision Processes, 86*(2), 197–215.

Thibaut, J., & Walker, L. (1975). *Procedural justice: A psychological analysis*. Hillsdale, NJ: Lawrence Erlbaum Associates.

Tyler, T. R. (1994). Psychological models of the justice motive: Antecedents of distributive and procedural justice. *Journal of Personality and Social Psychology, 67*, 850–863.

Tyler, T. R., & Bies, R. J. (1990). Beyond formal procedures: The interpersonal context of procedural justice. In J. Carroll (Ed.), *Applied social psychology and organizational settings* (pp. 77–98). Hillsdale, NJ: Lawrence Erlbaum Associates.

van den Bos, K. (2001). Fairness heuristic theory: Assessing the information to which people are reacting has a pivotal role in understanding organizational justice. In S. W. Gilliland, D. D. Steiner, & D. Skarlicki (Eds.), *Theoretical and cultural perspectives on organizational justice* (pp. 63–84). Greenwich, CT: Information Age Publishing.

van den Bos, K. (2005). What is responsible for the fair process effect? In J. Greenberg & J. A. Colquitt (Eds.), *Handbook of organizational justice* (pp. 273–300). Mahwah, NJ: Lawrence Erlbaum Associates.

van den Bos, K., & Lind, E. A. (2002). Uncertainty management by means of fairness judgments. In M. P. Zanna (Ed.), *Advances in experimental social psychology* (Vol. 34, pp. 1–60). San Diego, CA: Academic Press.

van den Bos, K., Peters, S. L., Bobocel, D. R., & Jan, F. Y. (2006). On preferences and the right thing: Satisfaction with advantageous inequity when cognitive processing is limited. *Journal of Experimental Social Psychology, 42*(3), 273–289.

Vermunt, R., & Steensma, H. (2005). How can justice be used to manage stress in organizations? In J. Greenberg & J. A. Colquitt (Eds.), *Handbook of organizational justice* (pp. 383–410). Mahwah, NJ: Lawrence Erlbaum Associates.

Walster, E., Walster, G. W., & Berscheid, E. (1978). *Equity: Theory and research*. New York, NY: Allyn & Bacon.

Weir, K. (2014). Not-so blank slates: What do infants understand about the social world? More than you think. *Monitor on Psychology, 45*(4), 32–35.

Wessel, J. L., & Steiner, D. D. (2015). Surface acting in service: A two context examination of customer power and politeness. *Human Relations, 68*, 709–730. http://dx.doi.org/10.1177/0018726714540731

Whitman, D. S., Caleo, S., Carpenter, N. C., Horner, M. T., & Bernerth, J. B. (2012). Fairness at the collective level: A meta-analytic examination of the consequences and boundary conditions of organizational justice climate. *Journal of Applied Psychology, 97*, 776–791.

Dirk D. Steiner

CORPORATE SOCIAL RESPONSIBILITY: AN OVERVIEW FROM AN ORGANIZATIONAL AND PSYCHOLOGICAL PERSPECTIVE

INTRODUCTION

Since the 1950s, the concept of corporate social responsibility (CSR) has continuously grown in importance, both among academics and practitioners (Aguinis & Glavas, 2012; Carroll, 1999; Waddock, 2004). Ninety-three percent of the world's 250 largest corporations by revenue now formally report on CSR (KPMG, 2015). In parallel, academia has also focused heavily on CSR with over 650 schools and universities formally committing to embedding CSR in teaching and research.[1] Moreover, in a search of the literature, we found 11,758 articles on CSR in peer-reviewed journals related to psychology.[2] Due to the vast and diverse extant CSR literature, there is much we already know about CSR.

However, CSR has historically been studied at the institutional and organizational levels of analysis with the individual level being largely overlooked until recently (Glavas, 2016b).[3] In order to address this gap, scholars in psychology and related fields (e.g., organizational behavior (OB), human resources) have been increasingly studying CSR (Gond, El Akremi, Swaen, & Babu, 2017). We now know a lot about topics at the individual level such as job seeking (Jones, Willness, & Madey, 2014), organizational identification (Farooq, Farooq, & Jasimuddin, 2014; Jones, 2010), perceived organizational support (Glavas & Kelley, 2014), and trust (de Roeck & Delobbe, 2012). Yet, there is still so much more that psychologists can contribute to CSR, such as developing multilevel models of CSR (Jones, Willness, & Glavas, 2017), exploring the dark side of CSR (Willness, forthcoming), and studying relevant topics such as work meaningfulness (Aguinis & Glavas, 2019), perceptions of CSR (Jones, forthcoming), and CSR attributions (Donia & Sirsly, 2016; Vlachos, Panagopoulos, & Rapp, 2013).

In order to help further integrate psychology with CSR, our article is structured as follows. First, we present a brief history and definitional development of CSR over the years, along with outlining its similarities/differences with overlapping concepts such as sustainability and corporate social performance (CSP). Second, we review the literature on CSR by analyzing across three levels of analysis (institutional, organizational, and individual). Third, we outline a non-exhaustive agenda for future research on CSR from a "psychological" perspective.

Thus, our article contributes to CSR by further accelerating the increasing CSR research by psychologists and related fields in the following ways. Our article offers a first stop and relatively general overview of past and current CSR trends so that those not familiar with CSR can find an approachable entry to the field, while those familiar with it may find an overview that provides clarity to a rather complex field. In addition, each part of our article outlines the implications of past and current trends of CSR so that scholars can understand the role that psychology and related fields might play in CSR. Finally, our future research agenda offers guidance for relevant CSR research—most notably, we recommend bridging CSR with fields of psychology such as developmental and cognitive psychology. To be clear upfront, our intent is not to further fragment the field by calling for more research only at the individual level of analysis; rather, we see the role of scholars who can explore micro-CSR as critical to being able to build multilevel models of CSR. In addition, our intent is not to provide another systematic review of CSR,[4] but instead to provide an overview for a wide audience that will hopefully inspire research from not only psychology but also multiple disciplines.

THE CONCEPT AND HISTORY OF CSR

Because there are numerous definitions of CSR—which we will partly cover later in this article—for purposes of clarity, the overarching definition that we use for CSR in this article is: "context-specific organizational actions and policies that take into account stakeholders' expectations and the triple bottom line of economic, social, and environmental performance" (Aguinis & Glavas, 2012, p. 933). As Aguinis and Glavas (2012) further state, although the definition of CSR refers to policies and actions by organizations, such policies and actions are influenced and implemented by actors at all levels of analysis (e.g., institutional, organizational, and individual).

Certain organizational activities, which could today be labeled as "socially responsible" date back centuries. Although social responsibility (SR) was already explored in academia from the 1930s (Berle, 1931; Dodd, 1932), the roots of the current SR movement mostly date back to the post-World War II period (Spector, 2008). Scholars (e.g., Carroll, 2008) generally trace the scholarly conceptualization of CSR to Howard R. Bowen's (1953) "foundational" book titled *Social Responsibilities of the Businessman (SRB)*. In this period, what we today refer to as corporate social responsibility (CSR) was then referred to as social responsibility (SR). Bowen (1953, p. 6) thus defined CSR as "the obligations of businessmen to pursue those policies, to make those decisions, or to follow those lines of action which are desirable in term of the objectives and values of our society." Bowen's view of CSR came from his careful analysis of the statements and discourses of close to 70 of the most prominent executives of the time (Bowen, 1953). It is important to note that *SRB* was more than just a normative book. As Bowen was essentially an economist, *SRB* theorized on explaining why business people were interested in CSR, but also reviewed critically the business case and legal arguments against CSR from an economic viewpoint (Acquier, Gond, & Pasquero, 2011).

Throughout the 1960s and 1970s, the United States was undergoing various social movements including civil rights, consumer rights, women's rights, and environmental movements (Carroll & Shabana, 2010). This changing social environment had pushed organizations toward accepting socially responsible practices, policies, and perspectives. This led to an expansion of the literature on the topic, which primarily focused on defining the actual meaning of CSR (e.g., Davis, 1967, p. 46), and how it is relevant for business and society (e.g., Walton, 1967). In this phase, the concept of CSR basically argued that being an organization in society comes with a series of responsibilities, and that as actors in societies, businesses should behave responsibly (Carroll, 2008). It also argued that this should be done voluntarily, and thus avoid problems that would otherwise emerge. However, the responsibilities rested on two fundamental principles of charity and stewardship. In practice, this was seen through corporate activities such as philanthropic programs and strategies, volunteering, and better community relationships.

The 1970s were a time when different definitions of CSR began to proliferate. Also, it was in this decade that similar/alternative concepts such as CSP and corporate social responsiveness were first introduced (Ackerman, 1973; Ackerman & Bauer, 1976). Although different scholars have used different definitions of CSR, and explained how it differs from related concepts, a widely accepted definitional contribution came from the Committee for Economic Development (CED) (Carroll, 1999). The CED, which was—and still is—one of the most influential business-led public policy organizations, in their publication *Social Responsibilities of Business Corporations*, proposed a so-called three-concentric-circle definition of CSR, including *inner* (i.e., basic efficiency related responsibilities), *intermediate* (i.e., social values and changing priorities), and *outer* (i.e., newly emerging responsibilities) *corporate social responsibilities* (Carroll, 1999). From a practical perspective, it was in the late 1970s that companies began to develop departments (e.g., public affairs departments) specialized for helping them bridge between corporate activities/decisions and external constituencies.

In the 1980s complementary concepts such as stakeholder management, CSP, and business ethics became more frequent (Carroll, 1999). During these years, the focus of CSR was on "ethical corporate cultures" and research was conducted on the link between CSR and financial performance (McGuire, Sundgren, & Schneeweis, 1988). Although the idea that being socially responsible was also good for business had existed for a long time (e.g., Bowen, 1953), the 1980s were a time when these ideas began to increase. This was the beginning of the "instrumental" arguments or "business case for CSR"—a perspective of CSR in which practitioners and academic researchers explored the usefulness of CSR for businesses by exploring its link to financial performance. This was also evident in some CSR definitions, such as that of Peter Drucker (1984), who proposed what he called a new meaning of CSR, in which business should "turn a social problem into economic opportunity and benefit, productive capacity, human competence, well paid job and wealth" (Drucker, 1984, p. 62).

Building on these developments, from the 1990s and onwards, even more research was conducted on the relationship between CSR and financial performance (Carroll, 2008). From a practical perspective, the 1990s were a time in which philanthropy and other forms of "corporate giving" expanded significantly, which led to the development of managers specialized in corporate giving, CSR, public affairs, and related areas (Waddock, 2004). On a global scale, multinational corporations (e.g., Coca-Cola, McDonalds, Nike) became more engaged in CSR, and some smaller companies (e.g., Ben and Jerry's, Patagonia, The Body Shop) built global reputations as a result of their CSR practices. These companies engage in a wide variety of activities in order to be more responsible to numerous stakeholders, including customers, suppliers, employees, and local communities. A key part of such activities has been various forms of sponsorship and philanthropy aimed at the development of local communities. While some organizations donate for strategic purposes, others make contributions solely because they want to be good corporate citizens (Lii & Lee, 2012). For instance, a famous example of a CSR activity is Microsoft's "Affordable Access Initiatives," through which they seek to empower billions of people worldwide who do not have affordable access to the Internet by providing internet infrastructure, but also providing free education programs to increase the level of information technology literacy. In addition to such philanthropic activities, companies like The Body Shop and Patagonia have focused on making their production more responsible by using sustainable packaging, using natural products in production, and lowering their carbon footprint. Thus, managing their supply chain in an ethical and sustainable way has become a key strategic goal for many organizations. More recently, CSR has become crucial internally, such as in human resource departments, where CSR principles have been implemented in the way organizations recruit, manage, and treat their members, making socially responsible human resource management an integral part of CSR initiatives and a key tool for the implementation of CSR objectives. Such activities have often gone beyond the provision of better work conditions or a higher salary, but also include recruiting policies that target socially responsible employees, offering CSR training to employees, and so forth. An overview with the "main types" and examples of CSR activities can be found in the Appendix.

The global popularization of CSR then led to the development of a large number of CSR books for practitioners (e.g., Esty & Winston, 2006; Hart, 2005; Kotler & Lee, 2008; Laszlo & Zhexembayeva, 2011) as well as CSR becoming a common subject in business schools around the world.[5] From an academic perspective, the empirical and conceptual literature that was published by scholars mostly focused on claiming a theoretical contribution, and was thus primarily framed toward contributing to different management theories (e.g., institutional theory, stakeholder theory). In recent years, the research on CSR has gone into different directions, with scholars using different paradigms and levels of analysis. This is discussed later in the review.

CSR AND SIMILAR CONCEPTS

As was explained above, in the last 30 years, the concept of CSR was complemented with similar concepts such as CSP, stakeholder theory, corporate sustainability (CS), and corporate responsibility (CR)/corporate citizenship (CC).[6] In this section, we outline each one of these concepts, and explain how these concepts differ to what we broadly understand as CSR. Please note that despite our depiction of these concepts as being distinct, these terms are sometimes used interchangeably with boundaries being blurred (Peloza, 2009; Waddock, 2004).

CSP. CSP provides a framework by which a company can assess its activities in and relation to society by taking into consideration all of its stakeholders and the natural environment. However, as with CSR, the exact definition of CSP is the subject of ongoing debate. Yet it is possible to categorize the definitions into two groups, depending on whether scholars have approached the concept empirically or conceptually (Gond & Crane, 2010).

The theoretical approach to CSP tends to view it as an umbrella concept that has a number of parts and dimensions, one of which is CSR (Gond & Crane, 2010). Carroll's (1979) three-dimensional conceptual model can be seen as the landmark of the CSP concept. Building on this, Wood (1991) further developed a more detailed, and later widely acknowledged CSP model that consists of *principles of CSR* (i.e., institutional, organizational, and individual principles), *processes of corporate social responsiveness* (i.e., environmental, stakeholder, and issues management), and *outcomes of corporate behavior*. The second, and differing, definitional approach to conceptualizing CSP refers to the way that it was assessed in the empirical literature (e.g., Clarkson, 1995; Hillman & Keim, 2001). In this context, CSP is primarily configured to capture and measure the activities—among which are CSR activities—and the societal impact of corporations (Gond & Crane, 2010). Overall, both groups of definitions have viewed CSP as a broader umbrella concept of which CSR is one, but albeit important, part.

Stakeholder Theory. Stakeholder theory, a theory popularized by Edward Freeman (1984), is based on the assumption that a company's relationship with all of its stakeholders—including the natural environment—is essential to understanding how a business operates and adds value. Freeman thus argued that relationships among stakeholders are the basis of value added and strategic initiatives. Stakeholder theory was also largely referred to as a response to the "shareholder approach," which was famously emphasized by Milton Friedman, and it asserts that "there is one and only one social responsibility of business—to use its resources and engage in activities designed to increase its profits so long as it ... engages in open and free competition, without deception or fraud" (Friedman, 1970). Thus, stakeholder theory expanded the view of business and managerial action being only responsible to shareholders, but also to all stakeholders of an organization. It is important to emphasize that stakeholder theory builds on organizational theory, explaining some aspects of organizational life such as firm performance, firms' actions/responses, stakeholder actions/responses, and stakeholder salience (Laplume, Sonpar, & Litz, 2008). Stakeholder theory thus evolved as the one of the first major theories attributed to explaining how, when, and why CSR is enacted. Stakeholder theory also signaled a shift of emphasis from trying to prove the business case for CSR to trying to actually understand CSR itself.

Corporate Sustainability. The concept of corporate sustainability (CS) was popularized in 1987 by a report published by the United Nations World Commission on Environment and Development (WCED). In this report, titled "Our Common Future"—or commonly known as the Brundtland Report—the WCED propagated the term *sustainable development*. The WCED argued that development is sustainable "if companies needs can be met without compromising the ability of future generations to meet their own needs" (WCED, 1987, p. 43). However, it was not until the 1990s that sustainability became a popular topic among business scholars. Moreover, it is important to note that sustainability has also been defined in different ways. While some scholars have used the concept of "ecological sustainability" to refer to the environmental issues of business, others have applied the WCED definition in a broader sense, by explaining it through a tri-dimensional construct which includes environmental, economic, and social dimensions (Bansal, 2005; Montiel, 2008).

While both sustainability and CSR tackle the relationship between business and society, and both have a similar conceptualization of the three dimensions (economic, social, and environmental), what differentiates them is that they emerged from different paradigms (Bansal & Song, 2016). As was explained before, CSR research started with a normative orientation, in which scholars explored the normative role of business in society, questioning unconstrained laissez-faire capitalism (Bansal & Song, 2016; Bowen, 1953; Walton, 1967). On the other hand, sustainability research served as a reaction to the ecological disruptions that happened as a result of economic development (Bansal & Song, 2016; Roome, 1992; WCED, 1987). While sustainability scholars focused on the interconnectedness between the economic, social, and environmental dimensions, the older CSR literature (e.g., Carroll, 1979) viewed CSR as an aspect that will supplement business (Montiel, 2008). However, in recent years, the distinctiveness between the two concepts has been blurred to the extent that researchers who study the intersection between business and society often struggle with their choice of constructs and literature (Bansal & Song, 2016).

CR/CC. During the 1990s, a new way of thinking about CSR was emerging, and CSR became a topic among business and strategy scholars around the world. From these studies, the concept of CR was developed, dropping the word "social" in order to reflect the importance of "responsibilities" in all corporate actions, decisions, behaviors, and impacts (Waddock, 2004). Thus, this concept integrally linked corporate practices, stakeholders, and responsibilities of all corporate relationships. It refers to the degree of (ir)responsibility that manifests in a company's strategy and operations on a daily basis. Similarly, and around the same time, the concept of CC developed from the British tradition of practitioners and management scholars, and its definition is essentially comparable to the term of CR (Waddock, 2004). The two terms integrate stakeholder relationships as part of their operationalization. Other than just focusing on social implications of business activities, the concepts incorporate issues related to a company's performance in respect to specific stakeholders and the natural environment. Therefore, stakeholder and environmental performance are central to CC/CR.

PRIOR CSR RESEARCH CLASSIFIED AT THE INSTITUTIONAL, ORGANIZATIONAL, AND INDIVIDUAL LEVELS OF ANALYSIS

In this section, we briefly review the theoretical and empirical literature on CSR. With its increasing importance, the phenomenon of CSR was studied across disciplines (e.g., environmental studies, law, management, psychology, sociology). As a result, and due to the multidisciplinary natures of the fields, CSR has been studied through different levels of analysis. Here we illustrate what we know about CSR by organizing the literature across three levels of analysis: institutional, organizational, and individual. Also, scholars at all levels of analysis have not only explored the outcomes of CSR, but also the underlying mechanisms that lead to these outcomes, along with the activities that serve as "triggers" of CSR activities. All three aspects are covered in this brief overview (for a more detailed analysis of each level of CSR see Aguinis & Glavas, 2012). To be clear upfront, although analyzing at different levels of analysis is a convenient approach that is often used, CSR is a multilevel construct that should ideally be studied from all levels of analysis at the same time (Aguinis & Glavas, 2012).

Institutional Level of Analysis. As was described in the section "The Concept and History of CSR," in the early years of the CSR field, scholars (e.g., Bowen, 1953; Walton, 1967) were interested in what they called the role of business in society, by exploring the responsibilities business has toward broader society. This implies that these scholars viewed CSR from what we today understand as an institutional level of analysis. Although there have been numerous attempts to define what an institution is, most scholars agree that institutions consist of three pillars which are *normative, cultural-cognitive,* and *regulative* (Scott, 1995). To give a few examples, if CSR is studied in relation to laws, it would be considered a regulatory pillar. On the other hand, if it is studied in relation to constructs that are shaped by stakeholders that are external to the firm (e.g., consumers) then it would be considered cultural-cognitive. Finally, if CSR is explored in relation to an "ethical" concern, that would be considered as "normative."

A relevant view of institutions to CSR is based around the concept of isomorphism (cf. Agle, Mitchell, & Sonnenfeld, 1999; Hoffman, 1999), which is defined as the similarity of the processes of structure of one organization to those of the other (DiMaggio & Powell, 1983). There are three main types of institutional isomorphism: normative, coercive, and mimetic. Normative isomorphism is driven by norms that are brought up by education, for example, and are then embedded into the organization (e.g., CSR codes of conduct). Coercive isomorphism involves pressures by other organizations that are dependent on cultural expectations of society (DiMaggio & Powell, 1983) such as stakeholder pressure on firms to engage in CSR. By contrast, mimetic isomorphism refers to the tendency of the organization to imitate another organization's structure (e.g., firms copying CSR practices of competitor firms), because it believes it is beneficial (DiMaggio & Powell, 1983).

When referring to institutional-level CSR outcomes, a commonly researched topic is the relationship between CSR and a firm's reputation. The basic assumption of such studies is that CSR would positively influence a firm's reputation, making it more attractive to their external stakeholders (e.g., McWilliams & Siegel, 2001). By empirically testing this, scholars have shown consistent findings regarding the positive relationship between CSR and a firm's reputation (e.g., Brammer & Pavelin, 2006; Lii & Lee, 2012; Turban & Greening, 1997), including reputation based on consumer loyalty (e.g., Maignan, Ferrell, & Hult, 1999). Other than reputational outcomes, more recently a number of CSR scholars have adopted what they call a political view of CSR (e.g., Fooks, Gilmore, Collin, Holden, & Lee, 2013; Scherer & Palazzo, 2007). Building on the ideas of Scherer and Palazzo (2007), scholars have started to explore the phenomenon in which private corporations engage in the provision of public goods (e.g., water, health, education). Scherer, Rasche, Palazzo, and Spicer (2016) conceptualize this phenomenon by introducing the umbrella concept of political CSR, which they define as those responsible business activities that turn corporations into political actors by engaging in public deliberations, collective decisions, and the provision of public goods.

In order to explain the CSR–outcome relationship, mediators have been studied at the institutional level, such as customer satisfaction (e.g., Lev, Petrovits, & Radhakrishnan, 2010), consumer trust (Vlachos, Tsamakos, Vrechopoulos, & Avramidis, 2009), and consumer–organization fit (e.g., Sen & Bhattacharya, 2001). On the other hand, the strength of the influence of CSR on institutional outcomes has been studied primarily by using moderating variables such as firm environment (e.g., Chatterji & Toffel, 2010), stakeholders (e.g., Russo & Fouts, 1997), and industry (e.g., Chiu & Sharfman, 2011). A key concept in this relationship is "stakeholder salience," which refers to the level of importance that organizations give to certain stakeholder groups (Mitchell, Agle, & Wood, 1997). By using a sample of companies from emerging economies, and drawing from literature on stakeholder salience (Mitchell et al., 1997), Jamali (2008) has shown how stakeholder management is affected by relational attributes (i.e., power, legitimacy, urgency) and the pressures they can exert on corporations. However, David, Bloom, and Hillman (2007) have shown that the relationship between CSR initiatives and outcomes is much more complex than initially theorized because stakeholder salience might influence managers to try to appease stakeholders through symbolic actions (i.e., lower-quality CSR that does not impact stakeholders as positively as substantive actions). These findings foreshadowed later work on micro-CSR in which it was shown that individuals react in different ways to CSR (e.g., both negative and positive) and thus have varying influences on the relationship between CSR and outcomes.

Although the aforementioned literature has described the institutional-level outcomes of CSR, along with the underlying mechanisms that lead to it, some scholars went a "step back" and asked the question: "what motivates these organizations to engage in CSR? Why do they do it in the first place?" In order to explain this, Aguilera, Rupp, Williams, and Ganapathi (2007) delved into CSR motives and outlined three groups of motives that pressure firms to engage in CSR. These authors created a multilevel model such that the motives apply to all levels of analysis. For purposes of this section, we refer to institutional motives. The first motives are *instrumental*, which they described as those that are driven by an organization's self-interest (e.g., reputation). The second type are *moral*, which refer to those motives that are driven by moral principles which are often influenced by society. Finally, the third type are *relational*, which refer to the concerns with relationships among different group members (e.g., fulfilling one's need to belong by engaging in CSR)—at the institutional level, this might be industry forces. However, as the motives imply, it is important to note that CSR activities are rarely a purely moral decision, but are often triggered by different stakeholders who have different expectations of the organization (Grunig, 1979). Building on this idea, a number of studies have explored the way consumers (e.g., Christmann & Taylor, 2006), shareholders (e.g., David et al., 2007), the media (Weaver, Treviño, & Cochran, 1999), and governments (Moon & Vogel, 2008) influence firms to engage in CSR. However, although these studies have shown that these stakeholders do influence organizations' CSR activities, the way they do so tends to differ. For example, when customers want to influence CSR they may do it through their evaluation and product purchasing (e.g., Sen & Bhattacharya, 2001), customer monitoring and expected sanctions (e.g., Christmann & Taylor, 2006), and discursive actions (e.g., Stole & Micheletti, 2013, p. 258). On the other hand, certain interest groups (e.g., nongovernmental organizations (NGOs)) may use public statements and other forms of public pressure in order to make companies more socially responsible. Overall, external stakeholders apply pressure by indirectly impacting an organization's financial resources and reputation (LaPlume et al., 2008).

In sum, by viewing CSR from an institutional level of analysis, scholars have demonstrated the important influence of different stakeholder groups and institutional forces on CSR activities. However, research has also shown that institutional forces may lead to primarily symbolic CSR, meaning that firms engage in these activities to superficially meet stakeholder demands, or meet the regulatory minimum (David et al., 2007). Finally, scholars have also shown that companies that engage in CSR are likely to increase their reputation and strengthen their customer loyalty (e.g., Brammer & Pavelin, 2006; Maignan et al., 1999).

Organizational Level of Analysis.   Although CSR was originally studied from an institutional level of analysis, to date the vast majority of CSR research has been conducted from what we understand as an organizational level of analysis (Aguinis & Glavas, 2012). An organizational level of analysis refers to studies that look at the impact that CSR has on organizations as a whole. As was described previously, since the 1990s, numerous scholars were interested in exploring the positive relationship between CSR and financial outcomes, along with the moderating and mediating effects that lead to it. All these attempts to measure the impact of CSR on financial performance can be broadly placed within an area of CSR research, which is today often labeled as "the business case for CSR." The business case for CSR refers to the underlying arguments that support the idea that the business community should advance their own CSR agendas (Carroll & Shabana, 2010). Thus, the business case for CSR is primarily concerned with the question of "how do businesses benefit from CSR?" (Carroll & Shabana, 2010, p. 85). Generally, there seems to be a significant and positive, albeit slight, relationship between CSR and financial performance (Orlitzky, Schmidt, & Rynes, 2003; Margolis, Elfenbein, & Walsh, 2009). However, Aguinis and Glavas (2019) put forward that there is great variance in the relationships—something that Orlitzky et al. (2003) also acknowledge in their meta-analysis—and that this variance cannot be understood without studying the differing effects CSR has on individuals.

Other than financial outcomes, a number of studies explored the relationship between CSR and non-financial outcomes. For example, by drawing from social identity theory, Turban and Greening (1997) found that CSR can attract better talent because of positive signaling effects on job seekers. Similarly, through their concept of "shared value," Porter and Kramer (2011) theorized that CSR should be used as a source of competitive advantage. They define shared value as the policies and operating practices that enhance the competitiveness of a company, while at the same time improving the economic and social conditions of the communities in which they operate. However, this concept was strongly criticized by Crane, Palazzo, Spence, and Matten (2014), who argued that it suffers from serious shortcomings: it ignores complex tensions that usually exist between social and economic goals, it is too simplistic about the challenges of business compliance, and it is based on a shallow conception of the corporations' role in society. Furthermore, a few studies have explored the impact of CSR and firm capabilities such as product quality (e.g., Johnson & Greening, 1999), operational efficiency (Sharma & Vredenburg, 1998), and management practices (Waddock & Graves, 1997). In addition to studying the effects of CSR on outcomes, scholars have also explored factors that influence these outcomes through the moderating role of financial resources such as financial performance (e.g., Brammer & Millington, 2004; Johnson & Greening, 1999) and slack resources (e.g., Bansal, 2003). Other commonly investigated moderators include firm size (e.g., Sharma, 2000) and firm visibility to the public (Fry, Keim, & Meiners, 1982). Overall, these studies show how financial resources, as well as additional resources and size of the organization, strengthen the relationship between CSR and outcomes.

Finally, scholars have explored organizational factors that motivate companies to engage in CSR, and in a sense, serve as predictors of CSR engagement. These studies have shown how the aforementioned instrumental motivation of firms—the perception that CSR is good for business—is likely to increase a firm's legitimacy (e.g., Sharma, 2000) and competitiveness (e.g., Bansal & Roth, 2000). However, this is not the only source of motivation for CSR because organizations can also to be motivated by normative reasons such as a sense of responsibility (e.g., Bansal & Roth, 2000) and higher-level morals (Aguilera et al., 2007).

In sum, when studying the relationship between CSR and financial outcomes, research has shown varied results. On the other hand, there are several non-financial outcomes that have shown to result from CSR. These include product quality, operational efficiency, and enhanced diversity. In addition to the effects of CSR on outcomes, research has shown that factors such as firm size, financial resources, and additional resources (e.g., firm visibility) strengthen the CSR–outcomes relationship. Finally, scholars have put forward that the motivation for an organization to engage in CSR can be both instrumental and normative (e.g., Aguilera et al, 2007; Bansal & Roth, 2000). Varied results might be due to outcomes of CSR being aggregated to the organizational level, which might result, for example, in a relatively neutral relationship between CSR and outcomes; but if CSR is unpacked to include the individual level, then results might vary widely with some individuals being positively affected while others negatively (Aguinis & Glavas, 2012, 2019). Therefore, we now turn to the different ways that individuals influence and are influenced by CSR.

Individual Level of Analysis.   Until recently, understanding CSR from the perspective of an individual was largely ignored by scholars (Gond et al., 2017). However, since 2010, there has been a rapid increase in the literature on individual-level research on CSR, now popularly called micro-CSR (Glavas, 2016b). Micro-CSR scholars suggest integrating organizational psychology and OB—as well as related disciplines such as organizational psychology and human resources—with CSR (Gond et al., 2017; Jones & Rupp, 2018). This literature provides insights into how CSR practices influence and/or are influenced by organizational members (Gond et al., 2017). Also, it serves as a response to the aforementioned varied results of CSR at the organizational level. By taking an individual level of analysis, micro-CSR scholars have unpacked the results, and found that, under certain conditions, CSR may influence some employees positively, while others negatively (Aguinis & Glavas, 2013). However, individual-level research should not just be limited to the study of employees, but should include individuals both inside (e.g., employees, managers, executives) and outside (e.g., perspective employees) the organization. This is why Gond et al. (2017) emphasized a "person-centric" rather than "employee-centric" perspective of micro-CSR.

Research on micro-CSR has shown that CSR has numerous positive effects on employees. Scholars have found positive effects of CSR on factors such as job satisfaction (e.g., Glavas & Kelley, 2014; Vlachos et al., 2013), organizational commitment (e.g., Ditlev-Simonsen, 2015), employee engagement (e.g., Glavas, 2016a; Glavas & Piderit, 2009), creativity (e.g., Brammer, He, & Mellahi, 2015; Glavas & Piderit, 2009), employee attachment (Lee, Park, & Lee, 2013), and knowledge sharing (Farooq, Payaud, Merunka, & Balette-Florence, 2014). Also, studies have shown that CSR is positively related to organizational identification, which suggests that by improving organizational reputation and prestige, CSR in turn makes employees prouder of working for the organization (de Roeck, El Akremi, & Swaen, 2016). This can be explained through social identity theory, which would suggest that if treating others well is part of an employee's self-concept, then they would show a stronger identification with the organization that treats them well (Dutton, Roberts, & Bednar, 2010). In addition, by exploring the impact of CSR on employees' trust in relationships (Muthuri, Matten, & Moon, 2009) as well as high-quality relationships among coworkers (Glavas & Piderit, 2009), scholars have put forward a relational view of CSR, which by its very nature should include caring for different stakeholders (Glavas & Kelley, 2014). This implies that organizations that put effort into building high-quality relationships with their external stakeholders could create a similar culture within the organization (Glavas, 2016b).

Although the majority of micro-CSR research has focused on exploring the relationship between CSR and individual-level outcomes, a smaller number of scholars have also explored the underlying mechanisms that lead to these outcomes. Understanding these underlying mechanisms contributes to the CSR literature, while at the same time providing novel insights for organizational psychologists (Glavas, 2016b). Such research has shown that the strength of the relationship between CSR and micro-level outcomes is moderated by individual differences such as gender (e.g., Brammer, Millington, & Rayton, 2007), national culture (e.g., Mueller, Hattrup, Spiess, & Lin Hi, 2012), ideology (Jones, 2010), moral identity (e.g., Rupp, Shao, Thornton, & Skarlicki, 2013), and project meaningfulness (Caligiuri, Mencin, & Jiang, 2013), as well as organizational-level cooperative norms (Shen & Benson, 2016). In addition to exploring the strength of the CSR–outcomes relationship, scholars have also studied the mechanisms through which CSR influences employees because it enables them to bring more of their whole selves to work (Glavas, 2016a). In a recent micro-CSR review article published by Glavas (2016b), he outlined four aspects of the whole-self, which could be found in earlier studies, such as *psychological safety, psychological availability, values congruence,* and *purpose.* Psychological safety refers to aspects such as organizational trust (e.g., de Roeck & Delobbe, 2012) and perceived organizational support (Glavas & Kelley, 2014), which have shown to be positively related to CSR. This implies that CSR can provide an organizational environment/ atmosphere in which employees feel a safe space to express who they truly are. Psychological availability arises from factors such as organizational pride (Jones, 2010), identification (Carmeli, Gilat, & Waldman, 2007), and prosocial identity (Grant, Dutton, & Rosso, 2008). Simply put, this means that employees are likely to feel good about themselves if they are working for an organization that is perceived as doing good for society and, as a result, they will reveal more of their true selves at work. Purpose and values congruence refers to situations in which, as a result of CSR activities, employees have a stronger alignment with the purpose and values of the organization (Gully, Phillips, Castellano, Han, & Kim, 2013; Spanjol,

Tam, & Tam, 2015). Thus, CSR enables employees to bring aspects of their selves to work which they might not have otherwise in cultures where the focus is, for example, on aggressive pursuit of short-term profit. As such, CSR provides fertile ground for scholars to explore a broad range of psychological constructs at work.

In summary, in recent years we have witnessed a rapid increase in individual-level CSR literature. By exploring the impact that CSR has on employees, scholars have provided a partial answer to the varied results of organizational-level CSR research. However, micro-CSR scholars have not only focused on employees of the organization, but also on other individuals outside the organization. The aforementioned research has shown the positive impact that CSR can have on a number of factors such as job satisfaction, employee engagement, and creativity among others. Finally, a smaller number of studies have tried to explain the underlying mechanisms (e.g., gender, national culture, moral identity) that influence the relationship between CSR and individual-level outcomes.

MOVING FORWARD

Thus far, we have presented a brief history and definitional development of CSR over the years, along with outlining its similarities/differences with similar and sometimes overlapping concepts such as CSP, stakeholder theory, sustainability, and CC. Also, we have presented a cross-disciplinary review of the CSR literature across three levels of analysis. In this section, we provide a non-exhaustive agenda for future research topics on CSR, along with potential research questions that could link CSR to different streams of psychology.

Future Research Topics.   Despite the valuable prior research conducted on psychological aspects of CSR, there is much room for future research. We provide a few illustrative examples, which are not meant to be exhaustive. If there is one overarching theme of future research, it is that the underlying relationships between CSR and outcomes as well as antecedents and CSR could be explored in more detail. Little is still known about how, when, and why CSR influences employees and vice versa (Aguinis & Glavas, 2019; Glavas, 2016b)—which is sometimes referred to as the black box of CSR. As mentioned, prior research has often focused on proving the business case that CSR has positive effects for the organization and its employees (Aguinis & Glavas, 2012). Similarly, much of the research at the individual level focuses on the positive effects of CSR on employees; however, in reality, employees vary in how they are affected by and how they influence CSR (Aguinis & Glavas, 2019). Therefore, numerous scholars have stated that CSR should move beyond the business case and the over-emphasis on studying only the positive effects of CSR (e.g., Margolis & Walsh, 2003; Wood, 2010). Moreover, at the individual level, scholars have called for micro-CSR to move beyond a similar emphasis on the study of positive individual outcomes of CSR (Aguinis & Glavas, 2017; Willness, forthcoming). Following are examples of potential future research topics.

The Dark Side of CSR.   As Willness (forthcoming) argues, the extant CSR literature has largely painted a positive picture of the effects of CSR. However, employees react both positively and negatively to CSR. Understanding the different variables that influence positive versus negative reactions can inform both theory and practice. For example, could employees perceive CSR as being extra-role activities which contribute to stress because they are already overburdened at work (Aguinis & Glavas, 2019; Glavas, 2016b)? If CSR is implemented symbolically (e.g., greenwashing, which employees see as a hypocritical promotion of values that do not exist in the company), could it even have a counter-effect, with employees having even lower organizational identification than if there was no CSR (Glavas & Godwin, 2013)?

Third-Party Mechanisms. Because CSR includes a focus on how others are treated *outside* the organization, it provides new fertile ground to go beyond exploring only the direct relationship between employer and employee as well as the treatment of others who are *inside* the organization (e.g., coworkers). For example, organizational justice has traditionally focused on how employees perceive that the organization is treating them or their coworkers (Rupp, 2011). Recently, scholars have begun studying the effects on employees of how the organization treats those *outside* the organization. As Rupp (2011) puts forward, perceptions of fairness toward external stakeholders (i.e., third-party justice) have positive effects on employees. For example, Rupp et al. (2013) found that when employees perceive the organization is treating others outside the organization fairly (i.e., CSR), they respond with higher levels of organizational citizenship behaviors and this relationship is strengthened by moral identity.

Organizational Identity and Identification. While "organizational identification" refers to organizational members' "cognitive linking between the definition of the organization and the definition of the self" (Dutton, Dukerich, & Harquail, 1994, p. 242), "organizational identity" refers to the characteristics of the organization that members believe to be central, enduring, and distinctive (Albert & Whetten, 1985). Although there has been a number of studies exploring the relationship between CSR and organizational identification (e.g., de Roeck & Delobbe, 2012), little is known about the role of CSR in constructing and maintaining an organization's identity. With an increasing number of social enterprises and social impact organizations, in which CSR is often not only an "additional" activity, but also a key characteristic, future research could explore the role of CSR as a central, enduring, and distinctive characteristic of the organization, and how it interplays with other organizational activities (e.g., decision-making, strategy).

Attribution Theory. In addition to organizational justice and social identity theory, there have been many other theories and approaches used to help explain the underlying mechanisms of CSR, such as social exchange theory, signaling theory, and meaningfulness (Aguinis & Glavas, 2019). One theory that is understudied in CSR, but is promising, is attribution theory. CSR is fertile ground for attributions because, as mentioned in the section "Third-Party Mechanisms," CSR represents what the organization does *outside* of its boundaries. As a result, employees form attributions about the organization based on strategies and practices in which they are often not directly involved, which then potentially lead to greater variance in perceptions among employees. Understanding how these attributions are formed based on third-party mechanisms could lead to novel insights. To our knowledge, prior CSR literature has only focused on causal attribution, yet attribution theory is a vast theory. Valuable studies to build upon are those by Donia and Sirsly (2016) and Vlachos et al. (2013).

Micro-Political CSR. Although our review did cluster the political CSR literature within an institutional level of analysis, this distinction can be somewhat problematic, because it overlooks the potential of bridging the literature of micro-CSR and political CSR. Scholars have outlined the importance of the cognitive and linguistic dimensions of CSR (e.g., Basu & Palazzo, 2008; Joutsenvirta, 2009), but no study to date, to our knowledge, has developed a theory on micro-level political CSR. Such an approach could have great potential in understanding issues such as sense-making and sense-giving, power, Machiavellianism, and responsible leadership (Frynas & Stephens, 2015).

Measurement Issues. As Jones and Rupp (2018) put forward in a review, one of the major issues that CSR is facing is that of measurement. Internal (i.e., CSR directed toward employees) and external (i.e., CSR directed toward external stakeholders) CSR are often confounded. Thus, internal CSR overlaps with many constructs already studied in psychology (e.g., organizational justice, perceived organizational support, and social exchange theory). Yet there might be differentiating effects of CSR when the external component is separately measured—for example, as mentioned, with the effects of third-party justice on employees' organizational citizenship behaviors (Rupp et al., 2013). Overall, one of the main reasons for the underdevelopment of micro-level CSR theory is the evident lack of measures for employee perceptions of CSR. Prior CSR research has mostly used measures of CSR at the organizational level which may or may not capture individual-level perceptions (Glavas & Kelley, 2014). For example, an organization might be highly rated in CSR on a specific instrument, but it is quite possible that many employees perceive the organization's CSR differently and that some employees might not even be aware of CSR. A recent scale that provides a path forward is that of El Akremi, Gond, Swaen, de Roeck, and Igalens (2018) who developed a new measure of corporate stakeholder responsibility (CStR).

Perceptions of CSR. Building on the prior point, relatively little is known about how perceptions of CSR are formed (Jones, forthcoming). Future research could inform how employees learn about CSR in the first place and then how subsequent judgments are formed. In addition, social learning theory could provide insight into this topic.

CSR Education. CSR has become widespread as a taught academic course around the world. More than 600 schools and universities are formally committed to embedding CSR in teaching and research.[7] However, we know very little about the actual impact that CSR education has on individuals. This is why future research could explore the impact of CSR education on individuals' perceptions, career choice, and the way that they actually engage with the concept of CSR in their workplace.

Other Topics. Numerous other topics are also quite relevant for CSR for which scholars have called for more research such as on meaningfulness (Aguinis & Glavas; 2019; Glavas, 2016b), tensions between individual and organizational CSR priorities (Hahn, Preuss, Pinkse, & Figge, 2014), social intrapreneurship (Hemingway, 2005), and the role of individual differences (Glavas, 2016b). Finally, although multilevel approaches to CSR have been discussed that involve the institutional, organizational, and individual levels, the leadership level is often overlooked—much more is needed to be studied in order to learn how and when leaders influence and are influenced by CSR (Pless, Maak, & Waldman, 2012; Waldman, 2014).

Future Research: Disciplinary Approaches. Prior psychology research in CSR has been primarily studied from the fields of organizational and social psychology. For example, a special issue on organizational psychology and CSR was published in *Frontiers in Psychology* (Jones, Willness, & Glavas, 2017). As mentioned, CSR has built on topics in organizational psychology such as organizational justice, perceived organizational support, and social exchange theory. In social psychology, numerous contributions have been made to CSR, most notably social identity theory has been widely used to explore CSR and organizational identification (e.g., de Roeck et al., 2016; Farooq et al., 2014; Jones, 2010). However, other disciplines could contribute as well. A few illustrative examples which are not exhaustive follow.

Developmental psychology could shed further light on why, how, and when CSR plays a role in the development of individuals. Especially interesting might be studying the relationship between life stages and CSR. As Glavas (2016b) noted in a review, prior literature, especially from the broader public press, has highlighted that younger generations are more interested in CSR (Meister, 2012). However, a recent meta-analysis found that this is not the case and there is actually a slightly positive and significant relationship with age (Wiernik, Ones, & Dilchert, 2013). One potential avenue for future research to study is if the older that individuals get, the more salient legacy becomes and thus it becomes more important to leave the world better for future generations. In other words, the importance of making money and/or promotion decreases, while improving society (i.e., CSR) becomes much more important.

Cognitive psychology could contribute to the still less developed literature on the relationship between CSR and decision-making. Although previous CSR research has briefly touched upon this topic (e.g., Pedersen, 2006), cognitive psychology could offer a perspective and methodological approach that could help us understand how CSR influences managers' decision-making, particularly in complex cases. These studies could thus explore questions, such as, if CSR contributes to the well-being of employees across all levels, how does it influence the ability of managers to conduct complex decision-making? Another way to bridge the CSR–cognitive psychology literature gap is by exploring the role of cognition and emotion in organizations. Specifically, organizations nowadays are considered as places in which employees deal with issues such as anxiety (Linden & Muschalla, 2007), depression (Caplan & Jones, 1975), and cognitive biases (Barnes, 1984). Future research could explore if and how CSR influences these issues among employees. For example, although CSR should be focused on well-being, could it sometimes actually increase anxiety and stress in cases where it adds additional extra-role work to an already busy workload? Glavas (2016a) found that higher levels of volunteering weakened the relationship between CSR and employee engagement.

In sum, there are numerous ways that the psychology of CSR could be explored. This section hopefully provides a sampling of potential topics and opens up other questions that scholars and practitioners might have.

Future Research: Tying it All Together. While there is a need for more individual-level research, we caution that future research needs to ensure it does not increasingly fragment the field of CSR. Prior research on CSR has already been fragmented even while being studied primarily at the macro and institutional levels (Aguinis & Glavas, 2012; Lee, 2008). Adding one more layer of analysis (i.e., individual) that is not multilevel will not only further divide the field of CSR, but also add to the already existing micro–macro divide in scholarship (Aguinis, Boyd, Pierce, & Short, 2011). Therefore, scholars have called for multilevel models of CSR (Aguilera et al., 2007; Aguinis & Glavas, 2019; Glavas, 2016b; Jones et al., 2017).

While multilevel models of CSR are quite rare (Glavas, 2016b), a few good examples of multilevel research in CSR exist that can provide inspiration for future research. For example, Aguilera et al. (2007) put forward a multilevel model in which instrumental, relational, and moral motives affect actors at all levels. As another example, Aguinis and Glavas (2019) propose a person-centric multilevel framework of how employees experience and make sense of work meaningfulness. They posit that employees not only find meaningfulness in their daily tasks, as prior research has shown, but also based on how the organization treats outsiders. Following these examples, future research could expand the traditional view of context being at the organizational level to a context that is at the institutional level.

CSR is a field that is holistic in nature. It involves human beings (i.e., employees, customers, and other stakeholders), the organization, and society. Arguably, other fields have not been as holistic in nature. For example, industrial-organizational psychology has often focused primarily on the relationship between the individual and the organization, while largely ignoring society. Thus, not only can psychology contribute to CSR, but CSR can also contribute to psychology by providing an opportunity for a more holistic approach.

ACKNOWLEDGMENTS

We thank the reviewers and Jean-Pascal Gond for their very constructive feedback that allowed us to improve this article.

FURTHER READING

Aguinis, H., & Glavas, A. (2012). What we know and don't know about corporate social responsibility: A review and research agenda. *Journal of Management, 38*(4), 932–968.

Carroll, A. B. (1999). Corporate social responsibility. Evolution of a definitional construct. *Business and Society, 38*(3), 268–295.

Carroll, A. B. (2008). A history of corporate social responsibility: Concepts and practices. In A. Crane, A. McWilliams, D. Matten, J. Moon, & D. Siegel (Eds.), *The Oxford handbook of corporate social responsibility* (pp. 19–46). New York: Oxford University Press.

Frynas, J. G., & Stephens, S. (2015). Political corporate social responsibility: Reviewing theories and setting new agendas. *International Journal of Management Reviews, 17*(4), 483–509.

Garriga, E., & Melé, D. (2004). Corporate social responsibility: Mapping the conceptual territory. *Journal of Business Ethics, 53*(1/2), 51–71.

Glavas, A. (2016). Corporate social responsibility and organizational psychology: An integrative review. *Frontiers in Psychology, 7*, 144.

Gond, J. P., El Akremi, A., Swaen, V., & Babu, N. (2017). The psychological microfoundations of corporate social responsibility: A person-centric systematic review. *Journal of Organizational Behavior, 38*(2), 225–246.

Jones, D. A. (forthcoming). The psychology of corporate social responsibility. In A. McWilliams, D. E. Rupp, D. S. Siegel, G. Stahl, & D. A. Waldman (Eds.), *The Oxford handbook of corporate social responsibility: Psychological and organizational perspectives.* Oxford, U.K.: Oxford University Press.

Jones, D. A., & Rupp, D. E. (2018). Social responsibility in and of organizations: The psychology of corporate social responsibility among organizational members. In N. Anderson, D. S. Ones, H. K. Sinangil, & C. Viswesvaran (Eds.), *Handbook of industrial, work, and organizational psychology* (2nd ed., pp. 333–350). SAGE.

Rupp, D. E., & Mallory, D. B. (2015). Corporate social responsibility: Psychological, person-centric, and progressing. *Annual Review of Organizational Psychology and Organizational Behavior, 2*(1), 211–236.

Waddock, S. (2004). Parallel universes: Companies, academics, and the progress of corporate citizenship. *Business and Society Review, 109*(1), 5–42.

Willness, C. R. (forthcoming). When CSR backfires: Understanding stakeholders' negative responses to corporate social responsibility. In A. McWilliams, D. E. Rupp, D. S. Siegel, G. Stahl, & D. A. Waldman (Eds.), *The Oxford handbook of corporate social responsibility: Psychological and organizational perspectives.* Oxford, U.K.: Oxford University Press.

REFERENCES

Ackerman, R. W. (1973). How companies respond to social demands. *Harvard Business Review, 51*(4), 88–98.

Ackerman, R. W., & Bauer, R. A. (1976). *Corporate social responsiveness.* Reston, VA: Reston Publishing.

Acquier, A., Gond, J. P., & Pasquero, J. (2011). Rediscovering Howard R. Bowen's legacy: The unachieved agenda and continuing relevance of social responsibilities of the businessman. *Business & Society, 50*(4), 607–646.

Agle, B. R., Mitchell, R. K., & Sonnenfeld, J. A. (1999). Who matters to CEOs? An investigation of stakeholder attributes and salience, corporate performance, and CEO values. *Academy of Management Journal, 42*(5), 507–525.

Aguilera, R. V., Rupp, D. E., Williams, C. A., & Ganapathi, J. (2007). Putting the S back in corporate social responsibility: A multilevel theory of social change in organizations. *Academy of Management Review, 32*(3), 836–863.

Aguinis, H., Boyd, B. K., Pierce, C. A., & Short, J. C. (2011). Walking new avenues in management research methods and theories: Bridging micro and macro domains. *Journal of Management, 37*(2), 395–403.

Aguinis, H., & Glavas, A. (2012). What we know and don't know about corporate social responsibility: A review and research agenda. *Journal of Management, 38*(4), 932–968.

Aguinis, H., & Glavas, A. (2013). Embedded versus peripheral corporate social responsibility: Psychological foundations. *Industrial and Organizational Psychology, 6*(4), 314–332.

Aguinis, H., & Glavas, A. (2019). On corporate social responsibility, sensemaking, and the search for meaningfulness through work. *Journal of Management, 45,* 1057–1086.

Albert, S., & Whetten, D. A. (1985). Organizational identity. *Research in Organizational Behavior, 7,* 263–295.

Bansal, P. (2003). From issues to actions: The importance of individual concerns and organizational values in responding to natural environmental issues. *Organization Science, 14*(5), 510–527.

Bansal, P. (2005). Evolving sustainably: A longitudinal study of corporate sustainable development. *Strategic Management Journal, 26*(3), 197–218.

Bansal, P., & Roth, K. (2000). Why companies go green: A model of ecological responsiveness. *Academy of Management Journal, 43*(4), 717–736.

Bansal, P., & Song, H. C. (2016). Similar but not the same: Differentiating corporate responsibility from sustainability. *Academy of Management Annals, 11*(1), 105–149.

Barnes, J. H. (1984). Cognitive biases and their impact on strategic planning. *Strategic Management Journal, 5*(2), 129–137.

Basu, K., & Palazzo, G. (2008). Corporate social responsibility: A process model of sensemaking. *Academy of Management Review, 33*(1), 122–136.

Berle, A. A. (1931). Corporate powers as powers in trust. *Harvard Law Review, 44*, 1049–1074.

Bowen, H. R. (1953). *Social responsibility of the businessman.* New York: Harpers & Brothers.

Brammer, S., He, H., & Mellahi, K. (2015). Corporate social responsibility, employee organizational identification, and creative effort: The moderating impact of corporate ability. *Group & Organization Management, 40*(3), 323–352.

Brammer, S., & Millington, A. (2004). The development of corporate charitable contributions in the UK: A stakeholder analysis. *Journal of Management Studies, 41*(8), 1411–1434.

Brammer, S., Millington, A., & Rayton, B. (2007). The contribution of corporate social responsibility to organizational commitment. *International Journal of Human Resource Management, 18*(10), 1701–1719.

Brammer, S. J., & Pavelin, S. (2006). Corporate reputation and social performance: The importance of fit. *Journal of Management Studies, 43*(3), 435–455.

Caligiuri, P., Mencin, A., & Jiang, K. (2013). Win–win–win: The influence of company-sponsored volunteerism programs on employees, NGOs, and business units. *Personnel Psychology, 66*(4), 825–860.

Caplan, R. D., & Jones, K. W. (1975). Effects of work load, role ambiguity, and type A personality on anxiety, depression, and heart rate. *Journal of Applied Psychology, 60*(6), 713.

Carmeli, A., Gilat, G., & Waldman, D. A. (2007). The role of perceived organizational performance in organizational identification, adjustment and job performance. *Journal of Management Studies, 44*(6), 972–992.

Carroll, A. B. (1979). A three-dimensional conceptual model of corporate performance. *Academy of Management Review, 4*(4), 497–505.

Carroll, A. B. (1999). Corporate social responsibility: Evolution of a definitional construct. *Business & Society, 38*(3), 268–295.

Carroll, A. B. (2008). A history of corporate social responsibility: Concepts and practices. In A. Crane, A. McWilliams, D. Matten, J. Moon, & D. Siegel (Eds.), *The Oxford handbook of corporate social responsibility*, (pp. 19–46). New York: Oxford University Press.

Carroll, A. B., & Shabana, K. M. (2010). The business case for corporate social responsibility: A review of concepts, research and practice. *International Journal of Management Reviews, 12*(1), 85–105.

Chatterji, A. K., & Toffel, M. W. (2010). How firms respond to being rated. *Strategic Management Journal, 31*(9), 917–945.

Chiu, S. C., & Sharfman, M. (2011). Legitimacy, visibility, and the antecedents of corporate social performance: An investigation of the instrumental perspective. *Journal of Management, 37*(6), 1558–1585.

Christmann, P., & Taylor, G. (2006). Firm self-regulation through international certifiable standards: Determinants of symbolic versus substantive implementation. *Journal of International Business Studies, 37*(6), 863–878.

Clarkson, M. E. (1995). A stakeholder framework for analyzing and evaluating corporate social performance. *Academy of Management Review, 20*(1), 92–117.

Crane, A., Palazzo, G., Spence, L. J., & Matten, D. (2014). Contesting the value of the shared value concept. *California Management Review, 56*, 2.

David, P., Bloom, M., & Hillman, A. J. (2007). Investor activism, managerial responsiveness, and corporate social performance. *Strategic Management Journal, 28*(1), 91–100.

Davis, K. (1967). Understanding the social responsibility puzzle: What does the businessman owe to society? *Business Horizons, 10*, 45–50.

De Roeck, K., & Delobbe, N. (2012). Do environmental CSR initiatives serve organizations' legitimacy in the oil industry? Exploring employees' reactions through organizational identification theory. *Journal of Business Ethics, 110*(4), 397–412.

De Roeck, K., El Akremi, A., & Swaen, V. (2016). Consistency matters! How and when does corporate social responsibility affect employees' organizational identification? *Journal of Management Studies*, 53(7), 1141–1168.

DiMaggio, P., & Powell, W. W. (1983). The iron cage revisited: Collective rationality and institutional isomorphism in organizational fields. *American Sociological Review*, 48(2), 147–160.

Ditlev-Simonsen, C. D. (2015). The relationship between Norwegian and Swedish employees' perception of corporate social responsibility and affective commitment. *Business & Society*, 54(2), 229–253.

Dodd, E. M. (1932). For whom are corporate managers' trustees? *Harvard Law Review*, 45, 1145–1163.

Donia, M. B., & Sirsly, C. A. T. (2016). Determinants and consequences of employee attributions of corporate social responsibility as substantive or symbolic. *European Management Journal*, 34(3), 232–242.

Drucker, P. (1984). The new meaning of corporate social responsibility. *California Management Review*, 26, 53–63.

Dutton, J. E., Dukerich, J. M., & Harquail, C. V. (1994). Organizational images and member identification. *Administrative Science Quarterly*, 39(2), 239–263.

Dutton, J. E., Roberts, L. M., & Bednar, J. (2010). Pathways for positive identity construction at work: Four types of positive identity and the building of social resources. *Academy of Management Review*, 35(2), 265–293.

El Akremi, A., Gond, J. P., Swaen, V., de Roeck, K., & Igalens, J. (2018). How do employees perceive corporate responsibility? Development and validation of a multidimensional corporate stakeholder responsibility scale. *Journal of Management*, 44(2), 619–657.

Esty, D. C., & Winston, A. S. (2006). *Green to gold: How smart companies use environmental strategy to innovate, create value, and build competitive advantage*. New Haven, CT: Yale University Press.

Farooq, M., Farooq, O., & Jasimuddin, S. M. (2014). Employees response to corporate social responsibility: Exploring the role of employees' collectivist orientation. *European Management Journal*, 32(6), 916–927.

Farooq, O., Payaud, M., Merunka, D., & Valette-Florence, P. (2014). The impact of corporate social responsibility on organizational commitment: Exploring multiple mediation mechanisms. *Journal of Business Ethics*, 125(4), 563–580.

Fooks, G., Gilmore, A., Collin, J., Holden, C., & Lee, K. (2013). The limits of corporate social responsibility: Techniques of neutralization, stakeholder management and political CSR. *Journal of Business Ethics*, 112(2), 283–299.

Freeman, R. E. (1984). *Strategic management: A stakeholder approach*. Boston, MA: Pitman.

Friedman, M. (1970). The social responsibility of business is to increase its profits. *New York Times Magazine*, September 13.

Fry, L. W., Keim, G. D., & Meiners, R. E. (1982). Corporate contributions: Altruistic or for-profit? *Academy of Management Journal*, 25(1), 94–106.

Frynas, J. G., & Stephens, S. (2015). Political corporate social responsibility: Reviewing theories and setting new agendas. *International Journal of Management Reviews*, 17(4), 483–509.

Glavas, A. (2016a). Corporate social responsibility and employee engagement: Enabling employees to employ more of their whole selves at work. *Frontiers in Psychology*, 7, 1–10.

Glavas, A. (2016b). Corporate social responsibility and organizational psychology: An integrative review. *Frontiers in Psychology*, 7, 1–13.

Glavas, A., & Godwin, L. N. (2013). Is the perception of "goodness" good enough? Exploring the relationship between perceived corporate social responsibility and employee organizational identification. *Journal of Business Ethics*, 114(1), 15–27.

Glavas, A., & Kelley, K. (2014). The effects of perceived corporate social responsibility on employee attitudes. *Business Ethics Quarterly*, 24, 165–202.

Glavas, A., & Piderit, S. K. (2009). How does doing good matter? Effects of corporate citizenship on employees. *Journal of Corporate Citizenship*, 36, 51–70.

Gond, J. P., & Crane, A. (2010). Corporate social performance disoriented: Saving the lost paradigm? *Business & Society, 49*(4), 677–703.

Gond, J. P., El Akremi, A., Swaen, V., & Babu, N. (2017). The psychological microfoundations of corporate social responsibility: A person-centric systematic review. *Journal of Organizational Behavior, 38*(2), 225–246.

Grant, A. M., Dutton, J. E., & Rosso, B. D. (2008). Giving commitment: Employee support programs and the prosocial sensemaking process. *Academy of Management Journal, 51*(5), 898–918.

Grunig, J. E. (1979). A new measure of public opinion on corporate social responsibility. *Academy of Management Journal, 22*(4), 738–764.

Gully, S. M., Phillips, J. M., Castellano, W. G., Han, K., & Kim, A. (2013). A mediated moderation model of recruiting socially and environmentally responsible job applicants. *Personnel Psychology, 66*(4), 935–973.

Hahn, T., Preuss, L., Pinkse, J., & Figge F. (2014). Cognitive frames in corporate sustainability: Managerial sensemaking with paradoxical and business case frames. *Academy of Management Review, 39*, 463–487.

Hart, S. L. (2005). *Capitalism at the crossroads: The unlimited business opportunities in solving the world's most difficult problems*. Upper Saddle River, NJ: Wharton School.

Hemingway, C. A. (2005). Personal values as a catalyst for corporate social entrepreneurship. *Journal of Business Ethics, 60*(3), 233–249.

Hillman, A. J., & Keim, G. D. (2001). Shareholder value, stakeholder management, and social issues: What's the bottom line? *Strategic Management Journal, 22*, 125–139.

Hoffman, A. J. (1999). Institutional evolution and change: Environmentalism and the US chemical industry. *Academy of Management Journal, 42*(4), 351–371.

Jamali, D. (2008). A stakeholder approach to corporate social responsibility: A fresh perspective into theory and practice. *Journal of Business Ethics, 82*(1), 213–231.

Johnson, R. A., & Greening, D. W. (1999). The effects of corporate governance and institutional ownership types on corporate social performance. *Academy of Management Journal, 42*(5), 564–576.

Jones, D. A. (2010). Does serving the community also serve the company? Using organizational identification and social exchange theories to understand employee responses to a volunteerism programme. *Journal of Occupational and Organizational Psychology, 83*(4), 857–878.

Jones, D. A. (forthcoming). The psychology of corporate social responsibility. In A. McWilliams, D. E. Rupp, D. S. Siegel, G. Stahl, & D. A. Waldman (Eds.), *The Oxford handbook of corporate social responsibility: Psychological and organizational perspectives*. Oxford, U.K.: Oxford University Press.

Jones, D. A., & Rupp, D. E. (2018). Social responsibility in and of organizations: The psychology of corporate social responsibility among organizational members. In N. Anderson, D. S. Ones, H. K. Sinangil, & C. Viswesvaran (Eds.), *Handbook of industrial, work, and organizational psychology* (2nd ed., pp. 333–350). London, UK: SAGE.

Jones, D. A., Willness, C. R., & Glavas, A. (2017). When corporate social responsibility (CSR) meets organizational psychology: New frontiers in micro-CSR research, and fulfilling a quid pro quo through multilevel insights. *Frontiers in Psychology, 8*, 520.

Jones, D. A., Willness, C. R., & Madey, S. (2014). Why are job seekers attracted by corporate social performance? Experimental and field tests of three signal-based mechanisms. *Academy of Management Journal, 57*(2), 383–404.

Joutsenvirta, M. (2009). A language perspective to environmental management and corporate responsibility. *Business Strategy and the Environment, 18*(4), 240–253.

Kotler, P., & Lee, N. (2008). *Corporate social responsibility: Doing the most good for your company and your cause*. Hoboken, NJ: John Wiley & Sons.

KPMG. (2015). *Currents of change: The KPMG survey of corporate responsibility reporting 2015*. https://assets.kpmg.com/content/dam/kpmg/pdf/2016/02/kpmg-international-survey-of-corporate-responsibility-reporting-2015.pdf

Laplume, A. O., Sonpar, K., & Litz, R. A. (2008). Stakeholder theory: Reviewing a theory that moves us. *Journal of Management, 34*(6), 1152–1189.

Laszlo, C., & Zhexembayeva, N. 2011. *Embedded sustainability: The next big competitive advantage.* Palo Alto, CA: Stanford University Press.

Lee, E. M., Park, S. Y., & Lee, H. J. (2013). Employee perception of CSR activities: Its antecedents and consequences. *Journal of Business Research, 66*(10), 1716–1724.

Lee, M. D. P. (2008). A review of the theories of corporate social responsibility: Its evolutionary path and the road ahead. *International Journal of Management Reviews, 10*(1), 53–73.

Lev, B., Petrovits, C., & Radhakrishnan, S. (2010). Is doing good good for you? How corporate charitable contributions enhance revenue growth. *Strategic Management Journal, 31*(2), 182–200.

Lii, Y. S., & Lee, M. (2012). Doing right leads to doing well: When the type of CSR and reputation interact to affect consumer evaluations of the firm. *Journal of Business Ethics, 105*(1), 69–81.

Linden, M., & Muschalla, B. (2007). Anxiety disorders and workplace-related anxieties. *Journal of Anxiety Disorders, 21*(3), 467–474.

Maignan, I., Ferrell, O. C., & Hult, G. T. M. (1999). Corporate citizenship: Cultural antecedents and business benefits. *Journal of the Academy of Marketing Science, 27*(4), 455–469.

Margolis, J. D., Elfenbein, H. A., & Walsh, J. (2009). Does it pay to be good...and does it matter? A meta-analysis of the relationship between corporate social and financial performance. Unpublished manuscript.

Margolis, J. D., & Walsh, J. P. (2003). Misery loves companies: Rethinking social initiatives by business. *Administrative Science Quarterly, 48*(2), 268–305.

McGuire, J. B., Sundgren, A., & Schneeweis, T. (1988). Corporate social responsibility and firm financial performance. *Academy of Management Journal, 31*(4), 854–872.

McWilliams, A., & Siegel, D. (2001). Corporate social responsibility: A theory of the firm perspective. *Academy of Management Review, 26*(1), 117–127.

Meister, J. (2012). Corporate social responsibility: A lever for a level for employee engagement and attraction. *Forbes,* June 7. https://www.forbes.com/sites/jeannemeister/2012/06/07/the-future-of-work-corporate-social-responsiblity-attracts-top-talent/#634310693f95

Mitchell, R. K., Agle, B. R., & Wood, D. J. (1997). Toward a theory of stakeholder identification and salience: Defining the principle of who and what really counts. *Academy of Management Review, 22*(4), 853–886.

Moon, J., & Vogel, D. (2008). Corporate social responsibility, government, and civil society. In A. Crane, A. McWilliams, D. Matten, J. Moon, & D. Siegel (Eds.), *The Oxford handbook of corporate social responsibility* (pp. 303–323). New York: Oxford University Press.

Montiel, I. (2008). Corporate social responsibility and corporate sustainability: Separate pasts, common futures. *Organization & Environment, 21*(3), 245–269.

Mueller, K., Hattrup, K., Spiess, S. O., & Lin-Hi, N. (2012). The effects of corporate social responsibility on employees' affective commitment: A cross-cultural investigation. *Journal of Applied Psychology, 97*(6), 1186.

Muthuri, J. N., Matten, D., & Moon, J. (2009). Employee volunteering and social capital: Contributions to corporate social responsibility. *British Journal of Management, 20*(1), 75–89.

Orlitzky, M., Schmidt, F. L., & Rynes, S. L. (2003). Corporate social and financial performance: A meta-analysis. *Organization Studies, 24*, 403–441.

Pedersen, E. R. (2006). Making corporate social responsibility (CSR) operable: How companies translate stakeholder dialogue into practice. *Business and Society Review, 111*(2), 137–163.

Peloza, J. (2009). The challenge of measuring financial impacts from investments in corporate social performance. *Journal of Management, 35*(6), 1518–1541.

Pless, N. M., Maak, T., & Waldman, D. A. (2012). Different approaches toward doing the right thing: Mapping the responsibility orientations of leaders. *Academy of Management Perspectives, 26*(4), 51–65.

Porter, M., & Kramer, M. R. (2011). Creating shared value. *Harvard Business Review, 89*(1), 62–77.

Roome, N. (1992). Developing environmental management strategies. *Business Strategy and the Environment*, *1*(1), 11–24.

Rupp, D. E. (2011). An employee-centered model of organizational justice and social responsibility. *Organizational Psychology Review*, *1*(1), 72–94.

Rupp, D. E., & Mallory, D. B. (2015). Corporate social responsibility: Psychological, person-centric, and progressing. *Annual Review of Organizational Psychology and Organizational Behavior*, *2*(1), 211–236.

Rupp, D. E., Shao, R., Thornton, M. A., & Skarlicki, D. P. (2013). Applicants' and employees' reactions to corporate social responsibility: The moderating effects of first-party justice perceptions and moral identity. *Personnel Psychology*, *66*(4), 895–933.

Russo, M. V., & Fouts, P. A. (1997). A resource-based perspective on corporate environmental performance and profitability. *Academy of Management Journal*, *40*(3), 534–559.

Scherer, A. G., & Palazzo, G. (2007). Toward a political conception of corporate responsibility: Business and society seen from a Habermasian perspective. *Academy of Management Review*, *32*(4), 1096–1120.

Scherer, A. G., Rasche, A., Palazzo, G., & Spicer, A. (2016). Managing for political corporate social responsibility: New challenges and directions for PCSR 2.0. *Journal of Management Studies*, *53*(3), 273–298.

Sen, S., & Bhattacharya, C. B. (2001). Does doing good always lead to doing better? Consumer reactions to corporate social responsibility. *Journal of Marketing Research*, *38*(2), 225–243.

Scott, W. R. (1995). *Organizations and institutions: Foundations for organizational science*. Thousand Oaks, CA: SAGE.

Sharma, S. (2000). Managerial interpretations and organizational context as predictors of corporate choice of environmental strategy. *Academy of Management Journal*, *43*(4), 681–697.

Sharma, S., & Vredenburg, H. (1998). Proactive corporate environmental strategy and the development of competitively valuable organizational capabilities. *Strategic Management Journal*, *19*(8), 729–753.

Shen, J., & Benson, J. (2016). When CSR is a social norm: How socially responsible human resource management affects employee work behavior. *Journal of Management*, *42*(6), 1723–1746.

Spanjol, J., Tam, L., & Tam, V. (2015). Employer–employee congruence in environmental values: An exploration of effects on job satisfaction and creativity. *Journal of Business Ethics*, *130*(1), 117–130.

Spector, B. (2008). "Business responsibilities in a divided world": The Cold War roots of the corporate social responsibility movement. *Enterprise & Society*, *9*(2), 314–336.

Stolle, D., & Micheletti, M. (2013). *Political consumerism: Global responsibility in action*. New York: Cambridge University Press.

Turban, D. B., & Greening, D. W. (1997). Corporate social performance and organizational attractiveness to prospective employees. *Academy of Management Journal*, *40*(3), 658–672.

Vlachos, P. A., Panagopoulos, N. G., & Rapp, A. A. (2013). Feeling good by doing good: Employee CSR-induced attributions, job satisfaction, and the role of charismatic leadership. *Journal of Business Ethics*, *118*(3), 577–588.

Vlachos, P. A., Tsamakos, A., Vrechopoulos, A. P., & Avramidis, P. K. (2009). Corporate social responsibility: Attributions, loyalty, and the mediating role of trust. *Journal of the Academy of Marketing Science*, *37*(2), 170–180.

Waddock, S. (2004). Parallel universes: Companies, academics, and the progress of corporate citizenship. *Business and Society Review*, *109*(1), 5–42.

Waddock, S. A., & Graves, S. B. (1997). Finding the link between stakeholder relations and quality of management. *Journal of Investing*, *6*(4), 20–24.

Waldman, D. A. (2014). Bridging the domains of leadership and corporate social responsibility. In D. Day (Ed.), *Handbook of leadership and organizations* (pp. 541–557). New York: Oxford University Press.

Walton, C. C. (1967). *Corporate social responsibilities*. Belmont, CA: Wadsworth.

WCED (World Commission on Environment and Development). (1987). *Our common future*. New York: Oxford University Press.

Weaver, G. R., Trevino, L. K., & Cochran, P. L. (1999). Integrated and decoupled corporate social performance: Management commitments, external pressures, and corporate ethics practices. *Academy of Management Journal, 42*(5), 539–552.

Wiernik, B., S., Ones, D., & Dilchert, S. (2013). Age and environmental sustainability: A meta-analysis. *Journal of Managerial Psychology, 28*(7/8), 826–856.

Willness, C. R. (forthcoming). When CSR backfires: Understanding stakeholders' negative responses to corporate social responsibility. In A. McWilliams, D. E. Rupp, D. S. Siegel, G. Stahl, & D. A. Waldman (Eds.), *The Oxford handbook of corporate social responsibility: Psychological and organizational perspectives.* Oxford, U.K.: Oxford University Press.

Wood, D. J. (1991). Corporate social performance revisited. *Academy of Management Review, 16*(4), 691–718.

Wood, D. J. (2010). Measuring corporate social performance: A review. *International Journal of Management Reviews, 12*(1), 50–84.

APPENDIX. TYPES AND EXAMPLES OF CSR ACTIVITIES

Types of CSR Activities	Purpose of Activity	Examples
External (e.g., supply chain and operations management)	Organization engages in CSR activity in order to manage their operations and supply chain in a more ethical and sustainable way.	Lowering carbon footprint of company operations. Switching to renewable energy. Collaborating only with Fairtrade suppliers.
Internal (e.g., employees)	CSR policies and practices directed at recruiting, managing, and educating employees, with the goal of creating a more socially responsible and motivated workforce.	Recruiting and retaining socially responsible employees. Engaging in CSR activities as a source of meaningfulness. Providing CSR training to employees.
Strategic sponsorship	Strategic investment in an activity to access the exploitable commercial potential associated with the sponsored entity or event.	Organizing public events with charity organizations in order to improve the reputation of the organization. Donating to charitable activities in order to get a tax break. Donating to local communities to get benefits from local governments.
Philanthropy	Contributing to a cause solely because the organization wishes to be a good corporate citizen without expecting direct benefit from it.	Donating to promote education in local communities. Development of roads and infrastructure. Donating to global charitable causes.

NOTES

1. See PRME (Principles for Responsible Management Education) (https://www.unprme.org/about).
2. A search was conducted of peer-reviewed articles with the ProQuest database PsycINFO using search terms of "corporate social responsibility" or "sustainability."
3. Due to differing definitions of levels of analysis, we refer to the individual level as being at the employee level of analysis, the macro level at the organizational level of analysis, and the institutional level being that which is studied outside of the organization (e.g., community, government, stakeholder groups). The exception is when members of a stakeholder group—such as customers—are studied at the individual level, then we refer to these studies as also being at the individual level of analysis.
4. For more comprehensive reviews of the CSR literature at the individual level see the following: Aguinis (2011); Glavas (2016a); Gond et al. (2017); Jones and Rupp (2018); Rupp and Mallory (2015).
5. See PRME (Principles for Responsible Management Education).
6. Although there are great benefits by dividing the literature based on levels of analysis, it also comes with shortcomings. One shortcoming is related to the fact that certain studies that are based on different paradigms (e.g., studies on political CSR) are often hard to cluster within a single level.
7. See PRME (Principles for Responsible Management Education).

Ante Glavas and Mislav Radic

Human Resources Psychology

HUMAN RESOURCE MANAGEMENT AND ORGANIZATIONAL PSYCHOLOGY

INTRODUCTION

Human resources management (HRM) can be broadly defined as "all those activities associated with the management of work and people in organizations" (Boxall & Purcell, 2011). It serves as a focus of study but also as an occupation for specialists and a day-to-day component of the work of line managers. HRM is a relatively new area of study, but research has burgeoned in recent years, and this article will examine some of the central research debates and research findings.

HRM may not at first sight appear to be an obvious candidate for inclusion under the banner of work and organizational psychology. It is, after all, a multidisciplinary area of research, often conducted at the organizational rather than the individual level of analysis. But it also incorporates many of the core activities typically associated with work and organizational (W/O) psychology ranging from topics such as selection and training to outcomes such as well-being, absenteeism, and labor turnover. It therefore serves as an integrative context within which to consider the work of W/O psychologists. At the same time, HRM has emerged as a major field of theorizing and research in its own right, with several specialist academic journals

• 1105

and large numbers of practitioners who label themselves as HR professionals, and it offers the promise of some integration across disciplines and across levels of analysis.

The article starts with a brief overview of influences on the emergence of HRM, emphasizing those disciplinary perspectives that lie beyond the usual territory of W/O psychology. Subsequent sections examine the nature of HRM, the kind of outcomes it is expected to influence, and the processes whereby HRM and outcomes might be related. Each of these is a continuing focus of theorizing and research. In each section, conceptual and empirical issues and evidence will be reviewed.

Disciplinary Influences. Three broad disciplinary perspectives have been particularly influential in informing the development of HRM theory and research. The first, reflecting the historical traditions of the application of HRM, is the sub-discipline of industrial relations. The second is the influence of business strategy, reflecting the location of some researchers in business schools and the potentially important role of effective HRM for business performance. The third influence is W/O psychology and the overlapping field of organizational behavior.

The practice of what we now describe as HRM emerged in the early decades of the 20th century. Those working in the field were initially described as welfare officers and then personnel managers. When there was a need to address industrial conflict, the role of the industrial relations manager increasingly came to the fore. In the 1930s, the study of industrial relations and, more broadly, relations at work began to emerge within universities. Well-known examples over the decades include the Hawthorne studies (Roethlisberger & Dickson, 1939), the work of Whyte (1955) and others on the role of pay and restriction of output, and Walton and McKersie's (1965) behavioral theory of labor negotiation. Those engaged in this type of research typically had backgrounds in sociology, economics, or psychology, providing an early multidisciplinary perspective. Topics for research included forms of industrial conflict ranging from strikes to absenteeism, systems for alleviating or preventing conflict such as collective bargaining, systems for workers' participation, and the influence of pay on behavior. By the 1970s, there were flourishing departments of industrial relations in universities in many countries, undertaking research and providing education to those seeking to pursue a career in industrial relations or personnel management. By the 1980s, patterns of industrial conflict began to change and eventually diminish, and academic industrial relations departments entered a slow decline, though several prominent journals remained. A number of researchers who once worked in these departments switched their research focus to HRM, often providing some of the most trenchant critical analysis of the field (see, e.g., Godard, 2004).

The influence of business strategy on HRM began to emerge in the 1980s. A major factor in this was the growth of teaching and research in the business schools, particularly in the United States. The initial argument, proposed in general normative terms, most notably by Porter (1985), but applied to HRM by, for example, Miles and Snow (1984), was that organizations had strategic choices about how to compete, and this should influence the approach organizations adopt to HRM. The most obvious distinction was whether to compete on the basis of cost minimization or some combination of quality and innovation. Each required rather different ways of managing people at work. A clear exposition of this was outlined by Schuler and Jackson (1987) who set out five steps. First, an organization has to clarify its mission and values. Second, and building on this, it has to determine its competitive strategy. Third, it needs to determine the kinds of employees and the sorts of behavior that will enable the strategy to be achieved. Fourth, the organization needs to determine the HR policies and practices that will help to ensure that the right employees are performing appropriately. Finally, organizations should check that employee behavior is actually aligned with the strategic goals.

Further interest in HRM from a strategic perspective was provided by advocacy of the resource-based view of the firm (Barney, 1991). This argued that to compete effectively, organizations needed to acquire and utilize resources that are rare, expensive, hard to replace, and not easily replicable. Part of the analysis, developed further by Barney and Wright (1998), was that human resources fitted these criteria better than other resources such as finance or machinery, which could more easily be copied. This boosted the idea of employees as "human resources," a term that causes distaste in some quarters.

The resource-based view of HRM placed considerable emphasis on the economic concept of human capital (Nyberg & Wright, 2015). For example, Lepak and Snell (1999) argued that organizations need to invest heavily in attracting, retaining, and utilizing "human capital" that is highly unique to the firm and highly valuable. In contrast, human capital that is valuable but plentiful is best acquired, perhaps by being brought in. Where human capital is unique but of low strategic value, it might be best to form an alliance. Finally, human capital that is low in value and uniqueness is perhaps best contracted in. This might appear to be a cost-effective strategy, and research has shown the benefits of a selective approach (Lepak & Snell, 2002). However, Peel and Boxall (2005) found that seeking to classify human capital is far from straightforward and likely to vary from firm to firm. We return to the topic of human capital later in the article.

The third major source of influence on HRM comes from work and organizational psychology and organizational behavior (hereafter just W/O psychology). The reason for this is straightforward; HR practices such as selection, training, appraisal, and reward are the bread and butter of the research and practice of W/O psychologists. HR practitioners are constantly on the lookout for the best practices to apply, and it is the W/O psychologists who undertake the research that provides them. Although the picture is mixed, many W/O psychologists and most of those who use the OB label now work in business schools and, with an interest in effective management, this makes the field of HRM a natural context for their research and consultancy. At the same time, W/O psychology has a particular focus on individual and group behavior and associated outcomes. This has helped to promote a more employee-centered, micro-level focus to HRM.

A distinctive feature of HRM is its ability to integrate features of the macro strategic perspective with the more micro-level perspective typically adopted by psychologists. Indeed, writers such as Wright and Boswell (2002) have argued that some integration of macro and micro areas is essential for the field to develop. A feature of an integrated perspective, and a key argument of advocates of HRM (see, e.g., Becker & Huselid, 1998; Jackson, Schuler, & Jiang, 2014), is that HRM should be viewed as a system. What this implies is that it is not enough to focus on selection, training, rewards, or job design; it is necessary to view the whole range of HR practices as an integrated whole and to ensure that they are aligned to provide "internal fit." If this approach succeeds, there should be a kind of gestalt whereby the sum is more than the parts.

The dominant research topic has been the relationship between HRM and outcomes, and in particular, organizational performance. However, researchers are increasingly exploring the relationship with employee well-being and the feasibility of mutual gains (Van de Voorde, Paauwe, & van Veldhoven, 2012). Some years ago, Guest (1997) noted that if research on HRM is to progress, there needs to be clearer theory and research concerning the nature and measurement of HRM, of outcomes and the nature of the relationships among them. Since then, either directly or indirectly, much of the research has addressed these three core issues. In the following sections, we consider each of these in turn.

THE NATURE OF HRM

A major and continuing challenge for research has been how to conceptualize and operationalize HRM. There are several interrelated issues that need to be addressed. What HR practices should be included in the general field of HRM? What is the underlying rationale for including specific practices? How much detail is required about each practice? Can and should practices be combined in any kind of bundles? Who should provide information about them? And what kinds of response categories are appropriate? All these questions have provided the focus for extensive conceptual and empirical work.

Diversity in Conceptualizations of HRM.
In several earlier articles on HRM, it was conventional to identify four broad topics that reflected the field. These were recruitment and selection, training and development, performance appraisal, and rewards (see, e.g., Fombrun, Tichy, & Devanna, 1984). However, this list omitted a range of issues concerning the employment relationship, such as job security, communication, and flexible work arrangements. Writing for general managers at Harvard, Beer, Spector, Lawrence, Quinn Mills, and Walton (1985) suggested that broad core topics that needed to be addressed included employee influence, human resource flows, reward systems, and work systems. These two differing approaches highlight the scope for diversity when studying HRM. It is therefore perhaps not surprising that when Becker and Gerhart (1996) reviewed the existing studies, they found a wide variety of practices being measured. Indeed, no one practice appeared in every study they reviewed. Several years and many studies later, two extensive reviews (Boselie, Dietz, & Boon, 2005; Combs, Liu, Hall, & Ketchen, 2006) found that little had changed with respect to the variety of practices used in studies. There was also considerable difference in the number of practices used; indeed, Combs et al. found that the number ranged between 2 and 13 with an average of 6.2. The variety of practices used to measure HRM makes comparison across studies highly problematic. This has not stopped such comparisons being made, notably in meta-analyses.

Alternative Rationales for Determining the Content of HRM.
There has clearly been a need to find some underlying rationale to determine which practices should be included in any study. One approach has been to focus on external and internal fit. In the case of external fit, as Porter (1985) and Schuler and Jackson (1987) have argued, the starting point is to determine the mission, values, and core goals of the organization and then determine its competitive strategy. Since the main goal of most private-sector organizations is to maximize

financial performance, it is those HR practices that help to achieve this that should be included. As researchers have accepted this logic, one consequence has been a change in language, so that many studies now don't refer to HR practices, but rather to high-performance work practices (HPWPs).

In public sector organizations, the mission and values may be rather different, and the concept of competitive strategy may be inappropriate. Furthermore, as Paauwe (2004) and others have pointed out, in Europe, with its focus on social partnership, legislation at European and national levels requires the application of a range of HR practices to promote issues such as health and safety at work, equal opportunities, and flexible working. Partly reflecting this perspective, and acknowledging the roots of HRM in the industrial relations tradition, scholars have outlined alternative bases for determining appropriate HR practices. In the United States, Walton (1985) argued that effective management of the contemporary workforce requires a shift from policies and practices seeking control to those that promote employee commitment. This has led to advocacy of what is termed *high commitment* (Wood & Albanese, 1995) or *high-involvement* HRM (Boxall & Macky, 2009). These terms suggest a rather different approach, reflected in the writing of Beer et al. (1985) that recognized the legitimacy of outcomes of concern to employees and other stakeholders.

One problem with an approach to HRM that starts from mission, values, and stakeholder interests is that it still leaves open the choice of practices and it does not clearly specify how those practices should be deployed. Therefore, though there can be agreement about the need to include practices such as selection and training, the specific features of such practices can remain unclear. For example, selection can be measured through the use of certain types of psychometric tests or the use of assessment centers. Alternatively, it can be measured in relation to its aims, such as by hiring those who demonstrate immediate competence in a specified job or those with a positive attitude toward learning. The complexities and choices in measuring these variables are familiar to W/O psychologists. The problem in measuring them in the context of HRM is that each practice is just one among several. As a result, it is not surprising that researchers have measured a wide and varied range of practices, and have done so in often rather different ways.

Internal Fit and the Role of HR Bundles. The aim of internal fit is to identify sets of HR practices (sometimes described as bundles) that will complement each other. The most frequently cited approach to achieve this is the so-called AMO model. This draws on Lawler's (1971) expanded version of expectancy theory. While expectancy theory proposes that motivation is a function of the perceived links among effort, performance, and rewards, Lawler extended this to propose that effective performance also depends on individuals having the appropriate ability and role. Applying this to HRM (Becker, Huselid, Pickus, & Spratt, 1997; Guest, 1997) it is suggested that the immediate goals of an HR system designed explicitly to ensure high performance are to ensure that employees have the ability (A), motivation (M), and opportunity (O) to contribute effectively. HR practices required to achieve these goals can then be clustered together in three broad bundles. For example, ability or competence may be generated through appropriate selection, training, and development practices. The quality of these practices can be greatly enhanced by building on the evidence base developed by W/O psychologists. However, this approach is not without its challenges. For example, there are potential substitution effects—should the focus be on selection of competence or the training of competence? Furthermore, some practices, including those linked to job design, can have an impact on both motivation and opportunity to contribute, thereby blurring the bundles.

The concept of bundles can also present a challenge for psychologists who have typically developed expertise in specific practices, since the argument concerning internal fit suggests that it is not enough to focus on practices that develop one of these outcomes because they are all important. For example, it is not helpful to have highly motivated but incompetent employees or to have highly competent employees who have no opportunity to use their knowledge and skills. So the notion of internal fit within an HR system implies that there need to be HR practices present that can contribute to each element of the AMO model.

Meta-analyses by Jiang, Lepak, Hu, and Baer (2012) and Subramony (2009) tested models based on the three AMO bundles of practices and also tested a single integrated measure of HRM. They found a better fit with the three bundles. Furthermore, each was associated with somewhat different outcomes. This is further support for the view that all three bundles need to be present to have a full impact. Subramony found that opportunity to contribute and motivation had a stronger impact than human capital, which on its own was non-significant. On the other hand, Jiang et al. found that each bundle on its own had a modest but significant impact on financial outcomes. Reflecting this, subsequent research has shown that human capital on its own can improve employee behavior and organizational performance (Crook, Todd, Combs, Woehr, & Ketchen, 2011). But the impact is not as great as the application of the three bundles. This is somewhat akin to research on the impact of selection and training effects that has consistently shown that high-quality application of both practices can enhance and benefit individual performance. When this is aggregated to the unit or organizational level, we might expect an impact on organizational performance (see, e.g., Aguinis & Kraiger, 2009; Schmidt & Hunter, 1998). Nevertheless, Subramony (2009) also showed that each bundle made a stronger contribution than any individual practice. Given these competing results, further research needs to establish the relative importance of individual HR practices, bundles of practices, and an aggregated measure.

Human Capital. Recent theorizing and research have given considerable prominence to the concept of human capital and the specific bundle of HR practices associated with it. As originally conceived by Becker (1964), the concept was quite wide-ranging and covered the knowledge and skills of individuals and also their information, ideas, and health. Ployhart and Moliterno (2011) have distinguished between cognitive abilities and other individual characteristics like personality, interests, and values, all of which, as they acknowledge, are typically considered at the individual level. However, they outline enabling factors such as task complexity and interdependencies that create conditions where these types of capital can be aggregated to the unit level and analyzed with respect to their impact on unit performance. Researchers have begun to consider human capital at the unit level as a collective set of capacities for management to utilize (see, e.g., Ployhart, Nyberg, Reilly, & Maltarich, 2014) and Nyberg and Wright (2015) argue that it offers an opportunity for multidisciplinary as well as multilevel research. Although interest in human capital is generating a large body of research, it is potentially limited by its focus on one element, the A within the AMO model.

Levels of Detail about HR Practices. After a decision about which HR practices to include in any study, there remains the issue of how much detail to seek. For example, it is possible with respect to training to ask about the presence of a training policy, hours of training provided, off-the-job versus on-the-job training, and so on. Indeed, the amount of formal training provision is one of the most frequently included items in studies of HRM. However, this is not without problems since it might refer to a goal to provide specified hours, it might refer to off-the-job formal training but ignore informal and incidental learning, and it may apply to only some of the employees. In short, even if the relevant HR practices can be identified, there are unresolved research questions about the level of detail and how far this should be standardized across practices.

Sources of Information about HR Practices. A further and increasingly widely researched question is who should provide information about HR practices. Researchers have noted a gap between intended and implemented practices (Khilji & Wang, 2006), and among those concerned with the impact of HRM on outcomes, it is argued that effective implementation is more important than the presence of a policy or practice (Bowen & Ostroff, 2004). Senior managers in HR departments may report that a practice such as universal annual appraisal is a firm company policy. However, employees will be in a better position to report whether they have actually received an appraisal in the past year or whether they have perceived and are actually aware of specific policies and practices even if they have not directly experienced them. An example might be policies and practices related to bullying and harassment. Therefore, while much of the research on HR practices has obtained information from senior managers, there is a strong case for collecting information from employees. This may not only increase accuracy, but also enhance reliability. However, the attractions of collecting data from senior managers include the ability to compare across many organizations and to collect data swiftly at an organizational level to permit assessment against organizational-level outcomes. While it is possible to aggregate employee data, collecting such data across many organizations is a complex and time-consuming activity. An alternative is to focus on an important category of employees and ask about the HR practices that apply to this group. This can offer some advantages in accuracy over asking about the workforce as a whole, but it risks ignoring the HR practices applied to the remainder of the workforce.

Response Categories for HR Practices. Researchers need to give consideration to the choice of response categories when collecting information about HR practices. Once again, the published research displays a wide range of approaches. In many cases, the logical response categories will be a straightforward "Yes/No" as in responses to questions such as "Have you received an appraisal in the past 12 months?" An alternative is to turn these questions into statements and use a Likert scale, typically from "strongly agree to strongly disagree," which permits a factor analysis of the responses, but also invites potentially inaccurate responses to categorical items. When the questions are directed to managers, an alternative to asking for categorical answers is to ask about the percentage of workers who are likely to have experienced a particular practice. This permits a more flexible response, although the accuracy of such responses is open to question and they present potential problems of aggregation, particularly if different practices apply to different categories of employees. There are therefore choices concerning the approach to adopt for response categories, with no consensus in sight.

Aggregating HR Practices. A final issue concerns how to aggregate practices. This issue was first addressed some years ago by Delery and Doty (1996) who tested competing theories and different ways of combining data to address both external fit, through a contingency approach linking practices to strategy, and internal fit, based on a simple count of practices in place and a configurational model that examined interactions between bundles of practices. It was found that there was no clear advantage to a configurational model. Subramony (2009) and Jiang et al. (2012) also found no consistent evidence that one bundle in the AMO model or that any combination of A, M, and O is superior in terms of its impact. Interestingly, this is similar to the findings in a meta-analysis of expectancy theory (van Eerde & Thierry, 1996). The most widely used approach over the years has been to provide a count of the practices that are reported to be present on the grounds that a greater number of practices indicates the strength of the HR system and therefore increases the likelihood that they will have an impact. Although this is a plausible argument, it ignores the likelihood that certain practices will be more important than others. It also supports a universalist model that holds that the same broad set of practices applies, irrespective of the context and strategy, a view that is not well supported by the research and that supporters of contingency theory find inherently implausible.

Identifying and Measuring HR Practices: A Summary. This brief overview has shown that there are major problems in conceptualizing and operationalizing the presence and application of the HR practices that constitute the HRM system. Much of the difficulty can be attributed to the complexities that arise from the lack of clear definitions of the content and boundaries of any HRM system, from the variety of perceived goals of the system and therefore the practices that deserve priority, and from the various levels of analysis at which the research is undertaken. These challenges are of a different order than those faced by W/O psychologists who have typically focused more narrowly on a specific practice at the individual or group level. However, the lesson of HRM for W/O psychology is that this type of detailed focus needs to be understood in its wider context, recognizing the risk that a specific practice can act as a proxy for a wider set of practices unless some way can be found of controlling for their influence. Researchers need to be clear about the underlying rationale for the kind of HRM they are exploring and be explicit about the reasons certain HR practices are included and what assumptions are being made about aggregation. Too many studies have lacked a theory or even an explanation for their choices of practices. It is also worth noting that the research, with its focus on HR practices likely to enhance performance, omits a number of important topics that are likely to be of interest to employees and have been the focus of extensive research by W/O psychologists, such as the role of careers and career management, equal opportunities, and work-life balance. Despite all the problems of identifying and measuring HR practices, and the unreliability that the diversity of practice indicates, the large body of research, reflected in the various meta-analyses (see, e.g., Combs et al., 2006; Jiang et al., 2012) consistently reveals a positive association at the organizational level between the use of more HR practices and financial outcomes.

THE OUTCOMES OF HRM

Most of the early research was concerned with the relationship between HRM and organizational performance and was conducted at the level of the organization. For example, in the early seminal study by Huselid (1995) who surveyed leading U.S. companies, outcomes included aggregated labor turnover and productivity, but the main focus was on various financial indicators, including market value of shareholder equity. In Jiang et al.'s (2012) meta-analysis, the main dependent variable was financial performance reflected in a variety of measures, including return on assets, return on equity, and a general measure of overall financial performance. The problem with the use of financial indicators is that they are subject to a wide variety of influences, including the vagaries of the economic system. Therefore, as a distal outcome, the size of the association with HRM is always likely to be quite weak. An alternative is to utilize more proximal measures that are organizationally relevant in the sense that they could have a financial impact but are more likely to be influenced by HRM. In other words, they can provide a test of mediation. This has led to the use of outcomes like labor turnover, productivity, and service quality. Two early studies in strip steel mills (Arthur, 1994; Ichniowski, Shaw, & Prennushi, 1997) explored the link between HRM and productivity. However, productivity has proved particularly challenging to measure, especially in the service sector, and in their meta-analysis, Combs et al. (2006) found that there was a stronger association between HRM and financial performance than between HRM and productivity. What this perhaps illustrates is that there are questions concerning both the reliability and validity of these outcome measures.

Identifying outcome measures can become greater at the unit level rather than the organizational level. One way of addressing this has been to obtain subjective assessments of outcomes from managers. This is the approach that has been adopted over the years by the British Workplace Employment Relations surveys that collect data from about 2,000 workplaces (see van Wanrooy et al., 2013). They ask managers to rate their performance on a variety of criteria against competitors they know about in the same sector. Analyses of the results where it is possible to compare against independent financial reports (e.g., in single unit organizations) show that there is a modest positive association between the subjective and more objective indicators (Forth & McNabb, 2008; see also Wall et al., 2004). However, in their meta-analysis, Combs et al. (2006) reported higher associations between HRM and performance where subjective rather than objective indicators of performance are used. There are some sectors where unit-level comparisons are feasible, including retail and banking, because organizations have a large number of more-or-less identical branches. Similar arguments are increasingly made about public-sector organizations such as hospitals and local authorities, and benchmarking has become popular based on assumptions about the validity of such comparisons. For relevant research on hospitals, see Givan, Avgar, and Liu, (2010) and West, Guthrie, Dawson, Borrill, and Carter (2006), and for local authorities, see Messersmith, Patel, Lepak, and Gould-Williams (2011).

Psychologists have been more interested in employee outcomes, and a growing number of studies explore the relationship between HRM and employee attitudes, behavior, and well-being. The choice of measure depends on whether the primary interest lies in organizational performance or employee well-being. In the case of the former, it can include individual-level performance, organizational citizenship behavior, absence, and labor turnover. When the main interest is in well-being, outcome measures include psychological contract fulfillment, perceptions of employment security, and perceived organizational support, as well as measures of stress, burnout, and engagement, and standard measures of job satisfaction and well-being (for a review, see Clinton & van Veldhoven, 2013). Almost all the research shows a positive association between the presence of more HR practices and more positive employee responses (see Clinton & van Veldhoven, 2013). However, a small minority of studies have revealed increases in levels of stress (see, e.g., Ramsay, Scholarios, & Harley, 2000). This has led critics such as Godard (2004) to argue that HRM is bad for workers because it is likely to result in work intensification and the consequent stress.

Although the evidence of negative consequences for employees is weak, the topic has generated interest in the extent to which HRM is associated with both higher organizational performance and improved employee well-being. The relatively few reported studies in which both have been measured have been reviewed by van de Voorde, Paauwe, and van Veldhoven (2012) and Peccei, van de Voorde, and van Veldhoven (2013). They find that the presence of more HR practices is associated with both higher performance and higher job satisfaction and organizational commitment. However, the evidence from the very few studies that have included health-related well-being measures, mainly indications of stress, is somewhat more equivocal, revealing a mix of positive, neutral, and negative outcomes for employees. It is unclear whether the studies with more negative results were utilizing high-performance work systems to enhance performance or high-commitment/high-involvement approaches that give higher priority to employee roles and outcomes. Future research exploring this issue will need to be clearer about the HRM strategy that underpins the type of practices adopted.

In summary, the research on HRM has predominantly explored outcomes that reflect organizational and managerial interests associated with performance. These have often been quite distal measures, such as financial performance, and have usually been collected at the organizational level. A smaller stream of research has explored employee outcomes like job satisfaction and well-being. As more proximal measures, these might be expected to reveal a stronger association with HRM. Relatively few studies have explored both organizational and employee outcomes. Those that have done so tend to show mutual benefits, but the results are somewhat inconsistent and seem to depend in part on the type of employee outcome under investigation. This is an area that would benefit from further research.

UNDERSTANDING THE RELATIONSHIP BETWEEN HRM AND OUTCOMES

The early research was primarily concerned with establishing a relationship between HRM and organizational performance, but much of the focus shifted to seek explanations for how or why there appears to be an association. The relatively limited body of research exploring the role of external fit of HR practices with the business strategy has failed to show any consistent impact on outcomes (Jackson, Schuler, & Jiang, 2014). Instead, most subsequent research has been based on internal fit and development and testing of linkage models. These typically propose that HR practices influence employee perceptions that in turn affect employee attitudes and behavior and subsequently employee performance. This can then be aggregated to proximal (e.g., productivity, service quality) and distal (e.g., financial) organizational performance. Elements and sometimes a complete linkage model have been tested, and research has typically reported support for the expected associations indicating full or partial mediation. The AMO model has been the most extensively tested, and the meta-analysis by Jiang et al. (2012) provides a good example of this. They linked measures of the HR bundles to indicators of human capital and motivation, and linked those in turn to labor turnover and internal measures of performance, and finally linked both of those to financial performance. They reported good evidence for these linkages and for partial mediation.

The AMO model suggests that HR practices succeed by leveraging employee behavior. Alternative models based on high-commitment or high-involvement rather than high-performance HRM utilize social exchange theory (Gong, Chang, & Cheun, 2010; Piening, Baluch, & Salge, 2013). The core argument is that if HR practices are used to enhance the commitment and involvement of employees and to ensure a positive employment relationship, this will in turn be positively perceived by employees at both an individual and collective level. It might, for example, be perceived in terms of fulfillment of the psychological contract (Rousseau & Greller, 1994) or in the form of perceived organizational support (Eisenberger, Cummings, Armeli, & Lynch, 1997). Based on the norm of reciprocity (Gouldner, 1960), employees can be expected to respond with positive attitudes and behavior. Research supports these linkages and shows an association with organizational commitment, organizational citizenship behavior, higher individual performance, and a lower propensity to quit the organization or be voluntarily absent (e.g., Kehoe & Wright, 2013; Takeuchi, Chen, & Lepak, 2009). Overall, therefore, there is consistent support for a linkage model. More research is needed to test competing explanations for these linkages and to understand why the strength of the association varies. Some issues, to which we now turn, offer possible explanations.

The Role of Employee Attributions. As the role of employees takes center stage in the analysis of the impact of HRM, it is recognized that to understand the effect of HRM on attitudes and behavior, it is first necessary to consider how employees perceive HR practices. Researchers have begun to use a form of attribution theory to explore how employees interpret management motives for adopting certain HR practices and to examine how their interpretation affects their attitudes and behavior. Nishii, Lepak, and Schneider (2008) researched attributions among employees in a large Japanese retail chain. They hypothesized that if employees attributed management's use of HR practices to a desire to enhance quality of service or employee well-being, then the response would be positive and would, in turn, have a positive effect on customer service. In contrast, if they were attributed to management's desire to enhance control over employees or to intensify work, then these negative attributions would feed through into less enthusiastic employee behaviors that would be reflected in customer evaluation of service quality in the branches. Their findings supported these hypotheses. Subsequent research by van de Voorde & Beijer (2015) tested the impact of well-being and performance attributions on individual employee outcomes and found that, as predicted, well-being attributions had a positive impact on commitment to the organization and on employee well-being, reflected in lower levels of job strain, whereas performance attributions resulted in higher levels of job strain. Both studies confirm the importance of understanding employee attributions in any model seeking to explain the links between HRM and outcomes.

Research on employee attributions highlights the potential role of signaling theory (Connelly, Certo, Ireland, & Reutzel, 2011), a variation on communication theory. To put it at its simplest, what do HR practices, singly or in combination, signal to employees? Rousseau and Greller (1994) used signaling theory to explain how HR practices communicated to workers the content of the psychological contract. Signaling theory formed the basis for an influential conceptual article by Bowen and Ostroff (2004) concerning the implementation of HRM. They support the view that it is not sufficient to have good HR practices in place; implementation is only likely to be effective if management can clearly signal the intentions behind the HR practices.

They argue that this is more likely to be achieved when there is what they call a "strong" HR system. They hypothesize that this will entail three features that need to be clearly signaled: high consensus, implying agreement among the relevant stakeholders about the viability and fairness of the HR practices; high distinctiveness, implying that HR practices should be visible, understandable, and relevant; and high consistency, implying that HR practices complement each other and are seen as aiding goal achievement. Bowen and Ostroff's approach suggests that strong leadership signaling support from the top of the organization is required to ensure a strong HR system and therefore an increased likelihood of effective implementation of HR practices.

Researchers have begun to test Bowen and Ostroff's propositions. A first step has been to develop measures of the three core components and the sub-elements that Bowen and Ostroff outline (see, e.g., Delmotte, De Winne, & Sels, 2012; Coelho, Cunha, Gomes, & Correia, 2015). A second step has been to test the validity of the model by studying the association of the dimensions with performance outcomes (see, e.g., Sanders, Dorenbosch, & De Reuver, 2008; Li, Frenkel, & Sanders, 2011; Pereira & Gomes, 2012). The results of these studies highlight the complexity of the model, suggesting that it would benefit from some simplification. Secondly, they indicate that the distinctiveness dimension appears to be more important than the other dimensions, and that the relative importance of the three dimensions of HRM system strength seems to vary across studies and perhaps across national cultures. Despite the enthusiasm with which some researchers have been exploring the Bowen and Ostroff model, there may be a case for revisiting some of the underlying dimensions.

The HR Implementation Process and Actors.   Research on attribution theory, signaling theory, and the strength of the HR system is concerned with HR implementation. It is based on recognition that the presence of HR practices is not enough to ensure that they have an impact. A related stream of research has explored the process of HR implementation by focusing more directly on the roles of the main actors. Guest and Bos-Nehles (2013) have outlined a descriptive framework that implicated several parties in the implementation process. Top management and senior HR managers have responsibility for deciding whether certain practices should be present. HR managers, perhaps with outside help from consultants and W/O psychologists, shape the quality of the practices. Line managers, with support from local HR managers, have to implement practices on a day-to-day basis, and in addition they need to be motivated to ensure that they are implemented in a high-quality rather than a ritualistic way. Finally, their impact depends on employees' perceptions of and attributions about the practices. There has been some concern that line managers may be a weak link in this process. Case studies led Hope Hailey, Farndale, and Truss (2005) to conclude that in the U.K., line managers were neither willing nor able to accept their HR implementation role. In contrast, Bos-Nehles (2010) found that Dutch managers were motivated to ensure effective implementation of HR but often lacked the time to do so (Bos-Nehles, 2010). A study of the implementation of policy and practice to address bullying and harassment in healthcare (Woodrow & Guest, 2014) found that although best HR practices were in place, they were invariably poorly implemented due mainly to lack of senior management support, but also to employees' perceptions that the HR systems were ineffective in helping to resolve incidents of bullying and harassment. This would appear to support Bowen and Ostroff's argument about the need for a strong HR system with top-level support.

The interest in HRM implementation has increased the focus on the role of HR specialists. There has been a longstanding stream of research on the role of HR managers reflecting concerns about their lack of power and influence (see, e.g., Legge, 1978; Ritzer & Trice, 1969; Guest & King, 2004). In a highly influential attempt to boost the role, Ulrich has presented a stream of writing and research outlining evolving ideas about the HR department structure, the various HR roles, and HR competencies required for effective performance by HR professionals (see Ulrich, 1997; Ulrich & Brockbank, 2005: Ulrich, Younger, Brockbank, & Ulrich, 2013). Underpinning his research was a desire to see the HR function contributing to effective HR implementation or, as he expressed it, moving from "doing" to "delivering."

Ulrich's ideas generated considerable excitement among HR professionals in several countries, resulting in a rush to implement them. However, they have also been the subject of extensive conceptual critiques (see, e.g., Caldwell, 2008) and empirical research (see, e.g., Buyens & De Vos, 2001; Wright, 2008), raising serious questions about the feasibility of implementing them beyond the context of large, predominantly U.S. private-sector organizations, something Ulrich himself recognized. Nevertheless, his work is important in highlighting the role of HR professionals who often serve as gatekeepers for the application of the research of W/O psychologists in organizations.

The Role of Individual Differences. As psychologists have become more interested in HRM, attention has begun to focus on individual differences. One illustration of this has been a broadening of the conceptualization of the characteristics that constitute human capital, reflected in the work of Ployhart and Moliterno (2011), including the role of personality and values as human capital. Another stream of research has been considering age and the question of whether specific HR practices or bundles of practices have a greater impact at different ages. The rationale for expecting that this might be the case draws on selection, optimization, and compensation (SOC) theory (Baltes, Staudinger, & Lindenberger, 1999). For example, Bal, Kooij, and De Jong (2013) and Kooij et al. (2013) have shown how developmental HR practices among younger workers and accommodative HR practices among older workers can enhance commitment and well-being. There would appear to be room to extend this approach to consider other individual differences such as gender and education, but also variations in employment circumstances like temporary employment and other forms of employment flexibility. For example, what sort of HR practices are most suitable for long-distance workers including those working from home?

The Use of Multilevel Analysis. Bowen and Ostroff's (2004) model builds on previous work by Ostroff and Bowen (2000) in arguing for a multilevel approach for understanding HRM processes and their impact. Ployhart and Moliterno (2011) make a similar point with respect to the aggregation of human capital. There is a strong case for multilevel analysis when employee attitudes and behavior form part of the study but the primary concern is with organizational performance, something that has become relatively common in recent research (see, e.g., Liao et al., 2009; Messersmith et al., 2011; Piening, Baluch, & Salge, 2013). Another context is when moderating variables are hypothesized to affect outcomes, requiring the use of moderated mediation. The kinds of moderating variables that have attracted most research attention are organizational climate and leadership, but there is room to extend this type of research to consider a potentially wide range of moderating variables, including exogenous factors like business sector and market conditions.

Comparative HRM.   HRM is potentially a very broad field, and its extensive scope can be illustrated through the large body of research and writing on comparative HR systems. While most multilevel analysis uses the organization as the highest level of analysis, a distinct body of research has explored HRM at the country level. This research studies comparative HR systems and the impact of national institutions and cultural factors in shaping the kind of HR practices that are likely to be acceptable and have impact. European countries typically have a stronger institutional framework, including legislation that requires certain practices to be in place. In a country such as the United States, organizations have fewer constraints on the HR practices they can choose whether or not to apply. Along with the major comparative studies of national cultures and leadership, the Cranet project (see, e.g., Mayehofer & Brewster, 2005) has for years been conducting standard surveys in many countries collecting data on HR practices, the structure of the HR function, and perceptions of impact. Rabl, Jayasinghe, Gerhart, and Kuhlmann (2014) have analyzed country differences in the strength of the HRM-performance relationship across studies reported in 29 countries. Although in all cases, the associations were positive, there were wide country differences in the average strength of the association, and their hypotheses about the influence of two dimensions of national culture, namely tight-loose properties and degree of flexibility, were not supported.

In policy terms, research on comparative HRM is particularly relevant for international organizations sending managers on overseas assignments. Schuler, Dowling, and De Cieri (1993) have provided an integrative framework within which to consider international HRM, including overseas assignments. Black and Mendenhall (1990) have explored issues in selection and more particularly cross-cultural training methods, while Black, Mendenhall, and Oddou (1991) have outlined the steps necessary for effective adjustment to an overseas assignment. Doherty, Dickmann, and Mills (2011) have explored motives among company-initiated and self-initiated overseas assignments, while Bolino (2007) has analyzed the implications of such assignments for career success. Comparative HRM therefore provides a good example of how HRM research can be considered at different levels of analysis, from different disciplinary perspectives, and from both conceptual and applied perspectives.

The Importance of Longitudinal Research.   Much of the reported research linking HRM and outcomes has been cross-sectional, raising questions about causality and leading to calls for longitudinal studies. Researchers have begun to answer this call. Birdi et al. (2008) examined the impact of three HR practices (training, teamwork, and empowerment) and four operational practices (total quality management, just-in-time, supply chain management, and advanced manufacturing techniques) on productivity in a large sample of manufacturing firms over a 22-year period. They found a positive impact of HR practices but not operational practices, and they also found no interaction between them. They reported a lengthy time lag of several years before any impact was significant. In contrast, Piening, Baluch, and Salge (2013), in a longitudinal study in healthcare, found support for a causal chain from employee perceptions to changes in job satisfaction to changes in patient satisfaction. However, they found that the impact was greatest in the first year and diminished thereafter. The longitudinal study in healthcare by West et al. (2006) reported a more direct association between the presence of more HR practices and mortality rates after controlling for a range of other potential influences.

Longitudinal studies have generally supported a causal ordering whereby HR practices affect outcomes. However, they have rarely considered the possibility of reverse causality. The potential for reverse causality is based on the assumption that high performance and, in particular, high financial performance create room for investment, including investment in human resources. There is also the possibility that working for a successful organization is a source of satisfaction that in turn further enhances performance, a conclusion that might be drawn from the longitudinal study of company-level performance and job satisfaction over a number of years reported by Schneider, Hanges, Smith, and Salvaggio (2003). In the context of HRM, Guest, Michie, Conway, and Sheehan (2003) reported an association between HRM and subsequent financial performance. However, when they controlled for prior performance, this association disappeared, raising questions about the causal ordering. It also raises wider questions about the size of impact of HRM, since few studies have taken into account prior financial performance. This point is strongly reinforced in a study by Shin and Konrad (2016) that used a longitudinal Canadian company-level data set to explore the relation over time between HRM and productivity. After controlling for past performance and past HRM, they found a modest positive two-way causal link between the variables, with each having an influence on the other over three two-year time lags. The study by Piening, Baluch, and Salge (2013) found support for a cyclical process whereby HRM affected outcomes and these in turn affected HR practices. But Van de Voorde, Paauwe, and van Veldhoven (2010), in a cross-lagged study, found that an "HR-indexed" measure of organizational climate had an impact on organizational performance, though there was no evidence of performance influencing climate.

These studies help to highlight the challenges of establishing the causal direction in the HRM-outcomes relationship and challenge the size of the associations reported in cross-sectional studies. When the outcome is financial performance, one of the problems is that it tends to be very stable from year to year, leaving only a small amount of variance to explain. The same may be the case for HR practices. There are also major challenges in controlling for other endogenous and exogenous variables. What may be needed are naturally occurring quasi-experimental studies, possibly at branch levels. At a micro level, W/O psychologists have been more successful in demonstrating causality with respect, for example, to interventions for improving selection, training, or job design. Since the distinctive feature of HRM is that it needs to be considered as a system of practices and is more typically explored at the unit or organizational level, this presents distinctive challenges of access over time and interpretation of results when other factors are hard to control for. Understanding the dynamics of changes in the use of HR practices may require in-depth longitudinal, qualitative studies along with the dominant quantitative research.

CONCLUSION

HRM provides an important context for research in W/O psychology. It incorporates the core practices and activities that constitute W/O psychologists' areas of expertise. HR departments often act as gatekeepers for W/O psychologists from outside the organization or as hosts for those working within it. HRM extends the traditional domain of W/O psychologists by incorporating strategic issues, and it raises ethical issues in terms of the "utilization" of employees that can sometimes spill over into "exploitation." It is therefore important that research on outcomes addresses the impact of employee well-being while at the same time recognizing the pragmatic political requirement to explore those contexts, conditions, policies, and practices that offer the potential for both high performance and high well-being. HRM is a broad topic that has attracted an extensive and growing body of research. It also raises a lot of challenging research questions. Its multilevel, multidisciplinary characteristics pose additional challenges for W/O psychologists. But it is an important applied subject with room to link theory, research, and application, and it is one to which W/O psychology is making an increasingly significant contribution.

FURTHER READING

Bockerman, P., Bryson, A., & Ilmakunnas, P. (2012). Does high involvement management improve worker well-being? *Journal of Economic Behavior and Organization, 84,* 660–680.

Boxall, P., Purcell, J., & Wright, P. (Eds.). (2007). *The Oxford handbook of human resource management.* Oxford: Oxford University Press.

Brewster, C., & Mayrhofer, W. (Eds.). (2012). *Handbook of research on comparative HRM.* Cheltenham, U.K.: Edward Elgar.

Cascio, W., & Boudreau, J. (2012). *A short introduction to strategic human resource management.* New York: Cambridge University Press.

Legge, K. (2005). *Human resource management: Rhetorics and realities.* Basingstoke, U.K.: Palgrave Macmillan.

Paauwe, J., Guest, D., & Wright, P. (2013). *HRM and performance: Achievements and challenges.* Chichester, U.K.: Wiley.

Pfeffer, J. (1998). *The human equation: Building profits by putting people first.* Boston: Harvard Business School Press.

Rynes, S., Giluk, T., & Brown, G. (2007). The very separate worlds of academic and practitioner periodicals in human resources management: Implications for evidence-based management. *Academy of Management Journal, 50*(5), 987–1008.

Thompson, P. (2011). The trouble with HRM. *Human Resource Management Journal, 21*(4), 355–367.

Warner, M. (Ed.). (2011). *Society and HRM in China.* London: Routledge.

REFERENCES

Aguinis, H., & Kraiger, K. (2009). Benefits of training and development for individuals and teams, organizations and society. *Annual Review of Psychology, 60,* 451–474.

Arthur, J. (1994). Effects of human resource management systems on manufacturing performance and turnover. *Academy of Management Journal, 37*(3), 670–687.

Bal, M., Kooij, T., & De Jong, S. (2013). How do developmental and accommodative hrm enhance employee engagement and commitment? The role of the psychological contract and SOC strategies. *Journal of Management Studies, 50*(4), 545–572.

Baltes, P., Staudinger, U., & Lindenberger, U. (1999). Lifespan psychology: Theory and application to intellectual functioning. *Annual Review of Psychology, 50,* 471–507.

Barney, J. (1991). Firm resources and sustained competitive advantage. *Journal of Management, 17*(1), 99–120.

Barney, J., & Wright, P. (1998). On becoming a strategic partner: The role of human resources in gaining competitive advantage. *Human Resource Management, 37*(1), 31–46.

Becker, G. (1964). *Human capital.* New York: Columbia University Press.

Becker, B., & Gerhart, B. (1996). The impact of human resource management on organizational performance: Progress and prospects. *Academy of Management Journal, 39*(4), 779–801.

Becker, B., & Huselid, M. (1998). High performance work systems and firm performance: A synthesis of research and managerial implications. In K. Rowland & G. Ferris (Eds.), *Research in personnel and human resource management* (pp. 53–101). Greenwich, CT: JAI Press.

Becker, B., Huselid, M., Pickus, P., & Spratt, M. (1997). HR as a source of shareholder value: Research and recommendations. *Human Resource Management, 36*(1), 39–48.

Beer, M., Spector, B., Lawrence, P., Quinn Mills, D., & Walton, R. (1985). *Human resource management: A general manager perspective.* New York: Free Press.

Birdi, K., Clegg, C., Patterson, M., Robinson, A., Stride, C., Wall, T., & Wood, S. (2008). The impact of human resource and operational management practices on company productivity: A longitudinal study. *Personnel Psychology, 61*(3), 467–501.

Black, S., & Mendenhall, M. (1990). Cross-cultural training effectiveness: A review and theoretical framework for further research. *Academy of Management Review, 15*(1), 113–136.

Black, S., Mendenhall, M., & Oddou, G. (1991). Towards a comprehensive model of international adjustment: An integration of multiple theoretical perspectives. *Academy of Management Review, 16*(2), 291–317.

Bolino, M. (2007). Expatriate assignments and intra-organizational career success: Implications for individuals and organizations. *Journal of International Business Studies, 38*(5), 819–835.

Boselie, P., Dietz, G., & Boon, C. (2005). Commonalities and contradictions in HRM and performance research. *Human Resource Management Journal, 15*(3), 67–94.

Bos-Nehles, A. (2010). *The line makes the difference: Line managers as effective HR partners.* Zutphen, The Netherlands: CPI Wohrmann.

Bowen, D., & Ostroff, C. (2004). Understanding HRM-performance linkages: The role of the "strength" of the HRM system. *Academy of Management Review, 29*(2), 203–221.

Boxall, P., & Macky, K. (2009). Research and theory on high performance work systems: Progressing the high involvement work stream. *Human Resource Management Journal, 19*(1), 3–23.

Boxall, P., & Purcell, J. (2011). *Strategy and human resource management* (3d ed.). Basingstoke, U.K.: Palgrave Macmillan.

Buyens, D., & De Vos, A. (2001). Perceptions of the value of the HR function. *Human Resource Management Journal, 11*(3), 70–89.

Caldwell, R. (2008). HR business partner competency models: Re-contextualising effectiveness. *Human Resource Management Journal, 18*(3), 275–294.

Clinton, M., & van Veldhoven, M. (2013). HRM and employee well-being. In S. Bach & M. Edwards (Eds.), *Managing human resources* (5th ed., pp. 364–388). Chichester, U.K.: Wiley.

Coelho, J., Cunha, R., Gomes, J., & Correia, A. (2015). Strength of the HR system: The development of a measure. *Journal of Industrial Engineering and Management, 8*(4), 1069–1086.

Combs, J., Liu, Y., Hall, A., & Ketchen, D. (2006). How much do high-performance work systems matter? A meta-analysis of their effects on organizational performance. *Personnel Psychology, 59*(3), 501–528.

Connelly, B., Certo, T., Ireland, D., & Reutzel, C. (2011). Signaling theory: A review and assessment. *Journal of Management, 37*(1), 39–67.

Crook, T., Todd, S., Combs, J., Woehr, D., & Ketchen, D. (2011). Does human capital matter? A meta-analysis of the relationships between human capital and firm performance. *Journal of Applied Psychology, 96*(3), 443–456.

Delery, J., & Doty, D. (1996). Modes of theorizing in strategic human resource management: Tests of universalistic, contingency and configurational performance predictions. *Academy of Management Journal, 39*(4), 802–835.

Delmotte, J., DeWinne, S., & Sels, L. (2012). Toward an assessment of perceived HRM system strength: Scale development and validation. *International Journal of Human Resource Management, 23*(7), 1481–1506.

Doherty, N., Dickmann, M., & Mills, T. (2011). Exploring the motives of company-based and self-initiated expatriates. *International Journal of Human Resource Management, 22*(3), 595–611.

Eisenberger, R., Cummings, J., Armeli, S., & Lynch, P. (1997). Perceived organizational support, discretionary treatment and job satisfaction. *Journal of Applied Psychology, 82*(5), 812–820.

Fombrun, C., Tichy, N., & Devanna, M. (1984). *Strategic human resource management.* New York: Wiley.

Forth, J., & McNabb, R. (2008). Workforce performance: A comparison of subjective and objective measures in the 2004 WERS. *Industrial Relations Journal, 39*(2), 104–123.

Givan, R., Avgar, A., & Liu, M. (2010). Having your cake and eating it? The relationship between HR and organizational performance in healthcare. *Advances in Industrial and Labor Relations, 17,* 31–67.

Godard, J. (2004). A critical assessment of the high performance paradigm. *British Journal of Industrial Relations, 42*(2), 439–478.

Gong, Y., Chang, S., & Cheung, S. (2010). High-performance work system and collective OCB: A collective social exchange perspective. *Human Resource Management Journal, 20*(2), 119–137.

Gouldner, A. (1960). The norm of reciprocity: A preliminary statement. *American Sociological Review, 25*(2), 161–178.

Guest, D. (1997). Human resource management and performance: A review and research agenda. *International Journal of Human Resource Management, 8*(3), 263–276.

Guest, D., & Bos-Nehles, A. (2013). HRM and performance: The role of effective implementation. In J. Paauwe, D. Guest, & P. Wright (Eds.), *HRM and performance: Achievements and challenges* (pp. 79–98). Chichester, U.K.: Wiley.

Guest, D., & King, Z. (2004). Power, innovation and problem-solving: The personnel manager's three steps to heaven? *Journal of Management Studies, 41*(3), 401–423.

Guest, D., Michie, J., Conway, N., & Sheehan, M. (2003). Human resource management and corporate performance in the UK. *British Journal of Industrial Relations, 41*(2), 291–314.

Hope Hailey, V., Farndale, E., & Truss, K. (2005). The HR department's role in organizational performance. *Human Resource Management Journal, 15*(3), 49–66.

Huselid, M. (1995). The impact of human resource management practices on turnover, productivity and organizational financial performance. *Academy of Management Journal, 38*(3), 635–672.

Ichniowski, C., Shaw, K., & Prennushi, G. (1997). The effects of human resource management practices on productivity: A study of steel finishing mills. *The American Economic Review, 87*(3), 291–313.

Jackson, S., Schuler, R., & Jiang, K. (2014). An aspirational framework for strategic human resource management. *Academy of Management Annals, 8*(1), 1–56.

Jiang, K., Lepak, D., Hu, J., & Baer, J. (2012). How does human resource management influence organizational outcomes? A meta-analytic investigation of mediating mechanisms. *Academy of Management Journal, 55*(6), 1264–1294.

Kehoe, R., & Wright, P. (2013). The impact of high-performance human resource practices on employees' attitudes and behaviors. *Journal of Management, 39*(2), 366–391.

Khilji, S., & Wang, X. (2006). "Intended" and "implemented" HRM: The missing linchpin in strategic human resource management research. *International Journal of Human Resource Management, 17*(7), 1171–1189.

Kooij, D., Guest, D., Clinton, M., Knight, T., Janson, P., & Dikkers, J. (2013). How the impact of HR practices on employee well-being changes with age. *Human Resource Management Journal, 23*(1), 18–35.

Lawler, E. (1971). *Pay and organizational effectiveness: A psychological view*. New York: McGraw-Hill.

Legge, K. (1978). *Power, innovation and problem-solving in personnel management*. London: McGraw-Hill.

Lepak, D., & Snell, S. (1999). The human resource architecture: Toward a theory of human capital allocation and development. *Academy of Management Review, 24*(1), 31–48.

Lepak, D., & Snell, S. (2002). Examining the human resource architecture: The relationships among human capital, employment and human resource configurations. *Journal of Management, 28*(4), 517–543.

Li, X., Frenkel, S., & Sanders, K. (2011). Strategic HRM as process: How HR system and organizational climate strength influence Chinese employee attitudes. *International Journal of Human Resource Management, 22*(9), 1825–1842.

Liao, H., Toya, K., Lepak, D., & Hong, Y. (2009). Do they see eye to eye? Management and employee perspectives of high-performance work systems and influence processes on service quality. *Journal of Applied Psychology, 94*(2), 371–391.

Mayrhofer, W., & Brewster, C. (2005). European human resource management: Researching developments over time. *Management Revue, 16*(1), 36–62.

Messersmith, J., Patel, P., Lepak, D., & Gould-Williams, J. (2011). Unlocking the black box: Exploring the link between high-performance work systems and performance. *Journal of Applied Psychology, 96*(6), 1105–1118.

Miles, R., & Snow, C. (1984). Fit, failure and the hall of fame. *California Management Review, 26*, 10–28.

Nishii, L., Lepak, D., & Schneider, B. (2008). Employee attributions of the "why" of HR practices: Their effects on employee attitudes and behaviors, and customer satisfaction. *Personnel Psychology, 61*(3), 503–545.

Nyberg, A., & Wright, P. (2015). 50 years of human capital research: Assessing what we know, exploring where we go. *Academy of Management Perspectives, 29*(3), 287–295.

Ostroff, C., & Bowen, D. (2000). Moving HR to a higher level: Human resource practices and organizational effectiveness. In K. Klein & W. Kozlowski (Eds.), *Multilevel theory, research and methods in organizations* (pp. 211–266). San Francisco: Jossey Bass.

Paauwe, J. (2004). *HRM and performance: Achieving long-term viability*. Oxford: Oxford University Press.

Peccei, R., van de Voorde, K., & van Veldhoven, M. (2013). HRM, well-being and performance: A theoretical and empirical view. In J. Paauwe, D. Guest, & P. Wright (Eds.), *HRM and performance: Achievements and challenges* (pp. 15–46). Chichester, U.K.: Wiley.

Peel, S., & Boxall, P. (2005). When is contracting preferable to employment? An exploration of management and worker perspectives. *Journal of Management Studies, 42*(8), 1675–1699.

Pereira, C., & Gomes, J. (2012). The strength of human resource practices and transformational leadership: Impact on organisational performance. *International Journal of Human Resource Management, 23*(20), 4301–4318.

Piening, E., Baluch, A., & Salge, T. (2013). The relationship between employees' perceptions of human resource systems and organizational performance: Examining mediating mechanisms and temporal dynamics. *Journal of Applied Psychology, 98*(6), 926–947.

Ployhart, R., & Moliterno, T. (2011). Emergence of the human capital resource: A multi-level model. *Academy of Management Review, 36*(1), 127–150.

Ployhart, R., Nyberg, A., Reilly, G., & Maltarich, M. (2014). Human capital is dead: Long live human capital resources. *Journal of Management, 40*(2), 371–398.

Porter, M. (1985). *Competitive advantage: Creating and sustaining superior performance*. New York: Free Press.

Rabl, T., Jayasinghe, M., Gerhart, B., & Kuhlmann, T. (2014). A meta-analysis of country differences in the high-performance work system-business performance relationship: The roles of national culture and managerial discretion. *Journal of Applied Psychology, 99*(6), 1011–1041.

Ramsay, H., Scholarios, D., & Harley, B. (2000). Employees and high-performance work systems: Testing inside the black box. *British Journal of Industrial Relations, 38*(4), 501–531.

Ritzer, G., & Trice, A. (1969). *An occupation in conflict.* Ithaca, NY: Cornell University Press.

Roethlisberger, F., & Dickson, W. (1939). *Management and the worker.* Cambridge, MA: Harvard University Press.

Rousseau, D., & Greller, M. (1994). Human resource practices: Administrative contract makers. *Human Resource Management, 33*(3), 385–401.

Sanders, K., Dorenbosch, L., & De Reuver, R. (2008). The impact of individual and shared employee perceptions of HRM on affective commitment: Considering climate strength. *Personnel Review, 37*(4), 412–425.

Schmidt, F., & Hunter, J. (1998). The validity and utility of selection methods in personnel psychology: Practical and theoretical implications over 85 years of research findings. *Psychological Bulletin, 124*(2), 262–274.

Schneider, B., Hanges, P., Smith, D., & Salvaggio, A. (2003). Which comes first: Employee attitudes or financial and market performance? *Journal of Applied Psychology, 88*(5), 836–851.

Schuler, R., & Jackson, S. (1987). Linking competitive strategies with human resource management practices. *Academy of Management Executive, 1*(3), 207–219.

Schuler, R., Dowling, P., & De Cieri, H. (1993). An integrative framework of strategic international human resource management. *Journal of Management, 19*(2), 419–459.

Shin, D., & Konrad, A. (2016). Causality between high-performance work systems and organizational performance. *Journal of Management.*

Subramony, M. (2009). A meta-analytic investigation of the relationship between HRM bundles and firm performance. *Human Resource Management, 48*(5), 745–768.

Takeuchi, R., Chen, G., & Lepak, D. (2009). Through the looking glass of a social system: Cross-lagged effects of high-performance work systems on employee attitudes. *Personnel Psychology, 62*(1), 1–29.

Ulrich, D. (1997). *Human resource champions.* Boston: Harvard Business School Press.

Ulrich, D., & Brockbank, W. (2005). *The HR value proposition.* Boston: Harvard Business School Press.

Ulrich, D., Younger, J., Brockbank, W., & Ulrich, M. (2013). The state of the HR profession. *Human Resource Management, 52*(3), 457–471.

Van de Voorde, K., & Beijer, S. (2015). The role of employee HR attributions in the relationship between high-performance work systems and employee outcomes. *Human Resource Management Journal, 25*(1), 62–78.

Van de Voorde, K., Paauwe, J., & van Veldhoven, M. (2010). Predicting business unit performance using employee surveys: Monitoring HRM-related changes. *Human Resource Management Journal, 20*(1), 44–63.

Van de Voorde, K., Paauwe, J., & Van Veldhoven, M. (2012). Employee well-being and the HRM-performance relationship: A review of quantitative studies. *International Journal of Management Reviews, 14*(4), 391–407.

Van Eerde, W., & Thierry, H. (1996). Vroom's expectancy model and work-related criteria: A meta-analysis. *Journal of Applied Psychology, 81*(5), 575–586.

Van Wanrooy, B., Bewley, H., Bryson, A., Forth, J., Freeth, S., Stokes, L., & Wood, S. (2013). *Employment relations in the shadow of recession.* Basingstoke, U.K.: Macmillan.

Wall, T., Michie, J., Patterson, M., Wood, S., Sheehan, M., Clegg, C., & West, M. (2004). On the validity of subjective measures of company performance. *Personnel Psychology, 57*(1), 95–118.

Walton, R. (1985). From control to commitment in the workplace. *Harvard Business Review, 63*(2), 77–84.

Walton, R., & McKersie, R. (1965). *A behavioral theory of labor negotiations.* New York: McGraw-Hill.

West, M., Guthrie, J., Dawson, J., Borrill, C., & Carter, M. (2006). Reducing patient mortality in hospitals: The role of human resource management. *Journal of Organizational Behavior, 27*(7), 983–1002.

Whyte, W. (1955). *Money and motivation: An analysis of incentives in industry.* New York: Harper.

Wood, S., & Albanese, M. (1995). Can we speak of high commitment management on the shop floor? *Journal of Management Studies,* 3(2), 215–247.

Woodrow, C., & Guest, D. (2014). When good HR gets bad results: Exploring the challenge of HR implementation in the case of workplace bullying. *Human Resource Management Journal,* 24(1), 38–56.

Wright, C. (2008). Reinventing human resource management: Business partners, internal consultants and limits to professionalization. *Human Relations,* 61(8), 1063–1086.

Wright, P., & Boswell, W. (2002). Desegregating HRM: A review and synthesis of micro and macro human resource management research. *Journal of Management,* 28(3), 247–276.

David E. Guest

PSYCHOLOGICAL CONTRACTS AND THE EMPLOYMENT RELATIONSHIP

INTRODUCTION

Employment usually means that two parties, the employer and the employee, have agreed to a contract. This contract basically describes the exchange of work tasks and subsequent remuneration. Written employment contracts also often include formal, sometimes legally regulated, entitlements and obligations for the two parties, such as duration of the contract and terms and conditions for its end. In addition to the formal agreement, the parties to the relationship form implicit perceptions of commitments and promises based on the interaction between them. This implicit part of the relationship is the *psychological contract* (PC). The relevance of this relationship as a metaphorical "contract" builds upon the exchange between parties, and the psychological content assumed to be relevant for the relationship beyond what is indicated in any formal or written agreement. The psychological aspect of the relationship extends beyond the economic contract by including factors other than ones that are financially motivating, such as personal development and career prospects (Herriot, 2001).

There is considerable support for the idea that implicit promises and expectations seem to be more important than the formal contract. The PSYCONES project (PSYchological CONtracts across Employment Situations) investigated both forms of contracts in a large European project (Guest, Isaksson, & De Witte, 2010). One major conclusion was that the psychological contract was more important than the formal employment contract for cultivating employees' well-being and positive attitudes toward their work.

HISTORY, DEFINITIONS, AND DEBATES

Describing employment as an *exchange relationship* consisting of both explicit and implicit parts began in the 1950s. Argyris (1960) used the concept to describe the impact of the interaction between the parties and assumed that a positive exchange between employer and employee could increase productivity. Kotter (1973) conducted one of the early empirical studies. He described the psychological contract as largely implicit, describing what the parties expect to give and receive as part of the employment (Kotter, 1973, p. 92). His study investigated reasons for high turnover rates among recently hired employees. Results showed that agreement regarding the expectations of both parties at the onset of employment was related to overall job satisfaction and lower turnover among newcomers.

Several researchers in the 1980s further examined this concept (e.g., Schein, 1980). Schein described the dynamics, development, and change of psychological contracts over time. The perceived entitlements of employees consisted of economic benefits but also of career and development prospects. Typical in this early work was the description by researchers of an exchange relationship between two parties that consisted of both formal and informal commitments as well as a psychological dimension.

The seminal work of Denise Rousseau (1990, 1995) made an important breakthrough in psychological contract theory. Her work was pioneering in the development of the contract metaphor and a description of the psychological contract in more detail. Her definition, in contrast to earlier research, stated that "the psychological contract consists of *individual* beliefs regarding the terms of an exchange agreement between individuals and their organisation" (Rousseau, 1995, p. 9). The focus was on *individual employees* and their subjective perceptions of both written, explicit promises and implicit beliefs. Early on, Rousseau outlined a few characteristics that are still accepted by most scholars and used for their research. Perhaps most important is defining the psychological contract as consisting of *promise-based beliefs* and a cognitively based mental model of the mutual entitlements and obligations of the relationship (Rousseau, 2001). In both cases, the beliefs are subjective interpretations of verbal or written promises or are based on observations and conversations with representatives of the organization. By using the words "belief" and "promise" instead of "expectation," Rousseau emphasized the greater stability of a promise as compared to an expectation. In contrast to an expectation, promises build upon a *trust* that the promises should be kept, which gives the psychological contract a certain stability.

Although Rousseau undoubtedly had and still has a large influence in the arena of psychological contracts, there are a number of ongoing debates about how to define and use this concept. The most critical of these has been about the definition of the psychological contract: perceived as being primarily focused on employees' individual perceptions, in line with Rousseau's definition, or more in line with the earlier scholars who focused on the perceptions of both parties in the relationship (e.g., Kotter 1973; Schein, 1980). The psychological contract could then be defined as "The perceptions of *both parties* to the employment relationship, organization and individual, of the reciprocal promises and obligations implied in that relationship" (Guest & Conway, 2002, p. 22). The main argument for this perspective is that the focus on the relationship of *two parties in interaction* would clearly have the potential to add new knowledge to earlier organizational research. David Guest (1998) argued that there are already a number of concepts and measures of employees' perceptions of the organization, such as job satisfaction, organizational commitment, and organizational support. Studies of both parties to the employee-employer relationship could explain more of the complexity and dynamics of interactions in the workplace and how this affects organizational performance and employee well-being.

Although there are ongoing debates about definitions and content, there seems to be a rather general agreement about the following (see also Conway & Briner, 2005):

- The psychological contract consists of *perceptions* of *promise-based beliefs* and is *implicit*.
- The perceptions shaping the psychological contract are affected by both individual and organizational factors.
- The psychological contract is about an *exchange* between the parties.
- The psychological contract builds on *perceptions of mutuality* (i.e., perceived agreement about the content).
- The psychological contract also builds on the social *norm of reciprocity* (Gouldner, 1960): that is, that services or presents should be reciprocated for a relationship to remain in balance (e.g., an eye for an eye).
- The psychological contract is based on *promises* of a more stable nature than expectations.
- The psychological contract is dynamic and affected by HR practices, organizational change, and individual behavior.

Although a majority of scholars until recently seem to favor Rousseau's definition and have investigated workers' individual perceptions, there are certainly advantages to embracing both perspectives, including attention to the exchange between parties. Recent trends in research seem to be moving toward the investigation of the dynamics and processes between parties, thus increasing interest in interactions and the management of the psychological contract (see, e.g., Rousseau, Hansen, & Tomprou, 2018). Further studies of individual employees' perceptions, as well as studies of the perceptions of both parties, could make important additional contributions to this field of research.

To increase the understanding of how contextual factors affect the psychological contract, Guest (2004) introduced the *state of the psychological contract*. In this case, the state should indicate the level of *trust* between parties, but also of *fairness*—that is, whether promises can be trusted and whether they were perceived as fair. According to Guest (2004), the state in an organization could indicate the quality of the employment relationship, and thus influence the psychological contract.

AREAS IN PREVIOUS RESEARCH

Although there has been a large increase in research about psychological contracts, the topics and research questions addressed have been fairly limited. The most popular areas will be described here, starting with efforts to investigate the content.

Content of the Psychological Contract.
Over the last three decades, there has been a great deal of research about the psychological contract, mostly with a focus on how *employees* perceive their organizations. Early research heavily concentrated on describing the *content of the psychological contract*, and generally investigated employees' perceptions of promises and commitments made by the organization. There were several challenges to expand that research, for example, to examine the bases of individuals' perceptions, to explore the understanding of implied promises, which could be partly unconscious, and to compare the psychological contracts of individuals. The early studies used interviews (e.g., Herriot, Manning, & Kidd, 1997) and described both employee and employer perceptions of the obligations of the organization

and its employees. Examples of organizational obligations were the provision of a safe work environment, introduction for newcomers, fair treatment, reasonable pay, and other benefits, including support and recognition. Both employers and workers described similar sets of obligations for the organization, although there was also some disagreement. Workers stressed security, safety, and fair treatment, while employers more often mentioned support and recognition. The level of actual agreement was somewhat higher when describing employees' obligations. Examples included working hours, honesty, loyalty to the organization and its customers, and work role flexibility. All in all, these early studies described rather traditional values and work-related commitments, also later reported in representative samples in the United Kingdom (described in Conway & Briner, 2005).

Questionnaires have become the most common way to investigate the content of the psychological contract. For the assessment of range and mean values of certain promises and commitments in a workplace, questionnaires have used lists of items. Respondents indicate whether a certain promise or commitment is perceived. This method has its shortcomings, for example, there is a need to discover new elements, identify changing conditions, and further explore the methods of measurement (see, e.g., Sherman & Morley, 2019).

Building on the metaphor and the use of contract theory in other disciplines such as law and economy, a conceptual distinction is often made between *transactional* and *relational* psychological contracts. In her early work, Rousseau (1990) described these two types of content as dimensions resulting from varying contract terms. At one end of the dimension, transactional contract terms describe a mostly monetary exchange: "a fair day's work for a fair day's pay." Terms and conditions would then be relatively unambiguous, including clear commitments and limited loyalty, and commonly used with a time-limited employment contract. The other end of the continuum was described as incorporating more dynamic, flexible benefits, including more nonmonetary social advantages. These conditions were often offered as part of open-ended employment contracts. Rousseau (1995) later distinguished between four different types of contracts. Adding to transactional and relational psychological contracts, she also described *transitional and balanced contracts*. The transitional PCs were described as quite clear and found mostly in short-term work, for example, work on an hourly basis. In contrast, the balanced psychological contracts were more specific regarding performance requirements and included both transactional and relational content.

Although the distinction between transactional and relational contracts has become popular and often used in research, its significance is still not entirely clear. It is not always transparent how these psychological contracts differ, and researchers have not always been able to distinguish between them in empirical studies (Conway & Briner, 2005). The structure and form of transactional and relational aspects of psychological contracts also remain unclear, that is, whether they are dimensions, continuous, or wholly different types. In a paper by Isaksson, De Cuyper, Bernhard Oettel, and De Witte (2010), the aim was to investigate whether temporary and permanent employment contracts were related to a transactional or relational content of psychological contracts. They tested this and found some support for a *layered model* of the content. The idea was that transactional terms formed the basis, and they were included in all psychological contracts regardless of the employment contract. Above this bottom layer, relational contracts terms could be added and were more commonly found for permanent employees. Additional studies are needed to further explore this and other ideas about how the content of the psychological contract is formed and structured. An additional form of psychological contract, the *ideological*, was suggested by Thompson and Bunderson (2003) as particularly relevant in occupations where values and principles form part of the motivation for work, such as clerical and human services work. This type of psychological contract has also been identified for voluntary work (Vantilborgh et al., 2014).

Antecedents of Psychological Contracts.

An important question both for theory and for practice concerns antecedents, or factors shaping employment contracts, described by Rousseau (1995) and others (e.g., McLean Parks, Kidder, & Gallagher, 1998) in terms of variations in employment arrangements. These and other authors have aimed to identify the most important features of employment contracts and relate them to psychological contract dimensions.

Results from a study by Sels, Janssens, and Van den Brande (2004) supported the significance of formal contract characteristics and added HR practices as a second antecedent shaping the nature of psychological contracts. Variations in employment contracts could concern:

- *Specificity*: whether employment conditions are more or less explicit.
- *Breadth or scope*: how extensive the contract is in terms of number of promises and commitments.
- *Stability*: if the contract is stable or dynamic and flexible over time.
- *Timeframe*: duration of contract and level of security.

McLean Parks et al. (1998) described additional features to this list, suggesting that multiple agency and volition were equally important. As this indicates, the relationship between the formal employment contract and the psychological contract and how they relate to different outcomes has been a challenge for researchers. It touches upon questions about contextual influence, including legal regulations and central collective agreements leading to possible variations between sectors and countries. Investigating the psychological contract meant probing whether laws and regulations and other possible obligations were actually perceived by employees to have resulted in specific promises or commitments made by their current employer.

The pan-European project PSYCONES thoroughly investigated the role and significance of employment contracts, as well as scrutinizing the possible intervening role of psychological contracts (Guest et al., 2010). In this study, time-limited contracts were compared to open-ended, permanent contracts. Outcomes concerned both attitudes toward the job and the organization, as well as employee well-being. Results cast some doubt on the commonly assumed difference between permanent and temporary forms of employment. Contrary to expectations, temporary employment related to a higher level of well-being and job satisfaction than permanent employment, even after controlling for a range of possible confounding factors. The critical role of the psychological contract was not the content. Results very clearly showed that fulfillment of promises, or not violating them, was by far the strongest predictor of both attitudes and well-being. This result was robust across the three sectors and the seven countries involved in the study.

A general conclusion from earlier research is that intra-organizational factors, such as HR policies and the practices used for deciding on the types and features of employment contracts, as well as the level of fulfillment of promises and commitments, have profound effects on both psychological contracts and the well-being of workers. Whether this conclusion is equally relevant with the emerging changes in employment arrangements remains a question open for research (see, e.g., Kochan, Riordan, Kowalski, Khan, & Yang, 2019).

Creation and Development of Psychological Contracts. Another area of great importance for research, and also for HR practice, has been how the psychological contract develops. The creation of a psychological contract between the two parties in the employment relationship starts early on, during recruiting and interviews. The basis for the PC is the communication during the first phase of recruiting, including information-seeking. Both parties bring with them expectations about the new job. The organization has more or less specific demands and competence requirements, and the goal is to find as good a candidate as possible. The job seeker brings social norms and personal expectations, often based on earlier work experience, but also from available information about the organization obtained from advertisements, web pages, and social contacts with organization representatives (Low, Bordia, & Bordia, 2016). The possible zone of negotiability during the employment process varies, both as a result of country variation in legislation and collective agreements and variations in organizational practice and culture (Schalk & Rousseau, 2000). HR policies and practices form the basis of the employment contract offered, as well as for the kind of employment relationships for which the organization aims. The building of trust is critical and some kind of reference-seeking is commonly used by both parties: from former employers by the employer and from other workers or unions by the job seeker.

The creation process continues during the first year of employment as an important part of socialization in the new workplace (De Vos, Buyens, & Schalk, 2003; Tomprou & Nikolau, 2010). Recent research has confirmed the interaction and exchange of information as decisive for the outcome of the socialization process. A longitudinal study by Woodrow and Guest (2017) shows how the formation of the psychological contract affects the outcome of the socialization process after six months. Critical factors for both parties are promise strength during the first month of employment and whether promises have been fulfilled after three months. The process was positively related to a broad set of outcomes such as lower stress, higher service quality, and organizational commitment.

The adaptation process during the socialization period can be described as a *unilateral* adaptation, when newcomers learn and adapt their own behavior and commitments to organizational requirements (De Vos et al., 2003). Second, a *bilateral or mutual* adaptation is necessary when employees learn how their own behavior is met and rewarded by organization representatives and colleagues. The dynamics of this process often involve disappointment when misunderstandings have not been corrected by both parties. In some cases, when disappointment concerns critical issues for either the organization or the recently recruited worker, a probationary period does not lead to continued work. Generally, however, some adaptation is necessary, and changes are made before the psychological contract is stabilized and accepted as reasonably balanced by both parties. Stability in this case could mean that both a zone of acceptance and tolerance limits have been formed (Schalk & Roe, 2007).

Several studies have described the exchange in the socialization period for newcomers (e.g., De Vos & Freese, 2011; Delobbe, Cooper-Thomas, & De Hoe, 2016). Results showed that a positive and engaged newcomer generally developed a positive relationship with both colleagues and managers. After about a year, the PC seems to have become relatively stable, which means that the exchange is assumed to be reasonably balanced. The shift from creation of the PC to what has been called the maintenance phase (see, e.g., Rousseau et al., 2018) means that the PC becomes a mental model with relative stability but is still dynamic and affected by experience in the workplace.

Negative Development and Its Consequences. Effects of promise breach or violation is undoubtedly the most heavily researched topic within psychological contract theory. Even though a relative stability has generally been obtained during the first year of employment, research has shown that deviations of some kind are commonly reported mostly by employees about the organization (Conway & Briner, 2002; Lester, Turnley, Bloodgood, & Bolino, 2002; Robinson & Rousseau, 1994). Positive deviations also occur, although these are seldom reported and rarely investigated by researchers.

Research about psychological contract breach and its consequences has been hampered by the frequent lack of distinction between breach and violation; this sometimes leads to unexpected and contradictory results. A seminal paper by Morrison and Robinson (1997) suggested the distinction between *breach*—the *cognitive* awareness that a promise has been broken—and *violation*—strong *emotional* reactions to a broken promise. The distinction is important because breach of a promise has been shown to lead to a wide range of possible responses (see, e.g., Dulac, Coyle-Shapiro, Henderson, & Wayne, 2008). Some incidents of breach can probably be described as part of everyday life in the workplace. A lot of issues leading to perceptions of breach can be resolved or even ignored as they are considered less important and thus have very limited effects on behavior and attitudes. In other cases, a broken promise can lead to strong feelings of disappointment and anger. The reaction can be either a response to one specific incident or the result of a process of incidents over time, as suggested by Morrison and Robinson (1997). In the latter case, a perceived breach leads to increased vigilance, and when efforts to resolve issues are followed by the absence of a response from the organization, it can lead to negative emotional reactions. A recent qualitative study by Welander, Astvik, and Isaksson (2017) described a process leading to exit, based on interviews with social workers. In this case, it was a process extended in time, with efforts from social workers to suggest solutions to problems. The lack of response from management often led to disappointment and eventually to the decision to leave.

Results from research about the consequences of breach have been convincing in showing strong negative effects on attitudes, both toward the job, such as job satisfaction and engagement, and toward the organization, in terms of organizational commitment and turnover intention (Conway & Briner, 2005; Zhao, Wayne, Glibkowski, & Bravo, 2007). In mostly cross-sectional studies, breach has been shown to be a relatively strong predictor of work attitudes, including turnover. Results are not as clear when it comes to work behavior. There are several explanations for contradictory results about actual quitting. Most important is perhaps that breach is not always a good predictor of quitting. When similar or better jobs are unavailable, exit is not always an option. There may also be other reasons to stay, for example, the availability of social networks and relations between workers. The concept of *job embeddedness* (Lee, Burch, & Mitchell, 2014) is relevant here as an explanation. The authors describe economic and social reasons why people choose to stay in jobs even after dramatic changes and conflicts.

Behavior options other than that of exit are of course available for employees and have been both suggested and tested empirically. Several researchers have suggested the exit-voice-loyalty-neglect (EVLN) model as a useful conceptual framework describing employees' responses to changes in the psychological contract (see, e.g., Rousseau, 1995; Turnley & Feldman, 1999; Zhao et al., 2007). Hirschman (1970) initially developed the ideas behind the EVLN model, and Farrell (1983) and Rusbult, Farrell, Rogers, and Mainous (1988) further expanded it. Apart from *exit*, the responses suggested were *voice* (involvement by protest and suggestion) and *loyalty* (reduced loyalty and commitment), suggested by Hirschman. Farrell added *neglect* as a fourth passive destructive form. There are few longitudinal studies of the processes leading to different behavior outcomes. An exception is a study by Akhtar, Bal, and Long (2016) showing that fulfillment of the psychological contract appeared to be a critical factor in the decision process. Frequency of change was related to lower loyalty and negatively to exit, voice, and neglect, with fulfillment as a mediating factor. These studies have been cross-sectional so there is clearly a need for studies conducted over time, describing both the process and alternative outcomes.

MEASUREMENT AND METHODS OF INVESTIGATION

Surveys have become dominant as a method for data collection in PC research, and although variation has increased slightly, there is still a need to discuss whether the methods used really capture the content of the psychological contract this way. The surveys in use often present a predefined set of questions and items with few possibilities for respondents to describe deviations or to expand their own ideas about the content. The result is often reported in terms of mean values and variation is seldom discussed. Although alternative approaches have been tested, such as diaries (Conway & Briner, 2002), laboratory experiments (Lambert, 2011), and vignettes (Montes & Zweig, 2009), a question remains as to whether the methods really capture the psychological contract (Freese & Schalk, 2008; Sherman & Morley, 2019).

Problems with conducting longitudinal studies regarding consequences and development have gradually been resolved with the use of shorter time spans and forms of data other than traditional questionnaires, for example, diaries (Griep et al., 2018), interviews and documents (Schalk, De Ruiter, Van Loon, Kuijpers, & Van Regenmortel, 2018), short scales, and single items (Griep & Vantilborgh, 2018). Important contributions could clearly be obtained from in-depth interviews and other forms of qualitative data, preferably repeated over time.

An additional issue for research over the years has been the recurrent question about who represents the organization. The simple way to solve this has been to ask the HR managers, but this issue could benefit from more in-depth investigation. Part of the problem has been that organizations have many managers and the inconsistency or lack of continuity that this engenders requires further investigation for researchers to be able to fully understand the processes involved in developing and maintaining a stable psychological contract. The relationship to the organization could be assumed to change when HR policies and practices change, as this often means that power relations change. The resulting social processes need further attention.

Furthermore, worker unions are powerful in some European countries and they could have a positive role, for example, in suggesting solutions for the reparation of psychological contracts, as a resource for employees. The question about parties to the relationship was labeled single-party versus multiparty perspectives in a recent article focusing on measurement in PC research (Sherman & Morley, 2019). The issue of who the parties to the deal are becomes increasingly important in a changing labor market with new jobs in the so-called gig economy increasing, leading to changing employment relationships (Kochan et al., 2019).

RESEARCH ISSUES AND EMERGING NEW TOPICS

Despite the fact that psychological contract theory has been massively researched over the last 50 years, the topics investigated have been fairly limited and narrow in scope. There are a number of gaps in research on the content of the psychological contract as well as several areas of great interest which have remained almost totally unexplored. The first unexplored area regards positive development, maintenance, and repair after breaches. The second area builds on the definition of the relationship as consisting of two parties interacting, and this area has more apparent gaps. Previous research has almost exclusively concentrated on investigating the PC with a narrow focus on employees' perceptions of the organization. Investigating both parties to the relationship could add important knowledge for the organization about management and change. Another area regards new forms of employment relationships which call for a broader perspective, where factors outside *one* employing organization could have an influence and the parties are less clear (Kochan et al., 2019).

Positive Development, Dynamics, and Processes.   There seems to be a general growing interest in the processes involved in creating, maintaining, and managing relationships in the workplace using psychological contract theory (see, e.g., Rousseau et al., 2018).

Until very recently, an almost totally neglected area has been the *maintenance* of the psychological contract as part of keeping relative stability, a constructive climate in the workplace, and good relationships. There is quite a lot of research about the development and creation of psychological contracts, but what happens in the daily interaction in the workplace is not as well known. Although breaches are reported, employees also often seem to be fairly satisfied with their work and their relationship to their employing organization. A model by Schalk and Roe (2007) about the zones of acceptance and tolerance limits for deviations was an important contribution early on, but empirical studies over time would be warranted here. The quality of the relationship between leaders and employees, communication between them, and how the organization responds to complaints or suggestions by employees could decide whether a breach incident is easily resolved and a positive climate preserved or not. A relational perspective with reciprocity in focus could contribute with ideas and hypotheses about processes involved in maintaining a balanced relationship. There are several reasons for the lack of reports about the fulfillment of promises and positive development. One important reason is the cognitive bias in our thinking that favors memories of negative experiences to a higher degree than positive ones (Tversky & Kahneman, 1992). Second, the imbalance in power could lead employees to feel that they deserve more than was promised ("It's not more than right"). This power imbalance could also explain why employees seem to perceive breaches of the PC more often and to perceive inducements more negatively than their supervisors (Lester et al., 2002).

The focus of earlier research on employees' perceptions and negative effects becomes obvious in the lack of studies of *fulfillment* of promises and positive deviations from the psychological contract. Early studies (e.g., by Rousseau, 1990) assumed that the negative effects of breach had a much stronger impact than fulfillment, and generally fulfillment was seen as the opposite end of a continuum. A study by Conway, Guest, and Trenberth (2011) showed that the effects of the two could be differentiated. Supported by longitudinal data, and in line with the theory of negative bias, the negative effect of breach on attitudes and well-being was shown to be stronger over time than the positive effect of fulfillment. These recent studies are part of a broader interest in processes, development, and change of the psychological contract.

Thus, the breach concept needs to be further studied, especially with a focus on positive outcomes such as repair and recovery. In recent years, an increasing number of studies have investigated the effects of breach over relatively short periods of time with new forms of data analysis, which seems very promising. One such example is a study by Solinger et al. (2016) showing that employees after 10 weeks appeared to have recovered from a breach incident as shown in commitment levels. The study used weekly measures and experience sampling and also revealed nonlinear components in post-breach trajectories of recovery. The traditional use of questionnaires followed up within months does not always capture processes involving perceptions and emotions in the workplace.

Recent work regarding the functional or dysfunctional development of behavior following violation is part of this emerging line of research. In the last few years, there has been a growing interest in what happens after violation, from the perspective of the organization. Tomprou, Rousseau, and Hansen (2015) describe a post-violation model with four different pathways of behavior, two of them positive and the others negative. The model suggests that the outcome of organizational efforts to resolve problems and deal with negative emotions from employees is largely influenced by the possibility of mobilizing resources and engagement from both parties involved. In a study using four-wave longitudinal data from both questionnaires and qualitative interviews, results supported the interaction between the two parties as critical for a possible repair (Bankins, 2015). What happens with emotions after violation seems largely to depend on responses by the organization. The study by Solinger, Hofmans, Bal, and Jansen (2016), describing different trajectories over time for employees, provided some support for the four outcomes in the model. Most important for the recovery in terms of breach resolution success, as measured by organizational commitment, was how important specific promises were for the individual and then how the organization reacted in terms of support. Also, resources among employees and available support in the surrounding context need to be further investigated. There is reason to believe that support from unions and labor organizations, as well as a good climate in which to negotiate solutions, could be important to evaluate.

The increasing interest of scholars in the interaction processes involved in the maintenance of a positive relationship, and recently also in the repair of broken promises, could be seen as an increasing interest in the broader definition of the psychological contract, which emphasizes the two parties to the relationship and the interaction between them. This could also lead to an increasing interest in the employer side and the meaning of exchange and reciprocity from the other party to the deal.

Perceptions of Two Interacting Parties.   If the definition of psychological contracts builds on the interaction between the two parties, with a focus not only on the perceptions of employees but also on the organization and the processes involved in interactions that then shape the employment-organization relationship (EOR), there are a range of issues to investigate. Support for this orientation has come from studies confirming the idea of the norm of reciprocity as a building block for the psychological contract. This norm suggests giving something in return when receiving benefits, or the opposite, reducing contributions after reductions from the other party (Coyle-Shapiro & Kessler, 2002; Tekleab & Taylor, 2003). This is an area in need of expanded research, and specified as part of process studies. An interesting example recently reported concerned the changing behavior of employees in reaction to a perceived violation (Griep & Vantilborgh, 2018). Using weekly survey data over 10 weeks, they reported that accumulating reports of breach over time was related to intensifying violation feelings, which in turn was related to increasing counterproductive work behavior. There are still gaps in research related to the individual psychological contract and especially regarding employees' promises and commitments as perceived by both parties.

How do workers perceive their own obligations in the organization? How is this related to the employment contract and relationship to the organization? What are the effects for the organization of differences in employees' perceptions of entitlements? Increased knowledge about workers' perceptions of obligations could stimulate studies about the exchange and how it is looked at. Issues related to the basis for the exchange, such as reciprocity and mutuality, could be further examined, as can how these factors relate to a broader range of outcomes. Further study should be stimulated by the counterintuitive result that mutuality or agreement on the terms and conditions involved seems to be very low (Isaksson et al., 2010).

There are also gaps in research examining an *organization's perspectives* on promises and commitment as part of psychological contracts. Reasons for this are both theoretical and methodological. Questions about whether organizations can actually have psychological contracts and if so, who is going to represent the organization, have hampered the research over the years. There is a lot of knowledge about motivating factors at work and what a reasonable exchange *should* entail in terms of obligations, such as work tasks and loyalty in exchange for a reasonable salary. A closer look at both parties to the contract and the agreement on PC terms, or level of mutuality and its consequences, would also be interesting to pursue further. Broadening the discussion about parties to the deal could perhaps stimulate further research about contextual factors affecting the psychological contract.

MANAGING THE PSYCHOLOGICAL CONTRACT—PRACTICAL IMPLICATIONS

Psychological contract theory has thus far been an area for psychological research expanding into management studies. There is a great potential in further connecting this theory, with its focus on the EOR, to relational leadership theory and management of human resources. A definite advantage of the theory and the concept of psychological contracts is its close connection to and its applicability for management. It is easy to understand concepts such as contract, exchange, and balance both for managers and employees.

From a practical management perspective, the implicit and promise-based nature of the psychological contracts is a challenge but with great potential. Both HR strategies and aligned practices could be developed and contribute to a dynamic HR management with a focus on the relationship between the organization and its employees. In a recent review, Coyle-Shapiro, Pereira Costa, Doden, and Chang (2019) present a list of possible organizational actions, both to prevent psychological contract breach and to manage the aftermath of breaches. During recruiting and selection of staff, it seems critical not to make promises you cannot keep or to overestimate inducements and rewards, but to strive for clear job descriptions and demands, and to offer extra support and feedback for new recruits. To avoid breaches, HR management could include providing credible explanations and support to overcome breaches.

There are many good examples of applicable research showing the importance of HR policies and practices and their relevance for the psychological contract in this respect. A study by Sonnenberg, Koene, and Paauwe (2011) clearly supports the use of HR practices to contribute to employees' assessment of mutual demands of the employment relationship and to avoid violations of the psychological contract. Results in a longitudinal study by Guest and Conway (2002) highlighted three aspects of organizational communication for the psychological contract: during initial entry, in day-to-day work, and future-oriented, as being critical for less frequent occurrences of breach and for a more positive impact of HR policies and practices on attitudes and behavior.

Continued work and empirical studies are needed to clarify the interaction in post-breach maintenance and repair in order to further inform managers in strategic work and the handling of organizational change and development. Using psychological contract theory for strategy and practice in HR management is a challenge, and future research is needed to contribute to this development (Paauwe, Guest, & Wright, 2013). Two studies of relevance for this challenge are described here. First, a classic study by an American research team investigated different forms of employment relations from the perspective of the organizations (Tsui et al., 1997). They described two balanced relationships with a match between entitlements and obligations and labeled them *quasi-spot* and *mutual investment*, distinguished by level of engagement by the parties. Two unbalanced forms described were *over-* and *under-investment* on employees. Results showed that mutual investment and over-investment were related to positive outcomes both on attitudes and on behavior.

Differences in employment policies are of course commonly used in relation to different employment contracts and shape the content of an employer's promises, and thus the content of the psychological contract. The second study, by Kalleberg and Rognes (2000), showed five areas that could be used by employers if efforts were made to manage employment relations. Results indicated that transactional and relational features were used differently for limited contracts than for open-ended and long-term contracts. The features used were *communication of information* (temporary contracts were given narrow information and open-ended contracts received a much broader scope); *compensation* (performance related or not); *timeframe* (level of security); and *investments in training and skills development* and *flexibility* (static vs. dynamic). Kalleberg and Rognes concluded that there was a positive association between more relational, as opposed to transactional, contracts and positive attitudes and intention to stay with the company. Although these two studies were not typically describing psychological contracts, they provide good examples of the exchange relationship entailed in employment and about organizational strategies and their consequences. This is clearly an area in need of more research with both theoretical and practical value.

CONCLUDING REMARKS

Clearly there is enough evidence to say that the psychological contract is a useful theory for understanding the employment relationship, and how agreement or disagreement, very often based on unwritten promises, is perceived and affects attitudes, behavior, and well-being at work. Research has been almost overflowing in the last decades and has confirmed the relevance of this notion. Much is about keeping promises, not making promises you cannot keep, because the way the EOR is managed will have consequences for attitudes and behavior. Still, there are many unanswered questions for research concerning the parties involved, exchange, balance, and processes involved in maintaining and changing the EOR.

REFERENCES

Akhtar, M. N., Bal, M., & Long, L. (2016). Exit, voice, loyalty, and neglect reactions to frequency of change, and impact of change. *Employee Relations*, 38(4), 536–562.

Argyris, C. (1960). *Understanding organizational behavior*. Homewood, IL: Dorsey Press.

Bal, P. M., De Lange, A. H., Jansen, P. G. W., & Van Der Velde, M. E. G. (2008). Psychological contract breach and job attitudes: A meta-analysis of age as a moderator. *Journal of Vocational Behavior*, 72(1), 143–158.

Bankins, S. (2015). A process perspective on psychological contract change: Making sense of, and repairing, psychological contract breach and violation through employee coping actions. *Journal of Organizational Behavior*, 36(8), 1071–1095.

Conway, N., & Briner, R. (2002). A daily diary study of affective responses to psychological contract breach and exceeded promises. *Journal of Organizational Behavior*, 23(3), 287–302.

Conway, N., & Briner R. (2005). *Understanding psychological contracts at work: A critical evaluation of theory and research*. Oxford: Oxford University Press.

Conway, N., Guest, D., & Trenberth, L. (2011). Testing the differential effects of changes in psychological contract breach and fulfillment. *Journal of Vocational Behavior*, 79(1), 267–276.

Coyle-Shapiro, J., & Kessler, I. (2000). Consequences of the psychological contract for the employment relationship: A large scale survey. *Journal of Management Studies*, 37(7), 903–930.

Coyle-Shapiro, J., & Kessler, I. (2002). Exploring reciprocity through the lens of the psychological contract: Employee and employer perspectives. *European Journal of Work and Organizational Psychology*, 11(1), 69–86.

Coyle-Shapiro, J., Pereira Costa, S., Doden, W., & Chang, C. (2019). Psychological contracts: Past, present, and future. *Annual Review of Organizational Psychology and Organizational Behavior*, 6, 145–169.

De Vos, A., Buyens, D., & Schalk, R. (2003). Psychological contract development during organizational socialization: Adaptation to reality and the role of reciprocity. *Journal of Organizational Behavior*, 24(5), 537–559.

De Vos, A., & Freese, C. (2011). Sensemaking during organizational entry: Changes in newcomer information seeking and the relationship with psychological contract fulfillment. *Journal of Occupational and Organizational Psychology*, 84(2), 288–314.

Delobbe, N., Cooper-Thomas, H., & De Hoe, R. (2016). A new look at the psychological contract during organizational socialization: The role of newcomers' obligations at entry. *Journal of Organizational Behavior, 37*(6), 845–867.

Dulac, T., Coyle-Shapiro, J., Henderson, D., & Wayne, S. (2008). Not all responses to breach are the same: The interconnection of social exchange and psychological contract processes in organizations. *Academy of Management Journal, 51*(6), 1079–1098.

Farrell, D. (1983). Exit, voice, loyalty, and neglect as responses to job dissatisfaction: A multidimensional scaling study. *Academy of Management Journal, 26*(4), 596–607.

Freese, C., & Schalk, R. (2008). How to measure the psychological contract? A critical criteria-based review of measures. *South African Journal of Psychology, 38*(2), 269–286.

Gouldner, A. W. (1960). The norm of reciprocity: A preliminary statement. *American Sociological Review, 25*, 161–178.

Griep, Y., & Vantilborgh, T. (2018). Reciprocal effects of psychological contract breach on counterproductive and organizational citizenship behaviors: The role of time. *Journal of Vocational Behavior, 104*, 141–153.

Griep, Y., Vantilborgh, T., Baillien, E., & Pepermans, R. (2015). The mitigating role of leader-member exchange when perceiving psychological contract violation: A diary survey study among volunteers. *European Journal of Work and Organizational Psychology, 25*(2), 254–271.

Guest, D. E. (1998). Is the psychological contract worth taking seriously? *Journal of Organizational Behavior, 19*, 649–664.

Guest, D. E. (2004). The psychology of the employment relationship: An analysis based on the psychological contract. *Applied Psychology: An International Review, 53*(4), 541–555.

Guest, D. E., & Conway, N. (2002). Communicating the psychological contract: An employer perspective. *Human Resource Management Journal, 12*(2), 22–38.

Guest, D., Isaksson, K., & De Witte, H. (2010). *Employment contracts and psychological contracts among European workers.* Oxford: Oxford University Press.

Herriot, P. (2001). *The employment relationship: A psychological perspective.* London: Routledge.

Herriot, P., Manning, W. E. G., & Kidd, J. (1997). The content of the psychological contract. *British Journal of Management, 8*(2), 151–162.

Hirschman, A. (1970). *Exit, voice, and loyalty: Responses to decline in firms, organizations, and states.* Cambridge, MA: Harvard University Press.

Isaksson, K., De Cuyper, N., Bernhard Oettel, C., & De Witte, H. (2010). The role of the formal employment contract in the range and fulfilment of the psychological contract: Testing a layered model. *European Journal of Work and Organizational Psychology, 19*(6), 696–716.

Kalleberg, A. L., & Rognes, J. (2000). Employment relations in Norway: Some dimensions and correlates. *Journal of Organizational Behavior, 21*(3), 315–335.

Kochan, T., Riordan, C., Kowalski, A., Khan, M., & Yang, D. (2019). The changing nature of employee and labor-management relationships. *Annual Review of Organizational Psychology and Organizational Behavior, 6*, 195–219.

Kotter, J. P. (1973). The psychological contract: Managing the joining-up process. *California Management Review, 15*, 91–99.

Lambert, L. (2011). Promised and delivered inducements and contributions: An integrated view of psychological contract appraisal. *Journal of Applied Psychology, 96*(4), 695–712.

Lee, T. W., Burch, T., & Mitchell, T. (2014). The story of why we stay: A review of job embeddedness. *Annual Review of Organizational Psychology and Organizational Behavior, 1*, 199–216.

Lester, S., Turnley, W., Bloodgood, J., & Bolino, M. (2002). Not seeing eye to eye: Differences in supervisor and subordinate perceptions of and attributions for psychological contract breach. *Journal of Organizational Behavior, 23*(1), 39–56.

Low, C., Bordia, P., & Bordia, S. (2016). What do employees want and why? An exploration of employees' preferred psychological contract elements across career stages. *Human Relations, 69*(7), 1457–1481.

McLean Parks, J., Kidder, D., & Gallagher, D. (1998). Fitting square pegs into round holes: Mapping the domain of contingent work arrangements onto the psychological contract. *Journal of Organizational Behavior, 19,* 697–730.

Montes, S., & Zweig, D. (2009). Do promises matter? An exploration of the role of promises in psychological contract breach. *Journal of Applied Psychology, 94*(5), 1243–1264.

Morrison, E. W., & Robinson, S. (1997). When employees feel betrayed: A model of how psychological contract violation develops. *Academy of Management Review, 22*(1), 226–256.

Paauwe, J., Guest, D. E., & Wright, P. (2013). *HRM & performance: Achievements and challenges.* London: Wiley.

Robinson, S., & Rousseau, D. (1994). Violating the psychological contract: Not the exception but the norm. *Journal of Organizational Behavior, 15*(3), 245–259.

Rousseau, D. M. (1990). New hire perceptions of their own and their employer's obligations: A study of psychological contracts. *Journal of Organizational Behavior , 11*(5), 389–400.

Rousseau, D. M. (1995). *Psychological contracts in organizations: Understanding written and unwritten agreements.* Thousand Oaks, CA: SAGE.

Rousseau, D. M. (2001). Schema, promise and mutuality: The building blocks of the psychological contract. *Journal of Occupational and Organizational Psychology, 74,* 511–541.

Rousseau, D. M., Hansen, S., & Tomprou, M. (2018). A dynamic phase model of psychological contract processes. *Journal of Organizational Behavior, 39*(9), 1081–1098.

Rusbult, C., Farrell, D., Rogers, G., & Mainous, A. (1988). Impact of exchange variables on exit, voice, loyalty, and neglect: An integrative model of responses to declining job satisfaction. *Academy of Management Journal, 31*(3), 599–627.

Schalk, R., De Ruiter, M., Van Loon, J., Kuijpers, E., & Van Regenmortel, M. R. F. (2018). Actively coping with violation: Exploring upward dissent patterns in functional, dysfunctional and desert patterns of psychological contract end states. *Frontiers in Psychology, 9,* 54. https://dx.doi.org/10.3389/fpsyg.2018.00054

Schalk, R., & Roe, R. (2007). Towards a dynamic model of the psychological contract. *Journal for the Theory of Social Behavior, 37*(2), 167–182.

Schalk, R., & Rousseau, D. (2000). *Psychological contracts in employment: Cross-national perspectives.* Thousand Oaks, CA: SAGE.

Schein, E. H. (1980). *Organizational psychology.* Englewood Cliffs, NJ: Prentice-Hall.

Sels, L., Janssens, M., & Van den Brande, I. (2004). Assessing the nature of psychological contracts: A validation of six dimensions. *Journal of Organizational Behavior, 25*(4), 461–488.

Sherman, U., & Morley, M. (2019). What do we measure and how do we elicit it? The case for the use of repertory grid technique in multi-party psychological contract research. *European Journal of Work and Organizational Psychology.* Published online September, in press. https://dx.doi.org/%2010.1080/1359432X.2019.1668844

Solinger, O., Hofmans, J., Bal, P. M., & Jansen, P. (2016). Bouncing back from psychological contract breach: How commitment recovers over time. *Journal of Organizational Behavior, 37*(4), 494–514.

Sonnenberg, M., Koene, B., & Paauwe, J. (2011). Balancing HRM: The psychological contract of employees: A multi-level study. *Personnel Review, 40*(6), 664–682.

Tekleab, A. G., & Taylor, M. S. (2003). Aren't there two parties in an employment relationship? Antecedents and consequences of organization-employee agreement on contract obligations and violations. *Journal of Organizational Behavior, 24*(5), 585–608.

Thompson, J. A., & Bunderson, J. S. (2003). Violations of principle: Ideological currency in the psychological contract. *Academy of Management Review, 28*(4), 571–586.

Tomprou, M., & Nikolaou, I. (2010). A model of psychological contract creation upon organizational entry. *Career Development International, 16*(4), 342–363.

Tomprou, M., Rousseau, D., & Hansen, S. (2015). The psychological contracts of violation victims: A post-violation model. *Journal of Organizational Behavior, 36*(4), 561–581.

Tsui, A., Pearce, J., Porter, L., & Tripoli, A. (1997). Alternative approaches to the employee-organization relationship: Does investment in employees pay off? *Academy of Management Journal, 40*(5), 1089–1121.

Turnley, W., & Feldman, D. (1999). The impact of psychological contract violations on exit, voice, loyalty, and neglect. *Human Relations, 52*(7), 895–922.

Tversky, A., & Kahneman, D. (1992). Advances in prospect theory: Cumulative representation of uncertainty. *Journal of Risk and Uncertainty, 5*, 297–323.

Vantilborgh, T., Bidee, J., Pepermans, R., Willems, J., Huybrechts, G., & Jegers, M. (2014). Effects of ideological and relational psychological contract breach and fulfilment on volunteers' work effort. *European Journal of Work and Organizational Psychology, 23*(2), 217–230.

Welander, J., Astvik, W., & Isaksson, K. (2017). Corrosion of trust: Violation of psychological contracts as a reason for turnover amongst social workers. *Nordic Social Work Research, 7*(1), 67–79.

Woodrow, C., & Guest, D. (2017). Knowledge acquisition and effective socialization: The role of the psychological contract. *Journal of Occupational and Organizational Psychology, 90*(4), 587–595.

Zhao, H., Wayne, S., Glibkowski, B., & Bravo, J. (2007). The impact of psychological contract breach on work-related outcomes: A meta-analysis. *Personnel Psychology, 60*(3), 647–680.

Kerstin Isaksson

PERSONNEL SELECTION

INTRODUCTION

Personnel selection is one of the most critical processes in the study of human work behavior because it determines the efficacy of many other issues of human resource management (Guion, 1998; Salgado, Viswesvaran, & Ones, 2001). Personnel selection is used by organizations to decide which of the applicants for a job is the most appropriate for a particular position. In this sense, it is a decision-making process about the suitability of the candidates (Salgado & Moscoso, 2008).

As a scientific discipline, it began around 1900, when the principles and methods of psychology were applied to personnel decisions in Europe and the United States (Salgado, Anderson, & Hülsheger, 2010; Vinchur & Koppes Bryan, 2012). To this regard, as Vinchur and Koppes Bryan (2012) noted, the advances in the area are intimately tied to the advances in assessment and measurement procedures and in statistical developments.

This applied process requires carrying out several steps. First, an analysis of the job must be done in order to ascertain the specific characteristics of the position (e.g., tasks and duties). The second step involves identifying the specific individual requirements (e.g., cognitive abilities, job knowledge, skills, personality, experience, and other characteristics) needed for carrying out efficiently specified tasks and duties. This information is typically obtained through job analysis (García-Izquierdo, Díaz-Vilela, & Moscoso, 2015; Pearlman & Sanchez, 2010; Sanchez & Levine, 2012). Sometimes, these individual characteristics are called competencies (e.g., Schippman et al., 2000). The third step determines the degree to which candidates meet the individual requirements identified in step 2. In other words, candidates are evaluated using a variety of assessment procedures (e.g., cognitive test, job knowledge test, interview, assessment center, among others) to estimate their proficiency in requirements. Finally, the data collected can be used to predict future organizational behavior (e.g., job performance, training proficiency, turnover, promotions, career success, leadership potential, and many others). These organizational behaviors are typically named criteria. Therefore, personnel selection is a predictive process consisting of two kinds of variables: (a) predictors, that is, the assessment procedures; and (b) criteria, that is, the employee's behavior and the outcomes the organization seeks to obtain.

Nevertheless, we should not overlook that candidates also make decisions, that is, together with the organizational perspective, the candidate perspective must also be considered (e.g., the applicant perceptions and reactions), regarding the hiring process (Anderson, Born, & Cunningham-Snell, 2001; Anderson, Salgado, & Hülsheger, 2010).

This article reviews and summarizes the research literature on personnel selection and is organized into four main sections. The first section examines the different approaches to personnel selection. The second section reviews the most relevant assessment procedures according to their psychometric properties. Consequently, in the second section, the validity of cognitive ability tests, personality inventories, interviews, job knowledge tests, work sample tests, assessment centers, and other procedures are summarized. The third section reviews applicant perceptions and reactions. The fourth section presents the issue of combining data from different predictors (i.e., multiple prediction, incremental validity) to optimize efficacy. Finally, conclusions are provided.

PERFORMANCE MEASUREMENT AND APPROACHES TO PERSONNEL SELECTION

What is to be predicted? What behaviors and outcomes are relevant for organizations and candidates? Based on what we know currently about the procedures used in hiring decisions, these are probably the most crucial questions for an effective personnel selection process. These two questions underscore the issue of performance measurement on the one hand, and the perspectives on the selection process on the other.

For a century, it was believed that the aim of personnel selection was to predict overall job performance and that overall job performance was a single entity, whether assessed using a single global dimension or as a composite of multiple dimensions (Salgado, 2015; Schmidt, Hunter, & Ones, 1992). However, today we know that some assessment procedures can predict some performance-related behaviors and outcomes (e.g., task performance) very efficiently but they are poor predictors of other performance-related behaviors (e.g., contextual performance, counterproductive work behaviors, leadership potential, and so on). Thus, the first step in personnel selection is to determine the performance criteria for the future employees.

There is currently a large consensus among researchers that the job performance domain includes at least three main subdomains: task proficiency, contextual (citizenship) performance, and counterproductive performance. Task performance is defined as the proficiency with which employees perform core technical activities that are relevant for the job (Borman,

Bryant, & Dorio, 2010). Task performance can be subdivided into individual performance and work-team performance. Contextual performance (also called citizenship performance) relates to the contributions of the employee to the organizational, social, and psychological environment to help to accomplish organizational goals (Borman et al., 2001; Dorsey, Cortina, & Luchman, 2010; Hoffman & Dilchert, 2012). Empirical evidence has shown that there is some degree of interrelationship among the three subdomains (Conway, 1996). Contextual performance has been subdivided into two narrower dimensions: interpersonal performance and job dedication (Van Scotter & Motowidlo, 1996). Counterproductive performance has been defined as any intentional behavior of an employee viewed by the organization as contrary to its legitimate interests (Sackett & De Vore, 2001, p. 145). Two further subdimensions of counterproductive performance have been identified, that is, a subdimension related to interpersonal counterproductive behaviors, for example, abusive supervision, aggression, bullying; and a subdimension related to organizational counterproductive behaviors, for example, hurts, voluntary absenteeism, low effort (Hoffman & Dilchert, 2012; Rotundo & Spector, 2010). There is also meta-analytic evidence that, after controlling for halo error and reliability, there is a general factor in job performance rating (Viswesvaran, Schmidt, & Ones, 2005). This factor explained 60% of the total variance. With regard to the interrater reliability of job performance ratings, .52 is the average value found in independent meta-analytic studies for overall job performance (Salgado, in press; Salgado et al., 2003b; Salgado & Moscoso, 1996; Viswesvaran, Ones, & Schmidt, 1996). Figure 1 represents the performance domain and its dimensions and subdimensions.

In addition to criterion, a further issue to be appraised refers to the theoretical traditions related to personnel selection. Several authors have identified two main perspectives in personnel selection (Anderson, Lievens, van Dam, & Ryan, 2004; Anderson, Salgado, Schinkel,

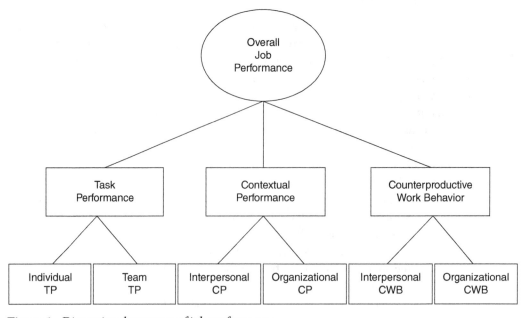

Figure 1. Dimensional structure of job performance.

& Cunningham-Snell, 2008; Schuler, 1993). The first perspective is the predictivist, which in essence aims to establish the *person-job fit*. According to this perspective, selection procedures are predictors of future job performance, and candidates are seen as "subjects" to selection procedures. The second perspective is constructivist, emphasizing that candidates, as well as organizations, make decisions in personnel selection. According to Anderson and his colleagues, the constructivist perspective sees selection as an opportunity for information exchange and to explore if a future working relationship would be viable. Therefore, from the constructivist perspective, personnel selection focuses not only on ensuring person-job fit but also *person-organization fit* and *team-organization fit*. In this context, person-organization fit is conceptualized as the adjustment between the candidate's values and the organizational values and culture, whereas team-organization fit is conceptualized as the adjustment between the candidate's competencies, attitudes, and abilities, and the immediate working environment of the group. The constructivist perspective is closely related to the Attraction-Selection-Attrition (ASA) paradigm (Schneider, 1987; Schneider, Goldstein, & Smith, 1995). According to the ASA paradigm, "the people make the place." This means that the attributes of employees (e.g., abilities and personality) are the most relevant factors of job performance and that candidates are differentially attracted to jobs. On their part, organizations try to select employees they see compatible with organizational culture and climate and that can be compatible for a number of different jobs. Over time, employees who do not fit in well are more likely to leave. The consequence of this process is a homogenization of employees' characteristics who work at the organization.

PERSONNEL SELECTION PROCEDURES

Regardless of which selection approach is used, that is, the predictivist or the constructivist perspective, the appropriateness of the hiring decision will depend upon the criterion-related validity of assessment procedures used for making decisions. As for recent estimates on the criterion-related validity of the procedures most commonly used in practice, the following sections will report the validity estimates provided for the most robust studies of validity generalization, based on the psychometric meta-analysis methods of Hunter and Schmidt (2004; Schmidt & Hunter, 2014). In all likelihood, psychometric meta-analysis has been the most significant methodological development in work and organizational psychology and in personnel selection for the last 40 years. Psychometric meta-analysis can be defined as a quantitative integration of multiple research results that correct measurement error, sampling error, and several other artifactual errors, providing the most robust estimate of the operational validity of selection procedures.

Several comprehensive reviews of the validity of personnel procedures have been published in the last 15 years (e.g., Salgado & Moscoso, 2008; Salgado, Viswesvaran, & Ones, 2001; Schmidt & Hunter, 1998). The current review will focus on the procedures most commonly used in practice, and on the most recent criterion-related validity evidence. Selection procedures can be classified by two types: procedures for assessing constructs and procedures that are assessment methods (Hunter & Hunter, 1984). The main difference between a construct and an assessment method resides in the fact that the latter consists in grouping several constructs or measures. In other words, an assessment method is an aggregate

1144 • PERSONNEL SELECTION

of other variables. More recently, assessment procedures have been classified in terms of reflective measures and formative measures (Edwards & Bagozzi, 2000). The first type of measures include the procedures for assessing constructs (e.g., cognitive test, job experience, and personality inventories), and the second type of measures are the assessment methods (e.g., interviews, situational judgment tests, and assessment centers). Using Hunter and Hunter's (1984) and Edwards and Bagozzi's (2000) classifications as the basis for subdividing the different procedures, the criterion-related validity of the personnel procedures is presented in two subsections.

Criterion-Related Validity of Reflective-Assessment (Constructs) Procedures.

The findings of the meta-analyses are summarized in Table 1, which shows the estimate of operative validity for the most common reflective procedures used in personnel selection for predicting overall job performance. It should be noted that the operative validity was estimated using the correlation between a predictor and a criterion after correction of artifactual errors. Typically, the observed correlation is corrected for measurement error in the criterion measure, and range restriction in the predictor.

General and Specific Cognitive Ability Tests.
General cognitive ability (GCA) can be defined as the capacity of a person to learn some material rapidly and accurately in optimal conditions of instruction. Therefore, less time taken and greater accuracy reflect greater GCA. There are several structural models of cognitive ability, most of them consisting of a general cognitive ability and several specific cognitive abilities (see Salgado, in press, for a comprehensive review). Among the specific cognitive abilities most frequently used in personnel selection we find abstract reasoning, spatial-mechanical reasoning, verbal reasoning, numerical reasoning, perceptual ability, and memory; but there are many other specific abilities. For example, the taxonomy of Fleishman and Reilly (1992) included inductive and deductive reasoning, verbal fluency, selective attention, and vigilance, among others.

Research on the criterion-related validity of cognitive ability measures in personnel selection is divided into two main approaches (see Salgado, in press; Schmitt, 2014, for exhaustive reviews). One approach contends that specific cognitive abilities do not add validity beyond the validity of GCA. In contrast, the other approach sustains that specific cognitive abilities can show incremental validity beyond GCA (e.g., Lang et al., 2010).

The meta-analytic findings across the globe obtained over the last 35 years have demonstrated that (1) CGA tests or a combination of several specific cognitive ability tests are the most valid predictor of overall job performance for all types of occupations (Hunter, Schmidt, & Le, 2006; Salgado et al., 2003a; Schmidt, Oh, & Le, 2006), and that .62 is the best estimate of operational validity; (2) The sizes of the estimates of criterion-related operational validity are similar across countries (Salgado, in press; Salgado & Anderson, 2003); (3) Job complexity is an important moderator of the validity of cognitive ability tests (Hunter & Hunter, 1984; Hunter et al., 2006; Salgado et al., 2003a; Schmidt et al., 2006); (4) Specific cognitive tests are also valid predictors of overall performance, but their validity is smaller than the GCA validity (Salgado et al., 2003b); (5) Cognitive tests are the most valid predictors of task performance, but they are less valid for predicting contextual performance, and they are not valid predictors of counterproductive work behavior (Gonzalez-Mule et al., 2014); (6) Cognitive

Table 1. Operational Validity Estimates of Reflective-Assessment Procedures

Criterion	Procedure	Validity
Overall Job Performance	General Cognitive Ability	.62
	Numerical Ability	.52
	Spatial Ability	.51
	Perceptual Ability	.52
	Verbal Ability	.38
	Memory	.56
	Conscientiousness	.39
	Emotional Stability	.20
	Extroversion	.12
	Openness	.22
	Agreeableness	.16
	Job Experience	.25
Task Performance	General Cognitive Ability	.62
	Conscientiousness	.25
	Emotional Stability	.08
	Extroversion	.09
	Openness	.12
	Agreeableness	.10
	Job Experience	.25
Contextual Performance	General Cognitive Ability	.24
	Conscientiousness	.32
	Emotional Stability	.16
	Extroversion	.22
	Openness	.03
	Agreeableness	.18
Overall Counterproductive Work Behavior	General Cognitive Ability	−.02
	Conscientiousness	−.34
	Emotional Stability	−.15
	Extroversion	−.14
	Openness	.02
	Agreeableness	−.33

tests show evidence of ethnic differences but they do not produce differential prediction (Berry et al., 2014).

Personality Inventories. The recent advances in the domain of personality at work have been largely due to the use of a construct-oriented approach in which the Five Factor Model (FFM) of personality has become the preferred model for Work and Organizational Psychology researchers (Hough & Ones, 2001). The seminal work by Barrick and Mount (1991), Hough (1992), and Tett et al. (1991) was crucial for demonstrating that personality dimensions were relevant predictors of overall job performance and, on the basis of this pioneering research, many studies were conducted in the following years. Furthermore, many surveys conducted around the world since the 1950s have shown that practitioners typically included personality measures in the personnel selection processes.

In the last 25 years, many hundreds of primary studies and dozens of meta-analyses have examined the validity of personality measures as predictors in personnel selection. The FFM proved to be a successful taxonomy for classifying the various measures included in validity studies, and we now have a better understanding of the validity of the Big Five.

Based on the best meta-analytical data available, the following conclusions can be drawn: (1) The taxonomy of the personality traits derived from the FFM has proved to be a very useful framework for organizing the various single measures and is now accepted as the paradigm in the field. The use of this taxonomy allowed personnel selection researchers to adequately respond to the concerns of Ghiselli (1966; Schmitt et al., 1984), Guion and Gottier (1965), and Schmitt et al. (1984) regarding the lack of a widely accepted personality model; (2) Conscientiousness is the best personality predictor of job performance and counterproductive behaviors, and it has shown validity generalization across samples, occupations, and countries. Operational validity of conscientiousness was found to be .39 when a quasi-ipsative forced-choice format was used (Salgado, Anderson, & Tauriz, 2015; Salgado & Tauriz, 2014); (3) Emotional stability was the second most relevant personality predictor of job performance and counterproductive work behaviors; (4) Conscientiousness, emotional stability, and agreeableness are the most valid predictors of overall counterproductive behaviors, interpersonally oriented counterproductive behaviors, and organizationally oriented counterproductive behaviors (Berry et al., 2007); (5) Conscientiousness, emotional stability, and agreeableness showed incremental validity over GCA for predicting overall job performance (Salgado & De Fruyt, 2006); (6) The format of the personality inventory is an important moderator of the criterion-related validity of the Big Five dimensions, so that the validity increases dramatically when quasi-ipsative forced-choice formats are used (Salgado, Anderson, & Tauriz, 2015; Salgado & Tauriz, 2014); and (7) The facets of the Big Five do not show evidence of criterion-related validity for predicting job performance when the validity of the factor is residualized (Salgado et al., 2015; Salgado, Moscoso, & Berges, 2013).

With regard to the criterion-oriented personality scales (COPS), meta-analyses have shown they were predictors of job performance and counterproductive behaviors. The most researched COPS were integrity tests. Technically, these are compounds (i.e., formative procedures), but they are included here as they include personality constructs only. The validity of personality-based integrity tests has been estimated at .37 for predicting job performance, and .42 for overall counterproductive behaviors (Ones, Viswesvaran, & Schmidt, 1993).

The nomological net of these measures suggests hypotheses for explaining why they predict job performance and counterproductivity. Integrity tests have been found to mainly consist of conscientiousness, emotional stability, and agreeableness (Ones et al., 1993; Ones & Viswesvaran, 2001). Thus, the joint effect of these three basic personality dimensions explains the large validity of this personality measure.

The conclusions of the cumulated research is that the Big Five personality dimensions are important variables for predicting and explaining overall job performance, task performance, contextual performance, and counterproductive work behaviors (see Judge et al., 2013; and Salgado, Moscoso, & Anderson, 2013, for a review), and that personality inventories measure variables that are not assessed by other selection methods, and hence provide unique and non-overlapping variance for explaining the criterion space. Consequently, practitioners in personnel selection can confidently use them for making personnel decisions.

Job Experience. In the practice of personnel selection, job experience is usually conceptualized as the number of years of experience on the same or similar job (McDaniel, Schmidt, & Hunter, 1988). Therefore, the length of service is used as a proxy of the experience on the job. Notwithstanding, this measure conveys no information on past performance of the job (Schmidt & Hunter, 1998).

Schmidt and Hunter (1998) indicated that the average operational validity of job experience was .25. In another meta-analysis, Schmidt, Hunter, and Outerbridge (1986) found a nonlinear relationship between job experience and job performance. Job performance increased linearly up to five years of job experience, and after that, the relationship became increasingly horizontal. When the amount of job experience was five years or less, the operational validity was .33 for predicting supervisory ratings of job performance (Schmidt et al., 1986).

Criterion-Related Validity of Formative-Assessment (Methods) Procedures.
The findings of the meta-analyses for the most common formative measures used in personnel selection are shown in Table 2, which includes the operational validity of three types of employment interviews, work sample test, job knowledge test, situational judgment test, assessment center, biodata, and reference checks.

Employment Interview. In numerous surveys across many countries, the interview showed to be the most extensively used procedure for personnel selection (Salgado et al., 2001). These surveys show that practically all candidates must get through at least one interview during the hiring process. For this reason, the employment interview can be considered the foremost standard formative-assessment procedure.

Since 1984, a number of meta-analyses have examined both criterion-oriented validity as well as construct validity evidence in the selection interview. Prior to 1984, several narrative reviews on the empirical data regarding the reliability and validity of the interview concluded that the employment interview was unreliable and that its validity was practically zero (see Moscoso, 2000). The first meta-analysis of the criterion-related validity of the interview (Hunter & Hunter, 1984) agreed with this conclusion and showed that validity was very small (operational validity of .14). This raised the paradox that the most commonly used procedure for predicting applicant's job performance was incapable of predicting it.

1148 • PERSONNEL SELECTION

Table 2. Operational Validity Estimates of Formative-Assessment Procedures

Criterion	Procedure	Validity
Overall Job Performance	Behavioral Structured Interview	.62
	Conventional Structured Interview	.37
	Unstructured Employment Interview	.20
	Work Sample Test	.33
	Job Knowledge Tests	.45
	Situational Judgment Test	.26
	Assessment Center	.37
	Biodata	.33
	Reference Check	.26

However, research conducted during the last 25 years has shown that the selection interview was not a single and unitary method. Employment interviews have been classified using a twofold scheme of the structure and content of the questions (Salgado & Moscoso, 2002). These authors found three main types of interviews: unstructured interviews, conventional structured interviews, and behavioral structured interviews (other classifications were suggested by Huffcut, Roth, & McDaniel, 1996; and McDaniel et al., 1994). Unstructured interviews have no fixed format regarding the content of the questions and the assessment of the answers. Conventional structured interviews ask the same questions to the candidates and can rate the answers using the same form. The majority of the questions of unstructured and conventional interviews focus on attitudes and opinions (Janz, Hellervik, & Gilmore, 1986). The behavioral structured interview is a category of interview that poses the following characteristics (Salgado & Moscoso, 2006): (a) The questions are based on a job analysis, using typically the critical incident technique; (b) The job analysis also serves to identify the main job dimensions that should be assessed with the interview; (c) The same questions are asked to all the candidates; (d) The same procedure is used for all candidates; (e) In many cases, the candidate answers are assessed using behavioral anchoring rating scales (BARS); (f) The interviewer is previously trained in this technique; (g) The decision is made only when all the candidates have been interviewed.

A meta-analysis of the nomological network of structured interviews found that conventional structured interviews appeared to be mainly measuring general cognitive ability and personality variables, that is, they focus on the intrinsic variables of the applicants (Salgado & Moscoso, 2002). With regard to behavioral structured interviews, these authors found that this type of interview mainly assessed job knowledge and job experience. Consequently, this interview type seems to be concentrated on finding out whether the applicant would perform well in the job.

Several meta-analyses have reported the criterion-related validity of employment interviews (e.g., Huffcut & Arthur, 1994; McDaniel et al., 1994; Salgado, Gorriti, & Moscoso, 2007; Wiesner

& Cronshaw, 1988). A meta-analysis of behavioral structured interviews found an operational validity of .62 (Salgado & Moscoso, 2006). In comparison, conventional structured interviews showed an operational validity of .35, and the operational validity of the unstructured interviews was .20 (Huffcut, Roth, & McDaniel, 1996).

Work Sample Tests. Work sample tests can be defined as hands-on simulations of part or all of the job content (Schmidt & Hunter, 1998). Work samples have been used extensively for selecting skilled workers, but they have the limitation that they can only be used with candidates who already know the job. In other words, candidates do not need to be trained as they have experience on the job.

The largest meta-analysis ever carried out on the criterion-related validity of work sample tests for predicting job performance found operational validity was .33 (Roth, Bobko, & McFarland, 2005). Roth and colleagues (2005) also examined the correlation between general cognitive ability and work sample tests and found a correlation of .38, which agrees with the correlation reported in a previous meta-analysis by Schmidt, Hunter, and Outerbridge (1986).

Job Knowledge Test and Situational Judgment Test. As the term indicates, job knowledge tests are procedures for examining the extent to which the candidate possesses the knowledge required for a particular job. This category of tests can include at least two types of procedures: job knowledge tests and situational judgment tests. Like the work sample tests, job knowledge tests can be used only for experienced candidates (Schmidt & Hunter, 1998).

With regard to the operational validity of job knowledge tests, Hunter and Hunter (1984) reported a coefficient of .48 for predicting overall job performance. For situational judgment tests, McDaniel and colleagues (2001) reported an initial estimate of .34 for predicting job performance; and, more recently, in a second and more comprehensive meta-analysis McDaniel and his colleagues (2007) reported an operational validity of .26.

With regard to the correlation between job knowledge tests and GCA, Schmidt, Hunter, and Outerbridge (1986) found a correlation of .48. In the case of the situational judgment test, McDaniel et al. (2007) reported a correlation of .32 with GCA.

Assessment Centers. The assessment center method is a kind of job simulation that consists of a set of different exercises aimed at assessing several job dimensions (e.g., problem solving, interpersonal behavior, influence and persuasion, and so on). Another important characteristic of the assessment center method is that different raters assess the candidates. The assessment center can also include some traditional procedures such as cognitive ability tests, personality inventories, and interviews, together with less traditional procedures such as role-playing exercises, group discussion exercises, and in-basket tests. This last procedure is probably the most frequent exercise of an assessment center. It consists in presenting applicants with a set of memos, letters, telephone messages, and so on, similar to those they would have to deal with in the actual job. The individuals are asked to organize all this information, as they would be in the real job situation.

Several meta-analyses have been conducted to find the operational validity of overall assessment ratings as well the operational validity of the ratings of the dimensions. The seminal meta-analysis conducted by Gaugler et al. (1987) found an operational validity of .36 for predicting job performance when an overall assessment rating (OAR) was used. Twenty years later, Hermelin, Lievens, and Robertson (2007) found an operational validity of .28. Recently, the operational validity of most of the standard exercises of assessment centers, including oral presentations, in-basket tests, case analysis, leaderless group discussions, and role play was found to range from .18 to .26 (Hoffman et al., 2015). Based on these operational validities and in the intercorrelations among the exercises, the best estimate of the operational validity of the OAR seems to be the score reported by Gaugler et al. (1987).

Biodata. The biodata form consists of biographical data questions about the job and life experiences of each candidate. These questions have been chosen because of their correlation with job performance. Therefore, biodata are criterion-oriented procedures that are empirically derived. In this sense, the construction of a biodata form is similar, for instance, to the method used for the development of the main scales of the Minnesota Multiphasic Personality Inventory (MMPI) (e.g., hysteria; psychopathy). Biodata forms can include questions such as early experiences in the candidate's first job, in high school, in college, in hobbies, and other pursuits; but due to antidiscrimination legislation, they exclude questions about race, age, marital status, and other forbidden issues in many countries (Schmidt & Hunter, 1998).

A meta-analysis carried out by Rothstein and her colleagues (1990) showed an operational validity of .35 for predicting overall job performance and that the correlation with GCA is moderately large, around .50. This last correlation suggests that biodata indirectly reflect GCA, similarly as conventional structured interviews do.

Reference Check. This assessment method is used at the end of the selection process. Typically, it involves collecting information on a candidate from previous employers. The literature reviews suggest that reference checks are used similarly for high and low complexity jobs, and that there are no significant differences related to the size of the company (Chamorro-Premuzic & Furnham, 2010; Lado, 2012). In the practice of personnel selection, both reference check content and structure show a remarkable variety (Chamorro-Premuzic & Furnham, 2010).

With regard to the operational validity of reference checks, Hunter and Hunter (1984) found a coefficient of .26 for predicting overall job performance. Recently, the meta-analysis of Lado (2012) found reference checks correlated .25 with general cognitive ability and .17 with job experience.

APPLICANT PERCEPTIONS AND REACTIONS TO SELECTION PROCEDURES

Research conducted since 1990 suggests that candidates have preferences regarding the procedures used for making personnel decisions, and that such preferences can have important consequences for organizational practices of personnel selection (Viswesvaran & Ones, 2004). This research stems from two parallel lines. A first research line is based on the selection fairness model of Gilliland (1993; Steiner & Gilliland, 1996). This model distinguishes between procedural justice and distributive justice. Procedural justice refers to the fairness of the personnel selection processes. Distributive justice refers to the fairness of the selection decisions.

Related to Gilliland's fairness selection model is Schuler's (1993) social validity perspective that consists of four different aspects related to applicant perceptions of the selection process. These aspects are (a) Informativeness, defined as the degree of information provided to the applicant and perceived as useful; (b) Participation, that is, the degree to which applicants perceive they have a chance to participate and present themselves properly; (c) Transparency, that is, the extent to which the procedures used are transparent; and (d) Feedback, defined as the availability and extent of feedback provided by the organization to the applicants, independently of their success in the selection process.

A meta-analysis carried out by Anderson, Salgado, and Hülsheger (2010) examined applicant perceptions and reactions using studies conducted in 17 countries spread worldwide through Europe, North America, Asia, and Africa. With small exceptions, interviews, work sample tests, and resumes were the procedures perceived most favorably. Cognitive tests, personality inventories, and references were also perceived quite favorably. Finally, personal contacts and graphology were perceived unfavorably. Anderson and colleagues (2010) also examined the relation between applicant reactions and the operational validity of the selection procedures. They found large correlations (over .60) between the operational validity of the procedures and the perceptions of favorability, scientific evidence, face validity, and opportunity to perform.

MULTIPLE PREDICTION OF JOB PERFORMANCE BASED ON THE MOST VALID PROCEDURES

Based on the validity of the different selection procedures and their interrelationships, the largest correlation can be estimated by combining a set of instruments. In the present case, the validity of selection processes consisting of two or three procedures for predicting several performance criteria was estimated, including overall, one task, and contextual performance, and overall interpersonal and organizational counterproductive work behaviors.

In the case of overall job performance and task performance, as general cognitive ability was the reflective predictor with the largest validity, it was the variable combined with a second predictor or with two additional predictors. In the case of contextual performance and counterproductive work behaviors, conscientiousness was the initial predictor to be supplemented with a second or a third predictor. The results of the two-variable prediction appear in Table 3, while those corresponding to the combinations of three predictors can be seen in Table 4.

With reference to overall job performance and task performance criteria, the best combination of two predictors was achieved using a GCA test supplemented with a behavioral structured interview (R=.77). The next best combination was a GCA test supplemented with a measure of the personality factor of conscientiousness (R=.74) or integrity test (R=.74). The third best option was the combination of GCA with a measure of job experience (R=.67). From here on, the contribution of the potential supplement predictors was relatively scant. For example, if a test of a specific cognitive ability (e.g., numerical reasoning) supplemented the GCA test, the second test increased GCA validity only slightly by .02. In the case of task performance, the results were similar.

1152 • PERSONNEL SELECTION

Table 3. Best Combinations of Two Procedures for Predicting Several Occupational Criteria

Criterion	Predictor Combination	R	R Square
Overall—Job Performance	GCA + BSI	.77	.60
Task—Performance	GCA + C	.68	.46
Contextual Performance	C + GCA	.41	.17
Overall—Counterproductive Work Behavior	C + ES	.52	.27
Interpersonal—Counterproductive Work Behavior	A + ES	.50	.25
Organizational—Counterproductive Work Behavior	C + A	.39	.16

Notes: GCA = general cognitive ability; BSI = behavioral structured interview; C = conscientiousness; EX = extroversion; A = agreeableness; ES = emotional stability.

Table 4. Best Combinations of Three Procedures for Predicting Several Occupational Criteria

Criterion	Predictor Combination	R	R Square
Overall—Job Performance	GCA + BSI + C	.84	.71
Contextual Performance	C + GCA + EX	.47	.22
Overall—Counterproductive Work Behavior	C + A + ES	.45	.20
Interpersonal—Counterproductive Work Behavior	A + ES + C	.52	.27
Organizational—Counterproductive Work Behavior	C + A + ES	.40	.16

Notes: GCA = general cognitive ability; BSI = behavioral structured interview; C = conscientiousness; EX = extroversion; A = agreeableness; ES = emotional stability.

For predicting contextual performance, the best combination of two predictors was a conscientiousness measure supplemented with a GCA test (R=.41). For the criterion of overall counterproductive work behaviors (OV-CWB), the best option was combining a measure of conscientiousness with a measure of emotional stability (R=.52). For interpersonal counterproductive behavior (I-CWB), the best combination was a measure of agreeableness supplemented with a measure of emotional stability (R=.50). Finally, for the criterion of organizational counterproductive work behavior (O-CWB), the best combination was conscientiousness supplemented by agreeableness (R=.39).

As shown in Table 4, there were two optimum combinations offering similar results when a combination of three procedures was used for predicting overall job performance. The best combination consists of a GCA test supplemented with a behavioral structured interview plus a conscientiousness inventory (R=.84). The second best combination was a GCA test supplemented with a behavioral interview and a job knowledge test. These two combinations had very good predictive outcomes. The choice of using one of the combinations or the other could be based on non-psychometric criteria, for instance, the costs of the instruments, the number of candidates, time available, and so on.

With regard to contextual performance, the best combination of three predictors was combining a conscientiousness measure supplemented by a GCA test, and an extroversion measure (R=.47). For innovative performance, the best combination was using a job knowledge test, plus a measure of openness, and a measure of emotional stability. For the criterion of overall CWB, the best predictive option was a personality-based compound of conscientiousness, agreeableness, and emotional stability (R=.45). For predicting interpersonal CWB, the optimum combination of three predictors was agreeableness, emotional stability, and conscientiousness (R=.52). Finally, for the criterion of organizational CWB, the best combination was conscientiousness, plus agreeableness, and emotional stability (R=.40).

ETHNIC GROUP DIFFERENCES AND BIASED PREDICTION

A relevant issue regarding the use of personnel selection procedures is whether they produce ethnic group differences and whether these differences can produce biased predictions. This issue is especially relevant in regards to cognitive tests and personality measures but also it is important for all personnel selection procedures. Schmitt (2014) concluded his review of this issue pointing out that the usual conclusion for at least the last two decades was that that the tests did not produce biased predictions for women and members of minority groups. The statistic Cohen's d is the effect size index used to establish whether there are subgroup differences. This effect size is computed by subtracting the minority group mean (e.g., Asian, African American, and Hispanics) from the majority group mean (typically, White) and dividing the difference by the pooled within-group standard deviation of the scores (Schmidt & Hunter, 2014).

In the last 20 years, it has been well documented that cognitive tests showed ethnic subgroup differences. This effect was found particularly in the United States (Berry et al., 2014; Berry & Zhao, 2014; Hough, Oswald, & Ployhart, 2001; Schmitt, Clause, & Pulakos, 1996; but it was also found in other countries such as The Netherlands (De Meijer et al., 2006; teNijenhuis & van der Flier, 1997), South Africa (Kriek & Dowdeswell, 2009), Sweden (Kvist & Gustafsson, 2008), and New Zealand (Guenole, Englert, & Taylor, 2003). In their review of this topic, Bobko and Roth (2013) updated the main findings on the Black-White subgroup differences. According to Bobko and Roth (2013), general cognitive ability tests show $d =.72$ for moderate complexity jobs and $d= .86$ for low complexity jobs. In the case of work sample tests, Bobko and Roth suggested an average $d = .73$. For situational judgment tests, these researchers suggested a weighted average $d = .38$. For biodata, the average d is .39 and for assessment centers, d is .56. Personality measures presented the lowest d values, with .04 for integrity tests and -.09 for conscientiousness. Finally, Bobko and Roth suggested that the Black-White differences range from .31 to .46 for structured interviews.

In the context of the ethnic group differences and biased prediction, it is important to distinguish between differential validity and differential prediction. On one hand, differential validity focuses on subgroup differences in the correlation between a selection procedure and an organizational outcome (e.g., job performance, productivity, salaries, satisfaction, and so on) as evidence of subgroup differences in procedure-outcome relationships. On the other hand, differential prediction focuses on subgroup differences in procedure-criterion unstandardized regression equations as evidence regarding to subgroup differences in procedure-criterion relationships. Recently, several articles reviewed the issue of differential validity and differential prediction (Berry et al., 2014; Berry & Zhao, 2014; Mattern & Patterson, 2013). After controlling for range restriction, Berry et al. (2014) found evidence of a small degree of differential validity in a cognitive test battery. More specifically, Berry et al. (2014) found that the average validity was smaller for Hispanics and African Americans than for Whites and Asians. With regard to differential prediction, empirical research carried out by Berry and Zhao (2014) and Mattern and Patterson (2013) agreed that cognitive ability tests overpredicted African American job performance. In other words, these researchers concluded that cognitive ability tests scores are not predictively biased against African American candidates in the employment setting, which is consistent with the conclusions of Schmitt (2014) mentioned above.

GENERAL CONCLUSION

In recent years, substantial progress in research and practice on personnel selection has been made around the world and many of the limitations that previously affected the field have been overcome. Currently, practitioners involved in personnel selection have a large number of valid assessment procedures and have access to a great deal of research that enables them to use the most appropriate set of instruments for their specific needs. Thus, the job of the practitioners has been strongly endorsed and their role in organizations is increasingly acknowledged and valued.

This article summarizes the operational validity of the 19 most common selection procedures used in current practice. The operational validity of each procedure was determined and the best combinations of pairs or triads of procedures were established. The best combinations were derived on the basis of the respective operational multiple correlation for predicting job performance criteria. Current state-of-the-art in personnel selection is capable of predicting these criteria and explaining over 60% of job performance variance based on individual differences. Future rises in the explained variance will be probably based on the development of new assessment technologies and on the development of new theoretical approaches for occupational situations.

FURTHER READING

Anderson, N., Ones, D. S., Sinangil, H. K., & Viswesvaran, C. (Eds.). (2001). *Handbook of industrial, work, and organizational psychology.* London: SAGE.

Evers, A., Anderson, N., & Voskuijl, O. (Eds.). (2005). *Handbook of personnel selection.* Oxford: Blackwell.

Farr, J. L., & Tippins, N. (Eds.). (2010). *Handbook of employee selection.* New York: Routledge.

Le, H., & Schmidt, F. L. (2006). Correcting for indirect range restriction in meta-analysis: Testing a new analytic procedure. *Psychological Methods, 11*(4), 416–438.

Morgeson, F. P., Campion, M. A., Dipboye, R. L., Hollenbeck, J. R., Murphy, K., & Schmitt, N. (2007). Reconsidering the use of personality tests in personnel contexts. *Personnel Psychology, 60*(3), 683–729.

Outz, J. L. (Ed.). (2010). *Adverse impact. Implications for organizational staffing and high stakes selection*. New York: Routledge.

Salgado, J. F. (2003). Predicting job performance using FFM and non-FFM personality measures. *Journal of Occupational and Organizational Psychology, 76*(3), 323–346.

Schmitt, N. (Ed.). (2012). *The Oxford handbook of personnel assessment and selection*. Oxford: Oxford University Press.

Society for Industrial and Organizational Psychology. (2003). *Principles for validation and use of the personnel selection procedures*. Bowling Green, OH: Author.

Tett, R. P., & Christiansen, N. D. (Eds.). (2013). *Handbook of personality at work*. New York: Routledge.

REFERENCES

Anderson, N., Born, M., & Cunningham-Snell, N. (2001). Recruitment and selection: Applicant perspectives and outcomes. In N. Anderson, D. S. Ones, H. K. Sinangil, & C. Viswesvaran (Eds.), *Handbook of industrial, work, and organizational psychology* (vol. 1, pp. 200–218). London: SAGE.

Anderson, N., Lievens, F., van Dam, K., & Ryan, A. M. (2004). Future perspectives on employee selection: Key directions for future research and practice. *Applied Psychology: An International Review, 53*(4), 487–501.

Anderson, N., Salgado, J. F., & Hülsheger, U. R. (2010). Applicant reactions in selection: Comprehensive meta-analysis into reaction generalization versus situational specificity. *International Journal of Selection and Assessment, 18*(3), 291–304.

Anderson, N., Salgado, J. F., Schinkel, S., & Cunningham-Snell, N. (2008). Staffing the organization: An introduction to personnel selection and assessment. In N. Chmiel (Ed.), *Introduction to work and organizational psychology* (pp. 257–280). Oxford: Blackwell.

Barrick, M. R., & Mount, M. K. (1991). The Big Five personality dimensions and job performance: A meta-analysis. *Personnel Psychology, 44*(1), 1–26.

Barrick, M. R., Mount, M. K., & Judge, T. (2001). Personality and performance at the beginning of the new millennium: What do we know and where do we go next? *International Journal of Selection and Assessment, 9*(1–2), 9–30.

Berry, C. M., Clark, M. A., & McClure, T. K. (2011). Racial/ethnic differences in the criterion-related validity of cognitive ability tests: A qualitative and quantitative review. *Journal of Applied Psychology, 96*(5), 881–906.

Berry, C. M., Cullen, M. J., & Meyer, J.M. (2014). Racial/ethnic subgroup differences in cognitive ability rest range restriction: Implications for differential validity. *Journal of Applied Psychology, 99*(1), 21–37.

Berry, C. M., Ones, D. S., & Sackett, P. R. (2007). Interpersonal deviance, organizational deviance, and their common correlates: A review and meta-analysis. *Journal of Applied Psychology, 92*(2), 361–364.

Berry, C. M., & Zhao, P. (2014). Addressing criticism of existing predictive bias research: Cognitive ability test scores still overpredict African Americans' job performance. *Journal of Applied Psychology, 96*(5), 881–906.

Bobko, P., & Roth, P. L. (2013). Reviewing, categorizing, and analyzing the literature on black–white mean differences for predictors of job performance: Verifying some perceptions and updating/correcting others. *Personnel Psychology, 66*(1), 91–126.

Borman, W. C., Bryant, R. H., & Dorio, J. (2010). The measurement of task performance as criteria in selection research. In J. L. Farr & N. Tippins (Eds.), *Handbook of employee selection* (pp. 439–462). New York: Routledge.

Borman, W. C., & Motowidlo, S. J. (1997). Task performance and contextual performance. *Human Performance, 10*(2), 99–109.

Borman, W. C., Penner, L. A., Allent, T. D., & Motowidlo, S. (2001). Personality predictors of citizenship performance. *International Journal of Selection and Assessment, 9*(1–2), 52–69.

Campbell, J. P., Gasser, M. B., & Oswald, F. L. (1996). The substantive nature of job performance variability. In K. R. Murphy (Ed.), *Individual differences and behavior in organizations*. San Francisco: Jossey-Bass.

Chamorro-Premuzic, T., & Furnham, A. (2010). *The psychology of personnel selection*. Cambridge, U.K.: Cambridge University Press.

Conway, J. (1996). Analysis and design of multitrait-multirater performance appraisal studies. *Journal of Management, 22*(1), 139–162.

De Meijer, L. A. L., Born, M. P., Terlouw, G., & van der Molen, H. T. (2006). Applicant and method factors related to ethnic score differences in personnel selection: A study at the Dutch police. *Human Performance, 19*, 219–251.

Dorsey, D. W., Cortina, J. M., & Luchman, J. (2010). Adaptive and citizenship-related behaviors at work. In J. L. Farr & N. Tippins (Eds.), *Handbook of employee selection* (pp. 463–487). New York: Routledge.

Edwards, J. R., & Bagozzi, R. P. (2000). On the nature and direction of relationships between constructs and measures. *Psychological Methods, 5*(2), 155–174.

Fleishman, E. A., & Reilly, M. E. (1992). *Handbook of human abilities: Definitions, measurements, and job and task requirements*. Palo Alto, CA: Consulting Psychologists Press.

García-Izquierdo, A. L., Díaz-Vilela, L., & Moscoso, S. (2015). Work analysis for personnel selection. In I. Nikolaou & J. K. Oostrom (Eds.), *Employee recruitment, selection, and assessment*. East Sussex, U.K.: Psychology Press.

Gaugler, B. B., Rosenthal, D. B., Thorton, G. C., & Bentson, C. (1987). Meta-analysis of assessment center validity. *Journal of Applied Psychology, 72*(3), 493–511.

Ghiselli, E. E. (1966). *The validity of occupational aptitude tests*. New York: Wiley.

Gilliland, S. W. (1993). The perceived fairness of selection systems: An organizational justice perspective. *Academy of Management Review, 18*(4), 694–734.

Gonzalez-Mule, E., Mount, M. K., & Oh, I-S. (2014). A meta-analysis of the relationship between general mental ability and nontask performance. *Journal of Applied Psychology, 99*(6), 1222–1243.

Guenole, N., Englert, P., & Taylor, P. J. (2003). Ethnic group differences in cognitive ability test scores within a New Zealand applicant sample. *New Zealand Journal of Psychology, 32*(1), 49–54.

Guion, R. M. (1998). *Assessment, measurement, and prediction for personnel decisions*. Mahwah, NJ: Erlbaum.

Guion, R. M., & Gottier, R. F. (1965). Validity of personality measures in personnel selection. *Personnel Psychology, 18*(1), 135–164.

Hermelin, E., Lievens, F., & Robertson, I. T. (2007). The validity of assessment centres for the prediction of supervisory performance ratings: A meta-analysis. *International Journal of Selection and Assessment, 15*(4), 405–411.

Hoffman, B. J., & Dilchert, S. (2012). A review of citizenship and counterproductive behaviors. In N. Schmitt (Ed.), *Personnel assessment and selection*. (pp 543–569). New York: Oxford University Press.

Hoffman, B. J., Kennedy, C. L., Lance, C. E., LoPilato, A. C., & Monahan, E. (2015). A review of the content, criterion-related, and construct-related validity of assessment center exercises. *Journal of Applied Psychology, 100*(4), 1143–1168.

Hough, L. M. (1992). The "Big Five" personality variables-construct confusion: Description versus prediction. *Human Performance, 5*(1–2), 139–155.

Hough, L.M., & Ones, D.S. (2001). The structure, measurement, validity, and use of personality variables in industrial, work and organizational psychology. In N. Anderson, D. S. Ones, H. K. Sinangil, & C. Viswesvaran (Eds.), *Handbook of industrial, work, and organizational psychology. Vol. 1: Personnel psychology* (pp. 233–277). London: SAGE.

Hough, L. M., Oswald, F. L., & Ployhart, R. E. (2001). Determinants, detection, and amelioration of adverse impact in personnel selection procedures: Issues, evidence, and lesson learned. *International Journal of Selection and Assessment, 9*(1–2), 152–194.

Huffcut, A. I., & Arthur, W. Jr. (1994). Hunter, and Hunter (1984) revisited: Interview validity for entry-level jobs. *Journal of Applied Psychology, 79*(2), 184–190.

Huffcut, A. I., Roth, P. L., & McDaniel, M. (1996). A meta-analytic investigation of cognitive ability in employment interview evaluations: Moderating characteristics and implications for incremental validity. *Journal of Applied Psychology, 81*(5), 459–473.

Hunter, J. E., & Hunter, R. F. (1984). Validity and utility of alternative predictors of job performance. *Psychological Bulletin, 96*(1), 72–98.

Hunter, J. E., & Schmidt, F. L. (2004). *Methods of meta-analysis: Correcting error and bias in research findings* (2d ed.). Newbury Park, CA: SAGE.

Hunter, J. E., Schmidt, F. L., & Le, H. (2006). Implications of direct and indirect range restriction for meta-analysis methods and findings. *Journal of Applied Psychology, 91*(3), 594–612.

Hurtz, G. M., & Donovan, J. J. (2000). Personality and job performance: The Big Five revisited. *Journal of Applied Psychology, 85*(6), 869–879.

Janz, T., Hellervik, L., & Gilmore, D. C. (1986). *Behavior description interviewing: New, accurate, cost effective.* Newton, MA: Allyn and Bacon.

Judge, T. A., Rodell, J. B., Klinger, E. R., Simon, L. S., & Crawford, E. R. (2013). Hierarchical representations of the five-factor model of personality in predicting job performance: Integrating three organizing frameworks with two theoretical perspectives. *Journal of Applied Psychology, 98*(6), 875–925.

Kreik, H., & Dowdeswell, K. (2009). *Adverse impact and validity evidence in South Africa: 12 years of data trends.* Unpublished manuscript, SHL South Africa.

Kvist, V., & Gustafsson, J. E. (2008). The relation between fluid intelligence and the general as a function of cultural background: A test of Cattell's Investment theory. *Intelligence, 36*(4), 422–436.

Lado, M. (2012). Reference cheks, general mental ability, and experience: A study of construct validity. *Revista de Psicología del Trabajo y de las Organizaciones, 28*(2), 119–131.

Lang, J. W. B., Kersting, M., Hülsheger, U. R., & Lang, J. (2010). General mental ability, narrower cognitive abilities, and job performance: The perspective of the nested-factors model of cognitive abilities. *Personnel Psychology, 63*(3), 595–640.

Mattern, K. D., & Patterson, B. F. (2013). Test of slope and intercept bias in college admissions: A response to Aguinis, Culpepper, and Pierce (2010). *Journal of Applied Psychology, 98*(1), 134–147.

McDaniel, M. A., Hartman, N. S., Whetzel, D. L., & Grubb, W. (2007). Situational judgment tests, response instructions, and validity: A meta-analysis. *Personnel Psychology, 60*(1), 63–91.

McDaniel, M. A., Morgeson, F. P., Finnegan, E. B., Campion, M. A., & Braverman, E. P. (2001). Use of situational judgment tests to predict job performance: A clarification of the literature. *Journal of Applied Psychology, 86*(4), 730–740.

McDaniel, M. A., Schmidt, F. L., & Hunter, J. E. (1988). A meta-analysis of the validity of methods for rating training and experience in personnel selection. *Personnel Psychology, 41*(2), 283–309.

McDaniel, M. A., Whetzel, D. L., Schmidt, F. L., & Maurer, S. (1994). The validity of employment interviews: A comprehensive review and meta-analysis. *Journal of Applied Psychology, 79*(4), 599–616.

Moscoso, S. (2000). Selection interview: A review of validity evidence, adverse impact and applicant reactions. *International Journal of Selection and Assessment, 8*(4), 356–363.

Ones, D. S., & Viswesvaran, C. (2001). Integrity test and other criterion-focused occupational personality scales (COPS) used in personnel selection. *International Journal of Selection and Assessment, 9*(1–2), 31–39.

Ones, D. S., Viswesvaran, C., & Schmidt, F. L. (1993). Comprehensive meta-analysis of integrity tests. *Journal of Applied Psychology, 78*(4), 679–703.

Pearlman, K., & Sanchez, J. I. (2010). Work analysis. In J. L. Farr & N. Tippins (Eds.), *Handbook of employee selection* (pp. 73–98). New York: Routledge.

Roth, P. L., Bobko, P., & McFarland, L. A. (2005). A meta-analysis of work sample test validity: Updating and integrating some classical literature. *Personnel Psychology*, 58(4), 1009–1037.

Rothstein, H. R., Schmidt, F. L., Erwin, F. W., Owens, W. A., & Sparks, C. P. (1990). Biographical data in employment selection: Can validities be made generalizable? *Journal of Applied Psychology*, 75(2), 175–184.

Rotundo, M., & Spector, P. E. (2010). Counterproductive work behavior and withdrawal. In J. L. Farr & N. Tippins (Eds.), *Handbook of employee selection* (pp. 489–511). New York: Routledge.

Sackett, P. R., & DeVore, C. J. (2001). Counterproductive behaviors at work. In N. Anderson, D. S. Ones, H. K. Sinangil, & C. Viswesvaran (Eds.), *Handbook of industrial, work and organizational psychology: Vol 1.* (pp. 145–164) London: Sage.

Salgado, J. F. (2002). The Big Five personality dimensions and counterproductive behaviors. *International Journal of selection and Assessment*, 10(1–2), 117–125.

Salgado, J. F. (2003). Predicting job performance using FFM and non-FFM personality measures. *Journal of Occupational and Organizational Psychology*, 76(3), 323–346.

Salgado J. F. (2015). Estimating coefficients of equivalence and stability for job performance ratings: The importance of controlling for transient error on criterion measurement. *International Journal of Selection and Assessment*, 23(1), 37–44.

Salgado, J. F. (in press). Using ability tests in selection. In H. Goldstein, E. Pulakos, J. Passmore, & C. Semedo (Eds.), *Handbook of the psychology of recruitment, selection, and retention*. New York: Wiley/Blackwell.

Salgado, J. F., & Anderson, N. (2003). Validity generalization of GMA tests across countries in the European community. *European Journal of Work and Organizational Psychology*, 12(1), 1–17.

Salgado, J. F., Anderson, N., & Hülsheger, U. R. (2010). Psychotechnics and the forgotten history of modern scientific employee selection. In J. L. Farr & N. Tippins (Eds.), *Handbook of employee selection* (pp. 921–942). New York: Routledge.

Salgado, J. F., Anderson, N., Moscoso, S., Bertua, C., & De Fruyt, F. (2003a). International validity generalization of GMA and cognitive abilities: A European community meta-analysis. *Personnel Psychology*, 56(3), 573–605.

Salgado, J. F., Anderson, N., Moscoso, S., Bertua, C., De Fruyt, F., & Rolland, J. P. (2003b). A meta-analytic study of general mental ability validity for different occupation in the European community. *Journal of Applied Psychology*, 88(6), 1068–1081.

Salgado, J. F., Anderson, N., & Tauriz, G. (2015). The validity of ipsative and quasi-ipsative forced-choice personality inventories for different occupational groups: A comprehensive meta-analysis. *Journal of Occupational and Organizational Psychology*, 88(4), 797–834.

Salgado, J. F., & De Fruyt, F. (2005). Personality in personnel selection. In A. Evers, N. Anderson, & O. Voskuijl (Eds.), *Handbook of personnel selection* (pp. 174–198). London: Blackwell.

Salgado, J. F., Gorriti, M., & Moscoso, S. (2007). The structured behavioural interview and job performance in Spanish public administration: Psychometric properties and fairness reactions. *Psychology in Spain*, 12, 88–96.

Salgado, J. F., & Moscoso, S. (1996). Meta-analysis of interrater reliability of job performance ratings in validity studies of personnel selection. *Perceptual and Motor Skills*, 83, 1195–1201.

Salgado, J. F., & Moscoso, S. (2002). Comprehensive meta-analysis of the construct validity of the employment interview. *European Journal of Work and Organizational Psychology*, 11(3), 299–324.

Salgado, J. F., & Moscoso, S. (2003). Internet-based personality testing: Equivalence of measures and assessee's perceptions and reactions. *International Journal of Selection and Assessment*, 11(1), 194–203.

Salgado, J. F., & Moscoso, S. (2006). Utiliser les entretiens comportementaux structures pour la selection du personnel. In C. Levy-Leboyer, C. Louche, J. P. Rolland, & C. Louche (Eds.), *RH: Les apports de la psychologie du travail* (pp. 195–208). Paris: Les Editions d'Organization.

Salgado, J. F., & Moscoso, S. (2008). Personnel selection in industry and public administration: From the traditional view to the strategic view. *Papelesdel Psicólogo*, 29(1), 16–24.

Salgado, J. F., Moscoso, S., & Anderson, N. (2013). Personality and counterproductive work behavior. In R. P. Tett & N. D. Christiansen (Eds.), *Handbook of personality at work* (pp. 606–632). New York: Routledge.

Salgado, J. F., Moscoso, S., & Anderson, N. (2013). Corrections for criterion reliability in validity generalization: The consistency of Hermes, the utility of Midas. *Revista de Psicologia del Trabajo y de las Organizaciones*, 32(1), 1–7.

Salgado, J. F., Moscoso, S., & Berges, A. (2013). Conscientiousness, its facets, and the prediction of job performance ratings: Evidence against the narrow measures. *International Journal of Selection and Assessment*, 27(1), 74–84.

Salgado, J. F., Moscoso, S., Sanchez, J. I., Alonso, P., Choragwicka, B., & Berges, A. (2015). Validity of the five-factor model and their facets: The impact of performance measure and facet residualization on the bandwidth-fidelity debate. *European Journal of Work and Organizational Psychology*, 24(3), 325–349.

Salgado, J. F., & Tauriz, G. (2014). The Five-Factor Model, forced-choice personality inventories and performance: A comprehensive meta-analysis of academic and occupational validity studies. *European Journal of Work and Organizational Psychology*, 23(1), 3–30.

Salgado, J. F., Viswesvaran, C., & Ones, D.S. (2001). Predictors used for personnel selection: An overview of constructs, method and techniques. In N. Anderson, D. S. Ones, H. K. Sinangil, & C. Viswesvaran (Eds.), *Handbook of industrial, work, and organizational psychology. Vol. 1: Personnel psychology* (pp. 165–199). London: Sage.

Sanchez, J. I., & Levine, E. L. (2012). The rise and fall of job analysis and the future of work analysis. *Annual Review of Psychology*, 63(1), 397–425.

Schippman, J. S., Ash, R. A., Battista, M., Carr, L., Eyde, L. D., Hesketh, B., . . . Sanchez, J. I. (2000). The practice of competency modelling. *Personnel Psychology*, 53(3), 703–740.

Schmidt, F. L., & Hunter, J. E. (1998). The validity and utility of selection methods in personnel psychology: Practical and theoretical implications of 85 years of research findings. *Psychological Bulletin*, 124(2), 262–274.

Schmidt, F. L., & Hunter, J. E. (2014). *Methods of meta-analysis: Correcting error and bias in research findings* (3d ed.). Newbury Park, CA: SAGE.

Schmidt, F. L., Hunter, J. E., & Ones, D. S. (1992). Personnel selection. *Annual Review of Psychology*, 43(1), 627–670.

Schmidt, F. L., Hunter, J. E., & Outerbridge, A. N. (1986). Impact of job experience and ability on job knowledge, work sample performance, and supervision ratings of job performance. *Journal of Applied Psychology*, 71(3), 432–439.

Schmidt, F. L., Oh, I. S., & Le, H. (2006). Increasing the accuracy of corrections for range restriction: Implications for selection procedure validities and others research results. *Personnel Psychology*, 59(2), 281–395.

Schmitt, N. (2014). Personality and cognitive ability as predictors of effective performance at work. *Annual Review of Organizational Psychology and Organizational Behavior*, 1, 45–65.

Schmitt, N., Clause, C., & Pulakos, E. (1996). Subgroup differences associated with different measures of some common job relevant constructs. In C. L. Cooper & I. T. Robertson (Eds.), *International review of industrial and organizational psychology* (vol. 11, pp. 115–140). Chichester, U.K.: Wiley.

Schmitt, N., Gooding, R. Z., Noe, R. A., & Kirsch, M. (1984). Meta-analysis validity studies published between 1964 and 1982 and the investigation of study characteristics. *Personnel Psychology*, 37(3), 402–422.

Schneider, B. (1987). The people make the place. *Personnel Psychology*, 40(3), 437–453.

Schneider, B., Goldstein, H. W., & Smith, D. B. (1995). The ASA framework: An update. *Personnel Psychology*, 48(4), 747–779.

Schuler, H. (1993). Social validity of selection situations: A concept and some empirical results. In H. Schuler, J. L. Farr, & N. Schmitt (Eds.), *Personnel selection and assessment: Individual and organizational perspectives*. Mahwah, NJ: Erlbaum.

Steiner, D. D., & Guilliland, S.W. (1996). Fairness reactions to personnel selection techniques in France and the United States. *Journal of Applied Psychology, 81*(4), 124–141.

TeNijenhuis, J., & van der Flier, H. (1997). Comparability of GATB scores for immigrants and majority group members: Some Dutch findings. *Journal of Applied Psychology, 82*(5), 675–687.

Tett, R., Rothstein, M. G., & Jackson, D. J. (1991). Personality measures as predictors of job performance: A meta-analytic review. *Personnel Psychology, 44*(4), 703–742.

Van Scotter, J. R., & Motowidlo, S. (1996). Interpersonal facilitation and job dedication as separate facets of contextual performance. *Journal of Applied Psychology, 81*(5), 525–531.

Vinchur, A. J., & Koppess Bryan, L. L. (2012). A history of personnel selection and assessment. In N. Schmitt (Ed.), *The Oxford handbook of personnel assessment and selection* (pp. 9–30). Oxford: Oxford University Press.

Viswesvaran, C., & Ones, D.S. (2004). Importance of perceived personnel selection systems fairness determinants: Relations with demographic, personality, and job characteristics. *International Journal of Selection and Assessment, 12*(1–2), 172–186.

Viswesvaran, C., Ones, D., & Schmidt, F. L. (1996). Comparative analysis of the reliability of job performance ratings. *Journal of Applied Psychology, 81*(4), 557–574.

Viswesvaran, C., Schmidt, F. L., & Ones, D. S. (2005). Is there a general factor in ratings of job performance? A meta-analytic framework for disentangling substantive and error influences. *Journal of Applied Psychology, 90*(1), 108–131.

Wiesner, W. H., & Cronshaw, S. F. (1988). The moderating impact of interview format and degree of structure on interview validity. *Journal of Occupational Psychology, 61*(2), 275–290.

Jesús F. Salgado

JOB INSECURITY

BACKGROUND: WHY IS JOB INSECURITY (STILL) RELEVANT?

Since the publication of Greenhalgh and Rosenblatt's (1984) influential article, there has always been cause for concern about job (in)security. Greenhalgh and Rosenblatt advanced four such causes that still have resonance in the early 21st century (e.g., Lee et al., 2018; Shoss, 2017; Sverke & Hellgren, 2002): (a) periods of economic downturn, with the 2007–2008 financial crisis as a prototypical example and the COVID-19 pandemic and associated health crisis as an atypical example; (b) the stream of mergers and acquisitions that has intensified under globalization; (c) the ongoing change in labor markets following technological innovation and associated developments in artificial intelligence and automation; and (d) the decrease in labor unionization that has fundamentally shifted the employment relationship, which is further illustrated with the increase in flexible employment, the informal economy, and the gig economy.

DEFINITION: WHAT IS JOB INSECURITY?

The ever-present reality of job insecurity has led to a wealth of job insecurity studies, yet not a fundamentally different view on the notion job insecurity. Sverke et al. (2002, p. 243) define job insecurity as "the subjectively experienced anticipation of a fundamental and involuntary event related to job loss." Most other definitions are variations on the same underlying themes: job insecurity (a) is subjective, (b) signals job loss concern, and (c) is involuntary.

Job insecurity is subjective; that is, employees appraise their situation. This appraisal can be cognitive in terms of chances of job loss (e.g., "I think I will lose my job") or affective in terms of emotions associated with potential job loss (e.g., "I am afraid I will lose my job") (see Vander Elst et al., 2014a, for sample items). Those appraisals may reflect an objective reality such as high unemployment or employment involving a temporary contract, but the emphasis is on how it is perceived by the individual, which can induce significant variation.

Job insecurity expresses a concern about job loss. Employees reflect about potential threats to their present job, be it the job as entity (i.e., quantitative job insecurity) or valued job features (i.e., qualitative job insecurity). Quantitative job insecurity has been at the center of attention probably because the parallel with unemployment is easily made. They are "twins" (De Witte et al., 2019) in the sense that quantitative job insecurity concerns the anticipation of unemployment. By contrast, qualitative job insecurity has no such strong parallel, though this does not make it less relevant. Even in sectors with relative stability, employees may feel insecure about how their jobs will look in the future. To illustrate, threats related to automation and robotization have attracted mass media attention and may lead to concerns about dramatic changes in how jobs are designed (see Garz, 2012, on the impact of media coverage on job insecurity). Most studies in this article concern quantitative job insecurity. Studies on qualitative job insecurity are flagged when relevant.

Job insecurity is involuntary, implying an unwelcome change, not job loss because the individual leaves the job and organization by their own choice. Shoss (2017) challenged the idea that job insecurity is by definition involuntary: she argues that job loss concern may still be relevant, even when employees have, willingly and knowingly, accepted an insecure contract or when they have embraced insecurity as the new reality in some sectors or during some specific periods. This criticism highlights that the notion of volition may need more reflection; it may not be a matter of voluntary versus involuntary, but perhaps more a matter of a variety of underlying motives.

THEORY: WHAT IS PROBLEMATIC ABOUT JOB INSECURITY AND WHY?

Job insecurity, like most other phenomena studied under the heading of applied psychology, does not have its "own" theoretical framework. Instead, theoretical frameworks are borrowed from related disciplines and are mainly used to explain specific outcomes related to job insecurity, in particular (a) strain and motivation, (b) attitudes and behavior vis-à-vis the organization, and (c) social attitudes and behavior. At the heart of those theories is the idea that job insecurity is problematic. Table 1 summarizes the main ideas for each of these theories, along with key publications.

Job Insecurity and Strain.   Job insecurity has typically been studied from the perspective of occupational health and well-being. Outcomes that have been studied extensively are indicators of strain, in particular general or context-free well-being (e.g., health, psychosomatic complaints); work-related well-being (e.g., burnout, job satisfaction); and, to a lesser extent, indicators of motivation (e.g., work engagement).

Theories with a focus on occupational health and well-being share the idea that job insecurity presents a threat, and this threat causes strain. Theories come in two strands: a first set of theories focuses on understanding what is threatened, and a second set on underlying mechanisms that explain the relationship between job insecurity and strain. Those theories are often combined to explain what is threatened and how this causes strain.

What Is Threatened by Job Insecurity? Within the first set of theories, latent deprivation theory (Jahoda, 1982) and basic psychological need satisfaction from self-determination theory (Deci & Ryan, 2000) have attracted attention. Latent deprivation theory starts from the observation that work provides employees with benefits. Income is a manifest benefit, but work also brings latent benefits: collective purpose; societal status; time structure throughout the day, week, and year; and activation. Even those benefits that are usually latent become a priority concern when threatened, and this induces strain.

Self-determination theory has been used to argue that a fulfilling job addresses the basic psychological needs of autonomy (i.e., the desire to experience a sense of volition and choice), belongingness (i.e., desire to feel connected to others), and competence (i.e., the desire to have an effect on the environment and a sense of mastery) that are critical for optimal functioning. Conversely, job insecurity frustrates those needs and hence leads to strain. Job insecurity is involuntary (vs. autonomous), could create tension among colleagues (vs. a sense of belonging), and implies a lack of control (vs. competence). Unlike other theories, this framework has been used also to explain outcomes associated with qualitative job insecurity.

How and Why Is Job Insecurity a Threat? Within the second set of theories, the focus is not so much on what is threatened, but on how and why job insecurity presents a threat. Conservation of resources theory (Hobfoll et al., 2018) and transactional stress theory (Lazarus & Folkman, 1984) have been most influential.

Conservation of resources theory starts from the assumption that people strive to "conserve" (i.e., retain) resources, defend those resources against (potential) threats, and build resources to prevent such threats. Strain occurs upon threat or actual loss of resources. Job insecurity presents a threat to employment and associated manifest and latent benefits, clearly all resources. Individuals typically react by attempting to protect existing resources, the so-called "resource conservation hypothesis." The implication is that individuals withdraw from the stressor. Paradoxically, this reaction also consumes resources (e.g., time spent worrying), triggers further losses, and ultimately leaves employees strained. Another reaction could be that individuals, particularly those with many resources, bring in excess resources to address the threat caused by job insecurity, the so-called "resource investment hypothesis." Doing so buffers the negative outcomes associated with job insecurity. Yet, under chronic job insecurity, it contributes to depletion of resources over time.

The basic premise of transactional stress theory fits well with the notion of job insecurity, namely, that it is the individual's perception that matters. More specifically, stress is seen as the result of the person's appraisal of the situation along two stages. During primary appraisal, any particular situation is appraised in the form of harm (i.e., actual loss), challenge (i.e., opportunity for growth, given effort), or threat (i.e., anticipation of harm). When employees feel insecure, threat appraisals are most likely. Job insecurity presents a threat to employment.

Secondary appraisal concerns the evaluation of available coping resources vis-à-vis the threat. When insecure, available coping resources are likely insufficient. Job insecurity induces uncertainty and unpredictability, so that employees are not sure how to react, and this leaves them strained.

Job Insecurity and Organizational Attitudes and Behavior.

Job insecurity has also attracted attention from the perspective of organizational behavior, with a focus on employee attitudes vis-à-vis the organization (e.g., affective organizational commitment, turnover intention) and behavior (e.g., task performance, organizational citizenship behavior). This has mostly been studied using insights from social exchange theory, in which the basic idea is that employees and employers engage in a reciprocal exchange of resources. This exchange generates benefits for both parties so that they become interdependent (Cropanzano & Mitchell, 2005). Job insecurity may interrupt this exchange and induce imbalance in the employment relationship. This leads employees to re-evaluate their part of the deal and to withdraw their investments. Social exchange theory has been used in different ways in order to understand what is interrupted by job insecurity and the underlying mechanism.

What Is Interrupted by Job Insecurity? One stream of studies has focused on what aspect in the deal between employee and employer is threatened, using the notion of the psychological contract and psychological contract breach in particular. The psychological contract is the constellation of mutual expectations between employee and employer (Robinson & Rousseau, 1994). Under the traditional or so-called relational psychological contract, employees expect job security from their employer in return for loyalty. This leads to a mutual win in the form of a long-term, mutually satisfactory relationship. Job insecurity then presents a breach of the psychological contract, inducing imbalance in the relationship. Employees respond by reducing or withdrawing their part of the deal. The psychological contract perspective has had particular resonance in the context of flexible employment. The general idea is that job insecurity is more damaging for employees who consider job security as part of the deal with the employer, in particular permanent employees. It is comparatively less damaging for employees who do not anticipate job security (De Cuyper & De Witte, 2006).

Why Is the Interruption Caused by Job Insecurity Problematic? A second stream of research has focused on justice (Colquitt, 2001) in order to understand why job insecurity is potentially problematic for the employment relationship and associated outcomes. Job insecurity signals an unwelcome change in the employment relationship that is appraised as unjust in terms of overall, procedural, and/or distributive justice. This induces strain and leads to a re-evaluation of the employment relationship, so employees reduce their investments.

Job Insecurity and Social Attitudes and Behavior.

Job insecurity has also been linked to social attitudes and behavior, though this has attracted comparatively less attention. Social attitudes concern different aspects of trust, for example, trust in politicians, political parties, and institutions; and anti-egalitarian attitudes and associated voting intentions and behavior. This is mostly framed with reference to social identity theory (Tajfel & Turner, 1986). Job insecurity threatens one's identity as an employed person, and being employed (vs. unemployed) is the preferred social category status. In an attempt to confirm their desired identity, job-insecure employees may then derogate outgroup members and express more conservative attitudes (Selenko & De Witte, 2020).

Summary. Theories are used in view of explaining what makes job insecurity problematic, and how and why, with reference to specific outcomes. There are three core arguments: (a) job insecurity is a stressor causing strain; (b) job insecurity induces imbalance in the employment relationship, which leads employees to reduce loyalty and effort; and (c) job insecurity threatens a desired identity, which affects social attitudes and behaviors.

Note that the connection between outcome and theory was a matter of structuring the literature. It may wrongfully create the impression that those theories have not been used in relation to other outcomes. To illustrate, most theories that have been used to explain strain associated with job insecurity have been extended to organizational attitudes. Strain then is interpreted broadly, including withdrawal from the stressor and the stressful context (i.e., the job and the organization). As another illustration, social identity theory has also been used to explain poorer health and well-being among job-insecure employees.

ANTECEDENTS: WHAT CAUSES JOB INSECURITY?

Research on antecedents is relatively scarce and fragmented (Shoss, 2017). By way of illustration, reviews and meta-analyses addressing outcomes of job insecurity are plenty (see Table 2) but comparatively few for antecedents of job insecurity (for meta-analyses, see Jiang et al., 2020; Keim et al., 2014; for narrative reviews, see Lee et al., 2018; Shoss, 2017). There have been some attempts at arriving at a classification of potential sources of job insecurity. Those attempts mostly distinguish between different levels at which the source can be found: at the level of (a) the individual, (b) the job, (c) the organization, or (d) the larger environment. The following overview of antecedents relies heavily on the meta-analyses from Jiang et al. (2020) and Keim et al. (2014).

Individual Sources. Individual sources of job insecurity are tied to the person, with the strongest focus on socio-demographics and individual differences. Socio-demographics that have been used consistently in job insecurity studies are age, tenure, gender, type of contract (permanent vs. temporary, full-time vs. part-time) and occupational position (blue-collar vs. white-collar). The general idea is that labor market dynamics make the situation of specific groups objectively more insecure, and this drives appraisals. The evidence from meta-analyses suggests that this is the case for employees on temporary (vs. permanent) contracts and in blue-collar (vs. white-collar) positions. The association between temporary employment and job insecurity is not surprising; a temporary contract has been advanced as a form of objective job insecurity (De Cuyper & De Witte, 2006; Klandermans et al., 2010). The association between occupational position and job insecurity also highlight objective differences and may relate to the increase in knowledge jobs that is particularly threatening for blue-collar workers.

Three observations may need further comment and explanation. First, the observation that education and job insecurity are not significantly related may come as a surprise. It could be that the relationship is more complex. Employees with a lower (vs. higher) education may feel more insecure, yet Peiró et al. (2012) observed that also being overqualified is a risk factor.

Table 1. Theoretical Frameworks and Sample Publications

Theory	Sample Publications	Hypothesis
Strain		Job insecurity relates negatively to strain because . . .
Latent deprivation theory (Jahoda, 1982)	Selenko and Batinic (2013) Selenko et al. (2020)	Job insecurity threatens manifest and latent benefits of work.
Self-determination theory (Deci & Ryan, 2000)	Vander Elst et al. (2012)	Job insecurity frustrates basic psychological needs.
Conservation of resources theory (Hobfoll et al., 2018)	De Cuyper et al. (2012) König et al. (2010)	Job insecurity presents a resource threat.
Transactional stress theory (Lazarus & Folkman, 1984)	Jiang et al. (2020) Vander Elst et al. (2014b)	Job insecurity induces threat appraisals for which employees do not have appropriate coping resources.
Organizational attitudes and behavior		Job insecurity relates negatively to attitudes and behavior because . . .
Psychological contract (Robinson & Rousseau, 1994)	De Cuyper and De Witte (2006) Klandermans et al. (2010)	Job insecurity breaches the psychological contract between employee and employer.
Justice (Colquitt, 2001)	Lazauskaite-Zabielske et al. (2019) Piccoli and De Witte (2015)	Job insecurity induces injustice.
Social attitudes and behavior		Job insecurity affects social attitudes and behavior because . . .
Social identity theory (Tajfel & Turner, 1986)	Selenko and De Witte (2020) Selenko et al. (2017)	Job insecurity threatens one's identity as employed person.

Second, the evidence for age is less consistent. Age related negatively to job insecurity in the meta-analysis by Keim et al. (2014), yet this was not replicated in the meta-analysis of Jiang et al. (2020). It could be that age dynamics are quite complex. Older employees may feel more insecure because they have more to lose or because of negative age-related stereotypes, yet younger employees are more often employed on flexible contracts and are the first to be dismissed. Third, tenure, gender, and part-time versus full-time employment were not related to job insecurity, yet they are often used as control variables in job insecurity studies. Selection of control variables may need careful consideration.

Individual differences that have been studied are personality (often the "Big Five" personality traits), negative or positive affectivity, internal or external locus of control, and core self-evaluations. The general idea is that individual differences make some employees more prone to feel insecure and other employees more resilient. Results from the meta-analyses provide overall support for this idea. Some employees are more vulnerable than others. More recently, the emphasis shifts from more general individual resources to career-related resources, such as employability (De Cuyper et al., 2012) and career adaptability (Spurk et al., 2016). The available evidence to date suggests a weak to moderate negative relationship with job insecurity.

Job-Related Sources. Job-related sources are tied to the current job. The general idea ties in with insights from conservation of resources theory: high-quality jobs provide resources, whereas poor-quality jobs consume resources. Employees with a larger resource reservoir are less vulnerable and individuals with fewer resources more vulnerable to job loss, and this may explain differences in job insecurity. Meta-analytic results support this idea (Jiang et al., 2020): job resources (e.g., autonomy) are negatively related to job insecurity, and job demands (e.g., role conflict, role ambiguity, workload) are positively related to job insecurity.

Organizational Sources. Organizational sources of job insecurity mostly concern organizational change and change-related aspects, such as communication, participation, and justice. Organizational change is associated with feelings of job insecurity, yet frequent organizational communication, participative decision-making, and fairness reduce job insecurity. Organizational politics had the strongest predictive power regarding job insecurity in the meta-analysis by Jiang et al. (2020).

Environmental Sources. Comparisons of large data sets from various countries show considerable cross-national variation in the level of perceived job insecurity (e.g., Green, 2009), which can be attributed to affluence (Van Oorschot & Chung, 2015); the unemployment rate and its evolution (Lübke & Erlinghagen, 2014); and labor market policies, both passive (e.g., increasing unemployment benefits) and active (e.g., providing vocational training and stimulating job search efforts) (Van Oorschot & Chung, 2015). Affluence and labor market policies reduce perceived job insecurity, whereas unemployment rate obviously increases perceived job insecurity. Interestingly, social protection measures are far more important than the generosity of the welfare state (Anderson & Pontusson, 2007).

Summary. Sources of job insecurity are multiple. They can be tied to the person, the job, the organization, or the environment. There are obvious cross-links between the categories (de Bustillo & de Pedraza, 2010). For example, the general economic climate shapes individuals' perceptions of job insecurity, and probably in a stronger fashion among individuals with specific profiles along the idea of hyperresponsivity. For example, individuals with higher negative affectivity may be more sensitive and thus react more strongly to environmental sources of job insecurity (Debus et al., 2014). Yet few studies have examined those cross-links and interactions, surprisingly so because stressors are commonly seen as the result of the person–environment interface. This is most explicit in transactional stress theory. An exception is the study by Debus et al. (2014), who examine interactions between organizational factors (i.e., company performance) and employment conditions (i.e., type of contract) on the one hand, and personality on the other hand. Their findings show that personality explains more variance than organizational factors and employment conditions. This question regarding relative strength of antecedents and their interaction and embeddedness is an important route for future research.

OUTCOMES: WHAT ARE CONSEQUENCES OF JOB INSECURITY?

There are comparatively many studies on outcomes associated with job insecurity. The evidence accumulates in the same direction. Job insecurity brings about negative outcomes for (a) the individual and (b) the organization, and (c) job insecurity can also affect ("spill over to") outcomes beyond the current job, such as the family, the society, or the career. Table 2 presents an overview of key publications for the different categories, along with a summary of findings from meta-analyses (in bold) and narrative reviews (in italic) or, when those are unavailable, from empirical studies with a longitudinal design (in normal font).

The Individual: Strain. At the core of job insecurity research is the hypothesis that job insecurity increases strain in the form of poorer health and well-being, both work related and context free. This hypothesis has found overall support. To illustrate, Jiang and Lavaysse (2018) report a meta-correlation of 0.24 for work-related strain and –0.37 for job satisfaction, and between 0.12 and 0.30 for context-free strain (e.g., anxiety, depression). Longitudinal studies show that job insecurity is more likely to cause strain than vice versa (De Witte et al., 2016) and that those effects are long term (e.g., up to 14 years in the study by Barrech et al., 2018).

The Organization (and the Labor Union): Attitudes and Behavior. Job insecurity has also been related to outcomes that are relevant for the organization. Most studies address those outcomes using employee reports about their attitudes vis-à-vis the organization (e.g., affective organizational commitment and turnover intention) and their performance. The main hypothesis is that job insecurity leads employees to reduce their efforts and withdraw from the stressor in the form of lower commitment, higher turnover (intention), and poorer performance. Those are attempts to cope with imbalance in the employment relationship, and associated strain.

Regarding affective organizational commitment, the evidence shows that the relationship is negative or not significant. Most studies report a negative relationship, so job insecurity reduces affective organizational commitment. This has been found in longitudinal studies with varying time frames (e.g., Cheng et al., 2012; Huang et al., 2020). Some studies do not establish a significant relationship between job insecurity and affective organizational commitment, particularly studies with relatively longer time frames (e.g., Kinnunen et al., 2000).

Regarding turnover intention, most studies show a positive relationship, so job insecurity triggers the intention to leave the organization. This is found across studies and with different time lags (e.g., Allen et al., 2001; Glambek et al., 2014; Kinnunen et al., 2014). Perhaps the most cautious conclusion is that job insecurity certainly does not promote loyalty in the form of commitment or intention to stay, yet evidence on actual behavior is lagging behind.

An interesting observation is that job insecurity affects labor unions in a similar way; job insecurity associates negatively with labor union support, satisfaction, and commitment

(Sverke et al., 2004). A possible explanation could be that in some countries labor unions lack the capacity to protect individual members; at the same time, union membership is relatively costly: This could be perceived as imbalance in the relationship and hence a reason to withdraw. The exception is Sweden, where members felt more committed and loyal to their labor union when feeling insecure, probably related to the strength of the labor union in Sweden. In Belgium and Italy in particular, job insecurity related positively to labor union membership turnover among members, yet it also was a trigger for non-members to unionize (De Witte et al., 2012). This may suggest that employees seek unionization when they see a strong cause, yet also quit union membership when they feel the labor union does not or cannot provide sufficient protection.

Regarding performance, recent meta-analytic evidence suggests a negative relationship, –0.14 to –0.20, depending on the specific indicator (Jiang & Lavaysse, 2018; Sverke et al., 2019). This negative association is found across studies using different performance indicators. A specific category of performance concerns counterproductive work behavior: Job insecurity associates positively with counterproductive work behavior (Jiang & Lavaysse, 2018; Sverke et al., 2019) and is a strong predictor of workplace bullying (Van den Brande et al., 2016).

On a related note, a relatively recent line of job insecurity research has sought to link job insecurity with job preservation efforts (Shoss, 2017). Employees may act according to what they believe could be helpful or instrumental in avoiding job loss. This has sometimes been interpreted as meaning that job insecurity will push employees to work harder, whereas job security may lead to complacency. This interpretation is premature and inaccurate. One reason is that job preservation efforts are strategic and not necessarily connected to actual performance. For example, employees may also appear as if they are model employees, hard-working, and committed to organizational values, through impression management strategies (Hewlin et al., 2016; Probst et al., 2020). As another example, job-insecure employees may showcase those behaviors that are valued and/or noticed in the organization, but withdraw effort otherwise. Job-insecure employees may invest in adaptive behavior in organizations in which change is implemented (Lavigne et al., 2020) or in organizational citizenship behavior that is visible to supervisors (Shoss & Probst, 2012; Schumacher et al., 2020). Yet another example is that job-insecure employees may also try not to draw attention to themselves, for example by not voicing problems (Schreurs et al., 2015). Another reason is that Selenko et al. (2013) convincingly demonstrated that job security does not lead to complacency. They establish that the relationship between job insecurity and performance is U-shaped: performance is highest at lower levels of job insecurity and lowest at moderate levels of job insecurity, but only slightly higher at highest levels of job insecurity. In conclusion, job insecurity certainly does not have a positive effect on performance, though it might prompt strategic behavior among employees.

Spillover to Family, Society, and Career. Outcomes associated with job insecurity may not be bound to the present job or organization: Job insecurity may spill over to the family context, society, and career-related matters.

Concerning the work-family interface, Mauno et al. (2017) argue that job insecurity affects life outside work along loss cycles described in the conservation of resources theory. Resource loss following job insecurity may ultimately affect family-related issues through accumulation of losses. For example, job-insecure employees feel strained and take this strain home with them. The outcomes are twofold: job insecurity may spill over to family well-being or affect significant others (e.g., partner, children). Mauno et al. (2017) provide a systematic review of 25 studies addressing this matter, 16 on spillover to family well-being and 9 on effects on significant others.

Regarding spillover to family well-being, their conclusion is that job insecurity associates positively with conflicts between work and family (in both directions), and negatively with marital role quality and parental behaviors. To date, longitudinal evidence is limited to Nordic countries, where family research has flourished. Regarding effects on significant others, parental job insecurity affects children's well-being, motivation, and school performance. Yet, this should be interpreted with caution, as studies are few and mainly cross-sectional. Studies on how job insecurity affects the employee's partner are even fewer, and the relations in those studies are not significant.

Concerning impact on the society, job insecurity has been related to social attitudes and associated voting intentions. In multi-country samples, job insecurity related negatively to trust in politicians, political parties, and political institutions, and satisfaction with democratic performance (Wroe, 2014). Evidence from different countries suggests that this has implications for voting behavior. Job insecurity associates with voting for a populist party in Australia (Mughan et al., 2003) and the United States (Mughan & Lacy, 2002) and for an extreme right-wing party in Belgium (De Witte & Meuleman, 2007). Longitudinal studies seem to support these results. Job insecurity strengthened anti-egalitarian attitudes over time (Selenko & De Witte, 2020).

Concerning career-related matters, job insecurity has been related to perceived employability (i.e., the employee's appraisal of available job opportunities). Following general stress theories, job insecurity may lead to a passive response, and this may deplete employees' employability. Studies so far are few but consistently show a negative relationship between job insecurity and perceived employability. Job-insecure employees feel less employable. This relationship is reciprocal (De Cuyper et al., 2012) and has been established using between- and within-person designs (Mäkikangas et al., 2013). Van Hootegem et al. (2019) showed that this is perhaps not a matter of lack of motivation; rather, job-insecure employees were more willing to undertake training to strengthen their position in the external labor market, yet they may not be able to. It is unclear how this inability should be interpreted. A plausible assumption could be that job-insecure employees do not have access to organizational resources or do not have energy left to pursue such resources, or perhaps both.

Summary.   The evidence is remarkably consistent. Job insecurity causes poorer outcomes in the form of strain and poorer attitudes and behavior vis-à-vis the job and organization. In addition, job insecurity may spill over to other contexts, the family and society in particular, and over time to career-related matters. Some authors have hinted at the "scarring" effect of job insecurity, mostly in relation to health (e.g., Barrech et al., 2018). A convincing illustration comes from Wu et al. (2020), who show that chronic job insecurity relates to Big Five personality changes: an increase in neuroticism and decreases in agreeableness and conscientiousness. Those scarring effects may need further follow-up. This obviously requires longitudinal designs, which have become standard practice in job-insecurity research (De Witte et al., 2016). An avenue for future research

Table 2. Outcomes Associated With Job Insecurity in Meta-Analysis (in **bold**), Narrative Reviews (in *italic*), or Longitudinal Studies (normal font)

Key Outcome	Sample Publications	Core Findings
The individual		
Strain Health and well-being	**Cheng and Chan (2008)** *De Witte et al. (2016);* **Jiang and Lavaysse (2018); Sverke et al. (2002)**	The relationship between job insecurity and strain, both work related and context free, is positive.
The organization		
Affective organizational commitment	Cheng et al. (2012); Huang et al. (2020)	The relationship between job insecurity and organizational commitment is negative.
Turnover intention	Glambek et al. (2014); Kinnunen et al. (2014)	The relationship between job insecurity and turnover intention is positive.
Performance	**Jiang and Lavaysse (2018); Sverke et al. (2002); Sverke et al. (2019)**	The relationship between job insecurity and indicators of performance is negative.
Across contexts and time		
Work-family interface	*Mauno et al. (2017)*	Job insecurity spills over to family life and crosses over to children's well-being, motivation, and performance.
Society	Selenko and De Witte (2020)	Job insecurity affects societal attitudes and voting behavior.
Career-related matters	De Cuyper et al. (2012); Mäkikangas et al. (2013)	Job insecurity has a negative impact on career-related matters.

would be to have person-centric studies in which within-person changes are followed up over time (see Kinnunen et al., 2014; Mäkikangas et al., 2013; Schumacher et al., 2020, for examples).

MODERATORS: WHAT CAN BE DONE?

Studies on moderators come in two strands related to potential buffers and country comparisons. The first strand of studies has probed factors that could buffer the outcomes associated with job insecurity. The focus has been on moderators that are malleable, often in the form of personal or organizational resources that could be nurtured to good effect (e.g., by training). Examples of personal resources are perceived employability (e.g., Silla et al., 2009), occupational self-efficacy, and work locus of control (König et al., 2010). Examples of organizational resources are social support, fairness, leader–member exchange (Wang et al., 2015), communication (König et al., 2010), and participative decision-making (Probst, 2005).

Those studies have resonance for practice, for example, in thinking about and designing potential interventions. Yet, future research could add both depth and breadth. In terms of depth, the selection of moderators often appears ad hoc, without much theoretical rational. For example, many of the personal and organizational resources have been used as both antecedents of job insecurity and moderators in the relationship between job insecurity and outcomes. This may require further thought and debate and, in a later phase, studies that are designed with a view on testing moderators (e.g., by using purposive sampling of extreme populations or by rigorous interventions). In terms of breadth, many other moderators besides personal and organizational resources are possible, yet they have attracted comparatively little attention. In this respect, Shoss (2017) launched a call to probe moderators that could affect how job insecurity is appraised, for example, duration of the threat and volition. She also highlights potential vulnerabilities. This vulnerability view complements the resource-based view and emphasizes potential asymmetry. Aspects that buffer the relationship between job insecurity and outcomes can be fundamentally different from aspects that increase sensitivity.

Another strand of studies focuses on macro-level moderators. Job insecurity associates with negative outcomes, yet the strength of those relationships varies across countries (László et al., 2010). This has been related to both structural and cultural features. Examples of structural features that make job insecurity even more problematic are the economic crisis, which has hit some countries particularly hard (Lam et al., 2014), and income inequality at both country and state levels (Jiang & Probst, 2017). Probst and Jiang (2017), in a comparison of data from 19 European countries, showed that structural features should not be looked at in isolation. Rather, the combination of employment security protection with flexible work arrangements, typical for a flexicurity policy, buffered the relationship between job insecurity and strain. Conversely, employees on temporary contracts and those in the informal economy may be even more vulnerable in countries with strict employment protection regulation (Karabchuk & Soboleva, 2020). Examples of cultural values are enacted uncertainty avoidance or masculine orientation (Debus et al., 2012, 2020).

CONCLUSION: JOB INSECURITY AS HINDRANCE

Job insecurity is one of the stressors at work that has been consistently high on the policy and research agenda since the 1980s. To date, the evidence all converges to the same observation, namely, that job insecurity is a stressor causing overall negative outcomes on different aspects of individual functioning (health and well-being, attitudes, behavior) and in different domains (at work, work–family interface, society, career). This suggests that job insecurity for employees is a hindrance that is difficult to overcome and that could cause scars in the longer term. This conclusion holds even though some studies have explicitly addressed the hypothesis that job insecurity is a challenge with potential positive side effects (e.g., Piccoli et al., 2019). This observation has led to studies seeking to identify factors that could buffer the negative effects, mainly personal, job, or organizational resources. What is particularly worrisome is that job insecurity seems to be concentrated in employees with more precarious profiles, temporary and blue-collar workers in particular, and in jobs with fewer resources and more demands. These employees may find it more difficult to build personal resources or to gain access to job and organizational resources, leading to double jeopardy: they are both more job insecure and more heavily affected. This is certainly one of the areas that needs follow-up, also from the perspective of qualitative job insecurity. There is growing concern about how technology will change jobs, with the strongest impact for the more precious groups.

REFERENCES

Allen, T. D., Freeman, D. M., Russel, J. E. A., Reizenstein, R. C., & Rentz, J. O. (2001). Survivor reactions to organizational downsizing: Does time ease the pain? *Journal of Occupational and Organizational Psychology, 74*(2), 145–164. https://doi.org/10.1348/096317901167299

Anderson, C. J., & Pontusson, J. (2007). Workers, worries and welfare states: Social protection and job insecurity in 15 OECD countries. *European Journal of Political Research, 46*(2), 211–235. https://doi.org/10.1111/j.1475-6765.2007.00692.x

Barrech, A., Baumert, J., Gündel, H., & Ladwig, K.-H. (2018, June 18). The impact of job insecurity on long-term self-rated health: Results from the prospective population-based MONICA/KORA study. *BMC Public Health, 18*(754). https://doi.org/10.1186/s12889-018-5621-4

Cheng, G. H.-L., & Chan, D. K.-S. (2008). Who suffers more from job insecurity? A meta-analytic review. *Applied Psychology: An International Review, 57*(2), 272–303. https://doi.org/10.1111/j.1464-0597.2007.00312.x

Cheng, T., Huang, G.-H., Lee, C., & Ren, X. (2012). Longitudinal effects of job insecurity on employee outcomes: The moderating role of emotional intelligence and the leader-member exchange. *Asia Pacific Journal of Management, 29,* 709–728. https://doi.org/10.1007/s10490-010-9227-3

Colquitt, J. A. (2001). On the dimensionality of organizational justice: A construct validation of a measure. *Journal of Applied Psychology, 86*(3), 386–400. https://doi.org/10.1037/0021-9010.86.3.386

Cropanzano, R., & Mitchell, M. S. (2005). Social exchange theory: An interdisciplinary review. *Journal of Management, 31*(6), 874–900. https://doi.org/10.1177/0149206305279602

Debus, M., Kleinmann, M., König, C. J., & Winkler, S. (2020). Being tough versus tender: The impact of country-level and individual masculinity orientations as moderators of the relationship between job insecurity and job attitudes. *Applied Psychology: An International Review, 69*(3), 616–652. https://doi.org/10.1111/apps.12189

Debus, M. E., König, C. J., & Kleinmann, M. (2014). The building blocks of job insecurity: The impact of environmental and person-related variables on job insecurity perceptions. *Journal of Occupational and Organizational Psychology, 87*(2), 329–351. https://doi.org/10.1111/joop.12049

Debus, M. E., Probst, T. M., König, C. J., & Kleinmann, M. (2012). Catch me if I fall! Enacted uncertainty avoidance and the social safety net as country-level moderators in the job insecurity-job attitudes link. *Journal of Applied Psychology, 97*(3), 690–698. https://doi.org/10.1037/a0027832

de Bustillo, M. R., & de Pedraza, P. (2010). Determinants of job insecurity in five European countries. *European Journal of Industrial Relations, 16*(1), 5–20. https://doi.org/10.1177/0959680109355306

Deci, E. L., & Ryan, R. M. (2000). The "what" and "why" of goal pursuits: Human needs and the self-determination of behavior. *Psychological Inquiry, 11*(4), 227–268. https://doi.org/10.1207/S15327965PLI1104_01

De Cuyper, N., & De Witte, H. (2006). The impact of job insecurity and contract type on attitudes, well-being and behavioural reports: A psychological contract perspective. *Journal of Occupational and Organizational Psychology, 79*(3), 395–409. https://doi.org/10.1348/096317905X53660

De Cuyper, N., Mäkikangas, A., Kinnunen, U., Mauno, S., & De Witte, H. (2012). Cross-lagged associations between perceived external employability, job insecurity, and exhaustion: Testing gain and loss spirals according to the Conservation of Resources Theory. *Journal of Organizational Behavior, 33*(6), 770–788. https://doi.org/10.1002/job.1800

De Witte, H., De Cuyper, N., Vander Elst, T., Vanbelle, E., & Niesen, W. (2012). Job insecurity: Review of the literature and a summary of recent studies from Belgium. *Romanian Journal of Applied Psychology, 14*(1), 11–17.

De Witte, H., & Meuleman, B. (2007). Job insecurity and voting for an extreme right-wing party. In G. Loosveldt, M. Swyngedouw, & B. Cambre (Eds.), *Measuring meaningful data in social research* (pp. 93–111). Acco.

De Witte, H., Pienaar, J., & De Cuyper, N. (2016). Review of 30 years of longitudinal studies on the association between job insecurity and health and well-being: Is there causal evidence? *Australian Psychologist, 51*(1), 18–31. https://doi.org/10.1111/ap.12176

De Witte, H., Selenko, E., De Cuyper, N. (2019). Unemployment and job insecurity: Surprisingly identical twins. In T. Taris, M. Peeters, & H. De Witte (Eds.), *The fun and frustration of modern working life: Contributions from an occupational health psychology perspective; festschrift for Prof. Dr. Wilmar Schaufeli* (pp. 45–57). Pelckmans Pro.

Garz, M. (2012). Job insecurity perceptions and media coverage of labor market policy. *Journal of Labor Research, 33*(4), 528–544. https://doi.org/10.1007/s12122-012-9146-9

Glambek., M., Matthiesen, S. B., Hetland, J., & Einarsen, S. (2014). Workplace bullying as an antecedent to job insecurity and intention to leave: A 6-month prospective study. *Human Resource Management Journal, 24*(3), 255–268. https://doi.org/10.1111/1748-8583.12035

Green, F. (2009). Subjective employment insecurity around the world. *Cambridge Journal of Regions, Economy and Society, 2*(3), 343–363. https://dx.doi.org/10.1093/cjres/rsp003

Greenhalgh, L., & Rosenblatt, Z. (1984). Job insecurity: Toward conceptual clarity. *Academy of Management Review, 9*(3), 438–448. https://doi.org/10.2307/258284

Hewlin, P. F., Kim, S. S., & Song, Y. H. (2016). Creating facades of conformity in the face of job insecurity: A study of consequences and conditions. *Journal of Occupational and Organizational Psychology, 89*(3), 539–567. https://doi.org/10.1111/joop.12140

Hobfoll, S. E., Halbesleben, J., Neveu, J.-P., & Westman, M. (2018). Conservation of resources in the organizational context: The reality of resources and their consequences. *Annual Review of Organizational Psychology and Organizational Behavior, 5,* 103–128. https://doi.org/10.1146/annurev-orgpsych-032117 -104640

Huang, G.-H., Zhang, Y., Zhang, X., & Long, L. (2020, October 13). Job insecurity, commitment and proactivity towards the organization and one's career: Age as a condition. *Human Resource Management Journal.* https://doi.org/10.1111/1748-8583.12322

Jahoda, M. (1982). *Employment and unemployment: A social-psychological analysis.* Cambridge University Press.

Jiang, L., Hu, S., Näswall, K., López Bohle, S., & Wang, H.-J. (2020). Why and when cognitive job insecurity relates to affective job insecurity? A three-study exploration of negative rumination and the tendency to negative gossip. *European Journal of Work and Organizational Psychology, 29*(5), 678–692. https://doi.org /10.1080/1359432X.2020.1758669

Jiang, L., & Lavaysse, L. M. (2018). Cognitive and affective job insecurity: A meta-analysis and a primary study. *Journal of Management, 44*(6), 2307–2342. https://doi.org/10.1177/0149206318773853

Jiang, L., & Probst, T. M. (2017). The rich get richer, the poor get poorer: Country- and state-level income inequality moderates the job insecurity-burnout relationship. *Journal of Applied Psychology, 102*(4), 672–681. https://doi.org/10.1037/apl0000179

Jiang, L., Xu, X., & Wang, H.-J. (2020). A resources–demands approach to sources of job insecurity: A multi-level meta-analytic investigation. *Journal of Occupational Health Psychology.* http://dx.doi.org/10.1037/ocp0000267

Karabchuk, T., & Soboleva, N. (2020). Temporary employment, informal work and subjective well-being across Europe: Does labor legislation matter? *Journal of Happiness Studies, 21*(5), 1879–1901.

Keim, A. C., Landis, R. S., Pierce, C. A., & Earnest, D. R. (2014). Why do employees worry about their jobs? A meta-analytic review of predictors of job insecurity. *Journal of Occupational Health Psychology, 19*(3), 269–290. https://doi.org/10.1037/a0036743

Kinnunen, U., Mäkikangas, A., Mauno, S., De Cuyper, N., & De Witte, H. (2014). Development of perceived job insecurity across two years: Associations with antecedents and employee outcomes. *Journal of Occupational Health Psychology, 19*(2), 243–258. https://doi.org/10.1037/a0035835

Kinnunen, U., Mauno, S., Nätti, J., & Happonen, M. (2000). Organizational antecedents and outcomes of job insecurity: A longitudinal study in three organizations in Finland. *Journal of Organizational Behavior, 21*(4), 443–459. https://www.researchgate.net/publication/228079241_Organizational_antecedents_and_outcomes_of_job_insecurity_A_longitudinal_study_in_three_organizations_in_Finland

Klandermans, B., Hesselink, J. K., & van Vuuren, T. (2010). Employment status and job insecurity: On the subjective appraisal of an objective status. *Economic and Industrial Democracy, 31*(4), 557–577. https://doi.org/10.1177/0143831X09358362

König, C. J., Debus, M. E., Häusler, S., Lendenmann, N., & Kleinmann, M. (2010). Examining occupational self-efficacy, work locus of control and communication as moderators of the job insecurity-job performance relationship. *Economic and Industrial Democracy, 31*(4), 231–247. https://doi.org/10.1177/0143831X09358629

Lam, J., Fan, W., & Moen, P. (2014). Is insecurity worse for well-being in turbulent times? Mental health in context. *Society and Mental Health, 4*(1), 55–73. https://doi.org/10.1177/2156869313507288

László, K. D., Pikhart, H., Kopp, M. S., Bobak, M., Pajak, A., Malyutina, S., Salavecz, G., & Marmot, M. (2010). Job insecurity and health: A study of 16 European countries. *Social Science & Medicine, 70*(6), 867–874. https://doi.org/10.1016/j.socscimed.2009.11.022

Lavigne, K. N., Whitaker, V. L., Jundt, D. K., & Shoss, M. K. (2020). When do job insecure employees adapt to change? *Career Development International, 25*(3), 271–286.

Lazarus, R. S., & Folkman, S. (1984). *Stress appraisals and coping.* Springer.

Lazauskaite-Zabielske, J., Urbanaviciute, I., Vander Elst, T., & De Witte, H. (2019). Explaining the link between qualitative job insecurity and attitudes: The role of perceived overall justice. *Baltic Journal of Management, 14*(2), 330–344. https://doi.org/10.1108/BJM-08-2018-0293

Lee, C., Huang, G.-H., & Ashford, S. J. (2018). Job insecurity and the changing workplace: Recent developments and the future trends in job insecurity research. *Annual Review of Organizational Psychology and Organizational Behavior, 5*, 335–359. https://doi.org/10.1146/annurev-orgpsych-032117-104651

Lübke, C., & Erlinghagen, M. (2014). Self-perceived job insecurity across Europe over time: Does changing context matter? *Journal of European Social Policy, 24*(4), 319–336. https://doi.org/10.1177/0958928714538215

Mäkikangas, A., De Cuyper, N., Mauno, S., & Kinnunen, U. (2013). A longitudinal person-centred view on perceived employability: The role of job insecurity. *European Journal of Work and Organizational Psychology, 22*(4), 490–503. https://doi.org/10.1080/1359432X.2012.665230

Mauno, S., Cheng, T., & Lim, V. (2017). The far-reaching consequences of job insecurity: A review on family-related outcomes. *Marriage & Family Review, 53*(8), 717–743. https://doi.org/10.1080/01494929.2017.1283382

Mughan, A., Bean, C., & McAllister, I. (2003). Economic globalization, job insecurity and the populist reaction. *Electoral Studies, 22*(4), 617–633. https://doi.org/10.1016/S0261-3794(02)00047-1

Mughan, A., & Lacy, D. (2002). Economic performance, job insecurity and electoral choice. *British Journal of Political Science, 32*(3), 513–533.

Peiró, J. M., Sora, B., & Caballer, A. (2012). Job insecurity in the younger Spanish workforce: Causes and consequences. *Journal of Vocational Behavior, 80*(2), 444–453. https://doi.org/10.1016/j.jvb.2011.09.007

Piccoli, B., & De Witte, H. (2015). Job insecurity and emotional exhaustion: Testing psychological contract breach versus distributive injustice as indicators of lack of reciprocity. *Work & Stress, 29*(3), 246–263. https://doi.org/10.1080/02678373.2015.1075624

Piccoli, B., Reisel, W. D., & De Witte, H. (2019). Understanding the relationship between job insecurity and performance: Hindrance or challenge effect? *Journal of Career Development, 48*(2), 150–165. https://doi.org/10.1177/0894845319833189

Probst, T. M. (2005). Countering the negative effects of job insecurity through participative decision making: Lessons from the demand-control model. *Journal of Occupational Health Psychology, 10*(4), 320–329. https://doi.org/10.1037/1076-8998.10.4.320

Probst, T. M., & Jiang, L. (2017). European flexicurity policies: Multilevel effects on employee psychosocial reactions to job insecurity. *Safety Science, 100*(Part A), 83–90. https://doi.org/10.1016/j.ssci.2017.03.010

Probst, T. M., Jiang, L., & López-Bohle, S. A. (2020). Job insecurity and impression management: Which is the horse and which is the cart when it comes to job performance? *Career Development International, 25*(3), 306–324. https://doi.org/10.1108/CDI-04-2018-0119

Robinson, S. L., & Rousseau, D. M. (1994). Violating the psychological contract: Not the exception but the norm. *Journal of Organizational Behavior, 15*(3), 245–259. https://doi.org/10.1002/job.4030150306

Schreurs, B., Guenter, H., Jawahar, I. M., & De Cuyper, N. (2015). Speaking up when feeling job insecure: The moderating role of punishment and reward sensitivity. *Journal of Organizational Change Management, 28*(6), 1107–1128. https://doi.org/10.1108/JOCM-02-2015-0027

Schumacher, D., Schreurs, B., De Cuyper, N., & Grosemans, I. (2020, October 21). The ups and downs of felt job insecurity and job performance: The moderating role of informational justice. *Work & Stress.* https://doi.org/10.1080/02678373.2020.1832607

Selenko, E., & Batinic, B. (2013). Job insecurity and the benefits of work. *European Journal of Work and Organizational Psychology, 22*(6), 725–736. https://doi.org/10.1080/1359432X.2012.703376

Selenko, E., & De Witte, H. (2020, June 10). How job insecurity affects political attitudes: Identity threat plays a role. *Applied Psychology: An International Review.*

Selenko, E., Mäkikangas, A., Mauno, S., & Kinnunen, U. (2013). How does job insecurity relate to self-reported job performance? Analysing curvilinear associations in a longitudinal sample. *Journal of Occupational and Organizational Psychology, 86*(4), 522–542. https://doi.org/10.1111/joop.12020

Selenko, E., Mäkikangas, A., & Stride, C. B. (2017). Does job insecurity threaten who you are? Introducing a social identity perspective to explain well-being and performance consequences of job insecurity. *Journal of Organizational Behavior, 38*(6), 856–875. https://doi.org/10.1002/job.2172

Selenko, E., Stiglbauer, B., & Batinic, B. (2020). More evidence on the latent benefits of work: Bolstered by volunteering while threatened by job insecurity. *European Journal of Work and Organizational Psychology, 29*(3), 364–376. https://doi.org/10.1080/1359432X.2019.1706487

Shoss, M. K. (2017). Job insecurity: An integrative review and agenda for future research. *Journal of Management, 43*(6), 1911–1939. https://doi.org/10.1177/0149206317691574

Shoss, M. K., & Probst, T. M. (2012). Multilevel outcomes of economic stress: An agenda for future research. In P. Perrewe, C. Rosen, & J. Halbesleben (Eds.), *Research in occupational stress and well-being: The role of economic context on occupational stress and well-being* (Vol. 10, pp. 43–86). Emerald.

Silla, I., De Cuyper, N., Gracia, F. J., Peiró, J. M., & De Witte, H. (2009). Job insecurity and well-being: Moderation by employability. *Journal of Happiness Studies: An Interdisciplinary Forum on Subjective Well-Being, 10*(6), 739–751. https://doi.org/10.1007/s10902-008-9119-0

Spurk, D., Kauffeld, S., Meinecke, A. L., & Ebner, K. (2016). Why do adaptable people feel less insecure? Indirect effects of career adaptability on job and career insecurity via two types of perceived marketability. *Journal of Career Assessment, 24*(2), 289–306. https://doi.org/10.1177/1069072715580415

Sverke, M., & Hellgren, J. (2002). The nature of job insecurity: Understanding employment uncertainty on the brink of a new millennium. *Applied Psychology: An International Review, 51*(1), 23–42. https://doi.org/10.1111/1464-0597.0077z

Sverke, M., Hellgren, J., & Näswall, K. (2002). No security: A meta-analysis and review of job insecurity and its consequences. *Journal of Occupational Health Psychology, 7*(3), 242–264. https://doi.org/10.1037/1076-8998.7.3.242

Sverke, M., Hellgren, J., Näswall, K., Chirumbolo, A., De Witte, H., & Goslinga, S. (2004). *Job insecurity and union membership: European unions in the wake of flexible production.* Peter Lang.

Sverke, M., Låstad, L., Hellgren, J., Richter, A., & Näswall, K. (2019). A meta-analysis of job insecurity and employee performance: Testing temporal aspects, rating source, welfare regime, and union density as moderators. *International Journal of Environmental Research and Public Health, 16*(14), 2536. https://doi.org/10.3390/ijerph16142536

Tajfel, H., & Turner, J. C. (1986). The social identity theory of intergroup behavior. In S. Worchel & W. G. Austin (Eds.), *Psychology of intergroup relation* (pp. 7–24). Hall.

Van den Brande, W., Baillien, E., De Witte, H., Vander Elst, T., & Godderis, L. (2016). The role of work stressors, coping strategies and coping resources in the process of workplace bullying: A systematic review and development of a comprehensive model. *Aggression and Violent Behavior, 29*, 61–71. https://doi.org/10.1016/j.avb.2016.06.004

Vander Elst, T., De Witte, H., & De Cuyper, N. (2014a). The Job Insecurity Scale: A psychometric evaluation across five European countries. *European Journal of Work and Organizational Psychology, 23*(3), 364–380. https://doi.org/10.1080/1359432X.2012.745989

Vander Elst, T., Van den Broeck, A., De Cuyper, N., & De Witte, H. (2014b). On the reciprocal relationship between job insecurity and employee well-being: Mediation by perceived control? *Journal of Occupational and Organizational Psychology, 87*(4), 671–693. https://doi.org/10.1111/joop.12068

Vander Elst, T., Van den Broeck, A., De Witte, H., & De Cuyper, N. (2012). The mediating role of frustration of psychological needs in the relationship between job insecurity and work-related well-being. *Work & Stress, 26*(3), 252–271.

Van Hootegem, A., De Witte, H., De Cuyper, N., & Vander Elst, T. (2019). Job insecurity and the willingness to undertake training: The moderating role of perceived employability. *Journal of Career Development, 46*(4), 395–409.

van Oorschot, W., & Chung, H. (2015). Feelings of dual-insecurity among European workers: A multi-level analysis. *European Journal of Industrial Relations, 21*(1), 23–37.

Wang, H., Lu, C., & Siu, O. (2015). Job insecurity and job performance: The moderating role of organizational justice and the mediating role of work engagement. *Journal of Applied Psychology, 100*(4), 1249–1258.

Wroe, A. (2014). Political trust and job insecurity in 18 European polities. *Journal of Trust Research, 4*(2), 90–112. https://doi.org/10.1080/21515581.2014.957291

Wu, C.-H., Wang, Y., Parker, S. K., & Griffin, M. A. (2020). Effects of chronic job insecurity on Big Five personality change. *Journal of Applied Psychology, 105*(11), 1308–1326. http://dx.doi.org/10.1037/apl0000488

Nele De Cuyper and Hans De Witte

TRAINING FROM AN ORGANIZATIONAL PSYCHOLOGY PERSPECTIVE

WHAT IS TRAINING?

Organizational training has been defined in a number of ways over the years. A classic definition offered by Goldstein and Ford (2002) defined training as the systematic acquisition of skills, rules, concepts, or attitudes that result in improved performance in another environment. In another popular training text, Noe (2010) defined training as a planned effort by a company to facilitate employees' learning of job-related competencies. Note that the former definition focuses on acquisition (learning) by the trainee, whereas the latter emphasizes the deliberate effort by the organization. Further, Noe addresses competencies that are job-related, whereas Goldstein and Ford are more specific as to training content—what is acquired are "skills, rules, concepts, or attitudes" that facilitate performance improvement.

A more recent definition of training that builds on both these definitions was offered by Kraiger and Culbertson (2013), who defined training as the systematic processes initiated by the organization that result in the relatively permanent changes in the knowledge, skills, or attitudes of organizational members. This perspective is more useful than prior ones because it recognizes that learning can occur without training (e.g., incidental learning) *and* that training can occur without learning (in the case of ineffective training). It also highlights the following important properties of training: (1) Training is deliberate or intentional on the part of the organization, and thus is distinct from self-directed learning which is initiated by the employee either formally or informally (Noe, Clarke, & Klein, 2014); (2) The outcomes of training are multidimensional—individuals responsible for training (trainers, training managers, etc.) should be able to specify precise knowledge, skills, affect, or attitudes that can be acquired via training and that affect individual performance (Kraiger, Ford, & Salas, 1993); (3) Training is most effective when it is systematic, when processes are in place to determine training requirements, prepare learners, evaluate training outcomes, and support learners back in the work environment (Salas, Tannenbaum, Kraiger, & Smith-Jentsch, 2012).

Training and Learning.   While training does not guarantee learning, it is impossible to discuss training without referencing learning. What is learning? In the training literature, learning is often defined as simply what results from training: "Learning is a desired outcome of training when one acquires new knowledge or behavior through practice, study, or experience" (Salas, Tannenbaum, Kriger, & Smith-Jentsch, 2012, p. 77). A more useful definition tells us something about the process, or how the learner transitions from "not knowing" (or lacking a skill) to "knowing" (or executing the skill). In educational psychology, Mayer (2008, p. 761) provided a definition that includes the outcome but also incorporates the transitional processes:

> (learning is) a change in the learner's knowledge that is attributable to experience... [and] depends on... cognitive processing during learning and includes (a) selecting— attending to the relevant material; (b) organizing—organizing the material into a coherent

mental representation; and (c) integrating—relating the incoming material with existing knowledge from long-term memory.

If the concept of "change in knowledge" is expanded to include changes in behaviors or skills, affect or attitude, this becomes a useful working definition. It highlights both the role of experience (which can include training content) and the mental activity on the part of the learner that successfully encodes and stores the information.

Returning to the definition of training, we can slightly modify the definition offered by Kraiger and Culbertson (2013) to the following: Training as the systematic processes initiated by the organization that *facilitate* relatively permanent changes in the knowledge, skills, or affect/attitudes of organizational members. Members will learn with or without training, but successful training optimizes the acquisition, retention, and retrieval of training content. Training research then can be organized around approaches or interventions that best facilitate and support learning, as well as on ways of measuring change.

DOES TRAINING FACILITATE LEARNING?

For many decades, training research stagnated, leading Campbell (1971) in his *Annual Review* chapter to conclude that the field of training was "voluminous, non-empirical, non-theoretical, poorly written, and dull" (p. 565). Yet, 30 years later, Salas and Cannon-Bowers (2001) not only pronounced a "decade of progress" (in theory and research), but that we now had a "science of training." Instrumental in this development were three papers published in the late 1980s and early 1990s. First, Baldwin and Ford (1988) examined why knowledge and skills learned in training were not only evident back on the job. In developing their transfer of training model, they drew attention to the distinction between learning in training and transfer on the job, and highlighted the importance of understanding training as one event in a broader organizational context. Noe's (1986) training effectiveness model similarly adapted a systems perspective, but also included the internal world of the learner. According to Noe, while the extent to which training affects later trainee behavior and performance depends *in part* on training delivery, both organizational-level variables (e.g., organizational support) and within-person variables (e.g., trainee self-efficacy or motivation) are influential in driving training outcomes and worthy of research attention. In sum, both Baldwin and Ford and Noe argued that the effectiveness of the effectiveness of training depended as much or more on broader systems variables than on training delivery.

While these papers broadened our perspective of training effectiveness, Kraiger, Ford, and Salas (1993) focused attention *inward* to the mental processes of the learner. For decades, training practitioners and researchers emphasized "behavioral objectives" as the standard for designing and evaluating training—what the trainee could be expected to be able to *do* after training. This narrow focus ignored the so-called cognitive revolution in other areas of psychology (Gardner, 1987) that recognized that learning occurs in many ways including changes in appreciation (for), beliefs (in), understanding (of), mental models (about), and so forth. While Kraiger et al. was intended as more of a call for sharper training design, it had a significant impact on how training researchers have sought to evaluate training programs (Aguinis & Kraiger, 2009; Ford, Kraiger, & Merritt, 2010; Salas et al., 2012).

Evidence That Training Works. So, does training work? Cumulative evidence says yes. Salas et al. (2012) presented summaries of eight separate meta-analyses on training effectiveness. First, in an omnibus meta-analysis of all obtainable training studies, Arthur, Bennett, Edens, and Bell (2003) reported an overall effect size (d) of .63 for learning criteria and .62 for behavioral criteria. Taylor, Russ-Eft, and Chan (2005) examined the effectiveness of behavior modeling training, and found d's over 1.00 for knowledge criteria, .29 for attitudes, and .25 for behavioral outcomes. Keith and Frese (2008) found an average d of .44 across criteria for error management training. Finally, and not reported by Salas et al., Mattingly, Kraiger, and Huntington (2016) reported mean effect sizes across outcome types between .42 and .53 for emotional intelligence training.

Other meta-analyses reported by Salas et al. (2012) have examined the effectiveness of training in specific populations. Two meta-analyses have examined the effectiveness of training for managers. Examining *managerial training*, Burke and Day (1986) reported overall effect sizes of .34 to .38 for learning criteria and .49 for behavioral criteria. In a subsequent meta-analysis, Powell and Yalcin (2010) reported lower, but still positive effect sizes: .17 to .55 for learning criteria and .17 to .30 for behavioral criteria. Examining broader *managerial leadership development* (which includes training), Collins and Holton (2004) reported effect sizes of .35 for knowledge outcomes and .40 for behavioral criteria using rigorous pretest–posttest with control group designs, and stronger effect sizes with less rigorous designs.

Two additional meta-analyses addressed team training effectiveness. Salas, Nichols, and Driskell (2007) examined the effectiveness of three forms of team training: cross-training, team coordination and adaptation training, and guided team self-correction training. Across criterion types, the researchers reported mean effect sizes between .45 and .61. In a broader investigation of all forms of team training, Salas et al. (2008) reported mean d's of .42 for cognitive outcomes, .35 for affective outcomes, and .39 for performance outcomes.

While reported mean effect sizes differ based on the scope of the meta-analysis and the criterion of interest, all reported mean effect sizes were significant. What is the practical impact of training? In a gross exercise of combining apples and oranges, the median effect size reported across the aforementioned meta-analyses and criteria is .46, a "moderate"-sized effect (Cohen, 1988). A d of .46 would mean that the average participant in a training group would be at the 68th percentile of the control group distribution. Examined yet another way using the Binomial Effect Size Display (Randolph & Edmondson, 2005), a d value of .46 would mean, in practice, that while 38.8% of a control (no-training) group would be expected to improve, 62.1% of those receiving training would do so. Thus, training on average results in a 23% improvement over no training. Note that this effect size is for all forms of training; the expected effect size would likely be better if generated only from studies in which: (1) evaluation criteria are matched to training objectives (Kraiger & Jung, 1997); (2) principles of effective instruction are built into training (see Core Instructional Processes); and (3) the broader training system is designed to identify and support the learning of training needs (see Pretraining Influences).

CHARACTERISTICS OF EFFECTIVE TRAINING

Active Learning. Not all training is equally successful in achieving intended outcomes. Cumulative research has identified a number of training-related variables that characterize effective training. First, learning should be an active process of the trainee. Bell and Kozlowski (2008) characterized active learning approaches in training as those that encourage learners to ask questions, explore primary and peripheral content, seek feedback, and reflect on content and progress. Thus, active learning in instruction encourages ownership of material and investment in learning processes, thus distinguishing it from more passive learning modes such as listening to lectures or watching videos. In general, active learning can be facilitated by structuring training so that trainees have the opportunity and encouragement to question training content (e.g., would this principle apply in situations not covered in training?), spontaneously produce variations of content (e.g., what are other ways to build rapport with another person?), practice new skills, receive immediate and specific feedback (e.g., remember to put on your oxygen mask before assisting others), and reflect on new material (e.g., what were the three most important concepts you learned today)?

Self-Regulation.   Closely related to the practice of active learning is self-regulation. Self-regulation in learning is the "modulation of affective, cognitive, and behavioral processes throughout a learning experience to reach a desired level of achievement" (Sitzmann & Ely, 2011, p. 421). Self-regulation is generally a learner-centric process, one resulting from self-set mastery goals and one that can lead to a number of effective learner activities such as planning, monitoring, allocating effort and attention, and evaluating and responding to progress toward learning objectives. While it is speculated that there are individual differences in the extent to which learners spontaneously engage in self-regulatory activities (Winne, 1996), there is also experimental evidence that *prompting* self-regulation can result in effective learner practices and greater learning in training (e.g., Berthold, Nückles, & Renkl, 2007; Sitzmann, Bell, Kraiger, & Kanar, 2009; Sitzmann & Ely, 2010). For example, Sitzmann et al. reported two studies in which simple prompts inserted periodically in training slides (e.g., are you ready now to be tested?) significantly improved training performance. In a meta-analysis by Sitzmann and Ely (2011), self-regulatory mechanisms prompting goal level, persistence, effort, and self-efficacy played a significant instrument role in learning after accounting for prior knowledge and cognitive ability. Thus, it is important for training programs to be designed to both encourage self-regulation and assist learners to engage in effective self-regulation (DeRouin, Fritzsche, & Salas, 2005).

Training Structure.   One mechanism for encouraging self-regulation and increasing engagement is to provide sufficient structure. This includes providing program-level and module-level overviews of instructional objectives, helping learners understand the relevance of training content, and providing regular feedback on learning performance. It has been well-established that providing learners control over the instructional environment is either not productive or counterproductive (Kraiger & Jerden, 2007; Landers & Reddock, in press). In the absence of structure, learners may not engage in effective planning, or implement ineffective learning strategies (Sitzmann & Johnson, 2012). One strategy for providing structure is to provide an advanced organizer. An advanced organizer is an outline or framework of training content; examples include a list of learning objectives, a course outline, or examples of how the training is used back on the job (Mayer, 1979). Advanced organizers can help learners focus on what's important in training and have been found to improve learning (Luiten, Ames,

& Ackerson, 1980; Stone, 1983). In technology-distributed instruction, another option for providing structure is adaptive guidance (Bell & Kozlowski, 2002a, 2008, 2010). Adaptive guidance is a form of training that provides autonomy to learners to explore the training domain, while simultaneously providing them with diagnostic and interpretive information to assist their learning decisions. For example, the learning software may suggest that, based on their training performance, the trainee should review key material before moving on to another module.

Requiring Effort. In addition, it is important to make sure training is designed in a way that requires learners to exert "optimal effort" in training. What optimal is varies by content area and trainee, but training materials should neither be too hard nor too easy for learners. It is well established that those training conditions which accelerate skill acquisition often diminish retention and transfer of learned skills (Schmidt & Bjork, 1992). Though there are a number of reasons this may be so, a primary one is that skill acquisition can be accelerated through drill and practice, as well as by narrowing the variety in stimuli that elicit the desired response. In recreational sports, this is akin to learning tennis by hitting against a machine that always places the ball in the same space and at the same speed, but then floundering against an actual opponent who hits the ball to different locations.

One of the best ways to ensure effort during learning is to build practice variability into the learning paradigm (Schmidt & Bjork, 1992). Practice variability simply means that the learning and practice conditions are allowed to vary (randomly or systematically) across learning trials. In one training demonstration of this effect, Holladay and Quiñones (2003) had undergraduate trainees learn a complex computer-based computer naval air defense simulation making a series of decisions based on attributes of the enemy target. The number of attributes was either constant or variable, and—consistent with prior cognitive science research—participants demonstrated better learning outcomes in response to the variable practice attributes. Practice variability slows learner acquisition, but is thought to help learners build more complex mental models of task performance and enhance their self-efficacy for performance.

Two other mechanisms for promoting effortful learning are action learning and Desirable Difficulties. Previously discussed, action learning is an empirically supported strategy for increasing trainees' learner attention to training (Bell & Kozlowski, 2002a, 2010). Action learning also promotes control of the learning environment (preferably with instructional guidance) and is believed to trigger a number of inductive processes by learners such as inferring rules, principles, and performance strategies. In the cognitive domain, Bjork and Bjork (2011) recommend the Desirable Difficulties principle for increasing learner effort and improving retention. Desirable Difficulties refer to empirically supported instructional strategies that prompt learner cognitive effort in the form of encoding and retrieval processes involved in learning, comprehension, and remembering. Examples of Desirable Difficulties include spacing (rather than massing) learning sessions, interleaving training content from multiple domains, testing rather than restudying, or having learners generate definitions (rather than be told) (see Dunlosky, Rawson, Marsh, Nathan, & Willingham (2013). Both action learning and Desirable Difficulties work by promoting deeper processing and self-regulation in learners (Bell & Kozlowski, 2010; Bjork, Dunlosky, & Kornell, 2013).

Core Instructional Processes. Each of the training strategies discussed so far represent emergent methods for engaging learners and optimizing training effectiveness. Many are also rooted in modern theories of how we learn. However, there are a number of "tried-and-true" training practices that also increase training effectiveness. Noe and Colquitt (2002) conducted a broad qualitative review of training literature and identified six characteristics of well-designed instruction that enhance learning. They are as follows: (1) The purpose, objectives, and intended outcomes of training are clearly communicated to trainees. Consistent with Mayer's (2008) organizing step in learning, these can be communicated at the outset of training. They should also be provided when trainees register for (or are assigned to) training to ensure the proper mindset for training. (2) The training content is meaningful, and training assignments, examples, and exercises are relevant to the job. This both supports the integration of new information with prior knowledge (Mayer's third step), increases motivation to learn (Noe, 1986), especially for older learners (Callahan, Kiker, & Cross, 2003), and facilitates transfer of training (Baldwin & Ford, 1988). (3) Trainees are provided with instructional aids that can help them organize, learn, and recall training content. These aids facilitate selection and organizing processes (Mayer, 2008) and can also reduce cognitive load during learning (Seufert & Brünken, 2006). (4) Opportunities for practice in a safe environment are provided. Carefully designed practice increases cognitive effort during training and also facilitates later transfer. A safe environment encourages learners to take risks and make errors, which can be advantageous during learning (Keith & Frese, 2008). The benefits of practice for skill acquisition in a wide range of performance domains is well documented (McNamara, Hambrick, & Oswald, 2014). (5) Feedback on learning and mastery is provided by trainers, observers, peers, or the task itself. Again, the benefits of feedback on performance improvement are well established (Azevedo & Bernard, 1995; Hatala, Cook, Zendejas, Hamstra, & Brydges, 2014; Kluger & DeNisi, 1996). Specific feedback that is close in time to behaviors performed in training allows incorrect behaviors to be stopped before habits are acquired, reinforces positive behaviors, and facilitates self-regulation by learners. (6) Training enables learners to observe and interact with others. Allowing interactions among participants promotes observational learning in which trainees can both mimic high performers and see high performers rewarded (Decker & Nathan, 1985). Additionally, it is sometimes the case that trainers know the content too well and struggle to explain it to a novice, whereas a fellow trainee who just acquired new knowledge or a new skill may be able to help other trainees make the jump to understanding the new content. Finally, interaction with other learners is critical to socially deriving meaning in learning environments: "learners (can) interpret, clarify and validate their understanding through sustained dialogue (i.e., two-way communication) and negotiation" (Garrison, 1993, p. 202). Further, Kraiger (2008) argued that through this social negotiation during training, trainees learn social skills that will promote later sense-making and learning back on the job.

CHARACTERISTICS OF EFFECTIVE SYSTEMS FOR TRAINING

The extent to which trainees acquire and apply new knowledge and skills is not only a function of training delivery, but also the larger training system. Thus far, we have examined primarily instructional (in-training) processes. In this section, we examine factors before and after training takes place. As already noted, Noe (1986) was the first to call attention to individual-level and system-level influences on training impact. Since then, other researchers have proposed and tested even broader models of training effectiveness (e.g., Cannon-Bowers, Salas, Tannenbaum, & Mathieu, 1995; Colquitt, LePine, & Noe, 2000). Here training effectiveness refers to individual- and system-level influences on the extent to which knowledge and skills are learned, transferred to the job, and maintained. Following Salas et al. (2012), this discussion is divided into pretraining and posttraining influences.

Pretraining Influences.   One of the primary actions that an organization can do to increase training effectiveness is to conduct a training needs assessment (Goldstein & Ford, 2002). Conceptually, a training needs assessment is a multi-step process to ensure that training targets the requisite knowledge and skills for employees to do their jobs and to ensure that the organization at all levels is in position to support training efforts. In a classic needs assessment, three phases are conducted (Goldstein & Ford, 2002). An organizational assessment identifies whether there is organizational support (e.g., interest and resources) and whether training can be tied to broader organizational initiatives (e.g., lean production). To a large extent, the results of organizational assessment determine whether or not training is likely to be chosen as an intervention. The second phase is a job or task analysis, in which the key tasks to be training and/or the core skills to perform those tasks are identified. The job/task assessment identifies the training content. The third phase is a person analysis, in which the training participants are identified (e.g., low performers) and/or special characteristics of participants are investigated (e.g., familiarity and comfort with mobile learning). The former focus assumes that not all workers in a job will be assigned to training. The latter assumes that training can be customized to learner preferences or attributes. Both assumptions are often not valid in many training contexts.

Within the training field, there is also an implicit assumption that the three phases are conducted in the order presented, that is, that the organizational assessment precedes the job/task analysis, which in turn precedes the person analysis. However, there is no research that supports this ordering over another. Logically, if an organizational assessment reveals inadequate support and resources for training, there would be no need for the job and person analysis. However, it could also be the case that the decision to support training is dependent on what specifically needs to be trained or on how many employees have subpar performance. Further, assessing worker performance (part of the person analysis) could yield insights as to which tasks should be the focus of the job/task analysis. Although the three phases were proposed many decades ago (Goldstein, 1974; McGehee & Thayer, 1961), we still know very little about the practical implications over variations in their ordering.

A more recent training needs assessment model is more prescriptive about the order of steps and is also more practical in many applied contexts. Surface (2012) has proposed a four-phase training needs assessment (TNA) process, which consists of *Needs Identification Phase* (addressing whether or not a TNA should be conducted), *Needs Specification Phase* (identifying specific existing knowledge, skill, or performance gaps and determining whether learning can address those gaps), *Training Needs Assessment Phase* (aspects of traditional organizational, task, and person analyses, as determined by the prior phase), and *TNA Evaluation Phase* (determining the impact of earlier decisions during earlier phases on the identified gaps). The four-phase process has many potential advantages over prior models. Primarily, it helps stakeholders focus on critical decisions at different times. Additionally, decision-making (and analysis) resources are conserved, since an all-out organizational/task/personal analysis is only conducted as warranted. Finally, it clarifies for decision-makers that training is only one of many possible solutions to perceived performance gaps (cf. Robinson & Robinson, 1995).

Despite the practical importance of training needs assessment, there is little evidence that it is frequently done to support training design. Both the Association for Talent Development and *Training* magazine conduct yearly surveys of training practices in U.S. companies. Neither survey tracks expenditures or activities related to needs assessment. In the 2014 survey reported by *Training* (2014), they reported on 23 categories of anticipated expenditures for 2015. Although there is no category for TNA, there is one for "Content Development," and presumably some training professionals anticipating developing new content would conduct a needs assessment prior to doing so. Only 29% of surveyed companies reported plans to invest in content development, thus setting the upper bound on estimates of the frequency of TNA. A more somber estimate can be drawn from Arthur et al.'s (2003) meta-analysis of training effectiveness. The authors reported that for only 6% of the reported effect sizes was there a prior needs assessment.

While the disconnect between the importance and prevalence of needs assessment is more of a concern for practice than for science, there are nonetheless research implications. For one, it would be valuable to understand better why training needs assessment is not done more frequently. There are likely high perceived costs in time and resources, but it would be interesting to approach the problem from a cost–benefit approach. There are multiple financial benefits of conducting a needs assessment: unnecessary training is reduced, individuals who do not need to be trained are kept on the job and not sent to training, and training is designed to maximize training outcomes. Applied research could investigate whether training professionals are aware of the benefits and to what extent these benefits factor into training investment decisions relative to the costs of needs assessments. For example, at what point do the potential savings from a well-designed needs assessment outweigh the costs in the minds of training stakeholders? There have also been occasional calls for rapid or just-in-time training needs assessment in which training professionals are able to stand up micro training programs quickly in response to emerging performance problems (e.g., Leat & Lovell, 1997; Wilson, Jonassen, & Cole, 1993). The effectiveness of these approaches and their attractiveness and credibility relative to traditional training programs are also interesting research questions. Finally, broader questions of how best to position training in general and needs assessment in particular as strategic investments on the part of the organization bear greater attention from training researchers (Iqbal & Khan, 2011).

In addition to the importance of linking training content to a training needs assessment, the other critical factor to be addressed pretraining is to ensure trainees are motivated to learn. Motivation to learn refers to the extent to which trainees are willing to exert effort in a training environment (Noe & Schmitt, 1986) and consists of both perceived value of mastering the training content and their beliefs that they are capable of learning. Motivation to learn has a number of positive impacts on the training function—trainees are more likely to choose to attend training, they exert more effort and persist in training activities, and they are more likely to transfer learned skills to the job (Quiñones, 1995). Trainee motivation to learn is partly determined by individual characteristics including proactive and Big Five personality variables (Major, Turner, & Fletcher, 2006), as well as self-efficacy and a mastery orientation (see Colquitt, LePine, & Noe, 2000; Noe & Colquitt, 2002, for a review). However, motivation to learn is also influenced by factors under the control of the organization, including how the need for training is framed to trainees, for example, mandatory or optional, remedial or developmental (Baldwin, Magjuka, & Loher, 1991; Hicks & Klimoski, 1987; Tsai & Tai, 2003) and whether employees believe they were fairly chosen for training (Quiñones, 1995). Additionally, motivation to learn is greater when training is promoted as intrinsically beneficial to the learner (Kooij, De Lange, Jansen, Kanfer, & Dikkers 2011). Perceived or anticipated support for training can also affect motivation to learn. For example, when trainees perceive that the training is sanctioned by their supervisor, they will have the opportunity to use what they learned in training, and they will have both supervisor and peer support for training, their motivation for training is greater (Kim-Soon, Ahmad, & Ahmad, 2014). Finally, and not surprisingly, prior experiences in training can influence future motivation to learn. Sitzmann, Brown, Ely, and Kraiger (2009) measured motivation at multiple time points in one organization and found that trainees who had negative reactions to earlier training courses had lower training motivation in later courses. For more on organizational-level influences, see Colquitt and associates (Colquitt et al., 2000; Noe & Colquitt, 2002).

Motivation to learn could be assessed as part of a prior needs assessment, measured at the outset of training, or gauged by the trainer based on prior knowledge of the trainees and the course material. Given its importance to training outcomes, it is important that training be designed to maximize trainee motivation regardless of pre-existing levels. In general, motivation to learn can be maximized to the extent that supervisors have already communicated the importance and value of the training, the trainer or training materials clearly communicate what is to be learned and how this information is relevant and useful to trainees, training content links new information to prior knowledge of trainees or their prior experiences, and plans to support the trainee back on the job are clearly communicated.

Posttraining Influences. Training has been shown to have a significant impact on learning and performance outcomes in multiple meta-analyses. Training effectiveness can be enhanced through well-designed training that incorporates empirically supported instructional principles and best practices. It can also be enhanced through conducting a needs assessment to ensure that the training content is relevant to the organization and the trainees, and it can be enhanced through attention to trainees' motivation to learn. It can also be enhanced through posttraining factors that foster the implementation, maintenance, and generalization of knowledge and behaviors acquired in training.

Transfer of training refers to the extent to which trainees apply the knowledge, skills, and attitudes acquired in training and on the job (Baldwin & Ford, 1988; Baldwin, Ford, & Blume, 2009). Kraiger (2002) distinguished between implementing or displaying a behavior on the job, on the one hand, and the effectiveness of that behavior, on the other. While the goal of training is typically to improve trainee job performance (increase behavioral effectiveness), the immediate transfer goal should be that trainees carry out learned behaviors on the job (irrespective of effectiveness). For example, suppose a human resource specialist is instructed on how to ask probing questions in a structured interview. Transfer first occurs when the specialist uses probing questions during an actual structured interview. But, it could be the case that doing so is not "natural" and sounds forced, or there are some probes that work more effectively than others. There is evidence of transfer because the correct behaviors were displayed. Behavioral effectiveness, or performance, comes later with practice, feedback, and personalization of the questions. The immediate goal, however, is the display. In addition to personal and situational factors discussed in this section, training fidelity—the psychological and physical relationship between the training and work context—facilitates this form of transfer (Baldwin & Ford, 1988; Burke & Hutchins, 2007; Holton & Baldwin, 2003).

Baldwin and Ford (1988) further distinguished between maintenance and generalization. If a behavior that is attempted gets discarded, transfer has not occurred. The behavior must be learned well enough that it is repeated and maintained over time. Generalization refers to the extent to which the learned behavior is executed in response to situations beyond those covered in training. For example, if the human resource specialist applies similar probing questions for a variety of jobs, or when conducting exit interviews, generalization has occurred.

Transfer of training can be influenced by variables present before training, during training, and after training (Kraiger & Culbertson, 2013). For example, pretraining motivation to learn is related both to posttraining motivation to transfer (Kontoghiorghes, 2002, 2004) and to actual transfer of training (Gegenfurtner & Vauras, 2012)). Many of the training design factors previously discussed, such as practice variability, are positive influences on transfer of training. This section thus focuses primarily on posttraining factors.

Posttraining factors influencing the transfer of training back to the job can be divided into characteristics of the trainee, the work, peers and supervisors, and the transfer or organizational climate. These broad factors were evaluated empirically in a recent meta-analysis by Blume, Ford, Baldwin, and Huang (2010). With respect to trainee characteristics, not surprisingly, trainee motivation to transfer is predictive of actual transfer back to the job. In their meta-analysis of 89 studies, Blume et al. found a mean population correlation of .29 between motivation and actual transfer. Consistent with the Theory of Planned Behavior (Ajzen, 1991), trainees who intend to apply what they learned are more apt to do so. However, a number of trainee characteristics also predicted transfer, including cognitive ability ($\rho = .37$), conscientiousness ($\rho = .28$), pretraining self-efficacy ($\rho = .22$), learning goal orientation ($\rho = .16$), and job involvement ($\rho = .38$). Essentially, workers who are most likely to be the "best trainees" are also those most likely to succeed applying what they learned back on the job.

Another strong determinant of transfer is what Ford and colleagues referred to as "opportunity to perform," or the extent to which trainees can immediately apply what they learned to relevant job situations (Ford, Quiñones, Sego, & Sorra, 1992; Quiñones, Ford, Sego, & Smith, 1995). Opportunity to perform may be attenuated, for example, when a trainee is assigned to work that is different than what he or she was trained in or when there is organizational pressure for high job performance rather than experimenting with new job skills. Low opportunity to perform has a negative impact on trainee motivation to transfer (Seyler, Holton, Bates, Burnett, & Carvalho, 1998), which in turn is negatively related to actual transfer (Axtell, Maitlis, & Yearta, 1997).

Social support is important for learned skills to be attempted, maintained, and generalized on the job. Both peers and supervisors can support trainees by inquiring about what was learned, encouraging attempts to transfer, supporting mistakes, and reinforcing successful attempts (Rouiller & Goldstein, 1993; Tracey, Tannenbaum, & Kavanagh, 1995). Blume et al. (2010) reported a significant, positive effect for social support ($\rho = .21$), although they did not differentiate between the impact of peers or supervisors. While there is tremendous variability in the studies of the effectiveness of social support on transfer (Aguinis & Kraiger, 2009; Kraiger & Culbertson, 2013), when social support does positively impact transfer, research suggests it does so through the mediating effects of trainee self-efficacy, motivation to transfer, and mastery goal orientation (Chiaburu, Van Dam, & Hutchins, 2010).

Finally, the broader transfer climate can influence the extent to which knowledge and skills acquired in training are applied and maintained on the job. Fleishman, Harris, and Burtt (1955) was the first empirical study to show that a supportive climate (via the actions of managers) has an impact on the maintenance of trained behaviors. The first known measure of transfer climate was by Rouiller and Goldstein (1993), who used a critical incident approach to measure the situational cues (goals, social cues, and task cues) and consequences (feedback, reinforcers, and punishment) that either facilitate or inhibit transfer. Subsequently, Holton, Bates, and Ruona (2000) developed and conducted extensive validation on a broader, proprietary transfer climate measure.

While some individual studies have found that transfer climate improves transfer (e.g., Kontoghiorghes, 2004), other findings do not find significant effects (e.g., Cheng & Hampson, 2008). Blume et al. (2010) did report a significant, positive effect for transfer climate on actual transfer ($\rho = .27$), suggesting that transfer climate matters more often that it doesn't. Kraiger and Culbertson noted that it is important to distinguish between transfer *climate* and (objective) organizational support, which is often measured from the perspective of the trainee. Transfer climate is defined as an aggregation of trainees' perceptions of: (a) supervisor and peer support, (b) opportunity to perform, and (c) accountability and/or consequences for performing. Perceptions matter, but researchers who measure climate using perception-based measures run the risk of exaggerating effects via common method variance. For example, in their transfer meta-analysis, Blume et al., when possible, separated out studies with a same-source and same measurement context (SS/SMC) confound from ones that didn't. Specific to the effects of work environment of transfer, the effect size for SS/SMC ($\rho = .54$) was over twice that for ($\rho = .23$).

While transfer climate research is often limited due to methodological problems, it seems undeniable that transfer is more likely to occur when there are opportunities to perform coupled with peer/supervisor support, as well as accountability and consequences for either performing or not performing. There is also evidence to suggest that perceived transfer climate differs across organizations, or organizational units, suggesting that climate is "real" beyond the eyes of trainees. For example, Holton, Chen, and Naquin (2003) found strong, significant differences in scale scores for peer support, supervisory support, supervisor sanctions, and opportunity to use learning across eight different organizations. Additionally, Bates and Khasawneh (2005) found significant differences across 28 organizations in scale scores for transfer climate dimensions of transfer effort–performance expectations, performance–outcome expectations, performance self-efficacy beliefs, and openness to change perceptions, and, more importantly, found these climate variables mediated the relationship between learning organizational culture and innovation.

In total, evidence supports the importance of the immediate transfer environment to reinforce what was learned in training and encourage application to the job. Salas et al. (2012) provided a number of practical recommendations for organizations interested in promoting transfer, including conducting debriefings of training or critical job events related to training content (Berenholtz et al., 2009; Brock, McManus, & Hale, 2009), access to job aids and knowledge repositories with reminders about what was learned (Gallupe, 2001; Rosenberg, 1995), and establishing "communities of practice" with other learners to foster continuous learning (Wenger, 1998; Wenger, McDermott, & Snyder, 2002).

Training Evaluation. A final characteristic of effective training is comprehensive evaluation. Kraiger et al. (1993) defined training evaluation as the collection and analysis of data to understand whether training objectives were achieved and/or whether meeting those objectives resulted in improved job performance on the job. Training evaluation thus becomes important to organizational decision-making about training (Kraiger, 2002)—Is training designed in a way that trainees are learning? Do trainees like the training they are receiving, and do they want to continue taking more training? Do knowledge and skills acquired in training transfer to the job? Have the performance gaps identified in a needs assessment gone away? Training evaluation closes the loop.

For decades, training evaluation practice has been influenced primarily by Kirkpatrick's (Kirkpatrick & Kirkpatrick, 2006) "four levels model": Do trainees like the training, did they learn anything, did they change their behavior back on the job, and did changes of the job result in improved performance? The four levels consist of trainees' reactions to (or affect toward) the training content, whether or not they learned the training content, whether or not they change their behavior back on the job (as a result of being trained), and whether or not there is some organizational-level benefit to changes in job behavior.

While there are still training researchers who rely on the Kirkpatrick approach (e.g., Pineda-Herrero, Belvis, Moreno, Duran-Bellonch, & Ucar, 2011; Roszkowski & Soven, 2010), increasingly, researchers are recognizing the practical and theoretical shortcomings of this framework (e.g., Holton, 1996; Kraiger, 2002; Spitzer, 2005). In brief, the framework leads to a reflexive approach, with the goal of evaluation being to check more boxes (levels) rather than linking evaluation decisions to both the purpose of evaluation (Kraiger, 2002) and the learning constructs that are the focus of the training intervention (Kraiger, 2002; Kraiger et al., 1993).

In training research, there is evidence of more mindful training evaluation practices. Ford, Kraiger, and Merritt (2010) reviewed 125 studies citing Kraiger et al.'s learning outcomes taxonomy (1993) and found that researchers are increasingly adopting multidimensional approaches to understanding learning, measuring cognitive or affective change as measures of learning (instead of behavioral change alone), using increasingly sophisticated assessment methods (e.g., Davis & Yi, 2004; Day, Arthur, & Gettman, 2001), and measuring trainee affect other than training satisfaction (e.g., Bell & Kozlowski, 2002b; Wallhead & Ntoumanis, 2004).

Additionally, there have been a number of thoughtful papers on aspects related to technical evaluation issues. Arvey and Cole (1989) discussed the evaluation of evaluation data with control groups and pretest scores available, and demonstrated the advantage of using Analysis of Covariance in these situations. Yang, Sackett, and Arvey (1996) reviewed the importance of statistical power in training evaluation designs and recommended several strategies for increasing power when the number trained is constrained. However, Haccoun and Hamtiaux (1994) recognized that in many applied situations, a control group is not possible, and proposed a useful technique for inferring learning when there is not a control group or even a pretest. Sitzmann and Weinhardt (in press) presented a new training engagement model that recommends both multi-level and temporal considerations in evaluating training impact.

Finally, both training professionals and researchers will argue that while thorough evaluation is important, it is often difficult to achieve in practice. Organizations may resist evaluation because evaluation time detracts from training time, and negative evaluation outcomes can be threatening to training champions. Training researchers have responded with multiple strategies for building support for training evaluation. Brinkerhoff (2005) provided multiple methods for building support for linking evaluation practices to key strategic objectives of the organization. Nickols (2005) integrated stakeholder theory with evaluation practices, and both he and Kraiger, McLinden, and Casper (2004) discussed strategies for involving key stakeholders in the design of training evaluation.

FINAL THOUGHTS

The rate of change and need for adaptation in organizations is continually increasing. Challenges created by rapid design and prototyping, leaner organizations, and the global marketplace make it increasingly important that organizations compete on the basis of talent, rather than relying on customer loyalty or product design (Boudreau & Ramstad, 2005). However, there is cumulative evidence that continual investment in the training and development of employees results in a competitive edge for organizations (Park & Jacobs, 2011; Saks & Burke-Smalley, 2014; Tharenou, Saks, & Moore, 2007), particularly when coupled with effective staffing programs (Kim & Ployhart, 2014; Van Iddekinge, Ferris, Perrewé, Perryman, Blass, & Heetderks, 2009).

However, training practice and training research will continue to be challenged by changes in how work is done (e.g., increasing use of technology) and where we work (e.g., the virtual workplace). Information is more available and more rapidly disseminated than ever before, but more information doesn't necessarily mean more knowledge or better performance.

The argument has been continually made that training is most effective when systematic processes are followed—conducting a needs assessment, careful training design, planning and supporting transfer, and ongoing evaluation. As the demand on the workforce changes, and as the nature of work changes, it will be important for training professionals and training researchers to not only continue to push for systematic, mindful practice, but to evaluate continually whether those same processes should be preserved or warrant reexamination themselves.

REFERENCES

Aguinis, H., & Kraiger, K. (2009). Benefits of training and development for individuals and teams, organizations, and society. *Annual Review of Psychology, 60*, 451–474.

Ajzen, I. (1991). The theory of planned behavior. *Organizational Behavior and Human Decision Processes, 50*, 179–211.

Arthur Jr, W., Bennett Jr, W., Edens, P. S., & Bell, S. T. (2003). Effectiveness of training in organizations: A meta-analysis of design and evaluation features. *Journal of Applied Psychology, 88*, 234–245.

Arvey, R. D., & Cole, D. A. (1989). Evaluating change due to training. In I. L. Goldstein & Associates (Eds.), *Training and development in organizations* (pp. 89–117). San Francisco: Jossey-Bass.

Axtell, C. M., Maitlis, S., & Yearta, S. K. (1997). Predicting immediate and longer-term transfer of training. *Personnel Review, 26*, 201–213.

Azevedo, R., & Bernard, R. M. (1995). A meta-analysis of the effects of feedback in computer-based instruction. *Journal of Educational Computing Research, 13*, 111–127.

Baldwin, T. T., & Ford, J. K. (1988). Transfer of training: A review and directions for future research. *Personnel Psychology, 41*, 63–105.

Baldwin, T. T., Ford, J. K., & Blume, B. D. (2009). Transfer of training 1988–2008: An updated review and new agenda for future research. In G. P. Hodgkinson & J. K. Ford (Eds.), *International review of industrial and organizational psychology* (Vol. 24, pp. 41–70). Chichester, U.K.: Wiley.

Baldwin, T. T., Magjuka, R. J., & Loher, B. T. (1991). The perils of participation: Effects of choice of training on trainee motivation and learning. *Personnel Psychology, 44*, 260–267.

Bates, R., & Khasawneh, S. (2005). Organizational learning culture, learning transfer climate and perceived innovation in Jordanian organizations. *International Journal of Training and Development, 9*, 96–109.

Bell, B. S., & Kozlowski, S. W. (2002a). Adaptive guidance: Enhancing self-regulation, knowledge, and performance in technology-based training. *Personnel Psychology, 55*, 267–306.

Bell, B. S., & Kozlowski, S. W. J. (2002b). Goal orientation and ability: Interactive effects on self-efficacy, performance, and knowledge. *Journal of Applied Psychology, 87*, 497–505.

Bell, B. S., & Kozlowski, S. W. J. (2008). Active learning: Effects of core training design elements on self-regulatory processes, learning, and adaptability. *Journal of Applied Psychology, 93*, 296–316.

Bell, B. S., & Kozlowski, S. W. J. (2010). Toward a theory of learner-centered training design: An integrative framework of active learning. In S. W. J. Kozlowski & E. Salas (Eds.), *Learning, training, and development in organizations* (pp. 263–300). New York: Routledge.

Berenholtz, S. M. Schumacher, K., Hayanga, A. J. Simon, M., Goeschel, C., Pronovost, P. J. et al. (2009). Implementing standardized operating room briefings and debriefings at a large regional medical center. *Joint Commission Journal on Quality and Patient Safety, 35*, 391–397.

Berthold, K., Nückles, M., & Renkl, A. (2007). Do learning protocols support learning strategies and outcomes? The role of cognitive and metacognitive prompts. *Learning and Instruction, 17*, 564–577.

Bjork, E. L., & Bjork, R. A. (2011). Making things hard on yourself, but in a good way: Creating desirable difficulties to enhance learning. In M. A. Gernsbacher, R. W. Pew, L. M. Hough, & J. R. Pomerantz (Eds.), *Psychology and the real world: Essays illustrating fundamental contributions to society* (pp. 56–64). New York: Worth Publishers.

Bjork, R. A., Dunlosky, J., & Kornell, N. (2013). Self-regulated learning: Beliefs, techniques, and illusions. *Annual Review of Psychology, 64*, 417–444.

Blume, B. D., Ford, J. K., Baldwin, T. T., & Huang, J. L. (2010). Transfer of training: A meta-analytic review. *Journal of Management, 36*, 1065–1105.

Boudreau, J., & Ramstad, P. (2005). Talentship, talent segmentation, and sustainability: A new HR decision science paradigm for a new strategy definition, *Human Resource Management, 44*, 129–136.

Brinkerhoff, R. O. (2005). The success case method: A strategic evaluation approach to increasing the value and effect of training. *Advances in Developing Human Resources, 7*(1), 86–101.

Brock, G. W., McManus, D. J., & Hale, J. E. (2009). Reflections today prevent failures tomorrow. *Communications of the ACM, 52*, 140–144.

Burke, L. A. & Hutchins, H. M. (2007). Training transfer: An integrative literature review. *Human Resource Development Review, 6*, 263–96.

Burke, M. J., & Day, R. R. (1986). A cumulative study of the effectiveness of managerial training. *Journal of Applied Psychology, 71*, 232–245.

Callahan, J. S., Kiker, D. S., & Cross, T. (2003). Does method matter? A meta-analysis of the effects of training method on older learner training performance. *Journal of Management, 29*, 663–680.

Campbell, J. P. (1971). Personnel training and development. *Annual Review of Psychology, 22*, 565–602.

Cannon-Bowers, J. A., Salas, E., Tannenbaum, S. I., & Mathieu, J. E. (1995). Toward theoretically based principles of training effectiveness: A model and initial empirical investigation. *Military Psychology, 7*, 141–164.

Cheng, E. W., & Hampson, I. (2008). Transfer of training: A review and new insights. *International Journal of Management Reviews, 10*, 327–341.

Chiaburu, D. S., Van Dam, K., & Hutchins, H. M. (2010). Social support in the workplace and training transfer: A longitudinal analysis. *International Journal of Selection and Assessment, 18*, 187–200.

Cohen, J. (1988). *Statistical power analysis for the social sciences* (2nd ed.). Mahwah, NJ: Erlbaum.

Collins, D. B., & Holton, E. F., III. (2004). The effectiveness of managerial leadership development programs: A meta-analysis of studies from 1982 to 2001. *Human Resource Development Quarterly, 15*, 217–248.

Colquitt, J. A., LePine, J. A., & Noe, R. A. (2000). Towards an integrative theory of training motivation: A meta-analytic path analysis of 20 years of research. *Journal of Applied Psychology, 85*, 678–807.

Davis, F. D., & Yi, M. Y. (2004). Improving computer skill training: Behavior modeling, symbolic mental rehearsal, and the role of knowledge structures. *Journal of Applied Psychology, 89*, 509–523.

Day, E. A., Arthur, W., & Gettman, D. (2001). Knowledge structures and the acquisition of a complex skill. *Journal of Applied Psychology, 86*, 1022–1033.

Decker, P. J., & Nathan, B. R. (1985). *Behavior modeling training: Principles and applications.* New York: Praeger

DeRouin, R. E., Fritzsche, B. A., & Salas, E. (2005). Optimizing e-learning: Research-based guidelines for learner-controlled training. *Human Resource Management, 43*, 147–162.

Dunlosky, J., Rawson, K. A., Marsh, E. J., Nathan, M. J., & Willingham, D. T. (2013). Improving students' learning with effective learning techniques promising directions from cognitive and educational psychology. *Psychological Science in the Public Interest, 14*(1), 4–58.

Fleishman, E. A., Harris, E. F., & Burtt, H. E. (1955). *Leadership and supervision in industry* (Report No. 33). Columbus, OH: Bureau of Educational Research, The Ohio State University.

Ford, J. K., Kraiger, K., & Merritt, S. M. (2010). An updated review of the multidimensionality of training outcomes: New directions for training education research. In S. W. J. Kozlowski & E. Salas (Eds.), *Learning, training, and development in organizations* (pp. 135–168). New York: Routledge.

Ford, J. K., Quiñones, M. A., Sego, D. J., & Sorra, J. S. (1992). Factors affecting the opportunity to perform trained tasks on the job. *Personnel Psychology, 45*, 511–527.

Gallupe, B. (2001). Knowledge management systems: Surveying the landscape. *International Journal of Management Reviews, 3*, 61–77.

Gardner, H. (1987). *The mind's new science: A history of the cognitive revolution.* New York: Basic Books.

Garrison, D. R. (1993). A cognitive constructivist view of distance education: An analysis of teaching-learning assumptions. *Distance Education, 14*, 199–211.

Gegenfurtner, A., & Vauras, M. (2012). Age-related differences in the relation between motivation to learn and transfer of training in adult continuing education. *Contemporary Educational Psychology, 37*, 33–46.

Goldstein, I.L. (1974) *Training: Program development and evaluation.* Monterey, CA: Brooks/Cole.

Goldstein, I. L., & Ford, J. K. (2002). *Training in organizations: Needs assessment, development and evaluation* (4th ed.). Belmont, CA: Wadsworth.

Haccoun, R. R., & Hamtiaux, T. (1994). Optimizing knowledge tests for inferring learning acquisition levels in single group training evaluation designs: The internal referencing strategy. *Personnel Psychology, 47*, 593–604.

Hatala, R., Cook, D. A., Zendejas, B., Hamstra, S. J., & Brydges, R. (2014). Feedback for simulation-based procedural skills training: a meta-analysis and critical narrative synthesis. *Advances in Health Sciences Education, 19,* 251–272.

Hicks, W. D., & Klimoski, R. (1987). The process of entering training programs and its effect on training outcomes. *Academy of Management Journal, 30,* 542–552.

Holladay, C. L., & Quiñones, M. A. (2003). Practice variability and transfer of training: The role of self-efficacy generality. *Journal of Applied Psychology, 88,* 1094–1103.

Holton, E. F., Bates, R. A., & Ruona, W. E. (2000). Development of a generalized learning transfer system inventory. *Human Resource Development Quarterly, 11,* 333–360.

Holton, E. F., Chen, H. C., & Naquin, S. S. (2003). An examination of learning transfer system characteristics across organizational settings. *Human Resource Development Quarterly, 14,* 459–482.

Holton, E. F., III. (1996). The flawed four-level evaluation model. *Human Resource Development Quarterly, 7,* 5–21.

Holton, E. F., III, & Baldwin, T. T. (2003). Making transfer happen: An action perspective on learning transfer systems. In E. F. Holton III & T. T. Baldwin (Eds.), *Improving learning transfer in organizations* (pp. 3–15). San Francisco: Jossey-Bass.

Iqbal, M. Z., & Khan, R. A. (2011). The growing concept and uses of training needs assessment: A review with proposed model. *Journal of European Industrial Training, 35,* 439–466.

Keith, N., & Frese, M. (2008). Effectiveness of error management training: A meta-analysis. *Journal of Applied Psychology, 93,* 59–69.

Kim, Y., & Ployhart, R. E. (2014). The effects of staffing and training on firm productivity and profit growth before, during, and after the Great Recession. *Journal of Applied Psychology, 99,* 361–389.

Kim-Soon, N., Ahmad, N., & Ahmad, A. R. (2014). Moderating effects of work environment on motivation to learn and perceived training transfer: Empirical evidence from a bank. *Australian Journal of Basic and Applied Sciences, 8,* 344–361.

Kirkpatrick, D. L., & Kirkpatrick, J. D. (2006). *Evaluating training programs: The four levels* (3rd ed.). San Francisco: Berrett-Koehler.

Kluger, A. N., & DeNisi, A. (1996). The effects of feedback interventions on performance: A historical review, a meta-analysis, and a preliminary feedback intervention theory. *Psychological Bulletin, 119,* 254–284.

Kontoghiorghes, C. (2002). Predicting motivation to learn and motivation to transfer learning back to the job in a service organization: A new systemic model for training effectiveness. *Performance Improvement Quarterly, 15*(3), 114–129.

Kontoghiorghes, C. (2004). Reconceptualizing the learning transfer conceptual framework: Empirical validation of a new systemic model. *International Journal of Training and Development, 8,* 210–221.

Kooij, D. T., De Lange, A. H., Jansen, P. G., Kanfer, R. & Dikkers, J. S. (2011). Age and work-related motives: Results of a meta-analysis. *Journal of Organizational Behavior, 32,* 197–225.

Kraiger, K. (2002). Decision-based evaluation. In K. Kraiger (Ed.), *Creating, implementing, and maintaining effective training and development: State-of-the-art lessons for practice* (pp. 331–375). San Francisco: Jossey-Bass.

Kraiger, K. (2008). Transforming our models of learning and development: Web-based instruction as enabler of third-generation instruction. *Industrial and Organizational Psychology, 1,* 454–467.

Kraiger, K., & Culbertson, S. S. (2013). Understanding and facilitating learning: Advancements in training and development. In I. Weiner, N. Schmitt, & S. Highhouse (Eds.), *Handbook of psychology: Industrial and organizational psychology* (2d ed.) (pp. 244–261). Hoboken, NJ: Wiley.

Kraiger, K., Ford, J. K., & Salas, E. (1993). Application of cognitive, skill-based, and affective theories of learning outcomes to new methods of training evaluation. *Journal of Applied Psychology, 78,* 311–328.

Kraiger, K., & Jerden, E. (2007). A meta-analytic investigation of learner control: Old findings and new directions. In S. M. Fiore & E. Salas (Eds.), *Toward a science of distributed learning* (pp. 65–90). Washington, DC: American Psychological Association.

Kraiger, K., & Jung, K. M. (1997). Linking training objectives to evaluation criteria. In M. A. Quinones & A. Ehrenstein (Eds.), *Training for a rapidly changing workplace: Applications of psychological research* (pp. 151–175). Washington, DC: American Psychological Association.

Kraiger, K., McLinden, D., & Casper, W. J. (2004). Collaborative planning for training impact. *Human Resource Management, 43*, 337–351.

Landers, R. N., & Reddock, C. M. (in press). A meta-analytic investigation of objective learner control in web-based instruction. *Journal of Business and Psychology.*

Leat, M. J., & Lovell, J. M. (1997). Training needs analysis: weaknesses in the conventional approach. *Journal of European Industrial Training, 21*, 143–153.

Luiten, J., Ames, W., & Ackerson, G. (1980). A meta-analysis of the effects of advanced organizers on learning and retention. *American Educational Research Journal, 17*, 211–218.

MacNamara, B. N., Hambrick, D. Z., & Oswald, F. L. (2014). Deliberate practice and performance in music, games, sports, education, and professions: A meta-analysis. *Psychological Science, 25*, 1608–1618.

Major, D. A., Turner, J. E., & Fletcher, T. D. (2006). Linking proactive personality and the Big Five to motivation to learn and development activity. *Journal of Applied Psychology, 91*, 927–935.

Mattingly, V., Kraiger, K., & Huntington, H. (2016, April). *Can emotional intelligence be trained? A meta-analytic investigation.* Paper presented at the annual conference of the Society for Industrial-Organizational Psychology, Anaheim, CA.

Mayer, R. E. (1979). Twenty years of research on advance organizers: Assimilation theory is still the best predictor of results. *Instructional Science, 8*, 133–167.

Mayer, R. E. (2008). Applying the science of learning: Evidence-based principles for the design of multimedia instruction. *American Psychologist, 63*, 760–769.

McGehee, W., & Thayer, P. W. (1961). *Training in business and industry.* New York: Wiley.

Nickols, F. (2005). Why a stakeholder approach to evaluating training. *Advances in Developing Human Resources, 7*, 121–134.

Noe, R. A. (1986). Trainees' attributes and attitudes: Neglected influences on training effectiveness. *Academy of Management Review, 11*, 736–749.

Noe, R. A. (2010). *Employee training and development* (5th ed.). Boston: Irwin-McGraw.

Noe, R. A., Clarke, A. D. M., & Klein, H. J. (2014). Learning in the twenty-first-century workplace. *Annual Review of Organizational Psychology and Organizational Behavior, 1*, 245–275.

Noe, R. A., & Colquitt, J. A. (2002). Planning for training impact: Principles of training effectiveness. In K. Kraiger (Ed.), *Creating, implementing, and maintaining effective training and development: State-of-the-art lessons for practice* (pp. 53–79). San Francisco: Jossey-Bass.

Noe, R. A., & Schmitt, N. (1986). The influence of trainee attitudes on training effectiveness: Test of a model. *Personnel Psychology, 39*, 497–523.

Park, Y., & Jacobs, R. L. (2011). The influence of investment in workplace learning on learning outcomes and organizational performance. *Human Resource Development Quarterly, 22*, 437–458.

Pineda-Herrero, P., Belvis, E., Moreno, V., Duran-Bellonch, M. M., & Ucar, X. (2011). Evaluation of training effectiveness in the Spanish health sector. *Journal of Workplace Learning, 23*, 315–330.

Powell, K. S., & Yalcin, S. (2010). Managerial training effectiveness. *Personnel Review, 39*, 227–241.

Quiñones, M. A. (1995). Pretraining context effects: Training assignment as feedback. *Journal of Applied Psychology, 80*, 226–238.

Quiñones, M. A., Ford, J. K., Sego, D. J., & Smith, E. M. (1995). The effects of individual and transfer environment characteristics on the opportunity to perform trained tasks. *Training Research Journal, 1*, 29–49.

Randolph, J. J., & Edmondson, R. S. (2005). Using the binomial effect size display (BESD) to present the magnitude of effect sizes to the evaluation audience. *Practical Assessment Research & Evaluation, 10*(14), 1–7.

Robinson, D. G., & Robinson, J. C. (1995). *Performance consulting: Moving beyond training.* San Francisco: Barrett-Koehler.

Rosenberg, M.J. (1995). Performance technology, performance support, and the future of training: A commentary. *Performance Improvement Quarterly, 8,* 94–99.

Roszkowski, M. J., & Soven, M. (2010). Did you learn something useful today? An analysis of how perceived utility relates to perceived learning and their predictiveness of satisfaction with training. *Performance Improvement Quarterly, 23,* 71–91.

Rouiller, J. Z., & Goldstein, I. L. (1993). The relationship between organizational transfer climate and positive transfer of training. *Human Resource Development Quarterly, 4,* 377–390.

Saks, A. M., & Burke-Smalley, L. A. (2014). Is transfer of training related to firm performance? *International Journal of Training and Development, 18,* 104–115.

Salas, E., & Cannon-Bowers, J. A. (2001). The science of training: A decade of progress. *Annual Review of Psychology, 52,* 471–499.

Salas, E., DiazGranados, D., Klein, C., Burke, C. S., Stagl, K. C., Goodwin, G. F., & Halpin, S. M. (2008). Does team training improve team performance? A meta-analysis. *Human Factors, 50,* 903–933.

Salas, E., Nichols, D. R., & Driskell, J. E. (2007). Testing three team training strategies in intact teams: A meta-analysis. *Small Group Research, 38,* 471–488.

Salas, E., Tannenbaum, S. I., Kraiger, K., & Smith-Jentsch, K. A. (2012). The science of training and development in organizations: What matters in practice. *Psychological Science in the Public Interest, 13,* 74–101.

Schmidt, R. A., & Bjork, R. A. (1992). New conceptualizations of practice: Common principles in three paradigms suggest new concepts for training. *Psychological Science, 3,* 207–217.

Seufert, T., & Brünken, R. (2006). Cognitive load and the format of instructional aids for coherence formation. *Applied Cognitive Psychology, 20,* 321–331.

Seyler, D. L., Holton III, E. F., Bates, R. A., Burnett, M. F., & Carvalho, M. A. (1998). Factors affecting motivation to transfer training. *International Journal of Training and Development, 2,* 16.

Sitzmann, T., Bell, B. S., Kraiger, K., & Kanar, A. M. (2009). A multilevel analysis of the effect of prompting self-regulation in technology-delivered instruction. *Personnel Psychology, 62,* 697–734.

Sitzmann, T., Brown, K.G., Ely, K., & Kraiger, K. (2009). Motivation to learn in a military training curriculum: A longitudinal investigation. *Military Psychology, 21,* 534–551.

Sitzmann, T., & Ely, K. (2010). Sometimes you need a reminder: The effects of prompting self-regulation on regulatory processes, learning, and attrition. *Journal of Applied Psychology, 95,* 132–144.

Sitzmann, T., & Ely, K. (2011). A meta-analysis of self-regulated learning in work-related training and educational attainment: What we know and where we need to go. *Psychological Bulletin, 137,* 421–442.

Sitzmann, T., & Johnson, S. K. (2012). The best laid plans: Examining the conditions under which a planning intervention improves learning and reduces attrition. *Journal of Applied Psychology, 97,* 967–981.

Sitzmann, T., & Weinhardt, J. M. (2015). Training engagement theory: A multilevel perspective on the effectiveness of work-related training. *Journal of Management.* http://dx.doi.org/10.1177/0149206315574596

Spitzer, D. R. (2005). Learning effectiveness measurement: A new approach for measuring and managing learning to achieve business results. *Advancements in Developing Human Resources, 7,* 55–70.

Stone, C. L. (1983). A meta-analysis of advance organizer studies. *Journal of Experimental Education, 51,* 194–199.

Surface, E. A. (2012). Training needs assessment: Aligning learning and capability with performance requirements and organizational objectives. In M. A. Wilson, W. Bennett, S. Gibson, & G. M. Alliger (Eds.), *The handbook of work analysis: The methods, systems, applications and science of work measurement in organizations* (pp. 437–462). New York: Routledge Academic.

Taylor, P. J., Russ-Eft, D. F., & Chan, D. W. L. (2005). A meta-analytic review of behavior modeling training. *Journal of Applied Psychology, 90,* 692–709.

Tharenou, P., Saks, A. M., & Moore, C. (2007). A review and critique of research on training and organizational-level outcomes. *Human Resource Management Review, 17,* 251–273.

Tracey, J. B., Tannenbaum, S. I., & Kavanagh, M. J. (1995). Applying trained skills on the job: The importance of work environment. *Journal of Applied Psychology, 80*, 239–252.

Training Magazine (2014). 2014 industry report. *Training, 51*(11), 16–29. Retrieved from https://trainingmag.com/sites/default/files/magazines/2014_11/2014-Industry-Report.pdf

Tsai, W. C., & Tai, W. T. (2003). Perceived importance as a mediator of the relationship between training assignment and training motivation. *Personnel Review, 32*, 151–163.

Van Iddekinge, C. H., Ferris, G. R., Perrewé, P. L., Perryman, A. A., Blass, F. R., & Heetderks, T. D. (2009). Effects of selection and training on unit-level performance over time: A latent growth modeling approach. *Journal of Applied Psychology, 94*, 829–843.

Wallhead, T. L., & Ntoumanis, N. (2004). Effects of a sport education intervention on students' motivational responses in physical education. *Journal of Teaching in Physical Education, 23*, 4–18.

Wenger, E. (1998). *Communities of practice: Learning, meaning and identity*. New York: Cambridge University Press.

Wenger, E., McDermott, R. & Snyder, W. M. (2002). *Cultivating communities of practice*. Boston: Harvard Business School Press.

Wilson, B. G., Jonassen, D. H., & Cole, P. (1993). Cognitive approaches to instructional design. In G. Piskurich (Ed.), *The ASTD handbook of instructional technology, 4*, 21.1–21.22.

Winne, P. H. (1996). A metacognitive view of individual differences in self-regulated learning. *Learning and Individual Differences, 8*, 327–353.

Yang, H., Sackett, P. R., & Arvey, R. D. (1996). Statistical power and cost in training evaluation: Some new considerations. *Personnel Psychology, 49*, 651–668.

Kurt Kraiger

OVERQUALIFICATION IN THE WORKPLACE

INTRODUCTION

When employees are looking for jobs, typically they are looking for positions that will utilize, benefit from, and reward the skills, abilities, education, and other qualifications they bring to the workplace. Similarly, fit is a key concern for recruiters and hiring managers (Erdogan, Bauer, Peiró, & Truxillo, 2011a; Kristof-Brown, Zimmerman, & Johnson, 2005). However, due to reasons such as a weak economy and strong competition among highly educated job candidates, absence of perfect information about applicants and job characteristics, and frictions in the job market that prevent perfect matching of jobs and applicants such as the mobility of job applicants (Li & Miller, 2015), there are instances where employees accept positions for which they are overqualified. Overqualification refers to a situation where a person's qualifications including education, skills, training, and experience exceed job requirements in such a way that the individual has many skills and qualifications that are neither required nor utilized by the job (Erdogan et al., 2011a; Liu & Wang, 2012). Feldman (1996), two decades ago, made the case that overqualification is a type of underemployment. In other words, along with conditions such as working in a part-time job even though one prefers full-time employment, and working in a job with a significantly lower salary than the one held before, overqualification describes an undesirable work situation that falls short of full employment. Since

Feldman's (1996) and subsequently McKee-Ryan and Harvey's (2011) reviews, the topic remains of interest to scholars and practitioners alike.

In this article, the authors aim to synthesize, summarize, and critique the accumulated body of literature on the topic of overqualification. Our objective is to take stock of what we know about overqualification and present a roadmap for future scholars regarding where further work is needed. An exciting, but unusual, feature of the topic of overqualification is that it is an incredibly diverse body of literature with scholars in fields as diverse as labor economics, sociology, education, management, and psychology investigating the nature, causes, and implications of overqualification. It is possible for scholars within one field to neglect important developments in others and miss the opportunity to create synergies. Therefore, wherever possible, we do not limit our review to a specific subdiscipline and instead attempt to summarize and integrate the accumulated body of knowledge regardless of the source discipline.

WHAT EXACTLY IS OVERQUALIFICATION? HOW IS IT MEASURED?

Overqualification may take many different forms. The variety of different forms of overqualification and the diversity of the literatures focusing on the phenomenon resulted in a multiplicity of approaches to its measurement. Since overqualification is an umbrella-like term, a close look at its unique forms and classifications is useful to prevent overlooking the diversity of measurement approaches in this area.

Perhaps the most frequently studied form of overqualification, particularly by economists and education scholars, is the case of overeducation (Erdogan & Mansfield, 2016). Overeducated individuals occupy positions that significantly exceed educational qualifications needed by the job. Overeducation is regarded as a societal issue, as it could indicate overinvestment in human capital that goes underutilized by the jobs available. Therefore, the study of overeducation is of importance to scholars in labor economics and education. It is possible to also extrapolate to other qualifications that may exceed job requirements, such as overexperience, overskilling, or overtraining. However, it seems that whenever scholars focus on a single dimension on which an individual is overqualified, the focus has typically been on overeducation (e.g., Hersch, 1991).

When measuring overeducation, or any other skill or qualification on which overqualification occurs, there seem to be four distinct measurement approaches (Verhaest & Omey, 2006). *Direct self-assessment* refers to simply asking individuals if they feel overeducated for their jobs. *Indirect self-assessment* involves asking the individuals themselves their education level and asking them a separate question regarding the educational requirements of their jobs, using a difference score to operationalize overeducation. The *job analysis method* involves individuals reporting their own education level, whereas the job's education requirements are reported by a job analysis. Finally, the *realized matches approach* is where an education level is considered atypical for the job in question (such as one standard deviation above the occupational mean). Each of these approaches has their unique strengths as well as potential limitations. For example, problems associated with difference scores exist (Edwards, 2001; Edwards & Parry, 1993). Job analyst ratings of jobs are hard to come by, and this assessment is more likely to capture the job as it typically occurs in the economy, rather than how it is defined in a specific organization. The realized matches approach ignores the possibility of education inflation in an occupation: It is possible that a job that used to require a high school degree may now require a college degree without a corresponding upgrade of job demands. Asking individuals direct questions tackles these questions, but introduces self-enhancement bias, or other personality traits that may result in an individual looking down on a job. Furthermore, there are studies that present theoretical arguments and empirical evidence revealing the problematic nature of assuming that overeducation is a valid indicator of skill mismatch (Halaby, 1994).

Complicating the matter even further, whether overeducation should be calculated by examining a job's entry requirements or whether it should focus on what the job actually requires to perform it at an adequate level is unclear, and there are examples of both approaches in the literature. For example, Kler, Leeves, and Shankar (2015) use the metric of having education more than the minimum *required* to perform the job. Others such as Frenette (2000) utilize the difference between one's level of education and the level required to *get* the job, and Croce and Ghignoni (2015) ask whether one's educational degree is *necessary* to perform the job. Hersch (1995) asked whether the person has a higher level of education than the level the *average* person would need to *do* the job, not just to be hired. Still others use more vague wording such as having qualifications superior to the job (Frei & Sousa-Poza, 2012). Of course, a job's entry requirements may change over time, and individuals may have difficulty recollecting the entry requirements post entry.

Even measuring the "level of education one has" may be deceptively simple to gather, but it too comes with unintended consequences. Brynin and Longhi (2009) distinguished between years spent in education and degree earned and made the case that excess time spent in education may indicate lack of motivation or dedication to one's studies, and therefore degree earned may be a better metric. As this discussion of measurement approaches illustrates, measurement of individual dimensions on which overqualification may occur is inconsistent from study to study, making it difficult to summarize and extend prior work.

In the management and industrial/organizational psychology literatures, the focus is typically on perceived overqualification. There are two commonly utilized measures, both of them measuring different dimensions of overqualification, or the possession of skills and qualifications not required or utilized on the job. Johnson and Johnson's (2000b) scale of overqualification consists of two dimensions: Mismatch, or the possession of surplus qualifications that exceed the job requirements, and No Grow, or the absence of opportunities to use one's skills and learn new skills. In their validation study, Johnson, Morrow, and Johnson (2002) showed that the No Grow dimension actually showed higher correlations with outcomes such as work and supervisor satisfaction. However, the Mismatch dimension is the one most closely linked to the theoretical definition of overqualification (Maynard, Joseph, & Maynard, 2006). Therefore, subsequent research typically focused only on this dimension and its four-item scale, and excluded the No Grow dimension from analyses (e.g., Erdogan & Bauer, 2009; Hu et al., 2015). Johnson and Johnson's measure is actually based on Khan and Morrow's (1991) earlier measure. Its length and diverse content (it focuses on education-, experience-, and skill-based overqualification) often yields borderline reliabilities (Nunnally, 1978). For example, Johnson and Johnson (2000b) reported reliabilities of .73 and .70 in their two samples. As a replacement to this measure, Maynard et al. (2006) developed a longer (9 items), psychometrically sound, and validated measure that is more commonly in use. The original scale was validated in three separate studies using outcomes such as organizational commitment, turnover intentions, and facets of job satisfaction.

Finally, there is also a somewhat related cognitive overqualification scale by Fine and Nevo (2008). Cognitive overqualification refers to the extent to which an individual's cognitive abilities are neither required nor used by the job. Because it captures mental skills that exceed the level of job challenge involved in the position, it is proposed to be an important type of overqualification with implications for attitudes and performance. Fine and Nevo (2008) examined 156 call center representatives in the United States in their study and showed that cognitive overqualification was more strongly and negatively associated with job satisfaction compared to overall perceived overqualification. It was also positively related to training performance. In a separate study, cognitive overqualification has been shown to be positively related to being evaluated as a leader by one's peers and supervisors during a training program, and to negative attitudes toward the training program (Fine, 2007).

Measurement inconsistency remains an important concern in aggregating and making sense of the findings of overqualification literature. Oftentimes, studies of overqualification, and particularly overeducation, rely on single-item indicators and large national samples. The size, diversity, and representativeness of the sample come at the expense of valid measurement. For example, Wu, Luksyte, and Parker (2015) used the item "I have the skills to handle more demanding duties" to capture overqualification, which may also be tapping into concepts such as self-efficacy and confidence as much as overqualification. The nature of the overqualification studies often necessitates the use of large-scale studies where single-item measures are used, and it is important to ensure that these scales all measure the same underlying construct.

A distinction is made by Green and Zhu (2010) between real and formal overqualification, the former referring to individuals who are both overqualified and overskilled, and the latter referring to individuals who are overqualified while experiencing full skill utilization. In a more recent study, Maltarich, Reilly, and Nyberg (2011) made a powerful argument that perceived and objective overqualification may not necessarily capture the same phenomenon, and they may not be easily used as substitutes of each other. Objective overqualification is visible to others, involves qualifications that have market value, and could predict ease of movement across jobs. Perceived overqualification is psychological in nature and is more likely to reflect one's overall experiences and treatment at work, along with mismatched qualifications. For this reason, Maltarich and colleagues suggested that investigating the link between the two metrics and differentiating their implications are important research directions.

THEORETICAL FOUNDATIONS OF OVERQUALIFICATION

Perhaps the most commonly used theory to explain why felt overqualification is undesirable is the relative deprivation theory (Crosby, 1984). Relative deprivation occurs when an individual wants something, feels entitled to have it, and feels deprived of it. Employees who feel overqualified believe that given their skills, education, and abilities, they are entitled to a higher-quality job. This sense of deprivation is theorized to be associated with negative effects on job satisfaction (Johnson & Johnson, 2000a). Relative deprivation theory is a justice-based theory, and therefore other justice theories such as equity theory have also been proposed as potential explanations of the effects of felt overqualification (Feldman, 1996).

Feldman, Leana, and Bolino (2002) showed that relative deprivation acted as a mediator of the relationship between perceived underemployment and job attitudes.

In the education literature, the concept of habitus explains the effects of overeducation. Individuals going through the education system develop expectations regarding the characteristics of the "appropriate" job, with corresponding requirements of education, offerings of salary, working conditions, and identity. When these expectations are not met, they experience cognitive dissonance, and they perceive the job as "beneath them," mentally rejecting the position and experiencing dissatisfaction (Vaisey, 2006).

Status inconsistency theory (Blalock, 1966; Hope, 1975) has been used to explain the effects of overeducation. According to this perspective, mismatch between the realized positions of a person in different status hierarchies is a cause for concern. For example, a college-educated person in a job where the typical job incumbent holds a high school degree is an example of status inconsistency. This situation indicates a social status discrepancy and leads to social stress. Garcy (2015) predicted that a status panic is likely among individuals who find themselves in this situation. What distinguishes a status inconsistency explanation to perceived overqualification from a relative deprivation-based explanation is the explicit focus on social status expectations that come from one's qualifications. According to this view, the person suffers not necessarily because of a mismatch between one's jobs and skills and a sense of skill underutilization. Similarly, the concern is not necessarily around the objective characteristics of the job such as pay. What this perspective emphasizes is around the feeling of status deprivation. Burris (1983) argued that one possible outcome of this would be that these individuals would pay greater attention to the status conferring features of their lives and seek to satisfy their status needs through emphasizing certain distinctions peripheral to their work. This theory may also be used to predict that overqualified employees will behave in a way that will increase their social credentials. Collins and Long (2015) showed a connection between overeducation and engagement in volunteering behavior. This finding may indicate an attempt by overqualified employees to achieve social status and standing. Friedland and Price (2003) attempted to distinguish the effects of overeducation from status underemployment, and found stronger negative effects on outcomes such as physical and mental health and well-being for status underemployment.

HOW TEMPORARY IS OVERQUALIFICATION?

Is overqualification temporary or relatively permanent? This is an important question in the overeducation literature, and there are theoretical arguments on both sides (Kiersztyn, 2013). On the one hand, individuals will not realistically get a sense of the qualification levels of the job until they start performing it. Once they start their position and realize a mismatch, one argument is that they should be able to upgrade quickly. In other words, it is assumed that individuals desire match, and once a mismatch is realized, they will take action by either changing jobs or negotiating for different duties to improve their match. The opposing argument though is that overqualification will act as a trap. Accepting a job for which one is overqualified will make job change difficult because their skills will atrophy with little opportunities for improvement or gaining new skills. Signaling theory of Spence (1973) may also be used to predict that overqualification will be a long-term phenomenon. According to this theory, skills acquired by the person are not always acquired with the purpose of being used on the actual job. The purpose of some skills and qualifications is to signal to recruiters that one is capable and valuable. Based on this rationale, a person who starts out overqualified will remain so over time.

There seems to be some evidence on both sides. For example, Alba-Ramirez (1993) used a sample of over 11,000 workers from Spain and showed that overeducated employees were younger and less experienced than adequately educated employees, and they improved their match over time, suggesting that overeducation is a way in which individuals acquire the experience they need and is a short-lived phenomenon. Vogtenhuber (2014), studying 15–34-year-olds in an Austrian sample, showed that individuals typically improved the level of match with their jobs over time. Frei and Sousa-Poza (2012) used the Swiss Household panel and showed that more than 60% of overqualified employees were not overqualified the next year and that 90% were able to escape overqualification in four years. Interestingly, in this particular study, those who escaped overqualification from one year to the next did not necessarily improve their match by changing employers: 87% of those who improved their match stayed with the same employer.

In contrast, Kiersztyn (2013) used Polish panel data to show that overeducated employees were four times more likely to be overeducated five years later compared to others. Sloane, Battu, and Seaman (1999) examined a large sample of British workers to find no support for the matching hypothesis. In fact, overeducated employees were likely to be those who had been unemployed before, and the greater the number of job changes employees experienced, the greater was the level of overeducation. These studies suggest that overeducation may not necessarily be resolved over time as individuals improve their match through job changes. Instead, there is some evidence that overeducation may have scarring effects.

WHAT CAUSES OVERQUALIFICATION?

There are many factors that are thought to result in the condition of being or feeling overqualified for one's job. For example, Johnson and Johnson (2000a) noted that the increase in job applicant qualifications faster than jobs that required these qualifications is a key reason for overqualification. Further, factors pushing job applicants to accept suboptimal positions, such as restructuring and layoffs, are increasingly common, and are among the culprits of the rise in employee overqualification. Wright (2014) proposed that many college graduates may in fact end up in positions that do not require those degrees, because their skills are deficient due to absence of rigor in their educational program. An examination of studies of predictors of overqualification typically focus on more micro factors and particularly job incumbent characteristics.

Education. The type, quality, and level of one's education is the natural first place to look at when examining antecedents of overqualification. In many parts of the world, including Asia and Europe, education is the beginning of one's career, and individuals start working only after completing their formal education. Further, when individuals are unable to secure a position that matches their level of education or aspirations, they may delay their job search by staying in school longer, which should have the effect of further overqualification down the line. Supporting this notion, Vogtenhuber (2014) examined over 4,000 employed individuals from the Austrian labor force survey and showed that vocational education reduced the likelihood of being overeducated in one's first job. In other words, gaining work experience during school years may present a smoother transition to the labor force, reducing overeducation. The type of education the person has is also a factor affecting overeducation. In a study of Canadian college graduates, those who reported having master's degrees, as well as humanities and arts majors reported higher overeducation, whereas other majors such as law or medicine carried low risk of overeducation (Frenette, 2000, 2004).

The quality of the diploma may also matter, but this is harder to assess. Lianos, Asteriou, and Agiomirgianakis (2004) examined Greek students who earned foreign degrees and came back to Greece to work. Among these employees, holding a degree from EU countries was associated with lower risk of overeducation compared to holding a degree from Balkan countries. Støren and Wiers-Jenssen (2010) compared local and foreign diploma earners in Norway, and showed that Norwegians educated in Norway had a lower likelihood of being overeducated compared to those with foreign diplomas.

Migrant Status. There also seems to be some evidence that migrant workers are more likely to experience overqualification. This may be explained by the skill compensation theory (Johnston, Khattab, & Manley, 2015) which suggests that employees who are deficient in some skills may accept jobs that make them overqualified in other ways, such as trading off of lack of experience with a surplus of education. Migrant employees may lack the social capital and country-specific skills that would make them more employable, resulting in a higher rate of overqualification. For example, Johnston et al. (2015) showed that East European migrants to Britain had greater levels of overeducation (they had atypically high levels of education in their occupations) compared to local workers, and their overeducation level was greater than that of West Europeans. In Canada, Livingstone (2010) showed that more recent immigrants to Canada reported greatest levels of overeducation compared to immigrants who had been in the country longer and compared to Canadian-born employees. In the United States, Madamba and De Jong (1997) found that immigrants were anywhere between 48% to as much as six times more likely than native-born employees to be overeducated for their jobs. Interestingly, this study found that fluency in English increased the chances of being overeducated, which may indicate that immigrants are more likely to end up in positions where they are overeducated, and even this situation may be possible only when they have sufficient language proficiency to obtain the job.

Factors that may help migrants to reduce their risk of overeducation were also identified. Griesshaber and Seibel (2015) showed in a study of 19 European countries that overeducation level was lower among active migrant members of voluntary associations compared to non-members, demonstrating the role of acculturation experiences.

Experience. Providing evidence that different dimensions of human capital may substitute for each other, there is evidence that overeducation levels are higher among those who have lower levels of experience and tenure (Sloane et al., 1999). At the same time, staying in a position for too long may result in a sense of overqualification as well. To the degree to which the person masters one's job without having the opportunity to improve one's skills, feelings of overqualification may develop. For example, Burke (1997) showed in a sample of

Canadian university graduates that years spent in one's job was positively related to perceived overeducation.

Job Search.   Job search is a costly investment, and it cannot continue indefinitely. In order to avoid remaining unemployed for too long, individuals may accept positions beneath their qualifications. This is a likely case particularly for the new entrants of the workforce. Thus, the investigation of job seekers' anticipations also has the potential to reveal an important antecedent of overqualification. In their three-wave study Guerrero and Hatala (2015) focused on job search intensity, but revealed surprising results. Perceived overqualification was lowest among those who did not search for a job intensely, but also had high levels of financial needs. This study indicates that more research is needed to investigate job seeker behaviors and eventual overqualification.

Sex.   Frank (1978) developed the "theory of differential overqualification" as an explanation for why women get paid less than men, and posited that married women have a greater risk of being overeducated for their jobs. Discussing the difficulty of optimizing job search in a dual-career couple, Frank argued that couples would solve this situation by optimizing the husband's job search first, deeming women to be the "tied movers" or "tied stayers." Particularly in cases where the couple moves to or chooses to stay in a small labor market, this would jeopardize the wife's job opportunities, restricting options and increasing the likelihood of their being overeducated for their jobs. There is some support for this theory, but the evidence is, much like the theory itself, dated, and findings would benefit from updating. For example, Büchel and Battu (2003) examined the 1995 data from the German Socioeconomic Panel and showed that married women had higher rates of overeducation compared to both unmarried women and men of all marital status. The theory most likely does not reflect the contemporary arrangements and societal changes in how married and unmarried dual-career couples make decisions, and it is unclear whether there is any truth in this theory today. At the same time, how dual-career couples make career-related decisions and deal with the overqualification of one or both members of the couple is an interesting research area.

The idea that migration may reduce overeducation, and that married women may be overeducated because they have difficulty migrating, seems to have some validity. Quinn and Rubb (2011) used the University of Michigan's panel study of income dynamics and showed that overqualification was in fact a predictor of migration for men and women in dual-career couples. Interestingly, migration increased the chances that men would be less likely to be overeducated for their subsequent jobs, whereas it was not effective in reducing overeducation in women. These results provide some further evidence that in dual-career couples, gender dynamics may play out in a way that disadvantages the female partner, affecting their rate of overeducation.

Age.   Age is another personal characteristic that has been associated with overqualification. There is some evidence that younger employees are more likely to be overqualified due to the absence of work experience and potential for taking some time to find one's match. For example, Hultin, Lundberg, Lundin, and Magnusson (2016) showed that in a large population survey of Sweden, younger people were more likely to be overeducated. Similar results were found for U.S. workers as well (Szydlik, 2002).

Interestingly, contradicting the expectation that younger workers are more likely to be overqualified, Madamba and De Jong (1997) showed that older workers (whom they defined as 46–64 years of age) were more likely to be overeducated for their jobs compared to 25–30-year-olds. The authors explained this unusual finding with the potential for displacement due to layoffs and inability to find sufficient quality employment following layoffs. It is also likely that worries over age discrimination and greater job embeddedness among these workers may prevent them from leaving their jobs even after they become experts in their position, leading to the feeling that they are overqualified for their current jobs. Finally, older workers may see their current positions as bridge employment, and choose or stay in positions where they are overqualified to reduce the mental overload and challenge that could be characteristic of better-fitting positions. Shultz, Olson, and Wang (2011) argued that because they would enter into overqualification knowingly, even though they may have higher levels of overqualification, they may experience fewer negative consequences in reaction to feeling overqualified.

Personality. Researchers considered the possibility that perceptions of overqualification may be a function of one's own personality. Narcissism is an interesting candidate as an antecedent. To the degree to which felt overqualification is the belief that one deserves a better job than currently held, extreme feelings of self-worth could be one explanation. Supporting this possibility, Lobene, Meade, and Pond (2015) studied the relationship between narcissism and perceived cognitive overqualification, demonstrating a significant relationship. Watt and Hargis (2010) identified boredom proneness as another personality trait increasing the likelihood of perceived overqualification, by showing a positive link between the two.

Job Characteristics. The characteristics of the position held, including how routine, repetitive, and meaningful the job is could be related to felt overqualification. This is because some jobs may be regarded so simple or so easy to master that regardless of one's qualifications, employees may feel that their qualifications exceed job requirements. This prediction found some support in the literature. Lobene et al. (2015) showed that among several antecedents of overqualification they examined, the repetitiveness of the job was the strongest predictor of perceived cognitive overqualification. Madamba and De Jong (1997) used U.S. census data and compared overeducation rates of employees in different industries and professions, and showed that managerial and professional workers had the lowest likelihood of being overeducated compared to other occupations. In a Spanish study, Sáez, González-Prieto, and Cantarero-Prieto (2016) showed that service workers were among those with the highest levels of overeducation.

Past Employment History. There is some evidence that overqualification may be more likely for employees who underwent a layoff or experienced unemployment. For example, Hultin et al. (2016) found in a Swedish sample that having experienced unemployment was a predictor of greater levels of overeducation in the current job.

Size of the Job Market. As a sign of mismatch between qualifications and the job, overeducation also is more likely in smaller job markets, which can either be a permanent feature stemming from high population and intense competition or a temporary characteristic of the market due to recession. In such cases, individuals may be able to reduce their chances of overqualification by increasing the size of their market through relocation and commuting. Note that for relocation and commuting, the dynamics are different compared to migrant workers. For migrants from a different country, lack of knowledge of the culture, lack of a social network, and language present barriers to a well-matching job, and employees settle down into positions lower than their qualifications. For domestic workers, moving to a bigger city or increasing commute time may improve the job match. Croce and Ghignoni (2015) analyzed data from a nationwide Italian survey to test this spatial flexibility hypothesis and showed that for those holding an upper secondary degree, commuting reduced the risk of overeducation, whereas for college graduates, relocation reduced this risk. Contradicting these findings, Romaní, Casado-Díaz, and Lillo-Bañuls (2016) did not find a relationship between commuting and relocating. However, individual willingness to change residences to accommodate company needs reduced the probability of overeducation.

National Context.   System-wide exploration of overqualification is somewhat limited in number and mostly composed of theoretical discussions while there is a call for a multilevel perspective. Focusing on 24 European countries, Flisi, Goglio, Meroni, Rodrigues, and Vera-Toscano (2017) examined the frequency of overeducation and overskilling comparatively. The study examined the prevalence of overeducation and skill utilization across the sampled countries. The results showed that in Italy, Spain, and Ireland, overeducation was prevalent, but skill underutilization was not. In Scandinavian countries and Eastern European countries, overskilling was prevalent, but overeducation was not.

Similarly, Green and Henseke (2016) showed country-level differences in the prevalence of overeducation. In their study of 21 OECD countries, 50% of their Japanese sample was over-educated, whereas only 11% of the Finnish sample reported overeducation. Countries with low demand for college-educated workers had higher levels of overeducation. This and similar studies suggest that the national context may change the prevalence of overqualification, and this could potentially affect how employees react to overqualification.

HOW DOES OVERQUALIFICATION AFFECT EMPLOYEES?

Job Attitudes.   In a review article, Feldman (1996) proposed that underemployment, including felt overqualification, would be negatively related to job attitudes such as job satisfaction, organizational commitment, work involvement, and work motivation. There is some evidence for this. Interestingly, Johnson and Johnson (2000a), in their study of postal workers surveyed twice over two years, found no link between perceived overqualification and satisfaction with work itself. This is an unexpected finding, as the most salient outcome of perceived overqualification does not seem to be satisfaction with the actual work performed. Overqualification has been shown to be related to satisfaction with different aspects of one's job, including intrinsic, extrinsic, and social elements (Peiró, Agut, & Grau, 2010) suggesting that employee negative reactions may be due to dissatisfaction with social status and rewards associated with the job, rather than the work being performed.

Job Security.   Interestingly, despite their superior qualifications, overqualified employees do not seem to be experiencing greater security in their jobs. Perhaps their lack of attachment to the organization is apparent to employers, which results in lower levels of attachment on their part to the employee. Alternatively, to the degree to which overqualified employees withdraw from their jobs and withhold effort, they may be jeopardizing their positions. In any case, there is some evidence that overeducation negatively predicts job security (Kler et al., 2015) and this effect seems to be stronger following an economic crisis and for those employees who have partners.

Health and Well-Being. Implications of overqualification on employee health and physical and mental well-being are among other important avenues for investigation. Feldman's (1996) review posited negative implications of overqualification on well-being indicators such as life satisfaction, optimism, and self-esteem. Further, Feldman proposed relations on one's personal relationships such as those with one's spouse, friends, and children. Supporting this argument, Roh, Chang, Kim, and Nam (2014) found that the well-being, self-esteem, and life satisfaction levels of overqualified employees did not differ from unemployed individuals and were worse than those of the adequately employed.

Hultin et al. (2016) proposed that overqualification may be associated with poor health due to reasons including lower job satisfaction, higher social stress, lower cognitive resilience, and greater exposure to poor-quality work. Alternatively, they recognized that overqualification may be a *consequence* of poor health, as those in less than ideal health may have difficulty finding and keeping a job matching their qualifications and find themselves working in jobs beneath their skill levels.

There are a small number of investigations linking overqualification to health outcomes. For example, there is evidence of a link between overqualification and self-reported stress and depression (Bracke, Pattyn, & von dem Knesebeck, 2013; Johnson & Johnson, 1996). Johnson and Johnson (1997) found negative effects on self-rated health, but the magnitude of the effect was small. Further, the effects of overqualification on health were weaker for those employees who received emotional support from others. This finding supports the idea that overqualification is a type of stressor, and buffers of stress in the form of personal and job-related resources could be moderators of this relationship. Finally, Johnson and Johnson's (1999) follow-up showed positive correlations between perceived overqualification, self-reported depression, and self-reported declines in one's health. More recently, in a large population study, Garcy (2015) pointed to a link between overeducation and mortality rates, particularly mortality from cancer and alcohol, as well as suicide. In other words, there seems to be a connection between overqualification in one's job and health.

It is unclear whether the relationship between overqualification and health outcomes reflects a causal link. As a case in point, Hultin et al. (2016) examined a large sample of Swedish workers to show that there was in fact a relationship between overeducation and self-reported health, but only for women. No relationship was observed with mental health. More importantly, the observed relationship did not hold once the job's qualification level was controlled. In other words, the observed overqualification–health relationship may be due to the quality of the job rather than the surplus of the skills, with jobs that are routine and monotonous creating health risks. It is possible that the proposed link to health is too distal, and there may be factors that explain both overqualification and poor health. Findings such as Stenfors, Hanson, Oxenstierna, Theorell, and Nilsson's (2013) study on a large

Swedish sample which showed that overeducation was associated with cognitive difficulties (concentration, memory, decision-making, and ability to think clearly) could be explained by job characteristics, as routine and monotonous jobs could be regarded as hazards for mental well-being.

Finally, there is also some evidence that the effects on health may actually be favorable under some conditions. In a study contradicting others, Büchel (2002) examined German household panel data for 1984–1995 for low-qualification jobs and showed that overeducation was positively related to self-reported health. The author attributed this finding to choice, and predicted that employees pushed to jobs where they are overqualified and others who select the jobs where they are overqualified will have differing reactions.

An interesting research direction, where research is still scarce, relates to the link between overqualification and safety at work. A study of over 10,000 Canadian workers found that overeducation for the job increased both job injury risk and repetitive motion injury risk (Premji & Smith, 2013). One explanation for this finding could be job characteristics rather than the level of education exceeding job requirements. The authors of the study suggested a different and plausible mechanism: overeducation may result in lack of solidarity with co-workers, increasing the risk of injuries at work.

Wages. Overqualification involves taking a job beneath one's skill levels, and this often means accepting a job that pays less than what the individual could make given their skill levels. Scholars of overeducation are particularly interested in calculating returns to education for adequately matched and overqualified employees. The accumulated body of literature suggests that overeducated employees experience a wage penalty such that they make less than those who are at their education level but placed at jobs that match their qualifications, but these individuals make more than others who have less education than them (e.g., Rubb, 2003; Verhaest & Omey, 2006). For example, a college graduate working at a job that requires a high school education typically makes less than a college graduate working at a job that requires college, but makes more than a high school graduate working in a job that requires a high school degree.

In addition to an examination of actual wages, studies examined the link between overqualification and satisfaction with pay. This relationship has been shown to be negative (Johnson & Johnson, 2000a). In other words, even though there may in fact be a pay premium compared to what others who perform similar jobs are paid, overqualified employees may be aware that they should be making more relative to others at the same education level, which may explain their unhappiness with their pay.

In addition to viewing wages as a consequence of overqualification, it is possible to consider it an antecedent. Lobene et al. (2015) examined one's hourly wages as a predictor of felt overqualification, identifying a modest relationship. This is an interesting take on the nature of felt overqualification–wage and earnings relationship. In fact, wages may provide the cues that influence whether employees feel overqualified for their jobs. Controlling for job characteristics, higher-paid employees may report lower levels of overqualification, whereas lower-paid employees may feel a sense of entitlement toward a higher quality job, reporting higher levels of overqualification.

Finally, there is some evidence that overeducation may have lasting effects on one's wages in the long run. Verbruggen, van Emmerik, Van Gils, Meng, and de Grip (2015) showed that among the alumni of a Dutch university, overeducation measured one year post graduation had negative effects on one's wages 10 years post graduation. A likely explanation for this finding is skill obsolescence and the lack of opportunities for further skill development that may be prevalent in positions where the person is overeducated.

Performance.   Unlike attitudinal implications of perceived overqualification, there is some evidence that the effects of overqualification on job performance are often positive. To the degree to which overqualification means meeting and exceeding qualifications required by the job, there is reason to expect that overqualified employees may have a performance advantage due to their superior skills. At the same time, they are likely to experience lower levels of motivation, resulting in a situation where performance effects may be positive as long as they are motivated to perform. Supporting this argument, Fine and Nevo (2007) examined the relationship between cognitive overqualification and training performance, showing that there was no decline in the relationship between cognitive abilities and performance, even though there was a ceiling effect after a certain point. Fine and Nevo (2008), in a sample of call center representatives, showed positive relations between perceived overqualification and self- and manager-rated performance.

Finally, there are also studies demonstrating a negative relationship between perceived overqualification and job performance. Chen (2009) showed that perceived overqualification was negatively related to manager-rated job performance and organizational citizenship behaviors when manager–employee relationship quality was low. A systematic investigation of overqualification–performance relationship accounting for different measurement perspectives and dimensions of performance is warranted.

Proactive Behaviors and Creativity.   Because overqualified employees feel that they bring a higher skill set to their jobs, they may have the potential to engage in discretionary actions that will benefit the organization. Proactive behaviors and creativity are among such actions where overqualification may prove to be an advantage. There is some evidence that felt overqualification may have positive effects on proactive behaviors. For example, Zhang, Law, and Lin (2016) conducted two studies in China and showed that perceived overqualification was positively associated with employee proactive behaviors because overqualified employees expressed greater levels of role-based self-efficacy. Further, perceived overqualification has been shown to be related to creative behaviors. However, this was a conditional relationship such that overqualification was positively related to employee creativity only when employees perceived high levels of support from the organization (POS), and only when individuals had successfully negotiated idiosyncratic deals (i-deals, Luksyte & Spitzmueller, 2016). Recently, Lin, Law, and Zhou (2017) executed a three-wave time-lagged survey on 327 teachers and their immediate supervisors to investigate the conditions under which organizations may benefit from underemployed staff. They found that organizational identification moderated the underemployment and task-crafting relation. In other words, there are conditions under which organizations can take advantage of proactivity and creativity of these employees, by showing their support of them and allowing them to have unique arrangements that differ from other employees.

In contrast, there is also evidence that overqualification may result in a more rigid interpretation of one's role. Agut, Peiró, and Grau (2009) surveyed 638 young Spanish workers and showed that overeducation was negatively related to content innovation, and having high levels of personal initiative resulted in even lower levels of content innovation for overeducated workers. These results suggest a need for more work linking overqualification to proactivity, innovation, and creativity.

Counterproductive Work Behaviors. Perceived overqualification has been linked to behaviors that harm the organization, namely counterproductive work behaviors. For example, Liu, Luksyte, Zhou, Shi, and Wang (2015) demonstrated that perceived overqualification was associated with counterproductive behaviors directed at supervisors, such as speaking poorly about the supervisor, and those targeting the organization, including behaviors such as spending time on tasks unrelated to work.

Upward Mobility. In the overeducation literature, it has been proposed that overqualification is a "stepping stone" to a better job. In fact, career mobility theory (Sicherman & Galor, 1990) posited that overeducation may be beneficial for individuals by increasing their chances of upward mobility within or outside the organization. Overqualified employees may be ready for advancement to the next job, and therefore even though they may be overqualified for their current jobs, their advancement may be faster, and overqualification may be less dissatisfactory as a result. To date, investigations of career mobility theory typically took place in the overeducation literature with large national databases representing a large number of job types, and the theory did not find empirical support (e.g., Verhaest & Omey, 2006). In contradiction with the career mobility theory, Johnson and Johnson (2000a) showed a negative relationship between perceived overqualification and satisfaction with promotion opportunities, which suggests that overqualified employees may be thwarted in their upward advancement. At the same time, Hersch (1995) showed in a study of 451 employees in one organization that overeducation at organizational entry was associated with subsequent promotions received. This study also revealed that overeducation predicted a shorter training time. It is plausible that the relationship between overqualification and upward advancement is contingent on the position in question and the organization's philosophy regarding upward mobility.

Sikora, Thompson, Russell, and Ferris (2016) posited that overqualified employees whose upward mobility ambitions are thwarted are more likely to leave. Therefore, organizations may retain these employees by satisfying their career-related needs. Oftentimes, upward mobility may not be possible due to lack of opportunities, but they recommended that factors such as job crafting, opportunities to mentor others, and serving as informal leaders may be some of the ways through which career-related needs of employees can be satisfied. In other words, examining a broader set of indicators of mobility and advancement may increase our understanding of career implications of overqualification.

Interpersonal Relationships. How does feeling overqualified translate into one's relationship with, attitudes toward, and interactions with other organizational members such as coworkers? In an early qualitative work based on a small sample of low-level clerical workers, Burris (1983) found that overeducated employees reported feeling competitiveness from their coworkers and that they distanced themselves from their coworkers in an elitist manner. In fact, they actually reported socializing with their manager rather than coworkers.

Systematic examinations of how overqualification affects workplace relationships are rare. There are a small number of studies that indicated no relationship between overqualification and interpersonal relationship quality. Johnson and Johnson (2000a) found no relationship between overqualification and satisfaction with supervision. Chen (2009) examined, but did not find a relationship between perceived overqualification and citizenship behaviors targeting coworkers. It has been suggested that overqualified employees may play an informal leadership role and mentor others around them, which would add to their own reputation and social capital development (Russell, Ferris, Thompson, & Sikora, 2016), but this possibility has not yet been tested. One recent study (Deng et al., in press) found that the relationship between overqualification and coworker acceptance depended on the employee's own political skills. In other words, much like the rest of the literature, overqualification's relation with coworker interactions may be conditional.

Absenteeism and Turnover.   Perhaps the most logical outcome of overqualification is leaving one's job to improve the match between one's qualifications and job requirements. Of course, employees may achieve match through other means such as higher levels of empowerment, through idiosyncratic deals or job crafting. When a solution is not within reach, turnover is an expected reaction. Maynard and Parfyonova (2013) showed a positive link between perceived overqualification, job search, and turnover, and this relationship was stronger for employees higher in competence and growth needs. Erdogan and Bauer (2009) showed a positive link with turnover intentions and turnover only when psychological empowerment was low.

It is also plausible that employees psychologically leave their jobs while not quitting. Based on this rationale, employee feelings of overqualification should be positively related to absenteeism, lateness, and other behavioral forms of withdrawal. However, Lobene et al. (2015) found no relationship between perceived cognitive overqualification and self- or manager-rated absenteeism and tardiness.

The relationship between overqualification and turnover assumes that overqualified employees are not motivated to stay in the organization. At the same time, research also shows that overqualified employees may end up being pushed out of organizations due to not being viewed as valuable members of the organization. Supporting this idea, Peiró, Sora, and Caballer (2012) conducted a survey of over 3,000 Spanish employees and showed that perceived overqualification predicted perceived job insecurity.

HOW DOES OVERQUALIFICATION AFFECT ORGANIZATIONAL OUTCOMES?

Interestingly, studies of overqualification have been limited to its implications on individuals, rather than groups and organizations. This is a curious omission and an exciting research opportunity. Do organizations that hire highly skilled employees regardless of where they will be placed experience advantages such as improved creativity and flexibility? The argument in favor of positive effects is a human capital-based argument, suggesting that highly qualified workers may contribute to organizations in unpredictable and unanticipated ways. In contrast, it is also plausible that if the vast majority of employees in an organization are feeling over-qualified, this may result in a mass exodus from the organization, low morale, and feelings of being underutilized and underplaced. The only study speaking to this question to date is by Marchante and Ortega (2012), where they studied 1,427 workers in 70 hotels in Spain. Their analyses showed that the percentage of employees who reported having more education than job requirements was negatively related to hotel performance, as operationalized by per employee profitability. At the same time, having a high percentage of undereducated workers was worse for hotel performance compared to having a high percentage of overeducated workers.

MEDIATORS OF OVERQUALIFICATION

Why does perceived overqualification relate to attitudes and behaviors? A small number of studies tackled this question. Liu et al. (2015) examined the role of organization-based self-esteem and anger at one's employment situation as potential mediators of overqualification–counterproductive work behaviors targeting supervisors and the organization. They found support for their model in a sample of Chinese research and development employees. Luksyte, Spitzmueller, and Maynard (2011) examined person–job fit, psychological contracts, and cynicism toward one's job as mediators of the relation between perceived overqualification and self-rated counterproductive behaviors, finding support for only cynicism. What is interesting is that despite the prevalence of relative deprivation theory in explanations of the effects of overqualification, relative deprivation has rarely been incorporated into models of over-qualification as a mediating mechanism (cf. Feldman et al., 2002).

MODERATORS OF OVERQUALIFICATION

Researchers also turned their attention to delineating the boundary conditions of overqualification. Understanding when the effects of overqualification are stronger or weaker is useful to get a clearer sense of contexts and situations under which surplus qualifications affect employees and to possibly ensure that some of its negative effects are dealt with.

An important moderator of overqualification is the *sense of empowerment* employees experience at work. Erdogan and Bauer (2009) showed that the negative relationship between perceived overqualification and job satisfaction, and positive relations with turnover intentions and turnover, were contingent on the level of empowerment, such that overqualification had no relations with these outcomes when empowerment was high. Similarly, Wu et al. (2015) examined a related concept—job autonomy—in a sample obtained from nine European countries, and demonstrated that job autonomy alleviated the negative effects of felt over-qualification on job attitudes.

A recent example explored how *peers' feelings of overqualification* could interact with one's own. Hu et al. (2015) made the argument that the relative deprivation resulting from felt over-qualification would be less of a problem when peers are also highly overqualified. In this context, overqualified employees would still fit in with their group, and their feelings about the tasks at hand would be more favorable. Their study on information technology workers in China supported this prediction. In fact, felt overqualification had positive effects on perceived person–group fit and task significance in general, but these effects were much stronger when peer overqualification was high. The social context of overqualification seems to be important. In fact, Kler et al. (2015) used the Australian household panel to look at the effects of social context in a different manner: They showed that some of the negative effects of over-education on job satisfaction and pay satisfaction disappeared after a financial crisis, suggesting that being in the company of others who are experiencing anxiety may have changed the frame of reference of individuals.

Not all employees react equally negatively to perceived overqualification. For example, *personality traits and values* may determine how much dissonance employees experience in reaction to feelings of overqualification, and how readily they take action as a result. Maynard and Parfyonova (2013) showed that perceived overqualification was positively related to job search behavior more strongly for those who had high needs for competence and growth. Liu et al. (2015) identified justice sensitivity as a moderator. Employee reactions to perceived overqualification in the form of organization-based self-esteem and anger at one's employment situation were stronger for employees who reported higher levels of justice sensitivity. Interestingly, Lobene and Meade's (2013) study on teachers in the United States revealed unexpected findings. The authors predicted that employees with a calling orientation, or those who see their jobs not as a paycheck or a step in their career ladder but a way to achieve higher purpose, were more negatively affected by perceptions of overqualification. In contrast to the expectation that having a calling orientation could act as a buffer, employees performed at a lower level when they approached their jobs as a calling and they reported high perceived overqualification.

Interpersonal relationships have also been identified as a possible buffer against the negative effects of perceived overqualification. Alfes, Shantz, and van Baalen (2016) showed in a study in the Netherlands that leader–member exchange (LMX) and team cohesiveness acted as moderators of perceived overqualification with respect to job satisfaction.

FUTURE RESEARCH DIRECTIONS

What Are the Group-Level Effects of Overqualification?

To date, studies of overqualification tended to focus on individual level outcomes of overqualification, in the form of job attitudes, turnover, and well-being. An unanswered question is how a combination of overqualified and well-matched employees influences group dynamics, teamwork, and team outcomes. Researchers proposed that individual- and group-level implications of overqualification may differ. For example, Sierra (2011) suggested that at the team level, the average overqualification level in a team may affect team cohesion and collaboration, if employees see overqualified employees as outsiders. Composition of overqualified employees within the group may stimulate social comparison dynamics, and employees working in groups with high versus low average overqualification may be affected by it differently.

How Do Recruiters React to Overqualified Applicants?

Few studies focused on recruiter reactions toward overqualified applicants and the conditions under which an employee is regarded as overqualified and excluded from the applicant pool. Bewley (1998) interviewed 300 hiring influencers during a U.S. recession. In these interviews, interviewees reported negative attitudes toward overqualified job candidates with the expectation that they would soon leave or threaten their supervisors. In a 35-person interview-based study, Bills (1992) found that employers tolerate a certain level of overqualification in the job applicants. There were essentially four reasons recruiters reported for shying away from overqualified applicants: They might not stay long enough to justify investing in them, they would leave sooner, they would be overpriced, and there would be mistrust in their motives. This study also identified a zone of tolerance for some overqualification. In other words, in the minds of recruiters, there was a certain ceiling of qualifications that would be acceptable before labeling an applicant overqualified for the job. Finally, Kulkarni, Lengnick-Hall, and Martinez (2015) report the results of 24 interviews, suggesting that common concerns include interpersonal and management issues and attitudinal problems these employees are expected to encounter.

Experimental work around how recruiters react to overqualified applicants would add value to the literature and is an area where there is a clear gap. Theoretical work on this topic exists (e.g., Martinez, Lengnick-Hall, & Kulkarni, 2014), but empirical research remains rare. Athey and Hautaluoma (1994) conducted an experiment with 61 hiring managers, manipulating education, job status, and job gender stereotype and showed that hiring managers tended to favor the more highly educated resumes. Similarly, Thompson, Sikora, Perrewé, and Ferris (2015) conducted an experimental study to show that recruiters have a preference for overqualified resumes. These findings are at odds with the real-life difficulties overqualified job applicants report, and suggest that the experimental studies may require a greater level of realism.

Understanding how recruiters react to overqualified applicants is a critically important topic, particularly in line with the fact that most research on overqualification utilized existing employees and not overqualified job applicants. For example, it is not technically accurate to assume that just because perceived overqualification is negatively related to job attitudes, an overqualified job candidate will necessarily be unhappy at work. This is because an overqualified job applicant may not always develop a sense of perceived overqualification once hired, and those who do not feel overqualified when they were first hired may end up developing this perception over time. As Fine and Nevo (2011) observed, we need objective measures of overqualification as observed by hiring managers, and we need studies of overqualification as part of the hiring process.

Measurement Inconsistency. Overqualification literature suffers from measurement inconsistency. There is some convergence on Maynard et al.'s (2006) measure of perceived overqualification, which is a positive development. Much of the literature we reviewed utilizes different measures and oftentimes single-item, unvalidated measures have also been used. McKee-Ryan and Harvey (2011), in their review of underemployment literature, called for greater consistency of measurement, and we would like to underline the importance of measurement practices in arriving at a generalizable literature that offers stronger inferences to future scholars.

Expanding and Bridging Micro and Macro Levels of Investigation. A holistic overview of the overqualification literature reveals a relatively confusing picture due to the mixed and conflicting empirical results. Contradictory results exist in almost every aspect of overqualification studies, such as the effects of age as an antecedent, or the effects of overqualification on performance. These controversies might be resolved with multilevel research designs (Sierra, 2011) or by including country-level economic characteristics (Erdogan, Bauer,

Peiró, & Truxillo, 2011b) or organization-level conditions. For example, differences in the sense of collective deprivation among industries or countries might provide a justification to some of the conflicting findings (as for age) on individual antecedents or consequences of overqualification.

To conclude, overqualification is a theoretically and practically important construct and its systematic investigation is still in the beginning stages. Research to date indicates that the effects of overqualification on employees and organizations are likely to be contingent on the situation. This construct is still new in management and industrial/organizational psychology literatures and offers a better understanding of implications of misfit with one's job relative to studies examining misfit while disregarding its direction and nature.

FURTHER READING

Bolino, M. C., & Feldman, D. C. (2000). The antecedents and consequences of underemployment among expatriates. *Journal of Organizational Behavior, 21,* 889–911.

Gallo A. (2011). Should you hire an overqualified candidate? *Harvard Business Review.* Retrieved from https://hbr.org/2011/03/should-you-hire-an-overqualifi

King, W. L., & Hautaluoma, J. E. (1987). Comparison of job satisfaction, life satisfaction, and performance of overeducated and other workers. *Journal of Social Psychology, 127,* 421–433.

Maynard, D., & Feldman, D. C. (2011). (Eds.). *Underemployment: Psychological economic, and social challenges.* New York: Springer.

McKee-Ryan, F. M., Virick, M., Prussia, G. E., Harvey, J., & Lilly, J. D. (2009). Life after the layoff: Getting a job worth keeping. *Journal of Organizational Behavior, 30,* 561–580.

Yang, W., Guan, Y., Lai, X., She, Z., & Lockwood, A. J. (2015). Career adaptability and perceived overqualification: Testing a dual-path model among Chinese human resource management professionals. *Journal of Vocational Behavior, 90,* 154–162.

REFERENCES

Agut, S., Peiró, J. M., & Grau, R. (2009). The effect of overeducation on job content innovation and career-enhancing strategies among young Spanish employees. *Journal of Career Development, 36,* 159–182.

Alba-Ramirez, A. (1993). Mismatch in the Spanish labor market: Overeducation? *Journal of Human Resources, 28,* 259–278.

Alfes, K., Shantz, A., & van Baalen, S. (2016). Reducing perceptions of overqualification and its impact on job satisfaction: The dual roles of interpersonal relationships at work. *Human Resource Management Journal, 26,* 84–101.

Athey, T. R., & Hautaluoma, J. E. (1994). Effects of applicant overeducation, job status, and job gender stereotype on employment decisions. *Journal of Social Psychology, 134,* 439–452.

Bewley, T. F. (1998). Why not cut pay? *European Economic Review, 42,* 459–490.

Bills, D. B. (1992). The mutability of educational credentials as hiring criteria how employers evaluate atypically highly credentialed job candidates. *Work and Occupations, 19,* 79–95.

Blalock, H. M., Jr. (1966). The identification problem and theory building: The case of status inconsistency. *American Sociological Review, 31,* 52–61.

Bracke, P., Pattyn, E., & von dem Knesebeck, O. (2013). Overeducation and depressive symptoms: Diminishing mental health returns to education. *Sociology of Health & Illness, 35,* 1242–1259.

Brynin, M., & Longhi, S. (2009). Overqualification: Major or minor mismatch? *Economics of Education Review, 28,* 114–121.

Büchel, F. (2002). The effects of overeducation on productivity in Germany: The firms' viewpoint. *Economics of Education Review, 21*, 263–275.

Büchel, F., & Battu, H. (2003). The theory of differential overqualification: Does it work? *Scottish Journal of Political Economy, 50*, 1–16.

Burke, R. J. (1997). Correlates of under-employment among recent business school graduates. *International Journal of Manpower, 18*, 627–635.

Burris, V. (1983). The social and political consequences of overeducation. *American Sociological Review, 48*, 454–467.

Chen, Y. J. (2009). Associations of perceived underemployment with in-role and organisational citizenship behaviours: The beneficiary perspective. *Global Business and Economics Review, 11*, 317–331.

Collins, B. K., & Long, L. (2015). The underemployment puzzle: The effects of overqualification and involuntary part-time status on volunteering. *Public Administration Quarterly, 39*, 569–594.

Croce, G., & Ghignoni, E. (2015). Educational mismatch and spatial flexibility in Italian local labour markets. *Education Economics, 23*, 25–46.

Crosby, F. (1984). Relative deprivation in organizational settings. *Research in Organizational Behavior, 6*, 51–93.

Deng, H., Guan, Y., Wu, C. H., Erdogan, B., Bauer, T., & Yao, X. (in press). A relational model of perceived overqualification: The moderating role of interpersonal influence on social acceptance. *Journal of Management*. http://dx.doi.org/10.1177/0149206316668237

Edwards, J. R. (2001). Ten difference score myths. *Organizational Research Methods, 4*, 265–287.

Edwards, J. R., & Parry, M. E. (1993). On the use of polynomial regression equations as an alternative to difference scores in organizational research. *Academy of Management Journal, 36*, 1577–1613.

Erdogan, B., & Bauer, T. N. (2009). Perceived overqualification and its outcomes: The moderating role of empowerment. *Journal of Applied Psychology, 94*, 557–565.

Erdogan, B., Bauer, T. N., Peiró, J. M., & Truxillo, D. M. (2011a). Overqualified employees: Making the best of a potentially bad situation for individuals and organizations. *Industrial and Organizational Psychology: Perspectives on Science and Practice, 4*, 215–232.

Erdogan, B., Bauer, T. N., Peiró, J. M., & Truxillo, D. M. (2011b). Overqualification theory, research, and practice: Things that matter. *Industrial and Organizational Psychology: Perspectives on Science and Practice, 4*, 260–267.

Erdogan, B., & Mansfield, L. (2016). Overqualification. In Ricky Griffin (Ed.), *Oxford bibliographies in management*. New York: Oxford University Press.

Feldman, D. C. (1996). The nature, antecedents and consequences of underemployment. *Journal of Management, 22*, 385–407.

Feldman, D. C., Leana, C. R., & Bolino, M. C. (2002). Underemployment and relative deprivation among re-employed executives. *Journal of Occupational and Organizational Psychology, 75*, 453–471.

Fine, S. (2007). Overqualification and selection in leadership training. *Journal of Leadership & Organizational Studies, 14*, 61–68.

Fine, S., & Nevo, B. (2007). A phenomenon of overqualification in personnel psychology. *International Journal of Testing, 7*, 327–352.

Fine, S., & Nevo, B. (2008). Too smart for their own good? A study of perceived cognitive overqualification in the workforce. *The International Journal of Human Resource Management, 19*, 346–355.

Fine, S., & Nevo, B. (2011). Overqualified job applicants: We still need predictive models. *Industrial and Organizational Psychology: Perspectives on Science and Practice, 4*, 240–242.

Flisi, S., Goglio, V., Meroni, E. C., Rodrigues, M., & Vera-Toscano, E. (2017). Measuring occupational mismatch: Overeducation and overskill in Europe—Evidence from PIAAC. *Social Indicators Research, 131*, 1211–1249.

Frank, R. H. (1978). Why women earn less: The theory and estimation of differential overqualification. *The American Economic Review, 68*, 360–373.

Frei, C., & Sousa-Poza, A. (2012). Overqualification: Permanent or transitory? *Applied Economics, 44*, 1837–1847.

Frenette, M. (2000). Overqualified? Recent graduates and the needs of their employers. *Education Quarterly Review, 7*, 6–20.

Frenette, M. (2004). The overqualified Canadian graduate: The role of the academic program in the incidence, persistence, and economic returns to overqualification. *Economics of Education Review, 23*, 29–45.

Friedland, D. S., & Price, R. H. (2003). Underemployment: Consequences for the health and well-being of workers. *American Journal of Community Psychology, 32*, 33–45.

Garcy, A. M. (2015). Educational mismatch and mortality among native-born workers in Sweden: A 19-year longitudinal study of 2.5 million over-educated, matched and under-educated individuals, 1990–2008. *Sociology of Health & Illness, 37*, 1314–1336.

Green, F., & Henseke, G. (2016). Should governments of OECD countries worry about graduate underemployment? *Oxford Review of Economic Policy, 32*, 514–537.

Green, F., & Zhu, Y. (2010). Overqualification, job dissatisfaction, and increasing dispersion in the returns to graduate education. *Oxford Economic Papers, 62*, 740–763.

Griesshaber, N., & Seibel, V. (2015). Over-education among immigrants in Europe: The value of civic involvement. *Journal of Ethnic and Migration Studies, 41*, 374–398.

Guerrero, L., & Hatala, J. P. (2015). Antecedents of perceived overqualification: A three-wave study. *Career Development International, 20*, 409–423.

Halaby, C. N. (1994). Overeducation and skill mismatch. *Sociology of Education, 67*, 47–59.

Hersch, J. (1991). Education match and job match. *The Review of Economics and Statistics, 73*, 140–144.

Hersch, J. (1995). Optimal "mismatch" and promotions. *Economic Inquiry, 33*, 611–624.

Hope, K. (1975). Models of status inconsistency and social mobility effects. *American Sociological Review, 40*, 322–343.

Hu, J., Erdogan, B., Bauer, T. N., Jiang, K., Liu, S., & Li, Y. (2015). There are lots of big fish in this pond: The role of peer overqualification on task significance, perceived fit, and performance for overqualified employees. *Journal of Applied Psychology, 100*, 1228–1238.

Hultin, H., Lundberg, M., Lundin, A., & Magnusson, C. (2016). Do overeducated individuals have increased risks of ill health? A Swedish population-based cohort study. *Sociology of Health & Illness, 38*, 980–995.

Johnson, G. J., & Johnson, W. R. (1996). Perceived overqualification and psychological well-being. *Journal of Social Psychology, 136*, 435–445.

Johnson, G. J., & Johnson, W. R. (1997). Perceived overqualification, emotional support, and health. *Journal of Applied Social Psychology, 27*, 1906–1918.

Johnson, G. J., & Johnson, W. R. (1999). Perceived overqualification and health: A longitudinal analysis. *Journal of Social Psychology, 139*, 14–28.

Johnson, G. J., & Johnson, W. R. (2000a). Perceived overqualification and dimensions of job satisfaction: A longitudinal analysis. *Journal of Psychology, 134*, 537–555.

Johnson, G. J., & Johnson, W. R. (2000b). Perceived overqualification, positive and negative affectivity, and satisfaction with work. *Journal of Social Behavior and Personality, 15*, 167–184.

Johnson, W. R., Morrow, P. C., & Johnson, G. J. (2002). An evaluation of a perceived overqualification scale across work settings. *Journal of Psychology, 136*, 425–441.

Johnston, R., Khattab, N., & Manley, D. (2015). East versus West? Over-qualification and earnings among the UK's European migrants. *Journal of Ethnic and Migration Studies, 41*, 196–218.

Khan, L. J., & Morrow, P. C. (1991). Objective and subjective underemployment relationships to job satisfaction. *Journal of Business Research, 22*, 211–218.

Kiersztyn, A. (2013). Stuck in a mismatch? The persistence of overeducation during twenty years of the post-communist transition in Poland. *Economics of Education Review, 32*, 78–91.

Kler, P., Leeves, G., & Shankar, S. (2015). Nothing to fear but fear itself: Perceptions of job security in Australia after the global financial crisis. *Social Indicators Research, 123*, 753–769.

Kristof-Brown, A. L., Zimmerman, R. D., & Johnson, E. C. (2005). Consequences of individuals' fit at work: A meta-analysis of person–job, person–organization, person–group, and person–supervisor fit. *Personnel Psychology, 58*, 281–342.

Kulkarni, M., Lengnick-Hall, M. L., & Martinez, P. G. (2015). Overqualification, mismatched qualification, and hiring decisions: Perceptions of employers. *Personnel Review, 44*, 529–549.

Li, I. W., & Miller, P. W. (2015). Overeducation and earnings in the Australian graduate labour market: An application of the Vahey model. *Education Economics, 23*, 63–83.

Lianos, T. P., Asteriou, D., & Agiomirgianakis, G. M. (2004). Foreign university graduates in the Greek labour market: Employment, salaries and overeducation. *International Journal of Finance & Economics, 9*, 151–164.

Lin, B., Law, K., & Zhou, J. (2017). Why is underemployment related to creativity and OCB? A task crafting explanation of the curvilinear moderated relations. *Academy of Management Journal, 60*, 156–177.

Liu, S., Luksyte, A., Zhou, L., Shi, J., & Wang, M. (2015). Overqualification and counterproductive work behaviors: Examining a moderated mediation model. *Journal of Organizational Behavior, 36*, 250–271.

Liu, S., & Wang, M. (2012). Perceived overqualification: A review and recommendations for research and practice. *Research in Occupational Stress and Well Being, 10*, 1–42.

Livingstone, D. W. (2010). Job requirements and workers' learning: Formal gaps, informal closure, systemic limits. *Journal of Education and Work, 23*, 207–231.

Lobene, E. V., & Meade, A. W. (2013). The effects of career calling and perceived overqualification on work outcomes for primary and secondary school teachers. *Journal of Career Development, 40*, 508–530.

Lobene, E. V., Meade, A. W., & Pond, S. B., III. (2015). Perceived overqualification: A multi-source investigation of psychological predisposition and contextual triggers. *Journal of Psychology, 149*, 684–710.

Luksyte, A., & Spitzmueller, C. (2016). When are overqualified employees creative? It depends on contextual factors. *Journal of Organizational Behavior, 37*, 635–653.

Luksyte, A., Spitzmueller, C., & Maynard, D. C. (2011). Why do overqualified incumbents deviate? Examining multiple mediators. *Journal of Occupational Health Psychology, 16*, 279–296.

Madamba, A. B., & De Jong, G. F. (1997). Job mismatch among Asians in the United States: Ethnic group comparisons. *Social Science Quarterly, 78*, 524–542.

Maltarich, M. A., Reilly, G., & Nyberg, A. J. (2011). Objective and subjective overqualification: Distinctions, relationships, and a place for each in the literature. *Industrial and Organizational Psychology: Perspectives on Science and Practice, 4*, 236–239.

Marchante, A. J., & Ortega, B. (2012). Human capital and labor productivity: A study for the hotel industry. *Cornell Hospitality Quarterly, 53*, 20–30.

Martinez, P. G., Lengnick-Hall, M. L., & Kulkarni, M. (2014). Overqualified? A conceptual model of managers' perceptions of overqualification in selection decisions. *Personnel Review, 43*, 957–974.

Maynard, D. C., Joseph, T. A., & Maynard, A. M. (2006). Underemployment, job attitudes, and turnover intentions. *Journal of Organizational Behavior, 27*, 509–536.

Maynard, D. C., & Parfyonova, N. M. (2013). Perceived overqualification and withdrawal behaviours: Examining the roles of job attitudes and work values. *Journal of Occupational and Organizational Psychology, 86*, 435–455.

McKee-Ryan, F. M., & Harvey, J. (2011). "I have a job, but . . .": A review of underemployment. *Journal of Management, 37*, 962–996.

Nunnally, J. C. (1978). *Psychometric theory* (2d ed.). New York: McGraw-Hill.

Peiró, J. M., Agut, S., & Grau, R. (2010). The relationship between overeducation and job satisfaction among young Spanish workers: The role of salary, contract of employment, and work experience. *Journal of Applied Social Psychology, 40*, 666–689.

Peiró, J. M., Sora, B., & Caballer, A. (2012). Job insecurity in the younger Spanish workforce: Causes and consequences. *Journal of Vocational Behavior, 80*, 444–453.

Premji, S., & Smith, P. M. (2013). Education-to-job mismatch and the risk of work injury. *Injury Prevention, 19*, 106–111.

Quinn, M. A., & Rubb, S. (2011). Spouse overeducation and family migration: Evidence from the US. *Journal of Family and Economic Issues, 32*, 36–45.

Roh, Y. H., Chang, J. Y., Kim, M. U., & Nam, S. K. (2014). The effects of income and skill utilization on the underemployed's self-esteem, mental health, and life satisfaction. *Journal of Employment Counseling, 51*, 125–141.

Romaní, J., Casado-Díaz, J. M., & Lillo-Bañuls, A. (2016). On the links between spatial variables and over-education. *Applied Economics Letters, 23*, 652–655.

Rubb, S. (2003). Overeducation in the labor market: A comment and re-analysis of a meta-analysis. *Economics of Education Review, 22*, 621–629.

Russell, Z. A., Ferris, G. R., Thompson, K. W., & Sikora, D. M. (2016). Overqualified human resources, career development experiences, and work outcomes: Leveraging an underutilized resource with political skill. *Human Resource Management Review, 26*, 125–135.

Sáez, M. P., González-Prieto, N., & Cantarero-Prieto, D. (2016). Is over-education a problem in Spain? Empirical evidence based on the EU-SILC. *Social Indicators Research, 126*, 617–632.

Shultz, K. S., Olson, D. A., & Wang, M. (2011). Overqualified employees: Perspectives of older workers. *Industrial and Organizational Psychology: Perspectives on Science and Practice, 4*, 247–249.

Sicherman, N., & Galor, O. (1990). A theory of career mobility. *Journal of Political Economy, 98*, 169–192.

Sierra, M. J. (2011). A multilevel approach to understanding employee overqualification. *Industrial and Organizational Psychology, 4*, 243–246.

Sikora, D. M., Thompson, K. W., Russell, Z. A., & Ferris, G. R. (2016). Reimagining overqualified human resources to promote organizational effectiveness and competitive advantage. *Journal of Organizational Effectiveness: People and Performance, 3*, 23–42.

Sloane, P. J., Battu, H., & Seaman, P. T. (1999). Overeducation, undereducation and the British labour market. *Applied Economics, 31*, 1437–1453.

Spence, M. (1973). Job market signaling. *Quarterly Journal of Economics, 87*, 355–374.

Stenfors, C. U., Hanson, L. M., Oxenstierna, G., Theorell, T., & Nilsson, L. G. (2013). Psychosocial working conditions and cognitive complaints among Swedish employees. *PLoS ONE, 8*, e60637.

Støren, L. A., & Wiers-Jenssen, J. (2010). Foreign diploma versus immigrant background determinants of labour market success or failure? *Journal of Studies in International Education, 14*, 29–49.

Szydlik, M. (2002). Vocational education and labour markets in deregulated, flexibly coordinated and planned societies. *European Societies, 4*, 79–105.

Thompson, K. W., Sikora, D. M., Perrewé, P. L., & Ferris, G. R. (2015). Employment qualifications, person–job fit, underemployment attributions, and hiring recommendations: A three-study investigation. *International Journal of Selection and Assessment, 23*, 247–262.

Vaisey, S. (2006). Education and its discontents: Overqualification in America, 1972–2002. *Social Forces, 85*, 835–864.

Verbruggen, M., van Emmerik, H., Van Gils, A., Meng, C., & de Grip, A. (2015). Does early-career underemployment impact future career success? A path dependency perspective. *Journal of Vocational Behavior, 90*, 101–110.

Verhaest, D., & Omey, E. (2006). The impact of overeducation and its measurement. *Social Indicators Research, 77*, 419–448.

Vogtenhuber, S. (2014). The impact of within country heterogeneity in vocational specificity on initial job matches and job status. *Journal of Vocational Behavior, 85*, 374–384.

Watt, J. D., & Hargis, M. B. (2010). Boredom proneness: Its relationship with subjective underemployment, perceived organizational support, and job performance. *Journal of Business and Psychology, 25*, 163–174.

Wright, R. (2014). Student focused marketing: Impact of marketing higher education based on student data and input. *College Student Journal, 48*, 88–93.

Wu, C. H., Luksyte, A., & Parker, S. K. (2015). Overqualification and subjective well-being at work: The moderating role of job autonomy and culture. *Social Indicators Research, 121*, 917–937.

Zhang, M. J., Law, K. S., & Lin, B. (2016). You think you are big fish in a small pond? Perceived overqualification, goal orientations, and proactivity at work. *Journal of Organizational Behavior, 37*, 61–84.

Berrin Erdogan, Talya N. Bauer, and Aysegul Karaeminogullari

CAREERS AND CAREER DEVELOPMENT

INTRODUCTION: DEFINITION AND HISTORY

A career is typically defined as "the evolving sequence of a person's work experiences over time" (Arthur et al., 1989, p. 8). Careers have been studied in a wide variety of disciplines, including but not limited to psychology, management, and sociology (Gunz & Peiperl, 2007; Gunz et al., 2019). Following the Academy of Management Careers Division domain statement, the field of career studies could be characterized as "people's lifelong succession of work experiences, the structure of opportunity to work, and the relationship between careers and other aspects of life." Although research on careers has been around for over 100 years, it has become increasingly popular during the early 21st century (Wang & Wanberg, 2017).

The field of career studies dates back to the early 1900s, when the main topics of study were individual differences and mental testing (e.g., Thorndike, 1914) and occupational (or vocational, career) choice (e.g., Parsons, 1909). Studies primarily focused on creating occupational classifications, as well as studying people's vocational choices and the degree to which those would fit with their individual characteristics. This trend was taken to the next level after the 1950s, when two highly influential theories were published: the theory of vocational development (Super, 1957) and the theory of vocational choice (Holland, 1959). These two theories provided a framework for understanding people's vocational interests and their career development over time. The main emphasis in research was on preparing people to make "the right" occupational choice that would offer long-term secure and stable employment (Ginzberg, 1972). Until the late 1980s, careers research was dominated by studies on career choice, often using Super's and Holland's work as the theoretical foundation.

Career studies started to move from an employer-focused perspective to an employee-focused perspective after that time. This was a result of societal changes in job security and job transitions, which led scholars to start studying topics such as job search and individual career management (Wang & Wanberg, 2017). The research on occupational choice, which had primarily focused on matching an individual with a lifetime occupation, also started changing at this time. Because of a growing focus on individual competencies and behaviors, studies began to look at occupational choice as a dynamic, ongoing process rather than a once-in-a-lifetime decision (De Vos et al., 2019). The 1990s featured the introduction of protean career theory (Hall, 2002), boundaryless career theory (Arthur et al., 2005), and social cognitive career theory (Lent et al., 1994), which became hallmarks of the field and still are at the core of careers research. These theories primarily emphasize individual agency as the key to career development and management, moving away even further from the traditional organizational career perspective.

Since the 2000s, the field of career studies has diversified even more, while mostly retaining its strong emphasis on individual agency in career development. Several review articles have examined trends in the field (Akkermans & Kubasch, 2017; Baruch et al., 2015; Byington et al., 2019; Lee et al., 2014) and draw similar conclusions. Most notably, all of these reviews conclude that the topic of career success has been the most dominant theme in the field. Furthermore, careers research has focused on topics such as employability, individual career management, and career choice. The field has been dominated by quantitative studies and a focus on the micro (i.e., individual) level, thereby further moving away from its sociological roots (Akkermans & Kubasch, 2017; Baruch et al., 2015).

In the remainder of this article, a number of influential (a) career theories and (b) career topics will be discussed that have been highly influential in the field. These specific theories and topics were chosen because of their overall influence in the field in terms of citations, and the amount of scholarly work they have spurred. In addition, the choices were made based on review articles and chapters in the field of career studies that have provided overviews of the field, and distinguished similar theories and topics. Finally, some emerging theories and topics are also discussed, based on clear increases in their popularity in the field.

THEORIES IN THE FIELD OF CAREER STUDIES

This section discusses some of the most prominent theoretical perspectives in the field of career studies.

Protean Career Theory. Protean career theory (Hall, 1976; Mirvis & Hall, 1994) became a leading career theory in the 1990s and has been highly influential ever since. Protean career theory argues that it is not the organization but, rather, the individual that manages their career. In addition, the theory was one of the first to propagate the importance of psychological, or subjective, success for people's careers. Furthermore, this theory emphasizes that careers are not just about upward advancement but also (or, even more so) about free individual growth (Hall, 1996). Thus, in contrast to the aforementioned models of Super (1957) and Holland (1959), protean career theory is about an individual agentic approach to career development, driven by intrinsic motivation (Hall, 2002). In doing so, it also emphasizes a changing employment relationship, arguing that careers are less about relational, long-term commitments and more about transactional, shorter-term psychological contracts (Hall & Moss, 1998).

Protean career theory consists of three elements: the protean career concept (PCC), protean career orientation (PCO), and protean career path (PCP) (Gubler et al., 2014; Hall et al., 2018). PCC refers to the theoretical concept of protean careers, emphasizing the aforementioned individual agency toward career development. Hall (2002) introduced the notion of "metacompetencies," which influence the degree to which individuals can develop other competencies. In the PCC, the two key metacompetencies are adaptability and identity (sometimes also referred to as self-awareness). According to Hall (2002), individuals must be able to constantly adapt to changing circumstances in order to thrive in their career. Yet, being adaptable in itself is not enough, because individuals also need to be aware of their identity. Together, these two metacompetencies form the core of the PCC. The PCO is an individual attitude toward career development that emphasizes two main aspects: self-direction (which associates with the PCC notion of individual agency) and being values-driven (which associates with the PCC notion of intrinsic motivation and psychological success) (Briscoe et al., 2006). Similar to the proposed interactive effect of the PCC metacompetencies, the two PCO dimensions are also assumed to interact for optimal effects. Indeed, Briscoe et al. (2010) showed that being self-directed and values-driven, together, explained more variance in willingness to change than either of the two dimensions by itself. Finally, the PCP is the objective sequence of job moves, the actual individual career path connected to the elements of the PCC and PCO (Gubler et al., 2014; Hall et al., 2018).

Though protean career theory already gained traction in the 1990s, its popularity has steeply increased since 2000 (Hall et al., 2018). In particular, research on protean careers skyrocketed in 2006, likely because this year marks the publication of a validated scale for PCO (Briscoe et al., 2006). The majority of empirical studies has focused on PCO, whereas only a few studies have explicitly examined PCC and PCP (Gubler et al., 2014). One of those strands in the literature has focused on further scale validation and development. The Briscoe et al. (2006) scale is still the most widely used and has been validated in a wide range of cultures, although others have developed similar PCO scales (e.g., Baruch et al., 2015; Porter et al., 2016). The majority of PCO literature has examined its role as an antecedent of career behaviors and outcomes (Hall et al., 2018). Generally speaking, PCO is considered a "win-win" for individuals and organizations, as it can lead to enhanced career success, job and life satisfaction, as well as performance and commitment (Rodrigues et al., 2015). In their review of protean career studies, Hall et al. (2018) observed two interesting patterns in the literature. First, PCO does not necessarily have a uniform effect on outcomes, but its two dimensions of being self-directed and values-driven can differ in their role as antecedent. For example, being self-directed is a consistent predictor of subjective career success, whereas this is not always the case for the values-driven component. Second, although PCO implies an individual independence from organizations, findings thus far indicate that PCO is positively linked to organizational outcomes such as affective commitment and task performance.

To summarize, research on protean careers has become a hallmark of "new career" research. Empirical studies have primarily focused on protean career orientations as predictors of career outcomes, which leaves potential for further research (critically) examining the protean career concept and protean career paths (Gubler et al., 2014). There have been critiques on protean career theory that have argued that the protean career concept in itself is far from clear (Arnold & Cohen, 2008), for example that the term *values* is hardly clarified in the theory. Relatedly, some studies in non-Western countries found that the values aspect of the PCO scale by

Briscoe et al. (2006) did not emerge as expected (Hall et al., 2018). Furthermore, Gubler et al. (2014) note that the protean career concept has rarely been critically examined, despite attempts to refine the model. In response, Hall et al. (2018) developed an integrative model of protean career theory, which attempts to reply to those conceptual critiques. Future research now needs to empirically test this model and further examine the core conceptual characteristics of the protean career concept, as well as protean career paths.

Boundaryless Career Theory.   Boundaryless career theory emerged in the 1990s and gained popularity around the same time as protean career theory, within the context of a changing labor market with more structural and psychological flexibility (Arthur & Rousseau, 1996). The boundaryless career thereby describes emerging career patterns that are less dependent on traditional organizational career management (Guan et al., 2019). Although the boundaryless career has several meanings and was used in different ways in the past (Arthur & Rousseau, 1996; Guan et al., 2019), the concept of boundaryless careers often refers to "sequences of job opportunities that go beyond the boundaries of single employment settings" (DeFillippi & Arthur, 1994, p. 306). Objectively described, as an example, a traditional career with one single job within one single organization over one's lifetime can be described as the opposite of a boundaryless career. In contrast, a career that is composed of a pattern of different jobs, employers, and potentially occupations can be described as a prototypical boundaryless career pattern. However, reducing the boundaryless career to patterns of mobility between structural elements is an unnecessary, but often undertaken, reduction of the richness of the concept (Guan et al., 2019; Sullivan & Arthur, 2006). Indeed, Arthur et al. (2005) noted that it is not physical mobility per se that is key to the boundaryless career, but rather opportunities for mobility and independence from one's employer. Within boundaryless career theory, the mobility concept can be separated and combined within two dimensions that are subjectively represented within individuals: physical mobility (also called organizational mobility preference) and psychological mobility (also called boundaryless mindset, Sullivan & Arthur, 2006). Physical mobility is the actual movement between jobs, firms, occupations, and countries, whereas psychological mobility is the capacity to move as seen through the mind of the career actor (Sullivan & Arthur, 2006).

Empirically, boundaryless careers have mostly been operationalized or measured by either objective patterns of career moves (clearly representing the physical mobility aspect) or a scale that captures both components (physical and psychological mobility) via individual ratings. This scale should best be interpreted as boundaryless career *orientations* because it captures a subjective pleasure or willingness to move between organizations or structural elements (Sullivan & Arthur, 2006). Research on the concept has mostly been conceptual, qualitative, and quantitative. In particular, the availability of the boundaryless career orientation scale caused an increase in quantitative boundaryless career research. To provide some examples: a boundaryless career orientation is helpful for dealing with workplace insecurity (Briscoe et al., 2012), the physical mobility component is negatively related to different types of organizational commitment (Çakmak-Otluoğlu, 2012) and positively related to salary (Volmer & Spurk, 2011), proactive personality and entrepreneurial interests predict a boundaryless mindset (Uy et al., 2015), and core self-evaluations predict boundaryless careers through higher levels of perceived employability (Rodrigues et al., 2019). A review by Guan et al. (2019) also showed the complex relationships of the boundaryless career with career success, indicating there is no universal linear relationship.

In sum, the boundaryless career can be seen as one of the most influential career theories between 1995 and 2020 (Guan et al., 2019; Sullivan, 1999). The framework has generated a considerable body of research and provided new insights for career development. These insights appear to be valid across countries, though the specific mechanisms may differ depending on contextual factors (Guan et al., 2019). For example, external career mobility could be particularly effective in liberal labor market situations (Fasang et al., 2012), whereas internal mobility is more effective in countries characterized by long-term orientations (Biemann & Wolf, 2009). Overall, the boundaryless career framework has provided a metaphor for the changing world of work within the last decades (for a review on the topic see also Arthur, 2014). Nonetheless, scholars have also criticized aspects of boundaryless career theory, like flexibility as a burden (Baruch & Vardi, 2016), less than expected objective career moves within the labor market (Rodrigues & Guest, 2010), or measurement and conceptual criticism about the boundaryless career orientation scale (Wiernik & Kostal, 2019). Future research needs to integrate past research and those critical voices to build an actualized and future-oriented research agenda.

Career Construction Theory.   Career construction theory explains the interpretive and interpersonal processes through which individuals construct themselves, impose direction on their vocational behavior, and make meaning of their careers (Savickas, 2013; Savickas & Porfeli, 2012). Interestingly, career construction theory did not only inform and influence career research on a large scale (Rudolph et al., 2017), but also generated a practical counseling approach (Savickas, 2015). Career construction theory thereby addresses how individuals build careers through personal and social constructionism. It asserts that individuals construct representations of reality, yet they do not construct reality itself. Hence, career construction theory is a highly subjective approach about how individuals give sense, purpose, and meaning to their (past) career paths and decisions. Moreover, career construction theory can be applied to diverse career stages and tasks and was thereby consequentially researched, for example, within student, job market entry, or adult populations (Guan et al., 2014; Hirschi, 2010; Johnston, 2018; Spurk et al., 2016).

Although career construction theory has existed since the 1990s, the popularity of the theory has grown considerably and exponentially since 2010. The major reason for the explosion in career construction research was the development and measurement of one of its core constructs: career adaptability. The highly influential paper about the concept and measurement of career adaptability was published in 2012 (Savickas, 1997; Savickas & Porfeli, 2012) and triggered more than 100 empirical studies on the topic. Career adaptability is defined as "a psychosocial construct that denotes an individual's resources for coping with current and anticipated tasks, transitions, traumas in their occupational roles" (Savickas & Porfeli, 2012, p. 662). Within career construction theory, four sub-dimensions build the higher-order general career adaptability construct: concern (i.e., planning), control (i.e., decision-making, being decisive), curiosity (i.e., exploring, being inquisitive), and confidence (i.e., problem solving, being efficacious).

Furthermore, career construction theory (Hirschi et al., 2015; Savickas, 2005; Spurk et al., 2020) differentiates among (a) adaptivity (i.e., the psychological trait of willingness to meet the unfamiliar, complex, and ill-defined problems presented by vocational development tasks), (b) adaptability (i.e., the resource for coping with current and anticipated tasks, transitions, and traumas in their occupational roles), and (c) adapting (i.e., performing adaptive behaviors that address changing conditions, such as career planning, career exploration, or networking). This model was empirically tested and validated, for instance, by a study by Hirschi et al. (2015) and a meta-analysis by Rudolph et al. (2017). Further research showed that career adaptability is positively related to career and work outcomes, such as objective and subjective career success (Rudolph et al., 2017), well-being (Maggiori et al., 2013), job search strategies (Koen et al., 2010), employability (Spurk et al., 2016), and performance (Zacher, 2015). Moreover, a study by Spurk et al. (2020) showed changes in career adaptability go along with changes in proactive career behaviors and furthermore predict career satisfaction in a longitudinal manner. Career adaptability has now been studied across the globe, with most studies finding support for its basic premises in a variety of countries, such as in Italy and Switzerland (Santilli et al., 2017), the Czech Republic (Hlad'o et al., 2020), China (Ocampo et al., 2020), Malaysia (Ng et al., 2020), and Turkey (Karacan-Ozdemir, 2019).

In sum, since 2010, research has provided a solid basis for studying the nature, predictors, and outcomes of career adaptability and, more broadly speaking, career construction theory. Career adaptability surely can be seen as a central career self-management concept that helps to build more sustainable and successful careers. Nonetheless, there are first signs that not all components of career adaptability have the same meaning and importance for all outcomes (Rudolph et al., 2017) and that high levels of career adaptability can also decrease proactive career behaviors (Spurk et al., 2020). Furthermore, career adaptability should be seen as one important aspect of career construction theory, namely as a means for reaching purpose and sense within one's career. However, career construction theory also focuses on career narratives, life themes, and career counseling methods that have received less attention within empirical career construction research.

Social Cognitive Career Theory. Social cognitive career theory (SCCT) has its roots in social cognitive theory (Bandura, 1986, 1999, 2001), which was developed to hypothesize why people approached or avoided various activities or actions. It was also a theory of how people regulated their behaviors to attain goals (Usher & Schunk, 2018). Bandura hypothesized that individuals would engage in tasks where they felt confident of their ability to act. Bandura termed this self-efficacy. Sources of self-efficacy are in four main areas: previous performance accomplishments, vicarious observation of role models, verbal persuasion, and physiological states and arousal. One result of the focus on sources of self-efficacy is that it has made this theory particularly amenable to interventions to bolster self-efficacy at the individual, group, and community levels. Self-efficacy is also connected to outcome expectancies, or the expectations one has of the result of behavior. Similar sources of outcome expectations operate: performance accomplishments, vicarious learning, verbal persuasion, and physiological arousal. According to social cognitive theory, one may be confident of one's actions but still not engage in those goal-related activities if the outcomes expected are negative.

Based on Bandura's social cognitive theory, SCCT (Lent et al., 1994) was initially applied to work and career choices to predict career interests and career choices, as well as persistence at work and performance. Social cognitive career theory suggests that if one has confidence to perform tasks (self-efficacy) and believes positive outcomes (outcome expectations) will occur if they engage in that task, they will have higher interest in that area and will engage in actions to enact those choices. Self-efficacy and outcome expectancies are the perceptions of reality, as opposed to reality. Thus, someone might be perceived by others to be competent in an area, but not feel that they can engage in actions related to the area; that will be a stronger predictor of their actions than objective reality.

In 1981, Hackett and Betz (1981; Betz & Hackett, 1981) applied Bandura's social cognitive theory to women's traditional career choices, proposing that that low self-efficacy may be a reason that women continued to choose a limited number of occupations. Their work was expanded by Lent et al. (1994, 2002; Lent & Brown, 2006) into a full- fledged theoretical model of career choice. Their initial model also hypothesized that self-efficacy and outcome expectations in a specific domain (or area) predicted the development of interests in that area. For example, if one feels confident to engage in math-related tasks and thinks that positive outcomes will result from engaging in math-related tasks, one will develop interests in math, and be more likely to choose a career that involves math. The constructs are domain specific; thus, efficacy in math is not the same as efficacy in English or French.

Self-efficacy and outcome expectations come from the learning experiences individuals have (Lent et al., 1994, 2002). Learning experiences can come from accomplishments one has, watching others as role models, being encouraged by others, or the physiological arousal, such as excitement or anxiety that can lead one toward, or away from, engaging in career-related activities (Lent & Brown, 2013). SCCT proposes that gender, race, and other demographic variables help to form the opportunities for learning experiences that then help form self-efficacy beliefs and beliefs about outcome expectations. For example, if someone is from a high socioeconomic status (SES) family that provides a wide array of opportunities for their children, such as visits to museums, camps, tutoring, music lessons, and so on, they are more likely to have the learning experiences to form higher self-efficacy beliefs and positive outcome expectations. Thus, if someone previously did well in an area, watched role models succeed in that area, was verbally encouraged to engage in the area, and had excitement (or reduced anxiety) in that area, they would be more likely to have higher self-efficacy and outcome expectations.

SCCT also proposes that there are barriers and supports that influence decisions to pursue actions (Lent et al., 2002). Some are earlier than (distal to) the choice and others are more proximal to the choice. Examples of distal influences may be factors that influence learning experiences, such as gender-role socialization, impoverished learning environment, or increased opportunities, while proximal barriers and supports affect the implementation of choices, such as having a child or financial aid.

The first SCCT model was a career choice model (Lent et al., 1994, 2002). Subsequent to this model, Lent and Brown developed a *performance* model, which predicts the level of performance as well as the persistence an individual has in pursuing goals (Lent et al., 2002), as well as a satisfaction model (Lent & Brown, 2008). Finally, Lent and Brown (2013) developed a model of career self-management. This model was developed to integrate adaptive career-related behaviors, such as career decision-making and exploration, searching for work, advancing in a career, managing various transitions, and negotiating various roles (such as work and family) with developmental periods and life roles.

The social cognitive career model has generated a great deal of interest among researchers in vocational psychology, and has given rise to several meta-analyses of research on the various models, as well as on aspects of the model. Research has demonstrated support for the relationship between self-efficacy and interests and between self-efficacy and outcome expectations. In addition, there is empirical support for the influence of self-efficacy and outcome expectations in predicting interests, as well as predicting occupational choices and goals (Lent & Brown, 2019; Sheu et al., 2010). The relationships between supports and barriers proximal to goals were also supported, although to a more moderate degree (Lent & Brown, 2019). Meta-analyses of the various sources of learning experiences, described earlier, have found that performance accomplishments are related most strongly to self-efficacy beliefs, moderately to vicarious learning and persuasion, and not significantly to physiological arousal (Byars-Winston et al., 2017). These findings have been robust across a number of U.S. racial/ethnic groups. Lent (2020) concludes that "research provides support for many of SCCT's theoretical assumptions . . . and in understanding and facilitating the career development of persons across a number of diversity dimensions" (p. 149).

Other Theoretical Perspectives

Sustainable Careers. Van der Heijden and De Vos (2015) defined sustainable careers as: "sequences of career experiences reflected through a variety of patterns of continuity over time, thereby crossing several social spaces, characterized by individual agency, herewith providing meaning to the individual" (p. 7). In their conceptual article, De Vos et al. (2020) argue that career sustainability is a dynamic interplay between individual, contextual, and temporal issues. For example, individuals can enact agency and search for meaning in their careers (i.e., individual), yet this depends on, for example, organizational, cultural, and nonwork factors (i.e., contextual) and it can change over time (i.e., temporal). Two crucial concepts in this regard are proactivity and adaptability. First, proactivity means that individuals need to take charge of their context and their own development over time. Second, adaptability refers to individuals being able to adapt to changes in their context and over time. Together, this implies that there is constant interaction between individual, contextual, and temporal factors that need to be balanced. De Vos et al. (2020) further argue that career sustainability is about an ongoing person-career fit dynamic, in which individuals strive for alignment between their career aspirations and behaviors. Career sustainability indicators are happiness (e.g., engagement, success), health (e.g., workability), and productivity (e.g., performance, employability). An important aspect of the conceptual work of De Vos et al. is that sustainable career theorizing complements other career theories (e.g., boundaryless and protean career theory) that have focused predominantly on individual agency by also explicitly taking into account context and time. Sustainable careers are highly idiosyncratic and are, as a consequence, highly diverse (Van der Heijden et al., 2020). There is no one universal path to career sustainability, and the path toward career sustainability may be much more challenging in certain circumstances, such as during unemployment, when being part of a minority population, or during economic recessions. As such, the sustainable career framework by De Vos et al. offers an inclusive framework for analyzing long-term career outcomes.

Empirical findings in the area of sustainable career have provided initial support for its basic premises. For example, studies have highlighted the importance of alignment between individuals and organizations, showing that reduced workload initiatives and career customization programs are only effective when there are clear agreements between employees and employers (Kossek & Ollier-Malaterre, 2020; Straub et al. 2020). Furthermore, career sustainability can only be understood from a whole-life perspective, as nonwork factors, such as leisure activities and work-home balance, are critical to long-term career sustainability (De Hauw & Greenhaus, 2015; Hirschi et al., 2020; Kelly et al., 2020). Learning and employability are also key for sustainable careers (Blokker et al., 2019; Heslin et al., 2020). Overall, Van der Heijden et al. (2020) conclude that studies in the area of career sustainability have offered support for its proposed mechanisms, yet that more research is needed to fully capture its theoretical, conceptual, and methodological complexities.

Kaleidoscope Careers. The kaleidoscope career perspective was introduced within the context of gendered opting-out career research (Mainiero & Sullivan, 2005). Thereby, the kaleidoscope is seen as a metaphor that produces changing patterns when the tube is rotated and its glass chips fall into new arrangements. Similarly, women shift the pattern of their careers by rotating different aspects in their lives to arrange their roles and relationships in new ways. Although originally applied to women, the related "ABC" model has also been applied to men and mixed populations. Authenticity (A) relates to the question of whether people can be themselves in the midst of career chaos and role changes and thereby still be authentic. Balance (B) relates to the question of whether people who make a career decision can balance the parts of their life well enough so that there can be a coherent whole. Challenge (C) relates to the question of whether people can be sufficiently challenged if they accept specific career options. If all components (ABC) are met, the career will result in satisfaction and meaningfulness (Mainiero & Sullivan, 2005). Empirical research has shown that the ABC factors can differ between men and women and across the life span. For example, though challenge was similar for women and men as declining over time, balance became increasingly important for women in the mid-career phase but less important for men (Mainiero & Gibson, 2017).

Psychology of Working Theory. The psychology of working theory (PWT; Duffy et al., 2016) grew out of Blustein's psychology of working framework (Blustein, 2006), developed to address the work decisions of non–college bound individuals. As a theoretical framework, PWT incorporates a number of variables that other vocational theories do not include, such as economic constraints and marginalization, which lead to choices of decent work (or ability to find decent work). The theory conceptualizes decent work as predicted by economic constraints and marginalization, mediated by career adaptability and work volition, leading to positive outcomes such as social connectedness, survival needs, and self-determination, which, in turn, lead to well-being and job satisfaction. The construct of decent work follows the definition by the International Labour Organization (Duffy et al., 2016), which includes the five factors of: (a) physically safe work, that (b) has adequate free time and rest, (c) has adequate compensation, (d) offers access to health care, and (e) provides work-life balance.

The theory also predicts that four variables moderate the relationship between economic constraints, marginalization, career adaptability, work volition, and decent work: proactive personality, critical consciousness, social support, and external economic conditions. In sum, Duffy et al. (2016) predict that individuals who have high economic status and had few experiences with racism and sexism would have higher career adaptability and higher work volition, would find decent work, and would have positive career outcomes. But the theory really is designed to explain the opposite scenario, helping to understand how, for example, sexism, racism, and homophobia would interact with more economic constraints to explain how individuals may have lower career adaptability or work volition. Support was found for the perceptions of barriers due to race (Blustein et al., 2010), although in the same study, half of the high school students did not perceive racism as playing a role in career considerations. Though the theory is still quite nascent, the model is receiving extensive study, both quantitatively and qualitatively, including global research on decent work (Duffy et al., 2020).

Theories From Other Disciplines. The field of career studies has also adopted theories that originated in other, related fields. A few of them are discussed next.

Conservation of resources (COR) theory was originally proposed by Hobfoll (1989) to explain mechanisms related to stress, and has since been applied to work-related stress and resources. COR theory proposes that people strive to maintain their current level and type of resources, try to acquire new resources, and guard against the loss of resources (Hobfoll, 2002). The theory also proposes that people accrue resources to guard against loss of future resources, preventing a spiral of resource loss. Though COR theory began as a stress-oriented theory, it has moved beyond that area (for an overview, see Hobfoll et al., 2018). It has also become a popular theory in careers research, for example as a theoretical model to understand career success (Spurk et al., 2019), employability (Forrier et al., 2018), career hurdles (Ng & Feldman, 2014), and career sustainability (De Vos et al., 2020).

Human capital theory primarily focuses on the skills and knowledge that individuals acquire to enhance their performance and success in the labor market (Becker, 1964). Human capital is likely to be rewarded in the labor market and has specific relevance for career development research. First, the development of human capital from childhood via youth and adulthood to older individuals can be considered as one important aspect of career development per se. Second, human capital puts individuals at a competitive advantage compared to peers with lower human capital. According to the contest-mobility perspective of career success, therefore, individuals with higher levels of human capital (e.g., experience, tenure, skill levels, education, and social networks) usually also show higher levels of objective career success like income or promotions (Ng et al., 2005). However, with a shift toward more subjective criteria of careers, human capital theory has lost a bit of its momentum in the field of career studies, at least in terms of predicting objective career outcomes (Spurk et al., 2019) and employability (Forrier et al., 2018).

Social exchange theory (SET) (Cropanzano & Mitchell, 2005; Cropanzano et al., 2017) has been a highly influential theoretical perspective to examine employment relations (Cook et al., 2013). SET focuses on interdependent relationships between parties (e.g., employer and employee) as a series of reciprocal resource exchanges. High-quality employment relations are achieved when they are balanced (i.e., equal contributions from the parties involved) and of high level (i.e., there is a high amount of investment), which then lead to positive outcomes for employees (e.g., commitment, performance) and employers (e.g., retention of talent) (Cook et al., 2013; Cropanzano et al., 2017). In the field of career studies, SET has been used in a variety of topics, including employability (Forrier et al., 2018), organizational career management (Guan et al., 2015), and career opportunities and development (Kraimer et al., 2011).

TOPICS IN THE FIELD OF CAREER STUDIES

In this section, some of the key topics and concepts that have been researched in the field of career studies will be discussed.

Career Choice Across the Life Span. It is axiomatic that individuals are now making career decisions at nearly every stage of life, rather than making a one-off career choice at the start of one's professional career (De Vos et al., 2019). As briefly described in the historical overview at the start of this article, in the 1950s, Super's developmental theory (1957) was revolutionary in conceptualizing that there were developmental stages that characterized final career choice (usually at age 18–20). Super proposed, first, that vocational development is a process of making several decisions, and second, that vocational choice is an implementation of the self-concept. He also proposed that choices were the result of an interaction between self-concept and external feedback, occurring over time. Thus, career choices were thought to be the result of a sense of self—"what I should do"—in combination with external reality— "what others think I should, or could do." Often, of course, the latter is shaped by what others, or the external world, says that one cannot do, in part due to gender or racial socialization, or discrimination.

Super proposed five distinct life stages, each with developmental tasks appropriate for the mid-20th century. The first was Growth (ages 4 to 13), the second was Exploration (ages 14 to 24), the third was Establishment (ages 25 to 44), the fourth was Maintenance or Management (ages 45 to 65), and the fifth was Disengagement (over age 65) (Hartung, 2013). Each stage had its characteristic developmental tasks (Hartung, 2013): for example, individuals at the career exploration stage needed to understand their own interests and values before going on to implementing a choice task before the next state of establishment. If individuals mastered the tasks of one stage, they were thought to be prepared for the next stage. Successfully navigating developmental tasks of a stage was considered to be evidence of career maturity. Eventually, the construct of career maturity evolved to be thought of as career adaptability, which is part of career construction theory (Savickas, 2002, 2005).

In the more than 60 years since Super (1957) proposed this theory, significant support has been marshaled for the tasks related to vocational exploration and career choice, although the role of career choice itself has changed. When Super was proposing his theory, as was discussed in the brief historical overview section of this article, individuals (usually men) chose a career path in secondary school, prepared for that path, were hired by a firm that determined the path of their career, and stayed with the firm their entire working lives. Now, the loosening of the contract between the individual and the employer means that individuals make career choices throughout their lives. Thus, individuals explore options at many points throughout their working career, sometimes changing organizations and sometimes changing career paths.

Jiang et al. (2019) reviewed studies of career exploration from 2000 to 2019, defining career exploration as "an adaptive mechanism of personal agency that allows individuals to build their career adaptability and manage adaptations and renewals in their vocational development" (p. 338). They found that, regardless of the age at which individuals engaged in career exploration, the agency with which they explored their options was related to the outcomes. In other words, individuals who were motivated to explore options (at any age) had better career outcomes, such as higher self-efficacy related to career decision-making, more career adaptability, better person-job fit, and higher satisfaction with the choice.

Jiang et al. (2019) also note the limitations of career exploration research and call for more research to study the psychological processes underlying career exploration. The original process of career choice was proposed by Frank Parsons in 1909 to help impoverished boys in Boston earn a meaningful wage. His model, termed the matching model, consisted of encouraging young men to know themselves, know the world of work, and find true reasoning between the two. Known as the matching model, Parsons's work gave rise to many ways to help individuals "know themselves," such as inventories to assess abilities, interests, and values, and the rise of occupational information models such as the U.S. Department of Labor's O*Net, which helps individuals know about the world of work. But "true reasoning between the two" happened in a somewhat magical black box. Lent and Brown (2020) have proposed a career decision-making model that integrates research on dual-process models of reasoning. Their model updates Parsons's model to reflect individuals' tendency to make decisions quickly and without reflection, although most models of career decision-making assume that individuals are rational processors. They have also updated the model to include career sustainability, such as is necessary in contemporary careers (cf. De Vos et al., 2020).

Career Success.   Career success is one of the most prevalent outcome variables within career research (Ng et al., 2005; Spurk et al., 2019), and has been the most popular topic in the field of career studies (Akkermans & Kubasch, 2017). Career success is an outcome of a person's career experiences and may be defined as: "the accomplishment of desirable work-related outcomes at any point in a person's work experiences over time" (Arthur et al., 2005, p. 179). The distinction between objective career success and subjective career success has received much attention. Whereas objective career success is defined as directly observable by others and measurable in a standardized way (Arthur et al., 2005; Gunz & Heslin, 2005)—by weighing a person's career against societal norms concerning salary, job level, promotion history, or occupational prestige (Dries et al., 2008)—subjective career success is defined as the focal career actor's evaluation and experience of achieving personally meaningful career outcomes (Ng et al., 2005; Seibert et al., 2001; Shockley et al., 2016). Subjective career success is typically measured as career satisfaction (Greenhaus et al., 1990; Seibert et al., 2013) or perceived career success (Heslin, 2003; Turban & Dougherty, 1994), though a multidimensional evaluation of career facets, such as growth and development, personal life, and authenticity would seem to more accurately measure the construct (Shockley et al., 2016). The correlation between objective and subjective success reported in meta-analytical reviews typically has been small to moderate, ranging from 0.22 to 0.30 (Ng et al., 2005), with even smaller or nonsignificant correlations reported between indicators of objective success and specific subjective success facets (Shockley et al., 2016). It should be noted that scholars have argued and shown that the objective versus subjective career success distinction does not fully capture the richness of the career success construct and, for cross-cultural generalizability, needs to be complemented with additional factors such as non-work and social elements (Shen et al., 2015). The Cross-Cultural Collaboration on Contemporary Careers (5C) has conducted career research inquiries in more than 30 countries across the world and found that, overall, career success consists of financial security, financial success, learning and development, work-life balance, positive relationships, positive impact, and entrepreneurship (Mayrhofer et al., 2016).

Although there are calls to investigate also outcomes of career success (Spurk et al., 2019), the vast majority of research has focused on predictors of career success. A seminal meta-analysis on the topic thereby identified four broader classes of predictors: (a) human capital, (b) organizational sponsorship, (c) socio-demographics, and (d) stable individual differences (Ng et al., 2005). A review by Spurk et al. (2019) organized research on predictors of career success and its related theories within a resource management framework, suggesting several resources that predict the attainment of career success: human capital, roles and identity, (competitive) performance, social environment, work environment, career agency, stress and coping, stable traits, national culture, person-environment interactions, life span, career transitions, and hybrid approaches. Importantly, the review also suggested that those approaches can have differential importance for predicting objective versus subjective career success. Studies, for example, linked various organizational career management approaches via different explaining mechanisms with objective career success (Bagdadli & Gianecchini, 2019), showing that organizational embeddedness predicts promotions and career satisfaction (Kiazad et al., 2020) and that the relationship between telecommuting and objective career success is rather complex (Golden & Eddleston, 2020).

In sum, although the prediction of career success is a well-understood field, future research still can provide further insights by focusing on some specific topics: making sense of the theoretical heterogeneity in career success research, accounting for the theoretical differentiation of correlates of objective career success and subjective career success, focusing more on positive versus "dark side" outcomes of career success, and more clearly accounting for antecedent–career success–outcome dynamics and causalities (Spurk et al., 2019).

Employability. Another highly popular topic in the field of career studies is employability (Akkermans & Kubasch, 2017; Byington et al., 2019). The rising popularity of the concept aligns with the historical developments in career studies (see the brief historical overview at the start of this article) in which individual agency has become the primary paradigm through which to examine career development. Employability is typically characterized as an individual's employment potential in the internal and/or external labor market (Forrier & Sels, 2003), and it has been brought forward as an important employment security mechanism.

Different perspectives exist in the literature on employability. First, Fugate et al. (2004) coined the *dispositional approach* to employability, which argues that employability is an individual characteristic that can enhance adaptive behaviors and positive employment outcomes (Fugate & Kinicki, 2008). Their employability model consists of five main dimensions: work and career resilience, openness to changes at work, work and career proactivity, career motivation, and work identity. Second, Van der Heijde and Van der Heijden (2006) developed a *competence-based approach* to employability, which argues that a set of malleable employability competencies forms the basis for one's chances of employment. There are five employability competencies in their model: occupational expertise, anticipation and optimization, personal flexibility, corporate sense, and balance. Though the specific individual characteristics differ somewhat, both the dispositional and competence-based perspectives on employability emphasize the importance of being adaptable and proactive. Forrier et al. (2009) argued that these characteristics can all be considered a form of "movement capital" that enables individuals to obtain and retain employment. The third strand of literature is the *perceived employability approach*, which emphasizes the importance of an individual's perceptions of their own employability, based on personal (e.g., competencies) and structural (e.g., labor market opportunities) factors (Vanhercke et al., 2014). Perceived employability is typically categorized into internal (i.e., with the current organization) and external (i.e., outside of the current organization) employability. Forrier et al. (2015) argued that the three types of employability can be considered as a dynamic chain that involves movement capital (i.e., dispositional and competence-based employability) as an input-based approach of employability, and perceived employability as an outcome-based approach.

Empirical studies on employability have flourished since 2005, which was made possible by the development of validated scales on dispositional employability (Fugate & Kinicki, 2008), competence-based employability (Van der Heijde & Van der Heijden, 2006; Van der Heijden et al., 2018), and perceived employability (De Cuyper & De Witte, 2011; Rothwell & Arnold, 2007). Studies have thus far primarily focused on employability—across the three strands—as an antecedent of work- and career-related outcomes. For example, empirical evidence suggests that employability can enhance health and well-being (e.g., Berntson & Marklund, 2007; Berntson et al., 2008; De Cuyper et al., 2012), job performance (e.g., De Cuyper et al., 2014; Philippaers et al., 2019), and career success (Bozionelos et al., 2015; Lo Presti et al., 2018). There is some emerging research on employability as an outcome as well. For example, Blokker et al. (2019) showed that career competencies and career success enhanced employability, which, in line with the arguments of Spurk et al. (2019), suggests that employability and career success may be mutually reinforcing phenomena. Furthermore, studies have started to investigate how employability can be enhanced. One line of research in this area has focused on the so-called management paradox of employability, which refers to employers fearing investments in employability due to a fear of their best talents leaving (De Cuyper & De Witte, 2011). Interestingly, studies thus far mostly indicate that this paradox may not exist, as interventions and human resources practices seem to increase employability without necessarily increasing turnover or reducing commitment of employable workers (Akkermans et al., 2019; Nelissen et al., 2017; Philippaers et al., 2017; Rodrigues et al., 2020).

Despite the quick rise of employability in the field of career studies, there are also concerns about the development of research in this area. The most prominent critique has been the overly agentic focus of employability research, thereby overlooking the role of, for example, employers and other contextual factors (e.g., Akkermans & Kubasch, 2017; Clarke, 2018; Van Harten et al., 2020). Indeed, Forrier et al. (2018) argued that employability research suffers from three blind spots that have been ignored in studies thus far: employability is contextual (rather than purely an individual asset), employability is relational (rather than purely agentic), and employability is potentially polarizing (rather than a win for all). Regarding the latter, Forrier et al. (2018) argue that employability development may lead to a "Matthew effect" in which the highly employable develop even more employability, whereas those who lack employability may increasingly be at a disadvantage. Another issue with the current state-of-the-art in the literature is that the relationships between input-based and output-based approaches has not been firmly established yet. While intuitively appealing, these associations may be more complex than expected and may have suffered from methodological problems (Peeters et al., 2020).

Career Self-Management and Career Resources. Similar to the aforementioned literatures on career success and employability, research on career self-management and career resources has gained in popularity in line with the growing emphasis on individual agency in contemporary careers. Greenhaus et al. (2010, p. 12) define *career self-management* as "a process by which individuals develop, implement, and monitor career goals and strategies." Although the majority of studies on career self-management have focused on its behavioral nature (e.g., King, 2004), the overall consensus in the literature is that career self-management consists of a behavioral and a cognitive component (De Vos, De Clippeleer, et al., 2009). Cognitive aspects of career self-management refer to becoming aware of one's career aspirations, developing goals, and reflecting on career strategies (Lent & Brown, 2013), whereas behavioral aspects focus on actual behaviors to develop one's career, thereby emphasizing the importance of proactive behaviors (Parker et al., 2010).

An influential model of career self-management was presented by King (2004). She categorized career self-management into three dimensions: positioning behaviors, influence behaviors, and boundary management. Positioning behaviors focus on gaining contacts, skills, and experience; influence behaviors are about influencing significant others; and boundary management refers to actively balancing work and nonwork domains. These career self-management behaviors have been empirically linked to, among others, career success (Abele & Wiese, 2008; De Vos & Soens, 2008), reemployment quality (Zikic & Klehe, 2006), and positive work-related outcomes such as psychological contract fulfillment (Sturges et al., 2005) and affective commitment (De Vos, Dewettinck, et al., 2009). Career self-management is also an integral part of social cognitive career theory, specifically its career self-management model (Lent & Brown, 2013). This model, however, does not focus on specific behaviors but, rather, presents a career self-management model that can be applied to a wide range of behaviors. In particular, the career self-management model of social cognitive career theory argues that cognitive factors (e.g., self-efficacy beliefs and outcome expectations) feed into career goals and, subsequently, behaviors. Empirical research has shown support for this process model of career self-management, and has linked it, in particular, to career decidedness and career indecision (Brown & Lent, 2019).

A related stream of literature in the field of career studies has examined different types of *career resources* (sometimes referred to as career capital). Hirschi et al. (2018, p. 339) defined career resources as "anything that helps an individual attain his or her career goals." Based on Hirschi's model of career resources (2012), they developed a measurement of career resources that consists of four categories: (a) human capital career resources (e.g., expertise, soft skills), (b) environmental career resources (e.g., organizational and social support), (c) motivational career resources (e.g., career involvement and confidence), and (d) career management behaviors (e.g., networking, learning). The career resources framework was originally developed to present an overarching collection of predictors of career success and is based on several literature streams, of which the research on career competencies and career adaptability are the most prominent ones.

Research on career competencies emerged with the arrival of the protean and boundaryless career theories. Based on a review of the career competencies literature, Akkermans, Brenninkmeijer, et al. (2013) developed an integrative model of career competencies. According to their model, there are three overarching dimensions of career competencies, each consisting of two specific competencies. First, reflective career competencies are about creating an awareness of motivations and skills. Reflection on motivation taps into values and passions, whereas reflection on qualities focuses on strengths, shortcomings, and skills. Second, communicative career competencies are about being able to communicate with relevant stakeholders in one's career. Networking refers to having and being able to expand a relevant network, and self-profiling means that a person is able to present their competencies to the internal and external labor market. Third, behavioral career competencies are about the ability to proactively explore and construct a career. Work exploration focuses on actively exploring opportunities, and career control centers on the ability to influence learning and work processes by setting and pursuing career goals. Developing career competencies can, for example, enhance people's career success (Akkermans & Tims, 2017; Kuijpers et al., 2006), marketability (Eby et al., 2003), employability (Blokker et al., 2019), and work engagement (Akkermans, Schaufeli, et al., 2013).

A core element in career construction theory (see section on "Career Construction Theory"), career adaptability has been another influential career resource in the field of career studies. Career adaptability is a psychosocial resource that helps to cope with career-related tasks, transitions, and traumas (Savickas & Porfeli, 2012) and enables individuals to solve complex problems in their career (Hirschi et al., 2015). There are four career adaptability resources: being *concerned* about one's career-related future, exercising *control*, exploring possible selves through *curiosity*, and strengthening *confidence* to fulfill goals and aspirations. In line with the core elements of career construction theory, a meta-analysis by Rudolph et al. (2017) showed that career adaptability can enhance adaptivity (e.g., self-esteem), adapting (e.g., career planning), and adaptation (e.g., employability). Johnston (2018), in a systemic review of the career adaptability literature, concluded that career adaptability contributes to personal development and effectively undergoing career transitions throughout people's careers.

In all, although research on career self-management and career resources has evolved mostly separately, there are clear conceptual similarities. In particular, the cognitive aspects of career self-management seem to relate quite closely to the notion of career competencies and career adaptability. Indeed, Hirschi and Koen (in press) concluded that career resources are, in essence, conditional elements to successfully self-manage a career. Similarly, Tims and Akkermans (2020) integrated career self-management and career resources into a framework of *career crafting*, consisting of a cognitive component (i.e., proactive career reflection) and a behavioral component (i.e., proactive career construction). Research thus far has convincingly shown that career self-management and career resources are critical components of contemporary career development, and are important building blocks of career outcomes.

Organizational Career Management and Changing Employment Relations. Although most career theories have primarily highlighted the role of the individual and related career self-management (as discussed in the section on "Career Self-Management and Career Resources") within career development, organizational career management is still an important issue for individual career actors and organizations. On the one hand, labor market statistics across the globe, and specifically Europe, show that careers are still less boundaryless than predicted some decades ago (Dries & Verbruggen, 2012; Rodrigues & Guest, 2010). On the other hand, how organizational career paths can be fitted to the needs and values of high potentials and other employees is a major task within human resource management. Hence, organizational career management is theoretically and practically important and located at the intersection of careers, organizational behavior, and management research.

According to Baruch (2006), organizations face three major issues when managing the careers of their employees: (a) strategic managing of human capital, (b) global careers and their management, and (c) diversity–homogeneity versus heterogeneity. With the emergence of the sustainable career perspective (as briefly discussed in the section on "Other Theoretical Perspectives"), the sustainability aspects also revived further importance for organizational career management (De Vos et al., 2020; Van der Heijden et al., 2020). To reach those goals, organizations traditionally and currently imply several diverse measures. Some examples are: formal education/tuition reimbursement, performance appraisal for career planning, counseling by manager, lateral moves/job rotations, preretirement programs, succession planning, formal mentoring, career booklets/pamphlets, career workshops, assessment center, special needs (highfliers or dual-career couples), diversity management, and expatriation/repatriation (Baruch, 2006; Baruch & Peiperl, 2000). It goes beyond the scope of this article to describe those career management practices in more detail, and nearly every mentioned practice is related to its own stream of research: talent management (Dries, 2013), mentoring (Eby et al., 2008), assessment centers (Arthur Jr et al., 2003), or diversity management (Mor Barak et al., 2016). This signals how organizational career management is an interdisciplinary topic, yet, at the same time, that there is little interdisciplinary connectivity.

Importantly, because of the changing employment relationships with highly individual needs of employees and erosion of the traditional psychological contract between employer and employee (Baruch & Rousseau, 2019), more flexible and individualized organizational career management practices seem to be useful. From the traditional approaches, for example, mentoring or career coaching already include highly individualized approaches and seem to be specifically relevant in contemporary work environments. Moreover, the application of idiosyncratic deals (i-deals) has received attention within the past several years (Hornung et al., 2008; Liao et al., 2016; Rousseau, 2015). I-deals are "voluntary, personalized agreements of a nonstandard nature negotiated between individual employees and their employers regarding terms that benefit each party" (Rousseau et al., 2006, p. 978). Typically, i-deals are negotiated between employees and their managers. I-deals have been shown to be positively related to, for example, leader-member-exchange, affective organizational commitment, and job satisfaction (Liao et al., 2016).

A related career management practice is called career customization (Bal et al., 2015; Straub et al., 2020). Career customization provides employees with different options to customize their careers to meet their personal needs and has been suggested as a sustainable solution to the mismatch between traditional career models and the needs of today's workforce (Straub et al., 2020). For example, employees can customize their work schedule, location, load, role, and promotion speed according to their personal needs, which has shown positive effects on career outcomes (Straub et al., 2020). This is a promising tool within current organizational career management, but future research needs to investigate it and other more flexible career management practices in more detail.

Current developments in the labor market, such as alternative employment types (Ashford et al., 2018; Spreitzer et al., 2017; Spurk & Straub, 2020), raise questions about which workers will have access to such organizational career management practices. Gig work, which is a type of temporary contract work that connects self-employed workers directly with clients via a digital platform (Spreitzer et al., 2017), is potentially the most flexible type of work arrangement. Most important, it is still unclear who is responsible for those gig workers in terms of career management: are they the prototype of protean and boundaryless career actors, managing their careers fully by themselves (Kost et al., 2020), or should they receive organizational career management through the digital contracting platforms (Meijerink & Keegan, 2019)? Those (digitalized) labor market developments raise several challenges and questions for organizational career management and changing employment relationships that should be addressed in future career research.

Career Transitions and Career Shocks. As a result of careers becoming more complex and individualized, individuals increasingly need to navigate *career transitions* throughout the life span (Vuori et al., 2012). The term *career transition* typically refers to a change in work experiences, which can be a change in, for example, a job or occupation (Louis, 1980). Research has shown that individuals are making more transitions during their career at all levels of analysis: transitions between jobs, organizations, occupations, industries, and labor markets (Fouad & Bynner, 2008; Sullivan & Baruch, 2009). Research on career transitions has a rich and interdisciplinary tradition, being part of literatures in, for example, careers, human resource management, organizational behavior, international management, and sociology (Sullivan & Al Ariss, 2021). Similar to the literature on organizational career management, though, the literature on career transitions is highly fragmented, with a wide range of conceptualizations and theoretical perspectives underlying studies on career transitions (Sullivan & Al Ariss, 2021).

Despite the fragmentation in the literature, there is a wealth of knowledge about normative transitions (i.e., those transitions imposed by society) as well as idiosyncratic transitions (i.e., those transitions initiated by the individual). This article cannot discuss all the different strands that exist in the literature in-depth, yet it will discuss some of the major streams of literature and mention other avenues of research on career transitions. Most notably, career transition research has focused on school-to-work transitions, unemployment-to-work transitions, work-to-work transitions, and work-to-retirement transitions.

The school-to-work transition (sometimes referred to as university-to-work or college-to-work transition) is the period during which someone leaves school and starts their first employment (Akkermans et al., 2021; Ng & Feldman, 2007). Though not often explicitly mobilized, this literature has clear commonalities with the literature on vocational and career choice. Indeed, research on school-to-work transitions traditionally focused on preparing individuals for a major, one-off, transition into professional life, but it has shifted focus toward continuous learning and decision processes across one's life span (De Vos et al., 2019). Studies on successful (or adaptive) school-to-work transitions have typically focused on a combination of subjective and objective factors (Akkermans et al., 2015; Ng & Feldman, 2007), characterizing a successful transition in terms of employment quantity (e.g., employment status), quality (e.g., fit, over-qualification), and stability (e.g., temporary, permanent). Predictors of a successful school-to-work transition are, among others, socioeconomic status, parental support, school performance, decision-making and career-related competencies, and coping skills (Akkermans et al. 2015; Ng & Feldman, 2007).

The unemployment-to-work transition literature has predominantly focused on the job search process and reemployment success (Paul & Moser, 2009; Wanberg, 2012). Wanberg et al. (2002) emphasized the importance of job search effort (or intensity) and quality as part of the unemployment-to-work process, and categorized predictors of a successful transition into three main dimensions: labor market, human and social capital, and contextual variables. Often used indicators of a successful transition are speed and quality of reemployment, as well as indicators of fit (e.g., person-organization, person-job) (Wanberg et al., 2002; Wanberg, 2012). In a review of the existing literature, Van Hooft et al. (2020) showed that job search intensity leads to (re)employment quantity (i.e., number of interviews, number of job offers, employment status) but not to (re)employment quality (e.g., person-job fit). They argued that self-regulation and job search quality (i.e., the thoroughness with which a job search is conducted) are key to achieving higher quality employment outcomes.

Research on work-to-work transitions is perhaps the most fragmented element of the career transitions literature, as it encompasses a wide range of literatures and terminologies. For example, there is research on job transitions, organizational transitions (including turnover), occupational transitions, and the wider career/organizational mobility literature (including expatriation). Overall, a wide range of predictors and outcomes of work-to-work transitions has been found. For example, Blau (2000) and Griffeth et al. (2000) showed that individuals are more likely to engage in a transition (i.e., to leave their organization) when they are less satisfied and committed, when they experience high levels of stress, when they have little autonomy and few promotion opportunities, and when they perceive many alternatives. There is some emerging literature on occupational transitions as well. The antecedents of occupational turnover are mostly similar to organizational turnover, including low levels of satisfaction and commitment. However, there are also differences. Blau (2007) found that job insecurity related to organizational turnover, whereas work exhaustion related to occupational turnover. In addition, Zimmerman et al. (2020) showed that people who have higher amounts of non-core duties and who have a job in addition to their main job (i.e., moonlighting) were more likely to change occupations versus change organizations. In all, most of the literature on organizational and occupational transitions has focused on antecedents of turnover, rather than looking at the organization or occupation someone joins after the transition.

The work-to-retirement literature has mostly adopted a dual focus, studying preparation for retirement and adjustment after retirement (Wang & Wanberg, 2017). With regard to the former, studies have examined the timing of retirement, for example whether individuals decide to retire early, on time, or late (Fischer et al., 2016). Findings indicate that a range of predictors determines the timing of retirement. For example, people who are financially secure or are in poor health likely retire earlier, whereas individuals who are satisfied with and committed to their job are less likely to retire (Topa et al., 2018). Pak et al. (2019) argued that preferred retirement age can be extended if organizations offer job resources, such as autonomy, variety, and security. The adjustment literature has mostly investigated the health and well-being outcomes after retirement, as well as potential predictors of such outcomes (Barbosa et al., 2016). Research shows that people who are more employable at retirement can adjust better (Sullivan & Al Ariss, 2019). Furthermore, people who remain active in their work role tend to adjust better (Wang & Shultz, 2010), likely because there is an increased sense of continuity between before and after the transition.

Although the main emphasis in research on career transitions—and career studies in general—has been on individual agency and control, there is also an emerging literature on *career shocks*. A career shock can be defined as "a disruptive and extraordinary event that is, at least to some degree, caused by factors outside the focal individual's control and that triggers a deliberate thought process concerning one's career" (Akkermans et al., 2018, p. 4). Although there was a relatively rich literature on chance events and serendipity in the 1970s and 1980s, this stream of literature mostly disappeared with the introduction of the boundaryless and protean career theories. However, given the increasing complexity and unpredictability of careers, major unpredictable events—career shocks—are becoming increasingly salient in people's careers (Akkermans et al., 2020). Studies have shown that such shocks happen to the majority of people and can have long-term consequences for their careers (Hirschi, 2010). For example, experiencing career shocks can lead professionals to pursue further education (Seibert et al., 2013) and a positive shock could lead academics to become more engaged in their work (Kraimer et al., 2019). The literature on career shocks is still in a rather nascent stage, though some important lessons can already be formulated (Akkermans et al., 2020). First, career shocks interact with individual agentic factors to impact on career development. For example, Blokker et al. (2019) showed that career shocks were a boundary condition in the career competencies–career success–employability relationship, such that negative shocks weakened and positive shocks strengthened that process. Seibert et al. (2016) also argued that resilience and adaptability are key individual characteristics that can help deal with career shocks. Second, the impact of career shocks is not straightforward. For example, Kraimer et al. (2019) showed that career shocks could have differential impact on people in different career stages. Moreover, studies have shown that events that were, at first, negatively valenced, ultimately turned out to have positive effects for people's careers (e.g., Rummel et al., 2019; Seibert et al., 2013; Zikic & Klehe, 2006). Further research is needed to probe the theoretical mechanisms that explain the way in which career shocks can impact people's career development.

Other Topics

Work-Nonwork Interface. Super (1980) was a pioneer in considering the development of vocational choices within the context of other life roles. He outlined six roles individuals could hold, sometimes at the same time: child, student, homemaker, worker, citizen, and leisurite. These roles could interact throughout their lives. Thus, as a child, the child role was primary, but often was again a primary role as an adult caring for aging parents. Individuals play multiple roles in their lives, and those roles interact. He was, thus, one of the first to outline the need to understand the balance of work and family roles. In the decades since he proposed the concept of role salience and the possible conflict between roles, research on the relationship between work and family, or work and nonwork roles, has generated many studies and many theories. While some have focused on factors related to the conflict between work and family (e.g., Allen et al., 2020), others have focused on how one role enriches the other (Lapierre et al., 2018). Because not all work environments are the same in their support for their workers' balancing work and family, attention is starting to turn to organizational policies that help employees manage multiple roles (e.g., Bourdeau et al., 2019; French & Shockley, 2020). Furthermore, research is starting to explore the role of nonwork orientations and leisure activities as core parts of career development (Hirschi et al., 2020). Overall, the work-nonwork interface has become an important part of career studies, for example in terms of career success, career sustainability, career self-management, and global careers (for an overview, see Greenhaus & Kossek, 2014).

Calling. Between 2010 and 2020, calling became a highly researched topic within career development. Following Dobrow and Tosti-Kharas (2011), a calling can be defined as "a consuming, meaningful passion people experience toward a domain" (Dobrow & Tosti-Kharas, 2011, p. 1005). Thus, employees who experience a career calling are likely to perceive their involvement in their work as consuming and perceive their work domain as meaningful, too. As calling can be a guiding inner force for career decisions and paths, it possesses high relevance for career development. However, calling research has also been plagued by issues of concept clarity and differentiation between different calling conceptualizations (Thompson & Bunderson, 2019). Nonetheless, empirical insights have started to further develop scholarly knowledge on calling (cf. Lysova et al., 2019). A meta-analysis on the topic provides a comprehensive overview of different definitions and correlates of calling (Dobrow et al., 2019). For example, callings were more important for well-being concerned with self-realization and meaning than for well-being concerned with happiness and pleasure, reflecting calling's significance for deeper growth-oriented rather than more fleeting, pleasurable types of happiness. Moreover, callings were related to lower strain and more career and life satisfaction. Overall, it seems that experiencing a calling is beneficial for work and private life.

However, although studies have primarily examined positive effects of calling on careers and private lives, research has also mentioned potential dark sides of calling (Dobrow et al., 2019). Duffy et al. (2018) assumed in their calling model that calling in terms of a kind of "overcommitment" to the work domain might also trigger burnout, workaholism, and exploitation. Indeed, some studies linked calling with higher levels of workaholism (Hirschi et al., 2019; Keller et al., 2016). Such findings show that a more differentiated perspective on calling and its potential predictors and outcomes is necessary in future research (Dobrow et al., 2019). Generally, compared to research on outcomes of calling, research on predictors of calling is less frequent. Moreover, other topics for future research are the examinations of the processes and boundary conditions that link searching for a calling with presence of calling and living a calling (Dobrow et al., 2019; Duffy et al., 2018).

CONCLUSION

The field of career studies has been around for a long time, yet has gained momentum in the early 21st century across disciplines (e.g., psychology, management). The field is fragmented, though, as theories and concepts are typically used within certain silos: boundaryless career theory, for example, has been prominent in management research, whereas career construction theory has primarily been mobilized by vocational psychology scholars. This article aimed to provide an overview of the key theories and concepts in the broad field of career studies across disciplinary boundaries. Hopefully, this will provide a valuable collection of topics for anyone who wants to explore careers research, as well as a fruitful basis for interdisciplinary connections in research on careers and career development.

REFERENCES

Abele, A. E., & Wiese, B. S. (2008). The nomological network of self-management strategies and career success. *Journal of Occupational and Organizational Psychology, 81*(4), 733–749. https://doi.org/10.1348/0 96317907X256726

Akkermans, J., Blokker, R., Buers, C., Van Der Heijden, B. I. J. M., & De Vos, A. (2021). Ready, set, go! School-to-work transition in the new career. In A. Marshall & J. Symonds (Eds.), *Young adult development at the school-to-work transition: International pathways and processes* (pp. 77–106). Oxford University Press.

Akkermans, J., Brenninkmeijer, V., Huibers, M., & Blonk, R. W. B. (2013). Competencies for the contemporary career: Development and preliminary validation of the career competencies questionnaire. *Journal of Career Development, 40*(3), 245–267. https://doi.org/10.1177/0894845312467501

Akkermans, J., & Kubasch, S. (2017). #Trending topics in careers: A review and future research agenda. *Career Development International, 22*(6), 586–627. https://doi.org/10.1108/CDI-08-2017-0143

Akkermans, J., Nykänen, M., & Vuori, J. (2015). Practice makes perfect? Antecedents and consequences of an adaptive school-to-work transition. In J. Vuori, R. W. B. Blonk, & R. Price (Eds.), *Sustainable working lives—Managing work transitions and health throughout the life course.* (pp. 65–86). Springer. https://doi .org/10.1007/978-94-017-9798-6_5

Akkermans, J., Richardson, J., & Kraimer, M. L. (2020). The Covid-19 crisis as a career shock: Implications for careers and vocational behavior. *Journal of Vocational Behavior, 119*, 103434. https://doi.org/10.1016/j .jvb.2020.103434

Akkermans, J., Schaufeli, W. B., Brenninkmeijer, V., & Blonk, R. W. B. (2013). The role of career competencies in the Job Demands—Resources model. *Journal of Vocational Behavior, 83*(3), 356–366. https:// doi.org/10.1016/j.jvb.2013.06.011

Akkermans, J., Seibert, S. E., & Mol, S. T. (2018). Tales of the unexpected: Integrating career shocks in the contemporary careers literature. *SA Journal of Industrial Psychology, 44*, e1503. https://doi.org/10.4102 /sajip.v44i0.1503

Akkermans, J., & Tims, M. (2017). Crafting your career: How career competencies relate to career success via job crafting. *Applied Psychology: An International Review, 66*(1), 168–195. https://doi.org/10.1111 /apps.12082

Akkermans, J., Tims, M., Beijer, S., & De Cuyper, N. (2019). Should employers invest in employability? Examining employability as a mediator in the HRM–commitment relationship. *Frontiers in Psychology, 10*, Article 717. https://doi.org/10.3389/fpsyg.2019.00717

Allen, T. D., French, K. A., Dumani, S., & Shockley, K. M. (2020). A cross-national meta-analytic examination of predictors and outcomes associated with work–family conflict. *Journal of Applied Psychology, 105*(6), 539–576. https://doi.org/10.1037/apl0000442

Arnold, J., & Cohen, L. (2008). The psychology of careers in industrial and organizational settings: A critical but appreciative analysis. *International Review of Industrial and Organizational Psychology, 23*(1), 1–44. https://doi.org/10.1002/9780470773277.ch1

Arthur, M. B. (2014). The boundaryless career at 20: Where do we stand, and where can we go? *Career Development International, 19*(6), 627–640. https://doi.org/10.1108/CDI-05-2014-0068

Arthur, M. B., Hall, D. T., & Lawrence, B. S. (1989). *Handbook of career theory.* Cambridge University Press.

Arthur, M. B., Khapova, S. N., & Wilderom, C. P. M. (2005). Career success in a boundaryless career world. *Journal of Organizational Behavior, 26*(2), 177–202. https://doi.org/10.1002/job.290

Arthur, M. B., & Rousseau, D. M. (1996). Introduction: The boundaryless career as a new employment principle. In M. B. Arthur & D. M. Rousseau (Eds.), *The boundaryless career: A new employment principle for a new organizational era* (pp. 3–20). Oxford University Press.

Arthur, W., Jr., Day, E. A., McNelly, T. L., & Edens, P. S. (2003). A meta-analysis of the criterion-related validity of assessment center dimensions. *Personnel Psychology, 56*(1), 125–153. https://doi.org/10.1111/j.1744-6570.2003.tb00146.x

Ashford, S. J., Caza, B. B., & Reid, E. M. (2018). From surviving to thriving in the gig economy: A research agenda for individuals in the new world of work. *Research in Organizational Behavior, 38*, 23–41. https://doi.org/10.1016/j.riob.2018.11.001

Bagdadli, S., & Gianecchini, M. (2019). Organizational career management practices and objective career success: A systematic review and framework. *Human Resource Management Review, 29*(3), 353–370. https://doi.org/10.1016/j.hrmr.2018.08.001

Bal, P. M., Van Kleef, M., & Jansen, P. G. W. (2015). The impact of career customization on work outcomes: Boundary conditions of manager support and employee age. *Journal of Organizational Behavior, 36*(3), 421–440. https://doi.org/10.1002/job.1998

Bandura, A. (1986). *Social foundations of thought and action: A social cognitive theory.* Prentice Hall.

Bandura, A. (1999). Social cognitive theory of personality. In L. A. Pervin & O. P. John (Eds.), *Handbook of personality* (Vol. 2, pp. 154–196). Guilford Press.

Bandura, A. (2001). Social cognitive theory: An agentic perspective. *Annual Review of Psychology, 52*(1), 1–26. https://doi.org/10.1146/annurev.psych.52.1.1

Barbosa, L. M., Monteiro, B., & Murta, S. G. (2016). Retirement adjustment predictors—A systematic review. *Work, Aging and Retirement, 2*(2), 262–280. https://doi.org/10.1093/workar/waw008

Baruch, Y. (2006). Career development in organizations and beyond: Balancing traditional and contemporary viewpoints. *Human Resource Management Review, 16*(2), 125–138. https://doi.org/10.1016/j.hrmr.2006.03.002

Baruch, Y. (2014). The development and validation of a measure for protean career orientation. *The International Journal of Human Resource Management, 25*(19), 2702–2723. https://doi.org/10.1080/09585192.2014.896389

Baruch, Y., & Peiperl, M. (2000). Career management practices: An empirical survey and implications. *Human Resource Management, 39*(4), 347–366. https://onlinelibrary.wiley.com/doi/abs/10.1002/1099-050X%28200024%2939%3A4%3C347%3A%3AAID-HRM6%3E3.0.CO%3B2-C

Baruch, Y., & Rousseau, D. M. (2019). Integrating psychological contracts and ecosystems in career studies and management. *Academy of Management Annals, 13*(1), 84–111. https://doi.org/10.5465/annals.2016.0103

Baruch, Y., Szűcs, N., & Gunz, H. (2015). Career studies in search of theory: The rise and rise of concepts. *Career Development International, 20*(1), 3–20. https://doi.org/10.1108/CDI-11-2013-0137

Baruch, Y., & Vardi, Y. (2016). A fresh look at the dark side of contemporary careers: Toward a realistic discourse. *British Journal of Management, 27*(2), 355–372. https://doi.org/10.1111/1467-8551.12107

Becker, G. (1964). *Human capital theory.* University of Chicago Press.

Berntson, E., & Marklund, S. (2007). The relationship between perceived employability and subsequent health. *Work & Stress, 21*(3), 279–292. https://doi.org/10.1080/02678370701659215

Berntson, E., Näswall, K., & Sverke, M. (2008). Investigating the relationship between employability and self-efficacy: A cross-lagged analysis. *European Journal of Work and Organizational Psychology, 17*(4), 413–425. https://doi.org/10.1080/13594320801969699

Betz, N. E., & Hackett, G. (1981). The relationship of career-related self-efficacy expectations to perceived career options in college women and men. *Journal of Counseling Psychology, 28*(5), 399–410. https://doi.org/10.1037/0022-0167.28.5.399

Biemann, T., & Wolf, J. (2009). Career patterns of top management team members in five countries: An optimal matching analysis. *International Journal of Human Resource Management*, 20(5), 975–991. https://doi.org/10.1080/09585190902850190

Blau, G. (2000). Job, organizational, and professional context antecedents as predictors of intent for inter-role work transitions. *Journal of Vocational Behavior*, 56(3), 330–345. https://doi.org/10.1006/jvbe.1999.1718

Blau, G. (2007). Does a corresponding set of variables for explaining voluntary organizational turnover transfer to explaining voluntary occupational turnover? *Journal of Vocational Behavior*, 70(1), 135–148. https://doi.org/10.1016/j.jvb.2006.07.007

Blokker, R., Akkermans, J., Tims, M., Jansen, P., & Khapova, S. (2019). Building a sustainable start: The role of career competencies, career success, and career shocks in young professionals' employability. *Journal of Vocational Behavior*, 112, 172–184. https://doi.org/10.1016/j.jvb.2019.02.013

Blustein, D. L. (2006). *The psychology of working: A new perspective for career development, counseling, and public policy*. Lawrence Erlbaum.

Blustein, D. L., Murphy, K. A., Kenny, M. E., Jernigan, M., Pérez-Gualdrón, L., Castañeda, T., Koepke, M., Land, M., Urbano, A., & Davis, O. (2010). Exploring urban students' constructions about school, work, race, and ethnicity. *Journal of Counseling Psychology*, 57(2), 248–254. http://doi.org/10.1037/a0018939

Bourdeau, S., Ollier-Malaterre, A., & Houlfort, N. (2019). Not all work-life policies are created equal: Career consequences of using enabling versus enclosing work-life policies. *Academy of Management Review*, 44(1), 172–193. https://doi.org/10.5465/amr.2016.0429

Bozionelos, N., Kostopoulos, K., Van der Heijden, B., Rousseau, D. M., Bozionelos, G., Hoyland, T., Miao, R., Marzec, I., Jędrzejowicz, P., Epitropaki, O., Mikkelsen, A., Scholarios, D., & Van der Heijde, C. (2015). Employability and job performance as links in the relationship between mentoring receipt and career success: A study in SMEs. *Group & Organization Management*, 41(2), 135–171. https://doi.org/10.1177/1059601115617086

Briscoe, J. P., Hall, D. T., & DeMuth, R. L. F. (2006). Protean and boundaryless careers: An empirical exploration. *Journal of Vocational Behavior*, 69(1), 30–47. https://doi.org/10.1016/j.jvb.2005.09.003

Briscoe, J. P., Henagan, S. C., Burton, J. P., & Murphy, W. M. (2012). Coping with an insecure employment environment: The differing roles of protean and boundaryless career orientations. *Journal of Vocational Behavior*, 80(2), 308–316. https://doi.org/10.1016/j.jvb.2011.12.008

Briscoe, J. P., Hoobler, J. M., & Byle, K. A. (2010). Do "protean" employees make better leaders? The answer is in the eye of the beholder. *The Leadership Quarterly*, 21(5), 783–795. https://doi.org/10.1016/j.leaqua.2010.07.007

Brown, S. D., & Lent, R. W. (2019). Social cognitive career theory at 25: Progress in studying the domain satisfaction and career self-management models. *Journal of Career Assessment*, 27(4), 563–578. https://doi.org/10.1177/1069072719852736

Byars-Winston, A., Diestelmann, J., Savoy, J. N., & Hoyt, W. T. (2017). Unique effects and moderators of effects of sources on self-efficacy: A model-based meta-analysis. *Journal of Counseling Psychology*, 64(6), 645–658. https://doi.org/10.1037/cou0000219

Byington, E. K., Felps, W., & Baruch, Y. (2019). Mapping the journal of vocational behavior: A 23-year review. *Journal of Vocational Behavior*, 110, 229–244. https://doi.org/10.1016/j.jvb.2018.07.007

Çakmak-Otluoğlu, K. Ö. (2012). Protean and boundaryless career attitudes and organizational commitment: The effects of perceived supervisor support. *Journal of Vocational Behavior*, 80(3), 638–646. https://doi.org/10.1016/j.jvb.2012.03.001

Clarke, M. (2018). Rethinking graduate employability: The role of capital, individual attributes and context. *Studies in Higher Education*, 43(11), 1923–1937. https://doi.org/10.1080/03075079.2017.1294152

Cook, K. S., Cheshire, C., Rice, E. R. W., & Nakagawa, S. (2013). Social exchange theory. In J. DeLamater & A. Ward (Eds.), *Handbook of social psychology* (pp. 61–88). Springer Netherlands. https://doi.org/10.1007/978-94-007-6772-0_3

Cropanzano, R., Anthony, E. L., Daniels, S. R., & Hall, A. V. (2017). Social exchange theory: A critical review with theoretical remedies. *Academy of Management Annals, 11*(1), 479–516. https://doi.org/10.5465/annals.2015.0099

Cropanzano, R., & Mitchell, M. S. (2005). Social exchange theory: An interdisciplinary review. *Journal of Management, 31*(6), 874–900. https://doi.org/10.1177/0149206305279602

De Cuyper, N., & De Witte, H. (2011). The management paradox: Self-rated employability and organizational commitment and performance. *Personnel Review, 40*(2), 152–172. https://doi.org/10.1108/00483481111106057

De Cuyper, N., Mäkikangas, A., Kinnunen, U., Mauno, S., & Witte, H. D. (2012). Cross-lagged associations between perceived external employability, job insecurity, and exhaustion: Testing gain and loss spirals according to the Conservation of Resources Theory. *Journal of Organizational Behavior, 33*(6), 770–788. https://doi.org/10.1002/job.1800

De Cuyper, N., Sulea, C., Philippaers, K., Fischmann, G., Iliescu, D., & De Witte, H. (2014). Perceived employability and performance: Moderation by felt job insecurity. *Personnel Review, 43*(4), 536–552. https://doi.org/10.1108/PR-03-2013-0050

De Cuyper, N., Witte, H. D., & Emmerik, H. V. (2011). Temporary employment: Costs and benefits for (the careers of) employees and organizations. *Career Development International, 16*(2), 104–113. https://doi.org/10.1108/13620431111115587

De Hauw, S., & Greenhaus, J. H. (2015). Building a sustainable career: The role of work–home balance in career decision making. In A. De Vos & B. I. J. M. Van der Heijden (Eds.), *Handbook of research on sustainable careers* (pp. 223–238). Edward Elgar.

De Vos, A., Akkermans, J., & Van Der Heijden, B. I. J. M. (2019). From occupational choice to career crafting. In H. Gunz, M. Lazarova, & W. Mayrhofer (Eds.), *The Routledge companion to career studies* (pp. 128–142). Routledge.

De Vos, A., De Clippeleer, I., & Dewilde, T. (2009). Proactive career behaviours and career success during the early career. *Journal of Occupational and Organizational Psychology, 82*(4), 761–777. https://doi.org/10.1348/096317909X471013

De Vos, A., Dewettinck, K., & Buyens, D. (2009). The professional career on the right track: A study on the interaction between career self-management and organizational career management in explaining employee outcomes. *European Journal of Work and Organizational Psychology, 18*(1), 55–80. https://doi.org/10.1080/13594320801966257

De Vos, A., & Soens, N. (2008). Protean attitude and career success: The mediating role of self-management. *Journal of Vocational Behavior, 73*(3), 449–456. https://doi.org/10.1016/j.jvb.2008.08.007

De Vos, A., Van der Heijden, B. I. J. M., & Akkermans, J. (2020). Sustainable careers: Towards a conceptual model. *Journal of Vocational Behavior, 117*, Article 103196. https://doi.org/10.1016/j.jvb.2018.06.011

DeFillippi, R. J., & Arthur, M. B. (1994). The boundaryless career: A competency-based perspective. *Journal of Organizational Behavior, 15*(4), 307–324. https://doi.org/10.1002/job.4030150403

Dobrow, S. R., & Tosti-Kharas, J. (2011). Calling: The development of a scale measure. *Personnel Psychology, 64*(4), 1001–1049. https://doi.org/10.1111/j.1744-6570.2011.01234.x

Dobrow, S., Weisman, H., Heller, D., & Tosti-Kharas, J. (2019). Calling attention to 20 years of research: A comprehensive meta-analysis of calling. *Academy of Management Proceedings, 2019*(1), 12789. https://doi.org/10.5465/AMBPP.2019.199

Dries, N. (2013). The psychology of talent management: A review and research agenda. *Human Resource Management Review, 23*(4), 272–285. https://doi.org/10.1016/j.hrmr.2013.05.001

Dries, N., Pepermans, R., & Carlier, O. (2008). Career success: Constructing a multidimensional model. *Journal of Vocational Behavior, 73*(2), 254–267. https://doi.org/10.1016/j.jvb.2008.05.005

Dries, N., & Verbruggen, M. (2012). Fresh perspectives on the "new" career: Introduction to the special section. *Journal of Vocational Behavior, 81*(2), 269–270. https://doi.org/10.1016/j.jvb.2011.11.001

Duffy, R. D., Blustein, D. L., Allan, B. A., Diemer, M. A., & Cinamon, R. G. (2020). Introduction to the special issue: A cross-cultural exploration of decent work. *Journal of Vocational Behavior, 116*(Part A), Article 103351. https://doi.org/10.1016/j.jvb.2019.103351

Duffy, R. D., Blustein, D. L., Diemer, M. A., & Autin, K. L. (2016). The Psychology of Working Theory. *Journal of Counseling Psychology, 63*(2), 127–148. https://doi.org/10.1037/cou0000140

Duffy, R. D., Dik, B. J., Douglass, R. P., England, J. W., & Velez, B. L. (2018). Work as a calling: A theoretical model. *Journal of Counseling Psychology, 65*(4), 423–439. https://doi.org/10.1037/cou0000276

Eby, L. T., Allen, T. D., Evans, S. C., Ng, T., & DuBois, D. L. (2008). Does mentoring matter? A multidisciplinary meta-analysis comparing mentored and non-mentored individuals. *Journal of Vocational Behavior, 72*(2), 254–267. https://doi.org/10.1016/j.jvb.2007.04.005

Eby, L. T., Butts, M., & Lockwood, A. (2003). Predictors of success in the era of the boundaryless career. *Journal of Organizational Behavior, 24*(6), 689–708. https://doi.org/10.1002/job.214

Fasang, A. E., Geerdes, S., & Schomann, K. (2012). Which type of job mobility makes people happy? A comparative analysis of European welfare regimes. *International Sociology, 27*(3), 349–383. https://doi.org/10.1177/0268580911423048

Fisher, G. G., Chaffee, D. S., & Sonnega, A. (2016). Retirement timing: A review and recommendations for future research. *Work, Aging and Retirement, 2*(2), 230–261. https://doi.org/10.1093/workar/waw001

Forrier, A., De Cuyper, N., & Akkermans, J. (2018). The winner takes it all, the loser has to fall: Provoking the agency perspective in employability research. *Human Resource Management Journal, 28*(4), 511–523. https://doi.org/10.1111/1748-8583.12206

Forrier, A., & Sels, L. (2003). The concept employability: A complex mosaic. *International Journal of Human Resources Development and Management, 3*(2), 102–124. https://doi.org/10.1504/IJHRDM.2003.002414

Forrier, A., Sels, L., & Stynen, D. (2009). Career mobility at the intersection between agent and structure: A conceptual model. *Journal of Occupational and Organizational Psychology, 82*(4), 739–759. https://doi.org/10.1348/096317909X470933

Forrier, A., Verbruggen, M., & De Cuyper, N. (2015). Integrating different notions of employability in a dynamic chain: The relationship between job transitions, movement capital and perceived employability. *Journal of Vocational Behavior, 89*, 56–64. https://doi.org/10.1016/j.jvb.2015.04.007

Fouad, N. A., & Bynner, J. (2008). Work transitions. *American Psychologist, 63*(4), 241–251. https://doi.org/10.1037/0003-066X.63.4.241

French, K. A., & Shockley, K. M. (2020). Formal and informal supports for managing work and family. *Current Directions in Psychological Science, 29*(2), 207–216. https://doi.org/10.1177/0963721420906218

Fugate, M., & Kinicki, A. J. (2008). A dispositional approach to employability: Development of a measure and test of implications for employee reactions to organizational change. *Journal of Occupational and Organizational Psychology, 81*(3), 503–527. https://doi.org/10.1348/096317907X241579

Fugate, M., Kinicki, A. J., & Ashforth, B. E. (2004). Employability: A psycho-social construct, its dimensions, and applications. *Journal of Vocational Behavior, 65*(1), 14–38. https://doi.org/10.1016/j.jvb.2003.10.005

Ginzberg, E. (1972). Toward a theory of occupational choice: A restatement. *Vocational Guidance Quarterly, 20*(3), 2–9. https://doi.org/10.1002/j.2164-585X.1972.tb02037.x

Golden, T. D., & Eddleston, K. A. (2020). Is there a price telecommuters pay? Examining the relationship between telecommuting and objective career success. *Journal of Vocational Behavior, 116*, 103348. https://doi.org/10.1016/j.jvb.2019.103348

Greenhaus, J. H., Callanan, G. A., & Godshalk, V. M. (2010). *Career management.* SAGE.

Greenhaus, J. H., & Kossek, E. E. (2014). The contemporary career: A work–home perspective. *Annual Review of Organizational Psychology and Organizational Behavior, 1*(1), 361–388. https://doi.org/10.1146/annurev-orgpsych-031413-091324

Greenhaus, J. H., Parasuraman, S., & Wormley, W. M. (1990). Effects of race on organizational experiences, job performance evaluations, and career outcomes. *Academy of Management Journal, 33*(1), 64–86. https://doi.org/10.2307/256352

Griffeth, R. W., Hom, P. W., & Gaertner, S. (2000). A meta-analysis of antecedents and correlates of employee turnover: Update, moderator tests, and research implications for the next millennium. *Journal of Management, 26*(3), 463–488. https://doi.org/10.1177/014920630002600305

Guan, Y., Arthur, M. B., Khapova, S. N., Hall, R. J., & Lord, R. G. (2019). Career boundarylessness and career success: A review, integration and guide to future research. *Journal of Vocational Behavior, 110,* 390–402. https://doi.org/10.1016/j.jvb.2018.05.013

Guan, Y., Guo, Y., Bond, M. H., Cai, Z., Zhou, X., Xu, J., Zhu, F., Wang, Z., Fu, R., Liu, S., Wang, Y., Hu, T., & Ye, L. (2014). New job market entrants' future work self, career adaptability and job search outcomes: Examining mediating and moderating models. *Journal of Vocational Behavior, 85*(1), 136–145. https://doi.org/10.1016/j.jvb.2014.05.003

Guan, Y., Zhou, W., Ye, L., Jiang, P., & Zhou, Y. (2015). Perceived organizational career management and career adaptability as predictors of success and turnover intention among Chinese employees. *Journal of Vocational Behavior, 88,* 230–237. https://doi.org/10.1016/j.jvb.2015.04.002

Gubler, M., Arnold, J., & Coombs, C. (2014). Reassessing the protean career concept: Empirical findings, conceptual components, and measurement. *Journal of Organizational Behavior, 35*(S1), S23–S40. https://doi.org/10.1002/job.1908

Gunz, H. P., & Heslin, P. A. (2005). Reconceptualizing career success. *Journal of Organizational Behavior, 26*(2), 105–111. https://doi.org/10.1002/job.300

Gunz, H., Lazarova, M., & Mayrhofer, W. (2019). *The Routledge companion to career studies.* Routledge.

Gunz, H., & Peiperl, M. (2007). *Handbook of career studies.* SAGE.

Hackett, G., & Betz, N. E. (1981). A self-efficacy approach to the career development of women. *Journal of Vocational Behavior, 18*(3), 326–339. https://doi.org/10.1016/0001-8791(81)90019-1

Hall, D. T. (1976). *Careers in organizations.* Goodyear.

Hall, D. T. (1996). Protean careers of the 21st century. *The Academy of Management Executive, 10*(4), 8–16. https://doi.org/10.5465/ame.1996.3145315

Hall, D. T. (2002). *Careers in and out of organizations.* SAGE.

Hall, D. T., & Moss, J. E. (1998). The new protean career contract: Helping organizations and employees adapt. *Organizational Dynamics, 26*(3), 22–37. https://doi.org/10.1016/S0090-2616(98)90012-2

Hall, D. T., Yip, J., & Doiron, K. (2018). Protean careers at work: Self-direction and values orientation in psychological success. *Annual Review of Organizational Psychology and Organizational Behavior, 5*(1), 129–156. https://doi.org/10.1146/annurev-orgpsych-032117-104631

Hartung, P. J. (2013). The life-span, life-space theory of careers. In S. D. Brown & R. W. Lent (Eds.), *Career development and counseling: Putting theory and research to work* (pp. 83–114). John Wiley & Sons.

Heslin, P. A. (2003). Self- and other-referent criteria of career success. *Journal of Career Assessment, 11*(3), 262–286. https://doi.org/10.1177/1069072703254500

Heslin, P. A., Keating, L. A., & Ashford, S. J. (2020). How being in learning mode may enable a sustainable career across the lifespan. *Journal of Vocational Behavior, 117,* Article 103324. https://doi.org/10.1016/j.jvb.2019.103324

Hirschi, A. (2010). The role of chance events in the school-to-work transition: The influence of demographic, personality and career development variables. *Journal of Vocational Behavior, 77*(1), 39–49. https://doi.org/10.1016/j.jvb.2010.02.002

Hirschi, A. (2012). The career resources model: An integrative framework for career counsellors. *British Journal of Guidance & Counselling, 40*(4), 369–383. https://doi.org/10.1080/03069885.2012.700506

Hirschi, A., Herrmann, A., & Keller, A. C. (2015). Career adaptivity, adaptability, and adapting: A conceptual and empirical investigation. *Journal of Vocational Behavior, 87,* 1–10. https://doi.org/10.1016/j.jvb.2014.11.008

Hirschi, A., Keller, A. C., & Spurk, D. (2019). Calling as a double-edged sword for work-nonwork enrichment and conflict among older workers. *Journal of Vocational Behavior, 114*, 100–111. https://doi.org/10.1016/j.jvb.2019.02.004

Hirschi, A., & Koen, J. (in press). Contemporary career orientations and career self-management: A review and integration. *Journal of Vocational Behavior*.

Hirschi, A., Nagy, N., Baumeler, F., Johnston, C. S., & Spurk, D. (2018). Assessing key predictors of career success: Development and validation of the career resources questionnaire. *Journal of Career Assessment, 26*(2), 338–358. https://doi.org/10.1177/1069072717695584

Hirschi, A., Steiner, R., Burmeister, A., & Johnston, C. S. (2020). A whole-life perspective of sustainable careers: The nature and consequences of nonwork orientations. *Journal of Vocational Behavior, 117*, Article 103319. https://doi.org/10.1016/j.jvb.2019.103319

Hlad'o, P., Kvasková, L., Ježek, S., Hirschi, A., & Macek, P. (2020). Career adaptability and social support of vocational students leaving upper secondary school. *Journal of Career Assessment, 28*(3), 478–495. https://doi.org/10.1177/1069072719884299

Hobfoll, S. E. (1989). Conservation of resources: A new attempt at conceptualizing stress. *American Psychologist, 44*(3), 513–524. https://doi.org/10.1037/0003-066X.44.3.513

Hobfoll, S. E. (2002). Social and psychological resources and adaptation. *Review of General Psychology, 6*(4), 307–324. https://doi.org/10.1037/1089-2680.6.4.307

Hobfoll, S. E., Halbesleben, J., Neveu, J.P., & Westman, M. (2018). Conservation of resources in the organizational context: The reality of resources and their consequences. *Annual Review of Organizational Psychology and Organizational Behavior, 5*(1), 103–128. https://doi.org/10.1146/annurev-orgpsych-032117-104640

Holland, J. L. (1959). A theory of vocational choice. *Journal of Counseling Psychology, 6*(1), 35–45. https://doi.org/10.1037/h0040767

Hornung, S., Rousseau, D. M., & Glaser, J. (2008). Creating flexible work arrangements through idiosyncratic deals. *Journal of Applied Psychology, 93*, 655–664. https://doi.org/10.1037/0021-9010.93.3.655

Jiang, Z., Newman, A., Le, H., Presbitero, A., & Zheng, C. (2019). Career exploration: A review and future research agenda. *Journal of Vocational Behavior, 110*, 338–356. https://doi.org/10.1016/j.jvb.2018.08.008

Johnston, C. S. (2018). A systematic review of the career adaptability literature and future outlook. *Journal of Career Assessment, 26*(1), 3–30. https://doi.org/10.1177/1069072716679921

Karacan-Ozdemir, N. (2019). Associations between career adaptability and career decision-making difficulties among Turkish high school students. *International Journal for Educational and Vocational Guidance, 19*(3), 475–495. https://doi.org/10.1007/s10775-019-09389-0

Keller, A. C., Spurk, D., Baumeler, F., & Hirschi, A. (2016). Competitive climate and workaholism: Negative sides of future orientation and calling. *Personality and Individual Differences, 96*, 122–126. https://doi.org/10.1016/j.paid.2016.02.061

Kelly, C. M., Strauss, K., Arnold, J., & Stride, C. (2020). The relationship between leisure activities and psychological resources that support a sustainable career: The role of leisure seriousness and work-leisure similarity. *Journal of Vocational Behavior, 117*, Article 103340. https://doi.org/10.1016/j.jvb.2019.103340

Kiazad, K., Kraimer, M. L., Seibert, S. E., & Sargent, L. (2020). Understanding organizational embeddedness and career success: Who and what you know. *Journal of Organizational Behavior, 41*(7), 678–693. https://doi.org/10.1002/job.2464

King, Z. (2004). Career self-management: Its nature, causes and consequences. *Journal of Vocational Behavior, 65*(1), 112–133. https://doi.org/10.1016/S0001-8791(03)00052-6

Koen, J., Klehe, U.C., Van Vianen, A. E. M., Zikic, J., & Nauta, A. (2010). Job-search strategies and reemployment quality: The impact of career adaptability. *Journal of Vocational Behavior, 77*(1), 126–139. https://doi.org/10.1016/j.jvb.2010.02.004

Kossek, E. E., & Ollier-Malaterre, A. (2020). Desperately seeking sustainable careers: Redesigning professional jobs for the collaborative crafting of reduced-load work. *Journal of Vocational Behavior, 117*, Article 103315. https://doi.org/10.1016/j.jvb.2019.06.003

Kost, D., Fieseler, C., & Wong, S. I. (2020). Boundaryless careers in the gig economy: An oxymoron? *Human Resource Management Journal, 30*(1), 100–113. https://doi.org/10.1111/1748-8583.12265

Kraimer, M. L., Greco, L., Seibert, S. E., & Sargent, L. D. (2019). An investigation of academic career success: The new tempo of academic life. *Academy of Management Learning & Education, 18*(2), 128–152. https://doi.org/10.5465/amle.2017.0391

Kraimer, M. L., Seibert, S. E., Wayne, S. J., Liden, R. C., & Bravo, J. (2011). Antecedents and outcomes of organizational support for development: The critical role of career opportunities. *Journal of Applied Psychology, 96*(3), 485–500. https://doi.org/10.1037/a0021452

Kuijpers, M. A. C. T., Schyns, B., & Scheerens, J. (2006). Career competencies for career success. *The Career Development Quarterly, 55*(2), 168–178. https://doi.org/10.1002/j.2161-0045.2006.tb00011.x

Lapierre, L. M., Li, Y., Kwan, H. K., Greenhaus, J. H., DiRenzo, M. S., & Shao, P. (2018). A meta-analysis of the antecedents of work–family enrichment. *Journal of Organizational Behavior, 39*(4), 385–401. https://doi.org/10.1002/job.2234

Lee, C. I. S. G., Felps, W., & Baruch, Y. (2014). Toward a taxonomy of career studies through bibliometric visualization. *Journal of Vocational Behavior, 85*(3), 339–351. https://doi.org/10.1016/j.jvb.2014.08.008

Lent, R. W. (2020). Career development and counseling: A social cognitive framework. In S. D. Brown & R. W. Lent (Eds.), *Career development and counseling* (3rd ed., pp. 129–164). Wiley.

Lent, R. W., & Brown, S. D. (2006). Integrating person and situation perspectives on work satisfaction: A social-cognitive view. *Journal of Vocational Behavior, 69*(2), 236–247. https://doi.org/10.1016/j.jvb.2006.02.006

Lent, R. W., & Brown, S. D. (2008). Social cognitive career theory and subjective well-being in the context of work. *Journal of Career Assessment, 16*(1), 6–21. https://doi.org/10.1177/1069072707305769

Lent, R. W., & Brown, S. D. (2013). Social cognitive model of career self-management: Toward a unifying view of adaptive career behavior across the life span. *Journal of Counseling Psychology, 60*(4), 557–568. https://doi.org/10.1037/a0033446

Lent, R. W., & Brown, S. D. (2019). Social cognitive career theory at 25: Empirical status of the interest, choice, and performance models. *Journal of Vocational Behavior, 115*, Article 103316. https://doi.org/10.1016/j.jvb.2019.06.004

Lent, R. W., & Brown, S. D. (2020). Career decision making, fast and slow: Toward an integrative model of intervention for sustainable career choice. *Journal of Vocational Behavior, 120*, Article 103448. https://doi.org/10.1016/j.jvb.2020.103448

Lent, R. W., Brown, S. D., & Hackett, G. (1994). Toward a unifying social cognitive theory of career and academic interest, choice, and performance. *Journal of Vocational Behavior, 45*(1), 79–122. https://doi.org/10.1006/jvbe.1994.1027

Lent, R. W., Brown, S. D., & Hackett, G. (2002). Social cognitive career theory. In D. Brown & Associates (Eds.), *Career choice and development* (4th ed., Vol. 4, pp. 255–311). Jossey-Bass.

Liao, C., Wayne, S. J., & Rousseau, D. M. (2016). Idiosyncratic deals in contemporary organizations: A qualitative and meta-analytical review. *Journal of Organizational Behavior, 37*(S1), S9–S29. https://doi.org/10.1002/job.1959

Lo Presti, A., Pluviano, S., & Briscoe, J. P. (2018). Are freelancers a breed apart? The role of protean and boundaryless career attitudes in employability and career success. *Human Resource Management Journal, 28*(3), 427–442. https://doi.org/10.1111/1748-8583.12188

Louis, M. R. (1980). Career transitions: Varieties and commonalities. *Academy of Management Review, 5*(3), 329–340. https://doi.org/10.5465/amr.1980.4288836

Lysova, E. I., Dik, B. J., Duffy, R. D., Khapova, S. N., & Arthur, M. B. (2019). Calling and careers: New insights and future directions. *Journal of Vocational Behavior, 114*, 1–6. https://doi.org/10.1016/j.jvb.2019.03.004

Maggiori, C., Johnston, C. S., Krings, F., Massoudi, K., & Rossier, J. (2013). The role of career adaptability and work conditions on general and professional well-being. *Journal of Vocational Behavior, 83*(3), 437–449. https://doi.org/10.1016/j.jvb.2013.07.001

Mainiero, L. A., & Gibson, D. E. (2017). The kaleidoscope career model revisited: How midcareer men and women diverge on authenticity, balance, and challenge. *Journal of Career Development, 45*(4), 361–377. https://doi.org/10.1177/0894845317698223

Mainiero, L. A., & Sullivan, S. E. (2005). Kaleidoscope careers: An alternate explanation for the "opt-out" revolution. *Academy of Management Perspectives, 19*(1), 106–123. https://doi.org/10.5465/ame .2005.15841962

Mayrhofer, W., Briscoe, J. P., Hall, D. T. T., Dickmann, M., Dries, N., Dysvik, A., Kaše, R., Parry, E., & Unite, J. (2016). Career success across the globe: Insights from the 5C project. *Organizational Dynamics, 45*(3), 197–205. https://doi.org/10.1016/j.orgdyn.2016.07.005

Meijerink, J., & Keegan, A. (2019). Conceptualizing human resource management in the gig economy: Toward a platform ecosystem perspective. *Journal of Managerial Psychology, 34*(4), 214–232. https://doi .org/10.1108/JMP-07-2018-0277

Mirvis, P. H., & Hall, D. T. (1994). Psychological success and the boundaryless career. *Journal of Organizational Behavior, 15*(4), 365–380. https://doi.org/10.1002/job.4030150406

Mor Barak, M. E., Lizano, E. L., Kim, A., Duan, L., Rhee, M.K., Hsiao, H.Y., & Brimhall, K. C. (2016). The promise of diversity management for climate of inclusion: A state-of-the-art review and meta-analysis. *Human Service Organizations: Management, Leadership & Governance, 40*(4), 305–333. https://doi.org /10.1080/23303131.2016.1138915

Nelissen, J., Forrier, A., & Verbruggen, M. (2017). Employee development and voluntary turnover: Testing the employability paradox. *Human Resource Management Journal, 27*(1), 152–168. https://doi.org /10.1111/1748-8583.12136

Ng, S. I., Lim, Q. H., Cheah, J.H., Ho, J. A., & Tee, K. K. (2020). A moderated-mediation model of career adaptability and life satisfaction among working adults in Malaysia. *Current Psychology: A Journal for Diverse Perspectives on Diverse Psychological Issues*. Advance online publication. https://doi.org/10.1007 /s12144-020-00837-7

Ng, T. W. H., Eby, L. T., Sorensen, K. L., & Feldman, D. C. (2005). Predictors of objective and subjective career success: A meta-analysis. *Personnel Psychology, 58*(2), 367–408. https://doi.org/10.1111 /j.1744-6570.2005.00515.x

Ng, T. W. H., & Feldman, D. C. (2007). The school-to-work transition: A role identity perspective. *Journal of Vocational Behavior, 71*(1), 114–134. https://doi.org/10.1016/j.jvb.2007.04.004

Ng, T. W. H., & Feldman, D. C. (2014). A conservation of resources perspective on career hurdles and salary attainment. *Journal of Vocational Behavior, 85*(1), 156–168. https://doi.org/10.1016/j.jvb.2014.05.008

Ocampo, A. C. G., Reyes, M. L., Chen, Y., Restubog, S. L. D., Chih, Y.Y., Chua-Garcia, L., & Guan, P. (2020). The role of internship participation and conscientiousness in developing career adaptability: A five-wave growth mixture model analysis. *Journal of Vocational Behavior, 120*, Article 103426. https://doi .org/10.1016/j.jvb.2020.103426

Pak, K., Kooij, D. T. A. M., De Lange, A. H., & Van Veldhoven, M. J. P. M. (2019). Human resource management and the ability, motivation and opportunity to continue working: A review of quantitative studies. *Human Resource Management Review, 29*(3), 336–352. https://doi.org/10.1016/j.hrmr.2018.07.002

Parker, S. K., Bindl, U. K., & Strauss, K. (2010). Making things happen: A model of proactive motivation. *Journal of Management, 36*(4), 827–856. https://doi.org/10.1177/0149206310363732

Parsons, F. (1909). *Choosing a vocation*. Houghton Mifflin.

Paul, K. I., & Moser, K. (2009). Unemployment impairs mental health: Meta-analyses. *Journal of Vocational Behavior, 74*(3), 264–282. https://doi.org/10.1016/j.jvb.2009.01.001

Peeters, E. R., Akkermans, J., & De Cuyper, N. (2020). The only constant is change? Movement capital and perceived employability. *Journal of Career Assessment*, 28(4), 674–692. https://doi.org/10.1177/1069072720918195

Philippaers, K., De Cuyper, N., & Forrier, A. (2017). Employable, committed, and thus well-performing: A matter of interdependent forward-looking social exchange. *European Journal of Work and Organizational Psychology*, 26(5), 755–767. https://doi.org/10.1080/1359432X.2017.1351950

Philippaers, K., De Cuyper, N., & Forrier, A. (2019). Employability and performance: The role of perceived control and affective organizational commitment. *Personnel Review*, 48(5), 1299–1317. https://doi.org/10.1108/PR-04-2017-0098

Porter, C., Woo, S. E., & Tak, J. (2016). Developing and validating short form protean and boundaryless career attitudes scales. *Journal of Career Assessment*, 24(1), 162–181. https://doi.org/10.1177/1069072714565775

Rodrigues, R., Butler, C. L., & Guest, D. (2019). Antecedents of protean and boundaryless career orientations: The role of core self-evaluations, perceived employability and social capital. *Journal of Vocational Behavior*, 110, 1–11. https://doi.org/10.1016/j.jvb.2018.11.003

Rodrigues, R., Butler, C. L., & Guest, D. (2020). Evaluating the employability paradox: When does organizational investment in human capital pay off? *The International Journal of Human Resource Management*, 31(9), 1134–1156. https://doi.org/10.1080/09585192.2019.1704825

Rodrigues, R. A., & Guest, D. (2010). Have careers become boundaryless? *Human Relations*, 63(8), 1157–1175. https://doi.org/10.1177/0018726709354344

Rodrigues, R., Guest, D., Oliveira, T., & Alfes, K. (2015). Who benefits from independent careers? Employees, organizations, or both? *Journal of Vocational Behavior*, 91, 23–34. https://doi.org/10.1016/j.jvb.2015.09.005

Rothwell, A., & Arnold, J. (2007). Self-perceived employability: Development and validation of a scale. *Personnel Review*, 36(1), 23–41. https://doi.org/10.1108/00483480710716704

Rousseau, D. (2015). *I-deals: Idiosyncratic deals employees bargain for themselves.* Routledge.

Rousseau, D. M., Ho, V. T., & Greenberg, J. (2006). I-deals: Idiosyncratic terms in employment relationships. *Academy of Management Review*, 31(4), 977–994. https://doi.org/10.5465/amr.2006.22527470

Rudolph, C. W., Lavigne, K. N., & Zacher, H. (2017). Career adaptability: A meta-analysis of relationships with measures of adaptivity, adapting responses, and adaptation results. *Journal of Vocational Behavior*, 98(Supplement C), 17–34. https://doi.org/10.1016/j.jvb.2016.09.002

Rummel, S., Akkermans, J., Blokker, R., & Van Gelderen, M. (2019). Shocks and entrepreneurship: A study of career shocks among newly graduated entrepreneurs. *Career Development International*. https://doi.org/10.1108/CDI-11-2018-0296

Santilli, S., Marcionetti, J., Rochat, S., Rossier, J., & Nota, L. (2017). Career adaptability, hope, optimism, and life satisfaction in Italian and Swiss adolescents. *Journal of Career Development*, 44(1), 62–76. https://doi.org/10.1177/0894845316633793

Savickas, M. L. (1997). Career adaptability: An integrative construct for life-span, life-space theory. *The Career Development Quarterly*, 45(3), 247–259. https://doi.org/10.1002/j.2161-0045.1997.tb00469.x

Savickas, M. L. (2002). Career construction. In D. Brown & Associates (Eds.), *Career choice and development* (pp. 149–205). Jossey-Bass.

Savickas, M. L. (2005). The theory and practice of career construction. In S. D. Brown & R. W. Lent (Eds.), *Career development and counseling: Putting theory and research to work* (Vol. 1, pp. 42–70). Wiley.

Savickas, M. L. (2013). Career construction theory and practice. In R. W. Lent & S. D. Brown (Eds.), *Career development and counseling: Putting theory and research into work* (2nd ed., pp. 147–192). John Wiley & Sons.

Savickas, M. L. (2015). Designing projects for career construction. In R. A. Young, J. F. Domene, & L. Valach (Eds.), *Counseling and action* (pp. 13–31). Springer.

Savickas, M. L., & Porfeli, E. J. (2012). Career Adapt-Abilities Scale: Construction, reliability, and measurement equivalence across 13 countries. *Journal of Vocational Behavior, 80*(3), 661–673. https://doi.org/10.1016/j.jvb.2012.01.011

Seibert, S. E., Kraimer, M. L., & Heslin, P. A. (2016). Developing career resilience and adaptability. *Organizational Dynamics, 45*(3), 245–257. https://doi.org/10.1016/j.orgdyn.2016.07.009

Seibert, S. E., Kraimer, M. L., Holtom, B. C., & Pierotti, A. J. (2013). Even the best laid plans sometimes go askew: Career self-management processes, career shocks, and the decision to pursue graduate education. *Journal of Applied Psychology, 98*(1), 169–182. https://doi.org/10.1037/a0030882

Seibert, S. E., Kraimer, M. L., & Liden, R. C. (2001). A social capital theory of career success. *Academy of Management Journal, 44*(2), 219–237. https://doi.org/10.5465/3069452

Shen, Y., Demel, B., Unite, J., Briscoe, J. P., Hall, D. T., Chudzikowski, K., Mayrhofer, W., Abdul-Ghani, R., Bogicevic Milikic, B., Colorado, O., Fei, Z., Las Heras, M., Ogliastri, E., Pazy, A., Poon, J. M. L., Shefer, D., Taniguchi, M., & Zikic, J. (2015). Career success across 11 countries: Implications for international human resource management. *The International Journal of Human Resource Management, 26*(13), 1753–1778. https://doi.org/10.1080/09585192.2014.962562

Sheu, H. B., Lent, R. W., Brown, S. D., Miller, M. J., Hennessy, K. D., & Duffy, R. D. (2010). Testing the choice model of social cognitive career theory across Holland themes: A meta-analytic path analysis. *Journal of Vocational Behavior, 76*(2), 252–264. https://doi.org/10.1016/j.jvb.2009.10.015

Shockley, K. M., Ureksoy, H., Rodopman, O. B., Poteat, L. F., & Dullaghan, T. R. (2016). Development of a new scale to measure subjective career success: A mixed-methods study. *Journal of Organizational Behavior, 37*(1), 128–153. https://doi.org/10.1002/job.2046

Spreitzer, G. M., Cameron, L., & Garrett, L. (2017). Alternative work arrangements: Two images of the new world of work. *Annual Review of Organizational Psychology and Organizational Behavior, 4*(1), 473–499. https://doi.org/10.1146/annurev-orgpsych-032516-113332

Spurk, D., Hirschi, A., & Dries, N. (2019). Antecedents and outcomes of objective versus subjective career success: Competing perspectives and future directions. *Journal of Management, 45*(1), 35–69. https://doi.org/10.1177/0149206318786563

Spurk, D., Kauffeld, S., Meinecke, A. L., & Ebner, K. (2016). Why do adaptable people feel less insecure? Indirect effects of career adaptability on job and career insecurity via two types of perceived marketability. *Journal of Career Assessment, 24*(2), 289–306. https://doi.org/10.1177/1069072715580415

Spurk, D., & Straub, C. (2020). Flexible employment relationships and careers in times of the COVID-19 pandemic. *Journal of Vocational Behavior, 119*, 103435. https://doi.org/10.1016/j.jvb.2020.103435

Spurk, D., Volmer, J., Orth, M., & Göritz, A. S. (2020). How do career adaptability and proactive career behaviours interrelate over time? An inter- and intraindividual investigation. *Journal of Occupational and Organizational Psychology, 93*(1), 158–186. https://doi.org/10.1111/joop.12288

Straub, C., Vinkenburg, C. J., & Van Kleef, M. (2020). Career customization: Putting an organizational practice to facilitate sustainable careers to the test. *Journal of Vocational Behavior, 117*, 103320. https://doi.org/10.1016/j.jvb.2019.103320

Sturges, J., Conway, N., Guest, D., & Liefooghe, A. (2005). Managing the career deal: The psychological contract as a framework for understanding career management, organizational commitment and work behavior. *Journal of Organizational Behavior, 26*(7), 821–838. https://doi.org/10.1002/job.341

Sullivan, S. E. (1999). The changing nature of careers: A review and research agenda. *Journal of Management, 25*(3), 457–484. https://doi.org/10.1177/014920639902500308

Sullivan, S. E., & Al Ariss, A. (2019). Employment after retirement: A review and framework for future research. *Journal of Management, 45*(1), 262–284. https://doi.org/10.1177/0149206318810411

Sullivan, S. E., & Al Ariss, A. (2021). Making sense of different perspectives on career transitions: A review and agenda for future research. *Human Resource Management Review, 31*(1), 100727. https://doi .org/10.1016/j.hrmr.2019.100727

Sullivan, S. E., & Arthur, M. B. (2006). The evolution of the boundaryless career concept: Examining physical and psychological mobility. *Journal of Vocational Behavior, 69*(1), 19–29. https://doi.org/10.1016/j .jvb.2005.09.001

Sullivan, S. E., & Baruch, Y. (2009). Advances in career theory and research: A critical review and agenda for future exploration. *Journal of Management, 35*(6), 1542–1571. https://doi.org/10.1177/01492063 09350082

Super, D. E. (1957). *The psychology of careers.* Harper & Row.

Super, D. E. (1980). A life-span, life-space approach to career development. In D. Brown & Associates (Eds.), *Career choice and development* (pp. 197–261). Jossey-Bass.

Thompson, J. A., & Bunderson, J. S. (2019). Research on work as a calling...and how to make it matter. *Annual Review of Organizational Psychology and Organizational Behavior, 6*(1), 421–443. https://doi .org/10.1146/annurev-orgpsych-012218-015140

Thorndike, E. L. (1914). *Educational psychology: Vol 3. Mental work and fatigue and individual differences and their causes.* Teachers College. https://doi.org/10.1037/13796-000

Tims, M., & Akkermans, J. (2020). Job and career crafting to fulfill individual career pathways. In G. Carter & J. Hedge (Eds.), *Career pathways—School to retirement and beyond* (pp. 165–190). Oxford University Press. https://doi.org/10.1093/oso/9780190907785.003.0010

Topa, G., Depolo, M., & Alcover, C.M. (2018). Early retirement: A meta-analysis of Its antecedent and subsequent correlates. *Frontiers in Psychology, 8,* 2157. https://www.frontiersin.org/article/10.3389/fpsyg .2017.02157

Turban, D. B., & Dougherty, T. W. (1994). Role of protégé personality in receipt of mentoring and career success. *Academy of Management Journal, 37*(3), 688–702. https://doi.org/10.5465/256706

Usher, E. L., & Schunk, D. H. (2018). Social cognitive theoretical perspective of self-regulation. In D. H. Schunk & J. A. Greene (Eds.), *Handbook of self-regulation of learning and performance* (pp. 19–35). Educational Psychology Handbook Series. Routledge.

Uy, M. A., Chan, K.Y., Sam, Y. L., Ho, M.H. R., & Chernyshenko, O. S. (2015). Proactivity, adaptability and boundaryless career attitudes: The mediating role of entrepreneurial alertness. *Journal of Vocational Behavior, 86,* 115–123. https://doi.org/10.1016/j.jvb.2014.11.005

Van der Heijde, C. M., & Van der Heijden, B. I. J. M. (2006). A competence-based and multidimensional operationalization and measurement of employability. *Human Resource Management, 45*(3), 449–476. https://doi.org/10.1002/hrm.20119

Van der Heijden, B. I. J. M., & De Vos, A. (2015). Sustainable careers: Introductory chapter. In A. De Vos & B. I. J. M. Van der Heijden (Eds.), *Handbook of research on sustainable careers* (pp. 1–19). Edward Elgar.

Van der Heijden, B., De Vos, A., Akkermans, J., Spurk, D., Semeijn, J., Van der Velde, M., & Fugate, M. (2020). Sustainable career across the lifespan: Moving the field forward. *Journal of Vocational Behavior, 117,* Article 103344. https://doi.org/10.1016/j.jvb.2019.103344

Van der Heijden, B. I. J. M., Notelaers, G., Peters, P., Stoffers, J. M. M., De Lange, A. H., Froehlich, D. E., & Van der Heijde, C. M. (2018). Development and validation of the short-form employability five-factor instrument. *Journal of Vocational Behavior, 106,* 236–248. https://doi.org/10.1016/j.jvb.2018.02.003

Van Harten, J., De Cuyper, N., Guest, D., Fugate, M., Knies, E., & Forrier, A. (2020). Introduction to special issue on HRM and employability: Mutual gains or conflicting outcomes? *The International Journal of Human Resource Management, 31*(9), 1095–1105. https://doi.org/10.1080/09585192.2020.1740457

Van Hooft, E. A. J., Kammeyer-Mueller, J. D., Wanberg, C. R., Kanfer, R., & Basbug, G. (2020). Job search and employment success: A quantitative review and future research agenda. *Journal of Applied Psychology.* https://doi.org/10.1037/apl0000675

Vanhercke, D., De Cuyper, N., Peeters, E., & De Witte, H. (2014). Defining perceived employability: A psychological approach. *Personnel Review*, 43(4), 592–605. https://doi.org/10.1108/PR-07-2012-0110

Volmer, J., & Spurk, D. (2011). Protean and boundaryless career attitudes: Relationships with subjective and objective career success. *Zeitschrift für ArbeitsmarktForschung*, 43(3), 207–218. https://doi.org/10.1007/s12651-010-0037-3

Vuori, J., Toppinen-Tanner, S., & Mutanen, P. (2012). Effects of resource-building group intervention on career management and mental health in work organizations: Randomized controlled field trial. *Journal of Applied Psychology*, 97(2), 273–286. https://doi.org/10.1037/a0025584

Wanberg, C. R. (2012). The individual experience of unemployment. *Annual Review of Psychology*, 63(1), 369–396. https://doi.org/10.1146/annurev-psych-120710-100500

Wanberg, C. R., Hough, L. M., & Song, Z. (2002). Predictive validity of a multidisciplinary model of reemployment success. *Journal of Applied Psychology*, 87, 1100–1120. https://doi.org/10.1037/0021-9010.87.6.1100

Wang, M., & Shultz, K. S. (2010). Employee retirement: A review and recommendations for future investigation. *Journal of Management*, 36(1), 172–206. https://doi.org/10.1177/0149206309347957

Wang, M., & Wanberg, C. R. (2017). 100 years of applied psychology research on individual careers: From career management to retirement. *Journal of Applied Psychology*, 102(3), 546–563. https://doi.org/10.1037/apl0000143

Wiernik, B. M., & Kostal, J. W. (2019). Protean and boundaryless career orientations: A critical review and meta-analysis. *Journal of Counseling Psychology*, 66(3), 280–307. https://doi.org/10.1037/cou0000324

Zacher, H. (2015). Daily manifestations of career adaptability: Relationships with job and career outcomes. *Journal of Vocational Behavior*, 91, 76–86. https://doi.org/10.1016/j.jvb.2015.09.003

Zikic, J., & Klehe, U.-C. (2006). Job loss as a blessing in disguise: The role of career exploration and career planning in predicting reemployment quality. *Journal of Vocational Behavior*, 69(3), 391–409. https://doi.org/10.1016/j.jvb.2006.05.007

Zimmerman, R. D., Swider, B. W., & Arthur, J. B. (2020). Does turnover destination matter? Differentiating antecedents of occupational change versus organizational change. *Journal of Vocational Behavior*, 121, 103470. https://doi.org/10.1016/j.jvb.2020.103470

Jos Akkermans, Daniel Spurk, and Nadya Fouad

RETIREMENT

INTRODUCTION

Retirement is an important concept to study because the idea of retirement has changed over the decades, and retirement as it is known in the 21st century is not the same as the one that our ancestors experienced in the past (Zickar, 2012). People live longer thanks to better healthcare and thus stay at their jobs for longer periods of time. In fact, the average age of the workforce is continuing to grow as baby boomers have longer life expectancies and there are lower birth rates (Alley & Crimmins, 2007). Meanwhile, the youth labor force (aged 16 to 24 years) is entering the workforce later, which seems to be due to increased school attendance (e.g., graduate programs; Toossi, 2004). As a result, the interest in retaining good employees has risen, in order to avoid an employee shortage. Interestingly, Shultz and Adams (2007) noted that 2050's older workers are already part of the workforce today. Thus, studying the predictors and outcomes of retirement and the different paths available for older workers can improve expectations and lead to better predictions about changes in the future. While the population growth and rapid increase in women's participation in the workforce led to a growth of the baby boomers' labor market involvement during 1982–1992 (Toossi, 2004), the median age of the labor force increased from 34.6 years in 1982 to 40 years in 2002 (Chen & Scott, 2006). The employees who now compose the older worker population are likely to stay in the workforce for several reasons—namely, financial need, higher educational attainment, and improvements in health, among others. At the same time, almost 24% of the total U.S. workforce will be 55 or more years old in 2018 (Toossi, 2009). Thus, it is important to know what will happen socially and economically when these older workers decide to retire. Namely, the estimated percentage of population who will be aged 65 and over in 2050 is the highest for Japan (40.1%), Italy (31.0%), and Germany (30.1%), among other developed countries, and Brazil (26.8%) and Russia (25.7%) for developing countries. Furthermore, these percentages are always higher for females than males (Alcover, Topa, Parry, Fraccaroli, & Depolo, 2014).

RETIREMENT: DEFINITION, MEASUREMENT, AND BASIC CONCEPTS

Wang and Shi (2014) defined retirement as an individual's exit process from the workforce, which is usually accompanied by both a decrease in psychological commitment to work and an increase in behavioral withdrawal from work. In the past, retirement was perceived as a "crisis" that negatively impacted the retiree's well-being (van Solinge & Henkens, 2008). Subsequent research has acknowledged the beneficial effects of retirement. For example, Mein, Martikainen, Hemingway, Stansfeld, and Marmot (2003) found that retirement at age 60 was associated with an improvement in mental health and no change in physical health and that this effect was even more prevalent for individuals in high socioeconomic groups. Furthermore, retirement is of global significance and has economic and societal implications in the development of societies (Wang, 2012).

Retirement is used to refer to the withdrawal of older workers from paid work; "older" is typically taken to mean over the ages of 50 to 55 (Denton & Spencer, 2009). Feldman (1994) also specified that the term *retirement* should be used only when referring to jobs or career-path changes that occur after middle-age. Some research has compared the retirement decisions of older workers to those of previous generations. In 2004, the mean self-reported likelihood of employees working full time past the age of 65 was 33%, an increase from 27% in 1992 (Mermin, Johnson, & Murphy, 2007). This could be explained by longer life expectancies (Alley & Crimmins, 2007). Additionally, if employees leave an organization after middle-age, it does not mean that they will not go back to work in a different organization or even engage in entrepreneurial activities. Therefore, it is hard to conceptualize retirement, because it certainly means different things to different individuals and at distinct time points in their lives.

Indeed, it is hard to measure retirement because the concept is both fuzzy and fluid (Denton & Spencer, 2009), where "fuzzy" refers to its lack of precise measurement and "fluid" means the concept is modified over time as social conditions change. Denton and Spencer (2009) make the claim that an individual can be considered retired for the wrong reasons—namely, transitions at work could classify an individual as a retiree, yet that individual could return to the workforce at a later time. Likewise, someone who became disabled but continues working receives employment-related benefits and thus may be considered retired unintentionally. The authors postulate eight categories of retirement measures that have been proposed or used as indicators of retirement by researchers in the past; their utility is dependent on the research question at hand and the data available. The first three categories include measures based on labor force. These include nonparticipation in the labor force (e.g., individual is either in or out, without the possibility of in-between), reduction in hours worked and/or earning, and reduction in hours worked or earning below a minimum cutoff. The latter two represent a more realistic view of retirement, characterized by a gradual exit from the workplace. The fourth category is receipt of retirement/pension income, which is not a clear representation for full retirement because individuals might continue working with the same or different employer even after retirement. Different countries have different pension systems. For example, Japan, which has one of the most rapidly aging societies in the world, has raised the age of those entitled to full pensions to 65. Countries in Europe (at the European Commission level) follow less rigid laws and policies that incentivize prolonged working while maintaining anti-discrimination policies (Fraccaroli & Deller, 2015). Yao and Peng (2012) highlight the pension systems of four countries (two developing countries, China and India, and two developed countries, the United States and Germany) that together account for almost half of the population of the world. For the United States, Germany, and China, they described the three pillars of the old-age security system (i.e., social security, private pensions, and voluntary savings), as well as the issues and challenges relevant to these. India has a more complex old-age security system; thus, Yao and Peng examined the components and related issues of the Indian system separately, before drawing conclusions about the problems common to all four countries—namely, the problems of financial sustainability of the old-age security system are longevity and low birth rates for the developed countries and institution transition costs and highly generous benefits for developing countries.

The fifth and sixth categories, exit from one's main employer and change of career or employment in later life, respectively, may be less applicable for boomers and millennials, who are very mobile and have adopted the convention of changing employers far more frequently than previous generations, a phenomenon called "careerism" (Wesner & Miller, 2008). Careerism often manifests as a preference for changing employers to get ahead of one's competition (De Hauw & De Vos, 2010). The seventh category captured is the self-assessment of retirement, which is a useful indicator for the individual's state of mind but because of its subjectivity, can create conflict when comparing across individuals. Finally, Denton and Spencer (2009) created an eighth category for any combination of the seven operationalizations, which can be composed of both subjective and objective descriptions. Indeed, Gustman and Steinmeier (2001) proposed a measure of retirement based on four criteria: (a) exit from the main employer, (b) working fewer hours than before, (c) working hours below some minimal level, and (d) individual self-assessment of him- or herself as retired. According to Gustman and Steinmeier (2001), individuals would only be considered retired if they met all four criteria.

One popular way to conceptualize retirement is through the temporal process. The temporal process argues that there are three phases in an individual's retirement process: retirement planning, decision-making, and transition and adjustment (Shultz & Wang, 2011). This process allows researchers to investigate retirement as a step-by-step sequence, although researchers typically choose to investigate just one phase at a time because the process is not homogeneous across individuals. Doing so is successful as long as investigators realize that there is a bigger "retirement puzzle" to fill in that differs across retirees.

Retirement planning typically begins years before the individual desires to retire. Individuals start saving for retirement and discuss retirement plans with friends, family members, and current colleagues (Wang & Shi, 2014). The specific time when individuals first engage in retirement planning depends on several factors, such as the norms and institutions of the society or the organization (Moen, 1996). If the organization promotes (early) retirement, the individual will have more resources at work with which to engage in retirement planning. Taylor-Carter, Cook, and Weinberg (1997) have argued that retirement planning can be categorized as financial planning (focusing on private savings) and cognitive planning (exploring the possibilities of work and social interactions in the future). Both types of planning are important because they describe different aspects of the postretirement life that can be improved via preretirement planning. Financial planning allows the individual to engage in nonpaid activities during retirement, if desired, and reduces planning costs (e.g., economic and psychological barriers to acquiring information, calculating numbers, and developing a plan; van Rooij, Lusardi, & Alessie, 2011). Accordingly, research has shown that financial literacy is positively associated with retirement planning behavior, and that those individuals who are financially savvy are more likely to succeed in their planning via formal methods (Lusardi & Mitchell, 2011; van Rooij, Lusardi, & Alessie, 2011). Cognitive planning can reduce the anxiety associated with retirement (Macewen, Barling, Kelloway, & Higginbottom, 1995).

The retirement decision-making phase is more information-based than retirement planning and requires individuals to determine when they will retire. According to Feldman and Beehr (2011), an individual must consider his or her possible future and past experiences at work and compile this information to lay out the steps needed for retirement. The decision to retire is subjective because it depends on the person–environment fit at the time of decision-making. If the individual does not see a fit with his or her environment (workplace), that individual is more likely to opt for retirement than someone who believes there is a good fit with the environment. Although the decisions and transitions may differ substantially across individuals (some older workers successfully transition into retirement, while others do not), an employee's retirement decision is a major life event (Adams & Beehr, 1998) and thus should be studied carefully.

Finally, it is important to note that in the phase of retirement transition and adjustment, maladjustment to retirement can have negative implications for retirees, such as increased alcohol and drug use (Perreira & Sloan, 2001; Bacharach, Bamberger, Sonnenstuhl, & Vashdi, 2004, 2008) or decreased mental health (Wang, 2007). A certain level of physical and mental health is needed to successfully adjust to postretirement life (especially if bridge employment is anticipated). Retirees need to take opportunities to occupy their newly gained free time and help them adjust to the changes in their daily activities. For example, retirees can occupy themselves with leisure activities (e.g., spending time with friends), volunteer work (e.g., teaching young children at local schools), or various forms of paid work (e.g., bridge employment; Adams & Rau, 2011). Important to retirement adjustment is the fact that the impact of retirement varies not only across individuals, but also within individuals over time (Wang, Henkens, & van Solinge, 2011). The authors argue that retirees' adjustment-level changes are dependent on the resources (e.g., psychological or financial resources) they have, which are sure to fluctuate over time. For instance, an individual may engage in nonpaid activities during the beginning of his or her retirement life and soon realize that financial expectations are not being met. Consistency theory (e.g., Bell, 1979) posits that when retirees' expectations are not met, dissatisfaction occurs. The theory explains why this retiree would change activities to avoid dissatisfaction with his or her retired life (Beehr, 1986).

Other Important Concepts and How They Are Measured

Early Retirement.   Early retirees are defined as those individuals who "exit from an organizational position or career path of considerable duration" who are younger than 65 years old (Feldman, 1994, p. 287). There are potential problems associated with early retirement because it can leave the older worker's organization bereft of that employee's knowledge and skills; and, as von Bonsdorff, Huuhtanen, Tuomi, and Seitsamo (2009) noted, overall "Western countries are struggling to retain and hire competent employees" (p. 94). However, this view of retirement is subjective in the sense that "early" might mean different things to different people. Although certain countries and professions have mandatory retirement ages (e.g., 65 in Belgium and France, 70 years old in Brazil, and 65 years old for pilots in the United States), some countries classify mandatory retirement as illegal (e.g., Australia, New Zealand, and Canada). In countries that do not have mandatory retirement age, the decision is left up to the individual's interpretations as to when retirement is early or on time. Retiring on time can have important psychological implications (Kim & Moen, 2001; Williamson, Rinehart, & Blank, 1992) if employees fear being wrongly judged for retiring earlier or later than their peers. An individual with coworkers of similar age who are retiring will likely retire at a similar time to avoid a negative classification of being late in taking action. The decision to retire early can be seen as a combination of chance (e.g., higher socioeconomic status) and choice (Gould, 2006); older workers with a higher socioeconomic status will be more financially able to engage in early retirement (because they do not need the continued income after retirement). Moreover, some countries adopt certain norms that may also guide an individual's decision to retire. For example, Sweden has implemented more legal changes (i.e., flexibility for older workers) that show more support for later retirement than in many other countries (Isaksson, Johansson, & Palm, 2014).

Another reason for the subjectivity of early retirement is the perceived work–environment fit the older worker experiences; for example, older workers who are content in their jobs are less likely to engage in early retirement. The role loss accompanied by the exit from the desired work life would create an undesirable postretirement experience, which is consistent with consistency theory (Bell, 1979).

Despite the potential negative effects, early retirement can have significant positive outcomes for individuals. For example, individuals who retire early can enjoy more time with friends and family while they are physically and psychologically healthy (assuming that bad health is not the reason for retiring early). As long as employees' income and health are satisfactory, so, too, is their retirement likely to be satisfactory (Barfield & Morgan, 1978; Barnes-Farrell, 2003).

Phased Retirement.   Phased retirement suggests a gradual reduction in work hours with a long-term employer before engaging in full retirement. This kind of retirement is usually preferred by employees who are considering retirement (Chen & Scott, 2006) but may not yet have concrete plans yet. Reducing the number of hours at work can provide safety for employees who might not be ready for the full transition. Phased retirement can "give them a taste" of what their postretirement life will entail, and this can in turn help their transition by allowing them to make the necessary changes to fulfill their expectations. Phased retirement seems to be preferred by older workers. Research has shown that faculty members who chose phased retirement would have continued working full-time if their institution had not offered phased retirement (Ghent, Allen, & Clark, 2001). Indeed, "one-time, permanent retirements are now the exception, not the rule, among today's older Americans with full-time career jobs" (Cahill, Giandrea, & Quinn, 2006, p. 523). Phased retirement can also encourage older workers to work past their expected retirement age, allowing them to earn extra income that will improve their postretirement life. Phased retirement can benefit the institution by allowing it to retain competent older workers, and this sometimes has a significant impact on how the institution is viewed by outsiders (Allen, 2004).

A typical phased retirement program allows older workers to officially retire (sometimes even requires that they do), from which they are rehired by their previous organization at fewer (usually half the) hours and compensated for these reduced hours at their former hourly wage. Since employees are offered their former hourly wage, this option should be preferred by older workers over starting a new career elsewhere during retirement. Such retirees can claim their pensions while working half (or so) the time they used to, which increases the incentive to engage in phased retirement (Ghent, Allen, & Clark, 2001). Other incentives for phased retirement include government subsidies to big companies that retain older workers. This way, the government is able to report lower unemployment rates, and in turn, older workers can keep their jobs (e.g., in Japan; Usui, Colignon, & Rosen, 2014).

Bridge Employment.   Bridge employment is defined as participation in the labor force by older workers as they leave their career jobs and move toward complete labor force withdrawal (Shultz, 2003). Bridge employment is another way (like phased retirement) to help smooth the transition to full retirement so that retirees do not have to go immediately from working full-time to cessation of work. Bridge employment is very prevalent among preretired employees; the majority of employees leaving their full-time jobs first move to a bridge job (Cahill, Giandrea, & Quinn, 2006). One possible explanation for the preference of bridge employment among retirees is the concept of "not so big jobs" introduced by Moen (2007). The idea is that older workers want to be able to engage in some type of work during retirement but that it does not have to be the "big job" that they usually preferred during their careers. "Not so big jobs" allow retirees to have a little bit of career, leisure, or community participation by offering them flexible schedules to fit their needs and desires in each area of activities (Moen, 2007).

One advantage of bridge employment for the organization is that it allows employers to retain retired workers, and thus help maintain the skilled and experienced workforce who is already familiar with the organization's policies and procedures. In turn, this helps reduce the cost of replacing older workers (Wang & Shi, 2014). Since the 1980s, there has been a large increase in the number of individuals who decide to reenter the workforce after retirement (Hayward, Crimmins, & Wray, 1994). It is important to note that bridge employment can take two forms: career bridge employment (i.e., working in the same field as the career job) and bridge employment in a different field (Wang, Zhan, Liu, & Shultz, 2008). Thus, it is important to consider the predictors and corresponding outcomes of bridge employment and to understand that once older workers retire, they may not necessarily be finished contributing to their field. For instance, 40% of older workers who had opted for bridge employment in the Netherlands found a job in a different field (Henkens & van Solinge, 2014), and 60% of Swedish older workers' reason for retiring was to engage in leisure activities.

Like early retirement, bridge employment can constitute different things to different people. For this reason, bridge employment has been measured empirically in different ways in the past. Some researchers have opted to use dichotomous responses, asking retirees whether they participate in a part-time job; whereas others have directly asked their participants how many hours they work. Some researchers have used both these measures together to provide further evidence for their hypotheses (Zhan, Wang, & Shi, 2015). These researchers found consistent results regardless of whether they operationalized bridge employment as a status or as number of hours worked.

THEORETICAL FRAMEWORKS FOR RETIREMENT RESEARCH

The theories often applied in retirement research include role theory, continuity theory, and human-capital theory. These help explain retirees' roles inside and outside the organization, desire for continuity beyond retirement, and generic and specialized skills they will pass on, respectively. The perspectives discussed are the life-course perspective (interdependence with other life spheres in retirees' lives) and resource-based perspectives (available resources can determine planning, decisions, and adjustment in retirement). Moreover, the protean career model is different in that it emphasizes the process of retirement, and has helped individuate retirees. It is important to note that these theories, perspectives, and model are not necessarily mutually exclusive. Rather, simultaneously integrating and incorporating them in studies can help better capture the complex nature of retirement.

Role Theory. Role theory emphasizes the importance of two components during retirement adjustment: role exit and role transition. Depending on an individual's perception of his or her work role (e.g., whether that individual identifies with it), retirement might be seen as a negative or positive life event. For employees who are highly invested in their work roles, their feelings of self-worth are highly associated with the effectiveness with which they carry out their roles (Ashforth, 2001). With this in mind, retirement can be characterized as a role transition (Riley & Riley, 1994) in which work roles are weakened or even lost, and family or community roles are strengthened (Barnes-Farrell, 2003). This role loss can cause people to feel anxious or depressed, which may also lead to less well-being during retirement (Riley & Riley, 1994). The opposite can be true when retirees leave jobs that they find unpleasant and thus may be pleased with the role loss (Wang et al., 2011). For individuals who find their jobs stressful or burdensome, retirement can be seen as a relief and an opportunity to engage in different roles, such as family roles or community roles, in their newly acquired free time.

Resource-Based Perspective. The resource-based perspective looks at the fluctuations in retirees' adjustment as a function of the resources (and the changing levels or lack of them; Wang et al., 2011). Several elements can be considered resources for retirees' adjustment and well-being. For example, money is a resource that helps retirees maintain their lifestyles on a par with their preretirement lives. Other resources include cognitive resources (e.g., processing speed and working memory; Wang & Chen, 2006), motivational resources (e.g., self-efficacy; Dendinger, Adams, & Jacobson, 2005), financial resources (e.g., salary and pension; Damman, Henkens, & Kalmijn, 2011), social resources (e.g., social network and social support; Kim & Feldman, 2000), emotional resources (e.g., emotional stability and affectivity; Blekesaune & Skirbekk, 2012), and physical resources (e.g., muscle strength; Jex, Wang, & Zarubin, 2007). Wang (2007) suggested that a retiree's total capability to fulfill his or her needs is composed of these resources.

One of the advantages of using the resource-based perspective to examine retirees' adjustment and well-being is that it can accommodate for changes over a long period of time. Changes in resources are inevitable; thus, this perspective can help accurately capture the ups and downs of such changes. Retirees' resources at the reference point (e.g., the beginning of the retirement adjustment) can be compared to their total resources at different time points to assess whether there has been a significant decrease or increase or a lack of change that could affect their well-being (Wang, 2007). If a retiree's total resources at a certain point are lower than those at the reference point, the individual might experience a negative change in well-being. Another advantage of using the resource perspective to analyze changes in adjustment is that specific differences between current total resources and resources at the reference point can be pinpointed, and individuals can know the reason for their negative (or positive) change in well-being. Knowing the sources of their problem (e.g., loneliness due to reduced social life) can help retirees look for solutions specific to their situation (e.g., engagement in community-service activities).

Life-Course Perspective. The life-course perspective emphasizes that individuals make decisions that are contextually embedded. This means that retirement adjustment depends on the circumstances in which the adjustment may (or may not) occur. These circumstances derive from individual attributes of the retiree before entering retirement (e.g., demographic characteristics, financial and health status, and transition-related abilities and skills; Kim & Moen, 2002). These circumstances may also be shaped by individual life history (Orel, Ford, & Brock, 2004) or current-job-related experience (Wang et al., 2008). Elder (1995) emphasized two interrelated concepts that are central to understanding life-changing decisions in people's lives: interdependence, or linked lives, and timing. Interdependence refers to the connectedness between people and their actions, such that an individual's decision to retire will influence the social and financial environments of his or her relatives as well. Timing refers to the historical or social timing of transitions (e.g., from work to retirement) in individuals' lives.

Additionally, life-span theorists propose that if an individual has a flexible style in dealing with previous life transitions (e.g., career changes), is less socially integrated with their current work (e.g., does not establish significant social relations in their jobs), and has attributes that help smooth the transition (e.g., is high in openness), he or she will be more likely to transition smoothly and have a positive adjustment experience (Wang & Shultz, 2010). Individuals that value their time spent at their jobs will likely have a harder time at the time of exit.

Furthermore, the life-course perspective emphasizes that life spheres influence each other, so that the work life sphere influences and is influenced by other life spheres, such as the marital life sphere and the community life sphere, and so on. This is important in studying retirement transition and adjustment because it is clear that the nonwork life spheres will influence the decision to retire and the adaptation to retirement. Not only can adjustment problems transfer from one life sphere to another within a person, but other family members' life spheres can have an impact on the retiree's life. For example, problems in one partner's retirement experience can affect the quality of the other partner's retirement experience (van Solinge & Henkens, 2005). Interdependent life spheres are important to study because they provide retirees alternative spheres to engage in when they exit the workforce (Wang et al., 2011). The participation in alternative spheres offers retirees meaningful and desirable opportunities to adjust to their retirement (Zhan et al., 2015).

Continuity Theory. Continuity indicates a consistency of patterns over time, the connection between changes without any taxing disruptions (Atchley, 1999). Continuity theorists propose that if retirees can maintain their identity and self-concept during the retirement transition, they should not experience a significant change in their well-being. This idea is consistent with Atchley's claim, from over two decades ago, which says that "middle-aged and older adults attempt to preserve and maintain existing structures," and these individuals also prefer continuity (Atchley, 1989, p. 183). One way retirees can engage in continuity is to apply familiar strategies in different or new areas of their lives. Individuals who experience extreme difficulty in maintaining their identity and self-concepts during the transition from work to retirement life would experience negative change in well-being (e.g., psychological well-being). Another way retirees can maintain continuity is by viewing retirement as another career stage or by continuing to work during retirement (Kim & Feldman, 2000). Doing so would create standards based on past experience that retirees can hold in their postretirement lives. To the extent that their retirement activities match their expected standards, retirees would experience continuity.

Furthermore, two types of continuity have been proposed: internal and external. Internal continuity is related to mental and psychological states (e.g., self-efficacy, goals, skills); external continuity is related to environment-based features (e.g., social roles, living and transportation arrangements, income; von Bonsdorff & Ilmarinen, 2012; Atchley, 1999). These two types come into play when important decisions are to be made that may not allow for continuity. A balance between internal and external continuity permits retirees to use past life events to make decisions on future events. According to Atchley (1989), individuals can tolerate substantial life events without severely affecting their continuity; it is simply part of evolutionary changes (von Bonsdorff & Ilmarinen, 2012) that allow individuals to develop their identities over time.

Human-Capital Theory. Human capital theory focuses on generic (available to multiple organizations) and specialized (unique to parent organization) skills (Lepak & Snell, 1999). Employees' specialized skills benefit the organization the most, whereas employees with generic skills can have a higher potential benefit to themselves if they join the labor market in the future. A relatable way to look at the skills acquired from years of experience is using two categories of processes: documenting and interpersonal. These two categories serve as knowledge-transfer tools for organizations. Documenting processes focus on knowledge transfer via tangible, often written procedures and programs; interpersonal processes focus on knowledge transfer through social exchanges between employees who are leaving and those who are staying (Rau & Adams, 2012). These two approaches to viewing the skills and capabilities of older worker highlight the differences in the human capital that different employees may develop over time, which is critical to human capital theory.

The value of employees' human capital is influenced by many factors (e.g., newcomer training). The costs of training and development must be entered into the total value, since they are costs to the organization in acquiring human capital. Another big cost to organizations is the loss of good employees due to retirement, and management seems to be well aware of this. In a recent study, 71% of employers reported worrying about loss of knowledge resulting from older workers retiring (MetLife, 2009). Older workers leave organizations with the knowledge that they gained, but one way that they can extend their knowledge is by continuing to participate in work during postretirement life. Further, organizations can implement policies to make sure that older workers pass along this knowledge to younger workers before exiting the workforce. By having established policies, managers can worry less about the loss of knowledge resulting from retirees' leaving. For instance, organizations can include succession planning, structured job trainings, apprentice programs, and job shadowing or coaching, among others, to better preserve human capital (Rau & Adams, 2012).

Protean Career Model. The protean career model focuses on the person and his or her core values in career decision-making (Hall, 1976). The core values are personal freedom and growth, and the main goal for career development is psychological success (Hall, 2004). This is different from the traditional career model, which posits that the organization is in charge and the main success criteria is organization based (e.g., achieving high-level positions in an organization). The protean career model has been applied to the concept of retirement in past research, especially in conjunction with retirement transition and adjustment (Wang, Adams, Beehr, & Shultz, 2009; Kim & Hall, 2012). This model studies retirement as a part of older workers' career path—namely, as another step in their career development. In particular, Kim and Hall (2012) have called attention to using four patterns to describe possible paths during the late-life career transitions. Two of these describe individuals who for different reasons have had less mobility in their careers or jobs (i.e., one career, one life seekers and late passion followers); the other two comprise individuals who have switched between different careers because of misfits or other external motives (i.e., early strugglers following a path with a heart and multicareerers).

The protean career model is one of the few models that emphasizes the process of retirement much more than the decision to retire itself. By considering retirement as another career step, researchers can better understand the beneficial outcomes of different paths entering retirement. For example, employees can benefit from all the positive influences surrounding continued participation in the same (or different) work (e.g., learning, teaching, social support). In fact, employees have increasingly worked past their retirement age and indicated that they enjoy it (Kim & Hall, 2012). Interestingly, it seems that the benefits from continued workplace participation are not so much extrinsic (e.g., financially instrumental), but rather intrinsic (e.g., improving skills, attaining autonomy; Eichar, Norland, Brady, & Fortinsky, 1991). In sum, career transitions in a late career are significant because the employee has gained total self-identity by then (Kim & Hall, 2012).

EMPIRICAL FINDINGS REGARDING THE TEMPORAL PROCESS OF RETIREMENT

This section reviews empirical findings from retirement research that focus on identifying antecedents and outcomes of retirement processes. Regarding antecedents of retirement processes, several categories of variables are worth noting from a multilevel perspective (Wang & Shi, 2014). They are: individual attributes, job and organizational factors, family factors, and socioeconomic contexts. Individual attributes include demographic factors such as gender, age, and education. Job and organizational factors include characteristics of the individual's preretirement job, such as age- and retirement-related human-resource practices, workplace ageism, job characteristics, and job- and career-related attitudes. The family factors identified by Wang and Shi (2014) include social support, marital and dependent-care situations, and spouse's working situations. Finally, socioeconomic contextual factors include retirement support systems, cultural values and social norms regarding retirement, and economic and labor market conditions. Identifying these antecedents has critical practical value for managers and HR professionals, whose goal is to retain good employees for as long as possible for the sake of the organization.

Concurrently, outcomes of the retirement process are of great importance to society. The outcomes of retirement provide a way of measuring the success of the transition from full-time work to retirement. However, because retirement is not usually considered one event but, rather, a process, the outcomes studied should also be based on the different components of retirement processes. Wang and Shi (2014) specifically refer to three type of outcomes: financial well-being, physical well-being, and psychosocial well-being. Financial well-being is considered to be the extent to which retirees are satisfied with their level of financial status and able to cover their expenses. Physical well-being during retirement is considered to be the absence of physical diseases or functional limitations that could constrain an individual from participating in postretirement activities: part-time work or volunteering, among others. Lastly, psychosocial well-being is considered the level of effective psychological functioning the retiree has and whether he or she is content with it (Wang, 2012; Wang & Shi, 2014).

Antecedents and Outcomes of Retirement Planning. Individual attributes specifically related to retirement planning include but are not limited to socioeconomic status, gender, and attitudes toward retirement. One study looked at older workers from higher income brackets and found that they were less likely to engage in informal or formal planning than those from lower income brackets (Taylor & Geldhauser, 2007). Further, from a gender perspective, it appears that men, versus women, were more likely to save more for retirement (Glass & Kilpatrick, 1998). Employee attitudes toward retirement were examined by Kim and Moen (2001), who found that unfavorable attitudes about overall retirement were negatively related to planning and information-seeking about retirement. Kalokerinos, von Hippel, and Henry (2015) suggest that organizations implement job-attitudes interventions, since this can increase the likelihood of employment continuation with the same organization. Other organizational factors that affect retirement planning include the organizational incentives and supports associated with retirement planning, as well as the organization's general policies and the climate regarding older workers. Older workers can usually seek information from their older peers at work or from family and friends at social gatherings.

An individual's clarity about his or her financial state and goals is of importance to the outcomes of retirement planning, because it can influence the actions he or she takes during the planning process. Preretirement financial planning is associated with increased saving for retirement and improved budgeting, which can create stability for retirees during postretirement life (Hershey, Henkens, & Van Dalen, 2007). However, employees who have switched career paths repeatedly will be less likely to secure social security or pensions, which would have an effect on their financial well-being during retirement (Glass & Kilpatrick, 1998; O'Rand, 2003).

Antecedents and Outcomes of Retirement Decision-Making. The decision to retire can be impacted by several factors, sometimes simultaneously, as the life-course perspective explains. For instance, Soidre (2005) suggested that positive and negative attitudes that drove the decision to retire in a Swedish sample were different for males than for females (i.e., men with socially rewarding jobs were more likely to stay in the workforce). Regarding age, the older an individual is, the more likely it is that the individual will retire (e.g., Adams & Rau, 2004; Wang et al., 2008). Indeed, age is probably one of the strongest predictors of individuals' decisions to retire. Similarly, studies have found that employees with health problems are more likely to retire (Shultz & Wang, 2007) than employees who are healthy and that health problems have a stronger effect in predicting retirement decision-making than retirees' economic conditions (Dwyer & Mitchell, 1999). These findings have not changed from previous research that examined health limitations, amount of work the individual is able to do, and the likelihood of retiring (Hurd & Boskin, 1984). Sometimes it is not the employees' health that is a determinant of the decision to retire but the health of a close family member or spouse. Henkens and van Soligne's (2002) study showed that spouses often influence the retirement decisions made, and there is even evidence of coordination between the spouses on pension decisions and other investments (Shuey, 2004). In 2015, a study used the Survey of Health Ageing and Retirement in Europe (SHARE) to analyze retirees from 16 countries and found that one's social network, especially the spouse, is related to early exit from the workforce (Litwin & Tur-Sinai, 2015).

Some organizational factors also affect retirement decisions. The conditions of the organization that older workers would leave by entering retirement can have a positive or negative impact on them (as continuity theory explains). Employees working in negative work environments usually intend to decide to retire early (Wang & Shultz, 2010). For instance, employees having higher workloads and perceiving their jobs as stressful intended to retire early (Lin, 2001), and these findings were consistent with those found internationally among blue-collar employees with demanding work conditions, such as heavy lifting in Poland (Szubert & Sobala, 2005). Furthermore, in the United States, employees who are younger than age 65 run the risk of losing healthcare coverage from the organization before they are eligible for Medicare. In this case, older workers may be better off continuing to work for their organization (possibly via bridge employment) and maintaining their healthcare coverage until they are eligible for government-run insurances programs like Medicare. Thus, employees without employer health insurance are more likely to delay their retirement entrance (French & Jones, 2004). Mermin et al. (2007) found a similar effect on retirement decisions for social security eligibility age.

Lastly, retirees' circumstances before their decision to retire have a great impact on their psychosocial well-being. With an Australian sample, Mariappanadar (2013) found social retirement anxiety moderated the relationships between perceived financial preparedness and certain bridge-employment options. In accordance, older workers who are happy and feel strongly identified with their jobs might experience a decrease in well-being when entering retirement (Wang & Shi, 2014). Employees who experienced unemployment just before their retirement are more likely to enter retirement with low levels of psychosocial well-being (Marshall, Clarke, & Ballantyne, 2001; Pinquart & Schindler, 2007). Such a low point of reference for well-being can lead to worse psychological well-being in the future.

Antecedents and Outcomes of Transition and Adjustment to Retirement.

From a societal perspective, it is important to study the adjustment to retirement because it provides information about how to improve the quality of postretirement life for retirees. From a research perspective, it provides an opportunity for scholars to understand how people adjust to internal and external challenges after retirement (Wang et al., 2011). Some research has shown evidence that highly educated individuals with college degrees are more likely to engage in bridge employment than those who did not have a college degree (Wang & Shi, 2014), suggesting that having a college degree provided opportunities for these individuals to extend their career.

Similarly, stressful and demanding job conditions may drive employees to take bridge employment in a different field instead of in their own field or to fully retire (Wang et al., 2008, Gobeski & Beehr, 2009). In some research that has been done on employees' job and career attitudes, scholars have shown that organizational commitment (Adams, Prescher, Beehr, & Lepisto, 2002), job satisfaction (Wang et al., 2008), and job tenure (Kim & Feldman, 2000) are all related to the decision to retire or engage in bridge employment in a different field. Job characteristics, such as extra benefit packages (e.g., pension and health insurance) are related to early retirement (Kim & Feldman, 1998) as well.

One organizational factor it is important to consider is pressure from the organization. Organizations with norms and policies regarding appropriate age, increased flexibility, or that offer specific employment opportunities for older workers highly influence employees' decisions to engage in bridge employment with them, or elsewhere (Settersen & Hägestad, 1996, Rau & Adams, 2005). Flexibility, by allowing older workers to engage in leisure activities and bridge employment as they desire, can be a strong incentive to retain good older workers.

The interrelation in families' lives is also very important. Studies have shown that one spouse's retirement can strongly influence the retirement transition of the other (Pienta, 2003). Although the effect of marital status as an antecedent for retirement is much less clear than other family factors, some studies show a negative relationship between being married and engagement in bridge retirement (Davis, 2003). However, other studies have shown that marital status and marital quality are not related to such decisions (Wang et al., 2008). There may be other factors that could further explain the relationship between marital status and retirement decisions, such as work status of spouse, number of dependent children, or personality fit between the couple.

The decision to engage in bridge employment is part of the retirement transition. Many antecedents to bridge employment have been identified in the past (Zhan et al., 2015). Studies have found that age, years of education, health, work-related commitment, and preretirement job satisfaction were all related to retirees' decisions to engage in bridge employment (e.g., Gobeski & Beehr, 2009; Wang et al., 2008; Zhan, Wang, & Yao, 2013). Moreover, Kim and DeVaney (2005) found that self-employed individuals were more likely to engage in bridge employment, suggesting that entrepreneurs may work later than individuals in organizations. Furthermore, Zhan et al. (2015) found that among Chinese retirees in Beijing, there were motivational antecedents (e.g., status striving, communion striving, and generativity striving) to engagement in bridge employment, and that gender moderated some of the effects. Specifically, status striving refers to an individual's tendency to value social worth and standing; the authors found a significant positive association between status striving and bridge employment for males but not for females. In addition, communion striving refers to an individual's tendency to maintain social contracts, which has a positive relationship to bridge employment. Lastly, generativity striving alludes to transferring knowledge to younger people, which is also positively associated with bridge employment (Barrick Stewart, & Piotrowski, 2002; Kooij & Van De Voorde, 2011; Zhan et al., 2015). In general, studies examining the impact of bridge employment on retirees have found positive trends; for example, when compared to retirees who continued working without retirement, those engaged in bridge employment reported better mental health (Zhan et al., 2009).

Retirees' preretirement health status is most predictive of their physical well-being during retirement (Zhan, Wang, Liu, & Shultz, 2009). One way that retirees can increase their preretirement physical well-being is by engaging in healthy behaviors and habits (e.g., exercise, hygiene, abstaining from drugs and alcohol), which, in turn, can help them maintain their physical well-being during retirement (Wang, 2012). However, one thing that retirees sometimes have less control of after retirement is their health insurance and the range of medical conditions that are covered by their premiums. Stanton and Rutherford (2006) showed that retirees have a better physical well-being when their health insurance offers more extensive service coverage so that their out-of-pocket costs are lower. Furthermore, it has been shown that engaging in certain activities during retirement helps to maintain retirees' physical health (e.g., no differences were found in the physical well-being of those engaging in bridge employment versus those who have not retired; Zhan et al., 2009).

Moreover, there is no one prediction of psychosocial well-being for retirees, as two large studies have suggested. First, Wang (2007) showed that over an eight-year period, about 70% of retirees experienced minimum psychological well-being changes; about 25% experienced negative changes during the beginning of transition but then improved; and about 5% experienced positive changes overall. Pinquart and Schindler (2007) further validated these findings with a German sample and found that for the same groups, the percentages were similar: 75% experienced minor changes, 9% experienced a negative change followed by improvement during the transition, and 15% experienced a positive change in life satisfaction. In addition, though the Dutch government discourages people from retiring early, for older Dutch workers who retired involuntarily, a study found that bridge employment alleviated their decrease in life satisfaction (Dingemans & Henkens, 2014). These studies, taken together, show support for the multiple-pathway outcomes of retirement adjustment, demonstrating that the same decision can have different implications for different individuals. Furthermore, quality of marriage can have an impact on retirees' psychosocial well-being. Wang (2007) found that unhappy marriages were associated with negative changes in psychosocial well-being during retirement transition. This may point to one of the underlying mechanisms that connect marriage to well-being—companionship. Finally, some activities that may have a positive effect on retirees' psychosocial well-being include volunteering (Shultz, Morton, & Weckerle, 1998), retirement planning (Wang, 2007), and social goal setting (Petkoska & Earl, 2009).

CONCLUSION

In light of continued changes in the workforce (Toossi, 2004, 2009; Chen & Scott, 2006), it is important to acknowledge that the concept of retirement is changing as well. This article reviewed previous empirical and theoretical work on retirement. It included traditional retirement and other forms: phased retirement, early retirement, and bridge employment. Retirement is typically conceptualized using the temporal process (Shultz & Wang, 2011), which allows researchers to break retirement into different "phases" and explore the antecedents and outcomes at a deeper level.

The theories typically used to explain retirement processes include role theory, life-span theory, the protean career model, continuity theory, and the resource-based perspective. These theories can be further applied to look at retirement outcomes. As reviewed in this article, some of the outcomes given most attention in the past have included financial, physical, and psychosocial well-being (Wang & Shi, 2014). Studying current individual and organizational attributes can help predict what the workforce and their retirement will be like in the upcoming years.

FURTHER READING

Fasbender, U., Deller, J., Wang, M., & Wiernik, B. M. (2014). Deciding whether to work after retirement: The role of the psychological experience of aging. *Journal of Vocational Behavior, 84*, 215–224.

Fasbender, U., Wang, M., Voltmer, J., & Deller, J. (2016). The meaning of work for post-retirement employment decisions. *Work, Aging and Retirement, 2*, 12–23.

Shultz, K. S., & Wang, M. (2007). The influence of specific physical health conditions on retirement decisions. *International Journal of Aging and Human Development, 65*, 149–161.

Shultz, K., Wang, M., Crimmins, E., & Fisher, G. (2010). Age differences in the demand-control model of work stress: An examination of data from 15 European countries. *Journal of Applied Gerontology, 29*, 21–47.

van Dalen, H. P., Henkens, K., & Wang, M. (2015). Recharging or retiring older workers? Uncovering the age-based strategies of European employers. *Gerontologist, 55*, 814–824.

Wang M. (2012). *The Oxford handbook of retirement.* New York: Oxford University Press.

Wang, M., Burlacu, G., Truxillo, D., James, K., & Yao, X. (2015). Age differences in feedback reactions: The roles of employee feedback orientation on social awareness and utility. *Journal of Applied Psychology, 100*, 1296–1308.

Wang, M., Olson, D., & Shultz, K. (2013). *Mid and late career issues: An integrative perspective.* New York: Psychology Press.

Wöhrmann, A. M., Deller, J., & Wang, M. (2013). Outcome expectations and work design characteristics in post-retirement work planning. *Journal of Vocational Behavior, 83*, 219–228.

Wöhrmann, A. M., Deller, J., & Wang, M. (2014a). A mixed-method approach to post-retirement career planning. *Journal of Vocational Behavior, 84*, 307–317.

Wöhrmann, A. M., Deller, J., & Wang, M. (2014b). Postretirement career planning: Testing a model based on social cognitive career theory. *Journal of Career Development, 41*, 363–381.

REFERENCES

Adams, G. A., & Beehr, T. A. (1998). Turnover and retirement: A comparison of their similarities and differences. *Personnel Psychology, 51*, 643–665.

Adams, G. A., Prescher, J., Beehr, T. A., & Lepisto, L. (2002). Applying work-role attachment theory to retirement decision-making. *International Journal of Aging and Human Development, 54*, 125–137.

Adams, G. A., & Rau, B. L. (2004). Job seeking among retirees seeking bridge employment. *Personnel Psychology, 57*, 719–744.

Adams, G. A., & Rau, B. L. (2011). Putting off tomorrow to do what you want today: Planning for retirement. *American Psychologist, 66*, 180–192.

Alcover, C. M., Topa, G., Parry, E., Fraccaroli, F., & Depolo, M. (2014). Bridge employment: An introduction and overview of the handbook. In C. M. Alcover, G. Topa, E. Parry, F. Fraccaroli, & M. Depolo (Eds.), *Bridge employment: A research handbook* (pp. 3–24). New York: Routledge.

Allen, S. (2004). The value of phased retirement (NBER Working Paper Series No. 10531). Cambridge, MA: National Bureau of Economic Research.

Alley, D., & Crimmins, E. (2007). The demography of aging and work. In K. S. Shultz & G. A. Adams (Eds.), *Aging and work in the 21st century* (pp. 7–23). Mahwah, NJ: Lawrence Erlbaum.

Ashforth, B. (2001). *Role transitions in organizational life: An identity-based perspective.* Mahwah, NJ: Lawrence Erlbaum.

Atchley, R. C. (1989). A continuity theory of normal aging. *The Gerontologist, 29*, 183–190.

Atchley, R. C. (1999). Continuity theory, self, and social structure. In C. D. Ryff & V. W. Marshall (Eds.), *Families and retirement* (pp. 145–158). Thousand Oaks, CA: SAGE.

Bacharach, S. B., Bamberger, P. A., Sonnenstuhl, W. J., & Vashdi, D. (2004). Retirement, risky alcohol consumption and drinking problems among blue-collar workers. *Journal of Studies on Alcohol, 65*, 537–545.

Bacharach, S., Bamberger, P. A., Sonnenstuhl, W. J., & Vashdi, D. R. (2008). Retirement and drug abuse: The conditioning role of age and retirement trajectory. *Addictive Behaviors, 33*, 1610–1614.

Barfield, R. E., & Morgan, J. N. (1978). Trends in satisfaction with retirement. *The Gerontologist, 18*, 19–23.

Barnes-Farrell, J. L. (2003). Beyond health and wealth: Attitudinal and other influences on retirement decision-making. In G. A. Adams & T. A. Beehr (Eds.), *Retirement: Reasons, processes, and results* (pp. 159–187). New York: Springer.

Barrick, M. R., Stewart, G. L., & Piotrowski, M. (2002). Personality and job performance: Test of the mediating effects of motivation among sales representatives. *Journal of Applied Psychology, 87*, 43–51.

Beehr, T. A. (1986). The process of retirement: A review and recommendations for future investigation. *Personnel Psychology, 39*, 31–55.

Bell, B. D. (1979). Life satisfaction and occupational retirement beyond the impact year. *International Journal of Aging and Human Development, 9*, 31–50.

Blekesaune, M., & Skirbekk, V. (2012). Can personality predict retirement behaviour? A longitudinal analysis combining survey and register data from Norway. *European Journal of Ageing, 9*, 199–206.

von Bonsdorff, M. E., Huuhtanen, P., Tuomi, K., & Seitsamo, J. (2009). Predictors of employees' early retirement intentions: An 11-year longitudinal study. *Occupational Medicine, 60*, 94–100.

von Bonsdorff, M. E., & Ilmarinen, J. (2012). Continuity theory and retirement. In M. Wang (Ed.), *The Oxford handbook of retirement* (pp. 73–87). New York: Oxford University Press.

Cahill, K. E., Giandrea, M. D., & Quinn, J. F. (2006). Retirement patterns from career employment. *The Gerontologist, 46,* 514–523.

Chen, Y. P., & Scott, J. C. (2006). Phased retirement: Who opts for it and toward what end? *European Papers on the New Welfare, 6,* 16–28.

Damman, M., Henkens, K., & Kalmijn, M. (2011). The impact of midlife educational, work, health, and family experiences on men's early retirement. *Journals of Gerontology Series B: Psychological Sciences and Social Sciences, 66,* 617–627.

Davis, M. A. (2003). Factors related to bridge employment participation among private sector early retirees. *Journal of Vocational Behavior, 63,* 55–71.

De Hauw, S., & De Vos, A. (2010). Millennials' career perspective and psychological contract expectations: Does the recession lead to lowered expectations? *Journal of Business and Psychology, 25,* 293–302.

Dendinger, V. M., Adams, G. A., & Jacobson, J. D. (2005). Reasons for working and their relationship to retirement attitudes, job satisfaction and occupational self-efficacy of bridge employees. *International Journal of Aging and Human Development, 61,* 21–35.

Denton, F. T., & Spencer, B. G. (2009). What is retirement? A review and assessment of alternative concepts and measures. *Canadian Journal on Aging/La revue canadienne du vieillissement, 28,* 63–76.

Dingemans, E., & Henkens, K. (2014). Involuntary retirement, bridge employment, and satisfaction with life: A longitudinal investigation. *Journal of Organizational Behavior, 35,* 575–591.

Dwyer, D. S., & Mitchell, O. S. (1999). Health problems as determinants of retirement: Are self-rated measures endogenous? *Journal of Health Economics, 18,* 173–193.

Eichar, D. M., Norland, S., Michael Brady, E., & Fortinsky, R. H. (1991). The job satisfaction of older workers. *Journal of Organizational Behavior, 12,* 609–620.

Elder, G. H. (1995). The life course paradigm: Social change and individual development. In P. E. Moen, G. H. Elder, & K. E. Luscher (Eds.), *Examining lives in context: Perspectives on the ecology of human development* (pp. 101–139). Washington, DC: American Psychological Association.

Feldman, D. C. (1994). The decision to retire early: A review and conceptualization. *Academy of Management Review, 19,* 285–311.

Feldman, D. C., & Beehr, T. A. (2011). A three-phase model of retirement decision making. *American Psychologist, 66,* 193–203.

Fraccaroli, F., & Deller, J. (2015). Work, aging, and retirement in Europe: Introduction to the special issue. *Work, Aging and Retirement, 1,* 237–242.

French, E., & Jones, J. B. (2004). On the distribution and dynamics of health care costs. *Journal of Applied Econometrics, 19,* 705–721.

Ghent, L. S., Allen, S. G., & Clark, R. L. (2001). The impact of a new phased retirement option on faculty retirement decisions. *Research on Aging, 23,* 671–693.

Glass, J. C. Jr., & Kilpatrick, B. B. (1998). Gender comparisons of baby boomers and financial preparation for retirement. *Educational Gerontology: An International Quarterly, 24,* 719–745.

Gobeski, K. T., & Beehr, T. A. (2009). How retirees work: Predictors of different types of bridge employment. *Journal of Organizational Behavior, 30,* 401–425.

Gould, R. (2006). Choice or chance: Late retirement in Finland. *Social Policy and Society, 5,* 519–531.

Gustman, A. L., & Steinmeier, T. L. (2001–2002). Retirement and wealth. *Social Security Bulletin, 64,* 66–91.

Hall, D. T. (1976). *Careers in organizations.* Glenview, IL: Scott, Foresman.

Hall, D. T. (2004). The protean career: A quarter-century journey. *Journal of Vocational Behavior, 65,* 1–13.

Hayward, M. D., Crimmins, E. M., & Wray, L. A. (1994). The relationship between retirement life cycle changes and older men's labor force participation rates. *Journal of Gerontology, 49,* S219–S230.

Henkens, K., & van Solinge, H. (2002). Spousal influences on the decision to retire. *International Journal of Sociology, 32*, 55–74.

Henkens, K., & van Solinge, H. (2014). Bridge employment in the Netherlands. In C. M. Alcover, G. Topa, E. Parry, F. Fraccaroli, & M. Depolo (Eds.), *Bridge employment: A research handbook* (pp. 27–50). New York: Routledge.

Hershey, D. A., Henkens, K., & Van Dalen, H. P. (2007). Mapping the minds of retirement planners: A cross-cultural perspective. *Journal of Cross-Cultural Psychology, 38*, 361–382.

Hurd, M. D., & Boskin M. J. (1984). The effect of social security on retirement in the early 1970s. *Quarterly Journal of Economics, 99*, 767–790.

Isaksson, K., Johansson, G., & Palm, S. (2014). Bridge employment, a Swedish perspective. In C.-M. Alcover, G. Topa, E. Parry, F. Fraccaroli & M. Depolo (Eds.), *Bridge employment: A research handbook* (pp. 51–69). New York: Routledge.

Jex, S. M., Wang, M., & Zarubin, A. (2007). Aging and occupational health. In K. S. Shultz & G. A. Adams (Eds.), *Aging and work in the 21st century* (pp. 199–223). Mahwah, NJ: Lawrence Erlbaum.

Kalokerinos, E. K., von Hippel, C., & Henry, J. D. (2015). Job attitudes are differentially associated with bridge employment and phased retirement among older Australian employees. *Work, Aging and Retirement, 1*, 190–201.

Kim, H., & DeVaney, S. A. (2005). The selection of partial or full retirement by older workers. *Journal of Family and Economic Issues, 26*, 371–394.

Kim, J. E., & Moen, P. (2001). Is retirement good or bad for subjective well-being? *Current Directions in Psychological Science, 10*, 83–86.

Kim, J. E., & Moen, P. (2002). Retirement transitions, gender, and psychological well-being a life-course, ecological model. *Journals of Gerontology Series B: Psychological Sciences and Social Sciences, 57*, 212–222.

Kim, N., & Hall, D. T. (2012). Protean career model and retirement. In M. Wang (Ed.), *The Oxford handbook of retirement* (pp. 102–116). New York: Oxford University Press.

Kim, S., & Feldman, D. C. (1998). Healthy, wealthy, or wise: Predicting actual acceptances of early retirement incentives at three points in time. *Personnel Psychology, 51*, 623–642.

Kim, S., & Feldman, D. C. (2000). Working in retirement: The antecedents of bridge employment and its consequences for quality of life in retirement. *Academy of Management Journal, 43*, 1195–1210.

Kooij, D., & Van De Voorde, K. (2011). How changes in subjective general health predict future time perspective, and development and generativity motives over the lifespan. *Journal of Occupational and Organizational Psychology, 84*, 228–247.

Lepak, D. P., & Snell, S. A. (1999). The human resource architecture: Toward a theory of human capital allocation and development. *Academy of Management Review, 24*, 31–48.

Lin, T. C. (2001). Letter to the editor: Impact of job stress on early retirement intention. *International Journal of Stress Management, 8*, 243–247.

Litwin, H., & Tur-Sinai, A. (2015). The role of the social network in early retirement among older Europeans. *Work, Aging and Retirement, 1*, 340–349.

Lusardi, A., & Mitchell, O. S. (2011). Financial literacy and planning: Implications for retirement wellbeing (No. w17078). Cambridge, MA: National Bureau of Economic Research.

Macewen, K. E., Barling, J., Kelloway, E. K., & Higginbottom, S. F. (1995). Predicting retirement anxiety: The roles of parental socialization and personal planning. *Journal of Social Psychology, 135*, 203–213.

Mariappanadar, S. (2013). Do retirement anxieties determine bridge employment preference? A study among pre-retirees in the Australian construction industry. *Personnel Review, 42*, 176–204.

Marshall, V. W., Clarke, P. J., & Ballantyne, P. J. (2001). Instability in the retirement transition effects on health and well-being in a Canadian study. *Research on Aging, 23*, 379–409.

Mein, G., Martikainen, P., Hemingway, H., Stansfeld, S., & Marmot, M. (2003). Is retirement good or bad for mental and physical health functioning? Whitehall II longitudinal study of civil servants. *Journal of Epidemiology and Community Health, 57*, 46–49.

Mermin, G. B., Johnson, R. W., & Murphy, D. P. (2007). Why do boomers plan to work longer? *Journals of Gerontology Series B: Psychological Sciences and Social Sciences, 62*, S286–S294.

MetLife (2009). *The emerging retirement model study*. New York: Metropolitan Life Insurance Company.

Moen, P. (1996). A life course perspective on retirement, gender, and well-being. *Journal of Occupational Health Psychology, 1*, 131–144.

Moen, P. (2007). Not so big jobs and retirements: What workers (and retirees) really want. *Generations, 31*, 31–36.

O'Rand, A. (2003). Cumulative advantage and gerontological theory. *Annual Review of Gerontological Geriatrics, 22*, 14–30.

Orel, N. A., Ford, R. A., & Brock, C. (2004). Women's financial planning for retirement: The impact of disruptive life events. *Journal of Women and Aging, 16*, 39–53.

Perreira, K. M., & Sloan, F. A. (2001). Life events and alcohol consumption among mature adults: A longitudinal analysis. *Journal of Studies on Alcohol, 62*, 501–508.

Petkoska, J., & Earl, J. K. (2009). Understanding the influence of demographic and psychological variables on retirement planning. *Psychology and Aging, 24*, 245–251.

Pienta, A. M. (2003). Partners in marriage: An analysis of husbands' and wives' retirement behavior. *Journal of Applied Gerontology, 22*, 340–358.

Pinquart, M., & Schindler, I. (2007). Changes of life satisfaction in the transition to retirement: A latent-class approach. *Psychology and Aging, 22*, 442–455.

Rau, B. L., & Adams, G. A. (2005). Attracting retirees to apply: Desired organizational characteristics of bridge employment. *Journal of Organizational Behavior, 26*, 649–660.

Rau, B. L. & Adams, G. A. (2012). Aging, retirement, and human resources management: A strategic approach. In M. Wang (Ed.), *The Oxford handbook of retirement* (pp. 102–116). New York: Oxford University Press.

Riley, M. W., & Riley, J. W., Jr. (1994). Structural lag: Past and future. In M. W. Riley, R. L. Kahn, A. Foner, & K. A. Mack (Eds), *Age and structural lag: Society's failure to provide meaningful opportunities in work, family, and leisure* (pp. 15–36). Oxford: John Wiley.

van Rooij, M., Lusardi, A., & Alessie, R. J. (2011). Financial literacy, retirement planning, and household wealth (No. w17339). Cambridge, MA: National Bureau of Economic Research.

Settersten, R. A., & Hägestad, G. O. (1996). What's the latest? Cultural age deadlines for family transitions. *The Gerontologist, 36*, 178–188.

Shuey, K. M. (2004). Worker preferences, spousal coordination, and participation in an employer-sponsored pension plan. *Research on Aging, 26*, 287–316.

Shultz, K. S. (2003). Bridge employment: Work after retirement. In G. A. Adams & T. A. Beehr (Eds.), *Retirement: Reasons, processes, and results* (pp. 215–241). New York: Springer.

Shultz, K. S., & Adams, G. A. (2007). In search of a unifying paradigm for understanding aging and work in the 21st century. In K. S. Shultz & G. A. Adams (Eds.), *Aging and work in the 21st century* (pp. 303–319). Mahwah, NJ: Lawrence Erlbaum.

Shultz, K. S., Morton, K. R., & Weckerle, J. R. (1998). The influence of push and pull factors on voluntary and involuntary early retirees' retirement decision and adjustment. *Journal of Vocational Behavior, 53*, 45–57.

Shultz, K. S., & Wang, M. (2011). Psychological perspectives on the changing nature of retirement. *American Psychologist, 66*, 170–179.

Soidre, T. (2005). Retirement-age preferences of women and men aged 55–64 years in Sweden. *Ageing and Society, 25*, 943–963.

van Solinge, H., & Henkens, K. (2005). Couples' adjustment to retirement: A multi-actor panel study. *Journals of Gerontology Series B: Psychological Sciences and Social Sciences, 60*, S11–S20.

van Solinge, H., & Henkens, K. (2008). Adjustment to and satisfaction with retirement: Two of a kind? *Psychology and Aging, 23*, 422–434.

Stanton, M. W., & Rutherford, M. K. (2006, June). The high concentration of US health care expenditures (Publication No. 06–0060). Rockville, MD: Agency for Healthcare Research and Quality.

Szubert, Z., & Sobala, W. (2005). Current determinants of early retirement among blue-collar workers in Poland. *International Journal of Occupational Medicine and Environmental Health, 18*, 177–184.

Taylor, M. A., & Geldhauser, H. A. (2007). Low-income older workers. In K. S. Shultz & G. A. Adams (Eds.), *Aging and work in the 21st century* (pp. 25–50). Mahwah, NJ: Lawrence Erlbaum.

Taylor-Carter, M. A., Cook, K., & Weinberg, C. (1997). Planning and expectations of the retirement experience. *Educational Gerontology: An International Quarterly, 23*, 273–288.

Toossi, M. (2004). Labor force projections in 2012: The graying of the US workforce. *Monthly Labor Review, 127*, 37–57.

Toossi, M. (2009). Labor force projections to 2018: Older workers staying more active. *Monthly Labor Review, 132*, 30–51.

Usui, C., Colignon, R. A., & Rosen, D. (2014). The Japanese approach to bridge jobs. In C. M. Alcover, G. Topa, E. Parry, F. Fraccaroli, & M. Depolo (Eds.), *Bridge employment: A research handbook* (pp. 252–265). New York: Routledge.

Wang, M. (2007). Profiling retirees in the retirement transition and adjustment process: Examining the longitudinal change patterns of retirees' psychological well-being. *Journal of Applied Psychology, 92*, 455–474.

Wang, M. (2012). Health, fiscal, and psychological well-being in retirement. In J. W. Hedge & W. C. Borman (Eds.), *The Oxford handbook of work and aging* (pp. 570–584). New York: Oxford University Press.

Wang, M., Adams, G. A., Beehr, T. A., & Shultz, K. S. (2009). Career issues at the end of one's career: Bridge employment and retirement. In S. G. Baugh and S. E. Sullivan (Eds.), *Maintaining focus, energy, and options through the life span* (pp. 135–162). Charlotte, NC: Information Age Publishing.

Wang, M., & Chen, Y. (2006). Age differences in attitude change: Influences of cognitive resources and motivation on responses to argument quantity. *Psychology and Aging, 21*, 581–589.

Wang, M., Henkens, K., & van Solinge, H. (2011). Retirement adjustment: A review of theoretical and empirical advancements. *American Psychologist, 66*, 204–213.

Wang, M., & Shi, J. (2014). Psychological research on retirement. *Annual Review of Psychology, 65*, 209–233.

Wang, M., & Shultz, K. (2010). Employee retirement: A review and recommendations for future investigation. *Journal of Management, 36*, 172–206.

Wang, M., Zhan, Y., Liu, S., & Shultz, K. (2008). Antecedents of bridge employment: A longitudinal investigation. *Journal of Applied Psychology, 93*, 818–830.

Wesner, M. S., & Miller, T. (2008). Boomers and millennials have much in common. *Organization Development Journal, 26*, 89–96.

Williamson, R. C., Rinehart, A. D., & Blank, T. O. (1992). *Early retirement: Promises and pitfalls*. New York: Insight.

Yao, X., & Peng, H. (2012). Social security, pension systems, and retirement savings. In M. Wang (Ed.), *The Oxford handbook of retirement* (pp. 373–387). New York: Oxford University Press.

Zhan, Y., Wang, M., Liu, S., & Shultz, K. S. (2009). Bridge employment and retirees' health: A longitudinal investigation. *Journal of Occupational Health Psychology, 14*, 374–389.

Zhan, Y., Wang, M., & Shi, J. (2015). Retirees' motivational orientations and bridge employment: Testing the moderating role of gender. *Journal of Applied Psychology, 100*, 1319–1331.

Zhan, Y., Wang, M., & Yao, X. (2013). Domain specific effects of commitment on bridge employment decisions: The moderating role of economic stress. *European Journal of Work and Organizational Psychology, 22*, 362–375.

Zickar, M. J. (2012). The evolving history of retirement within the United States. In M. Wang (Ed.), *The Oxford handbook of retirement* (pp. 10–21). New York: Oxford University Press.

Mo Wang and Valeria Alterman

Organizational Outputs and Outcomes

WORK PERFORMANCE MANAGEMENT AND ASSESSMENT

THE PERFORMANCE MANAGEMENT CONUNDRUM

Performance management is "the broad collection of activities designed to maximize individual and, by extension, organizational performance. It includes setting expectations, measuring employee behaviors and results, providing coaching and feedback, and evaluating performance over time to use in decision-making. The purpose is to align individual efforts to achieve organizational goals" (Society for Human Resource Management [SHRM], 2017). While performance management is a well-established practice in organizations, its effectiveness has recently come into question. Proponents contend that it is essential for holding employees accountable for results and ensuring reward decisions are fair and merit based. Critics argue that it is too time consuming, disengaging for employees, and fails to improve performance (Adler et al., 2016; Culbert & Rout, 2010; Mueller-Hanson & Pulakos, 2018; Murphy, 2019, 2020; Pulakos et al., 2015; Pulakos & O'Leary, 2011).

How much time does performance management take? A study by Corporate Executive Board (CEB) found that performance management practices require an average of 210 hours per manager and 40 hours per employee each year (CEB, 2012), translating into significant costs. Deloitte made headlines when it publicly declared that it was spending approximately 2 million person hours per year on performance management activities with few discernable benefits (Buckingham & Goodall, 2015). In all, Gallup estimated that the cost of lost time spent on performance management activities was somewhere between $2.4 million and $35 million per year for a company with 10,000 employees (Wiegert & Harter, 2017).

Beyond concerns about the time required, employees and managers frequently complain that performance management is disengaging and demoralizing. A *Washington Post* headline perfectly captured this sentiment: "Study Finds That Basically Every Single Person Hates Performance Reviews" (McGregor, 2014). Research has shown that formal performance reviews can be demotivating to even the highest performing employees (Aguinis et al., 2011; Culbertson et al., 2013), leading to apathy and less effective performance.

Perhaps the most serious critique of performance management is that it doesn't lead to improved performance (DeNisi & Murphy, 2017; DeNisi & Smith, 2014; Murphy et al., 2018; Pulakos et al., 2015; Pulakos & O'Leary, 2011). The ultimate goal of performance management is to improve employee performance, which in turn should improve organizational performance. However, there is little evidence that it does either of these things in practice (Murphy, 2020).

Despite these criticisms, most organizations are unwilling to give up on performance management completely, choosing instead to seek ways to make it more efficient, empowering, and useful (Colquitt & Goldberg, 2020).

This article explores performance management's intended purposes, the evidence supporting it, and implications for the future.

PERFORMANCE MANAGEMENT PURPOSE

Desired goals for performance management frequently include the following (Aguinis, 2013; Colquitt & Goldberg, 2020; Mueller-Hanson & Pulakos, 2018; SHRM, 2017):

- Align individual actions to meet organizational goals, often through a process of cascading objectives.
- Set clear expectations for performance so that employees know how to succeed and are accountable for results.
- Develop employee skills by providing regular feedback and coaching.
- Improve communications between managers and employees by providing tools and structure for effective performance conversations.
- Inspire employees to improve their performance by rewarding results and behaviors in alignment with organizational goals and values.
- Evaluate performance consistently, accurately, and fairly.
- Use performance evaluation data to make fair, merit-based talent decisions and reward and retain high-performers.
- Provide documentation needed to defend against legal challenges.

Critics have observed that performance management tries to serve too many conflicting purposes, which results in it serving no single purpose particularly well (Colquitt, 2017;

Mueller-Hanson & Pulakos, 2018). Consequently, the reality of performance management is often far removed from its desired outcomes, for example:

- Employees and managers frequently struggle to identify meaningful, aligned goals that stay relevant during changing times. When performance goals are set yearly, as is typical, they quickly become out of date.
- Many employees complain they don't get useful feedback and coaching, and feedback does not guarantee performance improvement.
- Development and administrative goals are incompatible with each other. Employees can't be expected to candidly discuss their development needs while at the same time advocating that they are rated, and thus rewarded, at the highest possible levels.
- Performance ratings are notoriously unreliable and biased, calling into question their usefulness as the basis of talent decisions. For example, Scullen et al. (2000) found that 62% of the variance in performance ratings can be attributed to rater bias, while actual performance accounts for just 21% of the variance.
- The relationship between performance and rewards is complex, which makes pay-for-performance approaches challenging to administer.
- Performance documentation often fails to defend against legal challenges because terminated employees frequently have a history of receiving satisfactory reviews. In practice, organizations typically require additional steps and documentation to handle poor performance.

Why does performance management fail to live up to its expectations? Mueller-Hanson (2020) identified three major flaws in how it is implemented. First, it is often not designed in a strategic fashion that is closely aligned to supporting the organization's goals or priorities. Instead, it is developed in a piecemeal fashion based on "best practices" from high-profile companies without sufficient consideration of whether those practices will work within a company's unique context. Second, performance management practices are out of sync with how work is actually done in organizations. As Pulakos and Kantrowitz (2020) noted, organizations are facing unprecedented change, requiring new levels of adaptability, resilience, and agility. Yet performance management practices have been largely unchanged for the past several decades. For example, goals are often set at the beginning of the calendar year and then employees are evaluated on the extent to which the goals were achieved at the end of the year. Business rules and technology systems can make it difficult to change goals to keep up with changes in organizational priorities, making the goals less relevant by the end of the year. However, employees still need to demonstrate how goals were met or exceeded to receive a good rating. Third, performance management is often implemented without careful consideration of what purpose it should serve. While most organizations say that they want performance management to improve employee performance, in reality most systems are designed with other goals in mind, such as making compensation decisions (Colquitt & Goldberg, 2020) and include many practices that don't have demonstrable impact on individual or organizational performance.

This last flaw is perhaps the most serious threat to the usefulness of performance management. Mueller-Hanson and Pulakos (2018) argued that performance management should be designed with the singular purpose of facilitating performance, and research by Colquitt and

Goldberg (2020) suggests that organizations that prioritize this purpose are more satisfied with their performance management processes. Other goals may need to be addressed via different processes. For example, a separate rating approach may be most useful for making compensation decisions. In most organizations, however, performance management is a single process implemented in a yearly cycle. The next section breaks down this process into its major components and presents the research and practice supporting each.

PERFORMANCE MANAGEMENT PROCESS

Although specific performance management practices vary widely in organizations, most include the following common activities:

- setting expectations,
- monitoring progress and providing feedback,
- evaluating results, and
- using performance data to inform talent decisions.

Setting Expectations.   Clear expectations are the foundation of performance management. Knowing what is expected and how success will be measured are prerequisites for performing effectively. Organizations use a variety of means to set expectations, the most common of which are behavioral standards, individual performance goals, Key Performance Indicators (KPIs), or some combination of these.

Behavioral standards are usually organized into competencies or performance dimensions such as communication, collaboration, critical thinking, and so forth. They typically include performance examples, sometimes at multiple levels of effectiveness, that correspond to performance ratings (e.g., Meets Expectations vs. Exceeds Expectations). Behavioral standards can provide descriptive language to communicate how employees are expected to act, which is especially useful in the absence of objective measures of performance. The chief disadvantage is their inherent subjectivity (Pulakos et al., 2019).

Performance goals have grown in popularity since the early 2000s, and decades of research show that setting specific, difficult goals leads to higher performance (cf., Latham, 2016; Latham & Locke, 2007; Lock & Latham, 2013). Extensive guidance is available on setting effective goals, but one of the more popular approaches is to set "SMART" (Specific, Measurable, Achievable, Relevant, and Time-bound) goals. Latham (2016) described the conditions under which specific and difficult goals are most likely to improve performance: when employees (a) have the ability to attain the goal, (b) are committed to achieving the goal, (c) get regular feedback on their progress, and (d) have the resources needed to achieve the goal. A factor that doesn't impact the effectiveness of goals is who sets them—goals lead to higher performance if they are defined by the manager or employee, though having employees contribute to setting goals could lead to greater buy-in.

Although the link between goal setting and performance is quite strong, traditional ways of using goals in performance management may undermine their effectiveness (Mueller-Hanson & Pulakos, 2018). Performance goals often lack specificity, are not difficult enough to motivate performance, and don't provide a means of measuring progress. For example, goals set for performance management are typically expected to last a full year. However, research shows shorter time spans are generally better because individuals can get more immediate feedback on how they are doing (Latham & Locke, 2007), though ideal time frames for goals would depend on the nature of the work and organizational context. Additionally, when goal attainment is used as the basis of rewards, employees are more likely to try to "sandbag" by setting goals that are ostensibly difficult but actually easy to attain so that they are guaranteed higher ratings and thus higher rewards. Winters and Latham (2006) showed that goals set for performance evaluation tend to be easier and less likely to drive performance than goals set for learning purposes. Finally, goals are more motivating when employees can see visible progress toward attaining them (Latham, 2016), but progress on performance goals is often based on a manager's subjective judgements, which may not be apparent until performance is evaluated at the end of the year and is therefore too late to impact current performance.

In rapidly changing times and in situations where the path to attain the goal is uncertain, setting a learning goal may be superior to a specific performance goal (Latham, 2016). For example, setting a goal to increase revenue by X% will undermine rather than facilitate performance if employees don't specifically know how to increase revenue or if factors outside of their control (e.g., the economy) have a greater impact on revenue than any actions they can take. Instead, employees may perform better if the goal is focused on the actions most likely to contribute to increasing revenue. If the goal is then used to direct focus and inform development (rather than as the basis of a performance rating and reward), it takes the pressure off the employee, who can choose a more challenging goal without fear that missing it will negatively impact their career.

Despite these challenges, performance goals are a primary means of setting expectations in organizations. This is partly because they are perceived as facilitating the alignment of individual actions to organizational priorities (via a process of cascading goals from the organizational level through each successive layer on down) and the means to hold employees accountable for achieving tangible results. While behavioral standards can communicate organizational behaviors and values, goals define the more specific results employees are expected to achieve. Even learning goals can achieve these purposes, provided managers do a good job communicating organizational priorities and how employees can best contribute.

KPIs differ from performance goals in that they tend to be less individualized. Evaluating their attainment is usually based on objective metrics rather than subjective assessments. Examples may include sales, productivity, or efficiency targets; customer satisfaction scores; revenue; or profit. KPIs might apply to an entire business unit and/or to employees within a business unit.

KPIs can more easily be tied to organizational goals than behavioral standards, and they can often be assessed with existing data sources rather than requiring managers to make additional judgements. Employees may perceive KPIs as less susceptible to bias, but they are not without their pitfalls. Individual employees may not have complete control over results due to a variety of external factors. Additionally, KPIs may focus too much on objective outcomes such as finances and productivity without addressing important behaviors such as collaboration and communication. When too much pressure is placed on employees to achieve difficult financial targets, they may resort to unethical behavior to achieve them, especially if the organization's culture reinforces this behavior (e.g., Lawler, 2016).

Many organizations implement specific rules for how expectations are set. For example, all employees might be accountable for the same behavioral standards, and each person is also accountable for meeting specific performance goals (e.g., number of goals, formats, time frames, etc.). Such a strategy is often referred to as holding employees accountable for both the "what" and the "how"—that is, what should be accomplished and how it should be done.

A primary reason for standardizing expectations is to better fit them within available automated systems. Moreover, standardization makes it is easier for HR to oversee the process and ensure compliance. Too much standardization can result in a "check the box" mentality, however, especially if generic expectations are not perceived as relevant to all employees. If at all possible, it is preferable to allow expectations to fit the requirements of the role. For example, a group of customer service representatives may benefit very little from having individualized objectives if they all do similar work. Instead, a combination of well thought out KPIs (e.g., average time to resolve issues, customer satisfaction ratings) plus some behavioral standards may be more useful. In contrast, a project manager may benefit from individualized performance goals that are allowed to fit the timelines of individual projects rather than force-fit into a yearly cycle.

While allowing some flexibility is harder to manage, the potential payoff is significant. Freedom to set meaningful expectations that fit each employee's role will help them focus on how they can best support organizational goals. Moreover, flexibility in timing and format allows employees and managers to more rapidly adapt their focus during times of change.

In sum:

1. Behavioral standards are useful for communicating expectations, especially in relation to reinforcing organizational values, such as treating others with respect. However, using behavioral standards as a means of rating performance may not yield data reliable enough to use as the basis for decisions.
2. Performance goals are mostly likely to lead to higher performance when they are specific, challenging, and within the employee's control to achieve. Performance goals can be set by either the employee or the manager, but they should be clearly linked to important organizational outcomes, so they are meaningful to employees. The value of performance goals may be undermined if they are used as the basis of performance ratings and rewards; therefore, goals set for the purpose of directing focus and developing skills may be more useful.
3. KPIs such as sales, productivity, efficiency, and so forth are useful for some roles, especially where multiple people do similar work. Organizations should balance financial expectations with behavioral expectations to ensure employees are not under undue pressure to act unethically.
4. The "best" means of setting expectations is the one that fits the requirements of the role and allows flexibility in the timing and format of goals so that employees have meaningful expectations and can swiftly switch priorities as organizational needs change.

Monitoring Progress and Giving Feedback. Ongoing performance conversations that include progress reviews, feedback, and coaching are essential to performance management. However, in many organizations, these conversations take place only once or twice a year as part of a formal performance evaluation. Mueller-Hanson and Pulakos (2018) noted the distinction between periodic performance evaluations and ongoing progress measurement. Progress measurement entails checking in regularly to assess progress toward goals or expectations before the end result is achieved. Its purpose is to provide information needed to make course corrections in real time and improve future performance. In contrast, performance evaluation is backward looking, and its purpose is to evaluate results after the opportunity to perform has passed. Seeing progress toward goal attainment is an important part of why goals motivate behavior. Therefore, organizations seeking to improve employee performance would be well-served to reinforce the importance of ongoing conversations that provide an opportunity to measure progress and help employees overcome barriers to success.

A typical way of promoting regular performance conversations is to require monthly or quarterly check-ins between managers and employees. These need not be formal reviews and in fact are usually more informal so that both employees and managers feel more comfortable discussing barriers to performance and how to overcome them. Regular check-ins are opportunities to review progress and provide ongoing, timely coaching and feedback.

Feedback is a cornerstone of performance management, but the evidence for its effectiveness is mixed. For example, Kluger and DiNisi's classic meta-analysis on feedback effectiveness (1996) showed that feedback improves performance only about a third of the time. A third of the time it hurts performance, and a third of the time it has no impact on performance. Aguinis et al. (2011) and Culbertson et al. (2013) showed that even high-performing employees can be negatively impacted by feedback from formal reviews, making feedback a somewhat risky proposition.

David Rock's SCARF theory (2008) hypothesizes a possible explanation for these results. Rock suggests that being judged by others is a fundamental threat to one's status, which triggers stress hormones and can decrease performance. This trigger is rooted in evolution—early humans needed acceptance by others for their very survival. Anything that threatens one's standing in the group could be perceived as a threat to one's very existence. Therefore, receiving feedback is frequently perceived as a threat and negative reactions are likely.

Despite feedback's potential pitfalls, information about progress is essential for success, especially when employees are still new to or learning a task. Schneider and Ledford (2020) demonstrated that organizations with a high climate for feedback had better outcomes for employees and organizations in terms of positive perceptions of the impact of performance management on performance and motivation. They define feedback climate as the "bundle" of ways organizations emphasize the importance of effective feedback through training, communications, modeling from senior leaders, selecting and rewarding managers based on their ability to give effective feedback, and measuring the quality of feedback that employees receive.

Research on what makes for effective feedback shows that it has the greatest potential to influence performance when it is:

- about strengths and not just weaknesses (e.g., CEB, 2002; Kluger & DiNisi, 1996; London, 2003),
- specific and supported by examples (Ilgen et al., 1979),

- focused on behaviors and not personal characteristics (Kluger & DiNisi, 1996),
- diagnostic, reviewing the process of how results are achieved and not just the end results (Early et al., 1990),
- given in real time (van der Kleij et al., 2012), and
- perceived as accurate and fair by the recipient (Chartered Institute of Personnel and Development [CIPD], 2016). Perceptions of accuracy and fairness are improved when the source is credible (i.e., someone who is very familiar with the recipient's work and able to make well-informed judgements about its quality) and trustworthy (Ilgen et al., 1979; Taylor et al., 1984).

Mueller-Hanson and Pulakos (2018) observed that there is too much pressure on managers to be the sole source of feedback, which is problematic because managers may not be in a position to observe people's day-to-day work and can lack information to give meaningful feedback. Additionally, managers often fear (justifiably in many cases) negative reactions to feedback and avoid giving it altogether. Mueller-Hanson and Pulakos suggested organizations supplement manager observations with natural sources of feedback, such as objective metrics collected in the course of normal operations, customer survey results, and other similar datapoints. Feedback collected from others such as peers and direct reports can also provide useful insights to employees and has been shown to have more impact on desired outcomes than traditional formal feedback sessions alone (Ledford et al., 2016).

As technology and data science advances, collecting information about results will become easier and more automated. For example, customer satisfaction data can be collected and fed back to employees in real time, and feedback from peers can be collected from short pulse surveys via mobile applications. Other metrics such as production, error rates, money spent or saved, and so forth can be made more visible to employees and teams that are responsible for these results. These "substitutes" for traditional feedback will likely be perceived as more objective and result in greater acceptance than feedback based on manager judgements. In some cases, it may be possible to use this data to monitor progress, evaluate outcomes, and distribute rewards.

Too much emphasis on feedback by itself can minimize awareness of the environment's influence on performance. Forces outside the employee's control may have a bigger impact on results than individual skills or effort. In these situations, feedback won't improve performance without coaching to help employees navigate barriers to success. Feedback tends to be one way, with managers telling employees if their performance was effective or not and how it could be improved. In contrast, coaching empowers employees to discover the root causes of performance challenges and work collaboratively with managers to resolve them (Gregory & Levy, 2015). Similarly, feedforward (giving guidance on how to perform effectively in the future rather than rehashing the past) can be useful to impact performance without the defensiveness that can accompany feedback. Coaching is most effective when recipients are open to it, believe that they are able to improve, are motivated to improve, and trust the individual providing the coaching (Bozer & Jones, 2018).

In sum:

1. Seeing visible progress toward goal attainment is just as important as setting the goal itself; therefore, monitoring progress on an ongoing basis is critical. Once or twice a

year reviews come too late to impact current performance. Check-ins can be a useful way to assess progress if they are focused on how the work is progressing and problem solving to overcome barriers. This partnership approach (where the employee and manager work collaboratively to diagnose problems and develop solutions) can be more useful and less stressful than treating the check-ins as mini performance reviews in which the manager simply passes judgement on how the employee is doing.

2. Feedback does not always improve performance. To increase the chances of success, feedback should be strengths-based, specific, focused on behaviors and not personal characteristics, process instead of results oriented, timely, and delivered by credible and trustworthy sources with direct knowledge of the employee's work.

3. Managers are often the sole source of feedback in organizations, which can put the quality of feedback at risk. Manager feedback can be supplemented with feedback from other sources such as objective metrics and input from others. As technology advances, feedback "substitutes" may become more automated and easier to access by employees directly, resulting in greater acceptance and less defensiveness.

4. In addition to feedback, coaching is important for enhancing performance and is most effective when recipients are fully engaged in the process and are motivated to improve.

Evaluating Results. The typical culmination of performance management activities is an annual performance evaluation. Most organizations have some type of rating system whereby performance in relation to behavioral standards or performance goals is judged on a qualitative and/or quantitative scale. For example, a common rating method is a 5-point scale, with a 5 representing "outstanding," a 3 representing "meets expectations," and a 1 representing "unsatisfactory," or equivalent synonyms. Although organizations often put a lot of effort into defining their rating scales, decades of research have shown that the type of rating scale has little impact on reliability or accuracy (Landy & Farr, 1980).

A growing trend in performance management has been to eliminate ratings in favor of more ongoing check-ins and feedback. Proponents of the "no rating" approach cite human inability to rate accurately, negative impact of ratings on morale, and excessive time spent on the process as reasons to eliminate ratings. In contrast, rating proponents have pointed out that organizations use implicit ratings when making decisions about pay, thereby creating a "shadow" rating system that has the potential to exacerbate bias and would be difficult to defend against legal challenges (Adler et al., 2016).

The decision of whether or not to have ratings is largely a policy one. Ratings provide a means of documenting performance decisions but are not accurate reflections of performance. The concept of "accuracy" in ratings is problematic for a variety of reasons.

- No single objective measure of performance exists to which ratings can be compared to assess their accuracy (Pulakos et al., 2019). Objective measures, such as production or sales, often don't correlate with supervisory assessments of performance. Additionally, there is little to no relationship between performance ratings and business metrics such as revenue and profit. For example, in one-large scale study of rating accuracy, performance ratings were entirely uncorrelated with business unit performance. Business units with high performance ratings were no more likely to be profitable than units with low performance ratings (CEB, 2012).

- Humans are limited in the amount of information they can process. Managers encounter many performance examples in a single year, and it would be impossible for them to consider all of them when assigning a rating (Pulakos & O'Leary, 2009). Therefore, they revert to their overall impressions or noteworthy examples of performance that stand out from the rest, consistent with how humans naturally process large volumes of information (Landy & Farr, 1980).
- Different raters bring their own "frames-of-reference" or viewpoints and standards to any rating situation, which develop over time based on raters' individual experiences and attributes (Pulakos, 2009). The result is that raters rarely agree, even when they are observing the same behavior. Intensive rater training can help somewhat (DeNisi & Murphy, 2017), though most of the evidence comes from laboratory settings (e.g., Pulakos, 1984, 1986) that would be difficult to replicate.
- Raters often have many, often conflicting, goals when making judgements about performance. Murphy and Cleveland (1995) summarized several of these, such as maintaining interpersonal relationships, conforming to organizational norms, and attempting to raise the standing of the workgroup in the organization. These goals often carry so much weight that they outweigh managers' desire to accurately rate performance.

To mitigate these issues, some organizations use a forced ranking or rating process. In forced ranking, managers rank every person within a unit from 1 to N. In a forced rating distribution only a certain percentage of employees are allowed to get each rating. For example, only 10% of employees can be rated a "5," 25% can be rated a "4", and so on. Some organizations take the additional step of firing the 10%–15% of employees deemed to be the lowest performers. Forced ranking and rating has been shown to decrease rating inflation, a pervasive problem in which most ratings are clustered at the high end of the rating scale and do not differentiate well between employees. However, research demonstrates that any benefits diminish over time because after a few years the lower performers have left, and solid performers now must get low ratings and may perhaps lose their jobs (Scullen et al., 2010). Moreover, this approach has been associated with lower morale, unhealthy competition, and higher voluntary turnover among good performers (e.g., Warren, 2013).

Another attempt to improve performance ratings is framing the rating question in a different way. For example, Aguinis and Burgi-Tian (2020) propose a using performance promoter score to evaluate performance. The performance promoter score is based on the popular net promoter score (NPS), used in marketing to assess how likely customers are to recommend a business to others (Reichheld, 2003). NPS is correlated with an organization's profitability (van Doorn et al., 2013). Aguinis and Burgi-Tian propose that using a similar approach in performance management is a quick and valid way to measure performance for use in feedback, development, and decision-making. They suggest asking the following questions:

1. How likely is it that you would recommend working with [name of individual, workgroup, or unit] to a friend or a colleague?
2. Why did you provide the rating that you provided?
3. What would it take to raise the score just by 1 point?

The answer to the first question (as rated on a Likert scale) is the performance promoter score. Like the NPS in marketing, the performance promoter score is a single number that indicates how highly the employee is thought of by one or more raters. The answers to the second and third questions can provide rich feedback for development. The advantages of this approach are that it can be used to gather feedback from multiple sources and provide actionable recommendations for improvement. It yields a simple number that can be used to compare employees to each other for decision-making. The drawbacks are that employees might attempt to "game" the ratings by offering to trade high scores with coworkers and/or tend to rate their friends highly. Although Aguinis and Burgi-Tian offer advice on how to mitigate these pitfalls, it remains to be seen if this approach can overcome the challenges of traditional ratings.

Regardless of what performance rating approach is used, there is no solid evidence that using performance ratings has any impact on performance. Therefore, organizations must decide whether ratings are a good fit for the culture and useful for justifying talent decisions. In the absence of ratings, some organizations find that employees have more questions about how pay and other rewards are determined (e.g., Walter & Surface, 2020). Moreover, without an annual performance review conversation, employees are at risk of getting no feedback at all about their overall career prospects.

In sum:

1. Performance ratings are notoriously inaccurate and unreliable. A primary reason for their inaccuracy is that there is no single objective way to measure performance outside of ratings.
2. Forced rating and ranking approaches can reduce ratings inflation but tend to provide diminishing returns over time and can result in reduced morale and increased competition among employees.
3. Performance ratings do not lead to better performance; however, organizations may still find them useful as a forcing function to ensure employees get feedback at least once a year on their career prospects. Organizations should consider their culture, context, and goals when deciding whether to use performance ratings.

Using Performance Data in Talent Decisions.   Linking performance and rewards is an inherent part of many organizational cultures. The usual process entails calibrating performance ratings across managers or business units to ensure consistency and fairness. The organization may also issue guidance for how ratings translate into rewards (e.g., a rating of "Outstanding" would merit a pay increase of 5%–6% while a rating of "Meets Expectations" would merit a pay increase of 2%–3%). Calibration sessions are often time consuming and tedious, with managers frequently reporting that an inordinate amount of time is spent debating very small differences in ratings. Moreover, employees complain that calibration is a "black box" that provides little insight about how reward decisions are made.

Organizations often struggle with linking performance and rewards because (a) managers have difficulty making distinctions in performance, (b) performance is only one component of pay decisions, and (c) rewarding past performance does not necessarily lead to improved future performance. Many pay-for-performance systems are based on the assumption that performance is normally distributed—with equal numbers of high and low performers However, some research shows that a power law distribution better represents job performance, with the vast majority of people performing similarly and about 20% of the population significantly outperforming their peers (O'Boyle & Aguinis, 2012). This research suggests that it is relatively easy to identify the top performers but distinguishing among the other 80% will be not only difficult, but also not very useful.

Another practical challenge is that reward decisions are based on a variety of factors besides performance. For example, pay increases and bonuses are constrained by annual budgets. Labor market factors constrain salary ranges for most jobs. Similarly, performance may be a key consideration in determining who to promote, but a larger consideration is organizational need for individuals in higher-level positions and the employee's potential to perform effectively at a new job level. In fact, a common complaint is an overreliance on past performance in promotion decisions—high-performing individual contributors may not make effective leaders. Promoting someone as a "reward" for high performance often leads to disaster, and stories about bosses who were promoted based on technical rather than leadership skills are ubiquitous (Mueller-Hanson & Pulakos, 2018).

Finally, the whole rationale for pay-for-performance is based on the assumption that rewards will motivate higher performance. However, the relationship between pay and performance is complex. Pay is more likely to be a motivator when there is enough distinction to make a difference. Shaw and Mitra (2017) suggest a pay increase must be at least 5%–7% to be noticeable enough to increase motivation. Differentiated pay is also more likely to increase performance when employees see a clear link between their efforts and rewards, employees have control over the results they produce, and pay decisions are seen as transparent and fair (Shaw & Mitra, 2017).

The challenges of making meaningful links between pay and performance have led some organizations to use other methods of determining rewards. The most common strategies are to allow managers to make judgements about pay and establishing reward decision criteria that are distinct from performance ratings (Mueller-Hanson & Pulakos, 2018). With the first approach, managers are given a budget to work with and then given discretion over how to use this budget to make pay decisions. While managers may be in the best position to allocate rewards, the potential for legal challenges makes this a risky option.

A second approach is to use distinct decision criteria for rewards that are separate from performance ratings. For example, salary increases might be based on a rating scale that includes a combination of performance, the impact of the individual on the business, and the importance or scarcity of skills. Although these criteria define general guidelines for distributing pay increases, overall business goals and budget constraints will ultimately determine how much money is available to be distributed.

Regardless of how decisions are made, the way that the decisions are communicated has a significant impact on their perceived fairness. Employees who are satisfied with how their organization handles pay and performance linkages are more likely to want to stay with the organization and continue putting effort into their jobs (CEB, 2010). Years of organizational justice research have shown that perceptions of the fairness of both the outcome and the process used to arrive at the outcome are important predictors of employee satisfaction (e.g., Folger & Konovsky, 1989). Of course, most employees would prefer positive outcomes (e.g., a big pay increase) over negative outcomes (e.g., little or no pay increase) but are more likely to maintain a positive attitude about the organization and their manager if the process used to arrive at the outcome is perceived as fair (Colquitt et al., 2013; McFarlin & Sweeney, 1992). Effective reward conversations are straightforward, detailed enough to convey how decisions were made without sounding defensive, and explain how reward decisions fit business goals.

In sum:

1. Although linking performance and rewards is an inherent part of many organizational cultures, these linkages are challenging because (a) managers often struggle to distinguish performance among the majority of employees, (b) other factors besides performance may have a bigger impact on reward decisions, and (c) rewards don't always lead to better future performance.
2. Some organizations have attempted to use other methods besides performance ratings to make pay decisions. The two most common approaches are allowing managers discretion in making these decisions and using a separate rating scale for compensation that is distinct from performance ratings.
3. Regardless of how reward decisions are made, good communication to employees is essential for these decisions to be perceived as fair.

IMPLEMENTING PERFORMANCE MANAGEMENT

The success of any HR system rests on the strength of its implementation. A frequent complaint about performance management systems is the amount of time required to execute them. Setting goals, checking in to review progress, gathering feedback from multiple stakeholders, reviewing and rating performance at the end of the year, calibrating results across employees, conducting review conversations, and documenting everything in the performance management system requires many hours of effort. Technology platforms can streamline the process or cause additional frustration if they are not user friendly. Moreover, without a consistent set of business rules around how to conduct performance management activities, compliance is unlikely.

HR leaders have a number of considerations when implementing a new performance management system:

- *Purpose:* defining and communicating the intended outcomes of performance management;
- *Process:* mapping out the steps required to conduct performance management activities, their sequence, and how they fit together;
- *Technology:* procuring or developing technology (if any) that will be used to administer and document each step and to deliver real-time progress and results data directly to employees;
- *Training:* teaching managers and employees how to use the system and the supporting behaviors that make performance management effective (e.g., coaching and feedback);
- *Communication:* disseminating information about performance management and any changes to make adoption more likely; and
- *Governance:* requirements for compliance, oversight, and evaluation of the program's effectiveness.

Implementing performance management is just like any change management effort—a clear articulation of purpose, an explicit link of this purpose to the organization's mission, and strong communication are key. Senior leaders must be vocal and visible champions of the effort (SHRM, 2017). HR has an important role in implementation, but if the process feels like an HR initiative rather than a business initiative, it will ultimately be treated as a compliance exercise instead of as a value-added business activity. Creating a simple, flexible approach that is embedded in work to the extent possible is likely to lead to better acceptance and use (Pulakos et al., 2015).

CONCLUSION: THE FUTURE OF PERFORMANCE MANAGEMENT

Performance management is the HR process that managers and employees love to hate. Despite the many complaints that it is burdensome, demotivating, and of little value, it persists. Several of its components, such as goal setting and providing coaching and feedback, can improve performance under the right circumstances. Unfortunately, the way these components are implemented as part of performance management often undermines their effectiveness.

Given these challenges, it is sensible to ask where performance management is headed. Will the "no ratings" advocates gain traction to the point where most organizations have discarded the typical review in favor of more frequent check-ins? Or will the pendulum swing back again to a more traditional approach?

The worldwide COVID-19 pandemic in 2020–2021 likely forever changed the nature and structure of work. The need for greater flexibility to work remotely or balance the needs of work and family have made it difficult for managers to observe employees' day-to-day activities. In times of crisis and change, static performance goals, performance ratings, and performance-based merit-pay seem less essential. Many organizations are delaying performance management activities because of more pressing priorities, and it will be interesting to see if anyone misses them.

The long-term impact of the pandemic remains to be seen. However, it is likely that the trends of simplifying performance management, reducing bureaucratic processes, and increasing emphasis on regular coaching and feedback will continue. Also likely to continue is the search for the holy grail in performance management—evidence that it consistently improves individual and organizational performance. To date, this evidence is lacking, and the question of whether performance management "works" is rarely even asked. Murphy (2020) calls this lack of evidence "*the* crisis in performance management" and notes that how the field responds to this crisis will "largely determine the future of performance management" (p. 327, emphasis in original). Despite this pessimism, some evidence suggests that, done well, performance management can achieve many of its aims, such as aligning individual actions to organizational goals and providing a forcing function for coaching and feedback. Research by Ledford and Schneider (2018) shows that practices such as aligning individual goals to organizational priorities, providing developmental and ongoing feedback, and assessing competencies can have positive effects on developing, motivating, and retaining employees. They further found that a strong feedback culture has a positive effect on organizational performance. Colquitt and Goldberg's research (2020) showed that organizations perceive their performance management systems are more effective when they focus on coaching, feedback, and development. Unfortunately, their research also showed that many organizations are dissatisfied with the quality of coaching and feedback, reinforcing the need to strengthen these practices.

The evolution of performance management could follow several possible paths, but the two most likely are continued refinements along its present course or transformation into something new. If performance management were to continue along its present course, we might see more research on how to improve feedback, more alternatives to traditional performance ratings, and more technology designed to simplify the process and gather feedback from multiple sources.

A more radical transformation could take several forms, including abandoning it altogether. One less-drastic option would be to cease thinking of performance management as a single process that can meet myriad competing goals. Organizations frequently want performance management to do everything from empowering employees to informing pay decisions while at the same time improving individual and organizational performance. The difficulty in using a single performance management approach to accomplish all of these goals suggests that further efforts to fix it are likely doomed. Instead of searching for the holy grail performance management that serves all purposes it might be time to acknowledge that different goals require different strategies.

One possible path forward is to stop doing "performance management" and instead define distinct activities and processes that serve important, yet disparate goals in the organization. Table 1 shows an example of how different goals, currently under the umbrella of performance management, could be met via alternative means.

Such a strategy would not eliminate performance management but rather would break it up into distinct talent practices, each of which is evidence based and purpose driven. This suggestion

Table 1. Talent Strategies Aligned to Organizational Goals

Organizational Goals	Proposed Talent Strategies	Pitfalls to Avoid
Align employee actions to organizational priorities	Communicate organizational strategy and how employees contribute Define expectations relevant for each major job category via job descriptions and other communications Allow goal setting to be dynamic and tailored to the individual role	Rigid rules or requirements for setting performance goals that are applied in a one-size-fits-all approach Use ratings of goal attainment as the basis for rewards
Develop employee skills	Invest in training and experiential learning Improve leaders' ability to provide meaningful coaching and feedback Define and communicate career paths	Use the same process to drive development discussions and compensation decisions Use performance ratings and reviews to determine development needs

(Continued)

Table 1. Continued

Organizational Goals	Proposed Talent Strategies	Pitfalls to Avoid
Ensure employees are producing desired results	Give employees tools for gathering their own performance data from natural sources (e.g., customer feedback, productivity metrics, financial results); automate this data where possible for easier access Institute regular check-ins for discussing work progress Refocus manager roles to become partners and coaches, helping employees identify and overcome barriers to progress rather than serving as performance judges Recognize the importance of selecting the right people for the right role; consider a change in roles as one remedy to poor performance Recognize the impact of the environment on performance; if employees are struggling, consider how business processes and workflows can be changed to help people improve	Rely on the performance management system to handle chronic poor performance; instead, recognize that a separate process may be needed for people who are struggling to meet expectations
Distribute rewards fairly	Articulate a compensation strategy that clearly outlines all the factors that go into reward decisions (organizational budget, labor market costs, etc.) so that employees know how decisions are made Allocate rewards with distinct decision criteria that reflect business goals (e.g., pay more for high-value skills)—note that judgements about performance would be part of these criteria but not the sole criterion; communicate to employees that these decision criteria are for the purpose of making reward decisions Conduct adverse impact analysis and adjust practices as needed to ensure fairness across groups Teach managers how to communicate decisions effectively	Tie pay and performance together too tightly; instead acknowledge that the relationship is loose at best

is a bit more subtle than radical calls to "blow up" performance management as we know it. It doesn't lend itself to a single name or catch phrase. However, if Murphy's call (2020) to address the "crisis" of performance management is to be answered, it must begin with a focus on practices that are supported by research and consistent with organizational goals and build from there.

ACKNOWLEDGMENTS

The author would like to thank two anonymous reviewers for their excellent suggestions.

FURTHER READING

Adler, S. Campion, M., Colquitt, A., Grubb, A., Murphy, K., Ollander-Krane, R., & Pulakos, E. D. (2016). Getting rid of performance ratings: Genius or folly? A debate. *Industrial and Organizational Psychology, 9*, 219–252. http://doi.org/10.1017/iop.2015.106

Chartered Institute of Personnel and Development [CIPD]. (2016, December). *Could do better? Assessing what works in performance management* [Research report]. https://www.cipd.co.uk/knowledge /fundamentals/people/performance/what-works-in-performance-management-report

Colquitt, A. L. (2017). *Next generation performance appraisal: The triumph of science over myth and superstition.* Information Age.

DeNisi, A. S., & Murphy, K. R. (2017). Performance appraisal and performance management: 100 years of progress? *Journal of Applied Psychology, 102*, 421–433. http://doi.org/10.1037/apl0000085

Kluger, A. N., & DeNisi, A. S. (1996). The effects of feedback interventions on performance: A historical review, meta-analysis and a preliminary feedback intervention theory. *Psychological Bulletin, 119*, 254–284. http://doi.org/10.1037/0033-2909.119.2.254

Mueller-Hanson, R. A., & Pulakos, E. D. (2018). *Transforming performance management to drive performance: An evidence-based roadmap.* Routledge.

Murphy, K. R., Cleveland, J. N., & Hanscom, M. (2018). *Performance appraisal and management: Why does it fail and how can it be fixed?* SAGE.

Pulakos, E. D., Mueller-Hanson, R. A., & Arad, S. (2019). The evolution of performance management: Searching for value. *Annual Review of Organizational Psychology and Organizational Behavior, 6*, 249–271. http://doi.org/10.1146/annurev-orgpsych-012218-015009

Pulakos, E. D., & O'Leary, R. S. (2011). Why is performance management so broken? *Industrial and Organizational Psychology: Perspectives on Science and Practice, 4*(2), 146–164. http://doi.org/10.1111 /j.1754-9434.2011.01315.x

Society for Human Resource Management. (2017). *Performance management that makes a difference: An evidence-based approach.* https://www.shrm.org/hr-today/trends-and-forecasting/special-reports-and -expert-views/documents/performance%20management.pdf

REFERENCES

Adler, S. Campion, M., Colquitt, A., Grubb, A., Murphy, K., Ollander-Krane, R., & Pulakos, E. D. (2016). Getting rid of performance ratings: Genius or folly? A debate. *Industrial and Organizational Psychology, 9*, 219–252. http://doi.org/10.1017/iop.2015.106

Aguinis, H. (2013). *Performance management* (3rd ed.). Pearson.

Aguinis, H., & Burgi-Tian, J. (2020). Measuring performance during crises and beyond: The performance promoter score. *Business Horizons, 64*, 149–160. http://doi.org/10.1016/j.bushor.2020.09.001

Aguinis, H., Joo, H., & Gottfredson, R. K. (2011). Why we hate performance management—And why we should love it. *Business Horizons, 54*, 503–507. http://doi.org/10.1016/J.BUSHOR.2011.06.001

Bozer, G., & Jones, R. J. (2018). Understanding the factors that determine workplace coaching effectiveness: A systematic literature review. *European Journal of Work and Organizational Psychology, 27*(3), 342–361. http://doi.org/10.1080/1359432X.2018.1446946

Buckingham, M., & Goodall, A. (2015, April). Reinventing performance management. *Harvard Business Review.* https://hbr.org/2015/04/reinventing-performance-management

Chartered Institute of Personnel and Development [CIPD]. (2016, December). *Could do better? Assessing what works in performance management* [Research report]. https://www.cipd.co.uk/knowledge /fundamentals/people/performance/what-works-in-performance-management-report

Colquitt, A. L. (2017). *Next generation performance appraisal: The triumph of science over myth and superstition.* Information Age.

Colquitt, A., & Goldberg, E. (2020, December). *Designing performance management for impact: Practices that make a difference* [Research report].

Colquitt, J. A., Scott, B. A., Rodell, J. B., Long, D. M., Zapata, C. P., Conlon, D. E., & Wesson, M. J. (2013). Justice at the millennium, a decade later: A metaanalytic test of social exchange and affect-based perspectives. *Journal of Applied Psychology, 98*, 199–236. http://doi.org/10.1037/a0031757

Corporate Executive Board. (2002). *Building the high-performance workforce: A quantitative analysis of the effectiveness of performance management strategies.* CEB.

Corporate Executive Board. (2010). *Creating a pay-for-performance organization.* CEB.

Corporate Executive Board. (2012). *Driving breakthrough performance in the new work environment.* CEB.

Culbert, S. A., & Rout, L. (2010). *Get rid of the performance review! How companies can stop intimidating, start managing—And focus on what really matters.* Business Plus.

Culbertson, S. S., Henning, J. B., & Payne, S. C. (2013). Performance appraisal satisfaction: The role of feedback and goal orientation. *Journal of Personnel Psychology, 12*, 189–195. http://doi.org/10.1027/1866-5888/a000096

DeNisi, A. S., & Murphy, K. R. (2017). Performance appraisal and performance management: 100 years of progress? *Journal of Applied Psychology, 102*, 421–433. http://doi.org/10.1037/apl0000085

DeNisi, A., & Smith, C. E. (2014). Performance appraisal, performance management, and firm-level performance. *Academy of Management Annals, 8*, 127–179. http://doi.org/10.1080/19416520.2014.873178

Early, P. C., Northcraft, G. B., Lee, C., & Lituchy, T. R. (1990). The impact of process and outcome feedback on the relation of goal setting to task performance. *Academy of Management Journal, 33*, 87–105. http://doi.org/10.5465/256353

Folger, R., & Konovsky, M. A. (1989). Effects of procedural and distributive justice on reactions to pay raise decisions. *Academy of Management Journal, 32*, 115–130. http://doi.org/10.2307/256422

Gregory, J. B., & Levy, P. E. (2015). *Using feedback in organizational consulting.* American Psychological Association.

Ilgen, D. R., Fisher, C. D., & Taylor, M. S. (1979). Consequences of individual feedback on behavior in organizations. *Journal of Applied Psychology, 64*, 349–371. http://doi.org/10.1037/0021-9010.64.4.349

Kluger, A. N., & DeNisi, A. S. (1996). The effects of feedback interventions on performance: A historical review, meta-analysis and a preliminary feedback intervention theory. *Psychological Bulletin, 119*, 254–284. http://doi.org/10.1037/0033-2909.119.2.254

Landy, F. J., & Farr, J. L. (1980). Performance rating. *Psychological Bulletin, 87*, 72–107. http://doi.org/10.1037/0033-2909.87.1.72

Latham, G. (2016). Goal-setting theory: Causal relationships, mediators, and moderators. In *Oxford research encyclopedia of psychology.* Oxford University Press. http://doi.org/10.1093/acrefore/9780190236557.013.12

Latham, G. P., & Locke, E. A. (2007). New developments in and directions for goal-setting research. *European Psychologist, 12*, 290–300. http://doi.org/10.1027/1016-9040.12.4.290

Lawler, E. E. (2016, November 1). The Wells Fargo debacle: How proper reward practices can remedy a toxic culture. Forbes.com. https://www.forbes.com/sites/edwardlawler/2016/11/01/the-wells-fargo-debacle-how-proper-reward-practices-can-remedy-a-toxic-culture/2/#d9bebe22ff53

Ledford, G. E., Benson, G., & Lawler, E. E. (2016, August). *Cutting-edge performance management: 244 organizations report on ongoing feedback, ratingless reviews, and crowd-sourced feedback.* World at Work Research. Center for Effective Organizations.

Ledford, G., & Schneider, B. (2018). *Performance feedback culture drives business impact* [Research report]. I4CP and Center for Effective Organizations.

Locke, E. A., & Latham, G. P. (2013). *New developments in goal setting and task performance.* Routledge.

London, M. (2003). *Job feedback: Giving, seeking, and using feedback for performance improvement.* Erlbaum.

McFarlin, D. B., & Sweeney, P. D. (1992). Distributive and procedural justice as predictors of satisfaction with personal and organizational outcomes. *Academy of Management Journal, 35*, 626–637. http://doi.org/10.2307/256489

McGregor, J. (2014, January 27). Study finds that basically every single person hates performance reviews. *The Washington Post.* https://www.washingtonpost.com/news/on-leadership/wp/2014/01/27/study-finds-that-basically-every-single-person-hates-performance-reviews/?utm_term=.426470248841

Mueller-Hanson, R. A. (2020). The past, present and future of performance management. In E. D. Pulakos & M. Battista (Eds.), *Managing performance effectively in today's organizations* (pp. 289–317). Oxford University Press.

Mueller-Hanson, R. A., & Pulakos, E. D. (2018). *Transforming performance management to drive performance: An evidence-based roadmap.* Routledge.

Murphy, K. R. (2019). Performance evaluation will not die, but it should. *Human Resource Management Journal, 30*, 13–31. http://doi.org/10.1111/1748-8583.12259

Murphy, K. R. (2020). The past, present and future of performance management. In E. D. Pulakos & M. Battista (Eds.), *Managing performance effectively in today's organizations* (pp. 318–341). Oxford University Press.

Murphy, K. R., & Cleveland, J. N. (1995). *Understanding performance appraisal: Social, organizational, and goal-oriented perspectives.* SAGE.

Murphy, K. R., Cleveland, J. N., & Hanscom, M. (2018). *Performance appraisal and management: Why does it fail and how can it be fixed?* SAGE.

O'Boyle, E., Jr., & Aguinis, H. (2012). The best and the rest: Revisiting the norm of normality of individual performance. *Personnel Psychology, 65*, 79–119. http://doi.org/10.1111/j.1744-6570.2011.01239.x

Pulakos, E. D. (1984). A comparison of rater training programs: Error training and accuracy training. *Journal of Applied Psychology, 69*, 581–588. http://doi.org/10.1037/0021-9010.69.4.581

Pulakos, E. D. (1986). The development of a training program to increase accuracy with different rating formats. *Organizational Behavior and Human Decision Processes, 38*, 76–91. http://doi.org/10.1016/0749-5978(86)90027-0

Pulakos, E. D. (2009). *Performance management: A new approach for driving business results.* Wiley-Blackwell. http://doi.org/10.1002/9781444308747

Pulakos, E. D., & Kantrowitz, T. (2020). How performance management must change to drive adaptability, resilience, agility (ARA) and performance: An evidence-based view. In E. D. Pulakos & M. Battista (Eds.), *Managing performance effectively in today's organizations* (pp. 211–232). Oxford University Press.

Pulakos, E. D., Mueller-Hanson, R. A., & Arad, S. (2019). The evolution of performance management: Searching for value. *Annual Review of Organizational Psychology and Organizational Behavior, 6*, 249–271. http://doi.org/10.1146/annurev-orgpsych-012218-015009

Pulakos, E. D., Mueller-Hanson, R. A., Moye, N., & Arad, S. (2015). Performance management can be fixed: An on-the-job experiential learning approach for complex behavior change. *Industrial and Organizational Psychology: Perspectives on Science and Practice, 8*, 51–76. http://doi.org/10.1017/iop.2014.2

Pulakos, E. D., & O'Leary, R. S. (2009). Defining and measuring results of workplace behavior. In J. L. Farr & N. T. Tippins (Eds.), *Handbook of employee selection.* Erlbaum.

Pulakos, E. D., & O'Leary, R. S. (2011). Why is performance management so broken? *Industrial and Organizational Psychology: Perspectives on Science and Practice, 4*(2), 146–164. http://doi.org/10.1111/j.1754-9434.2011.01315.x

Reichheld, F. F. (2003). The one number you need to grow. *Harvard Business Review, 81*(12), 46–55.

Rock, D. (2008). SCARF: A brain-based model for collaborating with and influencing others. *NeuroLeadership Journal, 1*, 1–9.

Schneider, B., & Ledford, J. E. (2020). Climate for feedback: The key to performance management effectiveness. In E. D. Pulakos & M. Battista (Eds.), *Managing performance effectively in today's organizations* (pp. 185–210). Oxford University Press.

Scullen, S. S., Bergey, P. K., & Aiman-Smith, A. (2010). Forced distribution rating systems and the improvement of workforce potential: A baseline simulation. *Personnel Psychology, 58*, 1–32. http://doi.org/10.1111/j.1744-6570.2005.00361.x

Scullen, S. E., Mount, M. K., & Goff, M. (2000). Understanding the latent structure of job performance ratings. *Journal of Applied Psychology, 85*, 956–970. http://doi.org/10.1037/0021-9010.85.6.956

Shaw, J., & Mitra, A. (2017). The science of pay-for-performance systems: Six facts that all managers should know. *WorldatWork Journal, 26*, 19–27.

Society for Human Resource Management. (2017). *Performance management that makes a difference: An evidence-based approach.* https://www.shrm.org/hr-today/trends-and-forecasting/special-reports-and-expert-views/documents/performance%20management.pdf

Taylor, M. S., Fisher, C. D., & Ilgen, D. R. (1984). Individuals' reactions to performance feedback in organizations: Control theory perspective. In K. M. Rowland & G. R. Ferris (Eds.), *Research in personnel and human resource management* (pp. 81–124). JAI Press.

van der Kleij, F. M., Eggen, T. J., Timmers, C. F., & Veldkamp, B. P. (2012). Effects of feedback in a computer-based assessment for learning. *Computers & Education, 58*, 263–272. http://doi.org/10.3102/0034654314564881

van Doorn, J., Leeflang, P. S., & Tijs, M. (2013). Satisfaction as a predictor of future performance: A replication. *International Journal of Research in Marketing, 30*(3), 314–318. http://doi.org/10.1016/j.ijresmar.2013.04.002

Walter, M., & Surface, C. (2020). Medtronic's contrarian journey. In E. D. Pulakos & M. Battista (Eds.), *Managing performance effectively in today's organizations* (pp. 64–80). Oxford University Press.

Warren, T. (2013, November 11). Microsoft axes its controversial employee-ranking system. *The Verge.* http://www.theverge.com/2013/11/12/5094864/microsoft-kills-stack-ranking-internal-structure

Wiegert, B., & Harter, J. (2017). *Re-engineering performance management.* Gallup.

Winters, D., & Latham, G. P. (2006). The effect of learning versus outcome goals on simple versus a complex task. *Group and Organization Management, 21*, 236–250. http://doi.org/10.1037/a0013114

Rose Mueller-Hanson

THE PSYCHOLOGY OF WORK ENGAGEMENT

INTRODUCTION

The Truth about Burnout (Maslach & Leiter, 1997) proposed engagement with work as the opposite of burnout. This idea developed from observations that surveys across organizations or professions did not divide neatly into a burnout profile of exhaustion, cynicism, and inefficacy in contrast to all the normal people with nondescript psychological connections with their work life. Instead, the three subscales of the Maslach Burnout Inventory (MBI; Maslach, Jackson, & Leiter, 2017) reflected a smooth distribution, skewed in the positive direction. Samples included people who never or very rarely experienced exhaustion or cynicism and who felt efficacious nearly every day. This combination of scores reflected something more than the absence of burnout. It went beyond suggesting an adequate psychological connection with to work to describe an active state of energy, involvement, and efficacy. Maslach and Leiter (1997) deemed a strongly positive profile of MBI scores as worthy of a distinct label—engagement with work—that they proposed as a counterpart to the burnout profile.

Meta-analyses have questioned the extent to which burnout and engagement occupy distinct conceptual spaces. Most directly, Cole, Walter, Bedeian, and O'Boyle (2012) question their distinctiveness by noting strong correlations of the Utrecht Work Engagement Scale (UWES) with the Maslach Burnout Scale, the two measures' consistent relationships with organizational constructs, and the extent to which entering burnout into multiple regressions substantially reduced the power of work engagement as a predictor of organizational outcomes. Crawford, LePine, and Rich (2010) challenged the Job Demands/Resources prediction linking demands with burnout and resources with engagement. They found both demands and resources associated with burnout, while engagement, measured predominantly by the UWES, had distinct relationships with hindrance versus challenge demands. Further, MacKay, Allen, and Landis (2017) found that employee engagement, as assessed with various measures, made only modest contributions to explaining outcome variance beyond the power provided by various attitudinal measures. Overall, these meta-analyses find limited support for engagement's capacity to provide a unique perspective on work life.

THE CONCEPT OF WORK ENGAGEMENT

The UWES reliably captures a psychological connection with work that occupies the positive end of a spectrum that has negative connections, such as burnout, at the opposite end. Macey and Schneider (2008) noted that introducing a new positive construct into the thickly populated territory of organizational psychology or management studies presents serious challenges. For much of the past century the field has explored ways to assess employees' affiliation for their work and their workplaces. They essentially argue that construct redundancy presents a greater risk than construct neglect. In their overview of definitions and measures of engagement they find insufficient rigor in distinguishing new measures from established measures. They note instances in which writers simply relabeled job involvement or job satisfaction as engagement. In contrast, some studies have developed measures for specific subsets of engagement, specifically organizational engagement in contrast to job engagement (Saks, 2006).

In a comprehensive review of employee engagement, Macey and Schneider (2008) noted that research had identified a range of factors including personality qualities, management practices, and workplace social relationships that contribute to or inhibit engagement. They also presented engagement as a complex construct having qualities of both a state and a trait, and further presented engagement as a strategic orientation, in that employees assessed their work situations to evaluate the extent to which engagement behaviors would further their workplace aspirations. That is, engagement does not just happen to employees; some seek out opportunities for engagement as part of their career strategy.

Macey and Schneider (2008) criticize some measures as assessing the *conditions for engagement*, such as work-based friendships or supervisory attention, rather than assessing engagement per se. They singled out the UWES as having the distinct quality of a foundation of rigorous development as a measure. Analyses have supported the contention that the UWES defines work engagement as distinct from other positive work-related constructs (Christian, Garza, & Slaughter, 2011). However, others have found the UWES to overlap excessively with measures of burnout as well as organizational commitment and job performance. Byrne, Peters, and Weston (2016) concluded that the UWES overlapped considerably with other positive work-related constructs. They also noted that the UWES did not stand in direct opposition to burnout, although it did contrast with burnout in important ways. Although the UWES enjoys the status of the most widely used measure of work engagement, its use has its detractors.

MEASURING ENGAGEMENT

Although Kahn had introduced engagement as a construct in work psychology earlier (Kahn, 1990) research on work engagement proceeded at a modest pace until the introduction of the Utrecht Work Engagement Scale (Schaufeli, Salanova, González-Romá, & Bakker, 2002). In developing the work engagement scale Schaufeli and colleagues sought to define the construct with reference to the active presence of vigor and dedication rather than deducing engagement from the absence of exhaustion and cynicism, as with the MBI. The vigor subscale contrasts with exhaustion, while the dedication scale contrasts with cynicism. Schaufeli and colleagues introduced absorption as a feature of engagement because their theoretical model included a quality of flow as a part of engagement, and employees had noted the importance of absorption when interviewed about their experiences with work engagement. The developers of the UWES expressed reservations about the validity of efficacy as an element of burnout. They did not see fit to include efficacy as an aspect of engagement although they noted efficacy's relevance to the engagement construct. However, developing the scale as a direct contrast to the Maslach Burnout Inventory-General Scale (MBI-GS) required Schaufeli and colleagues (2002) to address a question presented by the professional efficacy scale. To capture burnout as a complex syndrome, the MBI uses negatively worded items to assess exhaustion and cynicism while using positively worded items to assess efficacy. The burnout syndrome includes high scores on exhaustion and cynicism and low scores on efficacy. The MBI has received criticism from the view that the relatively low correlations of the efficacy subscale with the other two subscales suggested that efficacy did not operate as part of a syndrome (Salanova, Grau, Cifre, & Llorens, 2000). In contrast, the consistently strong correlation of exhaustion with cynicism indicated that these two constructs defined the core burnout construct. Alternatively, the relatively independent status of efficacy leaves room for employees to experience exhaustion and cynicism with a positive sense of efficacy as a state distinct from the full burnout syndrome, which includes a negative sense of efficacy. They may attribute their exhaustion and cynicism to excessive demands aggravated by poor management practices while maintaining a strong sense of their own capabilities. This psychological connection with work could exist distinct from burnout. In that way, low efficacy may function as the active part of the burnout syndrome without moving in lockstep with the other two aspects of the syndrome. This framework follows the pattern found in medical syndromes. Some syndromes comprise highly correlated elements but in other instances the congruence of rarely combined elements define syndromes (Melnick, Powsner, & Shanafelt, 2017). The burnout syndrome includes both features.

In their analysis Schaufeli and colleagues (2002) contrast a single-factor model (engagement and burnout as opposite ends on a continuum) and a two-factor model of the three MBI subscales as one factor in contrast to the three UWES subscales as a second factor. Neither model met the criteria for a well-fitting confirmatory factor analysis (e.g., CFI of .83 and .85 respectively), nor did their model fit statistics differ markedly from one another. A modification that improved the fit adequately (CFI = .92) occurred through including the MBI efficacy subscale with the UWES subscales as one factor in contrast to a latent factor of exhaustion with cynicism. The resulting latent factors correlated at −.47 and −.62 in their two samples.

This analysis successfully established a positively constructed measure of engagement distinct from positive scores on the MBI; however, the results included caveats. First, the latent engagement variable in the final model that contrasted with burnout included a subscale of the MBI. The analysis did not delete the efficacy subscale, but included it with the UWES subscales in the final model. This approach did not align clearly with the authors' reservations about efficacy as an aspect of either burnout or engagement. Second, the −.62 correlation between the engagement and burnout factors for the employee sample did not entirely counter the argument that engagement and burnout function as opposite psychological connections with work. Although this correlation falls short of a perfect −1.00 that would indicate a complete opposite, $r = -.62$ for a sample of over 900 people does not argue convincingly that engagement and burnout function independently of one another. In many contexts, researchers would interpret a correlation of such magnitude as reflecting a strong relationship between two constructs.

The UWES has become a widely used measure of work engagement. The original 17-item scale produces the three subscales of vigor, dedication, and absorption. In contrast, researches often calculate a single engagement score from the 9-item short form (Schaufeli, Bakker, & Salanova, 2006) that includes items from each of the three subscales. Examinations of the 9-item UWES across many translations of the measure have produced mixed results, with some analyses confirming a three-factor structure and other analyses producing a single-factor solution (e.g., De Bruin & Henn, 2013; Schaufeli & De Witte, 2017). In light of these findings, researchers have at times reported the UWES as a single-factor engagement score. Schaufeli, Shimazu, Hakanen, Salanova, and De Witte (2017) have validated a three-item UWES that includes one item from each of the three subscales to produce a single-factor engagement score (Knight, Patterson, & Dawson, 2017). These three formats maintain consistency with the conceptual framework of work engagement comprising vigor, dedication, and absorption while accommodating a variety of research agendas. The full 17-item version supports delving into the distinct qualities of each subscale; the ultra-short version provides a metric for work engagement while placing the least burden on survey respondents. The UWES can provide this range of usage because work engagement functions as a unitary construct. The subscales differentiate clearly on factor analyses of the full scale but their high intercorrelations allow the combining of the items into a unitary measure of work engagement.

Psychological Connections with Work.   In addition to engagement's contrast with burnout, the field has also considered the distinction between engagement and workaholism.

Taris, Schaufeli, and Shimazu (2010) found these two experiences to share qualities, including an attraction to work and willingness to devote extensive time to it. However, engagement corresponded with measures of health and well-being while workaholism did not. Salanova, Del Líbano, Llorens, and Schaufeli (2014) examined this issue through a cluster analysis that distinguished four profiles: relaxed, engaged, workaholic, and burned out. The workaholic profile shared the engagement profile's qualities of energy, challenge, skills, and identification but differed markedly on pleasure, with workaholics finding less pleasure in their work. In contrast, the burnout profile shared the workaholic profile's lack of pleasure but scored negatively on all of the other qualities relative to the other profiles. These findings aligned well with the results of Taris and colleagues (2010).

Leiter and Maslach (2016) also used a person-oriented approach to identify distinct profiles of employees' psychological connections with work. Through latent profile analysis of two large samples of health care providers they identified five profiles based upon scores on the MBI-GS. In this approach they argued that energy, involvement, and efficacy—the constructs that underlie the three MBI subscales—relate to fundamental dimensions of employees' relationships to work. As such, distinct patterns of these three dimensions would identify fundamental ways of connecting or disconnecting with work.

Leiter and Maslach's (2016) analysis identified five profiles. Burnout (negative on all three subscales) and Engagement (positive on all three subscales) defined the two poles of the conceptual space. In addition, the analysis identified three additional profiles: Ineffective (negative only on efficacy), Overextended (negative only on energy), and Disengaged (negative only on cynicism). In relating the profiles to organizational constructs, they found that the Overextended had a negative view of workload demands but expressed indifference toward resources issues, such as community, control, and reward. In contrast, the Disengaged profile expressed indifference toward workload demands while expressing concerns about resource mismatches. The Burnout profile views both demands and resources negatively while the Engaged profile viewed demands and resources positively. The Ineffective profile occupied an intermediate position in that it expressed neutral view on both demands and resources that distinguished it from Engagement while stopping short of the distress associated with Overextended, Disengaged, and Burnout. This profile makes a definitive contribution to the conceptual space in characterizing a psychological connection with work that has a neutral quality. It defines a space for people who lack the enthusiasm of engagement without experiencing explicit distress regarding their work life.

A person-centered analysis (Mäkikangas, Schaufeli, Tolvanen, & Feldt, 2013) allows one to identify within a larger population subgroups with distinct and meaningful profiles that fall outside of the range expected on the basis of overall correlations alone. For example, the MBI exhaustion and cynicism scales have consistently large correlations but they do not occur in alignment in every instance. In contrast, the efficacy subscale does not correlate strongly with the other two MBI subscales, but the measure provides important information when they do all align. As Mäkikangas and colleagues (2013) demonstrated in their analysis, focusing on these distinct configurations of scores identifies considerable change and development within a population that appears highly stable on the basis of overall correlations.

THE JOB DEMANDS/RESOURCES MODEL

The Job Demands/Resources (J D/R) model (Demerouti, Bakker, Nachreiner, & Schaufeli, 2001) has guided a large proportion of the research on work engagement. Its first iteration focused on burnout, using the Oldenburg Burnout Inventory (OLBI) that measures exhaustion and disengagement (Demerouti, Bakker, De Jonge, Janssen, & Schaufeli, 2001). The model demonstrated a central concept that excessive demands contributed to exhaustion while shortages of resources contributed to disengagement. The model's use expanded with the introduction of the UWES as a positive measure of engagement, replacing the focus on the negatively worded disengagement subscale of the OLBI (Demerouti, Bakker, De Jonge et al., 2001). Over the subsequent years, a variety of studies have confirmed the core elements of the model. First, tests of the model have confirmed stronger relationships between demands and exhaustion than between demands and engagement. In parallel, results have confirmed stronger relationships between resources and engagement than between resources and exhaustion. Examinations of the model have also demonstrated that these patterns do not operate exclusively. They have shown weaker paths from resources to exhaustion and from demands to engagement as well as indirect effects (Bakker, Demerouti, & Sanz-Vergel, 2014).

Second, research has confirmed the J D/R model's contribution to predicting variety of organizational and personal outcomes (Bakker & Demerouti, 2014; Bakker, Schaufeli, Leiter, & Taris, 2008) with a focus on job performance. Bakker, Demerouti, and Schaufeli (2003) demonstrated the model's value in showing two distinct paths to important outcomes related to withdrawal. First, a path from exhaustion predicted illness that in turn predicted absences. Second, a path from resources predicted dedication that in turn predicted turnover intention. Nahrgang, Morgeson, and Hofmann (2011) provided parallel support to the two-pathway quality of the model in demonstrating a pathway from demands through exhaustion led to accidents while a path from resources through engagement led to compliance with safety culture. The inclusion of two distinct paths with related but different outcomes (turnover and absences) gives the model the potential to point toward a greater variety of actions to improve the quality of work life.

The J D/R model does not keep demands and resources entirely separate but includes interactions between demands and resources. J D/R accommodates the buffering functions such as the moderation by control of the relationship between demands and exhaustion (e.g., Karasek & Theorell, 1990). Parallel buffering effects occur through other resources, such as social support and performance feedback (Bakker, Demerouti, & Euwema, 2005; Xanthopoulou, Bakker, Demerouti, & Schaufeli, 2007).

The J D/R model has expanded to include personal as well as job resources as contributors to work engagement. The model depicts personal and job resources as mutually enhancing. Personal resources of consequence include resilience and self-management. These resources not only contribute to employees' potential for experiencing engagement, they also improve their potential for making use of available job resources. Xanthopoulou, Bakker, Demerouti, and Schaufeli (2007) reported that personal resources played a more active role in the relevance of job resources to engagement than they did in the relationship of job demands with exhaustion.

As Bakker, Demerouti, and Sanz-Vergel (2014) noted, the J D/R model draws its strength to a large part from its flexibility. The model's focus on resources and demands in the general sense accommodates a variety of strains and assets within an organization. This feature encourages comparisons across organizations in different sectors by accommodating the demands and resources that have distinct prevalence in those organizations. For example, although the actual demands and resources pertaining to the work of a hospital-based nurse differ in important ways form those pertaining to the life of a retail sales person, the general notion of balancing demands with resources has relevance for both.

INTERVENTIONS TO IMPROVE WORK ENGAGEMENT

Having identified engagement with work as a meaningful contributor to both well-being and performance, and having concluded that many workplaces maintain insufficient levels of work engagement among their employees, the question arises as to how to enhance engagement. As with many organizational issues, practitioners confront the intervention conundrum (Leiter & Cooper, 2017). While problems and shortcomings develop in organizations without expending any planning, resources, or effort, interventions to address such problems require impressive and sometimes forbidding quantities of planning, resources, and effort. However, intervention research brings the substantial benefit that the process of deliberately changing a phenomenon for the better demonstrates and deepens understanding. Work to improve engagement has benefitted from the field's positive focus. Employees need not acknowledge the presence of distress or discord among their employees. They can present efforts to improve engagement as a benefit to everyone involved.

In their meta-analysis of research in work engagement intervention, Knight, Patterson, and Dawson (2017) differentiated programs as building either personal or job resources, training leaders, or building engagement as an aspect of building workplace health. They found that programs designed to increase job resources and programs integrated into organizational well-being initiatives exhibited small but significant effects on improving engagement. They identified a temporal pattern regarding the UWES subcomponents in that the impact on vigor occurred promptly after intervention while the impact on dedication and absorption occurred later. However, follow-up assessments produced mixed results, with some gains diminishing over time while results in other studies sustained. The analysis did not find systematic variation in effectiveness across the four types of intervention (increasing personal resources, increasing job resources, leadership, or health promotion). The small number of studies (20) and the wide variation of specific programs within these four types prevented the authors from making definitive conclusions about the relative effectiveness of these approaches. The analysis did produce support for approaching work engagement intervention as a group project in contrast to individual training or coaching. The authors proposed that group formats might benefit from their greater potential to activate important job resources, such as social support.

Knight, Patterson, and Dawson (2017) noted the impact of logistic problems that plague organizational intervention research. Major events, including mergers, acquisitions, and redundancies occur during intervention implementation and follow-up periods disrupting programs and potentially affecting engagement. Individuals' choice to participate or drop out appear non-random, but associated with demographic features. The studies included in their meta-analysis varied considerably in the amount of available information about the thoroughness or adeptness of implementation. A weak effect may reflect an inappropriate procedure or an appropriate procedure improperly implemented. They encourage more thorough tracking of process to identify mechanisms of change.

The field remains far from a conclusive judgment on how to increase work engagement due to three inherent challenges. First, Knight, Patterson, and Dawson (2017) decry the paucity of intervention research. Despite work engagement enjoying a surge of research interest that generate publications only 20 studies met their straightforward criteria for inclusion in the meta-analysis. Second, even within their four types of intervention approach, studies varied greatly in specific procedures. The innovation apparent in the variety of intervention approaches came at the cost of comparability among the studies. They identified few points of reference among the diverse approaches. Third, the studies shed only modest light on the mechanisms through which their modest improvements in work engagement occurred.

Job Crafting. Enhancing job resources on the level of workgroups or organizational divisions requires more authority than individual employees can access. Increasing expertise, recruiting support staff, or purchasing equipment costs money. Although organizations regularly enhance resources in these ways, these occasions rarely provide opportunities for research on the impact on employees' engagement. Instead, research has focused on initiatives that enhance job resources on a more modest scale. Job crafting (Wrzesniewski & Dutton, 2001) occupies the intersection of individual and organizational intervention, in that it includes employee-initiated strategies to access resources and modify their work activities in ways they find personally meaningful. Job crafting works as an individual intervention in that the process coaches individuals on ways to enhance their personal interactions with work. Job crafting works as an organizational intervention in that rather than focusing on personal resources, skills, or attitudes, the process focuses on the people, activities, demands, and resources at work. As such, job crafting produces micro-level organizational change.

Demerouti, Bakker, and Gevers (2015) found that job crafting initiatives directed toward enhancing job resources increased work engagement. In turn, increased work engagement mediated a positive relationship of job crafting with creativity and with extra-role behavior. Both the improved access to resources and the associated positive experience of work increased employees' level of organizational citizenship.

Petrou, Demerouti, and Schaufeli (2018) noted variations in employees' use of job crafting in line with the elements of regulatory focus theory (Higgins, 1997) that distinguishes employees as promotion-focused (i.e., concerned with development) versus prevention-focused (concerned with duties). For promotion employees, effective communications about organizational change initiatives increased their job crafting behavior and their associated work engagement. In contrast, for prevention employees, inadequate communication about organizational change initiatives increased their job crafting behavior and their associated work engagement. Their job crafting activity appeared to function as a means of buffering the implications of communication gaps. This analysis indicated ways in which job crafting can operate in line with organizational agendas or operate as a means of assisting individuals to reduce the uncertainty introduced through organizational change.

Mäkikangas, Bakker, and Schaufeli (2017) found evidence that job crafting may require a high level of functioning prior to the intervention. Their analysis found positive effects for job crafting for individuals with preexisting positive affect, including self-efficacy. Further, job crafting worked more effectively in work units with an existing clear sense of mission, a positive bias toward innovation, and good working relationships with organizational leadership. So, thriving individuals in well-functioning work units gain more benefits from job crafting. This pattern supports the notion that initiatives that work well to address problems, such as burnout, may differ from initiatives that work well to enhance further the positive qualities of work life.

Liao, Wayne, and Rousseau (2016) examined a parallel approach, idiosyncratic deals (i-deals). I-deals have a more explicit status than job crafting action sin that employees negotiate idiosyncratic deals with their employers. Job crafting actions may occur more subtly. Job crafting employees may establish a new work pattern or access to new resources through a frank conversation with their supervisors. Alternatively, job crafting employees may operate on a less official scale, devising work initiatives with members of their work groups. On the most subtle scale, job crafting employees may simply nudge their work patterns in new directions without mentioning their plans to anyone. In contrast, employees negotiate i-deals and employers concur with a unique way of working for those who have successfully negotiated i-deals. Hornung and colleagues (2010) demonstrated that in addition to making positive contributions to employee recruitment and retention, i-deals contribute to increased work engagement.

Idiosyncratic deals present employers challenges in managing perceptions of fairness. Employees without i-deals may feel disadvantaged in their calculations of the balance of demands with rewards. Because i-deals form an official psychological contract, they may endure longer than the informal gains from job crafting.

These studies and others (e.g., Attridge, 2009) support the conclusion that organizational initiatives can improve work engagement through programs to improve workplace health, supervisory communication, organizational culture, and leadership.

THE DARK SIDE OF ENGAGEMENT

Work engagement has its dark side (Bakker, Albrecht, & Leiter, 2011). George (2011) noted that increased engagement need not invariably result in a win–win situation. Ideally, greater engagement leads to greater productivity and well-being, but productivity may at times come at the expense of well-being. As noted, the distinction between workaholism and work engagement rests on the extent to which employees find the work enjoyable. However, activities that employees have enjoyed at one time may not be enjoyed indefinitely. If engagement motivates employees to devote excessive time at work, the employer's gain in productivity may come at the cost of employees' health. Second, George (2011) pointed out that one employee crafting a job to reduce time on unpleasant or tedious tasks may dump these tasks upon their coworkers producing a win–lose situation among employees.

The concept of engagement always held a potential for a dark side. When Kahn (1990) first used the term *engagement* to describe employees' psychological connection with work, he presaged its complex implications for well-being by describing engagement as "harnessing" employees to their "work roles" (Kahn, 1990, p. 694). That phrasing casts some doubt upon work engagement as a win–win situation. The employer appears to win at the cost of employees' autonomy, at the least with potential adverse consequences for their health and well-being.

Sonnentag pointed toward mechanisms through which work engagement could affect well-being negatively. As found in Sonnentag, Binnewies, and Mojza (2010), work engagement predicted increases in future job demands in a time-lagged analysis. Additionally, increased demands predicted subsequent decreases in work engagement. From this perspective the enthusiasm inherent in work engagement could motivate employees to over-commit to work responsibilities. Halbesleben, Harvey, and Bolino (2009) reported similar concerns with increasing work demands. This mechanism could function to undermine efforts to sustain engagement in the long run.

Sonnentag argued for examining moderators to the relationship of work engagement with positive outcomes. She pointed out that Sonnentag, Mojza, Binnewies, and Scholl (2008) differentiated between engaged employees who could detach from work concerns during nonwork times from engaged employees who did not detach in this way. The former group reported more positive affective states at the end of the work week.

These considerations confirm that work engagement does not function as an absolute good. From the perspective of employees, initiatives to enhance work engagement need to anticipate the implications for employees' potential to fulfill their personal aspirations and to maintain their health while pursuing greater productivity. Initiatives need to anticipate the potential for overwhelming employees with increasing demands or to disrupt balances of work time with nonwork involvements. As with so much of organizational psychology, simplicity must also occur in moderation.

CONCLUSION

Work engagement has a future. The simplicity of the construct at first glance recedes to reveal a psychological connection with work with multiple facets and implications. Thorough examination of measurement issues have confirmed the UWES as an effective tool for assessing engagement as a positive construct. Much work remains to design and test interventions to improve work engagement and to package those processes into readily available programs.

FURTHER READING

Bakker, A. B. & Leiter, M. P. (Eds.) (2010). *Work engagement: A handbook of essential research and theory.* Hove, U.K.: Psychology Press. Translated into Japanese.

Bakker, A. B., Taris, T., & Leiter, M. P. (Eds.) (2008). Special Issue. Engagement at work: An emerging concept. *Work and Stress, 22*(3). https://www.tandfonline.com/toc/twst20/22/3

Demerouti, E., Bakker, A. B., Nachreiner, F., & Schaufeli, W. B. (2001). The job demands–resources model of burnout. *Journal of Applied Psychology, 86*(3), 499. https://psycnet.apa.org/doi/10.1037/0021-9010.86.3.499

Macey, W. H., & Schneider, B. (2008). The meaning of employee engagement. *Industrial and Organizational Psychology, 1*(1), 3–30. https://doi.org/10.1111/j.1754-9434.2007.0002.x

Saks, A. M. (2006). Antecedents and consequences of employee engagement. *Journal of Managerial Psychology, 21*(7), 600–619. https://psycnet.apa.org/doi/10.1108/02683940610690169

Salanova, M., Del Líbano, M., Llorens, S., & Schaufeli, W. B. (2014). Engaged, workaholic, burned-out or just 9-to-5? Toward a typology of employee well-being. *Stress and Health, 30*(1), 71–81. https://doi.org/10.1002/smi.2499

Schaufeli, W. B., Bakker, A. B., & Salanova, M. (2006). The measurement of work engagement with a short questionnaire: A cross-national study. *Educational and Psychological Measurement, 66*(4), 701–716. https://doi.org/10.1177%2F0013164405282471

Sonnentag, S., Binnewies, C., & Mojza, E. J. (2010). Staying well and engaged when demands are high: The role of psychological detachment. *Journal of Applied Psychology, 95*, 965–976. https://psycnet.apa.org/doi/10.1037/a0020032

Sonnentag, S., Mojza, E. J., Binnewies, C., & Scholl, A. (2008). Being engaged at work and detached at home: A week-level study on work engagement, psychological detachment, and affect. *Work and Stress, 22*, 257–276. https://dx.doi.org/10.1080/02678370802379440

Taris, T. W., Schaufeli, W. B., & Shimazu, A. (2010). The push and pull of work: About the difference between workaholism and work engagement. In A. B. Bakker & M. P. Leiter (Eds.), *Work engagement: A handbook of essential theory and research* (pp. 39–53). Hove, U.K.: Psychology Press.

REFERENCES

Attridge, M. (2009). Measuring and managing employee work engagement: A review of the research and business literature. *Journal of Workplace Behavioral Health, 24*(4), 383–398. https://doi.org/10.1080/15555240903188398

Bakker, A. B., Albrecht, S. L., & Leiter, M. P. (2011). Work engagement: Further reflections on the state of play. *European Journal of Work and Organizational Psychology, 20*(1), 7488. https://doi.org/10.1080/1359432X.2010.546711

Bakker, A. B., & Demerouti, E. (2014). Job demands–resources theory. In P. Chen (Ed.), *Wellbeing: A complete reference guide* (pp. 1–28). Chichester, U.K.: John Wiley and Sons. https://doi.org/10.1002/9781118539415.wbwell019

Bakker, A. B., Demerouti, E., & Euwema, M. C. (2005). Job resources buffer the impact of job demands on burnout. *Journal of Occupational Health Psychology 10*, 170–80, https://psycnet.apa.org/doi/10.1037/1076-8998.10.2.170

Bakker, A. B., Demerouti, E., & Schaufeli, W. B. 2003. Dual processes at work in a call centre: An application of the job demands–resources model. *European Journal of Work & Organizational Psychology. 12*, 393–417. https://psycnet.apa.org/doi/10.1080/13594320344000165

Bakker, A. B., Demerouti, E., & Sanz-Vergel, A. I. (2014). Burnout and work engagement: The JD–R approach. *Annual Review of Organizational Psychology and Organizational Behavior, 1*, 389–411. https://doi.org/10.1146/annurev-orgpsych-031413-091235

Bakker, A. B., Schaufeli, W. B., Leiter, M. P., & Taris, T. W. (2008). Work engagement: An emerging concept in occupational health psychology. *Work & Stress, 22*(3), 187–200. https://doi.org/10.1080/02678370802393649

Byrne, Z. S., Peters, J. M., & Weston, J. W. (2016). The struggle with employee engagement: Measures and construct clarification using five samples. *Journal of Applied Psychology, 101*(9), 1201. https://psycnet.apa.org/doi/10.1037/apl0000124

Christian, M. S., Garza, A. S., & Slaughter, J. E. (2011). Work engagement: A quantitative review and test of its relations with task and contextual performance. *Personnel Psychology, 64*(1), 89–136. https://doi.org/10.1111/j.1744-6570.2010.01203.x

Cole, M. S., Walter, F., Bedeian, A. G., & O'Boyle, E. H. (2012). Job burnout and employee engagement: A meta-analytic examination of construct proliferation. *Journal of Management, 38*, 1550–1581. https://psycnet.apa.org/doi/10.1177/0149206311415252

Crawford, E. R., LePine, J. A., & Rich, B. L. (2010). Linking job demands and resources to employee engagement and burnout: A theoretical extension and meta-analytic test. *Journal of Applied Psychology, 95*, 834. https://psycnet.apa.org/doi/10.1037/a0019364

De Bruin, G. P., & Henn, C. M. (2013). Dimensionality of the 9-item Utrecht Work Engagement Scale (UWES-9). *Psychological Reports, 112*(3), 788–799. https://doi.org/10.2466%2F01.03.PR0.112.3.788-799

Demerouti, E., Bakker, A. B., & Gevers, J. M. (2015). Job crafting and extra-role behavior: The role of work engagement and flourishing. *Journal of Vocational Behavior, 91*, 87–96. https://doi.org/10.1016/j.jvb.2015.09.001

Demerouti, E., Bakker, A. B., De Jonge, J., Janssen, P. P., & Schaufeli, W. B. (2001). Burnout and engagement at work as a function of demands and control. *Scandinavian Journal of Work, Environment & Health, 27*, 279–286. https://doi.org/10.5271/sjweh.615

Demerouti, E., Bakker, A. B., Nachreiner, F., & Schaufeli, W. B. (2001). The job demands–resources model of burnout. *Journal of Applied Psychology, 86*(3), 499. https://psycnet.apa.org/doi/10.1037/0021-9010.86.3.499

George, J. M. (2011). The wider context, costs, and benefits of work engagement. *European Journal of Work and Organizational Psychology, 20*(1), 53–59. https://psycnet.apa.org/doi/10.1080/1359432X.2010.509924

Halbesleben, J. R. B., Harvey, J., & Bolino, M. C. (2009). Too engaged? A conservation of resources view of the relationship between work engagement and work interference with family. *Journal of Applied Psychology, 94*, 1452–1465. https://psycnet.apa.org/doi/10.1037/a0017595

Higgins, E. T. (1997). Beyond pleasure and pain. *American Psychologist, 52*, 1280–1300. https://psycnet.apa.org/doi/10.1037/0003-066X.52.12.1280

Hornung, S., Rousseau, D. M., Glaser, J., Angerer, P., & Weigl, M. (2010). Beyond top–down and bottom–up work redesign: Customizing job content through idiosyncratic deals. *Journal of Organizational Behavior, 31*, 187–215. https://doi.org/10.1002/job.625

Kahn, W. A. (1990). Psychological conditions of personal engagement and disengagement at work. *Academy of Management Journal, 33*, 692–724. https://doi.org/10.5465/256287

Karasek, R. A., & Theorell, T. (1990). *Healthy work: Stress, productivity and the reconstruction of working life.* New York, NY: Basic Books.

Knight, C., Patterson, M., & Dawson, J. (2017). Building work engagement: A systematic review and meta-analysis investigating the effectiveness of work engagement interventions. *Journal of Organizational Behavior, 38*(6), 792–812. https://doi.org/10.1002/job.2167

Leiter, M. P. & Cooper, C. L. (2017). The state of the art in workplace wellbeing. In C. L. Cooper & M. P. Leiter (Eds.), *The Routledge companion to wellbeing at work* (pp. 1–11). London, U.K.: Routledge. https://doi.org/10.4324/9781315665979

Leiter, M. P. & Maslach, C. (2016). Latent burnout profiles: A new approach to understanding the burnout experience. *Burnout Research, 3*, 89–100. https://doi.org/10.1016/j.burn.2016.09.001

Liao, C., Wayne, S. J., & Rousseau, D. M. (2016). Idiosyncratic deals in contemporary organizations: A qualitative and meta-analytical review. *Journal of Organizational Behavior, 37*(S1), S9–S29. https://doi.org/10.1002/job.1959

Macey, W. H., & Schneider, B. (2008). The meaning of employee engagement. *Industrial and Organizational Psychology, 1*(1), 3–30. https://doi.org/10.1111/j.1754-9434.2007.0002.x

Mackay, M. M., Allen, J. A., & Landis, R. S. (2017). Investigating the incremental validity of employee engagement in the prediction of employee effectiveness: A meta-analytic path analysis. *Human Resource Management Review, 27*, 108–120. https://doi.org/10.1016/j.hrmr.2016.03.002

Mäkikangas, A., Bakker, A. B., & Schaufeli, W. B. (2017). Antecedents of daily team job crafting. *European Journal of Work and Organizational Psychology, 26*(3), 421–433. https://doi.org/10.1080/1359432X.2017.1289920

Mäkikangas, A., Schaufeli, W., Tolvanen, A., & Feldt, T. (2013). Engaged managers are not workaholics: Evidence from a longitudinal person-centered analysis. *Journal of Work and Organizational Psychology, 29*(3), 135–143.

Maslach, C., Jackson, S. E., & Leiter, M. P. (2017). *Maslach Burnout Inventory Manual* (4th ed.). Palo Alto, CA: Mindgarden Press.

Maslach, C. & Leiter, M. P. (1997). *The truth about burnout.* San Francisco, CA: Jossey Bass.

Melnick, E. R., Powsner, S. M., & Shanafelt, T. D. (2017). In reply—Defining physician burnout, and differentiating between burnout and depression. *Mayo Clinic Proceedings, 92*(9), 1456–1458. https://doi.org/10.1016/j.mayocp.2017.07.005

Nahrgang, J. D., Morgeson, F. P., & Hofmann, D. A. (2011). Safety at work: a meta-analytic investigation of the link between job demands, job resources, burnout, engagement, and safety outcomes. *Journal of Applied Psychology. 96*, 71–94. http://psycnet.apa.org/journals/apl/96/1/71/

Petrou, P., Demerouti, E., & Schaufeli, W. B. (2018). Crafting the change: The role of employee job crafting behaviors for successful organizational change. *Journal of Management, 44*(5), 1766–1792. https://doi.org/10.1177%2F0149206315624961

Saks, A. M. (2006). Antecedents and consequences of employee engagement. *Journal of Managerial Psychology, 21*(7), 600–619. https://psycnet.apa.org/doi/10.1108/02683940610690169

Salanova, M., Del Líbano, M., Llorens, S., & Schaufeli, W. B. (2014). Engaged, workaholic, burned-out or just 9-to-5? Toward a typology of employee well-being. *Stress and Health, 30*(1), 71–81. https://doi.org/10.1002/smi.2499

Salanova, M., Grau, R. M., Cifre, E., & Llorens, S. (2000). Computer training, frequency of usage and burnout: the moderating role of computer self-efficacy. *Computers in Human Behavior, 16*(6), 575–590. https://doi.org/10.1016/S0747-5632(00)00028-5

Schaufeli, W., & De Witte, H. (2017). Outlook work engagement in contrast to burnout: Real and redundant! *Burnout Research, 5*, 58–60. https://doi.org/10.1016/j.burn.2017.06.002

Schaufeli, W. B., Bakker, A. B., & Salanova, M. (2006). The measurement of work engagement with a short questionnaire: A cross-national study. *Educational and Psychological Measurement, 66*(4), 701–716. https://doi.org/10.1177%2F0013164405282471

Schaufeli, W. B., Salanova, M., González-Romá, V., Bakker, A. B. (2002). The measurement of engagement and burnout: A confirmatory factor analytic approach. *Journal of Happiness Studies, 3*, 71–92. https://doi.org/10.1023/A:1015630930326

Schaufeli, W. B., Shimazu, A., Hakanen, J., Salanova, M., & De Witte, H. (2017). An ultra-short measure for work engagement: The UWES-3 validation across five countries. *European Journal of Psychological Assessment, 33*, 1–15. https://psycnet.apa.org/doi/10.1027/1015-5759/a000430

Sonnentag, S., Binnewies, C., & Mojza, E. J. (2010). Staying well and engaged when demands are high: The role of psychological detachment. *Journal of Applied Psychology, 95*, 965–976. https://psycnet.apa.org/doi/10.1037/a0020032

Sonnentag, S., Mojza, E. J., Binnewies, C., & Scholl, A. (2008). Being engaged at work and detached at home: A week-level study on work engagement, psychological detachment, and affect. *Work and Stress, 22*, 257–276. https://dx.doi.org/10.1080/02678370802379440

Taris, T. W., Schaufeli, W. B., & Shimazu, A. (2010). The push and pull of work: About the difference between workaholism and work engagement. In A. B. Bakker & M. P. Leiter (Eds.), *Work engagement: A handbook of essential theory and research* (pp. 39–53). Hove, U.K.: Psychology Press.

Wrzesniewski, A., & Dutton, J. E. (2001). Crafting a job: Revisioning employees as active crafters of their work. *Academy of Management Review, 26*, 179–201. https://doi.org/10.5465/AMR.2001.4378011

Xanthopoulou, D., Bakker, A. B., Demerouti, E., & Schaufeli, W. B. (2007). The role of personal resources in the job demands–resources model. *International Journal of Stress Management, 14*, 121–41. https://psycnet.apa.org/doi/10.1037/1072-5245.14.2.121

Michael P. Leiter

CREATIVITY AT WORK

INTRODUCTION

Creativity at work is essential for organizations across different sectors in order to improve their organizational performance and overall effectiveness (Anderson, Potočnik, & Zhou, 2014). Creativity has been claimed as an essential ingredient for any successful organization—if employees and teams do not come up with novel and useful ideas, firms will be clueless regarding how to design their innovation efforts and what changes to implement in order to prosper in the competitive markets (Anderson, Potočnik, Bledow, Hulsheger, & Rosing, 2016). Some examples of employee creativity include the successful 3M Post-It Notes, an idea that came from an employee who found a marketable use for a pressure-sensitive, reusable adhesive in the 1970s. Another example of how a single employee revolutionized a specific product is reusable diapers. These became a huge market success after a Procter & Gamble engineer came up with the idea of using cellulose fibers instead of tissue paper to improve absorbency (Markides & Geroski, 2004). This chapter reviews and integrates the existing research on employee creativity that can help explain how novel and useful ideas such as these are generated.

CREATIVITY AT WORK DEFINED

One of the first conceptual definitions of creativity in the field of applied/organizational psychology was proposed by Amabile (1983) who suggested that "[a] product or response will be judged as creative to the extent that (a) it is both a novel and appropriate, useful, correct, or valuable response to the task at hand and (b) the task is heuristic rather than algorithmic" (p. 360). The importance of both novelty and value can be seen in Ford's (1996) definition, which argues creativity to be "a domain-specific, subjective judgment of the novelty and value of an outcome of a particular action" (p. 1115). Building on these operationalizations, creativity has been most commonly defined as the production of novel and useful ideas (Amabile, 1988; Montag, Maertz, & Baer, 2012) and oftentimes it is simply referred to as "idea generation" (Nijstad, Diehl, & Stroebe, 2003).

There are, however, other more recent definitions of creativity, such as the one by Shalley and Zhou (2008) who argued that "creativity can be described as both an outcome and a process. . . . As a process, creativity can involve continuously finding and solving problems and implementing new solutions . . . it is an iterative process, involving reflection and action, seeking feedback, experimenting, and discussing new ways to do things in contrast to just relying on habit or automatic behavior" (p. 4). Similarly, other scholars have suggested that creativity should be conceptualized from a process perspective whereby employees engage in different behaviors not necessarily according to some predetermined sequence but many times in an iterative and unpredictable fashion, such as problem formulation or definition, preparation or information gathering, idea generation, and idea evaluation or validation (Montag et al., 2012).

The existing literature suggests that the concept of creativity at work indeed refers to both outcomes (e.g., creative ideas) and processes that lead to these outcomes (e.g., idea generation, idea evaluation, etc.). However, it is also important to include the level of analysis at which the outcomes and processes evolve to the operationalization of creativity in order to capture the whole spectrum of creativity at work. In other words, it is argued that creativity refers to outcomes and a complex set of processes that may take place at both the individual employee level and the team level of analysis. Importantly, creativity has to be conceptually distinguished from innovation. Although it is difficult to draw a clear line between creativity and innovation, it has been generally argued that creativity refers to the generation of ideas and their evaluation in terms of usefulness and novelty, whereas innovation also involves their promotion or championing and implementation (Potočnik & Anderson, 2016). In order to provide a response to all of these points, Anderson et al. (2014, p. 1298) proposed that

> creativity and innovation at work are the process, outcomes, and products of attempts to develop new and improved ways of doing things. The creativity stage of this process refers to idea generation, and innovation to the subsequent stage of implementing ideas toward better procedures, practices, or products. Creativity and innovation can occur at the level of the individual, work team, organization, or at more than one of these levels combined, but will invariably result in identifiable benefits at one or more of these levels-of-analysis.

In the rest of this article, the theoretical frameworks and past research are reviewed, focusing specifically on creativity at work.

THEORETICAL FRAMEWORKS

A number of different theoretical perspectives and models have been propounded across the creativity literature. Perhaps the most influential theories that have also received substantial empirical support over the years are the componential theory of organizational creativity (Amabile, 1988) and the interactionist theory of organizational creativity (Woodman, Sawyer, & Griffin, 1993). Although they have received less research attention, other theories such as the model of individual creative action (Ford, 1996) and different process models of creativity (Baughman & Mumford, 1995; Drazin, Glynn, & Kazanjian, 1999; Montag et al., 2012; Reiter-Palmon & Ilies, 2004) also deserve a closer inspection.

Componential Theory of Organizational Creativity.   This model was built on the assumption that work environment shapes employee creativity by influencing individual components of creativity such as expertise, creative thinking skills, and intrinsic motivation (Amabile, 1988, 1997). Key features of work environment that influence these individual components are organizational motivation to innovate, resources, and managerial practices.

In terms of individual components, Amabile (1988, 1997) argues that expertise includes features like memory for factual knowledge, technical proficiency, and special talents. Creative thinking skills refer to a cognitive style that favors taking new perspectives on problems and the ability to explore new pathways. Whereas expertise and creative thinking skills have an influence on what an employee is potentially capable of, it is intrinsic task motivation that determines what a person will actually do (Amabile, 1988, 1997). Intrinsic motivation is present when a person is mainly "driven by deep interest and involvement in the work, curiosity enjoyment, or a personal sense of challenge" (Amabile, 1997, p. 44).

With regard to work environment components, organizational motivation to innovate refers to an orientation toward innovation and support for innovation, whereas the resources component represents any resource relevant to innovation, including finances, time availability, and personnel (Amabile & Conti, 1999). Finally, the management practices component refers to all management levels and is represented by such aspects as providing employees with challenging work, work group support, supervisory encouragement, and autonomy or freedom in the workplace.

In sum, according to this theory, employee expertise, creative thinking skills, and intrinsic motivation are key individual components of creativity, but work environment in terms of organizational motivation to innovate, resources, and managerial practices will also have an impact on these individual components and consequently on individual and small team creativity (Amabile, 1988, 1997). Previous research has provided substantial empirical support for the role of intrinsic motivation as a psychological mechanism that may explain the influences of work environment on employees' creativity; however, the other two components have received less research attention to date (Shalley, Zhou, & Oldham, 2004; Zhou & Shalley, 2010).

Interactionist Theory of Organizational Creativity.

Similarly to componential theory, the interactionist theory of organizational creativity also suggests that both individual and work environment factors influence creativity at work (Woodman et al., 1993). More specifically, this model argues that creativity is a result of a complex employee-environment interaction at different levels. For instance, creativity at the individual level is a function of antecedent conditions (e.g., past reinforcement history), cognitive style and ability (e.g., ideational fluency), personality (e.g., openness), relevant knowledge, motivation, and social influences (e.g., social facilitation), and contextual influences (e.g., task and time limitations). Team-level creativity is a result of employee creative behavior, the interaction between team members (e.g., group composition), group characteristics (e.g., cohesion), team processes (e.g., problem solving), and contextual influences (e.g., organizational size). In turn, organizational creativity is considered as a result of its teams' creative outputs and contextual influences, such as organizational culture and reward systems (Woodman et al., 1993).

Previous research has frequently applied this framework to explore how interactions between the contextual and individual aspects shape employee and team creativity at work (Shalley, Gilson, & Blum, 2009; Yuan & Woodman, 2010; Zhou & Shalley, 2010). Given its explicit focus on different levels of analysis, this model has great potential for exploring effects on creativity across different levels of analysis (Woodman et al., 1993).

Theory of Individual Creative Action. According to the theory of individual creative action, employees have to choose between two competing, conceptually independent, behavioral options—either to engage in creative actions or perform more routine, habitual actions (Ford, 1996). This model further suggests that the choice of what action to take is jointly influenced by three groups of factors such as sense-making processes, motivation, and knowledge and ability. In other words, individual creative action is a function of the combined influences of these different factors, and if any of them are lacking, an employee would not take creative action. In terms of sense-making factors, Ford (1996) suggests that a problem-finding orientation enhances creative actions, whereas automatic problem interpretation schema likely facilitates habitual actions. Among the group of motivational factors, goals (e.g., desired outcomes involve creativity, independence, and achievement), receptivity beliefs (e.g., creative actions are rewarded), capability beliefs (e.g., having confidence in being creative), and emotions (e.g., interest and anger) are suggested as drivers of creative actions. Regarding knowledge and ability, Ford (1996) suggests domain-related knowledge, behavioral abilities, and creative thinking ability to influence individual decisions whether to initiate creative versus habitual actions. For instance, diverse expertise, communication skills, and divergent thinking are all facilitators of creative actions, whereas narrow expertise and low social competence are initiators of habitual actions. This theory has not received much research attention, although some studies provided empirical support for some parts of the model (e.g., Janssen, 2005; Unsworth & Clegg, 2010).

Process Models of Creativity. There are several different models of creativity that can be categorized as process models due to their focus on the sequence of cognitive processes and actions that ultimately lead to creative outcomes—that is, novel and useful ideas (King, 1992; Montag et al., 2012). Traditionally, these models assumed that the creative process evolves in a standard sequence (e.g., Patrick, 1937; Wallas, 1926), but more recent empirical research has suggested that different stages in the creative process may take place simultaneously and/or in an unexpected sequence (Montag et al., 2012). Therefore, rather than focusing on the sequential nature of the creative process, it has recently been suggested that researchers should focus on different types of creative behaviors that take place in different stages of the creative process (Montag et al., 2012). Some of these process models include up to eight different behaviors related to the creative process (Mumford, Mobley, Uhlman, Reiter-Palmon, & Doares, 1991), whereas others focus on two (Drazin et al., 1999) or four behaviors (Baughman & Mumford, 1995). More specifically, early process models suggested preparation, incubation, illumination, and verification as key behaviors of the creative process (Patrick, 1937; Wallas, 1926). In another model, Mumford et al. (1991) suggested that the creative process involves problem construction, information encoding, category search, specification of best-fitting categories, combination and reorganization of best-fitting categories, idea evaluation, implementation, and monitoring. Interestingly, this model also includes implantation as part of the creative process, although idea implementation is essentially part of innovation. More recently, a shorter list of creative performance-related behaviors was suggested by Reiter-Palmon and Ilies (2004) who argued that problem construction, information search and encoding, generation of alternatives, and idea evaluation are key components of the creative process. What is common to all these process models is that most of them cover behaviors that are, in one way or another, related to problem formulation or problem definition, preparation or information gathering, idea generation, and idea evaluation or validation (Montag et al., 2012).

Summary.   Although there are other more specific models of creativity, particularly in the category of process models, the aforementioned theories are considered to be major frameworks in the field of creativity at work. Whereas process models of creativity focus specifically on the individual level, paying attention to different cognitive processes involved in creativity, all other models highlight the role of wider work and organizational context in fostering creativity at work. In the next section, the empirical research on different antecedents of employee creativity that have drawn upon these theoretical frameworks is reviewed and integrated.

ANTECEDENTS OF CREATIVITY AT WORK

Research on creativity at work has been increasing exponentially in the last three decades (Potočnik & Anderson, 2016). The majority of this research has explored the role of different antecedent variables at the individual level, although the literature has been witnessing an increasing number of studies conducted at the team level exploring team-level effects on both team creativity and individual employee creativity—so-called cross-level effects (Anderson et al., 2014). Some of the most recent research at both levels of analysis is summarized here, distinguishing between individual and contextual factors. Some recent studies regarding team-level creativity at work are also reviewed.

Individual Factors.   Research on the role of individual factors in employee creativity has mainly been driven by the componential and interactionist models of creativity exploring the role of different personality traits, self-concepts, abilities, skills, knowledge, expertise, motivation, moods, and emotions in creativity at work (Anderson et al., 2016; Anderson, De Dreu, & Nijstad, 2004). In terms of personality traits, openness to experience, proactive personality, and creative personality have been consistently found to foster employee creativity (Baer, 2010; Baer & Oldham, 2006; Gong, Cheung, Wang, & Huang, 2012; Raja & Johns, 2010; Tierney & Farmer, 2011; Wang & Cheng, 2010; Zhou, 2003). In contrast, other personality traits, such as conscientiousness, extroversion, and neuroticism that were found to predict a variety of employee behaviors like job performance, do not seem to have a direct effect on creativity. Following the interactionist approach (Woodman et al., 1993), some studies explored the boundary conditions under which their effects may be significant. For instance, Raja and Johns (2010) looked at job scope as a contextual moderator of the relationships between "Big Five" personality traits and creativity. Their results showed that both neuroticism and extroversion negatively predicted creativity when the job scope was high or, in other words, when employees had jobs that involved high skill variety, task identity, task significance, autonomy, and feedback (Hackman & Oldham, 1980). George and Zhou (2001) reported that conscientiousness may inhibit employee creativity, but only if supervisors engage in close monitoring and colleagues are unsupportive of creative attempts.

Related to personality traits are different self-appraisals or self-concepts such as self-efficacy and creative self-efficacy (i.e., individual beliefs of how able one is to produce creative ideas; Tierney & Farmer, 2002). These have been found to exhibit stronger relationships with creativity than the personality traits of the five-factor model (Potočnik, Anderson, & Latorre, 2015). According to the theory of individual creative action (Ford, 1996), self-efficacy is considered as one of the important motivational enablers of creative action, and empirical evidence has supported this assumption showing strong, positive effects of self-efficacy and creative self-efficacy on creativity at work (Clegg, Unsworth, Epitropaki, & Parker, 2002; Tierney & Farmer, 2002, 2011).

Drawing on the componential theory of creativity (Amabile, 1988), previous research explored what roles different abilities, skills, thinking styles, and knowledge play in employee creativity. One of the most consistent findings in this field has been the positive effect of creative ability, defined in terms of creativity-relevant skills, such as intuitive thinking and the use of imagination, on employee creativity (Choi, 2004; Choi, Anderson, & Veillette, 2009). Also, certain types of thinking or cognitive styles, such as intuitive, innovative, and creative, have been consistently related to creativity at work (Clegg et al., 2002; Shalley et al., 2004; Tierney, Farmer, & Graen, 1999). Employees characterized by these types of thinking styles are likely to process information from different paradigms simultaneously and have a propensity to take risks and hence come up with novel and useful ideas about how to do their tasks. More recent research has addressed the role of need for cognition, defined as an "individual dispositional tendency to engage in and enjoy thinking" (Cacioppo & Petty, 1982, cited in Wu, Parker, & De Jong, 2014, p. 1512), in creativity. Empirical evidence suggests that individuals scoring high on need for cognition generate more creative ideas (Dollinger, 2003) and also engage in more innovative behaviors (Wu et al., 2014).

In terms of knowledge and expertise as important individual components of creativity (Amabile, 1983, 1988), there is some research that has looked at the effects of job knowledge and job experience on creativity at work (Hammond, Neff, Farr, Schwall, & Zhao, 2011). Although job experience does not seem to be related to creative performance, there is evidence to suggest that job knowledge has positive effects on employee creativity (Choi, 2004). This finding is not surprising given that factual knowledge, technical proficiency, and domain-relevant skills could be considered as necessary to appreciate what improvements are needed and hence generate ideas to achieve them (Potočnik et al., 2015).

Also following the componential theory of creativity (Amabile, 1988), past research has explored the role of employee motivation in creativity. In this line of inquiry, one of the most consistent findings has been the positive effect of intrinsic motivation on creativity (Anderson et al., 2014; Shalley et al., 2004). Employees who are driven by the nature of their work and sense of accomplishment and enjoy doing the work for itself are more likely to generate novel and useful ideas. Recently, Grant and Berry (2011) reported another motivational facilitator of creativity—prosocial motivation. They observed that the effect of intrinsic motivation on creativity was enhanced when employees also exhibited high prosocial motivation. In terms of extrinsic motivation, although the componential theory of creativity (Amabile, 1988) and early research both suggest that extrinsic rewards may undermine creativity, more recent studies suggest that extrinsic incentives may positively affect creativity at work (Byron & Khazanchi, 2012), particularly when intrinsic motivation is already high (Hennessey & Amabile, 2010). However, the effects of extrinsic rewards have been studied in different contexts and they seem to be greater in experimental lab studies than in field studies (Gerhart & Fang, 2015). Much more work is thus needed to clarify the role of different types of motivations in employee creativity.

Finally, a considerable amount of research has explored the role of moods and emotions in creativity at work (Anderson et al., 2014). For instance, there has been consistent support for relationships between positive affect and positive moods and creativity (Binnewies & Wörnlein, 2011; Hammond et al., 2011). In contrast, the evidence about the role of negative affect and negative moods on creativity has been mixed and proved to be much more complex compared to the role of positive affect. For instance, Binnewies and Wörnlein (2011) observed no direct relationship between negative affect, as experienced in the morning, and daily creativity at work. This relationship was negative, however, for those employees who experienced lower levels of job control. Bledow, Rosing, and Frese (2012) explored a dynamic interplay between negative and positive affect and its role in fostering creativity at work. They found that employees exhibited higher levels of creativity if their experience of negative affect in the morning was followed by an affective shift that is, they experienced a decrease in negative affect and an increase in positive affect during the day. More research is needed to further uncover the underlying mechanisms of the affect–creativity link, particularly in relation to how contextual variables may shape this relationship. Next, creativity research that has addressed some of the contextual variables is discussed.

Contextual Factors. Drawing primarily upon the interactionist theory of creativity (Woodman et al., 1993), research has addressed a range of contextual factors as enablers of creativity at work. Contextual factors have also been explored as moderators of the relationships between individual factors and creativity at work to uncover the boundary conditions under which employees may be most creative. Past research has explored contextual factors in terms of task, social, and wider organizational contexts (Anderson et al., 2014, 2016).

Regarding task contexts, a substantial amount of research has provided strong support for the positive effects of job complexity on creativity at work (Anderson et al., 2014; Baer, Oldham, & Cummings, 2003; Tierney & Farmer, 2004). In contrast, more routine jobs—not necessarily less complex, but more automatic—could be expected to lead to lower creativity at work. Although the research on this matter is scarce, there is evidence against this assumption, suggesting that routinization also positively predicts creativity (Ohly, Sonnentag, & Pluntke, 2006). Other aspects related to task context are employee goals and how much creativity the job actually requires. Some studies found that the more employees are expected to engage in creative behaviors, the higher their actual creativity is (Unsworth & Clegg, 2010; Unsworth, Wall, & Carter, 2005).

Some research examining how time pressure affects employee creativity has provided mixed findings. On one hand, there is evidence showing the positive effects of daily time pressure on daily creativity, which suggests that having deadlines could enhance employee creativity (Ohly & Fritz, 2010). On the other hand, Baer and Oldham (2006) observed an inverted U-shaped relationship between time pressure and creativity when employees experienced high support for creativity and were characterized by high openness to experience. Some studies reported no significant relationship between time pressure and creativity at work (Ohly et al., 2006). Clearly, more research is needed to clarify the nature of the effects that time pressure may have on creativity at work.

In terms of social context, previous research has looked at how supervisors, coworkers, and even customers shape employee creativity (Anderson et al., 2014). The vast majority of this research looked at leadership and its role in creativity, providing evidence for the positive role of transformational leadership (Gong, Huang, & Farh, 2009; Shin & Zhou, 2003), benevolent leadership (Wang & Cheng, 2010), supervisory empowerment behaviors (Zhang & Bartol, 2010), and supervisory expectations for creativity (Tierney & Farmer, 2004). Overall, these studies suggest that when leaders and supervisors are supportive of their subordinates, are able to clearly communicate their expectations, and can stimulate and empower them, subordinates are more likely to exhibit higher creativity at work. Recently, Rujie, Janssen, and Shi (2015) showed that transformational leadership is related to employee creativity through follower relational identification with the leader. They further found that this indirect effect of transformational leadership on creativity was significant only when leaders set high creativity expectations. More studies such as this are needed to uncover the underlying mechanisms of leadership effects on employee creativity.

Apart from supervisors, peers or coworkers were also found to exert a significant influence on employee creativity. For instance, previous studies have found that creativity at work can be fostered when coworkers have high creativity-related expectations, are themselves highly creative, and provide support to their colleagues (Farmer, Tierney, & Kung-Mcintyre, 2003; Madjar, Oldham, & Pratt, 2002; Madjar, Greenberg, & Chen, 2011). In general terms, any agent in the employee social context who can provide feedback could be expected to influence employee creativity. Along these lines, De Stobbeleir, Ashford, and Buyens (2011) found that employees who were actively seeking feedback exhibited the highest levels of creativity. Similarly, Madjar and Ortiz-Walters (2008), using a sample of stylists from hairdressing salons, found significant effects of customer input and customer affect-based trust on stylist creativity.

Apart from exploring the impact of these different agents on employee creativity, a growing amount of research has focused on social networks and how these affect creativity at work (Baer, 2010; Perry-Smith, 2006; Perry-Smith & Shalley, 2003; Zhou, Shin, Brass, Choi, & Zhang, 2009). Different network characteristics, such as centrality and diversity, and personality characteristics, such as openness to experience may moderate the relationship between social ties and creativity.

In terms of wider organizational context, factors like organizational climate, bureaucratic practices, and perceived organizational support have been explored as predictors of employee creativity. Wang and Rode (2010) have explored the role of innovative organizational climate as a boundary condition of the transformational leadership-employee creativity link and found that when innovative climate was high and employees strongly identified with their manager, the positive relationship between transformational leadership and employee creativity was enhanced. Hirst, Van Knippenberg, Chin-Hui, and Sacramento (2011) explored the role of bureaucratic practices in terms of centralization and formalization as contextual moderators of the relationship between learning orientation and employee creativity. Although the majority of their findings suggested that less bureaucratic practices favor creativity, they also observed that less formalized practices strengthened the negative relationship between avoid orientation and employee creativity. Finally, perceived organizational support was also linked to creativity, particularly through the process of work team identification and success expectancy (Yu & Frenkel, 2013).

Team Creativity. With increasing reliance on teams in modern organizations, creativity research has recently expanded its inquiry into the team level, exploring factors like team structure, team composition, and team process variables, and the impact these may have on team creativity (Anderson et al., 2014). In terms of team composition, team diversity has been suggested as an important factor in team creativity. Shin and Zhou (2007) found that teams that are more diverse in terms of employee educational specialization or background are more creative, particularly when their supervisor is exhibiting a transformational leadership style. Regarding team processes, Farh, Lee, and Farh (2010) observed a curvilinear relationship between task conflict and team creativity at an early project team phase, such that creativity was highest at moderate levels of task conflict. Gilson and Shalley (2004) explored the role of a wide range of antecedents of team creativity and found that the more creative teams had tasks that required high levels of creativity, member interdependence, shared goals, and placed importance on participative problem solving and experienced a climate that was supportive of creativity.

Summary. Creativity at work has received substantial research attention over the recent years. Scholars interested in this field have explored a wide array of both individual and contextual factors (and interactions between both) as predictors of employee creativity. Although previous findings provide rich implications for both theory development (e.g., Bledow et al., 2012; Perry-Smith & Shalley, 2003) and practical recommendations, much more research is needed to provide conclusive evidence about how creativity unfolds over time and how factors at different levels of analysis influence individual and team creativity at work. Some of these avenues for future research are discussed next.

AVENUES FOR FUTURE RESEARCH

Creativity at work is a vibrant area of research. A substantial amount of work has been done in the field that has made significant contributions to our knowledge of how creativity at work unfolds both over time and across different levels of analysis and how it can be malleable in different contexts. However, based on the literature review presented here and considering recent methodological advances, particularly in terms of multilevel analyses, some directions for future research are suggested in order to further the understanding of creativity in modern workplaces.

First, future research should start revisiting the theoretical underpinnings of creativity at work. The major theoretical frameworks that guided the vast majority of research in the field were developed more than 20 years ago, and they may not adequately capture the fast-changing, complex, and global organizational environments of today (Anderson et al., 2014). Although a few conceptual pieces have been published more recently, these have tended to be rather narrow in focus and have not really been picked up by creativity researchers in their studies. Second, many so-called process models of creativity have been mushrooming in the literature, each suggesting their own fine-grained sub-processes or creativity-relevant behaviors (Montag et al., 2012). For the field to radically move forward, more research is needed at the conceptual level to bring these different models together and propose what antecedents could shape different creativity-relevant behaviors or sub-processes. But, and perhaps more important, in order to fully explore creativity at work, the theory building around process models of creativity should move beyond the micro, individual focus to include team and wider organizational and even societal contexts as factors influencing employee creative processes.

Furthermore, future research should start exploring creativity at work simultaneously with other dimensions of job performance. Given how much organizations today value creativity at work and expect their employees to be creative (e.g., creativity has become part of the formal appraisal systems in many organizations), there is still not enough evidence about how creative performance can be managed along with other, more routine dimensions of job performance. There is some research suggesting that different individual antecedents shape different dimensions of job performance; for instance, conscientiousness and general mental ability strongly predict routine performance, but not creativity, whereas openness predicts creativity, but not routine performance (Potočnik et al., 2015). More research is needed to uncover similar differential effects of contextual variables on both types of performance in order to understand how the working environment can be designed in a way to optimize specific types of behaviors.

The nature of teamwork has been changing with an increasing number of employees working, at least to some degree, in a virtual environment. The research on virtual teams, defined as teams in which members rely on information and communication tools (ICTs) to deliver a common goal (Maynard & Gilson, 2014), is almost completely lacking in creativity research. Taking into account that team processes are likely to unfold differently in virtual teams compared to face-to-face-teams (Maynard, Mathieu, Rapp, & Gilson, 2012), it cannot be assumed that findings on employee creativity in traditional settings can be generalized to a virtual environment. Future research should address this matter, starting with theory development on how virtual contexts may affect creative processes.

There is also a demonstrable need to simultaneously explore both creativity and innovation in future research. On one hand, studies that address only creativity at work are missing the final stage—idea implementation (Anderson et al., 2014, 2016). The production of novel and useful ideas is essential for idea implementation, but if ideas are not implemented, organizations do not benefit from them. On the other hand, the large majority of innovation research tends to merge the creativity stage with the implementation stage. Therefore, based on the current findings, a fine-tuned, clear understanding of what factors are at play at each stage of innovation is missing. Future research in this field is encouraged to add further evidence to this important issue.

Future research should also conduct more intervention studies to explore how employee creativity can be enhanced. Most of the creativity training programs include the creative problem-solving method, which consists of applying creative thinking to open-ended problems. For instance, companies like Quaker Oats have successfully used this method to solve a problem related to syrup blockages, and in general there is empirical evidence to suggest that this method could be effective for enhancing employee creativity (Puccio, Firestien, Coyle, & Masucci, 2006; Thompson, 2001). Other companies, such as IDEO, may focus specifically on the brainstorming stage of creative problem solving. The brainstorming method has been found highly effective for enhancing employee creativity, not only in terms of short-term results, such as increasing the number of generated ideas, but also in terms of long-term results, such as creating an innovation culture (Sutton & Hargadon, 1996). More research is needed, however, to explore the effectiveness of brainstorming and other creative problem-solving programs using experimental designs and employee samples.

Finally, although the field has witnessed some studies using samples from China, India, and South Korea, among others, the vast majority of creativity and innovation research has been conducted in Western countries (Anderson et al., 2014). More research is needed in different geographical areas around the world in order to understand how national cultures may shape creativity at work.

Based on the evidence presented here, creativity at work is clearly a flourishing research area. By addressing some of the gaps identified as areas for future research, however, more can be understood about the creative process at multiple levels and in a changing work environment. Researchers in the field are encouraged to tackle some of these issues in order to expand and develop the existing understanding of creativity in the workplace.

FURTHER READING

Amabile, T. M. (2000). Stimulate creativity by fueling passion. In E. A. Locke (Ed.), *Blackwell handbook of principles of organizational behavior* (pp. 331–341). Oxford: Blackwell.

Amabile, T. M., Conti, R., Coon, H., Lazenby, J., & Herron, M. (1996). Assessing the work environment for creativity. *Academy of Management Journal, 39*, 1154–1184.

Baas, M., De Dreu, C. W. K., & Nijstad, B. A. (2008). A meta-analysis of 25 years of mood-creativity research: Hedonic tone, activation, or regulatory focus? *Psychological Bulletin, 134*, 779–806.

George, J. M., & Zhou, J. (2007). Dual tuning in a supportive context: Joint contributions of positive mood, negative mood, and supervisory behaviors to employee creativity. *Academy of Management Journal, 50*, 605–622.

Liao, H., Liu, D., & Loi, R. (2010). Looking at both sides of the social exchange coin: A social cognitive perspective on the joint effects of relationship quality and differentiation on creativity. *Academy of Management Journal, 53*, 1090–1109.

Madjar, N., & Shalley, C. E. (2008). Multiple tasks' and multiple goals' effect on creativity: Forced incubation or just a distraction? *Journal of Management, 34*, 786–805.

Miron-Spektor, E., Gino, F., & Argote, L. (2011). Paradoxical frames and creative sparks: Enhancing individual creativity through conflict and integration. *Organizational Behavior and Human Decision Processes, 116*, 229–240.

Rank, J., Pace, V. L., & Frese, M. (2004). Three avenues for future research on creativity, innovation, and initiative. *Applied Psychology: An International Review, 53*, 518–528.

Richter, A. W., Hirst, G., van Knippenberg, D., & Baer, M. (2012). Creative self-efficacy and individual creativity in team contexts: Cross-level interactions with team informational resources. *Journal of Applied Psychology, 97*, 1282–1290.

To, M. L., Fisher, C. D., Ashkanasy, N. M., & Rowe, P. A. (2012). Within-person relationships between mood and creativity. *Journal of Applied Psychology, 97*, 599–612.

REFERENCES

Amabile, T. M. (1983). The social psychology of creativity: A componential conceptualization. *Journal of Personality and Social Psychology, 45*, 357–376.

Amabile, T. M. (1988). A model of creativity and innovation in organizations. *Research in Organizational Behavior, 10*, 123–176.

Amabile, T. M. (1997). Motivating creativity in organizations: On doing what you love and loving what you do. *California Management Review, 40*, 39–58.

Amabile, T. M., & Conti, R. (1999). Changes in the work environment for creativity during downsizing. *Academy of Management Journal, 42*, 630–640.

Anderson, N., de Dreu, C. K. W., & Nijstad, B. A. (2004). The routinization of innovation research: A constructively critical review of the state-of-the-science. *Journal of Organizational Behavior, 25*, 147–173.

Anderson, N., Potočnik, K., Bledow, R., Hulsheger, U. R., & Rosing, K. (2016). Innovation and creativity in organizations. In D. Ones, N. Anderson, C. Viswesvaran, & H. K. Sinangil (Eds.), *Handbook of industrial, work and organizational psychology*, 2d ed. London and New York: SAGE.

Anderson, N., Potočnik, K., & Zhou, J. (2014). Innovation and creativity in organizations: A state-of-the-science review and prospective commentary. *Journal of Management, 40*, 1297–1333.

Baer, M. (2010). The strength-of-weak-ties perspective on creativity: A comprehensive examination and extension. *Journal of Applied Psychology, 95*, 592–601.

Baer, M., & Oldham, G. R. (2006). The curvilinear relation between experienced creative time pressure and creativity: Moderating effects of openness to experience and support for creativity. *Journal of Applied Psychology, 91*, 963–970.

Baer, M., Oldham, G. R., & Cummings, A. (2003). Rewarding creativity: When does it really matter? *Leadership Quarterly, 14*, 569–586.

Baughman, W. A., & Mumford, M. D. (1995). Process-analytic models of creative capacities—Operations influencing the combination-and-reorganization process. *Creativity Research Journal, 8*, 37–62.

Binnewies, C., & Wörnlein, S. C. (2011). What makes a creative day? A diary study on the interplay between affect, job stressors, and job control. *Journal of Organizational Behavior, 32*, 589–607.

Bledow, R., Rosing, K., & Frese, M. (2012). A dynamic perspective on affect and creativity. *Academy of Management Journal, 56*, 432–450.

Byron, K., & Khazanchi, S. (2012). Rewards and creative performance: A meta-analytic test of theoretically derived hypotheses. *Psychological Bulletin, 138*, 809–830.

Cacioppo, J. T., & Petty, R. E. (1982). The need for cognition. *Journal of Personality and Social Psychology, 42*, 116–131.

Choi, J. N. (2004). Individual and contextual predictors of creative performance: The mediating role of psychological processes. *Creativity Research Journal, 16*, 187–199.

Choi, J. N., Anderson, T. A., & Veillette, A. (2009). Contextual inhibitors of employee creativity in organizations: The insulating role of creative ability. *Group & Organization Management, 34*, 330–357.

Clegg, C., Unsworth, K., Epitropaki, O., & Parker, G. (2002). Implicating trust in the innovation process. *Journal of Occupational & Organizational Psychology, 75*, 409–422.

De Stobbeleir, K. E. M., Ashford, S. J., & Buyens, D. (2011). Self-regulation of creativity at work: The role of feedback-seeking behavior in creative performance. *Academy of Management Journal, 54*, 811–831.

Dollinger, S. J. (2003). Need for uniqueness, need for cognition and creativity. *Journal of Creative Behavior, 37*, 99–116.

Drazin, R., Glynn, M., & Kazanjian, R. K. (1999). Multilevel theorizing about creativity in organizations: A sense-making perspective. *Academy of Management Review, 24*, 286–307.

Farh, J. L., Lee, C., & Farh, C. I. C. (2010). Task conflict and team creativity: A question of how much and when. *Journal of Applied Psychology, 95*, 1173–1180.

Farmer, S. M., Tierney, P., & Kung-Mcintyre, K. (2003). Employee creativity in Taiwan: An application of role identity theory. *Academy of Management Journal, 46*, 618–630.

Ford, C. M. (1996). A theory of individual creative action in multiple social domains. *Academy of Management Review, 21*, 1112–1142.

George, J. M., & Zhou, J. (2001). When openness to experience and conscientiousness are related to creative behavior: An interactional approach. *Journal of Applied Psychology, 86*, 513–524.

Gerhart, B., & Fang, M. (2015). Pay, intrinsic motivation, extrinsic motivation, performance, and creativity in the workplace: Revisiting long-held beliefs. *Annual Review of Organizational Psychology and Organizational Behavior, 2*, 489–521.

Gilson, L. L., & Shalley, C. E. (2004). A little creativity goes a long way: An examination of teams' engagement in creative processes. *Journal of Management, 30*, 453–470.

Gong, Y., Cheung, S., Wang, M., & Huang, J. (2012). Unfolding the proactive process for creativity: Integration of the employee proactivity, information exchange, and psychological safety perspectives. *Journal of Management, 38*, 1611–1633.

Gong, Y., Huang, J., & Farh, J. (2009). Employee learning orientation, transformational leadership, and employee creativity: The mediating role of employee creative self-efficacy. *Academy of Management Journal, 52*, 765–778.

Grant, A. M., & Berry, J. W. (2011). The necessity of others is the mother of invention: Intrinsic and prosocial motivations, perspective taking, and creativity. *Academy of Management Journal, 54*, 73–96.

Hackman, J. R., & Oldham, G. R. (1980). *Work redesign*. Reading, MA: Addison-Wesley.

Hammond, M. M., Neff, N. L., Farr, J. L., Schwall, A. R., & Zhao, X. (2011). Predictors of individual-level innovation at work: A meta-analysis. *Psychology of Aesthetics, Creativity, and the Arts, 5*, 90–105.

Hennessey B. A., & Amabile, T. M. (2010). Creativity. *Annual Review of Psychology, 61*, 569–698.

Hirst, G., Van Knippenberg, D., Chin-Hui Chen, & Sacramento, C. A. (2011). How does bureaucracy impact individual creativity? A cross-level investigation of team contextual influences on goal orientation-creativity relationships. *Academy of Management Journal, 54*, 624–641.

Janssen, O. (2005). The joint impact of perceived influence and supervisor supportiveness on employee innovative behaviour. *Journal of Occupational and Organizational Psychology, 78*, 573–579.

King, N. (1992). Modeling the innovation process: An empirical comparison of approaches. *Journal of Occupational and Organizational Psychology, 65*, 89–100.

Madjar, N., Greenberg, E., & Chen, Z. (2011). Factors for radical creativity, incremental creativity, and routine, noncreative performance. *Journal of Applied Psychology, 96*, 730–743.

Madjar, N., Oldham, G. R., & Pratt, M. G. (2002). There's no place like home? The contributions of work and nonwork creativity support to employees' creative performance. *Academy of Management Journal, 45*, 757–767.

Madjar, N., & Ortiz-Walters, R. (2008). Customers as contributors and reliable evaluators of creativity in the service industry. *Journal of Organizational Behavior, 29*, 949–966.

Markides, C. C., & Geroski, P. A. (2004). *Fast second: How smart companies bypass radical innovation to enter and dominate new markets.* San Francisco: Wiley.

Maynard, M. T., & Gilson, L. L. (2014). The role of shared mental model development in understanding virtual team effectiveness. *Group & Organization Management, 39*, 3–32.

Maynard, M. T., Mathieu, J. E., Rapp, T. L., & Gilson, L. L. (2012). Something(s) old and something(s) new: Modeling drivers of global virtual team effectiveness. *Journal of Organizational Behavior, 33*, 342–365.

Montag, T., Maertz, C. P., & Baer, M. (2012). A critical analysis of the workplace creativity space. *Journal of Management, 38*, 1362–1386.

Mumford, M. D., Mobley, M. I., Uhlman, C. E., Reiter-Palmon, R., & Doares, L. M. (1991). Process analytic models of creative capacities. *Creativity Research Journal, 4*, 91–122.

Nijstad, B. A., Diehl, M., & Stroebe, W. (2003). Cognitive stimulation and interference in idea generating groups. In P. B. Paulus & B. A. Nijstad (Eds.), *Group creativity: Innovation through collaboration* (pp. 137–159). New York: Oxford University Press.

Ohly, S., & Fritz, C. (2010). Work characteristics, challenge appraisal, creativity, and proactive behavior: A multi-level study. *Journal of Organizational Behavior, 31*, 543–565.

Ohly, S., Sonnentag, S., & Pluntke, F. (2006). Routinization, work characteristics and their relationships with creative and proactive behaviors. *Journal of Organizational Behavior, 27*, 257–279.

Patrick, C. (1937). Creative thought in artists. *Journal of Psychology, 4*, 35–73.

Perry-Smith, J. (2006). Social yet creative: The role of social relationships in facilitating individual creativity. *Academy of Management Journal, 49*, 85–101.

Perry-Smith, J., & Shalley, C. E. (2003). The social side of creativity: A static and dynamic social network perspective. *Academy of Management Review, 28*, 89–106.

Potočnik, K., & Anderson, N. (2016). A critical review of change management and innovation related concepts in management studies: Toward conceptual and operational clarity. *European Journal of Work and Organizational Psychology, 25*, 481–494. http://www.tandfonline.com/doi/pdf/10.1080/1359432X.2016.1176022?needAccess=true

Potočnik, K., Anderson, N. R., & Latorre, F. (2015). Selecting for innovation: Methods of assessment and the criterion problem. In I. Nikolaou & J. K. Oostrom (Eds.), *Employee recruitment, selection, and assessment: Contemporary issues for theory and practice* (pp. 209–227). London: Psychology Press and Routledge Academic.

Puccio, G. J., Firestien, R. L., Coyle, C., & Masucci, C. (2006). A review of the effectiveness of CPS training: A focus on workplace issues. *Creativity and Innovation Management, 15*, 19–33.

Raja, U., & Johns, G. (2010). The joint effects of personality and job scope on in-role performance, citizenship behaviors and creativity. *Human Relations, 63*, 981–1005.

Reiter-Palmon, R., & Ilies, J. J. (2004). Leadership and creativity: Understanding leadership from a creative problem-solving perspective. *Leadership Quarterly, 15*, 55–77.

Rujie, Q., Janssen, O., & Shi, K. (2015). Transformational leadership and follower creativity: The mediating role of follower relational identification and the moderating role of leader creativity expectations. *Leadership Quarterly, 26*, 286–300.

Shalley, C. E., Gilson, L. L., & Blum, T. C. (2009). Interactive effects of growth need strength, work context, and job complexity on self-reported creative performance. *Academy of Management Journal, 52*, 489–505.

Shalley, C. E., & Zhou, J. (2008). Organizational creativity research: A historical overview. In C. E. Shalley & J. Zhou (Eds.), *Handbook of organizational creativity* (pp. 3–31). Hillsdale, NJ: Lawrence Erlbaum.

Shalley, C. E., Zhou, J., & Oldham, G. R. (2004). The effects of personal and contextual characteristics on creativity: Where should we go from here? *Journal of Management, 30*, 933–958.

Shin, S. J., & Zhou, J. (2003). Transformational leadership, conservation, and creativity: Evidence from Korea. *Academy of Management Journal, 46*, 703–714.

Shin, S. J., & Zhou, J. (2007). When is educational specialization heterogeneity related to creativity in research and development teams? Transformational leadership as a moderator. *Journal of Applied Psychology, 92*, 1709–1721.

Sutton, R. I., & Hargadon, A. (1996). Brainstorming groups in context: Effectiveness in a product design firm. *Administrative Science Quarterly, 41*, 685–718.

Thompson, G. (2001). The reduction in plant maintenance costs using creative problem-solving principles. *Journal of Process Mechanical Engineering, 215*, 185–195.

Tierney, P., & Farmer, S. M. (2002). Creative self-efficacy: Its potential antecedents and relationship to creative performance. *Academy of Management Journal, 45*, 1137–1148.

Tierney, P., & Farmer, S. M. (2004). The Pygmalion process and employee creativity. *Journal of Management*, *30*, 413–432.

Tierney, P., & Farmer, S. M. (2011). Creative self-efficacy development and creative performance over time. *Journal of Applied Psychology*, *96*, 277–293.

Tierney, P., Farmer, S. M., & Graen, G. B. (1999). An examination of leadership and employee creativity: The relevance of traits and relationships. *Personnel Psychology*, *52*, 591–620.

Unsworth, K. L., & Clegg, C. W. (2010). Why do employees undertake creative action? *Journal of Occupational and Organizational Psychology*, *83*, 77–99.

Unsworth, K. L., Wall, T. D., & Carter, A. (2005). Creative requirement: A neglected construct in the study of employee creativity? *Group & Organization Management*, *30*, 541–560.

Wallas, G. (1926). *The art of thought*. New York: Harcourt.

Wang, A., & Cheng, B. (2010). When does benevolent leadership lead to creativity? The moderating role of creative role identity and job autonomy. *Journal of Organizational Behavior*, *31*, 106–121.

Wang, P., & Rode, J. C. (2010). Transformational leadership and follower creativity: The moderating effects of identification with leader and organizational climate. *Human Relations*, *63*, 1105–1128.

Woodman, R. W., Sawyer, J. E., & Griffin, R. W. (1993). Toward a theory of organizational creativity. *Academy of Management Review*, *18*, 293–321.

Wu, C., Parker, S. K., & de Jong, J. P. J. (2014). Need for cognition as an antecedent of individual innovation behavior. *Journal of Management*, *40*, 1511–1534.

Yu, C., & Frenkel, S. J. (2013). Explaining task performance and creativity from perceived organizational support theory: Which mechanisms are more important? *Journal of Organizational Behavior*, *34*, 1165–1181.

Yuan, F., & Woodman, R. W. (2010). Innovative behavior in the workplace: The role of performance and image outcome expectations. *Academy of Management Journal*, *53*, 323–342.

Zhang, X., & Bartol, K. M. (2010). Linking empowering leadership and employee creativity: The influence of psychological empowerment, intrinsic motivation, and creative process engagement. *Academy of Management Journal*, *53*, 107–128.

Zhou, J. (2003). When the presence of creative coworkers is related to creativity: Role of supervisor close monitoring, developmental feedback, and creative personality. *Journal of Applied Psychology*, *88*, 413–422.

Zhou, J., & Shalley, C. E. (2010). Deepening our understanding of creativity in the workplace: A review of different approaches to creativity research. In S. Zedeck (Ed.), *APA handbook of industrial and organizational psychology* (pp. 275–302). Washington, DC: APA.

Zhou, J., Shin, S. J., Brass, D. J., Choi, J., & Zhang, Z. (2009). Social networks, personal values, and creativity: Evidence for curvilinear and interaction effects. *Journal of Applied Psychology*, *94*, 1544–1552.

Kristina Potočnik and Neil Anderson

COUNTERPRODUCTIVE WORK BEHAVIORS

INTRODUCTION

Study of work performance has distinguished four elements—those concerned with the work task, those facilitating workplace and social relations (citizenship), those focused on adaptation and innovation, that contrast with those that disrupt and divert work activities (counterproductive work behaviors, CWBs) (Koopmans et al., 2011; Rotundo & Sackett, 2002). This article focuses on CWB, which, because of its covert nature, can be difficult for organizations to accurately discern and quantify; such behaviors disrupt organizations, as well as incurring considerable direct and indirect costs through thefts, losses, and accidents, with consequent reputation-loss, sanctions, and fines. Estimates, for example, of the costs of global financial fraud are calculated to be equivalent to 6.05% of GDP, equating to some $5.127 trillion, removing an average of 3–6% from the average organization balance sheet (Button et al., 2009). In addition, longitudinal organizational study reveals the deleterious cycles CWB creates, exacerbating employee stress and contributing further to such behaviors (Meier & Spector, 2013). Their consequences can extend beyond organizational boundaries, with potentially adverse impacts on a wide range of stakeholders, including customer-service users, their families, communities, and societies. In this article, CWB is defined, incorporating consideration of the types of activity and their structure and measurement. Four distinct perspectives are explored: the individual, situational, socio-cognitive, and moral licensing, to advance our understanding, and through this to improve the means of their detection, and to indicate better ways to deter and ameliorate these activities.

WHAT ARE COUNTERPRODUCTIVE BEHAVIORS?

Their Type and Structure.   CWBs are voluntary actions that violate important organizational and social norms, threatening the well-being of organizations, their employees, and service-users (Robinson & Bennett, 1995). They are significant for employers because they divert attention from the achievement of organizational goals, but they can also threaten the organization's long-term reputation and ultimate viability (Searle & Rice, 2020). CWBs can also lower psychological well-being and self-confidence, diminishing work and life satisfaction, and can impact health so as to reduce attendance and productivity and cause burnout (Fox et al., 2012; Hills & Joyce, 2013; O'Boyle et al., 2011; Samnani et al., 2014).

Prior meta-analytic study indicated CWB to be a distinct work behavior and negatively related to organizational citizenship behavior (OCB) (Dalal, 2005). However, research has revealed a more complex relationship between these two organizational dimensions, to which we return in our final section on moral licensing. Meta-analytic review confirms a general factor and various competing CWB taxonomies (Marcus et al., 2016). Research has dichotomized premeditated transgressive actions from those that are impulsive (Berkowitz, 1993), with considerable attention focused on discerning the different manifestations in CWB and their underlying structures. Critical review of prior study, however, suggests these different structural results may be an artifact of their discrete theoretical foundations (Marcus et al., 2016).

An area with greater consensus has been the distinguishing of CWB based on its target, separating organizationally directed actions (CWB-O) from those targeting an individual (CWB-I) (e.g., Robinson & Bennett, 1995). Further granularity has been added by the five-factor model that separates distinct CWB-O aspects, including organization-property destruction, job-specific shortcomings (production deviance), theft, and withdrawal, which are contrasted with interpersonally directed abuse (Spector et al., 2006). Subsequent meta-analytic scrutiny of these distinctions confirmed withdrawal as a more hidden and organizationally targeted deviance (Carpenter & Berry, 2017). "Production deviance," which involves a failure to follow standard organizational and/or professional processes, could blur these target distinctions as it endangers the safety of others, but it is also likely to be directed at the organization. However, without insight into the perpetrator's underlying motivations, their true target cannot be discerned. Marcus and colleagues' (2016) meta-analytic study indicated stronger support for a far more granular 11-facet taxonomy (Gruys & Sackett, 2003) as opposed to other less complex designs. Gruys and Sackett's (2003) 11-facet model expanded the previous binary organization and interpersonal target distinctions by adding the self, which is more apparent in behaviors such as drug or alcohol abuse (Marcus et al., 2016). These models are valuable in mapping transgressive behaviors, for instance in a large comparative study of health professionals' CWB that revealed the dominance of production deviances, such as a failure to properly record medical examinations or follow correct procedures (Searle et al., 2017). An enduring question, however, concerns how far these taxonomies capture actual behaviors, with evidence showing their value in indicating more frequent forms of deviance, but omitting rare extreme incidences such as the death of an individual (Searle & Rice, 2020).

A long-running debate has considered the hierarchy and structure of these forms of transgression, with conceptual argument contending interpersonally directed aggression to be the most severe, because it transgresses social norms (Bennett & Robinson, 2000). Empirical study of reporting behaviors reveals these distinctions to be more academic, with significant events more regularly reported (Bowling et al., 2020). Analysis of the misconduct of health professionals indicates relative similarity to many forms of transgressions, except for five behaviors that show critically different recidivistic patterns when studied over time (Spittal et al., 2015, 2019). They found elevated risk levels among professionals who abuse drugs or alcohol, steal, sexually harass and abuse, or have mental health issues, and they revealed different remediation and sanctions to be required to reduce the risk and adequately protect patients. (Why these anomalies arise is considered in the moral licensing section.) Their work highlights the importance of early misconduct detection for its subsequent and more successful remediation, because these professionals are more amenable to correction in the earlier stages of their careers, before these activities become ingrained and habitual.

Measurement. There has been considerable debate regarding the best way to measure CWB, with psychological study relying predominantly on self-report questionnaires, which are important in gathering data concerning less obvious activities, such as employee withdrawal. Collecting data on transgression is also improved through independent study, including anonymity, which can result in surprisingly candid reporting (Searle & Rice, 2018). The comparison of self-report data and that obtained by observations of others shows strong correlations, but that the former has incremental value by capturing a far wider range of transgressions than those seen by others (Berry et al., 2012). An important caveat, however, to the reliability of self-report has emerged from emotion and stress CWB studies, which reveal how individuals may not necessarily be aware of the way their behavior is declining, especially if they morally disengage (Fida et al., 2018). The reporting of others remains particularly important in the capture of severe transgressions (Bowling et al., 2020; Spittal et al., 2019). Four different perspectives on CWB are now reviewed.

PERPETRATOR PERSONALITY

Traditional approaches to understanding CWB have categorized "good" or "bad" employees, with considerable effort devoted to discerning the traits of "bad apples" (Kish-Gephart et al., 2010). Research into personality has notably contributed the "dark triad" (DT) of three facets: Machiavellianism, which involves a lack of concern for others, manipulating others to advance personal goals, and making individuals less normatively constrained in their social exchanges; narcissism, which includes attention-seeking and hypercompetitive behaviors that stem from the individual's delusions of grandeur and inflated self-view; and psychopathy, which comprises antisocial behavior emanating from the disregard for societal norms (LeBreton et al., 2018). Meta-analytic study reveals DT as more prevalent among men than women, and negatively related to Big Five's factor agreeableness, and Hexaco's honesty-humility model (Muris et al., 2017). Other Big Five personality factors associated with interpersonally and organizationally directed deviance include low conscientious and emotional stability (Berry et al., 2007). Conversely, those with lower DT levels are more likely to report others' CWB (Brock Baskin et al., 2020).

Scrutiny shows these DT factors are moderately correlated, with each significantly associated with CWB, with Machiavellianism and psychopathy also associated with reduced job performance (O'Boyle et al., 2012). Two contextual factors, however, are found to significantly moderate impacts: These include organizational culture, specifically cohesive workplaces that value duty and staff loyalty; and those in positions of authority. Closer examination indicates that while position of authority offers little constraint to those high in Machiavellianism, the adage about power corrupting is more evident among narcissists. Working in a more collective workplace may weaken CWB, but individual authority has fewer moderating consequences for those high in psychopathy. Psychopathy and Machiavellianism differ in their impacts on CWB through the mechanisms of moral disengagement, which is discussed in the social cognitive section (Egan et al., 2015). However, study of leaders with high levels of DT working in CWB-permissive contexts reveals the considerable challenges presented in working for someone who revels in the misfortunes of others (James et al., 2014).

Research has often failed to provide more granular exploration of DT, with studies of narcissism largely omitting scrutiny of the sub-facet, narcissistic vulnerability (LeBreton et al., 2018). Indeed, while CWB is usually associated with individual entitlement and exploitation of others, contrary results emerge for another narcissism facet, leadership authority (Grijalva & Newman, 2015). Similarly, the psychopathy facet, self-centered impulsive fearlessness, is rarely considered yet has revealed the associated organizational-directed CWB to be evident only among those with lower educational attainment and reduced interpersonal influence skills (Blickle & Schütte, 2017). By contrast, those with higher levels of education appear better able to manage their impulsivity, and therefore able to achieve more positive organizational outcomes. Paradoxically, results indicate that some level of DT may be important in effective leadership, but these benefits can rapidly unravel in less favorable situations, such as in response to psychological threat, physical exhaustion, cognitive overload, or stress (Kaiser et al., 2015). Critically, these unfavorable conditions can deplete individuals' resources to manage and suppress their less desirable impulses.

In summary, while individual differences have long been used to understand CWB, their current measurement may be oversimplistic, drawing largely from cross-sectional self-report studies, and with limited value in effectively discerning those with malevolent intent (Muris et al., 2017). This perspective does provide an important theoretical insight, but its utilization by an employing organization may be more limited (Levashina & Campion, 2006; Paulhus et al., 2013). Critically, more nefarious individuals may simply be better at adapting their responses to recruiters' requirements (Roulin & Bourdage, 2017). As a result, the application of personality to reducing CWB in organizations may be oversold, and indeed offer a false sense of confidence in being able to identify and deter those with high DT from entering a workplace (LeBreton et al., 2018). The fidelity between personality and distinct types of CWB is not apparent (Bragg & Bowling, 2018). Instead, it may be more valuable to consider CWB as an adaptive response (Dalal, 2005), an approach we now turn our attention to.

SITUATIONAL PERSPECTIVE

A seminal study of stress and coping (Lazarus & Folkman, 1984) focused on environmental demands (i.e., stressors) that face an individual. Strain manifests itself in various psychological forms, including anxiety, depression, and burnout, but can also trigger behavioral responses, such as withdrawal or increased aggression. These interrelations are the foundation of stress-emotion studies of CWB (Fox et al., 2001). In contrast to the previous approach, here the antecedents of CWB are found to arise from work situations, with efforts to discern the factors that undermine or overwhelm individuals, usually some form of trigger event or more pervasive frustrating context (Malik et al., 2020; Parker et al., 2020). Critically, CWB is positioned as a reactive consequence, and therefore, it is likely to be a far more widespread organizational phenomenon (Spector & Fox, 2005).

Key situations that create tangible stressors include those with interpersonal conflict, high levels of organizational constraint, and excessive workload, as well as those that reduce resources, specifically those concerned with support and decision-autonomy (Chen & Spector, 1992; Fox et al., 2001; Hershcovis et al., 2007). These contexts have significant affective consequences, thwarting and frustrating employees, which then deplete their self-regulatory resources that are central to containing negative behaviors (Baumeister et al., 1998).

An important approach to the study of stress-inducing circumstances involves the mapping of different CWB pathways, to reveal their distinct emotional precursors. Increasingly, attention has converged on the significance of negative affect (Fida et al., 2018; Kiefer, 2005), especially job-related affect (Krishnakumar et al., 2017). Research has found different emotions associated with distinct CWB, for example linking anger and anxiety to incivility and sabotage behaviors, while upset and boredom are more likely to produce withdrawal (Spector et al., 2006). By contrast, the relationship between emotion and theft appears more varied, and linked to perceived distributive injustice (Wilkin & Connelly, 2015). A further significant aspect of these stress-emotion-CWB relations has revealed that by undertaking CWB, an individual can actually alleviate their negative feelings (Shoss et al., 2016). Such results suggest that the capture of current emotions, rather than assessing stress per se, might be important in the early detection of CWB hotspots. However, care needs to be taken with this, as studies also show how organizational attempts to monitor and control employees erode their trust and actually lead to citizenship being replaced by CWB (Jensen & Raver, 2012; Yost et al., 2019).

A significant moderator to these stress-emotion-CWB pathways is individual difference; for instance, research indicates that trait anger and gender are significant moderators for CWB and occur more frequently for men than for women (Fida et al., 2015b; Hershcovis et al., 2007).

Situational studies have revealed the emergence of more pervasive CWB spirals of decline, where one person's CWB becomes another's source of stress, and so on; these insights underscore why stressful environments are likely to have far more widespread levels of misconduct (Spector et al., 2006). Further research into these emotional pathways also shows how employees' cognitions are reshaped, critically the de-coupling of negative affect from experiences, and in so doing offer an important psychological means to cope by allowing individuals to rationalize or diminish impact of their resultant deviant behaviors by assuaging their sense of guilt (Bandura, 1991). These more deviant cognitions can start very early in processes of workplace socialization and evolve through ongoing work experiences to create moral disengagement. Although this can reduce the strain individuals experience, it can also render the resultant deviant behaviors to be more benign (Fida et al., 2015a). (Moral disengagement is examined in more detail in the social cognitive section.) The reframing of cognitions can start as individual phenomena, but can soon become a pervasive self-serving view that is reinforced by others in a group, or across an entire workplace through their shared values, norms, and behavioral models (Rice & Searle, 2022). Studies highlight the critical role that leaders can play in this moral drift (Peng & Kim, 2020).

In summary, this perspective identifies the important role of affect in a process of CWB, positioning CWB to be an adaptive response to the diminishing context in which the individual is currently working. Significantly, this perspective enables a shift from simply focusing on an individual "bad apple" toward seeing CWB as a more widespread phenomenon, thus challenging as overly simplistic any individual scapegoating of CWB. Instead, attention is directed toward a wider stress-inducing context, highlighting how and why CWB can spread through a group, showing emotion not only to be an antecedent to CWB, but also a means for early detection of potential hotspots. However, in the absence of attention on the sources of stress, and better support to allow individuals to acquire more resources and better coping strategies, the potential of CWB remains; indeed, perversely by undertaking deviant actions, feelings of negative affect can be temporarily attenuated. Further, this perspective reveals a perverse coping response, with individuals cognitively reshaping their worlds, a phenomenon that can emerge surprisingly early in their employment enabling them to remain in these challenging workplaces. Next, a more complex approach is examined that combines some of the elements of the two previous perspectives.

SOCIO-COGNITIVE PERSPECTIVE

Bandura's (1986) seminal work on social cognitive theory provides one of the most significant advances in understanding deviant behavior. It adds insight into self-regulation and self-reflectiveness, through considering how moral agency is exercised, conceptualizing its proactive and inhibitory components. *Proactive components* are found in many occupations and evident in codes and standards, such as a doctor's Hippocratic Oath, which enshrines that actions should not further harm patients (Searle & Rice, 2020). *Inhibitory components* arise from the internalization of moral standards (Bandura, 1986), and therefore can vary according to different influences, including from peers, or national cultures (Westerman et al., 2007). Bandura distinguishes between three inhibitors. First is self-evaluation, which restrains an individual through either inwardly noting and then avoiding actions that violate their personal standards, or through their subsequent correction following an experience of guilt, which is a critical moral emotion (Greenbaum et al., 2020). The other two inhibitors are sanctions that lie beyond the individual and operate as fear-based deterrents. Social sanctions curtail individuals' activities through concern that others might disapprove and ostracize them, while legal sanctions focus on a fear of being caught and incurring punishment or fine.

However, Bandura (1986) offers an important psychological mechanism that helps individuals deactivate these aforementioned inhibitors, enabling them to cognitively dissociate their actions from these negative consequences. He develops moral disengagement as a dynamic means to reframe and neutralize deviant actions, by separating the behavior from its moral content through the use of four distinct "loci" that comprise eight moral disengagement mechanisms (Bandura, 1986, 2016). These processes significantly change how the event is regarded (Moore & Gino, 2013). Bandura implies a hierarchy for these different loci that he contends reveals the extent of their moral decline. Through these means an individual, in specific situations, can retain their moral commitment to ethical principles while concurrently performing norm-violating actions without feeling (at least temporarily) the more usual sense of conflict, guilt, shame, or even remorse. This dichotomization of the cognitive mechanisms offers insight into the associated cognitions, and through these important areas to focus on remediation and intervention.

The first locus is *behavioral* and distinguishes three cognitive rationalization processes that are designed to diminish the action's immorality and to reduce the enormity of what is being done. *Moral justification* renders immoral conduct as defensible, often making it appear an entirely reasonable course of action. *Euphemistic labeling* deliberately sanitizes the situation, using transformational words that change the immoral into something more respectable, for instance a shift from "killing people" to "collateral damage." Finally, *advantageous comparison* discounts the questionable behavior through making a comparison with another's far worse actions.

Bandura's (1986) second locus, *agency*, involves cognitively distorting perceptions of situational control and responsibility. This is done either through *displacing responsibility*, which pushes accountability for these actions onto some other decision-maker, often higher up the organization's hierarchy, or by *diffusing responsibility* onto a wider group. The third locus focuses on the *outcome*, disregarding or downplaying it by *distorting the consequences* of actions, or through simple *denial* that any, or specifically any negative, outcome arose. The final locus shifts attention onto the target, blaming them by means of *dehumanization*, which justifies such treatment on the grounds of these targets as being unworthy of the usual consideration or making them somehow subhuman; alternatively, *attribution of blame* places culpability for what occurred on the victim, thus diminishing the perpetrator's responsibility.

A further contribution from Bandura's (1986, 2016) work is to advance understanding of the creation, perpetuation, and even exacerbation of deviance by situating the individual in a wider context, which includes attention to a dynamic interplay of three critical codeterminants: personal, behavioral, and environmental. In this way he explains why some forms of behavior differ, as noted earlier in the study of professional misconduct that distinguished a higher risk of recidivism in five areas (Spittal et al., 2019). Social cognitive theory also reveals the important reciprocal mechanisms that both motivate and regulate these transgressive actions (Bandura, 2016).

Focusing on the personal, Bandura (1986, 2016) outlines how for some individuals behaviors can become self-reinforcing, drawing on biological and intrapsychic influences, such as their competence, beliefs, emotional states, goals, attitudes, and values, to allow how the environment is perceived to be altered, and thus the behaviors that can be undertaken in it. He reveals how the treatment an individual receives from others is shaped by stereotypes, derived from facets beyond their personal control, including responses to their gender, age, and physical characteristics. For example, those in high social status occupations, such as doctors, are found to receive more deferential reactions from others compared to those in less prestigious occupations, such as nurses (Searle et al., 2017). Through these different treatments, the means of social regulation becomes diminished, especially for those in higher-status roles. As a result, individuals can perceive the same environment in very different ways, leading them to believe that the rules simply do not apply to them in the same way they do to others.

In focusing on the context, Bandura (2016) distinguishes how environmental influences arise. First, *imposed* environments physically and socioculturally constrain the individual; however, the aforementioned moral disengagement mechanisms allow individuals to psychologically alter their perceptions of these constraints, positioning their *own* actions to be the exception. Far greater agency arises through the second influence—*selecting* environments—with individuals deliberately selecting more favorable contexts, such as through their career or workplace choices. For example, the decision to undertake agency or locum work maximizes autonomy, while minimizing the means for others to detect; the perpetrator simply moves on to another workplace as concerns about their antics start to be raised (Searle et al., 2017).

Selection also extends to particular social groups. Picking where, and with whom, to have work breaks allows the means to select like-minded people who are less likely to question and challenge the individual's actions, thus reducing the aforementioned social sanction that could help them check and self-regulate (Bandura, 2016). In this way these selected groups become important resources for perpetrators, enabling them to bolster their more permissive or deviant norms (Pina & Gannon, 2012). Selection also extends to the choice of target, deliberately choosing those who are more vulnerable, or whose resistance can be more easily overcome—specifically, those with less access to voice, lower status, or heightened economic dependency (O'Hare & O'Donohue, 1998); these targets are also likely to have less credibility as a witness, allowing the means to reduce legal sanctions (Easteal & Judd, 2008). High-status perpetrators are often protected, with organizational officials more reluctant to intervene (McDonald, 2012). Sadly, the resultant failure to even consider that something more nefarious might be occurring worsens the target's plight. As a result, targets' silence can appear acquiescent, because they simply perceive that nothing will be done if they raise their concerns (O'Leary-Kelly et al., 2009), or defensive, reflecting fears of subsequent reprisals from this more senior perpetrator (Hershcovis et al., 2021). Reinforced by the inaction of bystanders, perpetrators can, over time, perversely start to perceive that their wrongdoings are somehow sanctioned by those around them (Rice & Searle, 2022).

Finally, environments can be active and deliberately *created*, strategically constructed to better facilitate their perverse activities; they also intentionally foster networks designed to help them mitigate social and legal sanctions (Scott & Martin, 2006). Humor can provide an innocuous veneer to their antics, offering a means to reconstruct their actions as something more benign (Page et al., 2016). Using these combined strategies, perpetrators actively reduce social censure and their fear of ostracization, deliberately normalizing their deviant norms (Bandura, 2016). Through these accumulative means, networks of silence emerge that protect perpetrators and temporarily reduce reputational damage, enabling them not only to continue but even escalate their activities as they become more emboldened. Critically, deviant behaviors become cascaded as legitimate for others, insidiously altering workplace norms about both deviance and speak-up behaviors (Hershcovis et al., 2021). Over time, more CWB-tolerant cultures form (Russell & Oswald, 2016), particularly in contexts with high levels of competition and gendered power relations, where informal networks are particularly significant means of career advancement (Hennekam & Bennett, 2017). In this way, those with chronic predispositions engineer spaces that permit them to act out their proclivities undeterred (Page & Pina, 2018), while those with opposing views feel increasingly marginalized and eventually have to choose whether to collude by remaining silent or to leave the organization. The resultant context becomes significantly diminished in the operation and effectiveness of social sanction, and also reduced in the means to help these individuals self-regulate. Therefore, over time, only the fear of legal sanction remains to inhibit a perpetrator.

In summary, socio-cognitive theory indicates key mechanisms that operate to both create and inhibit CWB. Bandura (1986, 2016) outlines critical interwoven codeterminants, including individual, behavior, and environment, that comprise distinct social and cognitive mechanisms. This approach is important, as it identifies why *some* forms of behavior may for *some* individuals become compelling. It explains why sexual harassment and theft are higher-risk CWBs (Spittal et al., 2019). It outlines, too, the value of a more comprehensive approach in how to detect, deter, and ameliorate CWB in organizations. Next, the separation between OCB and CWB is challenged, to reveal their relationship as more complex than first apparent.

RELATIONS OF OCB AND CWB—MORAL-LICENSING PERSPECTIVE

In the section defining CWB, it was positioned as the opposite of organizational citizenship behavior (OCB) (e.g., Dalal, 2005; Sackett, 2002). However, closer scrutiny suggests such findings may be an artifact of study design, because these two behaviors are rarely measured together (Fox et al., 2012). Extant studies that include both of these discretionary behaviors reveal as overly simplistic a dichotomizing of "good" or "bad" people, and instead explore a significant temporal sequencing in their occurrence for individuals, to show that prosocial citizenship can precede subsequent CWB (Bolino & Klotz, 2015; Griep et al., 2021; Loi et al., 2020). Explanations of why such divergent behaviors should be enacted by the same individual offer intriguing insights that positions CWB as an unintended consequence of mandating good behavior (Klotz & Bolino, 2013).

Research has indicated some danger in making people feel compelled (Bolino et al., 2013) or obliged (Organ et al., 2006) to undertake OCB, rather than having it as something they can choose to do for themselves. Removing an individual's agency in the decision to act positively and altruistically can lead to unintended consequences, specifically providing a means to perceive that they are psychologically entitled to offset these "good" deeds against some subsequent "bad" activity.

Moral-licensing theory (Merritt et al., 2010; Miller & Effron, 2010) contends that by undertaking "good" actions, individuals acquire the psychological basis for their subsequent CWB, or to express their morally problematic attitudes. The theory outlines two important mechanisms. First, moral credits involve previously acquired moral capital derived through undertaking "good" deeds being offset against subsequent amoral actions. This acquired moral license is not domain-specific, with credits acquired in one domain being offset by actions in another; it also licenses both interpersonally and organizationally directed transgressions (Yam et al., 2017). While people can vary in the lower level of their "moral account," through their re-crediting efforts they can psychologically avoid consequent threats to their moral self-image (Zhong & Liljenquist, 2006); instead, they can retain their self-identity of being a "good" person.

Through the second mechanism, moral credentials, individuals can finesse their image as a moral person who does good (Miller & Effron, 2010). The historical precedent created by their prior good deeds enables the means to position current, and future, morally ambiguous actions to be construed as more acceptable. In this way, a "good" person is regarded as not acting badly, so the actions they take must therefore not be bad. As a result, dubious activities become transformed by virtue of their historically derived more positive self-image. Equally, those with prior "bad" deeds may struggle to have their subsequent good actions confirmed. Indeed, through this means those with "good" deeds are granted a "sense of entitlement to some moral laxity" (Zhong et al., 2009, p. 78). In this way, for instance, organizationally encouraged volunteering could provide a credit that entitles an individual latitude to undertake subsequent CWB (Loi et al., 2020).

Perceived organizational justice offers an important way to reduce the impact of moral licensing (Loi et al., 2020). In contexts with low organizational justice, employees can feel entitled, even justified, to engage in transgressive actions, by regarding their responses to be less morally discrediting (Klotz & Bolino, 2013). In this way, an organization with unequitable pay (low distributive and procedural justice) enables employees to feel justified in "taking back," rather than perceiving these actions as simply stealing (Greenberg, 2002). Yet people do not always seek revenge or payback, with moral identity (Aquino & Reed, 2002) an important moderator to individuals' injustice reactions. Extending insight into this further moral dimension adds greater nuance to explain why victims, and also observers of injustices, can seek revenge (Barclay et al., 2014). Such study also identifies the significant role of norms regarding moral behaviors. Thus, while workplaces can be important contexts to study CWB due to the accumulation of perceived breaches to employees' psychological contracts (Griep & Vantilborgh, 2018), they are also important in exploring restraint and how moral identity can alter responses to injustice (Skarlicki et al., 2016). Future study can add greater fidelity by extending how justice is measured to enable delineation of the consequences of different forms of injustice (Loi et al., 2020). To date, studies have been confirmed to examination of the importance of fair processes and rewarding ethical actions.

Further, diary-based study that has examined moral-licensing effects has indicated how the significant consequences of psychological entitlement can be diminished through the use of temporal reframing, which repositions individuals' attention on their future actions, rather than their past behavior (Griep et al., 2021). Therefore, rather than individuals seeing a *quid pro quo* from their past good deeds in licensing current CWB, it focuses on their future good deeds to alter self-serving intentions. This highlights how as social beings our moral compasses can be led adrift, distorted by our own individual and shared biases and bounded cognitions (Moore & Gino, 2013). A further temporal perspective that has received limited investigation arises where societal attitudes have evolved, or fresh critical insight is produced which requires revisiting of prior events, necessitating that individuals and society review again the morality of their behaviors as they become aware of the unintended consequences (Hershcovis et al., 2021; Rice & Searle, 2022). In this way moral compasses need regular checking and review (Moore & Gino, 2013).

In summary, this approach challenges as oversimplistic a dichotomy of "good" and "bad" individuals and reveals the dangers of prior "good" deeds in placing individuals beyond suspicion. Instead, it highlights the value of including a wider range of behaviors in studies, and the importance of considering moral identity along with temporal sequencing of actions. It reveals further individual difference facets and the cognitive dimensions that are significant to CWB, but also new approaches to moderate these outcomes. Moral-licensing theory also illuminates dangers in certain laudable occupations, such as being priests or doctors, which create moral credit and credentials that can then psychologically facilitate subsequent CWB. This approach outlines the powerful role of identity and the veneer of the "good person" in allowing individuals the means to avoid critically appraising their current behavior and its motivations. It highlights a value to reexamine our moral compasses, and to consider our current and future activities afresh.

CONCLUSIONS

This article has drawn attention to the considerable direct and indirect implications of CWB for individuals, organizations, and society. Through exploring four perspectives, we revealed divergent lenses as to how CWBs emerge, and different approaches to their detection and measurement, along with the means to contain, deter, and ameliorate them. Through these contrasting perspectives, some of the complex interactions of individual difference dimensions, but also behaviors, and their context emerge. It also charts important shifts in our understanding to reveal how we can all be capable of these activities, and the significance of further study of the temporal perspective to advancing our current understanding and study of this important topic.

REFERENCES

Aquino, K., & Reed, A. (2002). The self-importance of moral identity. *Journal of Personality and Social Psychology, 83*, 1423–1440.

Bandura, A. (1986). *Social foundations of thought and action*. Prentice Hall.

Bandura, A. (1991). Social cognitive theory of moral thought and action. In W. M. Kurtines & J. L. Gewirtz (Eds.), *Handbook of moral behavior and development* (Vol. 1, pp. 45–103). Erlbaum.

Bandura, A. (2016). *Moral disengagement: How people do harm and live with themselves.* Worth Publishers.

Barclay, L. J., Whiteside, D. B., & Aquino, K. (2014). To avenge or not to avenge? Exploring the interactive effects of moral identity and the negative reciprocity norm. *Journal of Business Ethics, 121*(1), 15–28. https://doi.org/10.1007/s10551-013-1674-6

Baumeister, R. F., Bratslavsky, E., Muraven, M., & Tice, D. M. (1998). Ego depletion: Is the active self a limited resource? *Journal of Personality and Social Psychology, 74*(5), 1252–1265. https://doi.org/10.1037/0022-3514.74.5.1252

Bennett, R. J., & Robinson, S. L. (2000). Development of a measure of workplace deviance. *Journal of Applied Psychology, 85*(3), 349–360. https://doi.org/10.1037/0021-9010.85.3.349

Berkowitz, L. (1993). *Aggression: Its causes, consequences, and control.* McGraw–Hill.

Berry, C. M., Carpenter, N. C., & Barratt, C. L. (2012). Do other-reports of counterproductive work behavior provide an incremental contribution over self-reports? A meta-analytic comparison. *Journal of Applied Psychology, 97*(3), 613–636. https://doi.org/10.1037/a0026739

Berry, C. M., Ones, D. S., & Sackett, P. R. (2007). Interpersonal deviance, organizational deviance, and their common correlates: A review and meta-analysis. *Journal of Applied Psychology, 92*(2), 410–424. https://doi.org/10.1037/0021-9010.92.2.410

Blickle, G., & Schütte, N. (2017). Trait psychopathy, task performance, and counterproductive work behavior directed toward the organization. *Personality and Individual Differences, 109*, 225–231. https://doi.org/10.1016/j.paid.2017.01.006

Bolino, M. C., & Klotz, A. C. (2015). The paradox of the unethical organizational citizen: The link between organizational citizenship behavior and unethical behavior at work. *Current Opinion in Psychology, 6*, 45–49. https://doi.org/10.1016/j.copsyc.2015.03.026

Bolino, M. C., Klotz, A. C., Turnley, W. H., & Harvey, J. (2013). Exploring the dark side of organizational citizenship behavior. *Journal of Organizational Behavior, 34*(4), 542–559. https://doi.org/10.1002/job.1847

Bowling, N. A., Lyons, B. D., & Burns, G. N. (2020). Staying quiet or speaking out: Does peer reporting depend on the type of counterproductive work behavior witnessed? *Journal of Personnel Psychology, 19*(1), 14–23. https://doi.org/10.1027/1866-5888/a000238

Bragg, C. B., & Bowling, N. A. (2018). Not all forms of misbehavior are created equal: Differential personality facet–counterproductive work behavior relations. *International Journal of Selection and Assessment, 26*(1), 27–35. https://doi.org/10.1111/ijsa.12200

Brock Baskin, M., Gruys, M. L., Winterberg, C. A., & Clinton, M. S. (2020). Monkey see, monkey do, monkey tell? Exploring the relationship between counterproductive work behavior engagement and the likelihood of reporting others. *Ethics & Behavior, 31*(7), 516–543. https://doi.org/10.1080/10508422.2020.1860767

Button, M., Lewis, C., & Tapley, J. (2009). Fraud typologies and the victims of fraud: Literature review. National Fraud Authority. https://researchportal.port.ac.uk/portal/files/1926122/NFA_report3_16.12.09.pdf

Carpenter, N. C., & Berry, C. M. (2017). Are counterproductive work behavior and withdrawal empirically distinct? A meta-analytic investigation. *Journal of Management, 43*(3), 834–863. https://doi.org/10.1177/0149206314544743

Chen, P. Y., & Spector, P. E. (1992). Relationships of work stressors with aggression, withdrawal, theft and substance use: An exploratory study. *Journal of Occupational and Organizational Psychology, 65*(3), 177–184. https://doi.org/10.1111/j.2044-8325.1992.tb00495.x

Dalal, R. (2005). A meta-analysis of the relationship between organizational citizenship behavior and counterproductive work behavior. *Journal of Applied Psychology, 90*(6), 1241–1255. https://doi.org/10.1037/0021-9010.90.6.1241

Easteal, P., & Judd, K. (2008). "She said, he said": Credibility and sexual harassment cases in Australia. *Women's Studies International Forum, 31*(5), 336–344. https://doi.org/10.1016/j.wsif.2008.08.009

Egan, V., Hughes, N., & Palmer, E. J. (2015). Moral disengagement, the dark triad, and unethical consumer attitudes. *Personality and Individual Differences, 76*, 123–128. https://doi.org/10.1016/j.paid.2014.11.054

Fida, R., Paciello, M., Tramontano, C., Fontaine, R. G., Barbaranelli, C., & Farnese, M. L. (2015a). An integrative approach to understanding counterproductive work behavior: The roles of stressors, negative emotions, and moral disengagement. *Journal of Business Ethics, 130*(1), 131–144. https://doi.org/10.1007/s10551-014-2209-5

Fida, R., Paciello, M., Tramontano, C., Fontaine, R. G., Barbaranelli, C., & Farnese, M. L. (2015b). "Yes, I can": The protective role of personal self-efficacy in hindering counterproductive work behavior under stressful conditions. *Anxiety, Stress & Coping, 28*(5), 479–499. https://doi.org/10.1080/10615806.2014.969718

Fida, R., Tramontano, C., Paciello, M., Guglielmetti, C., Gilardi, S., Probst, T. M., & Barbaranelli, C. (2018). "First, do no harm": The role of negative emotions and moral disengagement in understanding the relationship between workplace aggression and misbehavior. *Frontiers in Psychology, 9*(671), 1–17. https://doi.org/10.3389/fpsyg.2018.00671

Fox, S., Spector, P. E., Goh, A., Bruursema, K., & Kessler, S. R. (2012). The deviant citizen: Measuring potential positive relations between counterproductive work behaviour and organizational citizenship behaviour. *Journal of Occupational and Organizational Psychology, 85*(1), 199–220. https://doi.org/10.1111/j.2044-8325.2011.02032.x

Fox, S., Spector, P. E., & Miles, D. (2001). Counterproductive work behavior (CWB) in response to job stressors and organizational justice: Some mediator and moderator tests for autonomy and emotions. *Journal of Vocational Behavior, 59*(3), 291–309. https://doi.org/10.1006/jvbe.2001.1803

Greenbaum, R., Bonner, J., Gray, T., & Mawritz, M. (2020). Moral emotions: A review and research agenda for management scholarship. *Journal of Organizational Behavior, 41*(2), 95–114. https://doi.org/10.1002/job.2367

Greenberg, J. (2002). Who stole the money, and when? Individual and situational determinants of employee theft. *Organizational Behavior and Human Decision Processes, 89*(1), 985–1003. https://doi.org/10.1016/S0749-5978(02)00039-0

Griep, Y., Germeys, L., & Kraak, J. M. (2021). Unpacking the relationship between organizational citizenship behavior and counterproductive work behavior: Moral licensing and temporal focus. *Group & Organization Management, 46*(5), 819–856. https://doi.org/10.1177/1059601121995366

Griep, Y., & Vantilborgh, T. (2018). Reciprocal effects of psychological contract breach on counterproductive and organizational citizenship behaviors: The role of time. *Journal of Vocational Behavior, 104*, 141–153. https://doi.org/10.1016/j.jvb.2017.10.013

Grijalva, E., & Newman, D. A. (2015). Narcissism and counterproductive work behavior (CWB): Meta-analysis and consideration of collectivist culture, Big Five personality, and narcissism's facet structure. *Journal of Applied Psychology, 64*(1), 93–126. https://doi.org/10.1111/apps.12025

Gruys, M. L., & Sackett, P. R. (2003). Investigating the dimensionality of counterproductive work behavior. *International Journal of Selection and Assessment, 11*(1), 30–42. https://doi.org/10.1111/1468-2389.00224

Hennekam, S., & Bennett, D. (2017). Sexual harassment in the creative industries: Tolerance, culture and the need for change. *Gender, Work & Organization, 24*(4), 417–434. https://doi.org/10.1111/gwao.12176

Hershcovis, M. S., Turner, N., Barling, J., Arnold, K. A., Dupré, K. E., Inness, M., LeBlanc, M., & Sivanathan, N. (2007). Predicting workplace aggression: A meta-analysis. *Journal of Applied Psychology, 92*(1), 228–238. https://doi.org/10.1037/0021-9010.92.1.228

Hershcovis, M. S., Vranjes, I., Berdahl, J. L., & Cortina, L. M. (2021). See no evil, hear no evil, speak no evil: Theorizing network silence around sexual harassment. *Journal of Applied Psychology, 106*(12), 1834–1847.

Hills, D., & Joyce, C. (2013). A review of research on the prevalence, antecedents, consequences and prevention of workplace aggression in clinical medical practice. *Aggression and Violent Behavior, 18*(5), 554–569.

James, S., Kavanagh, P. S., Jonason, P. K., Chonody, J. M., & Scrutton, H. E. (2014). The Dark Triad, schadenfreude, and sensational interests: Dark personalities, dark emotions, and dark behaviors. *Personality and Individual Differences, 68*, 211–216. https://doi.org/10.1016/j.paid.2014.04.020

Jensen, J. M., & Raver, J. L. (2012). When self-management and surveillance collide: Consequences for employees' organizational citizenship and counterproductive work behaviors. *Group & Organization Management, 37*(3), 308–346. https://doi.org/10.1177/1059601112445804

Kaiser, R. B., LeBreton, J. M., & Hogan, J. (2015). The dark side of personality and extreme leader behavior. *Applied Psychology, 64*(1), 55–92. https://doi.org/10.1111/apps.12024

Kiefer, T. (2005). Feeling bad: Antecedents and consequences of negative emotions in ongoing change. *Journal of Organizational Behavior, 26*(8), 875–897. https://doi.org/10.1002/job.339

Kish-Gephart, J. J., Harrison, D. A., & Trevino, L. K. (2010). Bad apples, bad cases, and bad barrels: Meta-analytic evidence about sources of unethical decisions at work. *Journal of Applied Psychology, 95*(1), 1–31. https://doi.org/10.1037/A0017103

Klotz, A. C., & Bolino, M. C. (2013). Citizenship and counterproductive work behavior: A moral licensing view. *Academy of Management Review, 38*(2), 292–306. https://doi.org/10.5465/amr.2011.0109

Koopmans, L., Bernaards, C. M., Hildebrandt, V. H., Schaufeli, W. B., de Vet Henrica, C. W., & vander Beek, A. J. (2011). Conceptual frameworks of individual work performance: A systematic review. *Journal of Occupational and Environmental Medicine, 53*(8), 856–866. https://doi.org/10.1097/JOM.0b013e318226a763

Krishnakumar, S., Hopkins, K., & Robinson, M. D. (2017). When feeling poorly at work does not mean acting poorly at work: The moderating role of work-related emotional intelligence. *Motivation and Emotion, 41*(1), 122–134. https://doi.org/10.1007/s11031-016-9588-0

Lazarus, R. S., & Folkman, S. (1984). *Stress, appraisal, and coping.* Springer.

LeBreton, J. M., Shiverdecker, L. K., & Grimaldi, E. M. (2018). The dark triad and workplace behavior. *Annual Review of Organizational Psychology and Organizational Behavior, 5*(1), 387–414.

Levashina, J., & Campion, M. A. (2006). A model of faking likelihood in the employment interview. *International Journal of Selection and Assessment, 14*(4), 299–316. https://doi.org/10.1111/j.1468-2389.2006.00353.x

Loi, T. I., Kuhn, K. M., Sahaym, A., Butterfield, K. D., & Tripp, T. M. (2020). From helping hands to harmful acts: When and how employee volunteering promotes workplace deviance. *Journal of Applied Psychology, 105*(9), 944–958. https://doi.org/10.1037/apl0000477

Malik, A., Sinha, S., & Goel, S. (2020). The "screen"ing of you and me: Effects of COVID-19 on counterproductive work behaviors. *IEEE Engineering Management Review, 48*(3), 37–43.

Marcus, B., Taylor, O. A., Hastings, S. E., Sturm, A., & Weigelt, O. (2016). The structure of counterproductive work behavior: A review, a structural meta-analysis, and a primary study. *Journal of Management, 42*(1), 203–233. https://doi.org/10.1177/0149206313503019

McDonald, P. (2012). Workplace sexual harassment 30 years on: A review of the literature. *International Journal of Management Reviews, 14*(1), 1–17. https://doi.org/10.1111/j.1468-2370.2011.00300.x

Meier, L. L., & Spector, P. E. (2013). Reciprocal effects of work stressors and counterproductive work behavior: A five-wave longitudinal study. *Journal of Applied Psychology, 98*(3), 529–539. https://doi.org/10.1037/a0031732

Merritt, A. C., Effron, D. A., & Monin, B. (2010). Moral self-licensing: When being good frees us to be bad. *Social and Personality Psychology Compass, 4*(5), 344–357. https://doi.org/10.1111/j.1751-9004.2010.00263.x

Miller, D. T., & Effron, D. A. (2010). Psychological license: When it is needed and how it functions. In P. Z. Mark & M. O. James (Eds.), *Advances in experimental social psychology* (Vol. 43, pp. 115–155). Academic Press.

Moore, C., & Gino, F. (2013). Ethically adrift: How others pull our moral compass from true North, and how we can fix it. *Research in Organizational Behavior, 33*, 53–77. https://doi.org/10.1016/j.riob.2013.08.001

Muris, P., Merckelbach, H., Otgaar, H., & Meijer, E. (2017). The malevolent side of human nature: A meta-analysis and critical review of the literature on the dark triad (narcissism, Machiavellianism, and psychopathy). *Perspectives on Psychological Science*, 12(2), 183–204. https://doi.org/10.1177/174569 1616666070

O'Boyle, E. H., Forsyth, D. R., & O'Boyle, A. S. (2011). Bad apples or bad barrels: An examination of group- and organizational-level effects in the study of counterproductive work behavior. *Group & Organization Management*, 36(1), 39–69. https://doi.org/10.1177/1059601110390998

O'Boyle, E. H., Jr., Forsyth, D. R., Banks, G. C., & McDaniel, M. A. (2012). A meta-analysis of the dark triad and work behavior: A social exchange perspective. *Journal of Applied Psychology*, 97(3), 557–579. https://doi.org/10.1037/a0025679

O'Hare, E. A., & O'Donohue, W. (1998). Sexual harassment: Identifying risk factors. *Archives of Sexual Behavior*, 27(6), 561–580. https://doi.org/10.1023/a:1018769016832

O'Leary-Kelly, A. M., Bowes-Sperry, L., Bates, C. A., & Lean, E., R. (2009). Sexual harassment at work: A decade (plus) of progress. *Journal of Management*, 35(3), 503–536. https://doi.org/10.1177/014920 6308330555

Organ, D. W., Podsakoff, P. M., & MacKenzie, S. B. (2006). *Organizational citizenship behavior: Its nature, antecedents, and consequences*. SAGE.

Page, T. E., & Pina, A. (2018). Moral disengagement and self-reported harassment proclivity in men: The mediating effects of moral judgment and emotions. *Journal of Sexual Aggression*, 24(2), 157–180. https://doi .org/10.1080/13552600.2018.1440089

Page, T. E., Pina, A., & Giner-Sorolla, R. (2016). "It was only harmless banter!" The development and preliminary validation of the moral disengagement in sexual harassment scale. *Aggressive Behavior*, 42(3), 254–273. https://doi.org/10.1002/ab.21621

Parker, S. K., Knight, C., & Keller, A. (2020). Remote managers are having trust issues. *Harvard Business Review*, 30. https://hbr.org/2020/07/remote-managers-are-having-trust-issues

Paulhus, D. L., Westlake, B. G., Calvez, S. S., & Harms, P. D. (2013). Self-presentation style in job interviews: The role of personality and culture. *Journal of Applied Social Psychology*, 43(10), 2042–2059. https://doi .org/10.1111/jasp.12157

Peng, A. C., & Kim, D. (2020). A meta-analytic test of the differential pathways linking ethical leadership to normative conduct. *Journal of Organizational Behavior*, 41, 348–368. https://doi.org/10.1002/job.2427

Pina, A., & Gannon, T. A. (2012). An overview of the literature on antecedents, perceptions and behavioural consequences of sexual harassment. *Journal of Sexual Aggression*, 18(2), 209–232. https://doi.org/10 .1080/13552600.2010.501909

Rice, C., & Searle, R. H. (2022). The enabling role of internal organizational communication in insider threat activity—evidence from a high security organization. *Management Communication Quarterly*, 1–29. https://doi.org/10.1177/08933189211062250

Robinson, S. L., & Bennett, R. J. (1995). A typology of deviant workplace behaviors: A multidimensional scaling study. *Academy of Management Journal*, 38(2), 555–572. https://doi.org/10.2307/256693

Rotundo, M., & Sackett, P. R. (2002). The relative importance of task, citizenship, and counterproductive performance to global ratings of job performance: A policy-capturing approach. *Journal of Applied Psychology*, 87(1), 66–80. https://doi.org/10.1037/0021-9010.87.1.66

Roulin, N., & Bourdage, J. S. (2017). Once an impression manager, always an impression manager? Antecedents of honest and deceptive impression management use and variability across multiple job interviews. *Frontiers in Psychology*, 8, 1–13. https://doi.org/10.3389/fpsyg.2017.00029

Russell, B. L., & Oswald, D. (2016). When sexism cuts both ways: Predictors of tolerance of sexual harassment of men. *Men and Masculinities*, 19(5), 524–544. https://doi.org/10.1177/1097184X15602745

Sackett, P. R. (2002). The structure of counterproductive work behaviors: Dimensionality and relationships with facets of job performance. *International Journal of Selection and Assessment, 10*(1–2), 5–11. https://doi.org/10.1111/1468-2389.00189

Samnani, A.-K., Salamon, S. D., & Singh, P. (2014). Negative affect and counterproductive workplace behavior: The moderating role of moral disengagement and gender. *Journal of Business Ethics, 119*(2), 235–244. https://doi.org/10.1007/s10551-013-1635-0

Scott, G., & Martin, B. (2006). Tactics against sexual harassment: The role of backfire. *Journal of International Women's Studies, 7*(4), 111–125.

Searle, R., Rice, C., McConnell, A., & Dawson, J. (2017). Bad apples? Bad barrels? Or bad cellars? Antecedents and processes of professional misconduct in UK Health and Social Care: Insights into sexual misconduct and dishonesty. Professional Standards Authority, https://www.professionalstandards.org.uk/docs/default-source/publications/research-paper/antecedents-and-processes-of-professional-misconduct-in-uk-health-and-social-care.pdf

Searle, R. H., & Rice, C. (2018). Assessing and mitigating the impact of organisational change on counterproductive work behaviour: An operational (dis)trust based framework. Centre for Research and Evidence on Security Threats (CREST). https://crestresearch.ac.uk/cwb

Searle, R. H., & Rice, C. (2020). Making an impact in healthcare contexts: Insights from a mixed-methods study of professional misconduct. *European Journal of Work and Organizational Psychology, 30*(4), 470–481. https://doi.org/10.1080/1359432X.2020.1850520

Shoss, M. K., Jundt, D. K., Kobler, A., & Reynolds, C. (2016). Doing bad to feel better? An investigation of within- and between-person perceptions of counterproductive work behavior as a coping tactic. *Journal of Business Ethics, 137*(3), 571–587. https://doi.org/10.1007/s10551-015-2573-9

Skarlicki, D. P., van Jaarsveld, D. D., Shao, R., Song, Y. H., & Wang, M. (2016). Extending the multifoci perspective: The role of supervisor justice and moral identity in the relationship between customer justice and customer-directed sabotage. *Journal of Applied Psychology, 101*(1), 108–121. https://doi.org/10.1037/apl0000034

Spector, P. E., & Fox, S. (2005). The stressor-emotion model of counterproductive work behavior. In S. Fox & P. E. Spector (Eds.), *Counterproductive work behavior: Investigations of actors and targets* (pp. 151–174). American Psychological Association.

Spector, P. E., Fox, S., Penney, L. M., Bruursema, K., Goh, A., & Kessler, S. (2006). The dimensionality of counterproductivity: Are all counterproductive behaviors created equal? *Journal of Vocational Behavior, 68*(3), 446–460. https://doi.org/10.1016/j.jvb.2005.10.005

Spittal, M. J., Bismark, M. M., & Studdert, D. M. (2015). The PRONE score: An algorithm for predicting doctors' risks of formal patient complaints using routinely collected administrative data. *BMJ Quality & Safety, 24*(6), 360. https://doi.org/10.1136/bmjqs-2014-003834

Spittal, M. J., Bismark, M. M., & Studdert, D. M. (2019). Identification of practitioners at high risk of complaints to health profession regulators. *BMC Health Services Research, 19*(1), 380. https://doi.org/10.1186/s12913-019-4214-y

Westerman, J. W., Beekun, R. I., Stedham, Y., & Yamamura, J. (2007). Peers versus national culture: An analysis of antecedents to ethical decision-making. *Journal of Business Ethics, 75*(3), 239–252. https://doi.org/10.1007/s10551-006-9250-y

Wilkin, C. L., & Connelly, C. E. (2015). Green with envy and nerves of steel: Moderated mediation between distributive justice and theft. *Personality and Individual Differences, 72*, 160–164. https://doi.org/10.1016/j.paid.2014.08.039

Yam, K. C., Klotz, A. C., He, W., & Reynolds, S. J. (2017). From good soldiers to psychologically entitled: Examining when and why citizenship behavior leads to deviance. *Academy of Management Journal, 60*(1), 373–396. https://doi.org/10.5465/amj.2014.0234

Yost, A. B., Behrend, T. S., Howardson, G., Badger Darrow, J., & Jenson, J. M. (2019). Reactance to electronic surveillance: A test of antecedents and outcomes. *Journal of Business Psychology, 34*, 71–86. https://doi.org/10.1007/s10869-018-9532-2

Zhong, C.-B., & Liljenquist, K. (2006). Washing away your sins: Threatened morality and physical cleansing. *Science, 313*(5792), 1451–1452. https://doi.org/10.1126/science.1130726

Zhong, C.-B., Liljenquist, K., & Cain, D. M. (2009). Moral self-regulation: Licensing and compensation. In D. DeCremer (Ed.), *Psychological perspectives on ethical behavior and decision making* (pp. 75–89). Information Age Publishing.

Rosalind H. Searle

Occupational Health Psychology

OCCUPATIONAL HEALTH PSYCHOLOGY

INTRODUCTION

The US National Institute for Occupational Safety and Health provides the following definition for Occupational Health Psychology: "the application of psychology to improving the quality of work life, and to protecting and promoting the safety, health, and well-being of workers" (NIOSH, 2017). The key areas of occupational health psychology (OHP) are reviewed in this article in terms of theoretical perspectives, research evidence, and practical implications. Research in this important area has increased over recent years, with a number of academic journals that specialize in publishing in this area (e.g., the *Journal of Occupational Health Psychology, Stress and Health, Work and Stress*, and the *International Journal of Stress Management*) and professional organizations promoting OHP through conferences and research funding, including the European Association for Occupational Health Psychology (EAOHP) and the US Society for Occupational Health Psychology (SOHP). From a psychological perspective, health encompasses mental well-being, including resilience in face of challenges, rather than simply an absence of illness. Nevertheless, research has tended to focus on alleviating negative aspects (e.g., preventing disease and injury and reducing stress symptoms) rather than promoting positive ones. More recently, however, the positive psychology movement has encouraged researchers to view psychological health as a positive state, which can be

• 1339

facilitated through the development of resilience, thriving at work, and work engagement. Incorporating both these perspectives, we begin with a focus on occupational stress, which reflects one of the earliest and most researched topics in OHP, before extending our consideration to related areas, including workplace safety, work/nonwork boundaries, and organizational interventions.

OCCUPATIONAL STRESS

The stress-strain perspective is the dominant approach to understanding how sources of pressure in the workplace impact on employees' health and well-being. From this perspective, stress is a process, rather than being identified as specific work conditions or as outcomes. Sources of pressure in the workplace (stressors) may exert positive or negative effects on individuals, with negative effects leading to strain (i.e., a range of psychological and physical outcomes, or stress symptoms). Selye (1976, 1982) distinguished between "eustress" (good stress) and "distress" (bad stress), depending on the type of stressor encountered, with the experience of distress having negative physiological effects.

Sonnentag and Frese (2012) identified the major sources of job stress as physical, task-related, role-related, social, career-related, and traumatic events and stressful change processes. Within OHP, most theoretical and research attention has been focused on task-related stressors (related to time pressures, workload, and situational or organizational constraints that interfere with getting the job done); role stressors (role ambiguity, role overload, and role conflict); and social stressors (e.g., workplace bullying, harassment and aggression, incivility, and abusive supervision). While there has been a focus on stress arising from the work environment, the experience of stress also depends on individual factors, such as personality. For example, some people are more reactive in stressful situations, which makes them more susceptible to negative psychological or physiological effects; others self-select into stressful environments or are predisposed to thrive in stressful situations and so tend to see stressors as challenges to be overcome. Therefore, individual differences play a significant role in understanding the stress process as well as factors located in the work environment.

Impact on Physical and Mental Health. Exposure to stressors in the work environment results in a number of responses, including the release of neurochemicals in the brain and the associated physiological (e.g., increased pulse rate) and emotional/psychological (e.g., anxiety) reactions (Cooper, Dewe, & O'Driscoll, 2001). The onset of these responses is rapid, but they dissipate after the removal of the stressor and may have no lasting ill-effects. In the longer term, however, particularly with repeated or prolonged exposure to stressors, they can lead to physical symptoms and illness, which persist even after the period of stress is over (e.g., suppressed immune system; O'Leary, 1990). Common physical symptoms include musculoskeletal pain, headaches, fatigue, sleep disturbance, and gastrointestinal problems (Nixon, Mazzola, Bauer, Krueger, & Spector, 2011). Many of these symptoms can also manifest as physical illness: for example, gastrointestinal issues caused by the heightened levels of hormones excreted into the stomach during periods of stress can lead to conditions such as ulcers and irritable bowel syndrome. However, individuals vary substantially in how they respond to stressors and the extent to which stress acts as a risk factor for subsequent psychological and physical ill-health (Semmer, 2003).

Nixon et al. (2011) conducted a meta-analysis looking at links between work stressors and physical symptoms. Work stressors included a number of task-related (e.g., heavy workloads and organizational constraints, which constrain work efforts), role (e.g., lack of clarity about one's work role and conflict between work roles), and social stressors (e.g., interpersonal conflict at work, such as disagreements with one's manager or work colleagues). Based on a composite measure of physical symptoms, the following stressors had the largest effect sizes: organizational constraints ($\rho = .33$), role conflict ($\rho = .27$), interpersonal conflict ($\rho = .22$), workload ($\rho = .22$), and role ambiguity ($\rho = .15$). These effects were replicated for the longitudinal studies (i.e., demonstrating effects over time). Interpersonal conflict, organizational constraints, and workload had significant effects across all physical symptoms, whereas other stressors had stronger relationships with specific symptoms; for example, role ambiguity was only related to fatigue. (For a summary of the effects of stressors on stress outcomes, see Table 1.)

Table 1. Summary of Effects of Work Stressors on Health and Well-Being

Work Stressor	Physical Well-Being Outcome	Effect Size	Psychological Well-Being Outcome	Effect Size
Organizational constraints	Physical symptoms	.33/.40	Job satisfaction, emotional exhaustion, anxiety	−.39, .42, .50
Workload	Physical symptoms	.22	Emotional exhaustion	.65
Role conflict	Physical symptoms	.27	Emotional exhaustion, job satisfaction, anxiety, depression	.53, −.48, .43, .32
Role ambiguity	Physical symptoms	.15	Job satisfaction, anxiety, depression	−.46, .47, .28
Interpersonal conflict	Physical symptoms	.22		
Work-family interference (WFI)	Health problems, physical stress symptoms	.28, .29	Work-related burnout, general psychological strain	.38, .35
Family-work interference (FWI)	Health problems, physical stress symptoms	.24, .14	Work-related burnout, general psychological strain	.27, .21
Surface acting	Psychosomatic complaints	.44	Emotional exhaustion, depersonalization, psychological strain, job satisfaction	.44, .48, .42, −.33

(Continued)

1342 • OCCUPATIONAL HEALTH PSYCHOLOGY

Table 1. Continued

Work Stressor	Physical Well-Being Outcome	Effect Size	Psychological Well-Being Outcome	Effect Size
Workplace bullying	Physical health problems	.23	Anxiety, depression, burnout	.27, .34, .27
Abusive supervision			Depression, emotional exhaustion, job satisfaction, job tension	.24, .36, −.34, .24
Destructive leadership	Physical well-being	−.35	Job satisfaction, depression	−.34, .24

Note: Effect sizes of 0.20 are considered small, 0.50 moderate, and 0.8 large (Cohen, 1977).

The experience of strain is often associated with the psychological and emotional effects of stress. As with physical symptoms, the immediate feelings of "being stressed" (such as anxiety) dissipate when the stressful period is over, but the effects can also extend beyond this period to have lasting effects. Long-term psychological effects include anxiety and depression as well as negative job attitudes, such as job dissatisfaction. These effects can be just as strong, and even stronger, than the physical effects of stress. For example, Pindek and Spector (2016, p. 7) looked at the effects of organizational constraints (defined as "conditions at work that inhibit, interfere with, or fail to support an individual's performance of job tasks") encompassing a number of potential sources of stress (such as interpersonal conflicts and heavy workloads) with the emphasis on how these factors interfere with the ability to get the job done. They found that organizational constraints were associated with physical symptoms ($\rho = .40$), similar effect sizes for job satisfaction ($\rho = −.39$), and emotional exhaustion ($\rho = .42$). The strongest effect was found for anxiety ($\rho = .50$).

Prolonged and repeated exposure to work stressors can lead to physical and emotional exhaustion, feelings of alienation and withdrawal, and a loss of personal and professional efficacy. These physical and emotional responses are often described as being "burned out." Job burnout was originally proposed to capture the psychological outcomes from intense interpersonal interactions in the workplace, such as in customer service jobs and the caring professions; it comprises three dimensions—emotional exhaustion, depersonalization (cynicism), and (reduced) personal accomplishment (Maslach, 1982). Based on the stress-strain perspective, interpersonal interactions act as a source of stress (job demand), which results in strain (job burnout) (Leiter & Maslach, 1988). Emotional exhaustion has been proposed as deriving directly from job demands as a form of strain; while depersonalization reflects a defensive coping mechanism related to withdrawal, and (reduced) personal accomplishment as the erosion of self-efficacy (Leiter, 1993). Supportive evidence for job burnout was demonstrated by a meta-analysis (Lee & Ashforth, 1996) which showed that emotional exhaustion was most strongly associated with job demands: workload ($\rho = .65$), role stress ($\rho = .62$), role conflict ($\rho = .53$), and work pressure ($\rho = .50$). Depersonalization was most strongly related to low community bond ($\rho = −.46$) and low job satisfaction ($\rho = −.42$), as well as role stress ($\rho = .54$) and stressful events ($\rho = .50$), while personal accomplishment was most strongly associated with control coping ($\rho = .52$) but less so with job demands. A later meta-analysis (Alarcon, 2011) found a similar pattern of results, with a larger number of studies included. Burnout can lead to long-term mental and physical health problems, including increased risk of developing cardiovascular disease (Melamed, Shirom, Toker, Berliner, & Shapira, 2006) and depression (Toker & Biron, 2012). The effects of burnout over time can be mitigated, for example, by positive health behaviors, such as physical activity (Toker & Biron, 2012). Although burnout was first proposed in relation to specific occupations, it was later found to occur across a much broader range (Leiter & Schaufeli, 1996).

Stress is a process that has short-term effects, which may be manifest over the period of a workday, nested within longer-term time dynamics of weeks, months, and years (Griffin & Clarke, 2011). Ford and colleagues (2014) argued that both synchronous (where stressors and strain are measured at the same point in time) and lagged (where measures of stressors and strain are separated in time) effects between stressors and strain are important, but that lagged effects are often small and therefore difficult to detect without large samples in individual studies. Studies with synchronous measures may demonstrate the temporary effects of stressors over a short time period, while lagged effects show the effects of chronic stressors on strain over a longer time frame. Reviews of the variability of well-being suggest that lagged effects are generally smaller than synchronous measures but that well-being does vary over time. Mäkikangas, Kinnunen, Feldt, and Schaufeli (2016) showed that measures of burnout, job satisfaction, and work engagement varied significantly over time, with age and job changes most predictive of variability, such that younger workers and job changers experienced the greatest fluctuations in well-being.

Theories of Occupational Stress. There have been a number of theories developed to explain the occupational stress process. The most well-researched models of occupational stress are now summarized. While each theoretical approach has unique features and contributions to the understanding of occupational stress, they also share common aspects, such as adopting a stress-strain perspective.

Transactional Model of Stress. The transactional model of stress (Lazarus & Folkman, 1984) focuses on stress as a process, in which there is an ongoing interaction between the person and the environment. It describes two stages of cognitive appraisal: primary appraisal, in which the individual evaluates the stressor as personally relevant and potentially threatening (or not), and secondary appraisal, in which the individual evaluates their capability to cope and the coping mechanisms available to deal with the stressor. The extent to which the individual perceives that they are able to cope with the stressor determines their emotional reactions (such as tension, anxiety, anger, or frustration). Insight into the ways that situational cues prompt varying responses from individuals in the face of stressors has been gained through qualitative studies (e.g., Stevenson & Duxbury, 2018).

Coping has been defined as "the thoughts and behaviors used to manage the external and internal demands of situations that are appraised as stressful" (Folkman & Moskowitz, 2004, p. 745). Problem-solving coping involves altering the situation causing the distress (such as working harder or making changes to the work environment); emotion-focused coping, however, involves avoidance or reappraisal of the situation (Folkman, Lazarus, Dunkel-Schetter, DeLongis, & Gruen, 1986). There is evidence to suggest that emotion-focused coping has negative effects on mental health over time, as these coping mechanisms are typically maladaptive

(Aldwin & Revenson, 1987), while problem-solving coping strategies (such as direct coping) moderate the relationship between demands and mental health (Parkes, 1990).

Role Theory. The role theory model of stress focuses on the impact of role stressors (i.e., related to one's work role) on strain. Some of the earliest work on occupational stress focused on the effects of role ambiguity and role conflict (e.g., Kahn, Wolfe, Quinn, Snoek, & Rosenthal, 1964; Katz & Kahn, 1978). Role ambiguity refers to a lack of clarity about what one's work role entails, whereas role conflict refers to contradictory requirements from work roles. Role overload, which involves too many role requirements, may be viewed as a form of role conflict. Kahn and Byosiere (1992) developed a conceptual model linking organizational stressors (e.g., role ambiguity and role conflict) to stress-related responses in terms of behavioral, physiological, or psychological effects. There is strong evidence that high levels of role stress have a detrimental effect on well-being and psychological health. Jackson and Schuler (1985) reported moderate effects sizes for the relationships between role ambiguity and role conflict on measures of health and well-being: role ambiguity with job satisfaction ($\rho = -.46$) and anxiety ($\rho = .47$) and role conflict with job satisfaction ($\rho = -.48$) and anxiety ($\rho = .43$). Schmidt and colleagues (Schmidt, Roesler, Kusserow, & Rau, 2014) looked at the effects of role ambiguity and role conflict on mental health; they found that role ambiguity ($\rho = .28$) and role conflict ($\rho = .32$) had significant effects on depression.

Demands-Control and Demands-Control-Support Models. The demands-control (DC) and demands-control-support (DCS) models identify key work characteristics (job demands, job control, and social support), which are involved in the stress-strain process. The demands-control model (Karasek, 1979, 1989; Karasek & Theorell, 1990) proposes that excessive job demands lead to increased strain, where job demands are aspects of the job that require additional or sustained physical, psychological, or emotional effort (de Jonge & Dormann, 2003). However, the adverse effects of high job demands are mitigated (or buffered) when accompanied by high levels of job control, where job control refers to the extent to which there is control over decisions affecting the job (Karasek & Theorell, 1990). In an extension of this model, the demands-control-support model (Johnson, Hall, & Theorell, 1989), social support is proposed to act as an additional moderator in the stress-strain relationship, such that both job control and social support act as buffers against the adverse effects of job demands. There is meta-analytic support for the expected main effects of job demands, job control, and social support with measures of stress outcomes, such as burnout (de Lange, Taris, Kompier, Houtman, & Bongers, 2003; Luchman & González-Morales, 2013; van der Doef & Maes, 1999). Luchman and González-Morales (2013) found that task-related demands were positively related to emotional exhaustion ($\rho = .35$), while job control ($\rho = -.18$), supervisor support ($\rho = -.26$), and coworker support ($\rho = -.24$) were negatively related to emotional exhaustion.

However, the moderating effects of control and social support have been found less consistently than the main effects (van der Doef & Maes, 1999). For example, Van Yperen and Hagedoorn (2003) found that job control moderated the relationship between job demands and fatigue in their sample of nurses but did not find the hypothesized moderating effect of social support, or the three-way interaction (job demands × job control × social support). Based on a daily diary study of portfolio workers, Totterdell, Wood, and Wall (2006) found support for an additive model (with high demands, low control, and low support increasing psychological strain) but not an interactive model. Such studies demonstrate the difficulty of supporting theoretically relevant higher-level interactions empirically. (For a summary of the effects of mitigating factors in relation to stress outcomes, see Table 2.)

Conservation of Resources Model. The conservation of resources (COR) model (Hobfoll, 1989) has been utilized often in research studies as a stress-strain framework. The model proposes that people are motivated to protect their existing resources and gain new ones. Resources are those objects, conditions, or energies valued by people (e.g., knowledge, self-esteem, status, time away from work) that are important for adaptive functioning (Hobfoll, 1989) and defined as "anything perceived by the individual to help attain his or her goals" (Halbesleben, Neveu, Paustian-Underdahl, & Westman, 2014, p. 1338). Halbesleben et al. (2014) identify six basic tenets of COR theory: (1) resource loss is more salient than resource gain; (2) people must invest resources to gain resources and protect themselves from losing resources or to recover from resource loss; (3) individuals with more resources are better positioned for resource gains, but individuals with fewer resources are more likely to experience resource losses; (4) initial resource losses lead to future resource losses; (5) initial resource gains lead to future resource gains; and (6) lack of resources leads to defensive attempts to conserve remaining resources.

Resource loss (threat of loss or actual loss) is a more powerful motivator than resource gain, and so potential (or actual) resource loss acts as the main source of stress in the COR model and can result in stress outcomes, such as strain (Hobfoll, 1989; Westman, Hobfoll, Chen, Davidson, & Lasky, 2004). Meta-analyses linking resources (such as social support) to job burnout have provided support for COR model propositions (Halbesleben, 2006; Lee & Ashford, 1996). Coping mechanisms involve efforts to protect existing resources and restore resources following resource loss. The tendency for those who have experienced resource loss to lose further resources has been described as a "resource loss spiral"; for example, Demerouti, Bakker, and Bulters (2004) showed that work pressure resulted in work–family interference

Table 2. Effects of Mitigating Factors on Health and Well-Being

Mitigating Factors	Stress Outcome	Effect Size
Job control	Emotional exhaustion	−.18
Supervisor support	Emotional exhaustion	−.26
Coworker support	Emotional exhaustion	−.24
Job crafting	Job satisfaction, work engagement, job strain	.29, .45, −.13
Proactivity	Job satisfaction	.25
Recovery (psychological detachment, relaxation, mastery, control)	Fatigue	−.39, −.35, −.18, −.30
Recovery (psychological detachment, relaxation, mastery, control)	Vigor	.14, .24, .29, .31

and subsequent exhaustion, and, in turn, exhaustion led to increased work–family interference and more work pressure over time. Similarly, the tendency of those with resource gains to accumulate further gains has been called a "resource gain spiral." For example, in a longitudinal study over a 2-year period, Hakanen, Perhoniemi, and Toppinen-Tanner (2008) demonstrated the ongoing positive effects of job resources over time on work engagement and proactive behavior, which eventually led to the accumulation of further job resources.

The COR model has been used as the theoretical basis for understanding individuals' responses to stressful situations and the longer-term impacts on psychological well-being, particularly job burnout (Halbesleben, 2006; Lee & Ashford, 1996). It is a broadly based motivational theory, which has received wide support, but also presents areas for clarification and further research (Halbesleben et al., 2014; Hobfoll, Halbesleben, Neveu, & Westman, 2018).

Job Demands–Resources Model. Perhaps the most widely accepted and well-researched model of workplace stress is the job demands–resources model (JDR model). This model took its inspiration from the DC and DCS models but extended the range of demands and resources it considered as important to predicting job burnout (Bakker & Demerouti, 2017). Two types of working conditions—job demands and job resources—were identified and arranged in a dual-pathway model in which job demands were associated with exhaustion and a lack of job resources with disengagement (Demerouti, Bakker, Nachreiner, & Schaufeli, 2001). Job demands were defined as those "physical, psychological, social, or organizational aspects of the job that require sustained physical and/or psychological effort and are therefore associated with certain physiological and/or psychological costs" and job resources as "physical, psychological, social, or organizational aspects of the job that are functional in achieving work goals, reduce job demands and the associated physiological and psychological costs, or stimulate personal growth, learning, and development" (Bakker & Demerouti, 2017, p. 274). The dual pathways describe the negative effects of job demands as influencing health and well-being through a "health impairment pathway" and the positive effects of job resources promoting work engagement through a "motivational pathway."

There is empirical evidence that significant job demand–resource interactions occur, such that job resources act as a buffer against the adverse effects of job demands and therefore protect individuals against burnout, even when job demands are high (Bakker, Demerouti, & Euwema, 2005). Further research has extended the JDR model to examine the interactions between job demands, as the effects of some demands may be exacerbated by the presence of others; for example, the impact of emotional demands on sickness absence was accentuated in conditions of high workload (Van Woerkom, Bakker, & Nishii, 2016). The focus on job resources has also been extended to include personal resources (Xanthopoulou, Bakker, Demerouti, & Schaufeli, 2007). Personal resources are located within the person (e.g., self-efficacy, self-esteem) rather than the work environment. For example, in a daily diary study, Xanthopoulou, Bakker, Demerouti, and Schaufeli (2009) examined how daily fluctuations in job resources and personal resources impact on daily work engagement. They found that the daily level of job resources (autonomy, coaching, and team climate) influenced next-day personal resources (self-efficacy, organization-based self-esteem, and optimism) and work engagement.

The understanding of how job demands and resources influence health and well-being has been significantly advanced through the JDR framework, with additional insights through the combination of this model with COR theory, which helps to explain how resources influence behavior.

Challenge Hindrance Model.   The challenge-hindrance model (LePine, Podsakoff, & LePine, 2005) was proposed to address inconsistent findings about the relationship between stressors and job performance. Within this framework, stressors may be appraised as either challenges (e.g., workload) or hindrances (e.g., role ambiguity). Empirical work has supported this distinction, with workload being consistently appraised as a challenge and role ambiguity as a hindrance (Webster, Beehr, & Love, 2011). The distinction between challenge stressors and hindrance stressors was first derived empirically by Cavanaugh and colleagues (Cavanaugh, Boswell, Roehling, & Boudreau, 2000), who found that stressors formed two distinct factors: "stressful demands viewed by managers as obstacles to be overcome in order to learn and achieve" and "stressful demands viewed by managers as unnecessarily thwarting personal growth and goal attainment" (Lepine et al., 2005, p. 765). The challenge–hindrance framework predicts that challenge and hindrance stressors have differential effects on job performance, such that challenge stressors (such as role demands, pressure, time urgency, and workload) increase motivation and lead to improved performance, while hindrance stressors (constraints, hassles, role ambiguity, role and interpersonal conflict, role overload, supervisor-related stress, and organizational politics) decrease motivation and lead to reduced performance. Both types of stressor increase strain, but this is offset by the motivational effects of challenge stressors. Research evidence has supported a negative effect of hindrance stressors on job satisfaction but a positive relationship with challenge stressors (Cavanaugh et al., 2000; Podsakoff, LePine, & LePine, 2007).

In a longitudinal study, Crane and Searle (2016) demonstrated that exposure to challenge stressors can build stress resilience over time; challenge stressors build resources, while hindrance stressors are depleting, with increased resilience leading, in turn, to reduced strain over time. Challenge stressors can also have positive effects on thriving at work (Prem, Ohly, Kubicek, & Korunka, 2017).

Effort-Recovery Theory.   The effort-recovery theory (Meijman & Mulder, 1998) proposed that sufficient recovery during off-work time is needed to restore depleted resources and manage job demands effectively, safeguarding work performance and health (Geurts & Sonnentag, 2006). Higher job demands require greater levels of recovery for successful restoration (Sonnentag & Zijlstra, 2006). Psychological detachment is a specific form of recovery defined as disengaging psychologically from work during nonwork time; it involves not engaging in work or work-related tasks and not thinking about job-related issues (Sonnentag & Fritz, 2015). Based on effort-recovery theory, the stressor-detachment model (Sonnentag, 2010) proposes that psychological detachment plays an important role in the stressor-strain relationship, both mediating the effects of stressors on strain (where stressors impair recovery and increase strain) and also being a moderator of this relationship (where high psychological detachment attenuates the effects of stressors on strain). On a daily level, individuals need to detach from work during the evening before returning to work the next day; when individuals do not detach successfully from work, perhaps ruminating about previous events, or worrying about the next day's events, or even engaging in work-related activities, strain will remain high, instead of reducing. Becoming absorbed in leisure activities in the evening can help individuals become psychologically detached from work (e.g., Volman, Bakker, & Xanthopoulou, 2013); however, work engagement during the workday is predicted by both psychological detachment the previous evening and reattachment the next morning (i.e., mentally re-engaging with work) (Sonnentag & Kuhnel, 2016). A lack of recovery can lead to levels of strain remaining high and accumulating over time. Longer periods of psychological detachment, such as weekends and vacations, can help to restore strain to a lower level (e.g., de Bloom, Geurts, & Kompier, 2012).

Although there is strong empirical support for the detachment-stressor model, some studies have indicated that psychological detachment is not necessary for all individuals; for example, those who rate high in job involvement may enjoy thinking about work during nonwork time and do not experience strain as a result (Sonnentag & Fritz, 2015). The stressor-detachment model is specifically concerned with detaching from work during nonwork time, but micro-breaks during work have also been shown to have positive effects on the reduction of fatigue and the enhancement of vitality throughout the day (Zacher, Brailsford, & Parker, 2014). Other forms of recovery experiences include relaxation (i.e., having a low activation level), mastery (i.e., gaining challenges from learning something new outside work), and control (i.e., having autonomy over nonwork activities). Bennett, Bakker, and Field (2017) found that all forms of recovery experience were effective in reducing fatigue (psychological detachment, $\rho = -.39$; relaxation, $\rho = -.35$; mastery, $\rho = -.18$; control, $\rho = -.30$) and increasing vigor (psychological detachment, $\rho = .14$; relaxation, $\rho = .24$; mastery, $\rho = .29$; control, $\rho = .31$); although psychological detachment and relaxation were most effective at reducing fatigue, control and mastery were most effective at increasing vigor.

Emotional Labor.   A particular form of work that has high emotional demands (such as dealing with clients or customers in face-to-face or voice-to-voice interactions) creates a source of stress known as "emotional labor" (Hochschild, 1983). Emotional labor is associated with work that requires employees to display positive emotions in all client interactions, regardless of the demeanor of the client (e.g., arrogant, rude, or even aggressive) or their personal feelings. It is defined as the "effort, planning and control needed to express organizationally desired emotions during interpersonal transactions" (Morris & Feldman, 1996, p. 987). This is most common in customer service jobs (e.g., flight attendants, call centers, hotel staff, retail and sales staff), caring professions (e.g., nurses, doctors, social workers, healthcare professionals, and funeral directors), and social control jobs (e.g., police, prison guards, debt collectors, and bouncers; Humphrey, Pollack, & Hawver, 2008). Emotional demands in the workplace are strongly associated with job burnout (e.g., Zapf, Seifert, Schmutte, Mertini, & Holz, 2001) as they involve managing emotions so that organizational display rules are followed. Three types of emotion regulation have been identified: deep acting, surface acting, and emotion-rule dissonance (Grandey, 2000). Deep acting involves aligning felt emotions with required emotional displays, meaning that genuine emotions are protrayed; surface acting involves "putting on a mask" so that true feelings are suppressed while required emotional displays are faked. Emotion-rule dissonance refers to the discrepancy between felt and expressed emotions; it reflects an emotional state or felt tension due to person–role conflict. Surface acting is needed to actively regulate one's emotions to deal with the felt tension or conflict. This process involves cognitive effort and therefore drains mental resources, leading to strain (Martinez-Inigo, Totterdell, Alcover, & Holman, 2007).

In a meta-analysis, Hülsheger and Schewe (2011) found that surface acting was strongly associated with burnout, stress symptoms, and job dissatisfaction: emotional exhaustion (ρ = .44), depersonalization (ρ = .48), psychological strain (ρ = .42), psychosomatic complaints (ρ = .44), and job satisfaction (ρ = −.33). Emotion–rule dissonance had similar effects: emotional exhaustion (ρ = .40), depersonalization (ρ = .44), psychological strain (ρ = .39), psychosomatic complaints (ρ = .39), and job satisfaction (ρ = −.40). Deep acting, however, had near-zero relationships with burnout, stress symptoms, and job dissatisfaction, except for a small effect on psychosomatic complaints (ρ = .18). Surface acting is often regarded as an ineffective emotion regulation strategy, which leads to reduced well-being, and fails to enhance performance. Deep acting may be a more adaptive strategy as it leads to more rewarding interpersonal interactions. It is still depleting, but the adverse effects may be offset, leading to better job satisfaction and job performance (Wang, Seibert, & Boles, 2011). Humphrey, Ashforth, and Diefendorff (2015) argued that the most effective emotion regulation strategy with overall positive effects is displaying genuine and naturally occurring emotions, and so does not involve acting at all. This strategy would be adopted by those with high levels of work identification.

Workplace Harassment. As a particular form of social stressor, workplace harassment acts as a source of occupational stress. Bowling and Beehr (2006, p. 998) define workplace harassment as "interpersonal behavior aimed at intentionally harming another employee in the workplace"; it includes workplace bullying, abusive supervision, and social undermining. Victims are likely to blame not only the perpetrator for the harassment but also the organization, in terms of its climate and human resource practices. There is a process of attribution and reciprocity that usually results in negative reactions, potentially targeted at the perpetrator, the organization, or the self. Inward attributions are most likely to result in stress symptoms and impact upon well-being. Bowling and Beehr (2006) found that workplace harassment was associated with anxiety (ρ = .31), depression (ρ = .34), burnout (ρ = .39), frustration (ρ = .40), negative emotions at work (ρ = .46), (low) job satisfaction (ρ = −.39), and physical symptoms (ρ = .31). They also showed that while role stressors (role conflict and role ambiguity) accounted for more variance in depression and anxiety than workplace harassment, the latter was the stronger predictor of both burnout and physical symptoms. It is likely that poor working environments are the source of multiple stressors and that role stressors and workplace harassment often co-occur.

Abusive supervision is a more specific form of workplace harassment as it is perpetrated by supervisors toward their subordinates. Perceptions of abusive supervision act as a drain on the subordinate's resources, as cognitive and emotional resources are depleted by efforts to understand the abuse and consider its consequences, leading to strong emotional responses and burnout (especially emotional exhaustion) (Wheeler, Halbesleben, & Whitman, 2013). Hershcovis and colleagues (2007) showed that workplace aggression stems from the effect of both individual (e.g., trait anger) and situational (e.g., interpersonal conflict, poor leadership) factors. The theoretical underpinnings of abusive supervision relate to organizational justice theory, where subordinate perceptions of abusive supervision originate in a sense of injustice stemming from supervisory behaviors, subsequently reinforced through leader–subordinate exchanges and hypervigilance to threat detection (Klaussner, 2014). Mackey, Frieder, Brees, and Martinko (2017) found strong associations between abusive supervision and perceptions of authoritarian ($\rho = .41$) and ethical ($\rho = -.50$) leadership. Abusive supervision had a significant adverse impact on indicators of health and well-being: depression ($\rho = .24$), emotional exhaustion ($\rho = .36$), (low) job satisfaction ($\rho = -.34$), and job tension ($\rho = .24$). Schyns and Schilling (2013) focused on negative active leader behaviors, which they defined as "destructive leadership." Exposure to destructive leader behaviors over a long period of time results in reduced job satisfaction ($\rho = -.34$) and well-being, including life satisfaction and physical well-being ($\rho = -.35$), and increased stress symptoms, including exhaustion and depression ($\rho = .24$). For well-being, the negative effects of destructive leadership were stronger than the positive effects of constructive leadership. The authors noted that destructive leadership particularly influenced subordinates' experience of negative emotions, but the effect on stress symptoms (e.g., exhaustion and depression) was less, perhaps due to the influence of other factors, such as coping mechanisms.

Workplace bullying is characterized by "systematic and prolonged exposure to repeated negative and aggressive behavior of a primarily psychological nature, including non-behavior and acts of social exclusion" (Nielsen & Einarsen, 2012, p. 309). It captures a broader range of behavior than abusive supervision, as it includes coworkers, superiors, and subordinates. Nielsen and Einarsen (2012) reviewed both cross-sectional (i.e., measures taken at the same point in time) and longitudinal (i.e., measures taken at multiple points over time) studies of workplace bullying. Their findings suggested that the long-term negative effects on health and well-being are perpetuated as victims of bullying develop increased vulnerability to bullying over time. They reported synchronous effects for health and well-being outcomes: anxiety ($\rho = .27$), depression ($\rho = .34$), burnout ($\rho = .27$), and physical health problems ($\rho = .23$). Based on longitudinal effects on health and well-being, they found that baseline exposure to workplace bullying is significantly related to subsequent mental health problems ($\rho = .20$); furthermore, mental health problems at baseline were related to subsequent increased exposure to bullying ($\rho = .19$). These findings suggest a vicious circle, where those with mental health issues are more likely to be victims of bullying or are more sensitive to perceiving workplace behavior as bullying. Further research by Einarsen and Nielsen (2015) undertook a 5-year prospective study, which demonstrated evidence that baseline bullying led to significantly increased levels of psychological distress (anxiety and depression) over the 5-year period. This effect was found controlling for perceptions of victimization and a stressful work environment. Furthermore, baseline anxiety predicted subsequent exposure to bullying, supporting a vulnerable worker mechanism. However, both effects only held for men (not women), suggesting that men are especially at risk of these damaging psychological effects over time. Although workplace bullying can be perpetrated by supervisors, coworkers, or people from outside the organization (such as customers), Hershcovis and Barling (2010) found that the source makes little difference to the impact on mental and physical health.

Psychosocial Safety Climate. Psychosocial safety climate (PSC) has been defined as a facet-specific organizational climate for the psychological health of employees (Dollard &

Bakker, 2010). It has been identified as a precursor to job demands, which in turn relate to psychological health and well-being. It also acts as a moderator of the relationship between emotional demands and emotional exhaustion. Testing a multi-level model, Dollard and colleagues (2012) found that PSC at unit level influenced subsequent work conditions of nurses (workload and control) and psychological strain over a 24-month period. Support for the buffering effects of PSC has also been reported. For example, in a daily diary study, perceptions of PSC moderated the effects of job demands on fatigue and work engagement, demonstrating that a positive climate can help to attenuate the adverse effects of job demands on strain and accentuate the positive effects on engagement (Garrick et al., 2014). A high-PSC work environment, where the organization is viewed as valuing employee health and well-being, promotes feelings of "psychological safety" in which employees feel able to speak up and voice concerns. For example, victims of bullying are more likely to speak up about their experiences in a high-PSC environment, allowing resolution, whereas in a low PSC environment victims are more likely to acquiesce before leaving the organization (Kwan, Tuckey, & Dollard, 2016).

WORKPLACE SAFETY

Physical hazards, such as handling toxic materials or working at height, pose a danger to the safety of employees. Thus, working in hazardous environments presents a safety risk (i.e., increased likelihood of accidents and injuries). Physical hazards in the workplace not only pose safety risks but also act as a source of stress (e.g., worrying about one's personal safety), which can affect health and well-being. Nahrgang, Morgeson, and Hofmann (2011) found a significant relationship ($\rho = .28$) between physical hazards and indicators of well-being (anxiety, stress symptoms, and health). In addition, occupational stress can affect safety-related behavior (e.g., complying with safety rules and engaging in safety activities, such as training), which in turn affects accidents (Clarke, 2010, 2012; Nahrgang et al., 2011). Clarke (2012) demonstrated that hindrance stressors (i.e., job demands perceived as unmanageable) have a deleterious effect on safety-related behavior by reducing compliance with rules and regulations ($\rho = -.24$) and participation in safety citizenship behaviors, such as making safety suggestions ($\rho = -.34$) and increasing the likelihood of work accidents ($\rho = .14$). By contrast, challenge stressors (i.e., job demands that are perceived as challenging) had a near-zero effect on accidents and compliance but had a small effect on safety participation ($\rho = -.12$). Thus, hindrance stressors, which lead to psychological and physical strain, are most likely to affect not only health and well-being but also workplace safety.

In stressful situations psychological and physiological stress responses can have implications for workplace safety. In a cross-lagged panel study, Halbesleben showed that emotional exhaustion increased the use of safety workarounds, which in turn increased work injuries over time, where a safety workaround was defined as "a situation in which an employee devises a solution to address a real or perceived block in work flow" (2010, p. 2). Emotional exhaustion depletes individuals' resources, encouraging the use of shortcuts, which increases the risk of accidents. Using workarounds also means that problems are not reported, and therefore effective procedures are not developed as a result of feedback.

Safety Climate. A major antecedent of workplace accidents is organizational safety climate (Beus, Payne, Bergman, & Arthur, 2010; Clarke, 2006). Safety climate was first examined by Zohar (1980); it focuses on employees' perceptions of the work environment and reflects the extent to which safety is prioritized in the workplace. Neal and Griffin (2006) defined safety climate as shared perceptions of policies, procedures, and practices relating to safety in the workplace. As safety climate relates to shared perceptions, it is usually regarded as a group-level, rather than an individual-level, concept (Zohar, 2000). While safety priority is reflected in the "espoused" policies and practices of an organization (i.e., formal written documents), it is how these are "enacted" (i.e., experienced in practice) that influences employees' safety perceptions (Zohar, 2010). For example, a supervisor may endorse following safety rules but "turn a blind eye" to rule violations if tasks are performed more efficiently as a result. Thus, management commitment to safety, as reflected in managers' safety attitudes and actions, has emerged as an important aspect of safety climate (Flin, Mearns, O'Connor, & Bryden, 2000). It is often when there is high work pressure that production is prioritized over safety; therefore, a positive safety climate helps to ensure that safety is not sacrificed when production pressures are high. A positive safety climate is manifest throughout an organization and affects all areas of its operations and functioning, including communication, training, and opportunities for feedback. Christian, Bradley, Wallace, and Burke (2009) looked at lower-level dimensions of group-level safety climate as predictors of accidents; they found that the strongest associations were with perceptions of HR practices ($\rho = -.46$), safety systems ($\rho = -.38$), and management commitment ($\rho = -.36$). The wider organizational climate has a significant influence on perceptions of safety climate, with organizational aspects most influential, such as communication and information flow ($\rho = .72$), as well as the work group ($\rho = .51$) and leadership ($\rho = .51$) (Clarke, 2010). Nahrgang et al. (2011) found that social support ($\rho = -.44$) was closely related to safety climate, suggesting that support from coworkers (in addition to support from supervisors) shapes individuals' safety perceptions.

In a longitudinal study, Neal and Griffin (2006) demonstrated that group-level safety climate influenced safety motivation at an individual level, which affected individual safety behaviors over time. In addition, they found that safety behavior at group level was predictive of subsequent group-level accidents. The study suggested a motivational pathway for the effects of safety climate on work accidents that unfolded over time. Taking the direction of the effects into account, Beus et al. (2010) found that group-level safety climate was predictive of work injuries ($\rho = -.24$), and work injuries were predictive of subsequent group-level safety climate ($\rho = -.29$). Thus, there is likely to be a reciprocal relationship between safety climate and accidents over time.

Although most research has focused on the work environment, personality also has a role in safety at work. Early work on occupational accidents focused on the concept of "accident proneness," based on the finding that a small number of individuals were responsible for a disproportionately large number of accidents, leading to the hunt to identify the "accident prone personality" (Clarke, 2011). A specific personality profile has proven difficult to identify, but meta-analyses based on the "Big Five" (conscientiousness, agreeableness, extraversion, neuroticism, and openness) have shown that some personality traits are associated with accidents (Clarke & Robertson, 2005) and safety-related behavior (Beus, Dhanani, &

McCord, 2015). Those low on conscientiousness and low on agreeableness were more accident involved (Clarke & Robertson, 2005): conscientiousness ($\rho = .30$) and agreeableness ($\rho = .61$). This would suggest that people who are less diligent (e.g., at following rules or instructions) and those who are more aggressive (e.g., less co-operative and difficult to work with) are more likely to have work accidents. Furthermore, Beus et al. (2015) found that agreeableness, conscientiousness, and neuroticism are associated with safety behavior, controlling for perceptions of safety climate, reinforcing the interpretation that certain personality characteristics are influential in terms of safety behaviors, which in turn affect accident involvement.

Safety Leadership. Leadership has emerged as an important antecedent of safety climate and safety behaviors, including the type of leadership style (Clarke, 2013; Nielsen, Skogstad, Matthiesen, & Einarsen, 2016), the strength of the leader–subordinate relationship (Hofmann, Morgeson, & Gerras, 2003), and the extent to which leaders' words match their deeds (Leroy et al., 2012).

Based on social exchange theory, the quality of the relationship between the leader and each employee (i.e., leader–member exchange, or LMX) is related to the extent that employees feel obligated to reciprocate (e.g., citizenship behaviors). In terms of workplace safety, Hofmann et al. (2003) found that, in a positive safety climate, high LMX led to employees viewing safety citizenship as part of their role. Perceptions of leader integrity are also important to workplace safety. Where leaders are perceived to align their words with their actions (high behavioral integrity), employees are more likely to engage in safety-related behaviors, such as reporting errors (Leroy et al., 2012).

A number of leadership styles have been examined in relation to workplace safety in order to understand how leaders should act to encourage positive safety behavior. Both transformational leadership (i.e., inspirational and motivating behaviors) and active transactional leadership (i.e., correcting and directive behaviors) have been linked to safety climate and safety behaviors (Clarke, 2013). Perceptions of safety climate were closely associated with both transformational ($\rho = .48$) and active transactional ($\rho = .57$) leadership, and both types of leadership were associated with safety behavior, but transformational more so with participation ($\rho = .44$) and active transactional more so with compliance ($\rho = .41$). In a longitudinal study, Nielsen et al. (2016) found that constructive leadership had a significant positive effect on safety climate over time. Safety interventions have moved away from behavioral change initiatives at an individual level toward interventions that aim to improve the safety climate through leadership behaviors (e.g., Zohar & Polachek, 2017).

POSITIVE PSYCHOLOGY PERSPECTIVE

An approach based on positive psychology has led researchers to focus on building positive health and resilience rather than only eliminating or reducing negative aspects. While organizations can assist in efforts to design healthy workplaces that encourage work engagement, efforts to improve workplaces are also initiated by employees themselves (e.g., job crafting, proactive behavior).

Job Crafting. Job crafting refers to activities that individuals perform to actively shape their (perceptions of) job characteristics to create more meaningful work; the aim of these activities is to develop a better fit between the individual and their job (Wrzesniewski & Dutton, 2001). Job crafting can be viewed as a form of proactive behavior, where individuals adjust their work environment to increase resources, reduce hindrances, and increase challenges in order to improve psychological well-being (Tims & Bakker, 2010). Rudolph, Katz, Lavigne, and Zacher (2017) found that overall job crafting was positively related to job satisfaction ($\rho = .29$) and work engagement ($\rho = .45$) and negatively related to job strain ($\rho = -.13$). Structural (i.e., increasing job resources) and challenging (i.e., increasing challenging job demands) job-crafting strategies were most beneficial for well-being. Thus, activities that involve engaging in more challenges and building job resources are most effective and have the greatest benefits for employees, whereas reducing job demands can have an adverse effect on well-being. Petrou, Demerouti, and Schaufeli (2015) found a "vicious cycle" in which employees who experience exhaustion respond by decreasing their demands, which in turn leads to further exhaustion. This is possibly due to the effect of decreasing effort to meet demands creating the perception of increased workload. Although somewhat counterintuitive, reductions in strain are best achieved through increasing meaningful challenges, rather than reducing demands.

Proactivity. Proactive behavior has been defined as "taking initiative in improving current circumstances or creating new ones; it involves challenging the status quo rather than passively adapting to present conditions" (Crant, 2000, p. 436). Proactivity can take a number of different forms, including personal initiative, taking charge, and speaking up (voice). A meta-analysis conducted by Thomas, Whitman, and Viswesvaran (2010) examined the proactivity–job satisfaction relationship. Proactive behaviors were found to predict work satisfaction, as they help to develop greater job meaning. A reciprocal relationship is also possible as more satisfied employees may immerse themselves in work to a greater extent leading to more proactive behaviors. A significant relationship was found between proactive behaviors (voice) and work satisfaction ($\rho = .25$). Proactive behavior was also strongly associated with improved job performance: personal initiative ($\rho = .35$), taking charge ($\rho = .46$), and voice ($\rho = .30$) (Thomas et al., 2010).

Proactive behavior involves a high degree of cognitive effort and depletion of resources and might therefore be associated with job strain (Fay & Hüttges, 2017; Strauss, Parker, & O'Shea, 2017). Fay and Hüttges (2017) used a diary study to show that engaging in proactive behavior raised levels of daily cortisol output (using salvia samples), which indicates increased job strain. While Strauss et al. (2017) also found that proactive behavior was associated with job strain due to depletion of resources, this effect was offset by resource development through (autonomous) motivational processes. Proactive behavior only led to job strain when motivation was controlled (i.e., performed as a felt obligation) rather than autonomous (i.e., performed through intrinsic interest).

Callings. Work motivation has been found to affect people's work attitudes and emotional engagement with their work. People who identify their work as a "calling" experience greater life satisfaction and psychological well-being, because work is experienced as deeply meaningful

(Duffy & Dik, 2013). However, at the same time, it is possible that the sacrifices required to follow one's calling might have an adverse impact on well-being.

The type of motivation is an important intervening variable for understanding the impact of having a "calling" on psychological well-being and job strain. Conway, Clinton, Sturges, and Budjanovcanin (2015) looked at daily well-being and motivations through a diary study and found that daily positive well-being was mediated by intrinsic motivation. Calling motivation was also found to moderate the link from perceived calling to life satisfaction, such that life satisfaction was higher for those with greater motivation, as they were more likely to enact their calling and find meaning in it (Duffy, England, Douglass, Autin, & Allan, 2017).

Thriving at Work. Recent work has examined the workplace antecedents and health consequences of "thriving at work" defined as "a desirable subjective experience that helps individuals to understand what and how they are doing, and whether it is increasing their individual functioning and adaptability at work" (Spreitzer & Porath, 2014, p. 247). Thriving at work is associated with positive health and well-being, as positive experiences of vitality and learning help individuals to develop resilience to stress (Spreitzer, Porath, & Gibson, 2012; Walumbwa, Muchiri, Misati, Wu, & Meiliani, 2017).

Meeting challenge stressors in the workplace is an opportunity to build resilience to stress, so that future challenges create less job strain and increase thriving at work. For example, a diary study demonstrated that the daily experience of challenge stressors led to increased learning, which is a component of thriving at work (Prem et al., 2017).

WORK/NONWORK BOUNDARY

Managing the work/nonwork boundary is often a challenge for individuals and organizations. The relationship between these two domains offers the opportunity both for conflict (which drains resources and damages well-being) and enrichment (which builds resources and enhances well-being).

Work–Family Conflict. Work–family conflict (WFC) has been defined as "a form of interrole conflict in which the role pressures from the work and family domains are mutually incompatible in some respect" (Greenhaus & Beutell, 1985, p. 77). This means that one's role in the work domain interferes with one's family role (and vice versa). Research has shown that, like other forms of role conflict, work–family conflict has significant negative impact on health and well-being. In a meta-analysis, Amstad, Meier, Fasel, Elfering, and Semmer (2011) found that work interference from family (WIF) was associated with work-related burnout ($\rho = .38$), general psychological strain ($\rho = .35$), health problems ($\rho = .28$), and physical stress symptoms ($\rho = .29$); whereas family interference from work (FIW) was associated with work-related burnout ($\rho = .27$), general psychological strain ($\rho = .21$), health problems ($\rho = .24$), and physical stress symptoms ($\rho = .14$). Thus, WIF has more deleterious effects on general health and well-being than FIW, and the effects on job burnout are also more closely associated with WIF. Indeed, in a meta-analysis of longitudinal studies, Nohe, Meier, Sonntag, and Michel (2015) found that, controlling for FIW, only WIF predicts work-related strain. There is evidence of cross-domain effects, with work stress crossing over into family life more than family stress crosses over into work life (Ford, Heinen, & Langkamer, 2007), but the impact on health and well-being is stronger within domains. Job stressors ($\rho = .50$) and work role overload in particular ($\rho = .55$) affect WIF, and family stressors ($\rho = .40$), particularly family role conflict ($\rho = .36$) and family role overload ($\rho = .35$), are associated with FIW (Michel, Kotrba, Mitchelson, Clark, & Baltes, 2011). Most theoretical explanations for the relationship between WFC and strain have assumed that WFC leads to strain (e.g., based on effort-recovery theory), but reverse and reciprocal effects are also plausible, where those experiencing job strain are more likely to encounter work–family conflict. Nohe et al. (2015) found that WFC leads to strain but also that strain leads to WFC, resulting in a reciprocal relationship over time.

From an organizational perspective, support for employees trying to manage work/nonwork boundaries is important to safeguard health and well-being. Kossek, Pichler, Bodner, and Hammer (2011) found that both organizational support and supervisor support were important in relation to WFC: perceptions of conflict were reduced when employees believed the organization was supportive and when supervisors demonstrated specific supportive behaviors. It should also not be assumed that WFC is mainly an issue for women and that men do not need the same level of support. Shockley, Shen, DeNunzio, Arvan, and Knudsen (2017) found that both genders experience WFC in similar ways, and WFC had negative effects on health and well-being for both men and women. In a longitudinal analysis looking at spillover (effects of workload on own marital satisfaction) and crossover (effects of workload on spouse's marital satisfaction) over a 4-year period, Lavner and Clark (2017) found significant crossover effects but not spillover effects. Thus, people may be able to cope effectively with their own workloads but struggle more to cope with their partner's over longer time periods. This research emphasizes the importance of understanding the impact on work stress on family units, rather than the employee in isolation.

Work–Family Enrichment. Research has looked at the positive effects of the work–family relationship in terms of "work–family enrichment," defined as "the extent to which experiences in one role improve the quality of life in the other role" (Greenhaus & Powell, 2006, p. 73). Work–family enrichment can have positive effects on health and well-being (van Steenbergen & Ellemers, 2009). Carlson, Hunter, Ferguson, and Whitten (2014) examined the mechanisms underlying this relationship and found that work–family enrichment led to reduced psychological distress (i.e., experiencing negative emotions), which in turn increased both job satisfaction and family satisfaction.

Individual differences in how people manage work and nonwork boundaries may account for the different ways in which people experience work–family conflict or enrichment. Using a person-centered approach, Kinnunen, Rantanen, de Bloom, Mauno, Feldt, and Korpela (2016) found that those who protected nonwork time and kept work separate from nonwork had better recovery experiences and health outcomes.

Changes in Work Organization. The ways in which work is organized, such as flexible working and the use of new technology, has led to the blurring of boundaries between work and nonwork. This may create greater difficulty in disengaging from work, "switching off," and engaging in leisure activities, all of which aid recovery and maintain positive health and well-being.

Flexible working arrangements (FWAs), which allow employees flexibility in their work time (e.g., start and finish times, compressed hours, reduced load working, or part-time contracts) or location (e.g., working from home or mobile working) are often introduced by employers as a means of reducing WFC. Research evidence demonstrates that although flexible working is effective in reducing WFC, the effect tends to be small (Shockley & Allen, 2007). Nijp, Beckers, Geurts, Tucker, and Kompier (2012) found that FWAs led to enhanced work–life balance over time, but this did not necessarily lead to improved health and well-being. Positive effects depend on the extent to which FWAs are effective in reducing job burnout (Grzywacz, Carlson, & Shulkin, 2008) and increasing job resources, such as control (Allen, Johnson, Kiburz, & Shockley, 2013; Ter Hoeven & van Zoonen, 2015). Employers can benefit from having flexible working policies, as this leads to increased work engagement, but not always among those who make use of FWAs, as FWAs can lead to additional burdens (Timms et al., 2015). FWAs need to be implemented within a supportive organizational climate, so that job demands do not increase as a result, leading to reduced work engagement and increased job strain.

The use of new technology, such as smartphones and tablets, increases the availability of employees and can result in increased work demands. It also blurs the boundary between work and nonwork as it enables employees to remain connected to work during nonwork hours (e.g., checking, sending, and responding to email). Smartphone use has been found to reduce opportunities to engage in recovery through leisure activities (Derks, ten Brummelhuis, Zecic, & Bakker, 2014), and using a smartphone to work at night leads to increased depletion (via effects on sleep) and subsequent reduced work engagement the next morning (Lanaj, Johnson, & Barnes, 2014). However, the potential adverse effects on psychological health and well-being are moderated by high work engagement, clear organizational norms about availability during nonwork hours (Derks, van Duin, Tims, & Bakker, 2015), and the level of job control (Lanaj et al., 2014).

ORGANIZATIONAL INTERVENTIONS

In many countries organizations have a legal requirement to manage physical and psychosocial risks at work. Occupational stress may be viewed as a psychosocial risk factor, which can be managed through health and safety policies, practices, and procedures and targeted actions, such as interventions. Organizations implement a range of interventions to tackle occupational stress at an individual, group, or organizational level. The aim of an intervention may be to deal with stress symptoms (e.g., help employees to reduce the negative effects of work strain) or to prevent work stressors in the first place (e.g., through work redesign). Stress management interventions are generally effective at reducing the psychological effects of work stress, with Richardson and Rothstein (2008) reporting a moderate effect size for their overall effectiveness ($\rho = .53$). Stress management interventions often involve a combination of techniques to help employees reduce the effects of work stress. Although relaxation was used most frequently as an organizational intervention, Richardson and Rothstein (2008) reported that cognitive-behavioral therapy was the most effective individual technique. More recently, mindfulness interventions have been used to help employees achieve "a state of consciousness in which individuals attend to ongoing events and experiences in a receptive and non-judgmental way" (Hülsheger, Alberts, Feinholdt, & Lang, 2013, p. 310). Mindfulness can help to relieve the effects of stress but can also lead to longer-term resilience if adopted as an emotion regulation strategy, resulting in enhanced job satisfaction and reduced emotional exhaustion (Hülsheger et al., 2013).

Although stress management interventions have proven effective, one criticism of organizations relying on these interventions is that they tend to manage stress for employees who are already experiencing strain. Thus, they are aimed at treatment rather than prevention. Interventions that aim to prevent job strain often incorporate work redesign. Interventions with multiple foci (such as the NIOSH Total Worker Health program, which incorporates a focus on wellness as well as occupational health and safety) have proven effective in improving a range of employee outcomes (e.g., Anger et al., 2015). Holman and Axtell (2016) found that a job redesign intervention that increased job resources (job control and feedback) was effective at increasing employee health and well-being (alongside other employee outcomes). Another approach is to focus on building personal resources, which can have longer-term benefits for mental health, although this was found to be most effective for younger employees and those who were already showing signs of job strain (Vuori, Toppinen-Tanner, & Mutanen, 2012). As an alternative to top-down job redesign, job crafting interventions seek to facilitate individual efforts to craft job characteristics to provide a better person–job fit. By allowing employees control over job demands and resources, job crafting interventions (which involved increasing challenges, rather than decreasing demands) have been effective in reducing exhaustion, increasing work engagement (Gordon et al., 2018), and improving well-being (van Wingerden, Bakker, & Derks, 2017).

In addition, however, organizations need to be aware of the contribution that organizational culture and norms can make to employees' work behavior, so that excessive work patterns are not reinforced through cultural norms. For example, in a qualitative study, Kirrane, Breen, and O'Connor (2018) found that excessive work patterns are better understood as rooted in family background, educational experience, and professional norms, rather than characterizing individuals as being "addicted" to work. Organizations can help to mitigate the reinforcement of excessive work patterns by considering the effects of cultural norms within the workplace (e.g., expectations of permanent availability).

CONCLUSIONS

Occupational health psychology has taken strides as a sub-discipline of applied psychology, building influential theories, including the job demands-resources model (Bakker & Demerouti, 2017) and conservation of resources theory (Hobfoll et al., 2018). These have provided a theoretical framework for a substantial body of research, which aims to develop an understanding of how workplaces can be made into healthy, safe, and engaging environments. There has been significant uptake of ideas developed from OHP research, with organizations adopting a range of human resource practices (e.g., flexible working policies) and interventions (e.g., stress management and well-being programs), which promote employee well-being as well as organizational functioning.

REFERENCES

Alarcon, G. M. (2011). A meta-analysis of burnout with job demands, resources, and attitudes. *Journal of Vocational Behavior, 79*(2), 549–562. https://dx.doi.org/10.1016/j.jvb.2011.03.007

Aldwin, C. M., & Revenson, T. A. (1987). Does coping help? A reexamination of the relation between coping and mental health. *Journal of Personality and Social Psychology, 53*(2), 337–348. http://dx.doi.org/10.1037/0022-3514.53.2.337

Allen, T. D., Johnson, R. C., Kiburz, K. M., & Shockley, K. M. (2013). Work–family conflict and flexible work arrangements: Deconstructing flexibility. *Personnel Psychology, 66*(2), 345–376. http://dx.doi.org/10.1111/peps.12012

Amstad, F. T., Meier, L. L., Fasel, U., Elfering, A., & Semmer, N. K. (2011). A meta-analysis of work–family conflict and various outcomes with a special emphasis on cross-domain versus matching-domain relations. *Journal of Occupational Health Psychology, 16*(2), 151–169. http://dx.doi.org/10.1037/a0022170

Anger, W. K., Elliot, D. L., Bodner, T., Olson, R., Rohlman, D. S., Truxillo, D. M., . . . Montgomery, D. (2015). Effectiveness of Total Worker Health interventions. *Journal of Occupational Health Psychology, 20*(2), 226–247. http://dx.doi.org/10.1037/a0038340

Bakker, A. B., & Demerouti, E. (2017). Job demands-resources theory: Taking stock and looking forward. *Journal of Occupational Health Psychology, 22*(3), 273–285. http://dx.doi.org/10.1037/ocp0000056

Bakker, A. B., Demerouti, E., & Euwema, M. C. (2005). Job resources buffer the impact of job demands on burnout. *Journal of Occupational Health Psychology, 10*(2), 170–180. http://dx.doi.org/10.1037/1076-8998.10.2.170

Bennett, A. A., Bakker, A. B., & Field, J. G. (2017). Recovery from work-related effort: A meta-analysis. *Journal of Organizational Behavior.* https://dx.doi.org/10.1002/job.2217

Beus, J. M., Dhanani, L. Y., & McCord, M. A. (2015). A meta-analysis of personality and workplace safety: Addressing unanswered questions. *Journal of Applied Psychology, 100*(2), 481–498. http://dx.doi.org/10.1037/a0037916

Beus, J. M., Payne, S. C., Bergman, M. E., & Arthur, W. (2010). Safety climate and injuries: An examination of theoretical and empirical relationships. *Journal of Applied Psychology, 95*(4), 713–727. http://dx.doi.org/10.1037/a0019164

Bowling, N. A., & Beehr, T. A. (2006). Workplace harassment from the victim's perspective: A theoretical model and meta-analysis. *Journal of Applied Psychology, 91*(5), 998–1012. http://dx.doi.org/10.1037/0021-9010.91.5.998

Carlson, D. S., Hunter, E. M., Ferguson, M., & Whitten, D. (2014). Work-family enrichment and satisfaction: Mediating processes and relative impact of originating and receiving domains. *Journal of Management, 40*(3), 845–865. https://dx.doi.org/10.1177/0149206311414429

Cavanaugh, M. A., Boswell, W. R., Roehling, M. V., & Boudreau, J. W. (2000). An empirical examination of self-reported work stress among U.S. managers. *Journal of Applied Psychology, 85*(1), 65–74. http://dx.doi.org/10.1037/0021-9010.85.1.65

Christian, M. S., Bradley, J. C., Wallace, J. C., & Burke, M. J. (2009). Workplace safety: A meta-analysis of the roles of person and situation factors. *Journal of Applied Psychology, 94*(5), 1103–1127. http://dx.doi.org/10.1037/a0016172

Clarke, S. (2006). The relationship between safety climate and safety performance: A meta-analytic review. *Journal of Occupational Health Psychology, 11*(4), 315–327. http://dx.doi.org/10.1037/1076-8998.11.4.315

Clarke, S. (2010). An integrative model of safety climate: Linking psychological climate and work attitudes to individual safety outcomes using meta-analysis. *Journal of Occupational and Organizational Psychology, 83*(3), 553–578. http://dx.doi.org/10.1348/096317909X452122

Clarke, S. (2011). Accident proneness: Back in vogue? In R. J. Burke, S. Clarke, & C. L. Cooper (Eds.), *Occupational health and safety* (pp. 95–117). Farnham, Surrey, U.K.: Gower.

Clarke, S. (2012). The effect of challenge and hindrance stressors on safety behavior and safety outcomes: A meta-analysis. *Journal of Occupational Health Psychology, 17*(4), 387–397. http://dx.doi.org/10.1037/a0029817

Clarke, S. (2013). Safety leadership: A meta-analytic review of transformational and transactional leadership styles as antecedents of safety behaviors. *Journal of Occupational and Organizational Psychology, 86*(1), 22–49. http://dx.doi.org/10.1111/j.2044-8325.2012.02064.x

Clarke, S., & Robertson, I. T. (2005). A meta-analytic review of the Big Five personality factors and accident involvement in occupational and non-occupational settings. *Journal of Occupational and Organizational Psychology, 78*(3), 355–376. http://dx.doi.org/10.1348/096317905X26183

Cohen, J. (1977). *Statistical power analysis for the behavioral sciences.* Routledge.

Conway, N., Clinton, M., Sturges, J., & Budjanovcanin, A. (2015). Using self-determination theory to understand the relationship between calling enactment and daily well-being. *Journal of Organizational Behavior, 36*(8), 1114–1131. http://dx.doi.org/10.1002/job.2014

Cooper, C. L., Dewe, P., & O'Driscoll, M. P. (2001). *Organizational stress: A review and critique of theory, research, and applications.* Thousand Oaks, CA: SAGE.

Crane, M. F., & Searle, B. J. (2016). Building resilience through exposure to stressors: The effects of challenges versus hindrances. *Journal of Occupational Health Psychology, 21*(4), 468–479. http://dx.doi.org/10.1037/a0040064

Crant, J. M. (2000). Proactive behavior in organizations. *Journal of Management, 26*(3), 435–462. https://dx.doi.org/10.1177/014920630002600304

de Bloom, J., Geurts, S. A. E., & Kompier, M. A. J. (2012). Effects of short vacations, vacation activities and experiences on employee health and well-being. *Stress & Health, 28*(4), 305–318. http://dx.doi.org/10.1002/smi.1434

de Jonge, J., & Dormann, C. (2003). The DISC model: Demand-induced strain compensation mechanisms in job stress. In M. F. Dollard, H. R. Winefield, & H. R. Winefield (Eds.), *Occupational stress in the service professions* (pp. 43–74). London: Taylor & Francis.

de Lange, A. H., Taris, T. W., Kompier, M. A. J., Houtman, I. L. D., & Bongers, P. M. (2003). "The very best of the millennium": Longitudinal research and the demand-control-(support) model. *Journal of Occupational Health Psychology, 8*(4), 282–305. http://dx.doi.org/10.1037/1076-8998.8.4.282

Demerouti, E., Bakker, A. B., & Bulters, A. J. (2004). The loss spiral of work pressure, work–home interference and exhaustion: Reciprocal relations in a three-wave study. *Journal of Vocational Behavior, 64*(1), 131–149. https://dx.doi.org/10.1016/S0001-8791(03)00030-7

Demerouti, E., Bakker, A. B., Nachreiner, F., & Schaufeli, W. B. (2001). The job demands-resources model of burnout. *Journal of Applied Psychology, 86*(3), 499–512. http://dx.doi.org/10.1037/0021-9010.86.3.499

Derks, D., ten Brummelhuis, L. L., Zecic, D., & Bakker, A. B. (2014). Switching on and off . . . : Does smartphone use obstruct the possibility to engage in recovery activities? *European Journal of Work and Organizational Psychology, 23*(1), 80–90. http://dx.doi.org/10.1080/1359432X.2012.711013

Derks, D., van Duin, D., Tims, M., & Bakker, A. B. (2015). Smartphone use and work–home interference: The moderating role of social norms and employee work engagement. *Journal of Occupational and Organizational Psychology, 88*(1), 155–177. http://dx.doi.org/10.1111/joop.12083

Dollard, M. F., & Bakker, A. B. (2010). Psychosocial safety climate as a precursor to conducive work environments, psychological health problems, and employee engagement. *Journal of Occupational and Organizational Psychology, 83*(3), 579–599. http://dx.doi.org/10.1348/096317909X470690

Dollard, M. F., Opie, T., Lenthall, S., Wakerman, J., Knight, S., Dunn, S., Rickard, G., & MacLeod, M. (2012). Psychosocial safety climate as an antecedent of work characteristics and psychological strain: A multilevel model. *Work & Stress, 26*(4), 385–404. http://dx.doi.org/10.1080/02678373.2012.734154

Duffy, R. D., & Dik, B. J. (2013). Research on calling: What have we learned and where are we going? *Journal of Vocational Behavior, 83*(3), 428–436. https://dx.doi.org/10.1016/j.jvb.2013.06.006

Duffy, R. D., England, J. W., Douglass, R. P., Autin, K. L., & Allan, B. A. (2017). Perceiving a calling and well-being: Motivation and access to opportunity as moderators. *Journal of Vocational Behavior, 98*, 127–137. https://dx.doi.org/10.1016/j.jvb.2016.11.003

Einarsen, S., & Nielsen, M. B. (2015). Workplace bullying as an antecedent of mental health problems: A five-year prospective and representative study. *International Archives of Occupational and Environmental Health, 88*(2), 131–142. https://dx.doi.org/10.1007/s00420-014-0944-7

Fay, D., & Hüttges, A. (2017). Drawbacks of proactivity: Effects of daily proactivity on daily salivary cortisol and subjective well-being. *Journal of Occupational Health Psychology, 22*(4), 429–442. http://dx.doi.org/10.1037/ocp0000042

Flin, R., Mearns, K., O'Connor, P. & Bryden, R. (2000). Measuring safety climate: Identifying the common features. *Safety Science, 34*(1–3), 177–192. http://dx.doi.org/10.1016/S0925-7535(00)00012-6

Folkman, S., & Moskowitz, J. T. (2004). Coping: Pitfalls and promise. *Annual Review of Psychology, 55*(1), 745–774. https://dx.doi.org/10.1146/annurev.psych.55.090902.141456

Folkman, S., Lazarus, R. S., Dunkel-Schetter, C., DeLongis, A., & Gruen, R. J. (1986). Dynamics of a stressful encounter: Cognitive appraisal, coping, and encounter outcomes. *Journal of Personality and Social Psychology, 50*(5), 992–1003. http://dx.doi.org/10.1037/0022-3514.50.5.992

Ford, M. T., Heinen, B. A., & Langkamer, K. L. (2007). Work and family satisfaction and conflict: A meta-analysis of cross-domain relations. *Journal of Applied Psychology, 92*(1), 57–80. http://dx.doi.org/10.1037/0021-9010.92.1.57

Ford, M. T., Matthews, R. A., Wooldridge, J. D., Mishra, V., Kakar, U. M., & Strahan, S. R. (2014). How do occupational stressor-strain effects vary with time? A review and meta-analysis of the relevance of time lags in longitudinal studies. *Work & Stress, 28*(1), 9–30. http://dx.doi.org/10.1080/02678373.2013.877096

Garrick, A., Mak, A. S., Cathcart, S., Winwood, P. C., Bakker, A. B., & Lushington, K. (2014). Psychosocial safety climate moderating the effects of daily job demands and recovery on fatigue and work engagement. *Journal of Occupational and Organizational Psychology, 87*(4), 694–714. http://dx.doi.org/10.1111/joop.12069

Geurts, S. A. E., & Sonnentag, S. (2006). Recovery as an explanatory mechanism in the relation between acute stress reactions and chronic health impairment. *Scandinavian Journal of Work, Environment & Health, 32*(6), 482–492. http://dx.doi.org/10.5271/sjweh.1053

Gordon, H. J., Demerouti, E., Le Blanc, P. M., Bakker, A. B., Bipp, T., & Verhagen, M. A. M. T. (2018). Individual job redesign: Job crafting interventions in healthcare. *Journal of Vocational Behavior, 104*, 98–114. https://dx.doi.org/10.1016/j.jvb.2017.07.002

Grandey, A. A. (2000). Emotional regulation in the workplace: A new way to conceptualize emotional labor. *Journal of Occupational Health Psychology, 5*(1), 95–110. http://dx.doi.org/10.1037/1076%978998.5.1.95

Greenhaus, J. H., & Beutell, N. J. (1985). Sources of conflict between work and family roles. *Academy of Management Review, 10*(1), 76–88. http://dx.doi.org/10.5465/AMR.1985.4277352

Greenhaus, J. H., & Powell, G. N. (2006). When work and family are allies: A theory of work–family enrichment. *Academy of Management Review, 31*(1), 72–92. http://dx.doi.org/10.5465/AMR.2006.19379625

Griffin, M. A., & Clarke, S. (2011). Stress and well-being at work. In S. Zedeck (Ed.), *APA handbook of industrial & organizational psychology. Vol. 3. Maintaining, expanding and contracting the organization* (pp. 359–397). Washington, DC: American Psychological Association.

Grzywacz, J. G., Carlson, D. S., & Shulkin, S. (2008). Schedule flexibility and stress: Linking formal flexible arrangements and perceived flexibility to employee health. *Community, Work & Family, 11*(2), 199–214. http://dx.doi.org/10.1080/13668800802024652

Hakanen, J. J., Perhoniemi, R., & Toppinen-Tanner, S. (2008). Positive gain spirals at work: From job resources to work engagement, personal initiative and work-unit innovativeness. *Journal of Vocational Behavior, 73*(1), 78–91. https://dx.doi.org/10.1016/j.jvb.2008.01.003

Halbesleben, J. R. B. (2006). Sources of social support and burnout: A meta-analytic test of the conservation of resources model. *Journal of Applied Psychology, 91*(5), 1134–1145. http://dx.doi.org/10.1037/0021-9010.91.5.1134

Halbesleben, J. R. B. (2010). The role of exhaustion and workarounds in predicting occupational injuries: A cross-lagged panel study of health care professionals. *Journal of Occupational Health Psychology, 15*(1), 1–16. http://dx.doi.org/10.1037/a0017634

Halbesleben, J. R. B., Neveu, J., Paustian-Underdahl, S. C., & Westman, M. (2014). Getting to the "COR": Understanding the role of resources in conservation of resources theory. *Journal of Management, 40*(5), 1334–1364. https://dx.doi.org/10.1177/0149206314527130

Hershcovis, M. S., & Barling, J. (2010). Towards a multi-foci approach to workplace aggression: A meta-analytic review of outcomes from different perpetrators. *Journal of Organizational Behavior, 31*(1), 24–44. http://dx.doi.org/10.1002/job.621

Hershcovis, M. S., Turner, N., Barling, J., Arnold, K. A., Dupré, K. E., Inness, M., ... Sivanathan, N. (2007). Predicting workplace aggression: A meta-analysis. *Journal of Applied Psychology, 92*(1), 228–238. http://dx.doi.org/10.1037/0021-9010.92.1.228

Hobfoll, S. E. (1989). Conservation of resources: A new attempt at conceptualizing stress. *American Psychologist, 44*(3), 513–524. http://dx.doi.org/10.1037/0003-066X.44.3.513

Hobfoll, S. E., Halbesleben, J., Neveu, J., & Westman, M. (2018). Conservation of resources in the organizational context: The reality of resources and their consequences. *Annual Review of Organizational Psychology and Organizational Behavior, 5*, 103–128. http://dx.doi.org/10.1146/annurev-orgpsych-032117-104640

Hochschild, A. R. (1983). *The managed heart.* Berkeley, CA: University of California Press.

Hofmann, D. A., Morgeson, F. P., & Gerras, S. J. (2003). Climate as a moderator of the relationship between leader–member exchange and content specific citizenship: Safety climate as an exemplar. *Journal of Applied Psychology, 88*(1), 170–178. http://dx.doi.org/10.1037/0021-9010.88.1.170

Holman, D., & Axtell, C. (2016). Can job redesign interventions influence a broad range of employee outcomes by changing multiple job characteristics? A quasi-experimental study. *Journal of Occupational Health Psychology, 21*(3), 284–295. http://dx.doi.org/10.1037/a0039962

Hülsheger, U. R., Alberts, H. J. E. M., Feinholdt, A., & Lang, J. W. B. (2013). Benefits of mindfulness at work: The role of mindfulness in emotion regulation, emotional exhaustion, and job satisfaction. *Journal of Applied Psychology, 98*(2), 310–325. http://dx.doi.org/10.1037/a0031313

Hülsheger, U. R., & Schewe, A. F. (2011). On the costs and benefits of emotional labor: A meta-analysis of three decades of research. *Journal of Occupational Health Psychology, 16*(3), 361–389. http://dx.doi.org/10.1037/a0022876

Humphrey, R. H., Ashforth, B. E., & Diefendorff, J. M. (2015). The bright side of emotional labor. *Journal of Organizational Behavior, 36*(6), 749–769. http://dx.doi.org/10.1002/job.2019

Humphrey, R. H., Pollack, J. M., & Hawver, T. (2008). Leading with emotional labor. *Journal of Managerial Psychology, 23*(2), 151–168. https://dx.doi.org/10.1108/02683940810850790

Jackson, S. E., & Schuler, R. S. (1985). A meta-analysis and conceptual critique of research on role ambiguity and role conflict in work settings. *Organizational Behavior & Human Decision Processes, 36*(1), 16–78. https://dx.doi.org/10.1016/0749-5978(85)90020-2

Johnson, J. V., Hall, E. M., & Theorell, T. (1989). Combined effects of job strain and social isolation on cardiovascular disease morbidity and mortality in a random sample of the Swedish male working population. *Scandinavian Journal of Work Environment and Health, 15*(4), 271–279. http://dx.doi.org/10.5271/sjweh.1852

Kahn, R. L., & Byosiere, P. (1992). Stress in organizations. In M. D. Dunnette & L. M. Hough (Eds.), *Handbook of industrial and organizational* (2nd ed., Vol. 3, pp. 571–650). Palo Alto, CA: Consulting Psychologists Press.

Kahn, R. L., Wolfe, D. M., Quinn, R. P., Snoek, J. D., & Rosenthal, R. A. (1964). *Occupational stress: Studies in role conflict and ambiguity.* New York: Wiley.

Karasek, R., & Theorell, T. (1990). *Healthy work: Stress, productivity, and the reconstruction of working life.* Basic Books.

Karasek, R. A. (1979). Job demands, job decision latitude, and mental strain: Implications for job redesign. *Administrative Science Quarterly, 24*(2), 285–308. http://dx.doi.org/10.2307/2392498

Karasek, R. A. (1989). Control in the workplace and its health related aspects. In S. L. Sauter, J. J. Hurrell, & C. L. Cooper (Eds.), *Job control and work health* (pp. 129–159). New York: Wiley.

Katz, D., & Kahn, R. L. (1978). *The social psychology of organizations* (rev. ed.). New York: Wiley.

Kinnunen, U., Rantanen, J., de Bloom, J., Mauno, S., Feldt, T., & Korpela, K. (2016). The role of work–nonwork boundary management in work stress recovery. *International Journal of Stress Management, 23*(2), 99–123. http://dx.doi.org/10.1037/a0039730

Kirrane, M., Breen, M., & O'Connor, C. (2018). A qualitative investigation of the origins of excessive work behavior. *Journal of Occupational and Organizational Psychology, 91*(2), 235–260. http://dx.doi.org/10.1111/joop.12203

Klaussner, S. (2014). Engulfed in the abyss: The emergence of abusive supervision as an escalating process of supervisor-subordinate interaction. *Human Relations, 67*(3), 311–332. https://dx.doi.org/10.1177/0018726713493027

Kossek, E. E., Pichler, S., Bodner, T., & Hammer, L. B. (2011). Workplace social support and work-family conflict: A meta-analysis clarifying the influence of general and work-family specific supervisor and organizational support. *Personnel Psychology, 64*(2), 289–313. http://dx.doi.org/10.1111/j.1744-6570.2011.01211.x

Kwan, S. S. M., Tuckey, M. R., & Dollard, M. F. (2016). The role of the psychosocial safety climate in coping with workplace bullying: A grounded theory and sequential tree analysis. *European Journal of Work and Organizational Psychology, 25*(1), 133–148. http://dx.doi.org/10.1080/1359432X.2014.982102

Lanaj, K., Johnson, R. E., & Barnes, C. M. (2014). Beginning the workday yet already depleted? Consequences of late-night smartphone use and sleep. *Organizational Behavior and Human Decision Processes, 124*(1), 11–23. https://dx.doi.org/10.1016/j.obhdp.2014.01.001

Lavner, J. A., & Clark, M. A. (2017). Workload and marital satisfaction over time: Testing lagged spillover and crossover effects during the newlywed years. *Journal of Vocational Behavior, 101,* 67–76. https://dx.doi.org/10.1016/j.jvb.2017.05.002

Lazarus, R. L., & Folkman, S. (1984). *Stress, appraisal, and coping.* New York: Springer.

Lee, R. T., & Ashforth, B. E. (1996). A meta-analytic examination of the correlates of the three dimensions of job burnout. *Journal of Applied Psychology, 81*(2), 123–133. http://dx.doi.org/10.1037/0021-9010.81.2.123

Leiter, M. E. (1993). Burnout as a developmental process: Consideration of models. In W. B. Schaufeli, C. Maslach, & T. Marek (Eds.), *Professional burnout: Recent developments in theory and research* (pp. 237–250). Washington, DC: Taylor & Francis.

Leiter, M. P., & Maslach, C. (1988). The impact of interpersonal environment on burnout and organizational commitment. *Journal of Organizational Behavior, 9*(4), 297–308. http://dx.doi.org/10.1002/job.4030090402

Leiter, M. P., & Schaufeli, W. B. (1996). Consistency of the burnout construct across occupations. *Anxiety, Stress & Coping, 9*(3), 229–243. http://dx.doi.org/10.1080/10615809608249404

Lepine, J. A., Podsakoff, N. P., & Lepine, M. A. (2005). A meta-analytic test of the challenge stressor-hindrance stressor framework: An explanation for inconsistent relationships among stressors and performance. *Academy of Management Journal, 48*(5), 764–775. http://dx.doi.org/10.5465/AMJ.2005.18803921

Leroy, H., Dierynck, B., Anseel, F., Simons, T., Halbesleben, J. R. B., McCaughey, D., ... Sels, L. (2012). Behavioral integrity for safety, priority of safety, psychological safety, and patient safety: A team-level study. *Journal of Applied Psychology, 97*(6), 1273–1281. http://dx.doi.org/10.1037/a0030076

Luchman, J. N., & González-Morales, M. G. (2013). Demands, control, and support: A meta-analytic review of work characteristics interrelationships. *Journal of Occupational Health Psychology, 18*(1), 37–52. http://dx.doi.org/10.1037/a0030541

Mackey, J. D., Frieder, R. E., Brees, J. R., & Martinko, M. J. (2017). Abusive supervision: A meta-analysis and empirical review. *Journal of Management, 43*(6), 1940–1965. https://dx.doi.org/10.1177/0149206315573997

Mäkikangas, A., Kinnunen, U., Feldt, T., & Schaufeli, W. (2016). The longitudinal development of employee well-being: A systematic review. *Work & Stress, 30*(1), 46–70. http://dx.doi.org/10.1080/02678373.2015.1126870

Martinez-Inigo, D., Totterdell, P., Alcover, C. M., & Holman, D. (2007). Emotional labour and emotional exhaustion: Interpersonal and intrapersonal mechanisms. *Work & Stress, 21*(1), 30–47. http://dx.doi.org/10.1080/02678370701234274

Maslach, C. (1982). *Burnout: The cost of caring*. Englewood Cliffs, NJ: Prentice-Hall.

Meijman, T. F., & Mulder, G. (1998). Psychological aspects of workload. In P. J. D. Drenth & H. Thierry (Eds.), *Handbook of work and organizational psychology, Vol. 2. Work psychology* (pp. 5–33). Hove, U.K.: Psychology Press.

Melamed, S., Shirom, A., Toker, S., Berliner, S., & Shapira, I. (2006). Burnout and risk of cardiovascular disease: Evidence, possible causal paths, and promising research directions. *Psychological Bulletin, 132*(3), 327–353. http://dx.doi.org/10.1037/0033-2909.132.3.327

Michel, J. S., Kotrba, L. M., Mitchelson, J. K., Clark, M. A., & Baltes, B. B. (2011). Antecedents of work–family conflict: A meta-analytic review. *Journal of Organizational Behavior, 32*(5), 689–725. http://dx.doi.org/10.1002/job.695

Morris, J. A., & Feldman, D. C. (1996). The dimensions, antecedents, and consequences of emotional labor. *Academy of Management Journal, 21*(4), 989–1010. http://dx.doi.org/10.5465/AMR.1996.9704071861

Nahrgang, J. D., Morgeson, F. P., & Hofmann, D. A. (2011). Safety at work: A meta-analytic investigation of the link between job demands, job resources, burnout, engagement, and safety outcomes. *Journal of Applied Psychology, 96*(1), 71–94. http://dx.doi.org/10.1037/a0021484

National Institute for Occupational Safety and Health (NIOSH). (2017). *Occupational Health Psychology (OHP)*. https://www.cdc.gov/niosh/topics/ohp/default.html

Neal, A., & Griffin, M. A. (2006). A study of the lagged relationships among safety climate, safety motivation, safety behavior, and accidents at the individual and group levels. *Journal of Applied Psychology, 91*(4), 946–953. http://dx.doi.org/10.1037/0021-9010.91.4.946

Nielsen, M. B., & Einarsen, S. (2012). Outcomes of exposure to workplace bullying: A meta-analytic review. *Work & Stress, 26*(4), 309–332. http://dx.doi.org/10.1080/02678373.2012.734709

Nielsen, M. B., Skogstad, A., Matthiesen, S. B., & Einarsen, S. (2016). The importance of a multidimensional and temporal design in research on leadership and workplace safety. *Leadership Quarterly, 27*(1), 142–155. http://dx.doi.org/10.1016/j.leaqua.2015.08.003

Nijp, H. H., Beckers, D. G. J., Geurts, S. A. E., Tucker, P., & Kompier, M. A. J. (2012). Systematic review on the association between employee worktime control and work-non-work balance, health and well-being, and job-related outcomes. *Scandinavian Journal of Work, Environment & Health, 38*(4), 299–313. http://dx.doi.org/10.5271/sjweh.3307

Nixon, A. E., Mazzola, J. J., Bauer, J., Krueger, J. R., & Spector, P. E. (2011). Can work make you sick? A meta-analysis of the relationships between job stressors and physical symptoms. *Work & Stress, 25*(1), 1–22. http://dx.doi.org/10.1080/02678373.2011.569175

Nohe, C., Meier, L. L., Sonntag, K., & Michel, A. (2015). The chicken or the egg? A meta-analysis of panel studies of the relationship between work-family conflict and strain. *Journal of Applied Psychology, 100*(2), 522–536. http://dx.doi.org/10.1037/a0038012

O'Leary, A. (1990). Stress, emotion, and human immune function. *Psychological Bulletin, 108*(3), 363–382. http://dx.doi.org/10.1037/0033-2909.108.3.363

Parkes, K. R. (1990). Coping, negative affectivity, and the work environment: Additive and interactive predictors of mental health. *Journal of Applied Psychology, 75*(4), 399–409. http://dx.doi.org/10.1037/0021-9010.75.4.399

Petrou, P., Demerouti, E., & Schaufeli, W. B. (2015). Job crafting in changing organizations: Antecedents and implications for exhaustion and performance. *Journal of Occupational Health Psychology, 20*(4), 470–480. http://dx.doi.org/10.1037/a0039003

Pindek, S., & Spector, P. E. (2016). Organizational constraints: A meta-analysis of a major stressor. *Work & Stress, 30*(1), 7–25. http://dx.doi.org/10.1080/02678373.2015.1137376

Podsakoff, N. P., LePine, J. A., & LePine, M. A. (2007). Differential challenge stressor-hindrance stressor relationships with job attitudes, turnover intentions, turnover, and withdrawal behavior: A meta-analysis. *Journal of Applied Psychology, 92*(2), 438–454. http://dx.doi.org/10.1037/0021-9010.92.2.438

Prem, R., Ohly, S., Kubicek, B., & Korunka, C. (2017). Thriving on challenge stressors? Exploring time pressure and learning demands as antecedents of thriving at work. *Journal of Organizational Behavior, 38*(1), 108–123. http://dx.doi.org/10.1002/job.2115

Richardson, K. M., & Rothstein, H. R. (2008). Effects of occupational stress management intervention programs: A meta-analysis. *Journal of Occupational Health Psychology, 13*(1), 69–93. http://dx.doi.org/10.1037/1076-8998.13.1.69

Rudolph, C. W., Katz, I. M., Lavigne, K. N., & Zacher, H. (2017). Job crafting: A meta-analysis of relationships with individual differences, job characteristics, and work outcomes. *Journal of Vocational Behavior, 102*, 112–138. https://dx.doi.org/10.1016/j.jvb.2017.05.008

Schmidt, S., Roesler, U., Kusserow, T., & Rau, R. (2014). Uncertainty in the workplace: Examining role ambiguity and role conflict, and their link to depression—A meta-analysis. *European Journal of Work and Organizational Psychology, 23*(1), 91–106. http://dx.doi.org/10.1080/1359432X.2012.711523

Schyns, B., & Schilling, J. (2013). How bad are the effects of bad leaders? A meta-analysis of destructive leadership and its outcomes. *Leadership Quarterly, 24*(1), 138–158. https://dx.doi.org/10.1016/j.leaqua.2012.09.001

Selye, H. (1976). *Stress of life* (rev. ed.). New York: McGraw-Hill.

Selye, H. (1982). History and present status of the stress concept. In L. Goldberger & S. Breznitz (Eds.), *Handbook of stress* (pp. 7–17). New York: Free Press.

Semmer, N. K. (2003). Individual differences, work stress and health. In M. J. Schabracq, J. A. M. Winnubst, & C. L. Cooper (Eds.), *The handbook of work and health psychology* (pp. 83–120). Chichester, U.K.: Wiley.

Shockley, K. M., & Allen, T. D. (2007). When flexibility helps: Another look at the availability of flexible work arrangements and work–family conflict. *Journal of Vocational Behavior, 71*(3), 479–493. https://dx.doi.org/10.1016/j.jvb.2007.08.006

Shockley, K. M., Shen, W., DeNunzio, M. M., Arvan, M. L., & Knudsen, E. A. (2017). Disentangling the relationship between gender and work–family conflict: An integration of theoretical perspectives using meta-analytic methods. *Journal of Applied Psychology.* http://dx.doi.org/10.1037/apl0000246

Sonnentag, S. (2010). Recovery from fatigue: The role of psychological detachment. In P. L. Ackerman (Ed.), *Cognitive fatigue: The current status and future for research and application* (pp. 253–272). Washington, DC: American Psychological Association. http://dx.doi.org/10.1037/12343-012

Sonnentag, S., & Frese, M. (2012). Stress in organizations. In N. W. Schmitt & S. Highhouse (Eds.), *Handbook of psychology, Vol. 12. Industrial and organizational psychology* (2nd ed., pp. 560–592). Hoboken, NJ: Wiley.

Sonnentag, S., & Fritz, C. (2015). Recovery from job stress: The stressor-detachment model as an integrative framework. *Journal of Organizational Behavior, 36*(S1), S72–S103. http://dx.doi.org/10.1002/job.1924

Sonnentag, S., & Kuhnel, J. (2016). Coming back to work in the morning: Psychological detachment and reattachment as predictors of work engagement. *Journal of Occupational Health Psychology, 21*(4), 379–390. http://dx.doi.org/10.1037/ocp0000020

Sonnentag, S., & Zijlstra, F. R. H. (2006). Job characteristics and off-job activities as predictors of need for recovery, well-being, and fatigue. *Journal of Applied Psychology, 91*(2), 330–350. http://dx.doi.org/10.1037/0021-9010.91.2.330

Spreitzer, G. M., & Porath, C. (2014). Self-determination as nutriment for thriving: Building an integrative model of human growth at work. In M. Gagné (Ed.), *The Oxford handbook of work engagement, motivation, and self-determination theory* (pp. 245–258). New York: Oxford University Press.

Spreitzer, G., Porath, C. L., & Gibson, C. B. (2012). Toward human sustainability: How to enable more thriving at work. *Organizational Dynamics, 41*(2), 155–162. http://dx.doi.org/10.1016/j.orgdyn.2012.01.009

Stevenson, M., & Duxbury, L. (2018). Overloaded and stressed: A case study of women working in the health care sector. *Journal of Occupational Health Psychology.* http://dx.doi.org/10.1037/ocp0000111

Strauss, K., Parker, S. K., & O'Shea, D. (2017). When does proactivity have a cost? Motivation at work moderates the effects of proactive work behavior on employee job strain. *Journal of Vocational Behavior, 100*, 15–26. https://dx.doi.org/10.1016/j.jvb.2017.02.001

Ter Hoeven, T. L., & van Zoonen, W. (2015). Flexible work designs and employee well-being: Examining the effects of resources and demands. *New Technology, Work and Employment, 30*(3), 237–255. http://dx.doi.org/10.1111/ntwe.12052

Thomas, J. P., Whitman, D. S., & Viswesvaran, C. (2010). Employee proactivity in organizations: A comparative meta-analysis of emergent proactive constructs. *Journal of Occupational & Organizational Psychology, 83*(2), 275–300. http://dx.doi.org/10.1348/096317910X502359

Timms, C., Brough, P., O'Driscoll, M., Kalliath, T., Siu, O.L., Sit, C., & Lo, D. (2015). Flexible work arrangements, work engagement, turnover intentions and psychological health. *Asia Pacific Journal of Human Resources, 53*(1), 83–103. http://dx.doi.org/10.1111/1744-7941.12030

Tims, M., & Bakker, A. B. (2010). Job crafting: Towards a new model of individual job redesign. *South African Journal of Industrial Psychology, 36*(2), 1–9. http://dx.doi.org/10.4102/sajip.v36i2.841

Toker, S., & Biron, M. (2012). Job burnout and depression: Unraveling their temporal relationship and considering the role of physical activity. *Journal of Applied Psychology, 97*(3), 699–710. http://dx.doi.org/10.1037/a0026914

Totterdell, P., Wood, S., & Wall, T. (2006). An intra-individual test of the demands-control model: A weekly diary study of psychological strain in portfolio workers. *Journal of Occupational and Organizational Psychology, 79*(1), 63–84. http://dx.doi.org/10.1348/096317905X52616

Van der Doef, M., & Maes, S. (1999). The job demand-control (-support) model and psychological well-being: A review of 20 years of empirical research. *Work & Stress, 13*(2), 87–114. http://dx.doi.org/10.1080/026783799296084

Van Steenbergen, E. F., & Ellemers, N. (2009). Is managing the work–family interface worthwhile? Benefits for employee health and performance. *Journal of Organizational Behavior, 30*(5), 617–642. http://dx.doi.org/10.1002/job.569

Van Wingerden, J., Bakker, A. B., & Derks, D. (2017). Fostering employee well-being via a job crafting intervention. *Journal of Vocational Behavior, 100*, 164–174. https://dx.doi.org/10.1016/j.jvb.2017.03.008

Van Woerkom, M., Bakker, A. B., & Nishii, L. H. (2016). Accumulative job demands and support for strength use: Fine-tuning the job demands resources model using conservation of resources theory. *Journal of Applied Psychology, 101*(1), 141–150. http://dx.doi.org/10.1037/apl0000033

Van Yperen, N. W., & Hagedoorn, M. (2003). Do high job demands increase intrinsic motivation or fatigue or both? The role of job control and job social support. *Academy of Management Journal, 46*(3), 339–348. http://dx.doi.org/10.2307/30040627

Volman, F. E., Bakker, A. B., & Xanthopoulou, D. (2013). Recovery at home and performance at work: A diary study on self–family facilitation. *European Journal of Work and Organizational Psychology*, 22(2), 218–234. http://dx.doi.org/10.1080/1359432X.2011.648375

Vuori, J., Toppinen-Tanner, S., & Mutanen, P. (2012). Effects of resource-building group intervention on career management and mental health in work organizations: Randomized controlled field trial. *Journal of Applied Psychology*, 97(2), 273–286. http://dx.doi.org/10.1037/a0025584

Walumbwa, F. O., Muchiri, M. K., Misati, E., Wu, C., & Meiliani, M. (2017). Inspired to perform: A multilevel investigation of antecedents and consequences of thriving at work. *Journal of Organizational Behavior*. https://dx.doi.org/10.1002/job.2216

Wang, G., Seibert, S. E., & Boles, T. L. (2011). Synthesizing what we know and looking ahead: A meta-analytical review of 30 years of emotional labor research. In C. E. J. Härtel, N. M. Ashkanasy, & W. J. Zerbe (Eds.), *What have we learned? Ten years on* (pp. 15–43). Bingley, U.K.: Emerald.

Webster J. R., Beehr T. A., & Love K. (2011). Extending the challenge-hindrance model of occupational stress: The role of appraisal. *Journal of Vocational Behavior*, 79(2), 505–516. https://dx.doi.org/10.1016/j.jvb.2011.02.001

Westman, M., Hobfoll, S., Chen, S., Davidson, R., & Lasky, S. (2004). Organizational stress through the lens of conservation of resources (COR) theory. In P. Perrewé & D. Ganster (Eds.), *Research in occupational stress and well-being* (Vol. 5, pp. 167–220). Oxford: JAI Press/Elsevier Science.

Wheeler, A. R., Halbesleben, J. R. B., & Whitman, M. V. (2013). The interactive effects of abusive supervision and entitlement on emotional exhaustion and co-worker abuse. *Journal of Occupational and Organizational Psychology*, 86(4), 477–496. http://dx.doi.org/10.1111/joop.12034

Wrzesniewski, A., & Dutton, J. E. (2001). Crafting a job: Revisioning employees as active crafters of their work. *Academy of Management Review*, 26(2), 179–201. http://dx.doi.org/10.5465/AMR.2001.4378011

Xanthopoulou, D., Bakker, A. B., Demerouti, E., & Schaufeli, W. B. (2007). The role of personal resources in the job demands-resources model. *International Journal of Stress Management*, 14(2), 121–141. http://dx.doi.org/10.1037/1072-5245.14.2.121

Xanthopoulou, D., Bakker, A. B., Demerouti, E., & Schaufeli, W. B. (2009). Work engagement and financial returns: A diary study on the role of job and personal resources. *Journal of Occupational and Organizational Psychology*, 82(1), 183–200. http://dx.doi.org/10.1348/096317908X285633

Zacher, H., Brailsford, H. A., & Parker, S. L. (2014). Micro-breaks matter: A diary study on the effects of energy management strategies on occupational well-being. *Journal of Vocational Behavior*, 85(3), 287–297. http://dx.doi.org/10.1016/j.jvb.2014.08.005

Zapf, D., Seifert, C., Schmutte, B., Mertini, H., & Holz, M. (2001). Emotion work and job stressors and their effects on burnout. *Psychology & Health*, 16(5), 527–545. http://dx.doi.org/10.1080/08870440108405525

Zohar, D. (1980). Safety climate in industrial organizations: Theoretical and applied implications. *Journal of Applied Psychology*, 65(1), 96–102. http://dx.doi.org/10.1037/0021-9010.65.1.96

Zohar, D. (2000). A group-level model of safety climate: Testing the effect of group climate on micro-accidents in manufacturing jobs. *Journal of Applied Psychology*, 85(4), 587–596. http://dx.doi.org/10.1037//0021-9010.85.4.587

Zohar, D. (2010). Thirty years of safety climate research: Reflections and future directions. *Accident Analysis and Prevention*, 42(5), 1517–1522. http://dx.doi.org/10.1016/j.aap.2009.12.019

Zohar, D., & Polachek, T. (2017). Using event-level data to test the effect of verbal leader behavior on follower leadership perceptions and job performance: A randomized field experiment. *Group & Organization Management*, 42(3), 419–449. http://dx.doi.org/10.1177/1059601115619079

Sharon Clarke

WORK AND FAMILY

INTRODUCTION

Work-family research has evolved over many decades to include a wide range of issues related to the intersection of work and nonwork aspects of peoples' lives. Though researchers most commonly refer to this area as the study of work and family, research on the intersection of work and nonwork domains has come to include much broader definitions of nonwork roles, not limited only to roles within nuclear and extended family, but extending to roles within friendships, communities, leisure activities, and the self, as well. Thus, the term *work-life* has also commonly been used. In line with the focus of most existing literature on the family-specific domain within the broader nonwork domain, reference here is primarily to "family" components of nonwork. A summary of the state of the work-family field to date is provided. Additionally, various definitions of work-family integration and critical outcomes of work-family integration will be examined, and the workplace conditions and policies that can hinder or facilitate more successful work-family outcomes will be described.

THE HISTORY AND CURRENT STATE OF WORK AND FAMILY

Though the idea of work as it is conceptualized today did not exist in early hunter-gatherer societies, some scholars argue that activities in even such early human societies could be separated to a degree into work and nonwork categories. As society evolved toward agriculture and settlement, so too did the concept of work. With the development of ancient Greek and Roman society, the distinction between work and nonwork activities could be clearly seen in attitudes toward particular types of work, which continued to develop and change throughout history (Veal, 2004).

By the time widespread industrialization began, people had begun to focus on progress as a societal goal, rather than only an individual goal. One particularly important and relevant change occurred surrounding the widespread use of clocks (Veal, 2004). Many historians argue that the introduction of the clock began a focus on time-conscientiousness, in opposition to the previous orientation toward task completion (Thompson, 1967). The focus on time and lack of idleness has important implications for work and family. As modern society continued to develop, more emphasis was placed on structure of work and nonwork time and on material rewards from work (Veal, 2004). Taylorism, which refers to scientific management principles, popularized the trend of simplifying work (Taylor, 1911), starting a chain of significant changes to work life throughout the 1900s. The introduction of the Fair Labor Standards Act of 1938 brought the establishment of overtime laws and a reduction in the number of work hours per week. With lower numbers of work hours came an increase in nonwork hours.

Along with changes to work and nonwork hours, numerous demographic changes in work have continued to impact work-family issues since the 1970s. First, there has been a dramatic increase in the proportion of women participating in the workplace, bringing along a simultaneous increase in the proportion of dual-career couples. The U.S. Bureau of Labor Statistics (2015a) reported that female participation in the labor force has increased from 43.3% in 1970 to 57.0% in 2014, peaking at 60% in 1999. Specifically regarding dual-career couples, both partners were employed in 47.7% of all married couples in 2014, with an even greater percentage—60.2%—for married couples with children (U.S. Bureau of Labor Statistics, 2015b). These changes in the proportions of working women and dual-career couples have impacted work-family issues for both women and men. For example, mothers who are married and employed are still more likely to spend time providing child care and less likely to spend time in leisure than their male counterparts, and fathers in dual-career marriages spend more time doing household activities, such as housework and food preparation, than fathers whose partners do not work (U.S. Bureau of Labor Statistics, 2014a).

Second, in line with the larger population, the workforce is aging steadily, with greater proportions of workers age 55 and above and lower proportions of workers under age 24 than ever before. Labor force participation rates continue to increase dramatically for the 55- to 64-year-old population, the 65- to 74-year-old population, and even the 75-year-old and over population, with projections of further increases in coming decades (U.S. Bureau of Labor Statistics, 2014b). The aging of the workforce has several implications for work and family. For example, individuals age 45 to 64 are most likely to provide eldercare, closely followed by individuals age 65 and over (U.S. Bureau of Labor Statistics, 2015c). These individuals are often "sandwiched" between caretaking responsibilities for their children and for their aging parents (Neal & Hammer, 2007). In fact, in 2013 and 2014, 22% of eldercare providers also provided for children under age 18 (U.S. Bureau of Labor Statistics, 2015d).

Finally, as technology has developed, more options for flexible work arrangements, which allow flexibility around where or when work is completed (Rau & Hyland, 2002), have become available for greater numbers of employees to use (Kossek & Michel, 2010). Additionally, technology has brought about increasingly easy access to email, texts, and calls, meaning workers are often more connected across both domains (e.g., spending time accessing personal communication at work or accessing work communication during nonwork hours). Approximately 22% of holders of single jobs did at least some work from home on any given workday in 2010, compared to 37% of holders of multiple jobs (Bureau of Labor Statistics, 2015d). The trend toward increased flexibility around the time and place of work can benefit workers. Meta-analytic research found that flexible work arrangements are negatively associated with work interference with family, with differing effects across forms of flexibility (Allen, Johnson, Kiburz, & Shockley, 2013).

One essential way to face challenges related to work-family issues and to reap benefits of useful programs is through development of policies. The United States has begun some efforts to develop national regulations protecting work-family needs, such as the Family and Medical Leave Act (FMLA), but the United States remains far behind national policies implemented in other countries (Hammer, Cullen, & Shafiro, 2006; Hammer, Van Dyck, & Ellis, 2013). Even within the FMLA, only unpaid leave from work is guaranteed, meaning lower-wage workers are often not able to use the policy when needed (Hammer & Zimmerman, 2011). Since the passage of the FMLA, an increasing number of states and cities have implemented paid parental or family leave policies, temporary disability insurance, and paid sick leave policies (see Winston, 2014 for a recent detailed review of policies). Furthermore, the Affordable Care Act, enacted in 2010, provides additional family-related support at the national level through provision of breaks and facilities for breastfeeding mothers at work; however, research shows that low-income women and single mothers have less access to these provisions (Kozhimannil, Jou, Gjerdingen, & McGovern, 2016). In Europe and Asia, policies are far more advanced, including partially or fully paid leave and subsidized child care provisions, though policies remain varied even across European countries (Moss, 2012; Poelmans, Chinchilla, & Cardona, 2003). Of 184 countries reviewed, the United States is one of only six that does not provide paid parental leave; the other five countries are Liberia, Papua New Guinea, Samoa, Sierra Leone, and Swaziland (Heymann & McNeill, 2012).

Despite a lack of national policies supporting work-family needs, the United States has some of the strongest workplace policies and support systems of any in the world (Hammer et al., 2006). In fact, Hammer and colleagues (2006) argued that these strong workplace policies arose as a result of the lack of national policy, putting onus on organizations to respond to union demands and remain competitive with the policies of other organizations. However, these strong policies are almost exclusively available to higher-wage workers and large organizations, leaving lower-wage employees with little support, even though they are likely the most in need (Hammer et al., 2013).

THEORIES RELATED TO WORK AND FAMILY

Work-family scholars use a wide variety of theories to guide their research, but several theories have emerged that provide a strong foundation for understanding work-family issues. Matthews and colleagues (2016) surveyed leading work-family scholars and found that nearly all reported it is *very* or *extremely important* to incorporate theory into their research, but less than one-third of scholars reported that scholars are either *very* or *extremely effective* in actually incorporating theory. Thus, scholars continue to work to develop theory-based work-family research. Furthermore, Matthews and colleagues found that four theories emerged as most applicable to the examination of work-family issues: role theory, systems theory, conservation of resources theory, and boundary theory. These four theories—and recent developments related to them—will be described along with other relevant theories.

Primary Theories in Work-Family Research.   One foundational theory of work-family research is role theory (Kahn, Wolfe, Quinn, Snoek, & Rosenthal, 1964), which suggests that roles are determined by expectations others have about appropriate behavior. Role theory also suggests that role conflict, or tension experienced because of conflicting role pressures, occurs when individuals engage in roles that are mutually incompatible (Katz & Kahn, 1978). Inter-role conflict occurs between two such incompatible roles, such as work-to-family conflict (i.e., demands from the work role interfere with demands from the family role) and family-to-work conflict (i.e., demands from the family role interfere with demands from the work role).

Work-family research often relies on the scarcity hypothesis and the enhancement hypothesis, both of which are rooted in social identity theory (Mead, 1934; Stryker, 1968). The scarcity hypothesis posits that human energy is a limited resource, so participating in additional roles provides more opportunity for conflict (Goode, 1960). Alternatively, the enhancement hypothesis proposes that participating in additional roles provides more resources and opportunities for enhanced self-esteem, which can refuel energy (Marks, 1977). While the scarcity hypothesis is often used to support work-family conflict research, the enhancement hypothesis is often used to support work-family enrichment research (Hammer & Zimmerman, 2011). Social identity theory (i.e., the parent theory of the scarcity and enhancement hypotheses) posits that roles help build self-definition and guide behavior, as well as that meaningfulness derived from identities reduces stressors from those roles (Thoits, 1983, 1986).

Another foundational theory in work-family research is systems theory, which proposes that a system is made up of two or more related and interconnected parts (Bronfenbrenner, 1977; Hanson, 1995). According to Hanson (1995), when one part of a system is changed, all other parts of the system and related systems are impacted, sending a ripple effect throughout the system and back to the point of origin. Thus, the systems perspective emphasizes contextual understanding. Bronfenbrenner (1977), focusing on human development, argued for four interrelated systems: the microsystem, which is the individual and his or her immediate settings; the mesosystem, or the interactions between microsystems; the exosystem, which includes other social structures, both formal and informal, that influence behavior; and the macrosystem, or the society-level patterns reflecting values of the culture. These systems can easily be applied to work-family research, as scholars can examine the work and family domains, as well as aspects of the individual and society (Hammer & Zimmerman, 2011).

In line with both role theory and systems theory, Hammer and Zimmerman (2011) proposed an integrative work-family systems model, which integrates both conflict and enrichment perspectives. The work-family systems model posits that the work domain and family domain each serve as microsystems, connected in a larger mesosystem of the work-family interface, all nested within a broader exosystem that includes community, organizational, and family contextual factors, and a macrosystem that incorporates socioeconomic, legal, and political factors. This model provides a framework emphasizing the key role of context in individuals' experiences of work and family.

A third foundational theory is conservation of resources (COR) theory, which proposes that individuals strive to obtain, maintain, and protect resources, and stress occurs when individuals lose resources, feel threat of loss of resources, or do not gain resources when they expect to (Hobfoll, 1989, 2002). According to COR theory, resources are objects, personal characteristics, conditions, or energies of value to the individual or that serve to help the individual gain more resources. Additionally, COR theory has two central propositions (ten Brummelhuis & Bakker, 2012): loss spirals occur when resources are invested but fail to address a stressor or require further resource investment (i.e., resource loss leads to further resource loss) while gain spirals occur when resources generate other resources, such as when individuals gain resources and are better able to invest in gaining new resources, better equipped to handle stressors, or have substitute resources (Hobfoll, 2002). One key debate about COR theory has been over the definition of resources, with some researchers arguing that COR theory is deeply flawed because "anything good can be considered a resource" (Halbesleben, Neveu, Paustian-Underdahl, & Westman, 2014, p. 1337). Halbesleben and colleagues (2014) redefine resources as anything an individual perceives to help attain his or her goals.

Based on COR theory, ten Brummelhuis and Bakker (2012) developed a particularly relevant model called the work-home resources model. This model posits that resources can be categorized by the source (i.e., contextual or personal resources) and by transience (i.e., volatile or structural resources). Additionally, the theory proposes categories of key resources, which are stable personal resources, such as personality traits, that help individuals cope with stressors and gain other resources, and macroresources, which are characteristics of the larger economic, social, and cultural system. Furthermore, the model directly integrates the work and family domains, proposing that demands and resources from one domain impact personal resources, which in turn impact outcomes in the other domain. These processes are reflected in the theory as both daily and durable processes, accounting for both conflict and enrichment. The work-home resources model helps fill previous gaps in theory by defining resources with greater specificity than earlier theories, as well as by providing a theory that is specific to work-family research.

Finally, another foundational theory in work-family research is boundary theory (Ashforth, Kreiner, & Fugate, 2000; Zerubavel, 1991). Boundary theory focuses on outcomes related to how individuals create, maintain, or change boundaries that separate two entities, such as work and family (Allen, Cho, & Meier, 2014). Boundaries represent a way to classify parts of life, often based on separation by time or space (e.g., separating work time or place from the time or place an individual does not work in), and they can range from thick boundaries, which keep two entities separate, to thin boundaries, which blend the entities together. Kossek, Ruderman, Braddy, and Hannum (2012) found that boundary management profiles were related to positive and negative work and family outcomes. Boundary theory posits that there are macro- and microtransitions between the separated entities, with macrotransitions representing infrequent, permanent change and microtransitions representing frequent, recurring change (Ashforth et al., 2000). Work-family scholars typically focus on microrole transitions, such as the transition back and forth between work and home each day (Allen et al., 2014).

One theory closely related to boundary theory is border theory, which Clark (2000) proposed as a theory specifically about work-family balance. Borders can be physical, temporal, or psychological, and they divide what, where, and who individuals associate with work and family. As individuals move across borders between work and family, "border keepers," such as supervisors or spouses, are posited to help define and maintain borders. Furthermore, borders are proposed to vary in flexibility (i.e., how pliable the physical and temporal boundaries are; Hall & Richter, 1988) and permeability (i.e., how much an individual physically located in the work or family area psychologically or behaviorally engages with the other area). Overall, boundary theory and border theory share many concepts but arose from different areas of research (Allen et al., 2014); literature around related issues specific to the work-family field is often referred to as the boundary management literature.

Nippert-Eng (1996) proposed a continuum of segmentation to integration that refers to the degree of separation maintained between domains. High segmentation is characterized by inflexible and impermeable boundaries, while high integration is characterized by flexible and permeable boundaries. Integration/segmentation preferences are considered distinct from actual use of integration/segmentation (Allen et al., 2014), with preferences representing individual differences in the degree to which people favor merging versus separating work and family roles (Kreiner, 2006).

Two other key concepts in boundary management are the styles and tactics individuals use when transitioning between roles. Hall and Richter (1988) proposed three role transition styles: anticipatory (i.e., concern for destination domain exists prior to leaving current domain), discrete (i.e., concern begins upon arriving in destination domain), and lagged (i.e., concern begins after already present in destination domain). Kreiner and colleagues (2009) proposed a conceptualization of tactics, or strategies individuals use to produce the level and style of segmentation/integration they prefer, arguing that tactics can be behavioral, temporal, physical, or communication-based. Finally, Kossek and Lautsch (2012) proposed several "flexstyles": integrators (i.e., full blending of domains), separators (i.e., full separation of domains), and volleyers (i.e., use of both strategies at different times). Kossek and colleagues (2012) later built upon this approach by combining various characteristics linked with boundary management, including cross-role interruption behaviors, role identity centrality, and perceived boundary control, to create six possible styles (i.e., work warriors, overwhelmed reactors, family guardians, fusion lovers, dividers, and nonwork-eclectics).

Secondary Theories in Work-Family Research. Beyond the primary theories used in work-family research, several theories are increasingly common in the work-family literature. One such theory is social exchange theory (SET), which proposes that social exchange relationships develop from interactions that create obligation, such that both members of the relationship reciprocally provide resources the other person values (Emerson, 1976; Cropanzano & Mitchell, 2005). These resources include love, status, information, money, goods, and services (Foa & Foa, 1974, 1980; Cropanzano & Mitchell, 2005). SET gave rise to leader-member exchange (LMX) theory (Dansereau, Cashman, & Graen, 1973; Graen, 1976; Gerstner & Day, 1997), which focuses on the social exchange relationship between a supervisor (i.e., leader) and an employee (i.e., member). LMX is often applied to work-family research (e.g., Bagger & Li, 2014; Major & Morganson, 2011).

A second theory increasingly used in work-family research is person-environment (PE) fit theory (Caplan, 1983; Edwards, Caplan, & Van Harrison, 1998), which proposes that strain comes from the interaction of the person and their environment, rather than the person and environment separately. PE fit theory also proposes that there are subjective (i.e., as perceived by the person) and objective (i.e., actual) versions of both the person and their environment, meaning that fit between the person and environment can be classified as objective (i.e., objective person with objective environment) or subjective (i.e., subjective person with subjective environment), as well. Within the work-family literature, PE fit theory has been offered as a way to examine the work-family interface (Edwards & Rothbard, 2000; Matthews, Wayne, & Ford, 2014).

A third theory related to work-family research is the effort-recovery model (Meijman & Mulder, 1998), which proposes that effort at work leads to physiological, behavioral, and subjective responses known as load reactions. According to the model, negative load reactions are reversible through recovery experiences; however, when individuals are continuously exposed to demands, recovery cannot occur. Thus, load reactions accumulate, leading to more serious and longer-lasting outcomes. Within the work-family literature, the effort-recovery model has been used to link the work-family interface with concepts related to workload and recovery (e.g., Ilies et al., 2007; Moreno-Jiménez et al., 2009).

Matthews and colleagues (2016) present three additional theories that have not often been applied to the work-family field but may provide strong theoretical background for continued work-family research. First, the authors suggest adaptation theory, which posits that individual well-being decreases directly following exposure to a stressor, but that individuals adapt to the stressor and return to baseline well-being over time; similarly, individuals experience an increase in well-being following a positive stimulus, but adapt over time to return to baseline levels of well-being (Frederick & Loewenstein, 1999). Adaptation theory may help explain how stimuli and stressors related to work and family impact individuals over time. Second, affective events theory (AET) posits that events in the work environment lead to affective reactions, which in turn impact work attitudes and affect-driven behaviors (Weiss & Cropanzano, 1996). AET may help work-family scholars clarify and explain many work-specific and integrative work-family factors, such as affective, attitudinal, and behavioral responses. Finally, the theory of planned behavior (TPB) posits that behavioral intentions, stemming from an individual's expectancies about outcomes of the behavior, attitudes toward the behavior, normative beliefs about what other individuals would do, and perceived behavioral control of the behavior (i.e., perceptions about ability to perform the behavior) all lead to behavior performance (Ajzen, 1985). TPB may provide work-family researchers with an opportunity to further explore the work-family context through specific attitudes, behaviors, or behavioral intentions. Some research has extended these theories to the work-family literature (e.g., Carlson, Kacmar, Zivnuska, Ferguson, & Whitten, 2011; Matthews, Wayne, & Ford, 2014), but more work is needed to extend existing theories such as these to the work-family field, and to develop new theories that can guide future research.

CONSTRUCTS RELATED TO WORK AND FAMILY

Despite often being called "work-family" research, the term *family* can refer to a wide variety of nonwork roles, including non-family relationships, community, nonwork personal activities, and roles related to the self that do not involve others (e.g., Kreiner, 2006). Other terms that are commonly used to refer to the nonwork domain include *personal, life,* and *home.* The intersection between work and nonwork domains is often called the "work-family interface."

One framework that helps integrate understanding of various work-family interface constructs is the work-home perspective (Greenhaus & Kossek, 2014). This perspective argues that connections between work and nonwork domains can inherently be positive (e.g., work-family enrichment), negative (e.g., work-family conflict), or neither positive nor negative. The work-home perspective focuses on the priority individuals place on each domain, thus incorporating concepts from the boundary management literature. Furthermore, this perspective accounts for various social changes that impact work and family, such as the business environment (e.g., globalization), technology (e.g., portability of work), and diverse family structures (e.g., being "sandwiched" between child care and eldercare). Greenhaus and Kossek (2014) argue that adopting a work-home perspective can allow not only work-family scholars but also scholars across other areas of organizational research to better understand contemporary careers.

In an effort to better understand how individuals experience work and family domains and the interaction between them, scholars use several key constructs relating work and family domains. Broadly speaking, the links between work and family are bi-directional, such that the work domain can influence the family domain, the family domain can influence the work domain, or both can occur simultaneously. However, the effects one domain has on the other domain can be conceptualized as harmful (e.g., work-family conflict), beneficial (e.g., work-family enrichment), or can be focused on some other criteria (e.g., work-family balance). Furthermore, the relationship between work and family domains can be better understood through assessment of boundaries between domains (e.g., boundary management). These conceptions will be discussed in turn, along with evidence surrounding these constructs in the extant literature.

Work-Family Conflict and Work-Family Enrichment. The most common conceptualization of linking mechanisms between work and family differentiates between work-family conflict or stress and work-family enrichment. Work-family conflict or stress occurs when a work role and a nonwork role are not fully compatible and results in some type of physical or psychological strain (e.g., Greenhaus & Beutell, 1985), while work-family enrichment occurs when participation in one role benefits quality of life in the other role (e.g., Edwards & Rothbard, 2000). Work-family conflict and enrichment can both be categorized into different types. Work-family conflict is traditionally categorized as time-based, strain-based, and behavior-based (Greenhaus & Beutell, 1985). Time-based conflict occurs when time pressures in one role restrict how much time can be devoted to the other role (e.g., working overtime during a busy week at work). Strain-based conflict occurs when strain in one role impacts successful performance in the other role (e.g., lack of supervisor support for family needs). Behavior-based conflict occurs when patterns of behavior in one role are incompatible with behaviors in the other role (e.g., behaving in a loving way with a spouse yet responsible for discipline at work). Additionally, work-family enrichment has been sub-categorized into work-to-family and family-to-work enrichment. Work-to-family includes capital, affect, and development enrichment, while the family-to-work direction includes efficiency, affect, and development enrichment (Carlson, Kacmar, Wayne, & Grzywacz, 2006). These categories reflect the resources that Greenhaus and Powell (2006) propose may be acquired: skills and perspectives, psychological and physical, social-capital, flexibility, and material. Once resources are acquired, enrichment can occur through an affective pathway, whereby the increase in resources improves mood, which then spills over to promote better performance in the other role. Alternatively, Greenhaus and Powell (2006) propose that enrichment can occur through an instrumental pathway, when resources from one role transfer to the other role directly to increase performance in the other role.

One issue in the work-family field has been the wide variety of constructs assessed in the literature, often reflecting similar concepts and principles (e.g., Crain & Hammer, 2013). Though research on the negative side of the work-family interface quite consistently refers to constructs of work-family conflict or, more broadly, work-family interference, research on the positive side of the work-family interface has developed many similar constructs. For example, in addition to work-family enrichment, work-family positive spillover is defined as the transfer of affect, skills, behaviors, and values across work and family domains (Hanson, Hammer, & Colton, 2006). Work-family facilitation, another similar construct, is defined as the extent to which involvement in one domain provides benefits that help improve system functioning in the other domain (Wayne, Grzywacz, Carlson, & Kacmar, 2007).

Despite the similarity of the constructs on the positive side of the work-family interface, Carlson and colleagues (2006) argue that the distinctions between these constructs—though often subtle—warrant consideration during the measurement process. Wayne (2009) further suggests that these constructs are connected in that enrichment extends beyond positive spillover, with gains from one domain transferring to the other domain (i.e., positive spillover) to improve functioning in that domain (i.e., enrichment), and facilitation extends beyond enrichment, with improved individual functioning of enrichment (i.e., enrichment) leading to improved overall system functioning (i.e., facilitation). Because work-family research has focused primarily on individual outcomes and functioning, other researchers (e.g., Crain & Hammer, 2013; Greenhaus & ten Brummelhuis, 2013) will be followed here in utilizing *work-family enrichment* as the primary terminology.

Although work-family scholars are more consistent with terminology used to refer to the negative side of the work-family interface, the work-family conflict literature provides an illustrative example of challenges in defining roles. Despite broad use of the term *family* to refer to the nonwork domain, researchers sometimes choose to identify a particular area of the nonwork domain in their research to make more specific predictions and better understand the interface between two particular roles. For example, Wilson and Baumann (2015) studied the intersections of work, family, and personal roles, with the "personal" role referring to those activities an individual pursues because of their own interests, such as friendships, hobbies, or community. Other research has studied work-school conflict (e.g., Butler, 2007; Hammer, Grigsby, & Woods, 1998) and work-life conflict (e.g., Boswell & Olson-Buchanan, 2007). Although some studies measure specific nonwork roles, previous research has primarily used measures that are not construct validated or that combine all nonwork roles (Wilson & Baumann, 2015). One reason that combining nonwork roles may not always be ideal is that allocations of time and energy may not only be between work and nonwork, but rather between work and several different areas of the nonwork domain (Edwards & Rothbard, 2000).

Work-Family Balance. An additional area of work-family construct development has focused on the popular concept of work-family balance, which has been given many definitions over time. Despite the popularity of this term outside of scholarly research and numerous efforts to integrate the term into work-family research, many researchers continue to question the use of the term *balance* and its many definitions, as it may misrepresent the reality that working families face—often with little chance of achieving actual balance between work and nonwork domains (Hammer & Demsky, 2014).

Greenhaus and Allen (2011) provide a thorough discussion of past work-family balance definitions, which include: absence of work-family conflict, high involvement across multiple roles, and high effectiveness and satisfaction across multiple roles. Greenhaus and Allen (2011) then provide a new definition, intended to clarify the construct, as "an overall appraisal of the extent to which individuals' effectiveness and satisfaction with work and family roles are consistent with their life values at a given point in time" (p. 174). Other authors have built instead upon the idea of a typological view of work-family balance, which explicitly considers that conflict and enrichment can be experienced simultaneously in various combinations and levels (e.g., Demerouti & Geurts, 2004; Grzywacz, Butler, & Almeida, 2008). From this typological perspective, both directions of conflict and enrichment (i.e., work-to-family and family-to-work) are proposed to interact to create the overarching experience of work-family balance (Rantanen, Kinnunen, Mauno, & Tillemann, 2011; Rantanen, Kinnunen, Mauno, & Tement, 2013).

Wayne, Butts, Casper, and Allen (in press) present a study integrating these many definitions, stating that the central theme of the definitions is that balance is a global evaluation of the interface between work and family. Wayne and colleagues further argue that the various definitions of balance can be differentiated into four conceptualizations: additive spillover (i.e., work-family conflict is absent or enrichment is present), multiplicative spillover (i.e., low work-family conflict and high enrichment simultaneously), balance satisfaction (i.e., attitudes toward resource allocation across roles), and balance effectiveness (i.e., self-evaluation of meeting shared expectations across roles). Their study found that additive spillover was the most important predictor of work attitudes, but balance satisfaction and effectiveness together were the most important predictors of family satisfaction and job and family performance. Future researchers should consider using the framework provided by Wayne and colleagues to specify theoretical approaches to balance.

ANTECEDENTS RELATED TO WORK AND FAMILY

A great deal of research has been devoted to predictors of work-family conflict, with substantial work also focused on enrichment. Additional research emphasizes antecedents of balance; however, the focus here is primarily on conflict and enrichment, drawing from meta-analytic studies whenever possible, as continued lack of construct clarity around balance has led to comparatively unclear conclusions surrounding its antecedents. Note that most research distinguishes between the directions of work-family conflict and enrichment (i.e., work-to-family and family-to-work), as both antecedents and outcomes of these constructs often differ depending on the origin domain (e.g., Frone, Russell, & Cooper, 1992).

Work-Family Conflict.   Overall, meta-analytic evidence suggests that work factors are related more strongly to work-to-family conflict (WTFC) than to family-to-work conflict (FTWC), while only some family factors relate more strongly to FTWC, and demographic and individual factors are generally weakly related to both WTFC and FTWC (Byron, 2005). This supports the idea that WTFC and FTWC have unique antecedents and could thus require different interventions to address them.

Several individual differences are significant predictors of WTFC and FTWC. One primary individual difference variable work-family researchers have long shown interest in is gender. Traditionally, family is viewed as the domain associated more with women, with work being more associated with men (Hammer & Zimmerman, 2011). In line with this view of gender roles, scholars originally hypothesized that women would experience more FTWC, while men would experience more WTFC (e.g., Pleck, 1977). Meta-analytic studies have shown little support for this proposition, with one meta-analysis showing that that gender has a near-zero relationship with WTFC and is only weakly related to FTWC (Byron, 2005). However, the study showed that when more of the sample was made up of parents, there were greater sex differences in both WTFC and FTWC, with mothers experiencing higher levels of conflict than fathers.

In addition to gender, research shows that personality and dispositional factors can be significant predictors of work-family conflict. In a meta-analysis of work-family conflict antecedents, Michel and colleagues (2011b) found that internal locus of control had small, negative relationships with WTFC and FTWC, while negative affectivity/neuroticism had moderate, positive relationships with WTFC and FTWC and was one of the strongest predictors of WTFC of any in the meta-analysis. Additionally, a meta-analysis focusing specifically on dispositional antecedents found that negative affect, neuroticism, and self-efficacy were especially strong predictors of WTFC and FTWC, with negative traits seeming to make individuals more vulnerable to conflict, while positive traits seemed to protect against conflict (Allen et al., 2012).

Finally, some research has begun to address the role of national context. A meta-analysis found no significant differences in WTFC across cultural, institutional, and economic aspects of context. However, the meta-analysis did find that FTWC was higher in collectivistic (vs. individualistic) countries, countries with a higher economic gender gap, and countries other than the United States (Allen, French, Dumani, & Shockley, 2015). Other dimensions of culture have also been assessed as predictors of work-family conflict, including one study that examined multiple dimensions of culture across many European countries and found uncertainty avoidance to be negatively related to conflict (Ollo-López & Goñi-Legaz, 2015); however, research in this area remains sparse.

Another growing area of research on predictors of work-family conflict covers concepts related to boundary management. Research by Kossek and colleagues (2012) shows that actual segmentation is associated with decreased WTFC and FTWC. Additionally, they found that interruptions in one domain are relevant to conflict, such that family interruptions of work time are related to decreased WTFC and increased FTWC, while work interruptions of family time are linked to increased WTFC and decreased FTWC.

A variety of work-specific antecedents have also been tied to work-family conflict. Building upon previous work by Byron (2005), Michel and colleagues (2011b) conducted a meta-analysis and found that work role stressors (e.g., role ambiguity, time demands), work involvement (e.g., work centrality), workplace social support (e.g., supervisor support), and work characteristics (e.g., task variety, job autonomy) all significantly predict WTFC, while work role stressors and workplace social support significantly predicted FTWC. Byron (2005) found that work hours were moderately related to WTFC but only weakly to FTWC. Meta-analytic research by Allen and colleagues (2013) shows that flexible work arrangements are negatively associated with WTFC but had a nonsignificant relationship with FTWC. Additionally, this research shows evidence of a stronger relationship with flextime than flexplace and with flexplace use than flexplace availability, suggesting that the form of flexibility is important to consider.

Organizational members can also significantly impact work-family conflict. A meta-analysis by Kossek and colleagues (2011) found that work-family-specific supervisor support and organization support are more strongly related to WTFC than general supervisor support and organization support, respectively. A study by Butts, Becker, and Boswell (2015) focuses on daily experiences of receiving work-related electronic communication from organizational members during nonwork time. Results reveal significant impacts on employee emotions, whereby affective tone and time required by the communication are associated with anger, nication on WTF and anger mediates the relationship between affective tone and time required by the commu C.

Finally, family-specific antecedents have been tied to work-family conflict. Meta-analytic evidence from Michel and colleagues (2011b) shows that family stressors (e.g., parental demands), family social support (e.g., spousal support), and family climate all predict FTWC, while family stressors, family role involvement (e.g., family centrality), family social support, and family climate all predict WTFC. Byron's (2005) meta-analysis provides support for several additional family-related antecedents as well. For example, number of children is a significant predictor of WTFC and FTWC, though it was more strongly related to FTWC, while income was related to WTFC but not to FTWC.

Work-Family Enrichment. Due to its relative newness as a work-family construct, perhaps in addition to construct clarity issues, little meta-analytic evidence is available regarding predictors of work-family enrichment. However, as the area of work-family enrichment burgeons, other comprehensive resources are becoming available. In the seminal review article by Greenhaus and Powell (2006) a model of the work-family enrichment process was introduced. In addition, Crain and Hammer (2013) provide a thorough review of quantitative studies of work-family enrichment. This review will be summarized, as well as other individual studies that provide support for antecedents to be further explored in future research, examining individual, work-related, and family-related factors.

According to Crain and Hammer (2013), individual factors that have been shown to predict work-family enrichment include personality, core self-evaluations, positive affect/thinking, and secure attachment style. A meta-analysis by Michel and colleagues (2011a) found that extraversion, agreeableness, conscientiousness, and openness to experience are all positively related to overall work-family enrichment. Other individual studies (e.g., Wayne, Musisca, & Fleeson, 2004) provide evidence that includes specific directions of enrichment (i.e., work-to-family enrichment, or WTFE; family-to-work enrichment, or FTWE). One study of boundary management as a predictor of WTFE found that permeability preferences and perceived flexibility of the workplace predict job satisfaction, mediated by WTFE (Daniel & Sonnentag, 2016).

A greater amount of research examines work-related antecedents of enrichment, generally finding that work-related factors primarily predict WTFE, though some are also linked with FTWE (Crain & Hammer, 2013). For example, job burnout is negatively related to both WTFE and FTWE (Innstrand, Langballe, Espnes, Falkum, & Aasland, 2008), while family-supportive supervisor behaviors are positively related to both WTFE and FTWE (Hammer, Kossek, Yragui, Bodner, & Hanson, 2009). On the other hand, other work-related antecedents are thus far linked only to WTFE, such as organizational citizenship behaviors (Kwan & Mao, 2011), family-supportive organization perceptions (FSOP; Wayne, Casper, Matthews, & Allen, 2013), and schedule flexibility (Carlson, Grzywacz, & Kacmar, 2010). One longitudinal study of enrichment found that job satisfaction partially mediates the relationship between supervisory support and WTFE (Siu et al., 2015). Additionally, permeability of the work domain is associated with higher FTWE (Bulger, Matthews, & Hoffman, 2007).

Research on family-related antecedents of enrichment has generally found more support for the prediction of FTWE than WTFE, with a substantial portion of extant research focusing on support from nonwork sources, such as family, spouse, friends, and children (Crain & Hammer, 2013). Other relationship factors, such as relationship satisfaction, are also positively related to FTWE (e.g., Stevens, Minnotte, Mannon, & Kiger, 2007).

OUTCOMES RELATED TO WORK AND FAMILY

Work-family constructs have been tied to many important outcomes, including individual, work, and family factors. A review of this research will again focus on meta-analytic studies whenever possible to provide the most comprehensive review of the extant literature and will emphasize the role of conflict and enrichment, in line with the majority of existing work-family research.

Work-Family Conflict. The work-family conflict literature shows evidence of many important individual outcomes that are not specific to only work or family. A meta-analysis by Amstad and colleagues (2011) found that both work-to-family conflict (WTFC) and family-to-work conflict (FTWC) had the strongest relationships with domain-unspecific outcomes, rather than outcomes specific to work or family in particular. One commonly assessed area of domain-unspecific outcomes focuses on employee health and well-being. Amstad and colleagues (2011) found that WTFC and FTWC are moderately associated with general stress and that this outcome had the strongest meta-analytic relationships of the domain-unspecific outcomes explored. Another meta-analysis by Allen and colleagues (2000) shows that WTFC is associated with an increase in somatic and physical symptoms. Additionally, Allen and colleagues found that WTFC is related to general psychological strain, burnout, and depression. Regarding strain in particular, Nohe and colleagues (2015) performed a meta-analysis that provides evidence of reciprocal relationships of both WTFC and FTWC with strain across a variety of possible moderators. When examining work-specific strain as an outcome, Nohe and colleagues found that WTFC was supported as a predictor but not FTWC.

Evidence related to other specific health outcomes includes cardio-metabolic risk, psychological disorders, depressive symptoms, and sleep problems. A study by Berkman and colleagues (2015) found that WTFC was positively associated with cardio-metabolic risk, especially in younger employees, and that WTFC was associated with shorter sleep duration. Frone (2000) found that individuals experiencing WTFC were approximately 2 to 3 times more likely to have a mood, anxiety, or substance disorder, while individuals experiencing FTWC were approximately 9 to 30 times more likely to have a mood, anxiety, or substance disorder. Another study extended research on conflict and health beyond the individual alone, finding that conflict accounted for significant variance in depressive systems of both employees and their spouses (Hammer, Cullen, Neal, Sinclair, & Shafiro, 2005). Crain and colleagues (2014) found that WTFC, FTWC, and family-supportive supervisor behaviors together predict both objective and self-reported measures of sleep quality and quantity.

Work-specific outcomes are perhaps the most widely studied of all work-family conflict outcomes. Results of the meta-analysis by Amstad and colleagues (2011) found that WTFC shows stronger relationships with work-related outcomes, though both WTFC and FTWC are significantly associated with work outcomes. These results support the idea that relationships between conflict and outcomes are stronger when assessed using outcomes in the same domain as the origin of the conflict (i.e., the matching hypothesis). Another meta-analysis by Kossek and Ozeki (1998) found that both WTFC and FTWC are significantly related to decreased job satisfaction. A meta-analysis by Allen and colleagues (2000) found that WTFC is also linked to increased turnover and absenteeism, in addition to decreased organizational commitment and job performance; turnover intentions was the work-specific factor most strongly related to WTFC in the study. A study by Hammer and colleagues (2003) found similar results for FTWC, which was associated with higher absenteeism, tardiness, and interruptions at work. Another important workplace outcome linked to conflict is safety; Cullen and Hammer (2007) found that FTWC is related to decreased safety compliance and participation. Furthermore, Lapierre, Hammer, Truxillo, and Murphy (2012) found that FTWC is significantly related to cognitive failure at work, suggesting cognitive failure may be a mechanism explaining the link between FTWC and safety.

Research provides evidence of many family-specific outcomes of work-family conflict, as well. Amstad and colleagues (2011) found support for associations of both WTFC and FTWC with family-specific outcomes, including family-related stress and marital satisfaction; however, stronger relationships were found between FTWC and family-specific outcomes than between WTFC and family-specific outcomes, further supporting the matching hypothesis. Kossek and Ozeki's (1998) meta-analysis shows that increased WTFC and FTWC are both related to lower life satisfaction. Additionally, Allen and colleagues' (2000) meta-analysis shows that WTFC is related to decreased life satisfaction, marital satisfaction, and family satisfaction, with life satisfaction being the family-related outcome most strongly related to WTFC. Another meta-analytic study by Shockley and Singla (2011) found that WTFC has a stronger effect on family satisfaction for samples that include a greater proportion of males, while FTWC has a stronger effect on family satisfaction when samples include a greater proportion of females. Shockley and Singla also found that FTWC was more strongly related to family satisfaction than job satisfaction, while WTFC was more strongly related to job satisfaction than family satisfaction.

Work-Family Enrichment.   Research on work-family enrichment shows outcomes across individual, work, and family areas of life. One primary area of individual outcomes previously studied is health and well-being. Using a measure of work-family positive spillover, which is closely related to enrichment, Grzywacz and Marks (2000) found that higher family-to-work positive spillover is linked with decreased odds of problem drinking. Work-to-family positive spillover is related to increased odds of problem drinking. Another study by Hammer and colleagues (2005) found that positive spillover is related to depressive symptoms of both the individual and that person's spouse one year later. Summarizing various studies of enrichment and health, a meta-analytic review found that work-to-family enrichment (WTFE) and family-to-work enrichment (FTWE) are both positively related to physical and mental health (McNall, Nicklin, & Masuda, 2010). Research has also begun to examine the effects of national context on enrichment, most often focused on individualism and collectivism, but results remain inconsistent (Ollier-Malaterre, 2016).

Specifically within the work domain, several outcomes of enrichment are evident. A meta-analytic review of enrichment consequences shows that both WTFE and FTWE are positively related to job satisfaction and affective organizational commitment (McNall et al., 2010). Furthermore, the study shows that WTFE is more strongly related to work-specific variables, while FTWE is more strongly related to nonwork-specific variables. Thus, the originating domain in enrichment processes is more strongly related to outcomes in that domain. Crain and Hammer's (2013) review of work-family enrichment found several studies suggesting a negative relationship between WTFE and turnover intentions, while mixed results were found for FTWE and turnover intentions. A study by Odle-Dusseau and colleagues (2012) shows that WTFE predicted lower turnover intentions, and increased both organizational commitment and supervisor ratings of organizational support performance across a period of 5 months.

Within the family domain, work-family enrichment also impacts various outcomes. McNall and colleagues' (2010) meta-analysis showed significant effects of both WTFE and FTWE on family satisfaction. Furthermore, Shockley and Singla's (2011) meta-analysis found that WTFE had a relatively weak relationship with family satisfaction but was more strongly related to job satisfaction. Likewise, FTWE had a weak relationship with job satisfaction but a much stronger relationship with family satisfaction. This pattern of relationships provides evidence that reactions to enrichment may occur primarily in the origin domain, also known as the source attribution perspective (Shockley & Singla, 2011; Wayne, Musisca, & Fleeson, 2004).

ORGANIZATIONAL SUPPORT FOR WORK-FAMILY NEEDS

Within workplace policies supporting work-family needs, two important distinctions exist in the literature. First, scholars distinguish between formal and informal support. Formal supports are defined as policies, services, and benefits (Neal, Chapman, Ingersol-Dayton, & Emlen, 1993). One example of a formal organizational work-family policy is flexible work arrangements, or those work options that allow flexibility in time or place of work (Rau & Hyland, 2002). Flexible work arrangements are associated with a reduction in work-to-family conflict (Allen, Johnson, Kiburz, & Shockley, 2013). However, the relationship with family-to-work conflict is not significant across studies, so it is important to consider differential effects and conditions under which such formal policies are most beneficial (Allen et al., 2013). Formal supports also often come from national-level policies. Den Dulk and Peper (2016) reviewed national policies related to work-family issues in Organisation for Economic Cooperation and Development (OECD) member countries and found that maternity leave is the most established social policy. However, length of time given for maternity leave as well as other family supportive policies (e.g., paternity leave, child care) vary widely among countries.

Informal supports, on the other hand, are the "less prescribed practices that are manifested in a more positive work-family culture" (Hammer & Zimmerman, 2011, p. 416). One primary form of informal support organizations provide is through supervisor support (Hammer, Kossek, Zimmerman, & Daniels, 2007). When a policy or practice helps reduce negative outcomes of work-family conflict, it can be seen as family-supportive (Hammer, Cullen, Neal, Sinclair, & Shafiro, 2005). Thus, one especially important form of informal support is family-supportive supervisor behaviors (FSSB), which are behaviors supervisors exhibit that are supportive of employees' work-family needs (Hammer et al., 2007). Hammer and colleagues (2007) describe supervisors as the "linking pin" (p. 169) between availability of formal workplace support and development of work-family culture, or "the shared assumptions, beliefs, and values regarding the extent to which an organization supports and values the integration of employees' work and family lives" (Thompson, Beauvais, & Lyness, 1999, p. 392). Another important concept related to informal support is that of idiosyncratic employment arrangements (I-deals), which are informal employment arrangements that are negotiated between individual workers and their managers or organizations (Rousseau, 2005).

Second, researchers examine differences between availability and use of support. As Allen and colleagues' (2013) meta-analysis shows, the effects of organizational policies can be quite different, depending on consideration of availability versus use. The results of that study showed that flextime availability was more negatively associated with work-to-family conflict (WTFC) than was flextime use, while flexplace use was more negatively associated with WTFC than was flexplace availability. Thus, an important consideration for future research on policy may include deeper exploration of availability versus use; organizations may not realize that availability of policies is often enough to make a significant difference in employee outcomes, even if employees do not actually use the policy.

Evidence for the effectiveness of organizational support for work-family needs ranges across a wide variety of work-family policies and support structures. A meta-analysis of supervisor and organizational support constructs found that work-family-specific support is more strongly related to work-family conflict than general support (Kossek, Pichler, Bodner, & Hammer, 2011). This finding suggests that forms of support that are specific to work-family needs make an especially important difference in employees' work-family experiences, as well as that both supervisor and organizational support are important factors.

Another meta-analysis on work-family support policies found that availability and use of work-family support policies is related to job satisfaction, affective organizational commitment, and decreased turnover intentions (Butts, Casper, & Yang, 2013). Policy availability was actually more strongly related to outcomes than was use itself. Relationships of policy use and work attitudes were partially mediated by work-to-family conflict, showing that policy use partially serves to reduce conflict, thus improving employee outcomes. Butts and colleagues suggest that implementing multiple policies provides the best opportunity to meet employees' unique needs. Beyond policy availability and use, the study also showed that family-supportive organizational perceptions have larger effects than policy availability or use, suggesting that providing support is likely even more important than providing formal policies.

Another method of improving the support employees receive for work-family needs is to implement workplace interventions. Work-family-specific interventions are generally shown to be effective at improving employee outcomes. Hammer, Demsky, Kossek, and Bray (2015) provide a review of work-family interventions, highlighting several issues researchers and organizations face during implementation, such as organizational resource limitations (e.g., lack of resources to carry out studies), uneven adoption (e.g., flexible work arrangements are generally only available for higher-wage, professional-level workers), and lack of evidence-based solutions (e.g., organizations adopting interventions that are not scientifically validated). Additionally, Hammer and colleagues argue that existing work-family interventions can be broken into five categories: alternative work arrangements (e.g., telework), dependent care supports (e.g., subsidized childcare), training (e.g., family-supportive supervisor behavior training), work redesign initiatives (e.g., attempts to increase schedule control), and those interventions that combine multiple other types. Overall, their review concludes that most effects of work-family interventions on work-family outcomes, such as work-family conflict and work-family balance, have been positive.

One especially noteworthy work-family intervention comes from the Work, Family, and Health Network (WFHN), an interdisciplinary, collaborative group of researchers from multiple sites across the United States (King et al., 2012). The Work, Family, and Health Study (http://www.workfamilyhealthnetwork.org/), conducted by the WFHN, is a longitudinal randomized field experiment aimed at designing and testing an intervention to reduce work-family conflict and improve health and well-being of employees and their families (Bray et al., 2013; King et al., 2012). Pilot research for the study included conducting an intervention with grocery store workers, aimed at increasing family-supportive supervisor behaviors (FSSB). The intervention was found to successfully improve work and health outcomes for workers with high levels of family-to-work conflict (Hammer, Kossek, Anger, Bodner, & Zimmerman, 2011). Additional pilot research for the study examined implementation of the Results Only Work Environment (ROWE), which redesigned work to incorporate increased control over work time and supervisor focus on results of work (Kelly, Moen, & Tranby, 2011). Evidence shows ROWE benefits work-family balance (Kelly et al., 2011) and reduced turnover and turnover intentions (Moen, Kelly, & Hill, 2011).

Building upon this pilot research, the larger WFHN intervention targeted supportive supervisor behaviors and control over work as levers for change (King et al., 2012; Kossek, Hammer, Kelly, & Moen, 2014). The larger intervention used computer-based training, in-person participatory sessions, and supervisory behavior tracking to improve support for employees' work-family needs. The WFHN intervention has since shown evidence of ability to increase schedule control and FSSB (Kelly et al., 2014). Beyond influencing the direct intervention targets, research shows the intervention also reduces work-family conflict and increases family time adequacy (Kelly et al., 2014), increases objectively measured sleep duration and reduces sleep insufficiency (Olson et al., 2015), buffers against declines in employee safety compliance and organizational citizenship behaviors (Hammer et al., 2016), and increases parental time spent with children (Davis et al., 2015).

A review of work-family integration policies (Hammer, Van Dyck, & Ellis, 2013) provides several practical recommendations for best practices in work-family policy. First, the authors suggest using multi-level initiatives to intervene across multiple levels of the organization. Second, the authors suggest integrating policies with other internal organizational systems, such as performance management and human resources systems. Third, they advocate for considering individual differences, such as expanding policies to include broader work-life needs that benefit workers who do not have children or other traditional family responsibilities. Finally, the authors suggest that policies should seek to avoid possible "backlash" by striving for a high level of inclusiveness. Such inclusiveness may mean increasing support for employees without children or eldercare responsibilities.

As researchers and organizations work to improve upon existing interventions and build new approaches, Total Worker Health may prove particularly useful. Total Worker Health is a strategy developed by the National Institute for Occupational Health and Safety that focuses on integrating occupational safety and health protection with health promotion efforts to prevent injury and illness and increase overall health and well-being. Using a Total Worker Health framework, Hammer and Sauter (2013) reviewed research on chronic health outcomes associated with work-family conflict and stress and found that most research is based on correlational studies, rather than on programs and interventions to reduce conflict. Thus, future research should continue to explore interventions to improve work-family issues, perhaps through examination of resource loss or coping behaviors (Hammer & Sauter, 2013).

FUTURE DIRECTIONS IN WORK AND FAMILY

Although a great deal of research exists on work-family issues, particularly work-family conflict, several areas of research should be further examined. One such area is research on low-wage and shift workers. Working conditions contributing to work-family conflict and enrichment are frequently characteristic of lower-wage jobs, such as low levels of control over work, high work demands, low levels of supervisor support, shift work, and temporary work that can lead to unpredictable schedules, high degrees of job insecurity, and increased health and safety hazards. Despite these important aspects of lower-wage jobs, little research has examined low-wage samples, and a substantial amount of work is still needed to understand how work-family processes influence low-wage workers.

Beyond expanding research to lower-wage and shift workers, research can also work toward consideration of other roles, outside of the traditional family role. Wilson and Baumann (2015) developed and validated measures that incorporate personal life, in combination with work life and family life; these measures, as well as other new measures, can be used to build upon previous work that may be limited by restricted role definitions. Hammer and colleagues (2013) argue that the field is moving toward inclusion, and researchers should work to continue to expand understanding and support of roles that have not been traditionally studied.

Another area of future research might focus on diving deeper into current understanding of work-family issues through underused, theoretically justified methodologies. Greenhaus and ten Brummelhuis (2013) suggest that the work-home resources model (ten Brummelhuis & Bakker, 2012) is one theory that calls for a cross-domain approach and the use of longitudinal designs and daily diary designs to test various propositions of the model. Overall, the use of these approaches would help meet the call of many researchers (e.g., Hammer & Zimmerman, 2011; Casper, Eby, Bordeaux, Lockwood, & Lambert, 2007) who have previously argued for more longitudinal research. An alternative, much-needed approach to meeting this call is to target the long-term benefits of interventions and workplace policies and practices through such avenues as return on investment (e.g., Goetzel & Pronk, 2010), as well as business-relevant outcomes, such as firm-level performance (e.g., firm-level creativity, Hammer et al., 2013).

An additional area for future research is to work within other areas of organizational research to apply work-family concepts more broadly and build opportunities to help meet employees' work-family needs through new avenues. For example, Cleveland and Colella (2010) call for inclusion of employee health and well-being, as well as other nonwork criteria, such as work-family conflict, in the field of employee selection. While use of selection tools to predict work-family issues is highly problematic (e.g., penalizing applicants based on familial status or conditions and breaking discrimination laws regarding appropriate selection constructs), there are many other ways to incorporate work-family research into other areas of organizations. Ryan and Ployhart (2014) suggest, for example, focusing on time management or decision-making in the face of competing demands. By working with scholars from other areas of organizational research, work-family scholars can build new contributions, while also promoting understanding of—and concern for—employee health, well-being, and fairness.

Another budding area of work-family research is that of recovery from work, or the process of removing work demands and restoring resources lost during the workday (Meijman & Mulder, 1998). Recovery experiences are increasingly studied in relation to work-family issues. For example, Lapierre and colleagues (2012) found that psychological detachment (i.e., one of four recovery experiences outlined by Sonnentag and Fritz in their 2007 research) buffers the relationship between family-to-work conflict and work-related cognitive failure. Hammer and Demsky (2014) argue that more research is needed to understand the relationship between recovery and work-family concepts.

Researchers should additionally consider expanding the currently limited literature on national-level contextual factors that may be related to work-family issues. In their recent review of cross-national work-life research, Ollier-Malaterre and Foucreault (2017) note that, despite the increasing number of published theoretical rationales for cross-national work, few have been tested, and existing empirical research is often not backed by strong theoretical motivation. Additionally, some cultural factors have been explored individually (e.g., individualism-collectivism) in the work-family context, but much work remains to untangle the roles that other cultural factors play in work-family issues.

Finally, only a limited number of work-family interventions have been developed, and even fewer have been thoroughly evaluated. Future interventions could build upon support and work redesign interventions developed and evaluated by other researchers (e.g., the Work, Family, and Health Network intervention) or work to develop and evaluate entirely new interventions based on some of the many antecedents related to work and family that are supported by prior research.

CONCLUSION

The purpose has been to provide a broad overview of the work-family field, including important background information, theoretical frameworks, constructs, debates, and research on work and family components of individuals' lives, as well as the intersection between their various roles. As the workplace continues to change, with more dual-earner couples, an increasingly aging workforce, and surges of technology that facilitates flexible work arrangements (e.g., telecommuting), researchers and organizations work to explore relationships between work and family roles, develop policies and practices related to work and family, and build evidence-based interventions to improve organizations' abilities to meet employees' needs.

FURTHER READING

Amstad, F. T., Meier, L. L., Fasel, U., Elfering, A., & Semmer, N. K. (2011). A meta-analysis of work–family conflict and various outcomes with a special emphasis on cross-domain versus matching-domain relations. *Journal of Occupational Health Psychology, 16,* 151–169.

Byron, K. (2005). A meta-analytic review of work–family conflict and its antecedents. *Journal of Vocational Behavior, 67,* 169–198.

Crain, T. L., & Hammer, L. B. (2013). Work-family enrichment: A systematic review of antecedents, outcomes, and mechanisms. In A. B. Bakker (Ed.), *Advances in positive organizational psychology* (Vol. 1, pp. 303–328). Bingley, U.K.: Emerald.

Greenhaus J. H., & Allen, T. D. (2011). Work-family balance: A review and extension of the literature. In L. Tetrick & J. C. Quick (Eds.), *Handbook of occupational health psychology* (2d ed., pp. 165–183). Washington, DC: American Psychological Association.

Greenhaus, J. H., & Beutell, N. J. (1985). Sources of conflict between work and family roles. *Academy of Management Review, 10,* 76–88.

Greenhaus, J. H., & Powell, G. N. (2006). When work and family are allies: A theory of work-family enrichment. *Academy of Management Review, 31,* 72–92.

Hammer, L. B., & Zimmerman, K. L. (2011). Quality of work life. In S. Zedeck (Ed.), *American Psychological Association handbook of industrial and organizational psychology* (pp. 399–431). Washington, DC: American Psychological Association.

McNall, L. A., Nicklin, J. M., & Masuda, A. D. (2010). A meta-analytic review of the consequences associated with work–family enrichment. *Journal of Business and Psychology, 25,* 381–396.

REFERENCES

Ajzen, I. (1985). From intentions to actions: A theory of planned behavior. In J. Kuhl & J. Beckmann (Eds.), *Action-control: From cognition to behavior* (pp. 11–39). Heidelberg, Germany: Springer.

Allen, T. D., Cho, E., & Meier, L. L. (2014). Work–family boundary dynamics. *Annual Review of Organizational Psychology and Organizational Behavior, 1,* 99–121.

Allen, T. D., French, K. A., Dumani, S., & Shockley, K. M. (2015). Meta-analysis of work–family conflict mean differences: Does national context matter? *Journal of Vocational Behavior, 90,* 90–100.

Allen, T. D., Herst, D. E. L., Bruck, C. S., & Sutton, M. (2000). Consequences associated with work-to-family conflict: A review and agenda for future research. *Journal of Occupational Health Psychology, 5,* 278–308.

Allen, T. D., Johnson, R. C., Kiburz, K. M., & Shockley, K. M. (2013). Work–family conflict and flexible work arrangements: Deconstructing flexibility. *Personnel Psychology, 66,* 345–376.

Allen, T. D., Johnson, R. C., Saboe, K. N., Cho, E., Dumani, S., & Evans, S. (2012). Dispositional variables and work–family conflict: A meta-analysis. *Journal of Vocational Behavior, 80,* 17–26.

Ashforth, B. E., Kreiner, G. E., & Fugate, M. (2000). All in a day's work: Boundaries and micro role transitions. *Academy of Management Review, 25,* 472–491.

Bagger, J., & Li, A. (2014). How does supervisory family support influence employees' attitudes and behaviors? A social exchange perspective. *Journal of Management, 40,* 1123–1150.

Berkman, L. F., Liu, S. Y., Hammer, L., Moen, P., Klein, L. C., Kelly, E., et al. (2015). Work–family conflict, cardiometabolic risk, and sleep duration in nursing employees. *Journal of Occupational Health Psychology, 20,* 420–433.

Boswell, W. R., & Olson-Buchanan, J. B. (2007). The use of communication technologies after hours: The role of work attitudes and work-life conflict. *Journal of Management, 33,* 592–610.

Bray, J. W., Kelly, E. L., Hammer, L. B., Almeida D. M., Dearing, J. W., King R. B., et al. (2013). *An integrative, multilevel, and transdisciplinary research approach to challenges of work, family, and health* (RTI Press publication No. MR-0024-1303). Research Triangle Park, NC: RTI. http://www.rti.org/publication/integrative-multilevel-and-transdisciplinary-research-approach-challenges-work-family

Bronfenbrenner, U. (1977). Toward an experimental ecology of human development. *American Psychologist, 32,* 513–531.

Bulger, C., Matthews, R., & Hoffman, M. E. (2007). Work and personal life boundary management: Boundary strength, work/personal life balance, and the segmentation–integration continuum. *Journal of Occupational Health Psychology, 12,* 365–375.

Butler, A. B. (2007). Job characteristics and college performance and attitudes: A model of work–school conflict and facilitation. *Journal of Applied Psychology, 93*, 500–510.

Butts, M. M., Becker, W. J., & Boswell, W. R. (2015). Hot buttons and time sinks: The effects of electronic communication during nonwork time on emotions and work-nonwork conflict. *Academy of Management Journal, 58*, 763–788.

Butts, M. M., Casper, W. J., & Yang, T. S. (2013). How important are work–family support policies? A meta-analytic investigation of their effects on employee outcomes. *Journal of Applied Psychology, 98*, 1–25.

Caplan, R. D. (1983). Person-environment fit: Past, present, and future. In C. L. Cooper (Ed.), *Stress research* (pp. 35–77). New York: Wiley.

Carlson, D. S., Grzywacz, J. G., & Kacmar, K. M. (2010). The relationship of schedule flexibility and outcomes via the work-family interface. *Journal of Managerial Psychology, 25*, 330–355.

Carlson, D. S., Kacmar, K. M., Wayne, J. H., & Grzywacz, J. G. (2006). Measuring the positive side of the work–family interface: Development and validation of a work–family enrichment scale. *Journal of Vocational Behavior, 68*, 131–164.

Carlson, D., Kacmar, K. M., Zivnuska, S., Ferguson, M., & Whitten, D. (2011). Work-family enrichment and job performance: A constructive replication of affective events theory. *Journal of Occupational Health Psychology, 16*, 297–312.

Casper, W. J., Eby, L. T., Bordeaux, C., Lockwood, A., & Lambert, D. (2007). A review of research methods in IO/OB work-family research. *Journal of Applied Psychology, 92*, 28–43.

Clark, S. C. (2000). Work/family border theory: A new theory of work/family balance. *Human Relations, 53*, 747–770.

Cleveland, J. N., & Colella, A. (2010). Criterion validity and criterion deficiency: What we measure well and what we ignore. In J. L. Farr & N. T. Tippins (Eds.), *Handbook of employee selection* (pp. 551–567). New York: Routledge.

Crain, T. L., Hammer, L. B., Bodner, T., Kossek, E. E., Moen, P., Lilienthal, R., et al. (2014). Work–family conflict, family-supportive supervisor behaviors (FSSB), and sleep outcomes. *Journal of Occupational Health Psychology, 19*, 155–167.

Cropanzano, R., & Mitchell, M. S. (2005). Social exchange theory: An interdisciplinary review. *Journal of Management, 31*, 874–900.

Cullen, J. C., & Hammer, L. B. (2007). Developing and testing a theoretical model linking work-family conflict to employee safety. *Journal of Occupational Health Psychology, 12*, 266–278.

Daniel, S., & Sonnentag, S. (2016). Crossing the borders: The relationship between boundary management, work–family enrichment and job satisfaction. *International Journal of Human Resource Management, 27*, 407–426.

Dansereau, F., Cashman, J., & Graen, G. (1973). Instrumentality theory and equity theory as complementary approaches in predicting the relationship of leadership and turnover among managers. *Organizational Behavior and Human Performance, 10*, 184–200.

Davis, K. D., Lawson, K. M., Almeida, D. M., Kelly, E. L., King, R. B., Hammer, L., et al. (2015). Parents' daily time with their children: A workplace intervention. *Pediatrics, 135*, 875–882.

Demerouti, E., & Geurts, S. (2004). Towards a typology of work-home interaction. *Community, Work & Family, 7*, 285–309.

den Dulk, L., & Peper, B. (2016). The impact of national policy on work–family experiences. In T. D. Allen & L. T. Eby (Eds.), *Handbook of work and family* (pp. 300–314). Oxford: Oxford University Press.

Edwards, J. R., Caplan, R. D., & Van Harrison, R. (1998). Person-environment fit theory: Conceptual foundations, empirical evidence, and directions for future research. In C. L. Cooper (Ed.), *Theories of organizational stress* (pp. 28–67). Oxford: Oxford University Press.

Edwards, J. R., & Rothbard, N. P. (2000). Mechanisms linking work and family: Clarifying the relationship between work and family constructs. *Academy of Management Review, 25,* 178–199.

Emerson, R. M. 1976. Social exchange theory. *Annual Review of Sociology, 2,* 335–362.

Foa, E. B., & Foa, U. G. (1974). *Societal structures of the mind.* Springfield, IL: Charles C. Thomas.

Foa, E. B., & Foa, U. G. (1980). Resource theory: Interpersonal behavior as exchange. In K. J. Gergen, S. M. S. Martin, & R. H. Willis. (Eds.), *Social exchange* (pp. 77–94). New York: Plenum Press.

Frederick, S., & Loewenstein, G. (1999). Hedonic adaptation. In D. Kahneman, E. Diener, & N. Schwarz (Eds.), *Well being: The foundations of hedonic psychology* (pp. 302–329). New York: Russell Sage Foundation.

Frone, M. R. (2000). Work–family conflict and employee psychiatric disorders: The national comorbidity survey. *Journal of Applied Psychology, 85,* 888–895.

Frone, M. R., Russell, M., & Cooper, M. L. (1992). Antecedents and outcomes of work-family conflict: Testing a model of the work-family interface. *Journal of Applied Psychology, 77,* 65–78.

Gerstner, C. R., & Day, D. V. (1997). Meta-analytic review of leader–member exchange theory: Correlates and construct issues. *Journal of Applied Psychology, 82,* 827–844.

Goetzel, R. Z., & Pronk, N. P. (2010). Worksite health promotion: How much do we really know about what works? *American Journal of Preventive Medicine, 38,* S223–S225.

Goode, W. J. (1960). A theory of role strain. *American Sociological Review, 25,* 483–496.

Graen, G. (1976). Role making processes within complex organizations. In M. D. Dunnette (Ed.), *Handbook of industrial and organizational psychology* (pp. 1201–1245). Chicago: Rand McNally.

Greenhaus, J. H., & Kossek, E. E. (2014). The contemporary career: A work–home perspective. *Annual Review of Organizational Psychology and Organizational Behavior, 1,* 361–388.

Greenhaus, J. H., & Ten Brummelhuis, L. L. (2013). Models and frameworks underlying work-life research. In D. A. Major & R. Burke (Eds.), *Handbook of work-life integration among professionals: Challenge and opportunities* (pp. 14–34). Northampton, MA: Edward Elgar.

Grzywacz, J. G., Butler, A. B., & Almeida, D. M. (2008). Work, family, and health: Work–family balance as a protective factor against stresses of daily life. In A. Marcus-Newhall, D. F. Halpern, & S. J. Tan (Eds.), *The changing realities of work and family: A multidisciplinary approach.* Oxford: Wiley-Blackwell.

Grzywacz, J. G., & Marks, N. F. (2000). Reconceptualizing the work–family interface: An ecological perspective on the correlates of positive and negative spillover between work and family. *Journal of Occupational Health Psychology, 5,* 111–126.

Halbesleben, J. R., Neveu, J. P., Paustian-Underdahl, S. C., & Westman, M. (2014). Getting to the "COR": Understanding the role of resources in conservation of resources theory. *Journal of Management, 40,* 1334–1364.

Hall, D. T., & Richter, J. (1988). Balancing work life and home life: What can organizations do to help? *Academy of Management Executive, 2,* 213–223.

Hammer, L. B., Bauer, T. N., & Grandey, A. A. (2003). Work-family conflict and work-related withdrawal behaviors. *Journal of Business and Psychology, 17,* 419–436.

Hammer, L. B., Cullen, J. C., Neal, M. B., Sinclair, R. R., & Shafiro, M. V. (2005). The longitudinal effects of work-family conflict and positive spillover on depressive symptoms among dual-earner couples. *Journal of Occupational Health Psychology, 10,* 138–154.

Hammer, L. B., Cullen, J. C., & Shafiro, M. (2006). Work-family best practices. In F. Jones, R. Burke, & M. Westman (Eds.), *Work-life balance: A psychological perspective* (pp. 261–275). East Sussex, U.K.: Psychology Press.

Hammer, L. B., & Demsky, C. A. (2014). Introduction to work-life balance. In A. Day, E. K. Kelloway, & J. J. Hurrell (Eds.), *Workplace well-being: How to build psychologically healthy workplaces* (pp. 95–116). Hoboken, NJ: Wiley-Blackwell.

Hammer, L. B., Demsky, C., Kossek, E. E., & Bray, J. (2015). Work-family intervention research. In T. D. Allen & L. T. Eby (Eds.), *Handbook of work and family* (pp. 349–361). Oxford: Oxford University Press.

Hammer, L. B., Grigsby, T. D., & Woods, S. (1998). The conflicting demands of work, family, and school among students at an urban university. *Journal of Psychology, 132*, 220–226.

Hammer, L. B., Johnson, R. C., Crain, T. L., Bodner, T., Kossek, E. E., Davis, K. D., et al. (2016). Intervention effects on safety compliance and citizenship behaviors: Evidence from the Work, Family, and Health Study. *Journal of Applied Psychology, 101*(2), 190–208.

Hammer, L. B., Kossek, E. E., Anger, W. K., Bodner, T., & Zimmerman, K. L. (2011). Clarifying work–family intervention processes: The roles of work–family conflict and family-supportive supervisor behaviors. *Journal of Applied Psychology, 96*, 134–150.

Hammer, L. B., Kossek, E. E., Yragui, N. L., Bodner, T. E., & Hanson, G. C. (2009). Development and validation of a multidimensional measure of family supportive supervisor behaviors (FSSB). *Journal of Management, 35*, 837–856.

Hammer, L. B., Kossek, E. E., Zimmerman, K., & Daniels, R. (2007). Clarifying the construct of family supportive supervisory behaviors (FSSB): A multilevel perspective. In P. L. Perrewe & D. C. Ganster (Eds.), *Research in occupational stress and well-being* (Vol. 6, pp. 171–211). Amsterdam: Elsevier.

Hammer, L. B., & Sauter, S. (2013). Total worker health and work–life stress. *Journal of Occupational and Environmental Medicine, 55*, S25–S29.

Hammer, L. B., Van Dyck, S., & Ellis, A. (2013). Organizational policies supportive of work-life integration. In D. A. Major & R. Burke (Eds.), *Handbook of work-life integration among professionals: Challenges and opportunities* (pp. 288–309). Northampton, MA: Edward Elgar.

Hanson, B. G. (1995). *General systems theory beginning with wholes*. Washington, DC: Taylor & Francis.

Hanson, G. C., Hammer, L. B., & Colton, C. L. (2006). Development and validation of a multidimensional scale of perceived work–family positive spillover. *Journal of Occupational Health Psychology, 11*, 249–265.

Heymann, J., & McNeill, K. (2012). *Families at work: What we know about conditions globally*. Policy brief prepared for the United Nations Department of Economic and Social Affairs, Division for Social Policy and Development, United Nations Expert Group Meeting Session: "Good Practices in Family Policy Making."

Hobfoll, S. E. (1989). Conservation of resources: A new attempt at conceptualizing stress. *American Psychologist, 44*, 513–524.

Hobfoll, S. E. (2002). Social and psychological resources and adaptation. *Review of General Psychology, 6*, 307–324.

Ilies, R., Schwind, K. M., Wagner, D. T., Johnson, M. D., DeRue, D. S., & Ilgen, D. R. (2007). When can employees have a family life? The effects of daily workload and affect on work-family conflict and social behaviors at home. *Journal of Applied Psychology, 92*, 1368–1379.

Innstrand, S. T., Langballe, E. M., Espnes, G. A., Aasland, O. G. W., & Falkum, E. (2010). Work–home conflict and facilitation across four different family structures in Norway. *Community, Work & Family, 13*, 231–249.

Innstrand, S. T., Langballe, E. M., Espnes, G. A., Falkum, E., & Aasland, O. G. (2008). Positive and negative work–family interaction and burnout: A longitudinal study of reciprocal relations. *Work and Stress, 22*, 1–15.

Kahn, R. L., Wolfe, D. M., Quinn, R. P., Snoek, J. D., & Rosenthal, R. A. (1964). *Organizational stress: Studies in role conflict and ambiguity*. New York: Wiley.

Katz, D., & Kahn, R. L. (1978). *The social psychology of organizations* (2d ed.). New York: Wiley.

Kelly, E. L., Moen, P., Oakes, J. M., Fan, W., Okechukwu, C., Davis, K. D., et al. (2014). Changing work and work-family conflict evidence from the work, family, and health network. *American Sociological Review, 79*, 485–516.

Kelly, E. L., Moen, P., & Tranby, E. (2011). Changing workplaces to reduce work-family conflict schedule control in a white-collar organization. *American Sociological Review, 76*, 265–290.

King, R. B., Karuntzos, G., Casper, L. M., Moen, P., Davis, K. D., Berkman, L., et al. (2012). Work–family balance issues and work–leave policies. In R. J. Gatchel & L. Z. Schultz (Eds.), *Handbook of occupational health and wellness* (pp. 323–339). New York: Springer.

Kossek, E. E., Hammer, L. B., Kelly, E. L., & Moen, P. (2014). Designing work, family & health organizational change initiatives. *Organizational Dynamics, 43*, 53–63.

Kossek, E. E., & Lautsch, B. A. (2007). *CEO of me: Creating a life that works in the flexible job age.* Pearson Prentice Hall.

Kossek, E. E., & Lautsch, B. A. (2012). Work–family boundary management styles in organizations: A cross-level model. *Organizational Psychology Review, 2*, 152–171.

Kossek, E. E. & Michel, J. (2010). Flexible work schedules. In S. Zedeck (Ed.), *American Psychological Association handbook of industrial and organizational psychology* (pp. 535–572). Washington, DC: American Psychological Association.

Kossek, E. E., & Ozeki, C. (1998). Work–family conflict, policies, and the job–life satisfaction relationship: A review and directions for organizational behavior–human resources research. *Journal of Applied Psychology, 83*, 139–149.

Kossek, E. E., Pichler, S., Bodner, T., & Hammer, L. B. (2011). Workplace social support and work–family conflict: A meta-analysis clarifying the influence of general and work–family-specific supervisor and organizational support. *Personnel Psychology, 64*, 289–313.

Kossek, E. E., Ruderman, M. N., Braddy, P. W., & Hannum, K. M. (2012). Work–nonwork boundary management profiles: A person-centered approach. *Journal of Vocational Behavior, 81*, 112–128.

Kozhimannil, K. B., Jou, J., Gjerdingen, D. K., & McGovern, P. M. (2016). Access to workplace accommodations to support breastfeeding after passage of the Affordable Care Act. *Women's Health Issues, 26*, 6–13.

Kreiner, G. E. (2006). Consequences of work-home segmentation or integration: A person-environment fit perspective. *Journal of Organizational Behavior, 27*, 485–507.

Kreiner, G. E., Hollensbe, E. C., & Sheep, M. L. (2009). Balancing borders and bridges: Negotiating the work-home interface via boundary work tactics. *Academy of Management Journal, 52*, 704–730.

Kwan, H. K., & Mao, Y. (2011). The role of citizenship behavior in personal learning and work-family enrichment. *Frontiers of Business Research in China, 5*, 96–120.

Lapierre, L. M., Hammer, L. B., Truxillo, D. M., & Murphy, L. A. (2012). Family interference with work and workplace cognitive failure: The mitigating role of recovery experiences. *Journal of Vocational Behavior, 81*, 227–235.

Major, D. A., & Morganson, V. J. (2011). Coping with work-family conflict: A leader-member exchange perspective. *Journal of Occupational Health Psychology, 16*, 126–138.

Marks, S. R. (1977). Multiple roles and role strain: Some notes on human energy, time and commitment. *American Sociological Review, 42*, 921–936.

Matthews, R. A., Wayne, J. H., & Ford, M. T. (2014). A work–family conflict/subjective well-being process model: A test of competing theories of longitudinal effects. *Journal of Applied Psychology, 99*, 1173–1187.

Matthews, R. A., Wayne, J. H., & McKersie, S. J. (2016). Theoretical approaches to the study of work and family: Avoiding stagnation via effective theory borrowing. In T. D. Allen & L. T. Eby (Eds.), *Oxford handbook of work and family* (pp. 23–35). Oxford: Oxford University Press.

Mead, G. H. (1934). *Mind, self and society.* Chicago: University of Chicago Press.

Meijman, T. E., & Mulder, G. (1998). Psychological aspects of workload. In P. J. D. Drenth & H. Thierry (Eds.), *Handbook of work and organizational psychology: Work psychology* (Vol. 2, pp. 5–33). Hove, U.K.: Psychology Press.

Michel, J. S., Clark, M. A., & Jaramillo, D. (2011a). The role of the Five Factor Model of personality in the perceptions of negative and positive forms of work–nonwork spillover: A meta-analytic review. *Journal of Vocational Behavior, 79*, 191–203.

Michel, J. S., Kotrba, L. M., Mitchelson, J. K., Clark, M. A., & Baltes, B. B. (2011b). Antecedents of work–family conflict: A meta-analytic review. *Journal of Organizational Behavior, 32*, 689–725.

Moen, P., Kelly, E. L., & Hill, R. (2011). Does enhancing work-time control and flexibility reduce turnover? A naturally occurring experiment. *Social Problems, 58*, 69–98.

Moreno-Jiménez, B., Mayo, M., Sanz-Vergel, A. I., Geurts, S., Rodríguez-Muñoz, A., & Garrosa, E. (2009). Effects of work–family conflict on employees' well-being: The moderating role of recovery strategies. *Journal of Occupational Health Psychology, 14*, 427–440.

Moss, P. (2012). *International review of leave policies and related research*. London: International Network on Leave Policies and Research.

Neal, M. B., Chapman, N. J., Ingersol-Dayton, B., & Emlen, A. C. (1993). *Balancing work and caregiving for children, adults, and elders* (Vol. 3). Newbury Park, CA: SAGE.

Neal, M. B., & Hammer, L. B. (2007). *Working couples caring for children and aging parents: Effects on work and well-being*. Mahwah, NJ: Lawrence Erlbaum.

Nippert-Eng, C. E. (1996). *Home and work: Negotiating boundaries through everyday life*. Chicago: University of Chicago Press.

Nohe, C., Meier, L. L., Sonntag, K., & Michel, A. (2015). The chicken or the egg? A meta-analysis of panel studies of the relationship between work–family conflict and strain. *Journal of Applied Psychology, 100*, 522–536.

Odle-Dusseau, H. N., Britt, T. W., & Greene-Shortridge, T. M. (2012). Organizational work–family resources as predictors of job performance and attitudes: The process of work–family conflict and enrichment. *Journal of Occupational Health Psychology, 17*, 28–40.

Ollier-Malaterre, A. (2016). Cross-national work-life research: A review at the individual level. In T. D. Allen & L. T. Eby (Eds.), *Handbook of work and family* (pp. 315–330). Oxford: Oxford University Press.

Ollier-Malaterre, A., & Foucreault, A. (2017). Cross-national work-life research: Cultural and structural impacts for individuals and organizations. *Journal of Management, 43*(1), 111–136.

Ollo-López, A., & Goñi-Legaz, S. (2015). Differences in work–family conflict: Which individual and national factors explain them? *International Journal of Human Resource Management*, 1–27.

Olson, R., Crain, T. L., Bodner, T. E., King, R., Hammer, L. B., Klein, L. C., et al. (2015). A workplace intervention improves sleep: Results from the randomized controlled Work, Family, and Health Study. *Sleep Health, 1*, 55–65.

Pleck, J. H. (1977). The work-family role system. *Social Problems, 24*, 417–427.

Poelmans, S. A., Chinchilla, N., & Cardona, P. (2003). The adoption of family-friendly HRM policies: Competing for scarce resources in the labour market. *International Journal of Manpower, 24*, 128–147.

Rantanen, J., Kinnunen, U., Mauno, S., & Tement, S. (2013). Patterns of conflict and enrichment in work-family balance: A three-dimensional typology. *Work & Stress, 27*, 141–163.

Rantanen, J., Kinnunen, U., Mauno, S., & Tillemann, K. (2011). Introducing theoretical approaches to work-life balance and testing a new typology among professionals. In S. Kaiser, M. Ringlstetter, D. R. Eikhof, & M. Pina e Cunha (Eds.), *Creating balance? International perspectives on the work-life integration of professionals* (pp. 27–46). Berlin: Springer.

Rantanen, M., Mauno, S., Kinnunen, U., & Rantanen, J. (2011). Do individual coping strategies help or harm in the work–family conflict situation? Examining coping as a moderator between work–family conflict and well-being. *International Journal of Stress Management, 18*, 24–48.

Rau, B. L., & Hyland, M. A. M. (2002). Role conflict and flexible work arrangements: The effects on applicant attraction. *Personnel Psychology, 55*, 111–136.

Rousseau, D. M. (2005). *I-deals: Idiosyncratic deals employees bargain for themselves*. New York: M. E. Sharpe.

Ryan, A. M., & Ployhart, R. E. (2014). A century of selection. *Annual Review of Psychology, 65,* 693–717.

Shockley, K. M., & Singla, N. (2011). Reconsidering work–family interactions and satisfaction: A meta-analysis. *Journal of Management, 97,* 1077–1096.

Siu, O. L., Bakker, A. B., Brough, P., Lu, C. Q., Wang, H., Kalliath, T., et al. (2015). A three-wave study of antecedents of work–family enrichment: The roles of social resources and affect. *Stress and Health, 31,* 306–314.

Sonnentag, S., & Fritz, C. (2007). The Recovery Experience Questionnaire: Development and validation of a measure for assessing recuperation and unwinding from work. *Journal of Occupational Health Psychology, 12,* 204–221.

Stevens, D. P., Minnotte, K. L., Mannon, S. E., & Kiger, G. (2007). Examining the "neglected side of the work-family interface": Antecedents of positive and negative family-to-work spillover. *Journal of Family Issues, 28,* 242–262.

Stryker, S. (1968). Identity salience and role performance: The relevance of symbolic interaction theory for family research. *Journal of Marriage and the Family, 30,* 558–564.

Taylor, F. W. (1911). *Principles of scientific management.* New York: Harper.

Ten Brummelhuis, L. L., & Bakker, A. B. (2012). A resource perspective on the work–home interface: The work–home resources model. *American Psychologist, 67,* 545–556.

Thoits, P. A. (1983). Multiple identities and psychological well-being: A reformulation and test of the social isolation hypothesis. *American Sociological Review, 48,* 174–187.

Thoits, P. A. (1986). Social support as coping assistance. *Journal of Consulting and Clinical Psychology, 54,* 416–423.

Thompson, C. A., Beauvais, L. L., & Lyness, K. S. (1999). When work–family benefits are not enough: The influence of work–family culture on benefit utilization, organizational attachment, and work–family conflict. *Journal of Vocational Behavior, 54,* 392–415.

Thompson, J. D. (1967). *Organizations in action: Social science bases of administrative theory.* New York: McGraw-Hill.

U.S. Bureau of Labor Statistics. (2014a). *Time spent in primary activities and the percent of married mothers and fathers who did the activities on an average day by employment status and age of youngest own household child.* Bureau of Labor Statistics. http://www.bls.gov/tus/tables/a6_0913.pdf

U.S. Bureau of Labor Statistics. (2014b). *Labor force participation projected to fall for people under age 55 and rise for older age groups.* Bureau of Labor Statistics. http://www.bls.gov/opub/ted/2014/ted_20140106.htm

U.S. Bureau of Labor Statistics. (2015a). *Employment status of the civilian noninstitutional population 16 years and over by sex.* Bureau of Labor Statistics. http://www.bls.gov/cps/cpsaat02.pdf

U.S. Bureau of Labor Statistics. (2015b). *Employment characteristics of families summary.* Bureau of Labor Statistics. http://www.bls.gov/news.release/famee.nr0.htm

U.S. Bureau of Labor Statistics. (2015c). *Unpaid eldercare in the United States.* Bureau of Labor Statistics. http://www.bls.gov/news.release/pdf/elcare.pdf

U.S. Bureau of Labor Statistics. (2015d). *Percent of population who worked on weekdays and weekend days.* Bureau of Labor Statistics. http://www.bls.gov/tus/charts/work.htm

Veal, A. J. (2004). A brief history of work and its relationship to leisure. In J. T. Haworth & A. J. Veal (Eds.), *Work and leisure* (pp. 15–33). New York: Routledge.

Wayne, J. H. (2009). Reducing conceptual confusion: Clarifying the positive side of work and family. In D. R. Crane & J. Hill (Eds.), *Handbook of families and work: Interdisciplinary perspectives* (pp. 105–140). Lanham, MD: University Press of America.

Wayne, J. H., Butts, M. M., Casper, W. J., & Allen, T. D. (in press). In search of balance: A conceptual and empirical integration of multiple meanings of work-family balance. *Personnel Psychology.*

Wayne, J. H., Casper, W. J., Matthews, R. A., & Allen, T. D. (2013). Family-supportive organization perceptions and organizational commitment: The mediating role of work–family conflict and enrichment and partner attitudes. *Journal of Applied Psychology, 98,* 606–622.

Wayne, J. H., Grzywacz, J. G., Carlson, D. S., & Kacmar, K. M. (2007). Work–family facilitation: A theoretical explanation and model of primary antecedents and consequences. *Human Resource Management Review, 17,* 63–76.

Wayne, J. H., Musisca, N., & Fleeson, W. (2004). Considering the role of personality in the work–family experience: Relationships of the big five to work–family conflict and facilitation. *Journal of Vocational Behavior, 64,* 108–130.

Weiss, H. M., & Cropanzano, R. (1996). Affective events theory: A theoretical discussion of the structure, causes and consequences of affective experiences at work. In B. M. Staw & L. L. Cummings (Eds.), *Research in organization behavior* (Vol. 19, pp. 1–74). Greenwich, CT: JAI Press.

Wilson, K. S., & Baumann, H. M. (2015). Capturing a more complete view of employees' lives outside of work: The introduction and development of new interrole conflict constructs. *Personnel Psychology, 68,* 235–282.

Winston, P. (2014). *Work–family supports for low-income families: Key research findings and policy trends.* U.S. Department of Health and Human Services. http://aspe.hhs.gov/hsp/14/WorkFamily/rpt_work-family.cfm

Zerubavel, E. (1991). *The fine line.* New York: Free Press.

MacKenna L. Perry and Leslie B. Hammer

WORK, STRESS, COPING, AND STRESS MANAGEMENT

INTRODUCTION

Work stress is a generic term that refers to work-related stimuli (aka job stressors) that may lead to physical, behavioral, or psychological consequences (i.e., strains) that affect both the health and well-being of the employee and the organization. Not all stressors lead to strains, but all strains are a result of stressors, actual or perceived. Common terms often used interchangeably with work stress are occupational stress, job stress, and work-related stress. Terms used interchangeably with job stressors include work stressors, and as the specificity of the type of stressor might include psychosocial stressor (referring to the psychological experience of work demands that have a social component, e.g., conflict between two people; Hauke, Flintrop, Brun, & Rugulies, 2011), hindrance stressor (i.e., a stressor that prevents goal attainment; Cavanaugh, Boswell, Roehling, & Boudreau, 2000), and challenge stressor (i.e., a stressor that is difficult, but attainable and possibly rewarding to attain; Cavanaugh et al., 2000).

Stress in the workplace continues to be a highly pervasive problem, having both direct negative effects on individuals experiencing it and companies paying for it, and indirect costs vis-à-vis lost productivity (Dopkeen & DuBois, 2014). For example, U.K. public civil servants' work-related stress rose from 10.8% in 2006 to 22.4% in 2013 and about one-third of the workforce has taken more than 20 days of leave due to stress-related ill-health, while well over 50% are present at work when ill (French, 2015). These findings are consistent with a report by the International Labour Organization (ILO, 2012), whereby 50% to 60% of all workdays are lost due to absence attributed to factors associated with work stress.

The prevalence of work-related stress is not diminishing despite improvements in technology and employment rates. The sources of stress, such as workload, seem to exacerbate with improvements in technology (Coovert & Thompson, 2003). Moreover, accessibility through mobile technology and virtual computer terminals is linking people to their work more than ever before (ILO, 2012; Tarafdar, Tu, Ragu-Nathan, & Ragu-Nathan, 2007). Evidence of this kind of mobility and flexibility is further reinforced in a June 2007 survey of 4,025 email users (over 13 years of age); AOL reported that four in ten survey respondents reported planning their vacations around email accessibility and 83% checked their emails at least once a day while away (McMahon, 2007). Ironically, despite these mounting work-related stressors and clear financial and performance outcomes, some individuals are reporting they are less "stressed," but only because "stress has become the new normal" (Jayson, 2012, para. 4).

This new normal is likely the source of psychological and physiological illness. Siegrist (2010) contends that conditions in the workplace, particularly psychosocial stressors that are perceived as unfavorable relationships with others and self, and an increasingly sedentary lifestyle (reinforced with desk jobs) are increasingly contributing to cardiovascular disease. These factors together justify a need to continue on the path of helping individuals recognize and cope with deleterious stressors in the work environment and, equally important, to find ways to help organizations prevent harmful stressors over which they have control, as well as implement policies or mechanisms to help employees deal with these stressors and subsequent strains. Along with a greater focus on mitigating environmental constraints are interventions that can be used to prevent anxiety, poor attitudes toward the workplace conditions and arrangements, and subsequent cardiovascular illness, absenteeism, and poor job performance (Siegrist, 2010).

Even the ILO has presented guidance on how the workplace can help prevent harmful job stressors (aka hindrance stressors) or at least help workers cope with them. Consistent with the view that well-being is not the absence of stressors or strains and with the view that positive psychology offers a lens for proactively preventing stressors, the ILO promotes increasing preventative risk assessments, interventions to prevent and control stressors, transparent organizational communication, worker involvement in decision-making, networks and mechanisms for workplace social support, awareness of how working and living conditions interact, safety, health, and well-being in the organization (ILO, n.d.). The field of industrial and organizational (IO) psychology supports the ILO's recommendations.

IO psychology views work stress as the process of a person's interaction with multiple aspects of the work environment, job design, and work conditions in the organization. Interventions to manage work stress, therefore, focus on the psychosocial factors of the person and his or her relationships with others and the socio-technical factors related to the work environment and work processes. Viewing work stress from the lens of the person and the environment stems from Kurt Lewin's (1936) work that stipulates a person's state of mental health and behaviors are a function of the person within a specific environment or situation. Aspects of the work environment that affect individuals' mental states and behaviors include organizational hierarchy, organizational climate (including processes, policies, practices, and reward structures), resources to support a person's ability to fulfill job duties, and management structure (including leadership). Job design refers to each contributor's tasks and responsibilities for fulfilling goals associated with the work role. Finally, working conditions refers not only to the physical environment, but also the interpersonal relationships with other contributors.

Each of the conditions that are identified in the work environment may be perceived as potentially harmful or a threat to the person or as an opportunity. When a stressor is perceived as a threat to attaining desired goals or outcomes, the stressor may be labeled as a hindrance stressor (e.g., LePine, Podsakoff, & Lepine, 2005). When the stressor is perceived as an opportunity to attain a desired goal or end state, it may be labeled as a challenge stressor. According to LePine and colleagues' (2005), both challenge (e.g., time urgency, workload) and hindrance (e.g., hassles, role ambiguity, role conflict) stressors could lead to strains (as measured by "anxiety, depersonalization, depression, emotional exhaustion, frustration, health complaints, hostility, illness, physical symptoms, and tension" [p. 767]). However, challenge stressors positively relate with motivation and performance, whereas hindrance stressors negatively relate with motivation and performance. Moreover, motivation and strains partially mediate the relationship between hindrance and challenge stressors with performance.

In order to (1) minimize any potential negative effects from stressors, (2) increase coping skills to deal with stressors, or (3) manage strains, organizational practitioners or consultants will devise organizational interventions geared toward prevention, coping, and/or stress management. Ultimately, toxic factors in the work environment can have deleterious effects on a person's physical and psychological well-being, as well as on an organization's total health. It behooves management to take stock of the organization's health, which includes the health and well-being of its employees, if the organization wishes to thrive and be profitable. According to Page and Vella-Brodrick's (2009) model of employee well-being, employee well-being results from subjective well-being (i.e., life satisfaction and general positive or negative affect), workplace well-being (composed of job satisfaction and work-specific positive or negative affect), and psychological well-being (e.g., self-acceptance, positive social relations, mastery, purpose in life). Job stressors that become unbearable are likely to negatively affect workplace well-being and thus overall employee well-being. Because work stress is a major organizational pain point and organizations often employ organizational consultants to help identify and remediate pain points, the focus here is on organizational development (OD) frameworks; several work stress frameworks are presented that together signal areas where organizations might focus efforts for change in employee behaviors, attitudes, and performance, as well as the organization's performance and climate. Work stress, interventions, and several OD and stress frameworks are depicted in Figure 1.

The goals are: (1) to conceptually define and clarify terms associated with stress and stress management, particularly focusing on organizational factors that contribute to stress and stress management, and (2) to present research that informs current knowledge and practices on workplace stress management strategies. Stressors and strains will be defined, leading OD and work stress frameworks that are used to organize and help organizations make sense of the work environment and the organization's responsibility in stress management will be explored, and stress management will be explained as an overarching thematic label; an area of study and practice that focuses on prevention (primary) interventions, coping (secondary) interventions, and managing strains (tertiary) interventions; as well as the label typically used to denote tertiary interventions. Suggestions for future research and implications toward becoming a healthy organization are presented.

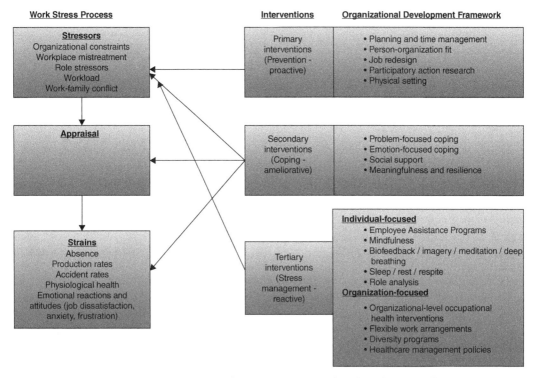

Figure 1. Organizational development frameworks to guide identification of work stress and interventions.

DEFINING STRESSORS AND STRAINS

Work-related stressors or job stressors can lead to different kinds of strains individuals and organizations might experience. Various types of stress management interventions, guided by OD and work stress frameworks, may be employed to prevent or cope with job stressors and manage strains that develop(ed).

Stressors. A job stressor is a stimulus external to an employee and a result of an employee's work conditions. Example job stressors include organizational constraints, workplace mistreatments (such as abusive supervision, workplace ostracism, incivility, bullying), role stressors, workload, work-family conflicts, errors or mistakes, examinations and evaluations, and lack of structure (Jex & Beehr, 1991; Liu, Spector, & Shi, 2007; Narayanan, Menon, & Spector, 1999). Although stressors may be categorized as hindrances and challenges, there is not yet sufficient information to be able to propose which stress management interventions would better serve to reduce those hindrance stressors or to reduce strain-producing challenge stressors while reinforcing engagement-producing challenge stressors.

Organizational Constraints. Organizational constraints may be hindrance stressors as they prevent employees from translating their motivation and ability into high-level job performance (Peters & O'Connor, 1980). Peters and O'Connor (1988) defined 11 categories of organizational constraints: (1) job-related information, (2) budgetary support, (3) required support, (4) materials and supplies, (5) required services and help from others, (6) task preparation, (7) time availability, (8) the work environment, (9) scheduling of activities, (10) transportation, and (11) job-relevant authority. The inhibiting effect of organizational constraints may be due to the lack of, inadequacy of, or poor quality of these categories.

Workplace Mistreatment. Workplace mistreatment presents a cluster of interpersonal variables, such as interpersonal conflict, bullying, incivility, and workplace ostracism (Hershcovis, 2011; Tepper & Henle, 2011). Typical workplace mistreatment behaviors include gossiping, rude comments, showing favoritism, yelling, lying, and ignoring other people at work (Tepper & Henle, 2011). These variables relate to employees' psychological well-being, physical well-being, work attitudes (e.g., job satisfaction and organizational commitment), and turnover intention (e.g., Hershcovis, 2011; Spector & Jex, 1998). Some researchers differentiated the source of mistreatment, such as mistreatment from one's supervisor versus mistreatment from one's coworker (e.g., Bruk-Lee & Spector, 2006; Frone, 2000; Liu, Liu, Spector, & Shi, 2011).

Role Stressors. Role stressors are demands, constraints, or opportunities a person perceives to be associated, and thus expected, with his or her work role(s) across various situations. Three commonly studied role stressors are role ambiguity, role conflict, and role overload (Glazer & Beehr, 2005; Kahn, Wolfe, Quinn, Snoek, & Rosenthal, 1964). Role ambiguity in the workplace occurs when an employee lacks clarity regarding what performance-related behaviors are expected of him or her. Role conflict refers to situations wherein an employee receives incompatible role requests from the same or different supervisors or the employee is asked to engage in work that impedes his or her performance in other work or nonwork roles or clashes with his or her values. Role overload refers to excessive demands and insufficient time (quantitative) or knowledge (qualitative) to complete the work. The construct is often used interchangeably with workload, though role overload focuses more on perceived expectations from others about one's workload. These role stressors significantly relate to low job satisfaction, low organizational commitment, low job performance, high tension or anxiety, and high turnover intention (Abramis, 1994; Glazer & Beehr, 2005; Jackson & Schuler, 1985).

Workload. Excessive workload is one of the most salient stressors at work (e.g., Liu et al., 2007). There are two types of workload: quantitative and qualitative workload (LaRocco, Tetrick, & Meder, 1989; Parasuraman & Purohit, 2000). Quantitative workload refers to the excessive amount of work one has. In a summary of a Chartered Institute of Personnel & Development Report from 2006, Dewe and Kompier (2008) noted that quantitative workload was one of the top three stressors workers experienced at work. Qualitative workload refers to the difficulty of work. Workload also differs by the type of the load. There are mental workload and physical workload (Dwyer & Ganster, 1991). Excessive physical workload may result in physical discomfort or illness. Excessive mental workload will cause psychological distress such as anxiety or frustration (Bowling & Kirkendall, 2012). Another factor affecting quantitative workload is interruptions (during the workday). Lin, Kain, and Fritz (2013) found that interruptions delay completion of job tasks, thus adding to the perception of workload.

Work-Family Conflict. Work-family conflict is a form of inter-role conflict in which demands from one's work domain and one's family domain are incompatible to some extent (Greenhaus & Beutell, 1985). Work can interfere with family (WIF) and/or family can interfere with work (FIW) due to time-related commitments to participating in one domain or another, incompatible behavioral expectations, or when strains in one domain carry over to the other (Greenhaus & Beutell, 1985). Work-family conflict significantly relates to work-related outcomes (e.g., job satisfaction, organizational commitment, turnover intention, burnout, absenteeism, job performance, job strains, career satisfaction, and organizational citizenship behaviors), family-related outcomes (e.g., marital satisfaction, family satisfaction, family-related performance, family-related strains), and domain-unspecific outcomes (e.g., life satisfaction, psychological strain, somatic or physical symptoms, depression, substance use or abuse, and anxiety; Amstad, Meier, Fasel, Elfering, & Semmer, 2011).

Strains. Individuals and organizations can experience work-related strains. Sometimes organizations will experience strains through the employee's negative attitudes or strains, such as that a worker's absence might yield lower production rates, which would roll up into an organizational metric of organizational performance. In the industrial and organizational (IO) psychology literature, organizational strains are mostly observed as macrolevel indicators, such as health insurance costs, accident-free days, and pervasive problems with company morale. In contrast, individual strains, usually referred to as job strains, are internal to an employee. They are responses to work conditions and relate to health and well-being of employees. In other words, "job strains are adverse reactions employees have to job stressors" (Spector, Chen, & O'Connell, 2000, p. 211). Job strains tend to fall into three categories: behavioral, physical, and psychological (Jex & Beehr, 1991).

Behavioral strains consist of actions that employees take in response to job stressors. Examples of behavioral strains include employees drinking alcohol in the workplace or intentionally calling in sick when they are not ill (Spector et al., 2000). Physical strains consist of health symptoms that are physiological in nature that employees contract in response to job stressors. Headaches and ulcers are examples of physical strains. Lastly, psychological strains are emotional reactions and attitudes that employees have in response to job stressors. Examples of psychological strains are job dissatisfaction, anxiety, and frustration (Spector et al., 2000). Interestingly, research studies that utilize self-report measures find that most job strains experienced by employees tend to be psychological strains (Spector et al., 2000).

LEADING FRAMEWORKS

Organizations that are keen on identifying organizational pain points and remedying them through organizational campaigns or initiatives often discover the pain points are rooted in work-related stressors and strains and the initiatives have to focus on reducing workers' stress and increasing a company's profitability. Through organizational climate surveys, for example, companies discover that aspects of the organization's environment, including its policies, practices, reward structures, procedures, and processes, as well as employees at all levels of the company, are contributing to the individual and organizational stress. Recent studies have even begun to examine team climates for eustress and distress assessed in terms of team members' homogenous psychological experience of vigor, efficacy, dedication, and cynicism (e.g., Kożusznik, Rodriguez, & Peiro, 2015).

Each of the frameworks presented advances different aspects that need to be identified in order to understand the source and potential remedy for stressors and strains. In some models, the focus is on resources, in others on the interaction of the person and environment, and in still others on the role of the person in the workplace. Few frameworks directly examine the role of the organization, but the organization could use these frameworks to plan interventions that would minimize stressors, cope with existing stressors, and prevent and/or manage strains. One of the leading frameworks in work stress research that is used to guide organizational interventions is the person and environment (P-E) fit (French & Caplan, 1972). Its precursor is the University of Michigan Institute for Social Research's (ISR) role stress model (Kahn, Wolfe, Quinn, Snoek, & Rosenthal, 1964) and Lewin's Field Theory. Several other theories have since evolved from the P-E fit framework, including Karasek and Theorell's (1990), Karasek (1979) Job Demands-Control Model (JD-C), the transactional framework (Lazarus & Folkman, 1984), Conservation of Resources (COR) theory (Hobfoll, 1989), and Siegrist's (1996) Effort-Reward Imbalance (ERI) Model.

Field Theory. The premise of Kahn et al.'s (1964) role stress theory is Lewin's (1997) Field Theory. Lewin purported that behavior and mental events are a dynamic function of the whole person, including a person's beliefs, values, abilities, needs, thoughts, and feelings, within a given situation (field or environment), as well as the way a person represents his or her understanding of the field and behaves in that space. Lewin explains that work-related strains are a result of individuals' subjective perceptions of objective factors, such as work roles, relationships with others in the workplace, as well as personality indicators, and can be used to predict people's reactions, including illness. Thus, to make changes to an organizational system, it is necessary to understand a field and try to move that field from the current state to the desired state. Making this move necessitates identifying mechanisms influencing individuals.

Role Stress Theory. Role stress theory mostly isolates the perspective a person has about his or her work-related responsibilities and expectations to determine how those perceptions relate with a person's work-related strains. However, those relationships have been met with somewhat varied results, which Glazer and Beehr (2005) concluded might be a function of differences in culture, an environmental factor often neglected in research. Kahn et al.'s (1964) role stress theory, coupled with Lewin's (1936) Field Theory, serves as the foundation for the P-E fit theory. Lewin (1936) wrote, "Every psychological event depends upon the state of the person and at the same time on the environment" (p. 12). Researchers of IO psychology have narrowed the environment to the organization or work team. This narrowed view of the organizational environment is evident in French and Caplan's (1972) P-E fit framework.

Person-Environment Fit Theory. The P-E fit framework focuses on the extent to which there is congruence between the person and a given environment, such as the organization (Caplan, 1987; Edwards, 2008). For example, does the person have the necessary skills and abilities to fulfill an organization's demands, or does the environment support a person's desire for autonomy (i.e., do the values align?) or fulfill a person's needs (i.e., a person's needs are rewarded). Theoretically and empirically, the greater the person-organization fit, the greater a person's job satisfaction and organizational commitment, the less a person's turnover intention and work-related stress (see meta-analyses by Assouline & Meir, 1987; Kristof-Brown, Zimmerman, & Johnson, 2005; Verquer, Beehr, & Wagner, 2003).

Job Demands-Control/Support (JD-C/S) and Job Demands-Resources (JD-R)

Model. Focusing more closely on concrete aspects of work demands and the extent to which a person perceives he or she has control or decision latitude over those demands, Karasek (1979) developed the JD-C model. Karasek and Theorell (1990) posited that high job demands under conditions of little decision latitude or control yield high strains, which have varied implications on the health of an organization (e.g., in terms of high turnover, employee ill-health, poor organizational performance). This theory was modified slightly to address not only control, but also other resources that could protect a person from unruly job demands, including support (aka JD-C/S, Johnson & Hall, 1988; and JD-R, Bakker, van Veldhoven, & Xanthopoulou, 2010). Whether focusing on control or resources, both they and job demands are said to reflect workplace characteristics, while control and resources also represent coping strategies or tools (Siegrist, 2010).

Despite the glut of research testing the JD-C and JD-R, results are somewhat mixed. Testing the interaction between job demands and control, Beehr, Glaser, Canali, and Wallwey (2001) did not find empirical support for the JD-C theory. However, Dawson, O'Brien, and Beehr (2016) found that high control and high support buffered against the independent deleterious effects of interpersonal conflict, role conflict, and organizational politics (demands that were categorized as *hindrance* stressors) on anxiety, as well as the effects of interpersonal conflict and organizational politics on physiological symptoms, but control and support did not moderate the effects between *challenge* stressors and strains. Coupled with Bakker, Demerouti, and Sanz-Vergel's (2014) note that excessive job demands are a source of strain, but increased job resources are a source of engagement, Dawson et al.'s results suggest that when an organization identifies that demands are hindrances, it can create strategies for primary (preventative) stress management interventions and attempt to remove or reduce such work demands. If the demands are challenging, though manageable, but latitude to control the challenging stressors and support are insufficient, the organization could modify practices and train employees on adopting better strategies for meeting or coping (secondary stress management intervention) with the demands. Finally, if the organization can neither afford to modify the demands or the level of control and support, it will be necessary for the organization to develop stress management (tertiary) interventions to deal with the inevitable strains.

Conservation of Resources Theory.

The idea that job resources reinforce engagement in work has been propagated in Hobfoll's (1989) Conservation of Resources (COR) theory. COR theory also draws on the foundational premise that people's mental health is a function of the person and the environment, forwarding that how people interpret their environment (including the societal context) affects their stress levels. Hobfoll focuses on resources such as objects, personal characteristics, conditions, or energies as particularly instrumental to minimizing strains. He asserts that people do whatever they can to protect their valued resources. Thus, strains develop when resources are threatened to be taken away, actually taken away, or when additional resources are not attainable after investing in the possibility of gaining more resources (Hobfoll, 2001). By extension, organizations can invest in activities that would minimize resource loss and create opportunities for resource gains and thus have direct implications for devising primary and secondary stress management interventions.

Transactional Framework. Lazarus and Folkman (1984) developed the widely studied transactional framework of stress. This framework holds as a key component the cognitive appraisal process. When individuals perceive factors in the work environment as a threat (i.e., primary appraisal), they will scan the available resources (external or internal to himself or herself) to cope with the stressors (i.e., secondary appraisal). If the coping resources provide minimal relief, strains develop. Until recently, little attention has been given to the cognitive appraisal associated with different work stressors (Dewe & Kompier, 2008; Liu & Li, 2017). In a study of Polish and Spanish social care service providers, stressors appraised as a threat related positively to burnout and less engagement, but stressors perceived as challenges yielded greater engagement and less burnout (Kożusznik, Rodriguez, & Peiro, 2012). Similarly, Dawson et al. (2016) found that even with support and control resources, hindrance demands were more strain-producing than challenge demands, suggesting that appraisal of the stressor is important. In fact, "many people respond well to challenging work" (Beehr et al., 2001, p. 126). Kożusznik et al. (2012) recommend training employees to change the way they view work demands in order to increase engagement, considering that part of the problem may be about how the person appraises his or her environment and, thus, copes with the stressors.

Effort-Reward Imbalance. Siegrist's (1996) Model of Effort-Reward Imbalance (ERI) focuses on the notion of social reciprocity, such that a person fulfills required work tasks in exchange for desired rewards (Siegrist, 2010). ERI sheds light on how an imbalance in a person's expectations of an organization's rewards (e.g., pay, bonus, sense of advancement and development, job security) in exchange for a person's efforts, that is a break in one's work contract, leads to negative responses, including long-term ill-health (Siegrist, 2010; Siegrist et al., 2014). In fact, prolonged perception of a work contract imbalance leads to adverse health, including immunological problems and inflammation, which contribute to cardiovascular disease (Siegrist, 2010). The model resembles the relational and interactional psychological contract theory in that it describes an employee's perception of the terms of the relationship between the person and the workplace, including expectations of performance, job security, training and development opportunities, career progression, salary, and bonuses (Thomas, Au, & Ravlin, 2003). The psychological contract, like the ERI model, focuses on social exchange. Furthermore, the psychological contract, like stress theories, is influenced by cultural factors that shape how people interpret their environments (Glazer, 2008; Thomas et al., 2003). Violations of the psychological contract will negatively affect a person's attitudes toward the workplace and subsequent health and well-being (Siegrist, 2010). To remediate strain, Siegrist (2010) focuses on both the person and the environment, recognizing that the organization is particularly responsible for changing unfavorable work conditions and the person is responsible for modifying his or her reactions to such conditions.

STRESS MANAGEMENT INTERVENTIONS: PRIMARY, SECONDARY, AND TERTIARY

Remediation of work stress and organizational development interventions are about realigning the employee's experiences in the workplace with factors in the environment, as well as closing the gap between the current environment and the desired environment. Work stress develops when an employee perceives the work demands to exceed the person's resources to cope and thus threatens employee well-being (Dewe & Kompier, 2008). Likewise, an organization's need to change arises when forces in the environment are creating a need to change in order to survive (see Figure 1). Lewin's (1951) Force Field Analysis, the foundations of which are in Field Theory, is one of the first organizational development intervention tools presented in the social science literature. The concept behind Force Field Analysis is that in order to survive, organizations must adapt to environmental forces driving a need for organizational change and remove restraining forces that create obstacles to organizational change. In order to do this, management needs to delineate the current field in which the organization is functioning, understand the driving forces for change, and identify and dampen or eliminate the restraining forces against change. Several models for analyses may be applied, but most approaches are variations of organizational climate surveys.

Through organizational surveys, workers provide management with a snapshot view of how they perceive aspects of their work environment. Thus, the view of the health of an organization is a function of several factors, chief among them employees' views (i.e., the climate) about the workplace (Lewin, 1951). Indeed, French and Kahn (1962) posited that well-being depends on the extent to which properties of the person and properties of the environment align in terms of what a person requires and the resources available in a given environment. Therefore, only when properties of the person and properties of the environment are sufficiently understood can plans for change be developed and implemented targeting the environment (e.g., change reporting structures to relieve, and thus prevent future, communication stressors) and/or the person (e.g., providing more autonomy, vacation days, training on new technology). In short, climate survey findings can guide consultants about the emphasis for organizational interventions: before a problem arises (aka stress prevention, e.g., carefully crafting job roles), when a problem is present, but steps are taken to mitigate their consequences (aka coping, e.g., providing social support groups), and/or once strains develop (aka stress management, e.g., healthcare management policies).

For each of the primary (prevention), secondary (coping), and tertiary (stress management) techniques the target for intervention can be the entire workforce, a subset of the workforce, or a specific person. Interventions that target the entire workforce may be considered organizational interventions, as they have direct implications on the health of all individuals and consequently the health of the organization. Several interventions categorized as primary and secondary interventions may also be implemented after strains have developed and after it has been discerned that a person or the organization did not do enough to mitigate stressors or strains (see Figure 1). The designation of many of the interventions as belonging to one category or another may be viewed as merely a suggestion.

Primary Interventions (Preventative Stress Management). Before individuals begin to perceive work-related stressors, organizations engage in stress prevention strategies, such as providing people with resources (e.g., computers, printers, desk space, information about the job role, organizational reporting structures) to do their jobs. However, sometimes the institutional structures and resources are insufficient or ambiguous. Scholars and practitioners have identified several preventative stress management strategies that may be implemented.

Planning and Time Management. When employees feel quantitatively overloaded, sometimes the remedy is improving the employees' abilities to plan and manage their time (Quick, Quick, Nelson, & Hurrell, 2003). Planning is a future-oriented activity that focuses on conceptual and comprehensive work goals. Time management is a behavior that focuses on organizing, prioritizing, and scheduling work activities to achieve short-term goals. Given the purpose of time management, it is considered a primary intervention, as engaging in time management helps to prevent work tasks from mounting and becoming unmanageable, which would subsequently lead to adverse outcomes. Time management comprises three fundamental components: (1) establishing goals, (2) identifying and prioritizing tasks to fulfill the goals, and (3) scheduling and monitoring progress toward goal achievement (Peeters & Rutte, 2005). Workers who employ time management have less role ambiguity (Macan, Shahani, Dipboye, & Philips, 1990), psychological stress or strain (Adams & Jex, 1999; Jex & Elaqua, 1999; Macan et al., 1990), and greater job satisfaction (Macan, 1994). However, Macan (1994) did not find a relationship between time management and performance. Still, Claessens, van Eerde, Rutte, and Roe (2004) found that perceived control of time partially mediated the relationships between planning behavior (an indicator of time management), job autonomy, and workload on one hand, and job strains, job satisfaction, and job performance on the other hand. Moreover, Peeters and Rutte (2005) observed that teachers with high work demands and low autonomy experienced more burnout when they had poor time management skills.

Person-Organization Fit. Just as it is important for organizations to find the right person for the job and organization, so is it the responsibility of a person to choose to work at the right organization—an organization that fulfills the person's needs and upholds the values important to the individual, as much as the person fulfills the organization's needs and adapts to its values. When people fit their employing organizations they are setting themselves up for experiencing less strain-producing stressors (Kristof-Brown et al., 2005). In a meta-analysis of 62 person-job fit studies and 110 person-organization fit studies, Kristof-Brown et al. (2005) found that person-job fit had a negative correlation with indicators of job strain. In fact, a primary intervention of career counseling can help to reduce stress levels (Firth-Cozens, 2003).

Job Redesign. The Job Demands-Control/Support (JD-C/S), Job Demands-Resources (JD-R), and transactional models all suggest that factors in the work context require modifications in order to reduce potential ill-health and poor organizational performance. Drawing on Hackman and Oldham's (1980) Job Characteristics Model, it is possible to assess with the Job Diagnostics Survey (JDS) the current state of work characteristics related to skill variety, task identity, task significance, autonomy, and feedback. Modifying those aspects would help create a sense of meaningfulness, sense of responsibility, and feeling of knowing how one is performing, which subsequently affects a person's well-being as identified in assessments of motivation, satisfaction, improved performance, and reduced withdrawal intentions and behaviors. Extending this argument to the stress models, it can be deduced that reducing uncertainty or perceived unfairness that may be associated with a person's perception of these work characteristics, as well as making changes to physical characteristics of the environment (e.g., lighting, seating, desk, air quality), nature of work (e.g., job responsibilities, roles, decision-making latitude), and organizational arrangements (e.g., reporting structure and feedback mechanisms), can help mitigate against numerous ill-health consequences and reduced organizational performance. In fact, Fried et al. (2013) showed that healthy patients of a medical clinic whose jobs were excessively low (i.e., monotonous) or excessively high (i.e., overstimulating) on job enrichment (as measured by the JDS) had greater abdominal obesity than those whose jobs were optimally enriched. By taking stock of employees' perceptions of the current work situation, managers might think about ways to enhance employees' coping toolkit, such as training on how to deal with difficult clients or creating stimulating opportunities when jobs have low levels of enrichment.

Participatory Action Research Interventions. Participatory action research (PAR) is an intervention wherein, through group discussions, employees help to identify and define problems in organizational structure, processes, policies, practices, and reward structures, as well as help to design, implement, and evaluate success of solutions. PAR is in itself an intervention, but its goal is to design interventions to eliminate or reduce work-related factors that are impeding performance and causing people to be unwell. An example of a successful primary intervention, utilizing principles of PAR and driven by the JD-C and JD-C/S stress frameworks is Health Circles (HCs; Aust & Ducki, 2004).

HCs, developed in Germany in the 1980s, were popular practices in industries, such as metal, steel, and chemical, and service. Similar to other problem-solving practices, such as quality circles, HCs were based on the assumptions that employees are the experts of their jobs. For this reason, to promote employee well-being, management and administrators solicited suggestions and ideas from the employees to improve occupational health, thereby increasing employees' job control. HCs also promoted communication between managers and employees, which had a potential to increase social support. With more control and support, employees would experience less strains and better occupational well-being.

Employing the three-steps of (1) problem analysis (i.e., diagnosis or discovery through data generated from organizational records of absenteeism length, frequency, rate, and reason and employee survey), (2) HC meetings (6 to 10 meetings held over several months to brainstorm ideas to improve occupational safety and health concerns identified in the discovery phase), and (3) HC evaluation (to determine if desired changes were accomplished and if employees' reports of stressors and strains changed after the course of 15 months), improvements were to be expected (Aust & Ducki, 2004). Aust and Ducki (2004) reviewed 11 studies presenting 81 health circles in 30 different organizations. Overall study participants had high satisfaction with the HCs practices. Most companies acted upon employees' suggestions (e.g., improving driver's seat and cab, reducing ticket sale during drive, team restructuring and job rotation to facilitate communication, hiring more employees during summer time, and supervisor training program to improve leadership and communication skills) to improve work conditions. Thus, HCs represent a successful theory-grounded intervention to routinely improve employees' occupational health.

Physical Setting. The physical environment or physical workspace has an enormous impact on individuals' well-being, attitudes, and interactions with others, as well as on the implications on innovation and well-being (Oksanen & Ståhle, 2013; Vischer, 2007). In a study of 74 new product development teams (total of 437 study respondents) in Western Europe, Chong, van Eerde, Rutte, and Chai (2012) found that when teams were faced with challenge time pressures, meaning the teams had a strong interest and desire in tackling complex, but engaging tasks, when they were working proximally close with one another, team communication improved. Chong et al. assert that their finding aligns with prior studies that have shown that physical proximity promotes increased awareness of other team members, greater tendency to initiate conversations, and greater team identification. However, they also found that when faced with hindrance time pressures, physical proximity related to low levels of team communication, but when hindrance time pressure was low, team proximity had an increasingly greater positive relationship with team communication.

In addition to considering the type of work demand teams must address, other physical workspace considerations include whether people need to work collaboratively and synchronously or independently and remotely (or a combination thereof). Consideration needs to be given to how company contributors would satisfy client needs through various modes of communication, such as email versus telephone, and whether individuals who work by a window might need shading to block bright sunlight from glaring on their computer screens. Finally, people who have to use the telephone for extensive periods of time would benefit from earphones to prevent neck strains. Most physical stressors are rather simple to rectify. However, companies are often not aware of a problem until after a problem arises, such as when a person's back is strained from trying to move heavy equipment. Companies then implement strategies to remediate the environmental stressor. With the help of human factors, and organizational and office design consultants, many of the physical barriers to optimal performance can be prevented (Rousseau & Aubé, 2010). In a study of 215 French-speaking Canadian healthcare employees, Rousseau and Aubé (2010) found that although supervisor instrumental support positively related with affective commitment to the organization, the relationship was even stronger for those who reported satisfaction with the ambient environment (i.e., temperature, lighting, sound, ventilation, and cleanliness).

Secondary Interventions (Coping).   Secondary interventions, also referred to as coping, focus on resources people can use to mitigate the risk of work-related illness or workplace injury. Resources may include properties related to social resources, behaviors, and cognitive structures. Each of these resource domains may be employed to cope with stressors. Monat and Lazarus (1991) summarize the definition of coping as "an individual's efforts to master demands (or conditions of harm, threat, or challenge) that are appraised (or perceived) as *exceeding* or *taxing* his or her resources" (p. 5). To master demands requires use of the aforementioned resources. Secondary interventions help employees become aware of the psychological, physical, and behavioral responses that may occur from the stressors presented in their working environment. Secondary interventions help a person detect and attend to stressors and identify resources for and ways of mitigating job strains. Often, coping strategies are learned skills that have a cognitive foundation and serve important functions in improving people's management of stressors (Lazarus & Folkman, 1991). Coping is effortful, but with practice it becomes easier to employ. This idea is the foundation for understanding the role of resilience in coping with stressors. However, "not all adaptive processes are coping. Coping is a subset of adaptational activities that involves effort and does not include everything that we do in relating to the environment" (Lazarus & Folkman, 1991, p. 198). Furthermore, sometimes to cope with a stressor, a person may call upon social support sources to help with tangible materials or emotional comfort. People call upon support resources because they help to restructure how a person approaches or thinks about the stressor.

Most secondary interventions are aimed at helping the individual, though companies, as a policy, might require all employees to partake in training aimed at increasing employees' awareness of and skills aimed at handling difficult situations vis-à-vis company channels (e.g., reporting on sexual harassment or discrimination). Furthermore, organizations might institute mentoring programs or work groups to address various work-related matters. These programs employ awareness-raising activities, stress-education, or skills training (cf., Bhagat, Segovis, & Nelson, 2012), which include development of skills in problem-solving, understanding emotion-focused coping, identifying and using social support, and enhancing capacity for resilience. The aim of these programs, therefore, is to help employees proactively review their perceptions of psychological, physical, and behavioral job-related strains, thereby extending their resilience, enabling them to form a personal plan to control stressors and practice coping skills (Cooper, Dewe, & O'Driscoll, 2011).

Often these stress management programs are instituted after an organization has observed excessive absenteeism and work-related performance problems and, therefore, are sometimes categorized as a tertiary stress management intervention or even a primary (prevention) intervention. However, the skills developed for coping with stressors also place the programs in secondary stress management interventions. Example programs that are categorized as tertiary or primary stress management interventions may also be secondary stress management interventions (see Figure 1), and these include lifestyle advice and planning, stress inoculation training, simple relaxation techniques, meditation, basic trainings in time management, anger management, problem-solving skills, and cognitive-behavioral therapy. Corporate wellness programs also fall under this category. In other words, some programs could be categorized as primary, secondary, or tertiary interventions depending upon when the employee (or organization) identifies the need to implement the program. For example, time management practices could be implemented as a means of preventing some stressors, as a way to cope with mounting stressors, or as a strategy to mitigate symptoms of excessive stressors. Furthermore, these programs can be administered at the individual level or group level. As related to secondary interventions, these programs provide participants with opportunities to develop and practice skills to cognitively reappraise the stressor(s); to modify their perspectives about stressors; to take time out to breathe, stretch, meditate, relax, and/or exercise in an attempt to support better decision-making; to articulate concerns and call upon support resources; and to know how to say "no" to onslaughts of requests to complete tasks. Participants also learn how to proactively identify coping resources and solve problems.

According to Cooper, Dewe, and O'Driscoll (2001), secondary interventions are successful in helping employees modify or strengthen their ability to cope with the experience of stressors with the goal of mitigating the potential harm the job stressors may create. Secondary interventions focus on individuals' transactions with the work environment and emphasize the fit between a person and his or her environment. However, researchers have pointed out that the underlying assumption of secondary interventions is that the responsibility for coping with the stressors of the environment lies within individuals (Quillian-Wolever & Wolever, 2003). If companies cannot prevent the stressors in the first place, then they are, in part, responsible for helping individuals develop coping strategies and informing employees about programs that would help them better cope with job stressors so that they are able to fulfill work assignments.

Stress management interventions that help people learn to cope with stressors focus mainly on the goals of enabling problem-resolution or expressing one's emotions in a healthy manner. These goals are referred to as problem-focused coping and emotion-focused coping (Folkman & Lazarus, 1980; Pearlin & Schooler, 1978), and the person experiencing the stressors as potential threat is the agent for change and the recipient of the benefits of successful coping (Hobfoll, 1998). In addition to problem-focused and emotion-focused coping approaches, social support and resilience may be coping resources. There are many other sources for coping than there is room to present here (see e.g., Cartwright & Cooper, 2005); however, the current literature has primarily focused on these resources.

Problem-Focused Coping. Problem-focused or direct coping helps employees *remove* or *reduce stressors* in order to reduce their strain experiences (Bhagat et al., 2012). In problem-focused coping employees are responsible for working out a strategic plan in order to remove job stressors, such as setting up a set of goals and engaging in behaviors to meet these goals. Problem-focused coping is viewed as an adaptive response, though it can also be maladaptive if it creates more problems down the road, such as procrastinating getting work done or feigning illness to take time off from work. Adaptive problem-focused coping negatively relates to long-term job strains (Higgins & Endler, 1995). Discussion on problem-solving coping is framed from an adaptive perspective.

Problem-focused coping is featured as an extension of control, because engaging in problem-focused coping strategies requires a series of acts to keep job stressors under control (Bhagat et al., 2012). In the stress literature, there are generally two ways to categorize control: internal versus external locus of control, and primary versus secondary control. Locus of control refers to the extent to which people believe they have control over their own life (Rotter, 1966). People high in internal locus of control believe that they can control their own fate whereas people high in external locus of control believe that outside factors determine their life experience (Rotter, 1966). Generally, those with an external locus of control are less inclined to engage in problem-focused coping (Strentz & Auerbach, 1988). Primary control is the belief that people can directly influence their environment (Alloy & Abramson, 1979), and thus they are more likely to engage in problem-focused coping. However, when it is not feasible to exercise primary control, people search for secondary control, with which people try to adapt themselves into the objective environment (Rothbaum, Weisz, & Snyder, 1982).

Emotion-Focused Coping. Emotion-focused coping, sometimes referred to as palliative coping, helps employees reduce strains without the removal of job stressors. It involves cognitive or emotional efforts, such as talking about the stressor or distracting oneself from the stressor, in order to lessen emotional distress resulting from job stressors (Bhagat et al., 2012). Emotion-focused coping aims to reappraise and modify the perceptions of a situation or seek emotional support from friends or family. These methods do not include efforts to change the work situation or to remove the job stressors (Lazarus & Folkman, 1991). People tend to adopt emotion-focused coping strategies when they believe that little or nothing can be done to remove the threatening, harmful, and challenging stressors (Bhagat et al., 2012), such as when they are the only individuals to have the skills to get a project done or they are given increased responsibilities because of the unexpected departure of a colleague. Emotion-focused coping strategies include (1) reappraisal of the stressful situation, (2) talking to friends and receiving reassurance from them, (3) focusing on one's strength rather than weakness, (4) optimistic comparison—comparing one's situation to others' or one's past situation, (5) selective ignoring—paying less attention to the unpleasant aspects of one's job and being more focused on the positive aspects of the job, (6) restrictive expectations—restricting one's expectations on job satisfaction but paying more attention to monetary rewards, (7) avoidance coping—not thinking about the problem, leaving the situation, distracting oneself, or using alcohol or drugs (e.g., Billings & Moos, 1981).

Some emotion-focused coping strategies are maladaptive. For example, avoidance coping may lead to increased level of job strains in the long run (e.g., Parasuraman & Cleek, 1984). Furthermore, a person's ability to cope with the imbalance of performing work to meet organizational expectations can take a toll on the person's health, leading to physiological consequences such as cardiovascular disease, sleep disorders, gastrointestinal disorders, and diabetes (Fried et al., 2013; Siegrist, 2010; Toker, Shirom, Melamed, & Armon, 2012; Willert, Thulstrup, Hertz, & Bonde, 2010).

Comparing Coping Strategies Across Cultures. Most coping research is conducted in individualistic, Western cultures wherein emotional control is emphasized and both problem-solving focused coping and primary control are preferred (Bhagat et al., 2010). However, in collectivistic cultures, emotion-focused coping and use of secondary control may be preferred and may not necessarily carry a negative evaluation (Bhagat et al., 2010). For example, African Americans are more likely to use emotion-focused coping than non–African Americans (Knight, Silverstein, McCallum, & Fox, 2000), and among women who experienced sexual harassment, Anglo American women were less likely to employ emotion focused coping (i.e., avoidance coping) than Turkish women and Hispanic American women, while Hispanic women used more denial than the other two groups (Wasti & Cortina, 2002).

Thus, whereas problem-focused coping is venerated in Western societies, emotion-focused coping may be more effective in reducing strains in collectivistic cultures, such as China, Japan, and India (Bhagat et al., 2010; Narayanan, Menon, & Spector, 1999; Selmer, 2002). Indeed, Swedish participants reported more problem-focused coping than did Chinese participants (Xiao, Ottosson, & Carlsson, 2013), American college students engaged in more problem-focused coping behaviors than did their Japanese counterparts (Ogawa, 2009), and Indian (vs. Canadian) students reported more emotion-focused coping, such as seeking social support and positive reappraisal (Sinha, Willson, & Watson, 2000). Moreover, Glazer, Stetz, and Izso (2004) found that internal locus of control was more predominant in individualistic cultures (United Kingdom and United States), whereas external locus of control was more predominant in communal cultures (Italy and Hungary). Also, internal locus of control was associated with less job stress, but more so for nurses in the United Kingdom and United States than Italy and Hungary. Taken together, adoption of coping strategies and their effectiveness differ significantly across cultures. The extent to which a coping strategy is perceived favorably and thus selected or not selected is not only a function of culture, but also a person's sociocultural beliefs toward the coping strategy (Morimoto, Shimada, & Ozaki, 2013).

Social Support. Social support refers to the aid an entity gives to a person. The source of the support can be a single person, such as a supervisor, coworker, subordinate, family member, friend, or stranger, or an organization as represented by upper-level management representing organizational practices. The type of support can be instrumental or emotional. Instrumental support, including informational support, refers to that which is tangible, such as data to help someone make a decision or colleagues' sick days so one does not lose vital pay while recovering from illness. Emotional support, including esteem support, refers to the psychological boost given to a person who needs to express emotions and feel empathy from others or to have his or her perspective validated. Beehr and Glazer (2001) present an overview of the role of social support on the stressor-strain relationship and arguments regarding the role of culture in shaping the utility of different sources and types of support.

Meaningfulness and Resilience. Meaningfulness reflects the extent to which people believe their lives are significant, purposeful, goal-directed, and fulfilling (Glazer, Kożusznik, Meyers, & Ganai, 2014). When faced with stressors, people who have a strong sense of meaning in life will also try to make sense of the stressors. Maintaining a positive outlook on life stressors helps to manage emotions, which is helpful in reducing strains, particularly when some stressors cannot be problem-solved (Lazarus & Folkman, 1991). Lazarus and Folkman (1991) emphasize that being able to reframe threatening situations can be just as important in an adaptation as efforts to control the stressors. Having a sense of meaningfulness motivates people to behave in ways that help them overcome stressors. Thus, meaningfulness is often used in the same breath as resilience, because people who are resilient are often protecting that which is meaningful.

Resilience is a personality state that can be fortified and enhanced through varied experiences. People who perceive their lives are meaningful are more likely to find ways to face adversity and are therefore more prone to intensifying their resiliency. When people demonstrate resilience to cope with noxious stressors, their ability to be resilient against other stressors strengthens because through the experience, they develop more competencies (Glazer et al., 2014). Thus, fitting with Hobfoll's (1989, 2001) COR theory, meaningfulness and resilience are psychological resources people attempt to conserve and protect, and employ when necessary for making sense of or coping with stressors.

Tertiary Interventions (Stress Management).

Stress management refers to interventions employed to treat and repair harmful repercussions of stressors that were not coped with sufficiently. As Lazarus and Folkman (1991) noted, not all stressors "are amenable to mastery" (p. 205). Stressors that are unmanageable and lead to strains require interventions to reverse or slow down those effects. Workplace interventions might focus on the person, the organization, or both. Unfortunately, instead of looking at the whole system to include the person and the workplace, most companies focus on the person. Such a focus should not be a surprise given the results of van der Klink, Blonk, Schene, and van Dijk's (2001) meta-analysis of 48 experimental studies conducted between 1977 and 1996. They found that of four types of tertiary interventions, the effect size for cognitive-behavioral interventions and multimodal programs (e.g., the combination of assertive training and time management) was moderate and the effect size for relaxation techniques was small in reducing psychological complaints, but not turnover intention related to work stress. However, the effects of (the five studies that used) organization-focused interventions were not significant. Similarly, Richardson and Rothstein's (2008) meta-analytic study, including 36 experimental studies with 55 interventions, showed a larger effect size for cognitive-behavioral interventions than relaxation, organizational, multimodal, or alternative. However, like with van der Klink et al. (2001), Richardson and Rothstein (2008) cautioned that there were few organizational intervention studies included and the impact of interventions was determined on the basis of psychological outcomes and not physiological or organizational outcomes. Van der Klink et al. (2001) further expressed concern that organizational interventions target the workplace and that changes in the individual may take longer to observe than individual interventions aimed directly at the individual.

The long-term benefits of individual-focused interventions are not yet clear either. Per Giga, Cooper, and Faragher (2003), the benefits of person-directed stress management programs will be short-lived if organizational factors to reduce stressors are not addressed too. Indeed, LaMontagne, Keegel, Louie, Ostry, and Landsbergis (2007), in their meta-analysis of 90 studies on stress management interventions published between 1990 and 2005, revealed that in relation to interventions targeting organizations only, and interventions targeting individuals only, interventions targeting both organizations and individuals (i.e. the systems approach) had the most favorable positive effects on both the organizations and the individuals. Furthermore, the organization-level interventions were effective at both the individual and organization levels, but the individual-level interventions were effective only at the individual level.

Individual-Focused Stress Management. Individual-focused interventions concentrate on improving conditions for the individual, though counseling programs emphasize that the worker is in charge of reducing "stress," whereas role-focused interventions emphasize activities that organizations can guide to actually reduce unnecessary noxious environmental factors.

Individual-Focused Stress Management: Employee Assistance Programs. When stress becomes sufficiently problematic (which is individually gauged or attended to by supportive others) in a worker's life, employees may utilize the short-term counseling services or referral services Employee Assistance Programs (EAPs) provide. People who utilize the counseling services may engage in cognitive behavioral therapy aimed at changing the way people think about the stressors (e.g., as challenge opportunity over threat) and manage strains. Example topics that may be covered in these therapy sessions include time management and goal setting (prioritization), career planning and development, cognitive restructuring and mindfulness, relaxation, and anger management. In a study of healthcare workers and teachers who participated in a 2–2.5-day comprehensive stress management training program (including 26 topics on identifying, coping with, and managing stressors and strains), Siu, Cooper, and Phillips (2013) found psychological and physical improvements were self-reported among the healthcare workers (for which there was no control group). However, comparing an intervention group of teachers to a control group of teachers, the extent of change was not as visible, though teachers in the intervention group engaged in more mastery recovery experiences (i.e., they purposefully chose to engage in challenging activities after work).

Individual-Focused Stress Management: Mindfulness. A popular therapy today is to train people to be more mindful, which involves helping people live in the present, reducing negative judgment of current and past experiences, and practicing patience (Birnie, Speca, & Carlson, 2010). Mindfulness programs usually include training on relaxation exercises, gentle yoga, and awareness of the body's senses. In one study offered through the continuing education program at a Canadian university, 104 study participants took part in an 8-week, 90-minute per group (15–20 participants per) session mindfulness program (Birnie et al., 2010). In addition to body scanning, they also listened to lectures on incorporating mindfulness into one's daily life and received a take-home booklet and compact discs that guided participants through the exercises studied in person. Two weeks after completing the program, participants' mindfulness attendance and general positive moods increased, while physical, psychological, and behavioral strains decreased. In another study on a sample of U.K. government employees, study participants receiving three sessions of 2.5 to 3 hours each training on mindfulness, with the first two sessions occurring in consecutive weeks and the third occurring about 3 months later, Flaxman and Bond (2010) found that compared to the control group, the intervention group showed a decrease in distress levels from Time 1 (baseline) to Time 2 (3 months after first two training sessions) and Time 1 to Time 3 (after final training session). Moreover, of the mindfulness intervention study participants who were clinically distressed, 69% experienced clinical improvement in their psychological health.

Individual-Focused Stress Management: Biofeedback/Imagery/Meditation/Deep Breathing. Biofeedback uses electronic equipment to inform users about how their body is responding to tension. With guidance from a therapist, individuals then learn to change their physiological responses so that their pulse normalizes and muscles relax (Norris, Fahrion, & Oikawa, 2007). The therapist's guidance might include reminders for imagery, meditation, body scan relaxation, and deep breathing. Saunders, Driskell, Johnston, and Salas's (1996) meta-analysis of 37 studies found that imagery helped reduce state and performance anxiety. Once people have been trained to relax, reminder triggers may be sent through smartphone push notifications (Villani et al., 2013).

Smartphone technology can also be used to support weight loss programs, smoking cessation programs, and medication or disease (e.g., diabetes) management compliance (Heron & Smyth, 2010; Kannampallil, Waicekauskas, Morrow, Kopren, & Fu, 2013). For example, smartphones could remind a person to take medications or test blood sugar levels or send messages about healthy behaviors and positive affirmations.

Individual-Focused Stress Management: Sleep/Rest/Respite. Workers today sleep less per night than adults did nearly 30 years ago (Luckhaupt, Tak, & Calvert, 2010; National Sleep Foundation, 2005, 2013). In order to combat problems, such as increased anxiety and cardiovascular artery disease, associated with sleep deprivation and insufficient rest, it is imperative that people disconnect from their work at least one day per week or preferably for several weeks so that they are able to restore psychological health (Etzion, Eden, & Lapidot, 1998; Ragsdale, Beehr, Grebner, & Han, 2011). When college students engaged in relaxation-type activities, such as reading or watching television, over the weekend, they experienced less emotional exhaustion and greater general well-being than students who engaged in resources-consuming activities, such as house cleaning (Ragsdale et al., 2011). Additional research and future directions for research are reviewed and identified in the work of Sonnentag (2012). For example, she asks whether lack of ability to detach from work is problematic for people who find their work meaningful. In other words, are negative health consequences only among those who do not take pleasure in their work? Sonnetag also asks how teleworkers detach from their work when engaging in work from the home. Ironically, one of the ways that companies are trying to help with the challenges of high workload or increased need to be available to colleagues, clients, or vendors around the globe is by offering flexible work arrangements, whereby employees who can work from home are given the opportunity to do so. Companies that require global interactions 24 hours per day often employ this strategy, but is the solution also a source of strain (Glazer, Kożusznik, & Shargo, 2012)?

Individual-Focused Stress Management: Role Analysis.   Role analysis or role clarification aims to redefine, expressly identify, and align employees' roles and responsibilities with their work goals. Through role negotiation, involved parties begin to develop a new formal or informal contract about expectations and define resources needed to fulfill those expectations. Glazer has used this approach in organizational consulting and, with one memorable client engagement, found that not only were the individuals whose roles required deeper re-evaluation happier at work (6 months later), but so were their subordinates. Subordinates who once characterized the two partners as hostile and akin to a couple going through a bad divorce, later referred to them as a blissful pair. Schaubroeck, Ganster, Sime, and Ditman (1993) also found in a three-wave study over a 2-year period that university employees' reports of role clarity and greater satisfaction with their supervisor increased after a role clarification exercise of top managers' roles and subordinates' roles. However, the intervention did not have any impact on reported physical symptoms, absenteeism, or psychological well-being. Role analysis is categorized under individual-focused stress management intervention because it is usually implemented after individuals or teams begin to demonstrate poor performance and because the intervention typically focuses on a few individuals rather than an entire organization or group. In other words, the intervention treats the person's symptoms by redefining the role so as to eliminate the stimulant causing the problem.

Organization-Focused Stress Management.   At the organizational level, companies that face major declines in productivity and profitability or increased costs related to health care and disability might be motivated to reassess organizational factors that might be impinging on employees' health and well-being. After all, without healthy workers, it is not possible to have a healthy organization. Companies may choose to implement practices and policies that are expected to help not only the employees, but also the organization with reduced costs associated with employee ill-health, such as medical insurance, disability payments, and unused office space. Example practices and policies that may be implemented include flexible work arrangements to ensure that employees are not on the streets in the middle of the night for work that can be done from anywhere (such as the home), diversity programs to reduce stress-induced animosity and prejudice toward others, providing only healthy food choices in cafeterias, mandating that all employees have physicals in order to receive reduced prices for insurance, company-wide closures or mandatory paid time off, and changes in organizational visioning.

Organization-Focused Stress Management: Organizational-Level Occupational Health Interventions.   As with job design interventions that are implemented to remediate work characteristics that were a source of unnecessary or excessive stressors, so are organizational-level occupational health (OLOH) interventions. As with many of the interventions, its placement as a primary or tertiary stress management intervention may seem arbitrary, but when considering the goal and target of change, it is clear that the intervention is implemented in response to some ailing organizational issues that need to be reversed or stopped, and because it brings in the entire organization's workforce to address the problems, it has been placed in this category. There are several more case studies than empirical studies on the topic of whole system organizational change efforts (see example case studies [http://www.hse.gov.uk/stress/casestudies.htm] presented by the United Kingdom's Health and Safety Executive). It is possible that lack of published empirical work is not so much due to lack of attempting to gather and evaluate the data for publication, but rather because the OLOH interventions themselves never made it to the intervention stage, the interventions failed (Biron, Gatrell, & Cooper, 2010), or the level of evaluation was not rigorous enough to get into empirical peer-review journals. Fortunately, case studies provide some indication of the opportunities and problems associated with OLOH interventions.

One case study regarding Cardiff and Value University Health Board revealed that through focus group meetings with members of a steering group (including high-level managers and supported by top management) and facilitated by a neutral, non-judgmental organizational health consultant, ideas for change were posted on newsprint, discussed, and areas in the organization needing change were identified. The intervention for giving voice to people who initially had little already had a positive effect on the organization, as absence decreased by 2.09% and 6.9% merely 12 and 18 months, respectively, after the intervention. Translated in financial terms, the 6.9% change was equivalent to a quarterly savings of £80,000 (Health & Safety Executive, n.d.). Thus, focusing on the context of change and how people will be involved in the change process probably helped the organization realize improvements (Biron et al., 2010). In a recent and rare empirical study, employing both qualitative and quantitative data collection methods, Sørensen and Holman (2014) utilized PAR in order to plan and implement an OLOH intervention over the course of 14 months. Their study aimed to examine the effectiveness of the PAR process in reducing workers' work-related and social or interpersonal-related stressors that derive from the workplace and improving psychological, behavioral, and physiological well-being across six Danish organizations. Based on group dialogue, 30 proposals for change were proposed, all of which could be categorized as either interventions to focus on relational factors (e.g., management feedback improvement, engagement) or work processes (e.g., reduced interruptions, workload, reinforcing creativity). Of the interventions that were implemented, results showed improvements on manager relationship quality and reduced burnout, but no changes with respect to work processes (i.e., workload and work pace) perhaps because the employees already had sufficient task control and variety. These findings support Dewe and Kompier's (2008) position that occupational health can be reinforced through organizational policies that reinforce quality jobs and work experiences.

Organization-Focused Stress Management: Flexible Work Arrangements.   Dewe and Kompier (2008), citing the work of Isles (2005), noted that concern over losing one's job is a reason for why 40% of survey respondents indicated they work more hours than formally required. In an attempt to create balance and perceived fairness in one's compensation for putting in extra work hours, employees will sometimes be legitimately or illegitimately absent. As companies become increasingly global, many people with desk jobs are finding themselves communicating with colleagues who are halfway around the globe and at all hours of the day or night (Glazer et al., 2012). To help minimize the strains associated with these stressors, companies might devise flexible work arrangements (FWA), though the type of FWA needs to be tailored to the cultural environment (Masuda et al., 2012). FWAs give employees some leverage to decide what would be the optimal work arrangement for them (e.g., part-time, flexible work hours, compressed work week, telecommuting). In other words, FWA provides employees with the choice of when to work, where to work (on-site or off-site), and how many hours to work in a day, week, or pay period (Kossek, Thompson, & Lautsch, 2015). However, not all employees of an organization have equal access to or equitable use of FWAs; workers in low-wage, hourly jobs are often beholden to being physically present during specific hours (Swanberg McKechnie, Ojha, & James, 2011). In a study of over 1,300 full-time hourly retail employees in the United States, Swanberg et al. (2011) showed that employees who have control over their work schedules and over their work hours were satisfied with their work schedules, perceived support from the supervisor, and work engagement.

Unfortunately, not all FWAs yield successful results for the individual or the organization. Being able to work from home or part-time can have problems too, as a person finds himself or herself working more hours from home than required. Sometimes telecommuting creates work-family conflict too as a person struggles to balance work and family obligations while working from home. Other drawbacks include reduced face-to-face contact between work colleagues and stakeholders, challenges shaping one's career growth due to limited contact, perceived inequity if some have more flexibility than others, and ambiguity about work role processes for interacting with employees utilizing the FWA (Kossek et al., 2015). Organizations that institute FWAs must carefully weigh the benefits and drawbacks the flexibility may have on the employees using it or the employees affected by others using it, as well as the implications on the organization, including the vendors who are serving and clients served by the organization.

Organization-Focused Stress Management: Diversity Programs. Employees in the workplace might experience strain due to feelings of discrimination or prejudice. Organizational climates that do not promote diversity (in terms of age, religion, physical abilities, ethnicity, nationality, sex, and other characteristics) are breeding grounds for undesirable attitudes toward the workplace, lower performance, and greater turnover intention (Bergman, Palmieri, Drasgow, & Ormerod, 2012; Velez, Moradi, & Brewster, 2013). Management is thus advised to implement programs that reinforce the value and importance of diversity, as well as manage diversity to reduce conflict and feelings of prejudice. In fact, managers who attended a leadership training program reported higher multicultural competence in dealing with stressful situations (Chrobot-Mason & Leslie, 2012), and managers who persevered through challenges were more dedicated to coping with difficult diversity issues (Cilliers, 2011). Thus, diversity programs can help to reduce strains by directly reducing stressors associated with conflict linked to diversity in the workplace and by building managers' resilience.

Organization-Focused Stress Management: Healthcare Management Policies. Over the past few years, organizations have adopted insurance plans that implement wellness programs for the sake of managing the increasing cost of health care that is believed to be a result of individuals' not managing their own health, with regular check-ups and treatment. The wellness programs require all insured employees to visit a primary care provider, complete a health risk assessment, and engage in disease management activities as specified by a physician (e.g., see frequently asked questions regarding the State of Maryland's Wellness Program). Companies believe that requiring compliance will reduce health problems, although there is no proof that such programs save money or that people would comply. One study that does, however, boast success, was a 12-week workplace health promotion program aimed at reducing Houston airport workers' weight (Ebunlomo, Hare-Everline, Weber, & Rich, 2015). The program, which included 235 volunteer participants, was deemed a success, as there was a total weight loss of 345 pounds (or 1.5 lbs per person). Given such results in Houston, it is clear why some people are also skeptical over the likely success of wellness programs, particularly as there is no clear method for evaluating their efficacy (Sinnott & Vatz, 2015).

Moreover, for some, such a program is too paternalistic and intrusive, as well as punishes anyone who chooses not to actively participate in disease management programs (Sinnott & Vatz, 2015). The programs put the onus of change on the person, though it is a response to the high costs of ill-health. The programs neglect to consider the role of the organization in reducing the barriers to healthy lifestyle, such as cloaking exempt employment as simply needing to get the work done, when it usually means working significantly more hours than a standard workweek. In fact, workplace health promotion programs did not reduce presenteeism (i.e., people going to work while unwell thereby reducing their job performance) among those who suffered from physical pain (Cancelliere, Cassidy, Ammendolia, & Côte, 2011). However, supervisor education, worksite exercise, lifestyle intervention through email, midday respite from repetitive work, a global stress management program, changes in lighting, and telephone interventions helped to reduce presenteeism. Thus, emphasis needs to be placed on psychosocial aspects of the organization's structure, including managers and overall organizational climate for on-site presence, that reinforces such behavior (Cancelliere et al., 2011). Moreover, wellness programs are only as good as the interventions to reduce work-related stressors and improve organizational resources to enable workers to improve their overall psychological and physical health.

CONCLUDING REMARKS

Future Research.   One of the areas requiring more theoretical and practical attention is that of the utility of stress frameworks to guide organizational development change interventions. Although it has been proposed that the foundation for work stress management interventions is in organizational development, and even though scholars and practitioners of organization development were also founders of research programs that focused on employee health and well-being or work stress, there are few studies or other theoretical works that link the two bodies of literature.

A second area that requires additional attention is the efficacy of stress management interventions across cultures. In examining secondary stress management interventions (i.e., coping), some cross-cultural differences in findings were described; however, there is still a dearth of literature from different countries on the utility of different prevention, coping, and stress management strategies.

A third area that has been blossoming since the start of the 21st century is the topic of hindrance and challenge stressors and the implications of both on workers' well-being and performance. More research is needed on this topic in several areas. First, there is little consistency by which researchers label a stressor as a hindrance or a challenge. Researchers sometimes take liberties with labels, but it is not the researchers who should label a stressor but the study participants themselves who should indicate if a stressor is a source of strain. Rodríguez, Kozusznik, and Peiró (2013) developed a measure in which respondents indicate whether a stressor is a challenge or a hindrance. Just as some people may perceive demands to be challenges that they savor and that result in a psychological state of eustress (Nelson & Simmons, 2003), others find them to be constraints that impede goal fulfillment and thus might experience distress. Likewise, some people might perceive ambiguity as a challenge that can be overcome and others as a constraint over which he or she has little control and few or no resources with which to cope. More research on validating the measurement of challenge versus hindrance stressors, as well as eustress versus distress, and savoring versus coping, is warranted. Second, at what point are challenge stressors harmful? Just because people experiencing challenge stressors continue to perform well, it does not necessarily mean that they are healthy people. A great deal of stressors are intellectually stimulating, but excessive stimulation can also take a toll on one's physiological well-being, as evident by the droves of professionals experiencing different kinds of diseases not experienced as much a few decades ago, such as obesity (Fried et al., 2013). Third, which stress management interventions would better serve to reduce hindrance stressors or to reduce strain that may result from challenge stressors while reinforcing engagement-producing challenge stressors?

A fourth area that requires additional attention is that of the flexible work arrangements (FWAs). One of the reasons companies have been willing to permit employees to work from home is not so much out of concern for the employee, but out of the company's need for the focal person to be able to communicate with a colleague working from a geographic region when it is night or early morning for the focal person. Glazer, Kożusznik, and Shargo (2012) presented several areas for future research on this topic, noting that by participating on global virtual teams, workers face additional stressors, even while given flexibility of workplace and work time. As noted earlier, more research needs to be done on the extent to which people who take advantage of FWAs are advantaged in terms of detachment from work. Can people working from home detach? Are those who find their work invigorating also likely to experience ill-health by not detaching from work?

A fifth area worthy of further research attention is workplace wellness programing. According to Page and Vella-Brodrick (2009), "subjective and psychological well-being [are] key criteria for employee mental health" (p. 442), whereby mental health focuses on wellness, rather than the absence of illness. They assert that by fostering employee mental health, organizations are supporting performance and retention. Employee well-being can be supported by ensuring that jobs are interesting and meaningful, goals are achievable, employees have control over their work, and skills are used to support organizational and individual goals (Dewe & Kompier, 2008). However, just as mental health is not the absence of illness, work stress is not indicative of an absence of psychological well-being. Given the perspective that employee well-being is a state of mind (Page & Vella-Brodrick, 2009), we suggest that employee well-being can be negatively affected by noxious job stressors that cannot be remediated, but when job stressors are preventable, employee well-being can serve to protect an employee who faces job stressors. Thus, wellness programs ought to focus on providing positive experiences by enhancing and promoting health, as well as building individual resources. These programs are termed "green cape" interventions (Pawelski, 2016). For example, with the growing interests in positive psychology, researchers and practitioners have suggested employing several positive psychology interventions, such as expressing gratitude, savoring experiences, and identifying one's strengths (Tetrick & Winslow, 2015). Another stream of positive psychology is psychological capital, which includes four malleable functions of self-efficacy, optimism, hope, and resilience (Luthans, Youssef, & Avolio, 2007). Workplace interventions should include both "red cape" interventions (i.e., interventions to reduce negative experiences) and "green cape" interventions (i.e., workplace wellness programs; Polly, 2014).

A Healthy Organization's Pledge. A healthy workplace requires healthy workers. Period. Among all organizations' missions should be the focus on a healthy workforce. To maintain a healthy workforce, the company must routinely examine its own contributions in terms of how it structures itself; how it reinforces communications among employees, vendors, and clients; how it rewards and cares for its people (e.g., ensuring they get sufficient rest and can detach from work); and the extent to which people at the upper levels are truly connected with the people at the lower levels. As a matter of practice, management must recognize when employees are overworked, unwell, and poorly engaged. Management must also take stock of when it is doing well and right by its contributors and maintain and reinforce the good practices, norms, and procedures. People in the workplace make the rules; people in the workplace can change the rules. How management sees its employees and values their contribution will have a huge role in how a company takes stock of its own pain points. Providing employees with tools to manage their own reactions to work-related stressors and consequent strains is fine, but wouldn't it be grand if organizations took better notice about what they could do to mitigate the strain-producing stressors in the first place and take ownership over how employees are treated?

REFERENCES

Abramis, D. J. (1994). Work role ambiguity, job satisfaction, and job performance: Meta-analyses and review. *Psychological Report, 75*, 1411–1433.

Adams, G. A., & Jex, S. M. (1999). Relationships between time management, control, work–family conflict, and strain. *Journal of Occupational Health Psychology, 1*, 72–77.

Alloy, L. B., & Abramson, L. Y. (1979). Judgment of contingency in depressed and nondepressed students: Sadder but wiser? *Journal of Experimental Psychology: General, 108*, 441–483.

Amstad, F. T., Meier, L. L., Fasel, U., Elfering, A., & Semmer, N. K. (2011). A meta-analysis of work-family conflict and various outcomes with a special emphasis on cross-domain versus matching-domain relations. *Journal of Occupational Health Psychology, 16*, 151–169.

Assouline, M., & Meir, E. I. (1987). Meta-analysis of the relationship between congruence and well-being measures. *Journal of Vocational Behavior, 31*, 319–332.

Aust, B., & Ducki, A. (2004). Comprehensive health promotion interventions at the workplace: Experiences with health circles in Germany. *Journal of Occupational Health Psychology, 9*, 258–270.

Bakker, A. B. Demerouti, E., Sanz-Vergel, A. I. (2014). Burnout and work engagement: The JD-R approach. *Annual Review of Organizational Behavior, 1*, 389–411.

Bakker, A. B., van Veldhoven, M. J. P. M., & Xanthopoulou, D. (2010). Beyond the demand-control model: Thriving on high job demands and resources. *Journal of Personnel Psychology, 9*, 3–16.

Beehr, T. A., Glaser, K. M., Canali, K. G., & Wallwey, D. A. (2001). Back to basics: Re-examination of demand control theory of occupational stress. *Work & Stress, 15*, 115–130.

Beehr, T. A., & Glazer, S. (2001). A cultural perspective of social support in relation to occupational stress. In P. Perrewé, D. C. Ganster, & J. Moran (Eds.), *Research in occupational stress and well-being* (pp. 97–142). Amsterdam: JAI Press.

Bergman, M. E., Palmieri, P. A., Drasgow, F., & Ormerod, A. J. (2012). Racial/ethnic harassment and discrimination, its antecedents, and its effect on job-related outcomes. *Journal of Occupational Health Psychology, 17*, 65–78.

Bhagat, R. S., Krishnan, B., Nelson, T. A., Leonard, K. M., Ford, D. J., & Billing, T. K. (2010). Organizational stress, psychological strain, and work outcomes in six national contexts: A closer look at the moderating influences of coping styles and decision latitude. *Cross Cultural Management, 17*, 10–29. http://www .dx.doi.org/10.1108/13527601011016880

Bhagat, R. S., O'Driscoll, M. P., Babakus, E., Frey, L., Chokkar, J., Ninokumar, B. H., et al. (1994). Organizational stress and coping in seven national contexts: A cross-cultural investigation. In G. P. Keita & J. J. Hurrell (Eds.), *Job stress in a changing workforce: Investigating gender, diversity, and family issues* (pp. 93–105). Washington, DC: American Psychological Association. http://dx.doi.org/10.1037/10165-006

Bhagat, R. S., Segovis, J. C., & Nelson, T. A. (2012). *Work stress and coping in the era of globalization.* New York: Routledge.

Billings, A. G., & Moos, R. H. (1981). The role of coping responses and social resources in attenuating the stress of life events. *Journal of Behavioral Medicine, 4*, 139–157.

Birnie, K., Speca, M., & Carlson, L. E. (2010). Exploring self-compassion and empathy in the context of mindfulness-based stress reduction (MBSR). *Stress & Health, 26*, 359–371.

Biron, C., Gatrell, C., & Cooper, C. L. (2010). Autopsy of a failure: Evaluating process and contextual issues in an organizational-level work stress intervention. *International Journal of Stress Management, 17*, 135–158.

Bowling, N. A., & Kirkendall, C. (2012). Workload: A review of causes, consequences, and potential interventions. In J. Houdmont, S. Leka, & R. Sinclair (Eds.), *Contemporary occupational health psychology* (Vol. 2) (pp. 221–238). Chichester, U.K.: Wiley.

Breaugh, J. A., & Colihan, J. P. (1994). Measuring facets of job ambiguity: Construct validity evidence. *Journal of Applied Psychology, 79*, 191–202.

Bruk-Lee, V., & Spector, P. E. (2006). The social stressors-counterproductive work behaviors link: Are conflicts with supervisors and coworkers the same? *Journal of Occupational Health Psychology, 11*, 145–156. http://dx.doi.org/10.1037/1076-8998.11.2.145

Cancelliere, C., Cassidy, J. D., Ammendolia, C., & Côte, P. (2011). Are workplace health promotion programs effective at improving presenteeism in workers? A systematic review and best evidence synthesis of the literature. *BMC Public Health, 11*, 395–406.

Caplan, R. D. (1987). Person–environment fit in organizations: Theories, facts, and values. In A. W. Riley & S. J. Zaccaro (Eds.), *Occupational stress and organizational effectiveness* (pp. 103–140). New York: Praeger.

Cartwright, S., & Cooper, C. L. (2005). Individually targeted interventions. In J. Barling, E. K. Kelloway, & M. R. Frone (Eds.), *Handbook of work stress* (pp. 607–622). Thousand Oaks, CA: SAGE.

Cavanaugh, M. A., Boswell, W. R., Roehling, M. V., & Boudreau, J. W. (2000). An empirical examination of self-reported work stress among U.S. managers. *Journal of Applied Psychology, 85*, 65–74. http://dx.doi .org/10.1037/0021-9010.85.1.65

Chong, D. S. F., van Eerde, W., Rutte, C. G., & Chai, K. H. (2012). Bringing employees closer: The effect of proximity on communication when teams function under time pressure. *Journal of Product Innovation Management, 29*, 205–215.

Chrobot-Mason, D., & Leslie, J. B. (2012). The role of multicultural competence and emotional intelligence in managing diversity. *Psychologist-Manager Journal, 15*, 219–236.

Cilliers, F. (2011). Individual diversity management and salutogenic functioning. *International Review of Psychiatry, 23*, 501–507.

Claessens, B. C., Van Eerde, W., Rutte, C. G., & Roe, R. A. (2004). Planning behavior and perceived control of time at work. *Journal of Organizational Behavior, 25*, 937–950. http://www.dx.doi.org/10.1002/job.292

Cooper, C. L., Dewe, P. D., & O'Driscoll, M. P. (2011). Employee assistance programs: Strengths, challenges, and future roles. In J. C. Quick & L. E. Tetrick (Eds.), *Handbook of occupational health psychology* (2d ed.) (pp. 337–356). Washington, DC: American Psychological Association.

Cooper, C. L., Dewe, P. J., & O'Driscoll, M. P. (2001). *Organizational stress: A review and critique of theory, research, and applications.* Thousand Oaks, CA: SAGE.

Coovert, M. D. & Thompson, L. F. (2003). Technology and workplace health. In J. C. Quick & L. E. Tetrick (Eds.), *Handbook of occupational health psychology* (pp. 221–241). Washington, DC: American Psychological Association.

Dawson, K. M., O'Brien, K. E., & Beehr, T. A. (2016). The role of hindrance stressors in the job demand-control-support model of occupational stress: A proposed theory revision. *Journal of Organizational Behavior, 37*(3), 397–415. http://dx.doi.org/proxy-ub.researchport.umd.edu/10.1002/job.2049

Dewe, P., & Kompier, M. (2008). *Foresight mental capital and wellbeing project: Wellbeing and work: Future challenges.* London: The Government Office for Science.

Dopkeen, J. C., & DuBois, R. (2014). *Stress in the workplace: A policy synthesis on its dimensions and prevalence.* White paper. University of Illinois Chicago, Center for Employee Health Studies, School of Public Health. http://hdl.handle.net/10027/18751

Dwyer, D. J., & Ganster, D. C. (1991). The effects of job demands and control on employee attendance and satisfaction. *Journal of Organizational Behavior, 12*, 595–608.

Ebunlomo, E. O., Hare-Everline, N., Weber, A., & Rich, J. (2015). Development of a comprehensive 12-week health promotion program for Houston Airport System. *Texas Public Health Journal, 67*(1), 11–13.

Edwards, J. R. (2008). Person-environment fit in organizations: An assessment of theoretical progress. *The Academy of Management Annals, 2*, 167–230.

Etzion, D., Eden, D., & Lapidot, Y. (1998). Relief from job stressors and burnout: Reserve service as a respite. *Journal of Applied Psychology, 83*, 577–585.

Firth-Cozens, J. (2003). Doctors, their wellbeing, and their stress: It's time to be proactive about stress— and prevent it. *British Medical Journal, 326*, 670–671.

Flaxman, P. E., & Bond, F. W. (2010). Worksite stress management training: Moderated effects and clinical significance. *Journal of Occupational Health Psychology, 15*, 347–358.

Folkman, S., & Lazarus, R. S. (1980). An analysis of coping in a middle-aged community sample. *Journal of Health and Social Behavior, 21*, 219–239. http://dx.doi.org/10.2307/2136617

French, J. R. P., Jr., & Caplan, R. D. (1972). Organizational stress and individual strain. In A. Marrow (Ed.), *The failure of success.* New York: AMACOM.

French, J. R. P., Jr., & Kahn, R. L. (1962). A programmatic approach to studying the industrial environment and mental health. *Journal of Social Issues, 18*, 1–48.

French, S. (2015, May 27). *PCS workload and work-life balance survey 2013.* London: Public and Commercial Services Union. http://pcs.org.uk/download.cfm?docid=451A8ABE-D3A8-4FDA-8149C0320A91CCA6

Fried, Y., Laurence, G. A., Shirom, A., Melamed, S., Toker, S., Berliner, S., & Shapira, I. (2013). The relationship between job enrichment and abdominal obesity: A longitudinal field study of apparently healthy individuals. *Journal of Occupational Health Psychology, 18*, 458–468.

Frone, M. R. (2000). Interpersonal conflict at work and psychological outcomes: Testing a model among young workers. *Journal of Occupational Health Psychology, 5*, 246–255.

Giga, S. I., Cooper, C. L., & Faragher, B. (2003). The development of a framework for a comprehensive approach to stress management interventions at work. *International Journal of Stress Management, 10,* 280–296.

Glazer, S. (2008). Cross-cultural issues in stress and burnout. In J. R. B. Halbesleben (Ed.), *Handbook of stress and burnout in health care* (pp. 79–93). Huntington, NY: Nova Science Publishers.

Glazer, S., & Beehr, T. A. (2005). Consistency of the implications of three role stressors across four countries. *Journal of Organizational Behavior, 26,* 467–487.

Glazer, S., Kożusznik, M. W., Meyers, J. H., & Ganai, O. (2014). Cultural implications of meaningfulness as a resource to mitigate work stress. In S. Leka & R. Sinclair (Eds.), *Contemporary occupational health psychology: Global perspectives on research and practice* (Vol. 3) (pp. 114–130). Hoboken, NJ: Wiley.

Glazer, S., Kożusznik, M. W., & Shargo, I. A. (2012). Global virtual teams: A cure for—or a cause of—stress. In P. L. Perrewé, J. Halbesleben, & C. Rosen (Eds.), *Research in occupational stress and well being: The role of the economic context on occupational stress and well being* (Vol. 10, pp. 213–266). Bingley, U.K.: Emerald.

Glazer, S., Stetz, T. A., & Izso, L. (2004). Effects of personality on subjective job stress: A cultural analysis. *Personality and Individual Differences, 37,* 645–658.

Greenhaus, J. H., & Beutell, N. J. (1985). Sources of conflict between work and family roles. *Academy of Management Review, 10,* 76–88.

Hackman, J. R., & Oldham, G. R. (1980). *Work redesign.* Reading, MA: Addison-Wesley.

Hauke, A., Flintrop, J., Brun, E., & Rugulies, R. (2011). The impact of work-related psychosocial stressors on the onset of musculoskeletal disorders in specific body regions: A review and meta-analysis of 54 longitudinal studies. *Work & Stress, 25,* 243–256. http://www.dx.doi.org/10.1080/02678373.2011.614069

Health & Safety Executive (n.d.). *Cardiff and Value University Health Board—A stress case study.* http://www.hse.gov.uk/stress/casestudies/cardiff-vale-university-health.htm

Heron, K. E., & Smyth, J. M. (2010). Ecological momentary interventions: Incorporating mobile technology into psychosocial and health behaviour treatments. *British Journal of Health Psychology, 15,* 1–39.

Hershcovis, M. (2011). "Incivility, social undermining, bullying…oh my!": A call to reconcile constructs within workplace aggression research. *Journal of Organizational Behavior, 32,* 499–519. http://www.dx.doi.org/10.1002/job.689

Higgins, J. E., & Endler, N. S. (1995). Coping, life stress, and psychological and somatic distress. *European Journal of Personality, 9,* 253–270. http://www.dx.doi.org/10.1002/per.2410090403

Hobfoll, S. E. (1989). Conservation of resources: A new attempt at conceptualizing stress. *American Psychologist, 44,* 513–524.

Hobfoll, S. E. (1998). *Stress, culture, and community: The psychology and philosophy of stress.* New York: Plenum Press.

Hobfoll, S. E. (2001). The influence of culture, community, and the nested-self in the stress process: Advancing Conservation of Resources Theory. *Applied Psychology: An International Review, 50,* 337–421.

International Labour Organization. (2012, July 5). Why stress at work matters. International Labour Organization. http://www.ilo.org/global/about-the-ilo/newsroom/comment-analysis/WCMS_184786/lang--en/index.htm

International Labour Organization. (n.d.). Psychosocial risks and work-related stress. International Labour Organization. http://www.ilo.org/safework/areasofwork/workplace-health-promotion-and-well-being/WCMS_108557/lang--en/index.htm

Jackson, S. E., & Schuler, R. S. (1985). A meta-analysis and conceptual critique of research on role ambiguity and role conflict in work settings. *Organizational Behavior and Human Decision Processes, 36,* 16–78.

Jayson, S. (2012, January 11). Yeah, we're stressed but dealing with it; Americans report a decrease in stress for the first time in five years, maybe because it's just the new normal. *USA Today.* http://www.lexisnexis.com.proxy-ub.researchport.umd.edu/lnacui...1255%2Fformatted_doc&fromCart=false&jobHandle=2827%3A526151255

Jex, S. M., & Beehr, T. A. (1991). Emerging theoretical and methodological issues in the study of work-related stress. *Research in Personnel and Human Resources Management, 9,* 311–365.

Jex, S. M., & Elaqua, T. C. (1999). Time management as a moderator of relations between stressors and employee strain. *Work & Stress, 13,* 182–191.

Johnson, J. V., & Hall, E. M. (1988). Job strain, workplace social support, and cardiovascular disease: A cross-sectional study of a random sample of the Swedish working population. *American Journal of Public Health, 78,* 1336–1342.

Kahn, R. L., Wolfe, D. M., Quinn, R. P., Snoek, J. D., & Rosenthal, R. A. (1964). *Organizational stress: Studies in role conflict and ambiguity.* New York: Wiley.

Kannampallil, T. G., Waicekauskas, K., Morrow, D. G., Kopren, K. M., & Fu, W. (2013). External tools for collaborative medication scheduling. *Cognition, Technology & Work, 15,* 121–131.

Karasek, R. A. (1979). Job demands, job decision latitude, and mental strain: Implications for job redesign. *Administrative Science Quarterly, 24,* 285–308.

Karasek, R. A., & Theorell, T. (1990). *Healthy work: Stress, productivity, and the reconstruction of working life.* New York: Basic Books.

van der Klink, J. J. L., Blonk, R. W. B., Schene, A. H., & van Dijk, F. J. H. (2001). The benefits of interventions for work-related stress. *American Journal of Public Health, 91,* 270–276.

Knight, B. G., Silverstein, M., McCallum, T. J., & Fox, L. S. (2000). A sociocultural stress and coping model for mental health outcomes among African American caregivers in southern California. *The Journals of Gerontology: Series B: Psychological Sciences and Social Sciences, 55B,* 142–150. http://www.dx.doi .org/10.1093/geronb/55.3.P142

Kossek, E. E., Thompson, R. J., Lautsch, B. A. (2015). Balanced workplace flexibility: Avoiding the traps. *California Management Review, 57,* 5–25.

Kożusznik, M., Rodriguez, I., & Peiró, J. M. (2012). Cross-national outcomes of stress appraisal. *Cross Cultural Management, 19,* 507–525.

Kożusznik, M., Rodriguez, I., & Peiró, J. M. (2015). Eustress and distress climates in teams: Patterns and outcomes. *International Journal of Stress Management, 22,* 1–23.

Kristof-Brown, A. L., Zimmerman, R. D., & Johnson, E. C. (2005). Consequences of individuals' fit at work: A meta-analysis of person-job, person-organization, person-group, and person-supervisor fit. *Personnel Psychology, 58,* 281–342.

LaMontagne, A. D., Keegel, T., Louie, A. M., Ostry, A., & Landsbergis, P. A. (2007). A systematic review of the job-stress intervention evaluation literature, 1990–2005. *International Journal of Occupational and Environmental Health, 13,* 268–280.

LaRocco, J. M., Tetrick, L. E., & Meder, D. (1989). Differences in perceptions of work environment conditions, job attitudes, and health beliefs among military physicians, dentists, and nurses. *Military Psychology, 1,* 135–151.

Lazarus, R. S., & Folkman, S. (1984). *Stress, appraisal, and coping.* New York: Springer.

Lazarus, R. S., & Folkman, S. (1991). The concept of coping. In A. Monat & R. S. Lazarus (Eds.), *Stress and coping: An anthology* (3d ed.) (pp. 189–206). New York: Columbia University Press.

LePine, J. A., Podsakoff, N. P., & LePine, M. A. (2005). A meta-analytic test of the challenge stressor-hindrance stressor framework: An explanation for inconsistent relationships among stressors and performance. *Academy of Management Journal, 48,* 764–775.

Lewin, K. (1936). *Principles of topological psychology.* New York: McGraw-Hill.

Lewin K. (1951). *Field theory in social science.* New York: Harper and Row.

Lewin, K. (1997). *Resolving social conflicts & Field theory in social science.* Washington, DC: American Psychological Association. Previously published in 1948 and 1951.

Lin, B. C., Kain, J. M., & Fritz, C. (2013). Don't interrupt me! An examination of the relationship between intrusions at work and employee strain. *International Journal of Stress Management, 20,* 77–94.

Liu, C., & Li, H. (2017) Stressor and stressor appraisals: The moderating effect of task efficacy. *Journal of Business and Psychology*, 1–14. http://www.dx.doi.org/10.1007/s10869-016-9483-4

Liu, C., Liu, Y., Spector, P. E., Shi, L. (2011). The interaction of job autonomy and conflict with supervisor in China and the United States: A qualitative and quantitative comparison. *International Journal of Stress Management, 18,* 222–245.

Liu, C., Spector, P. E., & Shi, L. (2007). Cross-national job stress: A quantitative and qualitative study. *Journal of Organizational Behavior, 28,* 209–239.

Luckhaupt, S. E., Tak, S., Calvert, G. M. (2010). The prevalence of short sleep duration by industry and occupation in the National Health Interview Survey. *Sleep, 33,* 149–159.

Luthans, F., Youssef, C. M., & Avolio, B. J. (2007). *Psychological capital: Developing the human competitive edge.* New York: Oxford University Press.

Macan, T. H. (1994). Time management: Test of a process model. *Journal of Applied Psychology, 79,* 381–391.

Macan, T. H., Shahani, C., Dipboye, R. L., & Philips, A. P. (1990). College students' time management: Correlations with academic performance and stress. *Journal of Educational Psychology, 82,* 760–768.

Masuda, A. D., Poelmans, S. A. Y., Allen, T. D., Spector, P. E., Lapierre, L. M., Cooper, C. L., et al. (2012). Flexible work arrangements availability and their relationship with work-to-family conflict, job satisfaction, and turnover intentions: A comparison of three country clusters. *Applied Psychology: An International Review, 61,* 1–29.

McMahon, M. (2007). Think you might be addicted to email? You're not alone. AOL. http://ir.aol.com/phoenix.zhtml?c=147895&p=irol-newsArticle&ID=1354021

Monat, A., & Lazarus, R. S. (Eds.). (1991). *Stress and coping: An anthology* (3d ed.). New York: Columbia University Press.

Morimoto, H., Shimada, H., & Ozaki, K. (2013). Does stressor evaluation mediate sociocultural influence on coping selection? An investigation using Japanese employees. *International Journal of Stress Management, 20,* 1–19.

Narayanan, L., Menon, S., & Spector, P. E. (1999). A cross-cultural comparison of job stressors and reactions among employees holding comparable jobs in two countries. *International Journal of Stress Management, 6,* 197–212.

National Sleep Foundation. (2005). Segment profiles. National Sleep Foundation. http://www.sleepfoundation.org/sites/default/files/Sleep_Segments.pdf

National Sleep Foundation. (2013). How much sleep do adults need? National Sleep Foundation. http://www.sleepfoundation.org/article/white-papers/how-much-sleep-do-adults-need

Nelson, D. L., & Simmons, B. L. (2003). Health psychology and work stress: A more positive approach. In J. C. Quick & L. E. Tetrick (Eds.), *Handbook of occupational health psychology* (pp. 97–119). Washington, DC: American Psychological Association.

Norris, P. A., Fahrion, S. L., & Oikawa, L. O. (2007). Autogenic biofeedback training in psychophysiological therapy and stress management. In P. M. Lehrer, R. L. Woolfolk, & W. E. Sime (Eds.), *Principles and practices of stress management* (3d ed., pp. 175–205). New York: Guilford.

Ogawa, N. (2009). Stress, coping behavior, and social support in Japan and the United States. *Dissertation Abstracts International Section A, 69,* 3802.

Oksanen, K., & Ståhle, P. (2013). Physical environment as a source for innovation: Investigating the attributes of innovative space. *Journal of Knowledge Management, 17,* 815–827.

Page, K. M., & Vella-Brodrick, D. A. (2009). The "what," "why" and "how" of employee well-being: A new model. *Social Indicators Research, 90,* 441–458.

Parasuraman, S., & Cleek, M. A. (1984). Coping behaviors and managers' affective reactions to role stressors. *Journal of Vocational Behavior, 24,* 179–193. http://www.dx.doi.org/10.1016/0001-8791(84)90005-8

Parasuraman, S., & Purohit, Y. S. (2000). Distress and boredom among orchestra musicians: The two faces of stress. *Journal of Occupational Health Psychology, 5*, 74–83.

Pawelski, J. O. (2016). Defining the "positive" in positive psychology: Part II. A normative analysis. *Journal of Positive Psychology, 11*, 357–365. http://www.dx.doi.org/10.1080/17439760.2015.1137628

Pearlin, L. I., & Schooler, C. (1978). The structure of coping. *Journal of Health and Social Behavior, 19*, 2–21. http://dx.doi.org/10.2307/2136319

Peeters, M. A. G., & Rutte, C. G. (2005). Time management behavior as a moderator for the job demand-control interaction. *Journal of Occupational Health Psychology, 1*, 64–75.

Peters, L. H., & O'Connor, E. J. (1980). Situational constraints and work outcomes: The influence of a frequently overlooked construct. *Academy of Management Review, 5*, 391–397.

Peters, L. H., & O'Connor, E. J. (1988). Measuring work obstacles: Procedures, issues, and implications. In F. D. Schoorman & B. Schneider (Eds.), *Facilitating work effectiveness* (pp. 105–123). Lexington, MA: Lexington Books.

Polly, S. (2014, July 2). Workplace well-being is not an oxymoron. *Positive Psychology News Daily.* http://www.positivepsychologynews.com/news/shannon-polly/2014070229282

Quick, C. J., Quick, J. D., Nelson, D. L., & Hurrell, J. J. (2003). *Preventive stress management in organizations.* Washington, DC: APA.

Quillian-Wolever, R. E., & Wolever, M. E. (2003). Stress management at work. In J. C. Quick & L. E. Tetrick (Eds.), *Handbook of occupational health psychology* (pp. 355–375). Washington, DC: American Psychological Association. http://dx.doi.org/10.1037/10474-017

Ragsdale, J. M., Beehr, T. A., Grebner, S., & Han, K. (2011). An integrated model of weekday stress and weekend recovery of students. *International Journal of Stress Management, 18*, 153–180.

Richardson, K. M., & Rothstein, H. R. (2008). Effects of occupational stress management intervention programs: A meta-analysis. *Journal of Occupational Health Psychology, 13*, 69–93.

Rodríguez, I., Kozusznik, M. W., & Peiró, J. M. (2013). Development and validation of the Valencia Eustress-Distress Appraisal Scale. *International Journal of Stress Management, 20*, 279–308.

Rothbaum, F., Weisz, J. R., & Snyder, S. S. (1982). Changing the world and changing the self: A two-process model of perceived control. *Journal of Personality and Social Psychology, 42*, 5–37.

Rotter, J. B. (1966). Generalized expectancies for internal versus external control of reinforcement. *Psychological Monographs, 80*, 609.

Rousseau, V., & Aubé, C. (2010). Social support at work and affective commitment to the organization: The moderating effect of job resource adequacy and ambient conditions. *Journal of Social Psychology, 150*, 321–340.

Saunders, T., Driskell, J. E., Johnston, J., & Salas, E. (1996). The effect of stress inoculation training on anxiety and performance. *Journal of Occupational Health Psychology, 1*, 170–186.

Schaubroeck, J., Ganster, D. C., Sime, W. E., & Ditman, D. (1993). A field experiment testing supervisory role clarification. *Personnel Psychology, 46*, 1–25.

Selmer, J. (2002). Coping strategies applied by Western vs overseas Chinese business expatriates in China. *International Journal of Human Resource Management, 13*, 19–34.

Siegrist, J. (1996). Adverse health effects of high effort/low reward conditions. *Journal of Occupational Health Psychology, 1*, 27–41.

Siegrist, J. (2010). Effort-reward imbalance at work and cardiovascular diseases. *International Journal of Occupational Medicine and Environmental Health, 23*, 279–285.

Siegrist, J., Dragano, N., Nyberg, S. T., Lunau, T., Alfredsson, L., Erbel, R., et al. (2014). Validating abbreviated measures of effort-reward imbalance at work in European cohort studies: The IPD-Work consortium. *International Archives of Occupational and Environmental Health, 87*, 249–256.

Sinha, B. K., Willson, L. R., & Watson, D. C. (2000). Stress and coping among students in India and Canada. *Canadian Journal of Behavioural Science/Revue canadienne des sciences du comportement, 32*(4), 218–225. http://dx.doi.org/10.1037/h0087118

Sinnott, J., & Vatz, R. E. (2015, March 13). Maryland doesn't trust state employees to manage their health. *Baltimore Sun*. http://www.baltimoresun.com/news/opinion/oped/bs-ed-wellness-program-20150315 -story.html

Siu, O. L., Cooper, C. L., & Phillips, D. R. (2013, July 1). Intervention studies on enhancing work well-being, reducing burnout, and improving recovery experiences among Hong Kong health care workers and teachers. *International Journal of Stress Management, 21*, 69–84. http://dx.doi.org/10.1037 /a0033291

Sonnentag, S. (2012). Psychological detachment from work during leisure time: The benefits of mentally disengaging from work. *Current Directions in Psychological Science, 21*, 114–118.

Sørensen, O. H., & Holman, D. (2014). A participative intervention to improve employee well-being in knowledge work jobs: A mixed-methods evaluation study. *Work & Stress, 28*, 67–86.

Spector, P. E., Chen, P. Y., & O'Connell, B. J. (2000). A longitudinal study of relations between job stressors and job strains while controlling for prior negative affectivity and strains. *Journal of Applied Psychology, 85*, 211–218.

Spector, P. E., & Jex, S. M. (1998). Development of four self-report measures of job stressors and strains: Interpersonal Conflict at Work Scale, Organizational Constraints Scale, Quantitative Workload Inventory, and Physical Symptoms Inventory. *Journal of Occupational Health Psychology, 3*, 356–367.

State of Maryland. (n.d.). Wellness program frequently asked questions. Maryland.gov. http://www.dbm .maryland.gov/benefits/Documents/Wellness%20Program%20FAQ.pdf

Strentz, T., & Auerbach, S. M. (1988). Adjustment to the stress of simulated captivity: Effects of emotion-focused versus problem-focused preparation on hostages differing in locus of control. *Journal of Personality and Social Psychology, 55*, 652–660. http://dx.doi.org/10.1037/0022-3514.55.4.652

Swanberg, J. E., McKechnie, S. P., Ojha, M. U., & James, J. B. (2011). Schedule control, supervisor support and work engagement: A winning combination for workers in hourly jobs? *Journal of Vocational Behavior, 79*, 613–624.

Tarafdar, M., Tu, Q., Ragu-Nathan, B. S., & Ragu-Nathan, T. (2007). The impact of technostress on role stress and productivity. *Journal of Management Information Systems, 24*, 301–328.

Tepper, B. J., & Henle, C. A. (2011). A case for recognizing distinctions among constructs that capture interpersonal mistreatment in work organizations. *Journal of Organizational Behavior, 32*, 487–498. http:// www.dx.doi.org/10.1002/job.688

Tetrick, L. E., & Winslow, C. J. (2015). Workplace stress management interventions and health promotion. *Annual Review of Organizational Psychology and Organizational Behavior, 2*, 583–603.

Thomas, D. C., Au, K., & Ravlin, E. C. (2003). Cultural variation and the psychological contract. *Journal of Organizational Behavior, 24*, 451–471.

Toker, S., Shirom, A., Melamed, S., & Armon, G. (2012). Work characteristics as predictors of diabetes incidence among apparently healthy employees. *Journal of Occupational Health Psychology, 17*, 259–267.

Velez, B. L., Moradi, B., & Brewster, M. E. (2013). Testing the tenets of minority stres theory in workplace contexts. *Journal of Counseling Psychology, 60*, 532–542.

Verquer, M. L., Beehr, T. A., & Wagner, S. H. (2003). A meta-analysis of relations between person–organization fit and work attitudes. *Journal of Vocational Behavior, 63*, 473–489.

Villani, D., Grassi, A., Cognetta, C., Toniolo, D., Cipresso, P., & Riva, G. (2013). Self-help stress management training through mobile phones: An experience with oncology nurses. *Psychological Services, 10*, 315–322.

Vischer, J. C. (2007). The effects of the physical environment on job performance: Towards a theoretical model of workspace stress. *Stress & Health, 23*, 175–184.

Wasti, S. A., & Cortina, L. M. (2002). Coping in context: Sociocultural determinants of responses to sexual harassment. *Journal of Personality and Social Psychology, 83*, 394–405. http://dx.doi.org/10.1037/0022 -3514.83.2.394

Willert, M. V., Thulstrup, A. M., Hertz, J., & Bonde, J. P. (2010). Sleep and cognitive failures improved by a three-month stress management intervention. *International Journal of Stress Management, 17*, 193–213. http://dx.doi.org/10.1037/a0019612

Xiao, Q., Ottosson, I., & Carlsson, I. (2013). Stressors and coping strategies in Chinese and Swedish students at a Swedish university. *Chinese Journal of Clinical Psychology, 21*, 309–312.

Sharon Glazer and Cong Liu

BULLYING AND HARASSMENT IN THE WORKPLACE

INTRODUCTION

Exposure to systematic and ongoing mistreatment, abuse, ostracism, and victimization by colleagues and superiors at work, often denoted as exposure to workplace bullying and harassment, has been thoroughly documented to cause a wide range of negative outcomes for those targeted. These outcomes include mental and physical health problems (Conway et al., 2018; Verkuil et al., 2015), reduced job satisfaction and organizational commitment (Nielsen & Einarsen, 2012), and even risk of expulsion from working life (Glambek et al., 2015). Studies have also shown how it may negatively and severely afflict bystanding colleagues, the organization itself, and even the society at large (Hoel et al., 2020; Mikkelsen et al., 2020). Prevalence rates are now relatively well-established across the globe (Van de Vliert et al., 2013), affecting some 3%–20% of the working population (Nielsen et al., 2010; Zapf et al., 2020).

Carroll M. Brodsky was among the first to describe the phenomenon, based on employee complaints filed in California and Nevada in the 1970s, in his 1976 book entitled *The Harassed Worker*. Brodsky described five types of such harassment, namely, scapegoating, name-calling, physical abuse, sexual harassment, and work pressure. Systematic research first appeared from the mid-1990s, much inspired by the pioneering work of Heinz Leymann (1990b), who in his role as an inspector in the Swedish labor Inspectorate came across a similar phenomenon, which he labeled "adult mobbing." Common for all these accounts was the repeated and persistent exposure to negative, unwanted, and illegitimate behaviors at work, behaviors that placed targets in a cornered position with few resources to defend themselves, resulting in vast negative outcomes for those exposed, even resulting in severe stigma and victimization (Brodsky, 1976). Since the turn of the millennium, research and public interest has exploded all over the globe, making workplace bullying and harassment one of the most studied phenomena in contemporary work and organizational psychology. This article will review the burgeoning literature to summarize existing knowledge on workplace bullying and harassment's nature, outcomes, and antecedents and risk factors.

THE CONCEPT OF WORKPLACE BULLYING AND HARASSMENT: THE NAME OF THE GAME

While *mobbing* has been the term used in many European countries, *workplace bullying* has been the most widely used term in the English-speaking countries as well as in the scholarly literature, at least within the European research tradition (see Einarsen et al., 2020), with *harassment* typically being used in official and legal documents to secure a wide definition of the behaviors and situations involved. Yet, as interest spread around the globe and ever more nuanced knowledge emerged on its many shapes and shades, a range of labels have been presented to describe various aspects of the underlying phenomenon, including *mistreatment, undermining, emotional abuse, scapegoating, victimization,* and *incivility* to name but a few (see Notelaers & Van der Heijden, 2021, for an overview). The introduction of such a plethora of concepts and terms has especially been characteristic of the North American literature, creating some confusion and lack of a coherent literature in the field (see Keashly et al., 2020, for an overview). Yet, while there most certainly may be some nuances to these concepts and their foci, they all refer to situations of systematic and ongoing unwanted, negative, illegitimate, and unnecessary behaviors in the working environment, directed at one or more employees by their peers or superiors, deeply resented by the recipient(s), and in breach of ethical and even legal norms of proper workplace conduct.

One of the most well-established and widely accepted definitions of workplace bullying has been presented by the first author and colleagues (Einarsen et al., 2003, 2020, p. 26):

> Bullying at work means harassing, offending, socially excluding someone or negatively affecting someone's work. In order for the label bullying (or mobbing) to be applied to a particular activity, interaction or process it has to occur repeatedly and regularly (e.g., weekly) and over a period of time (e.g., about 6 months). Bullying is an escalating process in the course of which the person confronted may end up in an inferior position becoming the target of systematic negative social acts. A conflict cannot be called bullying if the incident is an isolated event or if two parties of approximately equal "strength" are in conflict.

A core element in this definition is the "systematic negative social acts." These acts may be direct—including verbal abuse, accusations, and public humiliation—but also more subtle and indirect, including gossiping, rumor spreading, and social non-inclusion (Einarsen et al., 2009; Notelaers et al., 2019). They may furthermore be work-related in nature, causing a difficult, stressful, or even dangerous working situation, or they may be more person-related, such as persistent criticism and sarcasm, being yelled at, or acts of social exclusion (see also Rosander & Blomberg, 2019). Therefore, bullying is strictly speaking not about single and isolated episodes or events, but rather refers to behaviors that are repeatedly and persistently directed toward one or more person(s) by others in the work environment (Einarsen et al., 2020).

FOCUSING ON TARGET OR PERPETRATOR—EARLY OR LATER PHASES?

One may choose to focus on the perpetrator(s), who may show particularly unacceptable levels of aggression and hostile behavior toward others in the working environment. Alternatively, the focus may be on targets, who may be exposed to negative behaviors from many sources including the non-support from managers and employers, and where it is the total toll of the experience(s) that is at the heart of the problem. While the concept of workplace bullying traditionally takes the latter approach, concepts such as incivility tend to have the former as the focus. While the concept of incivility tends to focus on situations of relatively low intensity, the concept of workplace bullying and harassment has traditionally studied the range of the problem from the more subtle and indirect—yet systematic—all the way up to highly escalated situations where the target is severely stigmatized and victimized by the experience, as shown in the presented definition.

A GRADUALLY ESCALATING PROCESS

A core element of the definition is therefore that bullying may take the form of a gradually escalating process, indicating that bullying may exist at different levels of intensity and frequencies of the said negative acts (see also Notelaers et al., 2006). Hence, bullying is not a strict "either-or" phenomenon, but rather a gradually evolving process where targets in early phases are subjected to indirect or discreet behaviors that may be difficult to pinpoint (Einarsen, 2000). In later phases, more direct aggression may arise, and individuals may end up in an inferior position where they are targets of systematic negative acts with an increased risk of experiencing severe trauma and deterioration of work ability, health, and well-being (see also Einarsen, 1999). Accordingly, one may think of bullying as an end state with its accompanying consequences and the severe victimization of the target. Yet, one may also view and measure bullying as a more or less escalated process with less frequent yet still systematic exposure to bullying behaviors (labeled by some as incivility; Cortina et al., 2001). Both these levels of bullying are related to lowered health and well-being and are seen as stressful and unwanted by the target. On a sidenote: One may even study the phenomenon of bullying as experiences of specific negative acts happening on a daily or weekly basis, which is done ever more frequently when employing a diary design when studying the phenomenon (Hoprekstad et al., 2019; Rodríguez-Muñoz et al., 2022).

The last central characteristic of workplace bullying, according to this definition, is an imbalance of power between the perpetrator(s) and the target(s) (Einarsen et al., 1994). Typically, the target will perceive that they have few resources, if any, to defend themself against these negative acts. Such a power imbalance may be preexisting, such as in superior–subordinate relationships, but may also evolve due to the process and the constant exposure, leaving one of the parties in an increasingly vulnerable position vis-à-vis the perpetrator(s).

THE ROLE OF INTENT

A distinction exists in operational definitions regarding the issue of perpetrators' "intent to harm." One tradition, often anchored in aggression theory, sees this as central in all interpersonal forms of aggression (Keashly et al., 2020; Neuman & Baron, 1997), marking a distinction from mere accidental episodes where the result may have been harmful, but where the behavior itself was not intended to cause such harm. Scholars following this tradition classify workplace bullying as purposeful aggressive behavior on the part of the perpetrator, thus including intent to harm in the operational definition (Bowling & Beehr, 2006; Keashly et al., 2020).

In contrast, those who use the concept of incivility often define it as "low-intensity deviant behaviour with ambiguous intent to harm the target, in violation of workplace norms for mutual respect" (Andersson & Pearson, 1999, p. 457). Most studies of more systematic workplace bullying tend to have a target perspective, looking at the total toll of perceived exposure by a given target, often from a range of actors. When having the targets in focus, the intent of each individual perpetrator is of less relevance and even more difficult to measure from a methodological perspective (see Einarsen et al., 2020 for a more detailed discussion). Hence, the main theoretical argument here is that the level of exposure that one person is experiencing is likely the sum of many small acts by several potential perpetrators and bystanders—that could even be written off as insignificant or simply thoughtless in and of themselves but when accumulated over time may add up to a significant level of perceived victimization by the target. Furthermore, if intent were to be included as a central element of the definition, it would fall to the perpetrator(s) to decide whether their behavior should be categorized as bullying or not (Einarsen et al., 2020).

The target's own *perception* of the perpetrators' intent, on the other hand, may be important in determining whether the target interprets and subsequently labels their experience as bullying or not (Einarsen et al., 2020; Keashly, 2001). When the duration of the exposure is long, many targets make sense of the situation by attributing their experiences to intent to cause harm of the perpetrator(s), with the ultimate goal of pushing the target out of the organization (Vartia, 1996; Zapf, 1999). Yet, neither intent nor perceived intent is included in the measurement methods used to capture exposure to bullying from either research tradition (see also Nielsen et al., 2020).

MEASURING WORKPLACE BULLYING

Measuring bullying and harassment in the workplace may be challenging, as it is a complex, multifaceted, and somewhat subjective construct. When assessing bullying among children, a variety of observation methods and peer/teacher nominations have been applied, in addition to other data sources such as self-report, projective techniques, and psycho-physiological measurements (Olweus, 2013). Studies such as these have provided useful information on different aspects of bully/victim problems, although some data sources, including peer nominations, have been criticized for not being well-suited for prevalence estimation (Solberg & Olweus, 2003). In the field of adult bullying, most researchers use self-report questionnaires, employing two main techniques.

A *self-labeling* approach to measuring workplace bullying uses a single-item question of perceived victimization from bullying within a specific duration (e.g., the last 6 months). Most frequently, this single-item question is presented along with a theoretical definition of bullying (see e.g., Einarsen & Skogstad, 1996; Nielsen et al., 2010; O'Moore et al., 2003) often with a five- or seven-point frequency scale, usually ranging from "never bullied" to "bullied daily" (Cowie et al., 2002). Other studies use simple dichotomous (yes/no) response categories (Finne et al., 2011). Where this cut-off criterion should be set, then, is an ongoing debate. While some follow the criterion set by Leymann (1996) of experiencing bullying at least weekly during the last 6 months, others argue that many of the thresholds frequently used in the bullying literature are more or less arbitrary and lack a solid theoretical foundation (see e.g., Hutchinson et al., 2017). Accordingly, some researchers take the position that every respondent who indicates any level of exposure to bullying should be defined as a self-labeled victim (e.g., Berthelsen et al., 2011; Glambek et al., 2015).

This approach has several advantages, as it requires very little space in a questionnaire and is easy to administer. Explicitly asking respondents whether or not they consider themselves victims of bullying ensures high face validity (Nielsen et al., 2020) and provides information regarding the respondents' subjective view of themselves as a victim. Yet, the inherent subjectivity of this approach leaves it vulnerable to potential biases and misconceptions (Lewis et al., 2008). It may be difficult to admit or accept—both to oneself and to others—being a victim, resulting in a reluctance for victims to self-identify even if their experiences correspond to the formal definition of bullying. Moreover, this approach offers no insight into the nature of the negative behaviors involved (Nielsen et al., 2020). Accordingly, its usefulness may be limited when studying a bullying situation in the early stages of escalation. It is, however, highly appropriate when the goal is to capture the experiences of long-term exposed individuals who regard themselves as severely victimized by the process. Keep in mind though, that it seems to provide a rather conservative estimate with lower prevalence rates than does the following approach (Nielsen et al., 2010).

A *behavioral experience* approach to measuring workplace bullying employs an inventory with a list of specific acts and behaviors typical for bullying scenarios (Notelaers & Van der Heijden, 2021). Respondents are asked how often they have been subjected to each of these, often over the last 6 months, without explicitly mentioning the term *workplace bullying*. Several inventories have been developed, with the Leymann Inventory of Psychological Terror (Leymann, 1990a) and especially the Negative Acts Questionnaire (NAQ-R/NAQ; Einarsen & Raknes, 1997; Einarsen et al., 2009) by far the most frequently employed scales (Nielsen et al., 2020). The NAQ-R consists of 22 items measuring three types of negative social behavior at work, namely, person-oriented bullying (including social isolation), work-related bullying, and physically intimidating bullying, with a nine-item short version excluding the latter but retaining the items of social exclusion (SNAQ; Notelaers et al., 2019). Subsequently, a four-item version of the SNAQ has been employed in studies utilizing quantitative diary designs (e.g., Hoprekstad et al., 2019). The validity of the NAQ/NAQ-R/SNAQ has been established in a range of studies from around the globe, yet this also results in a range of slightly different versions in use (see Nielsen et al., 2020).

Using multiple items in a reliable and validated inventory provides a nuanced picture of the intensity and nature of the exposure (including person-related, work-related, and physically intimidating bullying). One may further statistically model the frequency and thereby the repeated nature of the experiences, providing important insights into the progress of different forms of bullying over time for different categories of respondents, at least when using appropriate statistical techniques and longitudinal designs (e.g., Latent Class Cluster analysis; Notelaers et al., 2006; Reknes et al., 2021). However, this approach does not provide any information explicitly relating to the assumed imbalance of power between the target and the perpetrator. In an effort to investigate this potential limitation, Nielsen et al. (2017) studied the moderating effect of respondents' perceived "ability to defend" against exposure to bullying behaviors on the relationship between such exposure and symptoms of anxiety. Interestingly, the results showed that while ability to defend did act as a buffer against anxiety at low to moderate levels of exposure to negative behaviors, the ability to defend no longer seemed to have the desired protective effect when exposure was high. This indicates that high-level exposure over time in and of itself strips individuals of their ability to defend themselves against such behavior.

CONSEQUENCES AND OUTCOMES OF WORKPLACE BULLYING

Much bullying and harassment research to date has concentrated on uncovering its consequences, especially pertaining to individual outcomes among targets (Hogh et al., 2019; Mikkelsen et al., 2020). Meta-analytic studies have shown positive associations between bullying and mental health problems (Conway et al., 2018; Nielsen & Einarsen, 2012), most strongly in the form of posttraumatic stress symptoms, anxiety, and depression. A 2017 systematic review also suggested a positive association between bullying and suicidal ideation (Leach et al., 2017). Furthermore, bullying has been shown to be related to a wide range of physiological health problems, including sleep problems (Hansen et al., 2014), headache and bodily pain (Glambek et al., 2018; Saastamoinen et al., 2009), cardiovascular disease (Xu et al., 2019), and Type 2 diabetes (Xu et al., 2018). With regard to job-related outcomes, bullying has been linked to reduced job satisfaction and organizational commitment (Nielsen & Einarsen, 2012), and increased risk of sickness absence (Niedhammer et al., 2013; Nielsen et al., 2016), job insecurity and turnover intentions (Glambek et al., 2014), and expulsion from working life (Glambek et al., 2015). While the majority of research has been cross-sectional in nature, more and more data show longitudinal relationships, yet with a tendency to indicate a reciprocal relationship between exposure and mental health problems, perhaps indicating a vicious circle of events.

A somewhat surprising but still rather consistent finding is that the relationship between exposure to bullying and subsequent mental health problems seems to be strongest among individuals with presumably positive coping resources, high levels of resilience, and other traits and abilities generally related to good health and indicative of personal resources (see e.g., Nielsen et al., 2017). Hence, the findings indicate a reversed buffer effect of personal dispositions on the association between bullying exposure and mental health, with those low on personal resources seemingly being immune against further deterioration in health and well-being following new adverse experiences of this kind (see also Nielsen & Einarsen, 2018). Another conclusion may be that workplace bullying in the end is harmful to all irrespective of one's presumed personal resources.

With such a wide range of long-lasting detrimental effects at the individual level, it is reasonable to conclude that the presence of bullying and harassment also brings consequences for organizations and society at large. Particularly with regard to sickness absenteeism, turnover, and the risk of expulsion from working life, the financial costs of long-lasting bullying cases is estimated to be high (Hoel et al., 2020). Following the extreme detrimental outcomes for targets, one may also expect costs to arise within health services addressing mental health problems. In a study from a Norwegian mental health clinic, as many as 25%–30% of the referred patients presented with experiences of bullying (Aarestad et al., 2020). Yet on a positive note, evaluation studies of existing clinical treatment and rehabilitation programs addressing the aftermath of such experiences (Aarestad et al., 2022) indicated very positive results in terms of mental health improvement and return to work (see also Schwickerath & Zapf, 2020).

EXPLAINING THE PHENOMENON: ANTECEDENTS AND RISK FACTORS

A large body of research also exists on the antecedents of and risk factors for bullying, with more recent focus also on preventive organizational factors (Salin & Hoel, 2020). By knowing more about what triggers and hinders a bullying process, organizations stand a better chance of preventing and intervening in bullying scenarios. Yet, workplace bullying is a complex phenomenon, likely caused by an interplay of risk factors existing on many levels (Salin & Hoel, 2020; Zapf, 1999). Such a theoretical view is supported by empirical evidence that suggests that the reasons why bullying arises and develops are associated with individual factors (i.e., personality; Zapf & Einarsen, 2020), work-related and organizational characteristics (i.e., aspects of the job, work group, or the organization; Salin & Hoel, 2020), as well as societal-level factors (Van de Vliert et al., 2013).

Predatory bullying is a scenario in which the victim has done nothing to provoke or justify the treatment (Einarsen, 1999). Victims of predatory bullying often accidentally find themselves in a situation where the perpetrator is demonstrating power or otherwise exploiting others, who then may become a target by mere "circumstance." The actions of destructive leaders, demonstrating petty tyranny (Ashforth, 1994) or abusive supervision (Tepper, 2007), are illustrative. An employee may also become the target of bullying because they are seen as an "easy target" for pent-up stress and frustration in a work group or they may be the target due to stereotypes and discriminatory attitudes in the society at large.

Dispute-related bullying (Einarsen, 1999), on the other hand, sees bullying as the result of existing stress and frustration in the work group creating unresolved social conflicts and aggressive outlets, to the point where an imbalance of power between the involved parties has developed (Zapf & Gross, 2001). This notion is in line with Leymann (1996), who argued that bullying should be viewed as a four-stage process starting with a critical incident—usually an unresolved or badly managed interpersonal conflict—escalating into bullying and potential trauma.

This may raise the question of whether conflict and bullying are overlapping constructs or refer to two related, yet distinct, phenomena. Some longitudinal evidence supports the view that bullying is a distinct concept that is separate from that of interpersonal conflict and workplace aggression, both in its nature and in the related outcomes (Baillien et al., 2017). Moreover, a study by Notelaers et al. (2018) indicated that while interpersonal conflict, aggression, and workplace bullying seem to overlap at levels of low intensity, bullying clearly deviates from the other two constructs when it reaches higher levels of escalation. As such, interpersonal conflict may be viewed as a mechanism and mediator between important situational antecedents and risk factors for bullying as demonstrated in the three-way model on workplace bullying development (Baillien et al., 2009).

Interpersonal conflict has indeed been documented to be among the strongest risk factors of workplace bullying (Hauge et al., 2007; Zapf, 1999). Based on interview data, Baillien et al. (2009) found conflict escalation as one of three main pathways to workplace bullying. If a conflict escalates into harsh personified conflicts (Van de Vliert, 1984) it may over time lead to negative behavior, which may subsequently escalate into a workplace bullying scenario (Baillien et al., 2009). When conflicts reach this level of escalation, the end result may be attempts to manipulate, retaliate, eliminate, and destroy the other party (Glasl, 1982; Van de Vliert, 1984). This escalating nature of the relationship between conflicts and bullying, well described in the three-way model of Baillien et al. (2009), has also been substantiated by several studies looking at the mediating effect of relationship conflict on the positive association between task conflicts and exposure to bullying (Arenas et al., 2015; Baillien et al., 2016; Leon-Perez et al., 2015). An important limitation related to these mediation studies, however, is that the analyses relied on cross-sectional data, thereby limiting the validity of making causal inferences. Therefore, more research using longitudinal data is needed to investigate how interpersonal conflicts may be related to increased victimization from bullying over time. Yet, Baillien et al. (2014) showed that for perpetrators, their conflict management style predicted subsequent escalation from task and relationship conflict into increased bullying involvement.

WORK-RELATED RISK FACTORS FOR BULLYING

The idea of dispute-related bullying corresponds well with the work environment hypothesis (Einarsen et al., 1994, 2020)—and is anchored in the seminal work of Leymann (1990b, 1996), which adamantly holds that bullying is a result of the prevailing psychosocial work environment. According to this situational view, deficiencies in work design and a generally negative psychological work environment are likely to elicit stress and frustration in all exposed employees, which in turn may escalate into bullying scenarios. Leymann (1996) emphasized poor conflict management skills and a laissez-faire attitude by local managers as an important conditional factor. Brodsky (1976) argued further that harassment happens only in organizations that reward or at least allow it. In other words, conflicts, stressors, and interpersonal frustration will escalate into bullying only when supervisors deny or neglect their managerial duty to resolve the underlying conflict issue or are ineffective in preventing or stopping the bullying process (Hamre et al., 2021).

Empirical Findings on Prominent Risk Factors in the Working Environment. A large number of empirical studies support the theoretical claim that bullying seems to thrive in demanding workplaces, in which employees are exposed to organizational constraints and contradictory expectations and demands (Salin & Hoel, 2020). In their meta-analysis based on 90 separate samples Bowling and Beehr (2006) found that role ambiguity, role conflict, tyrannical leadership, laissez-faire leadership, decision authority, job insecurity, and job demands all predicted exposure to bullying. Accordingly, the authors concluded that "characteristics of the work environment (e.g., other stressors) might strongly contribute to workplace harassment" (Bowling & Beehr, 2006, p. 1005).

Two of the most frequently described work-related risk factors of workplace bullying are role ambiguity and role conflict (Bowling & Beehr, 2006; Van den Brande et al., 2016). Role ambiguity is a state in which the person has inadequate or uncertain information about expectations toward their position or role in the organization (Kahn et al., 1964), resulting in a lack of clarity about duties, objectives, and responsibilities needed to fulfill his or her role (Kahn et al., 1964; Rizzo et al., 1970). Role conflict refers to someone holding incompatible roles or perceiving simultaneous but incompatible expectations and demands so that compliance with one makes compliance with the other more difficult (Kahn et al., 1964; Rizzo et al., 1970). Both role ambiguity and role conflicts are associated with increased feelings of anger, anxiety, and tension (Spector & Goh, 2001) and are related to reports of bullying among both targets and perpetrators (Hauge et al., 2009), even in longitudinal studies (Balducci et al., 2012; Reknes et al., 2014).

Still, a few studies do report a prospective relationship between workplace bullying and subsequent experiences of role ambiguity and role conflict (i.e., reverse causality; Hauge, Skogstad, et al., 2011; Nielsen & Knardahl, 2015). Accordingly, the empirical evidence regarding the causal relationship between role stressors and workplace bullying is still somewhat inconsistent. This may in part be explained by the different time lags employed in various studies, with shorter time lags (i.e., 6 months–1 year) indicating the impact of work environment factors on bullying, while longer time lags (i.e., 2 years) show evidence of reverse causation (Balducci et al., 2012). If so, this is in line with the theoretical arguments in the work environment hypothesis (Einarsen et al., 2020), in that the presence of poor and stressful working conditions is a prerequisite for bullying to exist in the first place. Then, when bullying has become prevalent in the working environment, it is not unlikely that this will further sour an already unfavorable psychosocial climate at work, creating a vicious cycle.

Moreover, quantitative work demands, including exposure to a high workload and working under time pressure, are also well-documented as being work-related risk factors of bullying in the workplace (Van den Brande et al., 2016). Brodsky (1976) even argued that work pressure may be viewed as a form of harassment in and of itself. Work pressure may be understood as a type of quantitative job demand that has reached a level above what is considered normal or acceptable in a certain situation or for a given employee (Van Veldhoven, 2014).

Leadership and the Role of Managers. Finally, researchers have documented leadership as an important determining factor regarding the prevalence of bullying in the workplace. Most important, destructive forms of leadership—be they active or passive—may be direct predictors of subordinates' experiences of exposure and victimization (Balducci et al., 2021; Rai & Agarwal, 2018). In fact, laissez-faire leadership, characterized by a lack of support from the leader in stressful situations where there is a particular need for leadership, may in and of itself be perceived as bullying by subordinates (Hoel et al., 2010; Skogstad et al., 2007). Conversely, the presence of constructive forms of leadership is related to fewer instances of bullying in the work environment (see e.g., Hauge, Einarsen, et al., 2011; Tsuno & Kawakami, 2015).

In recent years, studies have emerged that also consider the role of leadership as a conditional factor that may either boost or prevent the further development of workplace bullying. More specifically, some studies have investigated the moderating effects of passive-avoidant and laissez-faire leadership on the relationship between various work constraints and workplace bullying (Ågotnes et al., 2018, 2021; Rodriguez-Munoz et al., 2012; Sischka et al., 2021). These studies all support the theoretical notion that workers in stressful environments are at a higher risk of becoming targets of workplace bullying when their immediate supervisor is exhibiting passive-avoidant and laissez-faire leadership behavior. This is in line with the seminal work of Brodsky (1976), in which he stated that harassment will flourish only in environments where such behaviors are allowed or even rewarded. More specifically, leaders who are not present when needed, and who do not intervene in situations characterized by high levels of work stress and escalating conflicts, are likely to allow or even encourage further escalation (Zapf & Gross, 2001).

Contrasting this detrimental exacerbating effect of passive-avoidant leadership, a few studies indicate that the presence of a strong climate for conflict management in the work environment is related to fewer instances of bullying in the workplace—even when risk factors are present (Hamre et al., 2021; Zahlquist et al., 2019). Thus, in organizations where employees share the perception that there are fair and effective procedures in place for managing interpersonal issues and conflicts with active and competent managers (Rivlin, 2001), potential perpetrators will be made aware that any type of negative social behavior directed toward fellow coworkers will not be tolerated while targets will receive aid if needed. This should effectively deter the bullying process before it has really had a chance to begin in the first place.

Another climate facet suggested as a protective organization-level factor is psychosocial safety climate (PSC)—conceptualized as the shared belief held by workers that their psychological safety and well-being is protected in the organization and supported by senior management (Dollard & Bakker, 2010). Longitudinal studies suggest that a strong psychological safety climate is related to less bullying (Bond et al., 2010; Dollard et al., 2017). There is also some cross-sectional evidence suggesting that a strong PSC may buffer the negative relationship between bullying and mental health problems, as well as the relationship between bullying and work engagement (Law et al., 2011). However, more research is needed on the role of both conflict management and psychosocial safety climate in the organization in alleviating both risks and outcomes.

INDIVIDUAL RISK FACTORS FOR BULLYING

Contrasting the work environment hypothesis, the individual disposition hypothesis highlights individual characteristics as potential precursors and risk factors of bullying. According to this view, specific characteristics, or combinations of characteristics, are likely to increase the risk of either becoming a target or being a perpetrator (Nielsen & Knardahl, 2015).

In relation to the target's risk of being exposed to bullying, two distinct "victim personalities" have been described, in line with victim precipitation theory (Elias, 1986). The *vulnerable victim* describes individuals who are seen as "easy targets" of bullying, because they are seemingly unable to defend themselves and unable to manage conflicts at work constructively (Zapf & Einarsen, 2020). They tend to score low on self-esteem, social competence, and aggression, and high on social anxiety and insecurity (Coyne et al., 2000; Matthiesen & Einarsen, 2007), making them likely to react with withdrawal when attacked.

Employees may also become victims of bullying simply by being an outsider or a nonprototypical member of a work group, resulting in the individual being forced into the role of a scapegoat (Glambek et al., 2020). In contrast, the *provocative victim* (Einarsen, 1999; Olweus, 1978) acts in ways that trigger aggressive behavior in others, are aggressive themselves, and/or are likely to respond aggressively when confronted with conflict or bullying behavior. It may also be that these individuals, to protect themselves, retaliate against any aggressor, becoming a perpetrator themselves. In his research on school bullying, Olweus (1978, 1993) characterized these "bully-victims" as displaying a combination of anxious and aggressive reaction patterns, and such adults have also been found to score low on self-esteem and social competence, but high on aggression (Matthiesen & Einarsen, 2007).

Although the issue of personality as a proposed antecedent of bullying is controversial and does not receive as strong empirical support as does the work environment hypothesis, some notable findings have been presented with regard to the five factor personality traits of bullying victims as risk factors for exposure to workplace bullying. Meta-analytic evidence showed that exposure is associated positively yet rather moderately with neuroticism, and negatively with extraversion, agreeableness, and conscientiousness (Nielsen, Glasø, et al., 2017). Moreover, a longitudinal study investigating the role of personality in the development of the bullying process showed that individuals with high levels of trait anxiety and trait anger are not only more likely to be exposed to more bullying in general, but their exposure is also more likely to escalate over time. Furthermore, this study showed that a bullying process involving targets with high trait anger is less likely to deescalate over time (Reknes et al., 2021).

When studying perpetrators, the so-called dark triad of personality traits (i.e., psychopathy, narcissism, and Machiavellianism; Baughman et al., 2012; Linton & Power, 2013), as well as high and/or unstable self-esteem (Baumeister et al., 2000; Matthiesen & Einarsen, 2007) and a lack of social competencies (Jenkins et al., 2012), seem to increase the probability of engaging in aggressive behavior toward others in the workplace. Research on personality traits and workplace deviance and aggression more broadly defined consistently shows robust relationships between high scores on neuroticism and low scores on agreeableness and conscientiousness among perpetrators (Berry et al., 2007; Jones et al., 2011). Perpetrators' negative affectivity has also been linked to engagement in workplace aggressive behavior (Hackney & Perrewé, 2018; Martinko et al., 2017).

Person-Related or Work-Related Risk Factors—Or a Combination?   Although personal characteristics of both victims and perpetrators likely influence the bullying process to some degree, researchers have argued against such a one-sided and mono-causal argument when trying to explain the development of workplace bullying (see e.g., Hauge et al., 2009). This point has been underscored in studies showing that risk factors in the work environment (i.e., role stressors and job demands) are directly related to bullying exposure, over and above the negative effect of respondents' individual characteristics (Balducci et al., 2011, 2012). Furthermore, in two cross-sectional studies, Reknes et al. (2019) showed that victims' scores on trait anger, trait anxiety, and negative affect strengthened the positive relationship between role conflicts and reports of exposure to bullying behaviors. The victim's personality was only a risk factor in combination with role stressors. In other words, the personality of the target may not in and of itself trigger such behaviors from others. Some evidence of such a person in situation interaction has been evident in studies by Vandevelde (2019), who have employed a person-environment fit perspective to predict workplace bullying. Results from these studies therefore indicate that explanations for why such processes occur and develop in the workplace must focus on the potential influence of the various situational and organizational factors that coexist in the work environment (Reknes et al., 2019).

CONCLUSIONS AND NEEDS FOR FURTHER DEVELOPMENT

While bullying research has come a long way since its infancy in the mid-1990s, there are still issues that need more attention, advances that need to be made, and limitations that must be overcome. What is known is that bullying is prevalent in all kinds of industries all over the world, with detrimental outcomes for those targeted as well as for organizations and society at large. While there is some evidence of individual-level characteristics being risk factors for involvement in bullying scenarios, the main risk factors are found in the organizations and in the working environment of work groups and departments—including how managers act and react in relation to these risk factors and when actual cases arise. The reasons for why bullying develops and results in detrimental consequences are, however, likely to be both complex and interwoven; therefore, no single explanation is sufficient on its own to accurately explain the bullying process (Baillien et al., 2009; Zapf, 1999).

Furthermore, most research conducted to date has focused on the experiences and reports of targets. As a result, there is still a lack of information about perpetrators. Although there exist some studies that have investigated bullying enactment (see e.g., Baillien, De Cuyper, et al., 2011; Baillien, Rodriguez-Muñoz, et al., 2011; Baillien et al., 2014; Baillien et al., 2019; Balducci et al., 2012; Glasø et al., 2009; Hauge et al., 2009; Lange et al., 2019), this field is still largely unexplored when not relying on targets' accounts.

Studying perpetrators comes with many challenges, however. Self-reports by perpetrators may be rather unreliable, as people may not be completely truthful nor cognizant when it comes to describing their own negative behavior. Social desirability may influence the respondents to underreport engagement in such behavior. Nielsen et al. (2020) have further argued that it would be highly difficult to gather adequate information about a bullying process from all relevant sources, and, even if it were possible, the inter-rater correlation between target and each individual perpetrator is likely to be low. An even more provoking view is that the victim-bully distinction may not be clear-cut in real-life ongoing bullying processes, where all involved may have been targeted and perpetrators, at least to some extent. Some argue that there may exist a bullying spiral in which targets of bullying become perpetrators, and vice versa (Vranjes et al., 2021, 2022). Furthermore, all involved may be exposed to poor leadership and deficiencies in the organization and management of work (see also Matsson & Jordan, 2022, who argue against a clear-cut target-perpetrator distinction).

Moreover, the study of bystanders and observers (Niven et al., 2020; Pouwelse et al., 2021) is another emerging research topic with promising findings. Although still in its infancy, this research also faces the risk of seeing this as another clear-cut role different from that of targets and perpetrators. Research has, however, shown that bystanders may be involved in more active roles on both sides of the situation.

In short, a range of intervention strategies to prevent and tackle workplace bullying has been proposed and may be implemented at the individual, organizational, and/or society level (see Zapf & Vartia, 2020, for an overview). Yet, reviews and meta-analysis that have evaluated the available empirical intervention studies have assessed most existing studies as having low-quality designs, resulting in inconclusive evidence (Escartín, 2016; Gillen et al., 2017; Hodgins et al., 2014). As such, there are no clear empirical indications as to which specific intervention strategies are most effective in preventing and/or reducing the problem. However, a qualitative study by Salin et al. (2020), based on interviews of 214 human resource (HR) professionals from around the globe, may give some indications of the most effective strategies from the perspective of people with actual experience in managing these types of cases in the workplace. The results indicate that strategies such as raising awareness, having anti-bullying policies, as well as good and constructive leadership are deemed the most effective preventive factors by many of the HR professionals. Yet, for handling actual cases, complaints and investigation procedures are the most often mentioned necessary tools. This further underscores that ensuring a strong conflict management climate in organizations may be a universal and low-risk intervention that could be expected to be highly effective as a protective factor against bullying.

Further, the research field has indeed seen an increased sophistication in the research designs and statistical analyses employed in empirical research, starting around 2010. Despite this, studies included in systematic reviews and meta-analyses of the relationships between antecedents, bullying, and its consequences are still predominantly based on self-reported, cross-sectional data analyzed at the individual level (Neall & Tuckey, 2014; Rai & Agarwal, 2016). Such data are useful yet come with inherent methodological issues, including the risk of common method variance (Podsakoff et al., 2003) and problems regarding causality. Furthermore, this constitutes a mere snapshot of what is theoretically seen as a constantly developing and changing process. Hence, a major challenge in the field is to actually study the process involved and the ongoing nature of "the beast" (see Reknes et al., 2021 for such an attempt).

As a response to these limitations, scholars are increasingly employing various longitudinal (see e.g., Balducci et al., 2012; Reknes et al., 2014; Tsuno & Kawakami, 2015) and multilevel (see e.g., Hauge, Einarsen, et al., 2011; Tuckey et al., 2017; Zahlquist et al., 2019) approaches, with interesting and useful findings when it comes to the possibility of prevention and effective intervention in bullying cases. Employing quantitative diary designs has also been shown to cast important light on the process involved as well as on short-term risk factors (Hoprekstad et al., 2019; Reknes et al., 2021; Zahlquist et al., 2022). In line with this, more studies also focus on the effect of various organizational-level interventions (see Einarsen & Einarsen, 2021 for a review). Yet, there is still much work to be done when it comes to understanding and documenting the effect of workplace bullying interventions, as such research faces a range of demanding methodological issues.

A final remark is that the presented theory and research is the dominant perspective on workplace bullying, seeing it as interpersonal in nature and focusing on social interaction between organizational members where bullying is acted out by organizational members against others. Yet, there are also proponents of a wider workplace bullying concept, including depersonalized forms of bullying. In this perspective, bullying may be viewed as "the routine subjugation of employees by contextual, structural and processual elements of organizational design, which are implemented by supervisors and managers who involuntarily resort to abusive and hostile behaviours in an impersonal way to achieve organizational effectiveness" (D'Cruz, 2015, p. 2). The basic question here is whether organization and its systems and rules can bully, or whether it is conducted by persons' voluntary behaviors. That there are systems, procedures, rules, norms, and methods applied in organizations that are abusive and constitute mistreatment of employees is not arguable. Whether scholars should include it in the very concepts of workplace bullying or find other more distinct concepts is, however, another matter.

REFERENCES

Aarestad, S. H., Einarsen, S. V., Hjemdal, O., Gjengedal, R. G. H., Osnes, K., Sandin, K., Hannisdal, M., Bjørndal, M. T., & Harris, A. (2020). Clinical characteristics of patients seeking treatment for common mental disorders presenting with workplace bullying experiences. *Frontiers in Psychology, 11.* https://doi.org/ft9c

Aarestad, S. H., Harris, A., Hjemdal, O., Gjengedal, R. G., Osnes, K., Sandin, K., Reme, S. E., Hannisdal, M., & Einarsen, S. V. (2022). Healing the wounds of workplace bullying: Evaluating mental health and workplace participation among victims seeking treatment for common mental disorders. *WORK: A Journal of Prevention, Assessment & Rehabilitation, 73*(4), 1379–1391.

Ågotnes, K. W., Einarsen, S. V., Hetland, J., & Skogstad, A. (2018). The moderating effect of laissez-faire leadership on the relationship between co-worker conflicts and new cases of workplace bullying: A true prospective design. *Human Resource Management Journal*, 28(4), 555–568. https://doi.org/gfprmc

Ågotnes, K. W., Skogstad, A., Hetland, J., Olsen, O. K., Espevik, R., Bakker, A. B., & Einarsen, S. V. (2021). Daily work pressure and exposure to bullying-related negative acts: The role of daily transformational and laissez-faire leadership. *European Management Journal*, 39(4), 423–433. https://doi.org/ghdxf4

Andersson, L. M., & Pearson, C. M. (1999). Tit for tat? The spiraling effect of incivility in the workplace. *The Academy of Management Review*, 24(3), 452–471. https://doi.org/czn8bc

Arenas, A., León-Pérez, J.-M., Munduate, L., & Medina, F. J. (2015). Workplace bullying and interpersonal conflicts: The moderation effect of supervisor's power. *Revista De Psicologia Social*, 30(2), 295–322.

Ashforth, B. (1994). Petty tyranny in organizations. *Human Relations*, 47(7), 755–778. https://doi.org/cc8cw7

Baillien, E., Bollen, K., Euwema, M., & De Witte, H. (2014). Conflicts and conflict management styles as precursors of workplace bullying: A two-wave longitudinal study. *European Journal of Work and Organizational Psychology*, 23(4), 511–524. https://doi.org/hb2t

Baillien, E., Camps, J., Van den Broeck, A., Stouten, J., Godderis, L., Sercu, M., & De Witte, H. (2016). An eye for an eye will make the whole world blind: Conflict escalation into workplace bullying and the role of distributive conflict behavior. *Journal of Business Ethics*, 137(2), 415–429. https://doi.org/fc8k

Baillien, E., De Cuyper, N., & De Witte, H. (2011). Job autonomy and workload as antecedents of workplace bullying: A two-wave test of Karasek's Job Demand Control Model for targets and perpetrators. *Journal of Occupational and Organizational Psychology*, 84(1), 191–208. https://doi.org/dpbwx6

Baillien, E., Escartín, J., Gross, C., & Zapf, D. (2017). Towards a conceptual and empirical differentiation between workplace bullying and interpersonal conflict. *European Journal of Work and Organizational Psychology*, 26(6), 1–12. https://doi.org/fc8q

Baillien, E., Griep, Y., Vander Elst, T., & De Witte, H. (2019). The relationship between organisational change and being a perpetrator of workplace bullying: A three-wave longitudinal study. *Work & Stress*, 33(3), 211–230. https://doi.org/jtq5

Baillien, E., Neyens, I., De Witte, H., & De Cuyper, N. (2009). A qualitative study on the development of workplace bullying: Towards a three way model. *Journal of Community & Applied Social Psychology*, 19(1), 1–16. https://doi.org/10.1002/casp.977

Baillien, E., Rodriguez-Muñoz, A., Van den Broeck, A., & De Witte, H. (2011). Do demands and resources affect target's and perpetrators' reports of workplace bullying? A two-wave cross-lagged study. *Work & Stress*, 25(2), 128–146. https://doi.org/cpgh4m

Balducci, C., Cecchin, M., & Fraccaroli, F. (2012). The impact of role stressors on workplace bullying in both victims and perpetrators, controlling for personal vulnerability factors: A longitudinal analysis. *Work & Stress*, 26(3), 195–212. https://doi.org/ggxtxb

Balducci, C., Conway, P. M., & van Heugten, K. (2021). The contribution of organizational factors to workplace bullying, emotional abuse and harassment. In P. D'Cruz, E. Noronha, E. Baillien, K. Harlos, A. Hogh, & E. G. Mikkelsen (Eds.), *Pathways of job-related negative behaviour: Handbooks of workplace bullying, emotional abuse and harassment* (Vol. 2, pp. 3–28). Springer. https://doi.org/hb2c

Balducci, C., Fraccaroli, F., & Schaufeli, W. B. (2011). Workplace bullying and its relation with work characteristics, personality, and post-traumatic stress symptoms: An integrated model. *Anxiety, Stress & Coping*, 24(5), 499–513. https://doi.org/fwxxqz

Baughman, H. M., Dearing, S., Giammarco, E., & Vernon, P. A. (2012). Relationships between bullying behaviours and the Dark Triad: A study with adults. *Personality and Individual Differences*, 52(5), 571–575. https://doi.org/fzf7hc

Baumeister, R. F., Bushman, B. J., & Campbell, W. K. (2000). Self-esteem, narcissism, and aggression: Does violence result from low self-esteem or from threatened egotism? *Current Directions in Psychological Science*, 9(1), 26–29. https://doi.org/bbwm3b

Berry, C. M., Ones, D. S., & Sackett, P. R. (2007). Interpersonal deviance, organizational deviance, and their common correlates: A review and meta-analysis. *Journal of Applied Psychology, 92*(2), 410–424. https://doi.org/b965s7

Berthelsen, M., Skogstad, A., Lau, B., & Einarsen, S. (2011). Do they stay or do they go? A longitudinal study of intentions to leave and exclusion from working life among targets of workplace bullying. *International Journal of Manpower, 32*(2), 178–193. https://doi.org/bk7rss

Bond, S. A., Tuckey, M. R., & Dollard, M. F. (2010). Psychosocial safety climate, workplace bullying, and symptoms of posttraumatic stress. *Organization Development Journal, 28*(1), 37.

Bowling, N. A., & Beehr, T. A. (2006). Workplace harassment from the victim's perspective: A theoretical model and meta-analysis. *Journal of Applied Psychology, 91*(5), 998–1012. https://doi.org/cxct22

Brodsky, C. M. (1976). *The harassed worker.* Lexington Books.

Conway, P. M., Hogh, A., Balducci, C., & Ebbesen, D. K. (2018). Workplace bullying and mental health. In P. D'Cruz, E. Noronha, E. Baillien, B. Catley, K. Harlos, A. Hogh, & E. G. Mikkelsen (Eds.), *Pathways of job-related negative behaviour* (pp. 1–27). Springer. https://doi.org/hb2g

Cortina, L. M., Magley, V. J., Williams, J. H., & Langhout, R. D. (2001). Incivility in the workplace: Incidence and impact. *Journal of Occupational Health Psychology, 6*(1), 64–80. https://doi.org/dthsvr

Cowie, H., Naylor, P., Rivers, I., Smith, P. K., & Pereira, B. (2002). Measuring workplace bullying. *Aggression and Violent Behavior, 7*(1), 33–51. https://doi.org/b69ttk

Coyne, I., Seigne, E., & Randall, P. (2000). Predicting workplace victim status from personality. *European Journal of Work and Organizational Psychology, 9*(3), 335–349. https://doi.org/bbrdwv

D'Cruz, P. (2015). *Depersonalized bullying at work: From evidence to conceptualization.* Springer. https://doi.org/jhxc

Dollard, M. F., & Bakker, A. B. (2010). Psychosocial safety climate as a precursor to conducive work environments, psychological health problems, and employee engagement. *Journal of Occupational and Organizational Psychology, 83*(3), 579–599. https://doi.org/fcnxcr

Dollard, M. F., Dormann, C., Tuckey, M. R., & Escartín, J. (2017). Psychosocial safety climate (PSC) and enacted PSC for workplace bullying and psychological health problem reduction. *European Journal of Work and Organizational Psychology, 26*(6), 844–857. https://doi.org/gk3ksx

Einarsen, K., & Einarsen, S. V. (2021). Combating workplace bullying: Interventions and the role of the organization's ethical infrastructure. In *The Wiley Blackwell handbook of bullying: A comprehensive and international review of research and intervention* (Vol. 1, pp. 538–557). Wiley Blackwell. https://doi.org/jhw9

Einarsen, S. (1999). The nature and causes of bullying at work. *International Journal of Manpower, 20*(1/2), 16–27. https://doi.org/fdf4s4

Einarsen, S. (2000). Harassment and bullying at work: A review of the Scandinavian approach. *Aggression and Violent Behavior, 5*(4), 379–401. https://doi.org/d542hv

Einarsen, S., Hoel, H., & Notelaers, G. (2009). Measuring exposure to bullying and harassment at work: Validity, factor structure and psychometric properties of the Negative Acts Questionnaire-Revised. *Work & Stress, 23*(1), 24–44. https://doi.org/cwz987

Einarsen, S., Hoel, H., Zapf, D., & Cooper, C. L. (2003). The concept of bullying at work: The European tradition. In S. Einarsen, H. Hoel, D. Zapf, & C. L. Cooper (Eds.), *Bullying and emotional abuse in the workplace: International perspectives in research and practice* (pp. 3–30). Taylor & Francis.

Einarsen, S., & Raknes, B. I. (1997). Harassment in the workplace and the victimization of men. *Violence and Victims, 12*(3), 247–263. https://doi.org/gf3kq6

Einarsen, S., Raknes, B. I., & Matthiesen, S. B. (1994). Bullying and harassment at work and their relationships to work environment quality: An exploratory study. *European Journal of Work and Organizational Psychology, 4*(4), 381–401. https://doi.org/cx8m4n

Einarsen, S., & Skogstad, A. (1996). Bullying at work: Epidemiological findings in public and private organizations. *European Journal of Work and Organizational Psychology, 5*(2), 185–201. https://doi.org/bg8fv3

Einarsen, S. V., Hoel, H., Zapf, D., & Cooper, C. L. (2020). The concept of bullying and harassment at work: The European tradition. In S. V. Einarsen, H. Hoel, D. Zapf, & C. L. Cooper (Eds.), *Bullying and harassment in the workplace: Theory, research, and practice* (3rd ed., pp. 3–53). CRC Press. https://doi.org/hcd4

Elias, R. (1986). *The politics of victimization: Victims, victimology, and human rights.* Oxford University Press.

Escartín, J. (2016). Insights into workplace bullying: Psychosocial drivers and effective interventions. *Psychology Research and Behavior Management, 9*, 157. https://doi.org/jtq6

Finne, L. B., Knardahl, S., & Lau, B. (2011). Workplace bullying and mental distress—A prospective study of Norwegian employees. *Scandinavian Journal of Work, Environment & Health, 37*(4), 276–287. https://doi.org/dv8rqh

Gillen, P. A., Sinclair, M., Kernohan, W. G., Begley, C. M., & Luyben, A. G. (2017). Interventions for prevention of bullying in the workplace. *Cochrane Database of Systematic Reviews, 1*(1), CD 009778. https://doi.org/gbvzdw

Glambek, M., Einarsen, S. V., & Notelaers, G. (2020). Workplace bullying as predicted by non-prototypicality, group identification and norms: A self-categorisation perspective. *Work & Stress, 34*(3), 279–299. https://doi.org/hcd5

Glambek, M., Matthiesen, S. B., Hetland, J., & Einarsen, S. (2014). Workplace bullying as an antecedent to job insecurity and intention to leave: A 6-month prospective study. *Human Resource Management Journal, 24*(3), 255–268. https://doi.org/f6d3vk

Glambek, M., Nielsen, M. B., Gjerstad, J., & Einarsen, S. (2018). Gender differences in the relationship between workplace bullying and subjective back and neck pain: A two-wave study in a Norwegian probability sample. *Journal of Psychosomatic Research, 106*, 73–75. https://doi.org/gc59nx

Glambek, M., Skogstad, A., & Einarsen, S. (2015). Take it or leave: A five-year prospective study of workplace bullying and indicators of expulsion in working life. *Industrial Health, 53*, 160–170. https://doi.org/hb2j

Glasl, F. (1982). The process of conflict escalation and roles of third parties. In G. B. J. Bomers & R. B. Peterson (Eds.), *Conflict management and industrial relations* (pp. 119–140). Springer.

Glasø, L., Nielsen, M. B., & Einarsen, S. (2009). Interpersonal problems among perpetrators and targets of workplace bullying. *Journal of Applied Social Psychology, 39*(6), 1316–1333. https://doi.org/10/fbvdsr

Hackney, K. J., & Perrewé, P. L. (2018). A review of abusive behaviors at work: The development of a process model for studying abuse. *Organizational Psychology Review, 8*(1), 70–92. https://doi.org/gfw5k6

Hamre, K. V., Fauske, M. R., Reknes, I., Nielsen, M. B., Gjerstad, J., & Einarsen, S. V. (2021). Preventing and neutralizing the escalation of workplace bullying: The role of conflict management climate. *International Journal of Bullying Prevention, 4*, 255–265. https://doi.org/gwmw

Hansen, Å. M., Hogh, A., Garde, A. H., & Persson, R. (2014). Workplace bullying and sleep difficulties: A 2-year follow-up study. *International Archives of Occupational and Environmental Health, 87*(3), 285–294. https://doi.org/f5vmzc

Hauge, L. J., Einarsen, S., Knardahl, S., Lau, B., Notelaers, G., & Skogstad, A. (2011). Leadership and role stressors as departmental level predictors of workplace bullying. *International Journal of Stress Management, 18*(4), 305.

Hauge, L. J., Skogstad, A., & Einarsen, S. (2007). Relationships between stressful work environments and bullying: Results of a large representative study. *Work & Stress, 21*(3), 220–242. https://doi.org/10/fg6c9x

Hauge, L. J., Skogstad, A., & Einarsen, S. (2009). Individual and situational predictors of workplace bullying: Why do perpetrators engage in the bullying of others? *Work & Stress, 23*(4), 349–358. https://doi.org/bmzpd9

Hauge, L. J., Skogstad, A., & Einarsen, S. (2011). Role stressors and exposure to workplace bullying: Causes or consequences of what and why? *European Journal of Work and Organizational Psychology, 20*(5), 610–630. https://doi.org/fjrrs5

Hodgins, M., MacCurtain, S., & Mannix-McNamara, P. (2014). Workplace bullying and incivility: A systematic review of interventions. *International Journal of Workplace Health Management, 7*(1), 54–71. https://doi.org/gfzwd5

Hoel, H., Cooper, C. L., & Einarsen, S. V. (2020). Organizational effects of workplace bullying. In S. V. Einarsen, H. Hoel, D. Zapf, & C. L. Cooper (Eds.), *Bullying and harassment in the workplace: Theory, research, and practice* (3rd ed., pp. 209–234). CRC Press. https://doi.org/hcd4

Hoel, H., Glasø, L., Hetland, J., Cooper, C. L., & Einarsen, S. (2010). Leadership styles as predictors of self-reported and observed workplace bullying. *British Journal of Management, 21*(2), 453–468. https://doi.org/c6qczn

Hogh, A., Clausen, T., Bickmann, L., Hansen, Å. M., Conway, P. M., & Baernholdt, M. (2019). Consequences of workplace bullying for individuals, organizations and society. In P. D'Cruz, E. Noronha, E. Baillien, B. Catley, K. Harlos, A. Hogh, & E. G. Mikkelsen (Eds.), *Pathways of job-related negative behaviour* (pp. 1–24). Springer. https://doi.org/hb2k

Hoprekstad, Ø. L., Hetland, J., Bakker, A. B., Olsen, O. K., Espevik, R., Wessel, M., & Einarsen, S. V. (2019). How long does it last? Prior victimization from workplace bullying moderates the relationship between daily exposure to negative acts and subsequent depressed mood. *European Journal of Work and Organizational Psychology, 28*(2), 164–178. https://doi.org/fc69

Hutchinson, M., Bradbury, J., Browne, G., & Hurley, J. (2017). Determining the optimal cut-off scores for the Workplace Bullying Inventory. *Nurse Researcher, 25*(3), 46. https://doi.org/gcpkgp

Jenkins, M. F., Zapf, D., Winefield, H., & Sarris, A. (2012). Bullying allegations from the accused bully's perspective. *British Journal of Management, 23*(4), 489–501. https://doi.org/cs68bd

Jones, S. E., Miller, J. D., & Lynam, D. R. (2011). Personality, antisocial behavior, and aggression: A meta-analytic review. *Journal of Criminal Justice, 39*(4), 329–337. https://doi.org/b43fqz

Kahn, R. L., Wolfe, D. M., Quinn, R. P., Snoek, J. D., & Rosenthal, R. A. (1964). *Organizational stress: Studies in role conflict and ambiguity.* John Wiley & Sons.

Keashly, L. (2001). Interpersonal and systemic aspects of emotional abuse at work: The target's perspective. *Violence and Victims, 16*(3), 233–268. https://doi.org/hcd3

Keashly, L., Tye-Williams, S., & Jagatic, K. (2020). By any other name: North American perspectives on workplace bullying. In S. V. Einarsen, H. Hoel, D. Zapf, & C. Cooper (Eds.), *Bullying and harassment in the workplace: Theory, research and practice* (3rd ed., pp. 55–101). CRC Press/Taylor and Francis. https://doi.org/jhxn

Lange, S., Burr, H., Conway, P. M., & Rose, U. (2019). Workplace bullying among employees in Germany: Prevalence estimates and the role of the perpetrator. *International Archives of Occupational and Environmental Health, 92*(2), 237–247. https://doi.org/jtq7

Law, R., Dollard, M. F., Tuckey, M. R., & Dormann, C. (2011). Psychosocial safety climate as a lead indicator of workplace bullying and harassment, job resources, psychological health and employee engagement. *Accident Analysis & Prevention, 43*(5), 1782–1793. https://doi.org/fc3dwz

Leach, L. S., Poyser, C., & Butterworth, P. (2017). Workplace bullying and the association with suicidal ideation/thoughts and behaviour: A systematic review. *Occupational and Environmental Medicine, 74*(1), 72–79. https://doi.org/f9gnkk

Leon-Perez, J. M., Medina, F. J., Arenas, A., & Munduate, L. (2015). The relationship between interpersonal conflict and workplace bullying. *Journal of Managerial Psychology, 30*(3), 250–263. https://doi.org/f7cmrz

Lewis, D., Sheehan, M., & Davies, C. (2008). Uncovering workplace bullying. *Journal of Workplace Rights, 13*(3), 281–301. https://doi.org/c64cbs

Leymann, H. (1990a). *Handbok för användning av LIPT-formuläret för kartläggning av risker för psykologisk vald* [Manual of the LIPT questionnaire for assessing the risk of psychological violence at work]. Violen.

Leymann, H. (1990b). Mobbing and psychological terror at workplaces. *Violence and Victims, 5*(2), 119–126. https://doi.org/fc82

Leymann, H. (1996). The content and development of mobbing at work. *European Journal of Work and Organizational Psychology, 5*(2), 165–184. https://doi.org/bbmkdj

Linton, D. K., & Power, J. L. (2013). The personality traits of workplace bullies are often shared by their victims: Is there a dark side to victims? *Personality and Individual Differences, 54*(6), 738–743. https://doi.org/f4rcsw

Martinko, M. J., Mackey, J. D., Michalak, R., & Ashkanasy, N. M. (2017). The effects of the interactions between subordinates' and supervisors' characteristics on subordinates' perceptions of abusive supervision. In N. Bowling & M. S. Hershcovic (Eds.), *Research and theory on workplace aggression* (pp. 93–120). Cambridge University Press. https://doi.org/jhxp

Matsson, A., & Jordan, T. (2022). Workplace bullying investigations: A complex endeavor for a complex problem. *Organizational Dynamics, 51*(2), 1–11. https://doi.org/gjq9rm

Matthiesen, S. B., & Einarsen, S. (2007). Perpetrators and targets of bullying at work: Role stress and individual differences. *Violence and Victims, 22*(6), 735–753. https://doi.org/czh8g9

Mikkelsen, E. G., Hansen, Å. M., Persson, R., Brygesen, M. F., & Hogh, A. (2020). Individual consequences of being exposed to workplace bullying. In S. V. Einarsen, H. Hoel, D. Zapf, & C. L. Cooper (Eds.), *Bullying and harassment in the workplace: Theory, research, and practice* (3rd ed., pp. 163–208). CRC Press. https://doi.org/gjc9pc

Neall, A. M., & Tuckey, M. R. (2014). A methodological review of research on the antecedents and consequences of workplace harassment. *Journal of Occupational and Organizational Psychology, 87*(2), 225–257. https://doi.org/f5whx5

Neuman, J. H., & Baron, R. A. (1997). Aggression in the workplace. In R. A. Giacalone & J. Greenberg (Eds.), *Antisocial behaviour in organizations* (pp. 37–67). SAGE.

Niedhammer, I., Chastang, J. F., Sultan-Taieb, H., Vermeylen, G., & Parent-Thirion, A. (2013, August). Psychosocial work factors and sickness absence in 31 countries in Europe. *European Journal of Public Health, 23*(4), 622–629. https://doi.org/f46bng

Nielsen, M. B., & Einarsen, S. (2012). Outcomes of exposure to workplace bullying: A meta-analytic review. *Work & Stress, 26*(4), 309–332. https://doi.org/gd3zdj

Nielsen, M. B., & Einarsen, S. V. (2018). What we know, what we do not know, and what we should and could have known about workplace bullying: An overview of the literature and agenda for future research. *Aggression and Violent Behavior, 42*, 71–83. https://doi.org/gfdgpk

Nielsen, M. B., Gjerstad, J., Jacobsen, D. P., & Einarsen, S. (2017). Does ability to defend moderate the association between exposure to bullying and symptoms of anxiety? *Frontiers in Psychology, 8*, 1953. https://doi.org/hcd9

Nielsen, M. B., Glasø, L., & Einarsen, S. (2017). Exposure to workplace harassment and the Five Factor Model of personality: A meta-analysis. *Personality and Individual Differences, 104*, 195–206. https://doi.org/fc79

Nielsen, M. B., Indregard, A.-M. R., & Øverland, S. (2016). Workplace bullying and sickness absence: A systematic review and meta-analysis of the research literature. *Scandinavian Journal of Work, Environment & Health, 42*(5), 359–370. https://doi.org/f83n3q

Nielsen, M. B., & Knardahl, S. (2015). Is workplace bullying related to the personality traits of victims? A two-year prospective study. *Work & Stress, 29*(2), 128–149. https://doi.org/hb2x

Nielsen, M. B., Matthiesen, S. B., & Einarsen, S. (2010). The impact of methodological moderators on prevalence rates of workplace bullying. A meta-analysis. *Journal of Occupational and Organizational Psychology, 83*(4), 955–979. https://doi.org/10.1348/096317909X481256

Nielsen, M. B., Notelaers, G., & Einarsen, S. V. (2020). Methodological issues in the measurement of workplace bullying. In S. V. Einarsen, H. Hoel, D. Zapf, & C. Cooper (Eds.), *Bullying and harassment in the workplace: Theory, research and practice* (3rd ed., pp. 235–265). CRC Press. https://doi.org/hcd4

Niven, K., Ng, K., & Hoel, H. (2020). The bystanders of workplace bullying. In S. V. Einarsen, H. Hoel, D. Zapf, & C. L. Cooper (Eds.), *Bullying and harassment in the workplace: Theory, research, and practice* (3rd ed., pp. 385–408). CRC Press. https://doi.org/jhxq

Notelaers, G., Einarsen, S., De Witte, H., & Vermunt, J. K. (2006). Measuring exposure to bullying at work: The validity and advantages of the latent class cluster approach. *Work & Stress, 20*(4), 289–302. https://doi.org/ffw3c6

Notelaers, G., Van der Heijden, B., Guenter, H., Nielsen, M. B., & Einarsen, S. V. (2018). Do interpersonal conflict, aggression and bullying at the workplace overlap? A latent class modeling approach. *Frontiers in Psychology, 9*, 1743. https://doi.org/gffz8r

Notelaers, G., Van der Heijden, B., Hoel, H., & Einarsen, S. (2019). Measuring bullying at work with the short-negative acts questionnaire: Identification of targets and criterion validity. *Work & Stress, 33*(1), 58–75. https://doi.org/fc7c

Notelaers, G., & Van der Heijden, B. I. (2021). Construct validity in workplace bullying and harassment research. In P. D'Cruz, E. Noronha, G. Notelaers, & C. Rayner (Eds.), *Handbooks of workplace bullying, emotional abuse and harassment: Concepts, approaches and methods* (Vol. 1, pp. 369–424). Springer. https://doi.org/hb2p

O'Moore, M., Lynch, J., & Daeid, N. N. (2003). The rates and relative risks of workplace bullying in Ireland, a country of high economic growth. *International Journal of Management and Decision Making, 4*(1), 82–95. https://doi.org/d6ngws

Olweus, D. (1978). *Aggression in the schools: Bullies and whipping boys.* Hemisphere.

Olweus, D. (1993). *Bullying at school: What we know and what can we do.* Blackwell.

Olweus, D. (2013). School bullying: Development and some important challenges. *Annual Review of Clinical Psychology, 9*, 751–780. https://doi.org/gfs3w8

Podsakoff, P. M., MacKenzie, S. B., Lee, J.-Y., & Podsakoff, N. P. (2003). Common method biases in behavioral research: A critical review of the literature and recommended remedies. *Journal of Applied Psychology, 88*(5), 879–903. https://doi.org/czw

Pouwelse, M., Mulder, R., & Mikkelsen, E. G. (2021). The role of bystanders in workplace bullying: An overview of theories and empirical research. In P. D'Cruz, E. Noronha, E. Baillien, B. Catley, K. Harlos, A. Høgh, & E. G. Mikkelsen (Eds.), *Pathways of job-related negative behaviour: Handbook of workplace bullying, emotional abuse and harassment* (Vol. 2, pp. 385–422). Springer. https://doi.org/jhxr

Rai, A., & Agarwal, U. A. (2016). Workplace bullying: A review and future research directions. *South Asian Journal of Management, 23*(3), 27.

Rai, A., & Agarwal, U. A. (2018). A review of literature on mediators and moderators of workplace bullying: Agenda for future research. *Management Research Review, 41*(7), 822–859. https://doi.org/fc7d

Reknes, I., Einarsen, S., Knardahl, S., & Lau, B. (2014). The prospective relationship between role stressors and new cases of self-reported workplace bullying. *Scandinavian Journal of Psychology, 55*(1), 45–52. https://doi.org/fc7h

Reknes, I., Einarsen, S. V., Gjerstad, J., & Nielsen, M. B. (2019). Dispositional affect as a moderator in the relationship between role conflict and exposure to bullying behaviors. *Frontiers in Psychology, 10.* https://doi.org/fc7j

Reknes, I., Notelaers, G., Iliescu, D., & Einarsen, S. V. (2021). The influence of target personality in the development of workplace bullying. *Journal of Occupational Health Psychology, 26*(4), 291–303. https://doi.org/gmmtqq

Rivlin, J. N. (2001). *Conflict management climate related to employment litigation* [PhD thesis]. ProQuest One Academic (275660626).

Rizzo, J. R., House, R. J., & Lirtzman, S. I. (1970). Role conflict and ambiguity in complex organizations. *Administrative Science Quarterly, 15*(2), 150–163. https://doi.org/fvqgjc

Rodríguez-Muñoz, A., Antino, M., León-Pérez, J. M., & Ruiz-Zorrilla, P. (2022). Workplace bullying, emotional exhaustion, and partner social undermining: A weekly diary study. *Journal of Interpersonal Violence, 37*(5–6), NP3650–NP3666. https://doi.org/jjcj

Rodriguez-Munoz, A., Gil, F., & Moreno-Jimenez, B. (2012). Organisational factors and workplace bullying: The moderating role of "laissez-faire" leadership. *Revista De Psicologia Social, 27*(2), 221–231. https://doi.org/hcfc

Rosander, M., & Blomberg, S. (2019). Levels of workplace bullying and escalation—A new conceptual model based on cut-off scores, frequency and self-labelled victimization. *European Journal of Work and Organizational Psychology, 28*(6), 769–783. https://doi.org/fgsw

Saastamoinen, P., Laaksonen, M., Leino-Arjas, P., & Lahelma, E. (2009). Psychosocial risk factors of pain among employees. *European Journal of Pain, 13*(1), 102–108. https://doi.org/fg6pwc

Salin, D., Cowan, R. L., Adewumi, O., Apospori, E., Bochantin, J., D'Cruz, P., Djurkovic, N., Durniat, K., Escartín, J., & Guo, J. (2020). Prevention of and interventions in workplace bullying: A global study of human resource professionals' reflections on preferred action. *The International Journal of Human Resource Management, 31*(20), 2622–2644. https://doi.org/gftkm9

Salin, D., & Hoel, H. (2020). Organizational risk factors of workplace bullying. In S. V. Einarsen, H. Hoel, D. Zapf, & C. Cooper (Eds.), *Bullying and harassment in the workplace: Theory, research, and practice* (3rd ed., pp. 305–329). CRC Press. https://doi.org/jhxt

Schwickerath, J., & Zapf, D. (2020). Inpatient psychotherapy of bullying victims. In S. V. Einarsen, H. Hoel, D. Zapf, & C. L. Cooper (Eds.), *Bullying and harassment in the workplace: Theory, research and practice* (3rd ed., pp. 593–626). CRC Press. https://doi.org/jhxv

Sischka, P. E., Schmidt, A. F., & Steffgen, G. (2021). The effect of competition and passive avoidant leadership style on the occurrence of workplace bullying. *Personnel Review, 50*(5), 535–559. https://doi.org/hcfd

Skogstad, A., Einarsen, S., Torsheim, T., Aasland, M. S., & Hetland, H. (2007). The destructiveness of laissez-faire leadership behavior. *Journal of Occupational Health Psychology, 12*(1), 80–92. https://doi.org/b8vzt7

Solberg, M. E., & Olweus, D. (2003). Prevalence estimation of school bullying with the Olweus Bully/Victim Questionnaire. *Aggressive Behavior, 29*(3), 239–268. https://doi.org/dcs4jb

Spector, P. E., & Goh, A. (2001). The role of emotions in the occupational stress process. In P. Perrewe & D. Ganster (Eds.), *Exploring theoretical mechanisms and perspectives* (pp. 195–232). Emerald. https://doi.org/fq2v84

Tepper, B. J. (2007). Abusive supervision in work organizations: Review, synthesis, and research agenda. *Journal of Management, 33*(3), 261–289. https://doi.org/fw3bm8

Tsuno, K., & Kawakami, N. (2015). Multifactor leadership styles and new exposure to workplace bullying: A six-month prospective study. *Industrial Health, 53*(2), 139–151. https://doi.org/10.2486/indhealth.2014-0152

Tuckey, M. R., Li, Y., & Chen, P. Y. (2017). The role of transformational leadership in workplace bullying: Interactions with leaders' and followers' job characteristics in a multi-level study. *Journal of Organizational Effectiveness: People and Performance, 4*(3), 199–217. https://doi.org/gc5rnp

Van de Vliert, E. (1984). Conflict—Prevention and escalation. In P. J. D. Drenth, H. Thierry, P. J. Willems, & C. J. de Wolff (Eds.), *Handbook of work and organizational psychology* (Vol. 1, pp. 521–551). John Wiley & Sons.

Van de Vliert, E., Einarsen, S., & Nielsen, M. B. (2013). Are national levels of employee harassment cultural covariations of climato-economic conditions? *Work & Stress, 27*(1), 106–122. https://doi.org/hb2w

Van den Brande, W., Baillien, E., De Witte, H., Vander Elst, T., & Godderis, L. (2016). The role of work stressors, coping strategies and coping resources in the process of workplace bullying: A systematic review and development of a comprehensive model. *Aggression and Violent Behavior, 29*, 61–71. https://doi.org/f8wv56

Van Veldhoven, M. (2014). Quantitative job demands. In M. C. Peeters, J. De Jonge, & T. W. Taris (Eds.), *An introduction to contemporary work psychology* (pp. 117–143). John Wiley & Sons.

Vandevelde, K. (2019). *Not fitting in: Person-environment fit as a parsimonious way in understanding workplace bullying*. KU Leuven.

Vartia, M. (1996). The sources of bullying–psychological work environment and organizational climate. *European Journal of Work and Organizational Psychology, 5*(2), 203–214. https://doi.org/fcjqcg

Verkuil, B., Atasayi, S., & Molendijk, M. L. (2015). Workplace bullying and mental health: A meta-analysis on cross-sectional and longitudinal data. *PLoS ONE, 10*(8), e0135225. https://doi.org/ggb7q5

Vranjes, I., Elst, T. V., Griep, Y., De Witte, H., & Baillien, E. (2022). What goes around comes around: How perpetrators of workplace bullying become targets themselves. *Group & Organization Management*. Online first.

Vranjes, I., Salin, D., & Baillien, E. (2021). Being the bigger person: Investigating the relationship between workplace bullying exposure and enactment and the role of coping in ending the bullying spiral. *Work & Stress, 36*(2), 183–201.

Xu, T., Hanson, L. L. M., Lange, T., Starkopf, L., Westerlund, H., Madsen, I. E., Rugulies, R., Pentti, J., Stenholm, S., & Vahtera, J. (2018). Workplace bullying and violence as risk factors for type 2 diabetes: A multicohort study and meta-analysis. *Diabetologia, 61*(1), 75–83. https://doi.org/gc2b59

Xu, T., Magnusson Hanson, L. L., Lange, T., Starkopf, L., Westerlund, H., Madsen, I. E., Rugulies, R., Pentti, J., Stenholm, S., & Vahtera, J. (2019). Workplace bullying and workplace violence as risk factors for cardiovascular disease: A multi-cohort study. *European Heart Journal, 40*(14), 1124–1134. https://doi.org/gfnq78

Zahlquist, L., Hetland, J., Einarsen, S. V., Bakker, A. B., Hoprekstad, Ø. L., Espevik, R., & Olsen, O. K. (2022). Daily interpersonal conflicts and daily exposure to bullying behaviors at work: The moderating roles of trait anger and trait anxiety. *Applied Psychology, 72*(3), 893–914. https://doi.org/jhj3

Zahlquist, L., Hetland, J., Skogstad, A., Bakker, A. B., & Einarsen, S. V. (2019). Job demands as risk factors of exposure to bullying at work: The moderating role of team-level conflict management climate. *Frontiers in Psychology, 10*, 1–11, Article 2017. https://doi.org/fc8r

Zapf, D. (1999). Organisational, work group related and personal causes of mobbing/bullying at work. *International Journal of Manpower, 20*(1/2), 70–85. https://doi.org/10/b926bk

Zapf, D., & Einarsen, S. V. (2020). Individual antecedents of bullying: Personality, motives and competencies of victims and perpetrators. In S. V. Einarsen, H. Hoel, D. Zapf, & C. L. Cooper (Eds.), *Bullying and harassment in the workplace: Theory, research and practice* (3rd ed., pp. 269–303). CRC Press. https://doi.org/hcd4

Zapf, D., Escartín, J., Scheppa-Lahyani, M., Einarsen, S. V., & Vartia, M. (2020). Empirical findings on prevalence and risk groups of bullying. In S. V. Einarsen, H. Hoel, D. Zapf, & C. L. Cooper (Eds.), *Bullying and harassment in the workplace: Theory, research and practice* (3rd ed., pp. 105–162). CRC Press. https://doi.org/hcd4

Zapf, D., & Gross, C. (2001). Conflict escalation and coping with workplace bullying: A replication and extension. *European Journal of Work and Organizational Psychology, 10*(4), 497–522. https://doi.org/fbmbx8

Zapf, D., & Vartia, M. (2020). Prevention and treatment of workplace bullying: An overview. In S. V. Einarsen, H. Hoel, D. Zapf, & C. L. Cooper (Eds.), *Bullying and harassment in the workplace: Theory, research, and practice* (3rd ed., pp. 457–495). CRC Press. https://doi.org/jhxx

Stale Einarsen and Kari Wik Ågotnes

BURNOUT IN ORGANIZATIONS

OVERVIEW

A striking aspect of the vast amount of research published on job burnout is the small progress that has been made to date on actually testing solutions to the problem. The work on interventions has been so meagre that it may well reflect some profound misconceptions. One possible source of this gap may be the contrasting definitions of burnout. A second potential source is a failure of researchers and human resource (HR) practitioners to differentiate burnout as a complex syndrome from distressed states in which only one of the defining dimensions of burnout is problematic.

Defining burnout as a difficulty in the relationship of people with their workplaces relocates the problem from within people to between people. Positioning burnout as an internal, psychological problem encourages individually oriented interventions, such as mindfulness and relaxation procedures. Although these techniques are useful in themselves, they have little or no impact on the problems people encounter at work. At best they help people tolerate bad situations with greater equanimity. Locating burnout between people and their workplace has a greater potential to encourage interventions that change the context in which people work.

A fundamental definitional issue has been between burnout as a three-part syndrome (exhaustion, cynicism, and inefficacy) and burnout as simply a synonym for exhaustion. Examining differences between situations characterized by the full burnout syndrome and those characterized solely by exhaustion sheds some light on the contrasting definitions. Meaningful contrasts between burnout and exhaustion may help to focus interventions more precisely.

When burnout is viewed as a relationship problem, defining moments occur during social encounters among people at work. These encounters, especially those with people in management positions, convey important information about the workplace culture. Improving the quality of these encounters provides a perspective on the advantages of a relationships approach to burnout.

DEFINITION OF BURNOUT

Three-Part Syndrome.   Burnout is a syndrome of exhaustion, cynicism, and inefficacy that reflects occupational stress that has not been successfully managed by employees, their workplaces, or both. In stating this definition as part of developing the new version of the International Classification of Diseases (ICD-11), the World Health Organization (2019) noted that burnout is not a form of mental illness but, in parallel with chronic unemployment, is a condition making people more susceptible to experiencing physical and mental illness.

This definition aligns with burnout as measured by the Maslach Burnout Inventory (MBI) (Maslach et al., 2017). The original MBI–Human Services Survey and the MBI Educators Survey labeled the subscales emotional exhaustion, depersonalization, and diminished personal accomplishment. The MBI–General Scale introduced the labels noted in the ICD-11 statement of exhaustion, cynicism, and diminished professional efficacy (Leiter & Schaufeli, 1996).

Contrasting Definitions of Burnout. Although the MBI has been the most widely used measure of burnout, researchers and organizational consultants have used other measures. Some measures, such as the Burnout Measure (Shirom & Melamed, 2006), depict burnout as exactly equivalent to exhaustion. Adherents of this approach have not clarified the rationale for referring to exhaustion as burnout. One possibility is that the colloquial use of the term *burnout* refers primarily to feeling tired. Another possible rationale is that the exhaustion subscale of the MBI often correlates more strongly with health measures than do the other MBI subscales. In any case, the implicit argument of the exhaustion only approach is that burnout is a contemporary term to refer to the longstanding construct of exhaustion at work. Following this direction, the Burnout Measure reduces items categorizing mental, physical, and emotional exhaustion into a single factor.

Another view has equated burnout with depression (Bianchi et al., 2015). This view is based on correlations of the exhaustion subscale of the MBI with aspects of depression measures. The relationship of burnout with depression is consistent with exhaustion being a defining aspect of both. However, exhaustion is a characteristic of many dysphoric states and traits, but not everything that includes exhaustion is the same thing. That would be parallel to arguing that every disease that includes a fever is the same disease and there is no virtue in differential diagnosis. Bianchi et al. (2015) pointed out that both depression and burnout correlate with workplace measure, which is consistent with depression as a mental illness that pertains to all life domains, while burnout pertains primarily to the workplace. They attend less to burnout pertaining less to nonwork domains while depression does pertain to nonwork domains.

A primary contrast of burnout with depression is that depression is a disease and burnout is an occupational condition in the ICD context. Although experiencing burnout may reflect workplace conditions that contribute to experiencing depression, depression as a disease pervades other aspects of a person's life. Specifically, burnout is operationalized with specific reference to the workplace whereas depression is not. Both can have ramifications beyond the workplace, but burnout per se as measured is a workplace phenomenon.

PROFILES

Conceptual Framework. Burnout is a three-part syndrome of exhaustion, cynicism, and inefficacy rather than a single dimension experience. There is no crisp dividing line between burnout and no burnout. The lack of a binary cutoff point to provide a definitive designation of burnout has been a matter of contention. The tension reflects the MBI's history of being developed to assess a social science construct that is often viewed as a disease. The issue is especially intense in writings on physician burnout. Physicians aspire to binary diagnoses: the patients either have a disease or they do not. A disease diagnosis prompts certain protocols that are appropriate only in the context of a diagnosis. The design of the MBI coupled with its status as an occupational condition defies this approach.

An approach that is especially prevalent in research on physician burnout is using a third of cutoff scores on each of the three MBI subscales. Scoring above the 67 percentile on exhaustion or cynicism or below the 33 percentile score on efficacy is a sign of high burnout. This approach encounters the problem inherent in any dichotomizing of a continuous scale. It loses valuable information by treating a difference of less than a point as equivalent to a difference of 7 (the full range on the MBI's 0 to 6 scale). This equivalence is not credible in light of the MBI scales being designed to reflect a matter of degree: bigger intervals in scores reflect bigger underlying differences. Furthermore, no research has established that scores on one side of the percentile line are associated with qualitatively different experiences than scores on the other side of that line. Characterizing these cutoff-derived scores as reflecting high burnout assumes that a third of the working public is at any time experiencing burnout. The problem becomes magnified in reports that label scoring beyond the cutoff on any one of the three MBI subscales as burnout that can lead to more than half of a sample being labeled as such.

ANALYTICAL APPROACHES

These uses of the MBI raises two questions: whether all three of the MBI subscales assess dimensions for which extreme negative scores reflect a meaningful problem for people at work, and whether these states are distinguishable from job burnout as defined as problematic experiences on all three of these dimensions. Person-focused analysis provides techniques for exploring these questions. Methods including cluster analysis and latent profile analysis (LPA) use iterative processes on large samples to determine whether scores on the three subscales of the MBI cluster in distinct ways. For example, if a cluster analysis or LPA determined that the only meaningful clusters were people scoring high, medium, and low on all three subscales, then person-focused analysis has little to offer beyond what one could discover by combining the three subscales into a summary score. The more highly correlated the three subscales, the more likely this pattern would emerge. However, among the MBI subscales, exhaustion and cynicism correlate strongly and each has low to moderate correlations with efficacy. This lower interdependency allows other patterns to emerge from person-focused analyses.

Person-focused analyses have found the MBI to yield interesting patterns with both cross-sectional and longitudinal analyses (Leiter & Maslach, 2016; Mäkikangas & Kinnunen, 2016; Mäkikangas et al., 2020). Leiter and Maslach (2016) described five worklife profiles:

- Engaged: Energy, Involvement, Efficacy
- Ineffective: Energy, Involvement, Inefficacy
- Overextended: Exhaustion, Involvement, Efficacy
- Disengaged: Energy, Cynicism, Efficacy
- Burnout: Exhaustion, Cynicism, Inefficacy

In this outline, energy, as the opposite of exhaustion, indicates that respondents feel they have access to sufficient energy to address work demands. Involvement, as the opposite of cynicism, indicates the capacity to maintain interest in people, ideas, and activities, and to feel enthusiasm for work. Efficacy is the direct assessment of the efficacy or personal accomplishment subscale that has positive wording such that a high score indicates greater efficacy—confidence in one's capacity to have an impact through one's work—and a low score indicates inefficacy.

Contrasting profiles on key areas of worklife found that the intermediate profiles—Ineffective, Overextended, and Disengaged—were associated with challenges that differed in intensity and in kind from those associated with burnout. Unsurprisingly, burnout was associated with negative scores on all areas of worklife while Engagement was associated with positive scores on those constructs.

The Ineffective profile reflected a positive assessment of workload and an average assessment of other areas of worklife in contrast to the positive view of these other areas in the Engaged profile (Leiter & Maslach, 2016). Regarding social encounters, the Ineffective profile not only reflected low frequencies of incivility but also relatively low frequencies of positive social encounters that were prevalent in the Engaged profile. Overall, the Ineffective profile was not reporting distress, but it did not have positive views of worklife either. The message was more that work was okay rather than that work was a source of meaning and fulfillment, as was the case with the Engaged profile.

The Overextended profile had one intense issue: workload was unmanageable. The assessment of other areas of worklife was moderate but the ratings of manageable workload were negative, in many instances as negative as was found for the Burnout profile. People in the Overextended profile were not cynical: they often loved their work and believed in it. They did not experience low efficacy: to some extent their intense workload confirmed that they were capable and perhaps indispensable. But they were exhausted and saw few opportunities to escape the pressure from work demands. People in the Overextended profile report both lower frequency of civility and more frequent incivility from others at work. The combination of unmanageable workload with strained social encounters makes for a more distressing and exhausting worklife.

Salvagioni et al. (2017) conducted a systematic review that confirmed that burnout pertains as much to the Overextended profile as to the Burnout profile in that many outcomes in studies they reviewed related primarily or exclusively to exhaustion. This is especially the case in studies assessing burnout with the Shirom and Melamed (2006) scale that essentially relabels exhaustion as burnout in that its items pertain only to exhaustion. Notwithstanding, chronic exhaustion at work remains a problem worthy of attention in itself. For example, in a systematic review of the literature Salvagioni et al. (2017) found exhaustion to be a predictor of the following physical consequences: hypercholesterolemia, type 2 diabetes, coronary heart disease, hospitalization due to cardiovascular disorder, musculoskeletal pain, changes in pain experiences, prolonged fatigue, headaches, gastrointestinal issues, respiratory problems, severe injuries, and mortality below the age of 45 years. Additional psychological effects include insomnia, depressive symptoms, use of psychotropic and antidepressant medications, hospitalization for mental disorders, and psychological ill-health symptoms (Armon et al., 2008; Bianchi et al., 2015; Hakanen et al., 2011; Salvagioni et al., 2017). These conditions can occur with both the Overextended and the Burnout profile because of their close association with exhaustion.

The Disengaged profile has a few complaints about workload, but, consistent with its high score on cynicism, experiences mismatches on other areas of worklife. People in the Disengaged profile reported lower scores on fairness and a poorer alignment of personal values with workplace values. There is less of a sense of control, consistent with complaints about micromanagement or lower trust in management at the workplace.

The Burnout profile combines the negative aspects of all three of the intermediate profiles. People in the Burnout profile report feeling overwhelmed by unmanageable workload as well as mismatches on the other areas of worklife. They report work experiences of unrewarding work that conflicts with their personal or professional values. They feel unfairly treated and lacking control over how they do their work. Their social encounters include frequent incivility and infrequent instances of appreciating, inclusion, and civility. Except for sharing Overextended's low rating of manageable workload, the Burnout profile is associated with more extreme negative scores on worklife than any other profile.

The most positive profile is labeled Engaged as it reflects a state of energetic involvement in work that confirms a sense of efficacy. The terminology follows the book *The Truth About Burnout* (Maslach & Leiter, 1997) that proposed engagement as the opposite pole from burnout in that it encompassed the positive pole on all three MBI subscales. Fortunately, the Engaged profile was the most frequent in person-focused analyses of the MBI (Leiter & Maslach, 2016).

BURNOUT AS A RELATIONSHIP PROBLEM

As a social psychological construct, burnout is more of a relationship problem than an individual problem. In contrast to clinical or personality perspectives that locate virtues and problems within people, social and organizational psychology locates them between people or between people and their social context, such as the workplace. People experiencing problems at work does not necessarily mean that individuals are flawed or have shortcomings in their capacity to work or to cope with adversity. Similarly, it does not signal shortcomings for the workplace in terms of unreasonable demands or toxicity in the workplace. Such problems, instead, indicate that the relationships of at least some people with the workplace are not going well. This perspective aligns with survey responses that repeatedly show that many people are managing well in settings where some people fit into Overextended or Burnout profiles. The same setting can be manageable for some and not for others.

Research methods often obscure the preponderance of a relationship perspective. The job demands–resources (JD–R) model (Demerouti et al., 2001) frames dynamics in terms of the setting primarily with a secondary reference to the role of personal resources in the likelihood of people experiencing burnout or work engagement. However, the vast majority of research evaluating this model derive information about job demands and the adequacy of job resources from individual employees completing surveys about their perceptions of their workplaces. As a result, the survey responses convey more immediately respondents' relationship with the workplace. People who are having difficulty with a workplace resource, such as a management information system, can provide valid critiques of those resources, but they filter those evaluations with the disappointments and frustrations they have experienced dealing with those resources. They are not objective evaluators. Similarly, the areas of worklife model (Leiter & Maslach, 2004, 2011) assesses employees' evaluation of manageable workload, control, reward, community, fairness, and values, yielding more immediately a picture of employees' relationship with their workplaces on those issues.

When the preponderance of responses casts doubt on the viability of key areas of worklife, leadership is well advised to examine possible shortcomings in policies, practices, and structures to find more workable solutions. However, when the evidence is less clear cut in locating problems within the work environment, a more fruitful approach could involve finding ways of allowing employees more latitude in interacting with those areas of worklife. Employees for whom things are already working well may be disrupted by global changes intended to improve the lot for some. Therefore, rather than change things for everyone, it may work better to open ways for employees to improve their interactions with the areas. Improving the capacity of first-line managers to have difficult but constructive conversations with their employees would increase the potential for developing better fits between employee aspirations and workplace conditions.

Meta-analyses of the burnout literature on healthcare providers have identified personal characteristics associated with burnout, such as anxiety and poor emotional intelligence (Pradas-Hernández et al., 2018). The personal characteristics identified are apt to present challenges in developing a positive relationship with work. For example, poor emotional intelligence can inhibit employees' capacity to express civility and respect in their social encounters with colleagues and supervisors. Such problems are especially likely in diverse and complex workplaces where employees' preconceptions about others are likely to fall short. Both anxiety and poor social intelligence have a potential to inhibit active listening and explicit expressions of appreciation that help people build supportive relationships with others at work. In contrast, flexibility as both a personal characteristic and a quality of workplaces allows for developing more viable relationships with work (Ruiz & Odriozola-González, 2017). Personal qualities are most relevant when they shape the relationships people develop with their workplaces.

Bauernhofer et al. (2018), using a person-oriented analysis, contrasted people in an Overextended profile (high exhaustion) with people with the full Burnout profile (high exhaustion, cynicism, and inefficacy), noting that the latter reported more extensive disruptions of their social relationships at work. These problems included difficult encounters with supervisors, colleagues, and service recipients. They argue that these problems call for organizational approaches for burnout while the Overextended profile leaves more individual-focused options for action.

Focusing on organizational outcomes encourages a relationship perspective on burnout and related conditions. That is, making individual distress associated with burnout the primary research focus keeps the focus on individuals rather than their work context. An important organizational focus has been patient safety in healthcare organizations. In their systematic review Hall et al. (2016) noted that 21 of 30 studies reviewed found burnout to be associated with patient safety. Although these studies used established burnout measures, measures of patient safety were inconsistent in content as well as quality. Despite these limitations, this research encourages a more organizational perspective on the syndrome. Their focus is not solely the health or well-being of employees, but the capacity of organizations to fulfill their missions.

The quality of supervisory and coworker relationships has been a primary focus of research on burnout for decades. Leiter and Maslach (1988) determined that coworker relationships were more closely related to the exhaustion aspects of burnout while supervisory relationships had broader connections across all three aspects of the syndrome, a pattern that has been confirmed in studies conducted since the 2010s (e.g., Charoensukmongkol et al., 2016). In a systemic review and meta-analysis O'Connor et al. (2018) emphasized the importance of the supervisory relationship in the development of job burnout. Regarding exhaustion, supervisors have control over assigning workload to employees. Even when attempting to even-handedly assign equal work across employees, individuals may vary considerably in their capacity to manage certain types of work. In addition, a critical relationship quality in the supervisory relationship is fairness. With the ongoing flow of day-to-day decisions that supervisors make in organizational life, employees have many occasions to judge the extent to which they perceive fairness. Any actions that can be judged as reflecting favoritism can have an impact on trust and respect going forward. Overall, social encounters with people in leadership positions, from immediate supervisors to CEOs, provide a medium through which employees experience the culture of an organization.

SOCIAL RELATIONSHIPS AND BURNOUT

Research on workplace civility and incivility has shifted attention from social support or general workplace culture to specific social encounters in which people participate at work on a regular basis (Cortina et al., 2001). The balance between respect and disrespect in day-to-day social encounters plays a major role in determining whether employees fulfill their need for belonging in the workplace community (Leiter, 2012). Following Deci and Ryan (1987) respect functions as a highly informative quality in workplace encounters regarding its potential for providing fulfillment of the core motives of belonging, efficacy, and autonomy. Disrespect essentially excludes its targets as valid members of the community; it conveys that they do not belong. Furthermore, to experience a sense of efficacy, people need more than to be simply tolerated within a community. They find fulfillment as respected and valued members of their workplace communities through their potential to contribute to its well-being, its mission, or both. Regarding autonomy, the capacity to take initiative in the workplace rests upon a foundation of respect. The respect and support of supervisors and colleagues provide a basis for taking initiative in ways that move beyond the usual workplace constraints.

An important focus within research on incivility is appreciating the power of subtle social behaviors that may not arise from a deliberate intent to disregard others. Earlier research on social mistreatment at work gave more weight to high intensity abusive behavior. The shifted focus to incivility has emphasized that a message of disrespect embedded in subtle actions can have equal impact to the implicit threats in abusive bullying (Hershcovis, 2011). In workplaces committed to some level of professional conduct for employees, low intensity incivility may be the preferred course because it allows negative behavior to stay within the letter of the workplace's code of conduct.

A workgroup-focused intervention that was successful in improving civility while reducing incivility found that improved civility mediated reductions in exhaustion and cynicism (Leiter et al., 2011). The series of facilitated sessions guided employees in broadening their awareness of the impact of incivility on one another. But rather than emphasizing negative behaviors, the primary strategies encouraged employees to increase the frequency of civil behavior to convey acceptance and appreciation of others. To some extent this approach changes the work environment, but it does so by focusing on the relationship of people with the workplace as mediated through their social encounters. Keeping the focus within intact workgroups encompasses the encounters that function as an ongoing part of their worklife. The CREW (civility, respect, and engagement with work) approach was embedded in the work environment with actions for participants to enact during their workdays. At subsequent sessions, the facilitator led discussions of their experiences in changing the pattern of social encounters at work.

TAKING ACTION

Intervention research divides into approaches that seek to change the workplace and those that seek to change individuals. Individual-focused interventions have operated primarily on relaxation, mindfulness, and building resilience (Awa et al., 2010). Maricuțoiu et al. (2016) found in a meta-analysis that these approaches primarily reduced exhaustion but had little discernable impact on the cynicism or inefficacy aspects of the syndrome. These studies included cognitive behavioral therapy (CBT), meditation, relaxation, interpersonal skill training, and job skill training. For example, Ghannam et al. (2020) provided medical residents with a 1-day training session that included defining the concept of stress, ways of detecting job stressors and stress outcomes, how to implement relaxation techniques (including sleep hygiene and breathing exercises), strategies for cognitive restructuring, and techniques for improving time management. Meanwhile, Hofer et al. (2018) used an even less intrusive intervention of providing participants with a self-help book based on principles from acceptance and commitment therapy (ACT) without any reference to participants' work context. Compared to a waiting list control group that had not yet received the book, the treatment group showed fewer indications of burnout at post-test.

A randomized control trial of a mindfulness-, acceptance-, and value-based intervention (MAV) for burnout, using a person-centered analysis, found the strongest impact on a variety of well-being measures was evident for the profile that showed an immediate increase in mindfulness skills coupled with a decrease in exhaustion (Kinnunen et al., 2020). That pattern presaged participants retaining the benefits to well-being at follow-up assessments occurring at 4 months and 8 months following the intervention. In contrast, those who did not combine skill acquisition with decreased exhaustion were unlikely to show subsequent benefits. Kinnunen et al. proposed that additional follow-up training sessions may be necessary when the initial uptake is not evident at the assessment immediately following the training.

Another individual-focused intervention in health care found that a combination of Hatha yoga and mindfulness exercises was helpful in reducing various stress indicators, including exhaustion on the MBI (Sallon et al., 2017). The specific impact on exhaustion was consistent with the stress-management quality of the intervention. The participants did not necessarily change their relationship with their work or their work setting, but they reduced the extent to which they experienced distress while continuing their existing work patterns.

Studies often applied interventions to people who did not necessarily evidence all three aspects of burnout in pre-tests, increasing the difficulty of identifying effects of the interventions. However, the predominant correlates of the three aspects of burnout are job characteristics, including long work shifts, heavy patient load, difficult access to work-related information, and poor supervisory relationships.

Organizational Interventions. Organizational-level interventions are difficult to design, implement, and assess. Researchers have little or no authority in organizational research settings. Research opportunities rest on their capacity to convince employees and managers to cooperate with their plans. Practical considerations as well as research ethics requires researchers to invite participants to understand the research plan, contributing to shaping how it is implemented and evaluated. These qualities run at odds with the standards of randomized control trials with regard to double blind formats and the designation of treatment and control groups. Evaluating the impact of interventions calls for innovative strategies to overcome subjective perspectives and to identify active mechanisms contributing to change (Nielsen et al., 2008). McKinley et al. (2017) noted the challenges in conducting meta-analysis of intervention studies using workshop formats, in that they could find little or no consistency across studies in the content of such interventions. They attributed this variation to weak theoretical frameworks, leaving much of the intervention design to be reactive to local issues.

Job crafting guides employees through a process of revising their relationship with work by modifying specific aspects of their work. The general principle is increasing activities that employees experience as engaging and reducing activities that they find tedious or meaningless. Although job requirements may prevent employees from completely relinquishing some activities, they explore the extent to which they can reduce the time that they devote to disengaging activities. Shifting time from tedious activities to engaging activities has the potential for improving relationships with work. In their quasi-experimental designed study van den Heuvel et al. (2015) used pre- and post-measurements among 86 employees of a Dutch police district. Participants completed a survey prior to the intervention (T1, pre-measure) and 1 or 2 weeks after the intervention (T2, post-treatment measure). All participants received an online feedback report after completing the pre- and post-questionnaire. In between pre- and post-measures, participants completed weekly diaries during the 4 weeks of job crafting. Of the 52 people who participated in the intervention at T1, 39 continued and participated at T2. This group (n = 39) formed the experimental group. A control group of 47 employees was created by requesting participants to ask a colleague with a similar job to fill in the same questionnaires. A distinctive outcome of this study was an increase in self-efficacy at work. By focusing on the day-to-day patterns of work, the intervention went beyond stress or exhaustion reduction. Instead, the authors argue, job crafting triggered a process of positive experiences, improving a sense of goal achievement in their work. By shifting time and effort away from tedious activities and toward valued activities, more of the workday became rewarding time. The control group showed none of these improvements in their self-efficacy at work.

In an extensive review of organizational health interventions, Burges et al. (2020) critiqued the research literature as lacking a theoretical foundation. Instead, many interventions appeared to operate on a trial-and-error manner, capitalizing on opportunities in a specific situation. This critique aligns with the power status of principals in such projects. Researchers are generally external agents requiring permission from organizational leaders whose priorities differ from those of research design. Progress on organizational interventions to address burnout has proceeded slowly. Although the nature of work changes over time, it does so without a systematic framework that could inform a theory of burnout.

CONCLUSION

Much is known about the correlates of burnout. However, much remains unclear about their sequences: which of these correlates are precursors? Which are consequences? Which are coincident with burnout? This ambiguity rests largely with research methodology in that the vast bulk of published research on the topic rests upon cross-sectional questionnaires. Even the smaller body of longitudinal research leaves many questions unresolved. Organizational settings have existed long before researchers arrive. Their initial questionnaires do not mark the beginning of a process. They drop into the middle of an ongoing stream. Even with a few longitudinal surveys, it is difficult to untangle the dependencies among constructs that evolve across the history of the organization. With some organizations this process can be long and complex.

Conceptually, it makes sense that causality occurs in multiple directions. For example, work demands that people perceive as excessive can cause fatigue. And fatigue can affect what people judge to be excessive in their workload. One direction need not have priority. Employees can be exhausted by their work demands. They can also arrive at work exhausted because of illness, personal life demands, or a dissipated lifestyle. The central idea is that exhaustion and work overload align with one another and that this alignment likely reflects causal links. However, it does not follow that those causal links are simple or unidirectional.

In that way, given the state of current knowledge, it may be more constructive to depict the connections among the burnout aspects and qualities of people and qualities of workplaces as maintaining a balance rather than stating that one element causes another. In the courses of things, events within the workplace can disrupt that balance. The disruption may improve things or worsen things for employees, but in either case, the elements find a new equilibrium that maintains for a time.

Whether to untangle causal pathways or to improve the quality of worklife, the critical need for burnout research is well-designed intervention studies that deliberately change the workplace to determine the impact on exhaustion, cynicism, and inefficacy. Despite consistent calls for more intervention research, it remains rare. Furthermore, few interventions attempt to change the workplace. Most intervention studies sought to improve employees' capacity to endure the workplace as it is. That is, stress management, which may include relaxation or cognitive behavioral therapy, leaves the workplace unchanged. The implicit assumption is that employees experiencing aspects of burnout have a deficit that can be corrected through training. It is not surprising that improvements occur most readily in the exhaustion aspect of the syndrome: better coping skills can help people avoid feeling overwhelmed. However, the other two aspects of the syndrome—cynicism and efficacy—fail to improve with better coping. These aspects of the syndrome may require the work itself to become more meaningful and fulfilling. Although one may hope that improved coping will enable employees to take measures to improve the workplace, these approaches do not explicitly provide skills for making such changes. Without a systematic approach to making such changes, the results would be difficult to explain or to propagate in other settings.

The key implication for research is that the primary focus lies in connections of people within the job. Simply assessing burnout and demographics tells something about the people but fails to shed light on how they connect or disconnect with the workplace. A more complete picture entails assessing not only the objective structures and processes of workplaces, but also how people understand those structures and processes. That information can begin to identify the points of matches and mismatches from the employees' perspective. Assessing employees' social encounters provides another perspective on mismatches in that it suggests that people who receive frequent incivility from others are not valued by their colleagues. Receiving frequent incivility from supervisors conveys disrespect toward recipients from the workplace, as actions by managers often serve as a proxy for workplace values. It may be that the mismatch is not solely from the employees' point of view but from the workplace perspective as well.

Viewing burnout as a relationship problem may encourage intervention research to address the workplace by locating problems between people rather than within people. Job crafting takes an important step in that direction in developing employees' capacity to shape their jobs in a bottom-up capacity. This practice opens possibilities for improving the fit between employees' aspirations and the job's characteristics. Improving workplace civility provides another source of progress in translating employees' general relationship with work to their social encounters with key people at work.

FURTHER READING

Bakker, A. B., Emmerik, H. V., & Euwema, M. C. (2006). Crossover of burnout and engagement in work teams. *Work and Occupations, 33*(4), 464–489.

Demerouti, E., Bakker, A. B., Nachreiner, F., & Schaufeli, W. B. (2001). The job demands-resources model of burnout. *Journal of Applied Psychology, 86*(3), 499.

Dreison, K. C., Luther, L., Bonfils, K. A., Sliter, M. T., McGrew, J. H., & Salyers, M. P. (2018). Job burnout in mental health providers: A meta-analysis of 35 years of intervention research. *Journal of Occupational Health Psychology, 23*(1), 18–30.

Eckleberry-Hunt, J., Kirkpatrick, H., & Barbera, T. (2018). The problems with burnout research. *Academic Medicine, 93*(3), 367–370.

Han, S., Shanafelt, T. D., Sinsky, C. A., Awad, K. M., Dyrbye, L. N., Fiscus, L. C., Trockel, M., & Goh, J. (2019). Estimating the attributable cost of physician burnout in the United States. *Annals of Internal Medicine, 170*(11), 784–790.

Maslach, C., & Leiter, M. P. (1997). *The truth about burnout.* Jossey Bass.

Maslach, C., Schaufeli, W. B., & Leiter, M. P. (2001). Job burnout. *Annual Review of Psychology, 52*(1), 397–422.

Rotenstein, L. S., Torre, M., Ramos, M. A., Rosales, R. C., Guille, C., Sen, S., & Mata, D. A. (2018). Prevalence of burnout among physicians: A systematic review. *JAMA, 320*(11), 1131–1150.

REFERENCES

Armon, G., Shirom, A., Shapira, I., & Melamed, S. (2008). On the nature of burnout–insomnia relationships: A prospective study of employed adults. *Journal of Psychosomatic Research, 65*(1), 5–12.

Awa, W. L., Plaumann, M., & Walter, U. (2010). Burnout prevention: A review of intervention programs. *Patient Education and Counseling, 78*(2), 184–190.

Bauernhofer, K., Bassa, D., Canazei, M., Jiménez, P., Paechter, M., Papousek, I., Fink, A., & Weiss, E. M. (2018). Subtypes in clinical burnout patients enrolled in an employee rehabilitation program: Differences in burnout profiles, depression, and recovery/resources-stress balance. *BMC Psychiatry, 18*(10), 1–13. https://doi.org/10.1186/s12888-018-1589-y

Bianchi, R., Schonfeld, I. S., & Laurent, E. (2015). Burnout–depression overlap: A review. *Clinical Psychology Review, 36*(1), 28–41.

Burgess, M. G., Brough, P., Biggs, A., & Hawkes, A. J. (2020). Why interventions fail: A systematic review of occupational health psychology interventions. *International Journal of Stress Management, 27*(2), 195–207. https://doi.apa.org/doi/10.1037/str0000144

Charoensukmongkol, P., Moqbel, M., Gutierrez-Wirsching, S., & Shankar, R. (2016). The role of coworker and supervisor support on job burnout and job satisfaction. *Journal of Advances in Management Research*, 13(1), 1–10. https://doi.org/10.1108/JAMR-06-2014-0037

Cortina, L. M., Magley, V. J., Williams, J. H., & Langhout, R. D. (2001). Incivility in the workplace: Incidence and impact. *Journal of Occupational Health Psychology*, 6(1), 64–80.

Deci, E. L., & Ryan, R. M. (1987). The support of autonomy and the control of behavior. *Journal of Personality & Social Psychology*, 53(6), 1024–1037. https://psycnet.apa.org/doi/10.1037/0022-3514.53.6.1024

Demerouti, E., Bakker, A. B., De Jonge, J., Janssen, P. P., & Schaufeli, W. B. (2001). Burnout and engagement at work as a function of demands and control. *Scandinavian Journal of Work, Environment & Health*, 27(4), 279–286.

Ghannam, J., Afana, A., Ho, E. Y., Al-Khal, A., & Bylund, C. L. (2020). The impact of a stress management intervention on medical residents' stress and burnout. *International Journal of Stress Management*, 27(1), 65–73. https://doi.apa.org/doi/10.1037/str0000125

Hakanen, J. J., Bakker, A. B., & Jokisaari, M. (2011). A 35-year follow-up study on burnout among Finnish employees. *Journal of Occupational Health Psychology*, 16(3), 345–360.

Hall, L. H., Johnson, J., Watt, I., Tsipa, A., & O'Connor, D. B. (2016). Healthcare staff wellbeing, burnout, and patient safety: A systematic review. *PLoS ONE*, 11(7), e0159015. https://doi.org/10.1371/journal.pone.0159015

Hershcovis, M. (2011). "Incivility, social undermining, bullying...oh my!": A call to reconcile constructs within workplace aggression research. *Journal of Organizational Behavior*, 32(3), 499–519.

Hofer, P. D., Waadt, M., Aschwanden, R., Milidou, M., Acker, J., Meyer, A. H., Lieb, R., & Gloster, A. T. (2018). Self-help for stress and burnout without therapist contact: An online randomised controlled trial. *Work & Stress*, 32(2), 189–208. https://doi.org/10.1080/02678373.2017.1402389

Kinnunen, S. M., Puolakanaho, A., Mäkikangas, A., Tolvanen, A., & Lappalainen, R. (2020). Does a mindfulness-, acceptance-, and value-based intervention for burnout have long-term effects on different levels of subjective well-being? *International Journal of Stress Management*, 27(1), 82–87. https://doi.apa.org/doi/10.1037/str0000132

Leiter, M. P. (2012). *Analyzing and theorizing the dynamics of the workplace incivility crisis*. Springer.

Leiter, M. P., Laschinger, H. K. S., Day, A., & Gilin-Oore, D. (2011). The impact of civility interventions on employee social behavior, distress, and attitudes. *Journal of Applied Psychology*, 96(6), 1258–1274.

Leiter, M. P., & Maslach, C. (1988). The impact of interpersonal environment on burnout and organizational commitment. *Journal of Organizational Behavior*, 9(4), 297–308.

Leiter, M. P., & Maslach, C. (2004). Areas of worklife: A structured approach to organizational predictors of job burnout. In P. Perrewé & D. C. Ganster (Eds.), *Emotional and physiological processes and positive intervention strategies* (pp. 91–134). Research in Occupational Stress and Well Being: 3. Elsevier.

Leiter, M. P., & Maslach, C. (2011). *Areas of worklife scale manual* (5th ed.). Mindgarden.

Leiter, M. P., & Maslach, C. (2016). Latent burnout profiles: A new approach to understanding the burnout experience. *Burnout Research*, 3(4), 89–100. https://doi.org/10.1016/j.burn.2016.09.001

Leiter, M. P., & Schaufeli, W. B. (1996). Consistency of the burnout construct across occupations. *Anxiety, Stress, & Coping*, 9(3), 229–243.

Mäkikangas, A., & Kinnunen, U. (2016). The person-oriented approach to burnout: A systematic review. *Burnout Research*, 3(1), 11–23. https://doi.org/10.1016/j.burn.2015.12.002

Mäkikangas, A., Leiter, M. P., Kinnunen, U., & Feldt, T. (2020). Profiling development of burnout over eight years: Relation with job demands and resources. *European Journal of Work and Organizational Psychology*, 1–12. https://doi.org/10.1080/1359432X.2020.1790651

Maricuțoiu, L. P., Sava, F. A., & Butta, O. (2016). The effectiveness of controlled interventions on employees' burnout: A meta-analysis. *Journal of Occupational and Organizational Psychology*, 89(1), 1–27. https://doi.org/10.1111/joop.12099

Maslach, C., Jackson, S. E., & Leiter, M. P. (2017). *Maslach burnout inventory manual* (4th ed.). Mindgarden Press.

Maslach, C., & Leiter, M. P. (1997). *The truth about burnout.* Jossey Bass.

McKinley, T. F., Boland, K. A., & Mahan, J. D. (2017). Burnout and interventions in pediatric residency: A literature review. *Burnout Research, 6*(1), 9–17. https://doi.org/10.1016/j.burn.2017.02.003

Nielsen, K., Randall, R., Yarker, J., & Brenner, S. O. (2008). The effects of transformational leadership on followers' perceived work characteristics and psychological well-being: A longitudinal study. *Work & Stress, 22*(1), 16–32.

O'Connor, K., Neff, D. M., & Pitman, S. (2018). Burnout in mental health professionals: A systematic review and meta-analysis of prevalence and determinants. *European Psychiatry, 53*(1), 74–99.

Pradas-Hernández, L., Ariza, T., Gómez-Urquiza, J. L., Albendín-García, L., De la Fuente, E. I., & Cañadas-De la Fuente, G. A. (2018). Prevalence of burnout in paediatric nurses: A systematic review and meta-analysis. *PLoS ONE, 13*(4), e0195039. https://doi.org/10.1371/journal.pone.0195039

Ruiz, F. J., & Odriozola-González, P. (2017). The predictive and moderating role of psychological flexibility in the development of job burnout. *Universitas Psychologica, 16*(4), 1–8. https://doi.org/10.11144/Javeriana.upsy16-4.pmrp

Sallon, S., Katz-Eisner, D., Yaffe, H., & Bdolah-Abram, T. (2017). Caring for the caregivers: Results of an extended, five-component stress-reduction intervention for hospital staff. *Behavioral Medicine, 43*(1), 47–60. https://doi.org/10.1080/08964289.2015.1053426

Salvagioni, D. A. J., Melanda, F. N., Mesas, A. E., González, A. D., Gabani, F. L., & de Andrade, S. M. (2017). Physical, psychological and occupational consequences of job burnout: A systematic review of prospective studies. *PLoS ONE, 12*(10), e0185781. https://doi.org/10.1371/journal.pone.0185781

Shirom, A., & Melamed, S. (2006). A comparison of the construct validity of two burnout measures in two groups of professionals. *International Journal of Stress Management, 13*(2), 176.

van den Heuvel, M., Demerouti, E., & Peeters, M. C. W. (2015). The job crafting intervention: Effects on job resources, self-efficacy, and affective well-being. *Journal of Occupational and Organizational Psychology, 88*(3), 511–532. https://doi.org/10.1111/joop.12128

World Health Organization. (2019, May 28). *Burn-out an "occupational phenomenon": International Classification of Diseases.* https://www.who.int/mental_health/evidence/burn-out/en/

Michael P. Leiter and Jo Wintle

ORGANIZATIONAL DEHUMANIZATION

INTRODUCTION

Twenty-first-century workers face a substantial risk of being brought closer to the status of instruments and further away from humanity. While undergoing ever-changing technological breakthroughs, organizations may undertake restructuring processes aimed at reducing the size of the workforce while still coping with the same workload (Caesens et al., 2017). On top of these issues, a considerable number of workers across the globe work in hazardous and inhumane conditions ranging from unsafe practices to modern slavery (Christ et al., 2020). Many modern workplaces may thus be impersonal environments where personal subjectivity collides with capitalistic injunctions (Bell & Khoury, 2011), formal bureaucratic procedures (Caesens et al., 2017), or indecent work conditions (Christ et al., 2020), to name a few. Providing fertile ground for employees' perceptions of being treated as tools owned and used by their organization for its own ends (Caesens et al., 2017), these challenges spotlight the need for psychological considerations of employees' perceptions of a dehumanized relationship with their employing organizations (Bell & Khoury, 2011). In line with this, researchers have started to examine the negative side of the employee–organization relationship through the concept of organizational dehumanization (e.g., Bell & Khoury, 2011; Caesens et al., 2017), defined as "the experience of an employee who feels objectified by his or her organization, denied personal subjectivity, and made to feel like a tool or instrument for the organization's ends" (Bell & Khoury, 2011, p. 170).

Given its deleterious consequences for both employees and organizations (e.g., Caesens et al., 2017), organizational dehumanization has attracted increasing scholarly attention. This work has provided significant empirical evidence of its nomological network. Specifically, various categories of antecedents and consequences, as well as explaining and moderating mechanisms, of organizational dehumanization have been identified (e.g., Bell & Khoury, 2011, 2016; Caesens et al., 2019; Caesens et al., 2017; Lagios et al., 2021; Nguyen, Dao et al., 2021; Stinglhamber et al., 2021; Taskin et al., 2019). As part of these necessary efforts to advance theory regarding employees' perceptions of being dehumanized by their organization (e.g., Stinglhamber et al., 2021), this article pursues different aims. First, it briefly summarizes the historical background behind the concept of organizational dehumanization in order to clarify its conceptualization and its operationalization in the field of work and organizational psychology. Second, it clarifies how organizational dehumanization differs conceptually from related constructs in the psychological literature such as perceived organizational support, perceived organizational obstruction, or working objectification. Third, it reviews past research findings to provide an integrated view of the nomological network of organizational dehumanization including its antecedents and consequences as well as its explaining and moderating mechanisms. Finally, it identifies promising directions for future research.

HISTORICAL BACKGROUND, CONCEPTUALIZATION, AND OPERATIONALIZATION

Before entering the field of organizational psychology, the concept of dehumanization drew the interest of social psychologists (for reviews, see Haslam, 2006; Haslam & Loughnan, 2014). According to Haslam (2006), dehumanization is commonly referred to as the result of the process by which an individual is made to feel deprived of human attributes, which leads her or him to feel more like an animal or machine. In other words, one's human characteristics are being denied (Haslam & Loughnan, 2014). Most empirical research on dehumanization draws on Haslam's (2006) theoretical model that distinguishes animalistic dehumanization from mechanistic dehumanization. It is argued that when dehumanized, an individual is being denied humanness, which can be understood in two senses (Haslam, 2006). On the one hand, humanness may be understood in a comparative way that involves comparing humans with other animals, resulting in the identification of "human uniqueness" (i.e., the characteristics that differentiate humans from other animals) (Haslam, 2006). On the other hand, humanness may also be thought of in a noncomparative way when seeking to identify "human nature" (i.e., the characteristics that are typical of or fundamental to humans) (Haslam, 2006). When individuals are denied human uniqueness attributes, they are likely to be reduced to the status of animals "and seen as childlike, immature, coarse, irrational, or backward" (Bastian & Haslam, 2010, p. 107), which refers to animalistic dehumanization (Haslam, 2006). When they are denied human nature attributes, individuals are likely to be reduced to the status of objects or machines "and seen as cold, rigid, inert, and lacking emotion and agency" (Bastian & Haslam, 2010, p. 107), which refers to mechanistic dehumanization (Haslam, 2006). Alongside Haslam's (2006) dual model, scholars suggest that the key components of the denial of humanity are property (i.e., the commodification of an individual); violability (i.e., failure to consider a person's physical well-being); fungibility (i.e., treatment of a person as interchangeable); instrumentality (i.e., use of a person for one's own ends); and lack of autonomy, subjectivity, and experience (Nussbaum, 1995).

Primary scientific investigations of dehumanization focused on ethnicity and genocides (e.g., Kelman, 1973). Later on, other social issues such as disability (e.g., O'Brien, 1999), gender (e.g., Vaes et al., 2011), mental illnesses (e.g., Martinez et al., 2011), and medical relationships (e.g., Vaes & Muratore, 2013) were considered through the lens of dehumanization. Therefore, dehumanization has been described as a subtle everyday phenomenon that could also pervade individuals' professional life (Christoff, 2014).

The overwhelming majority of earlier work on dehumanization considered the phenomenon from the perpetrators' perspective by investigating to what extent and in which circumstances laypeople tend to dehumanize targets (Demoulin et al., 2021). As a result, the targets' perspective has been largely overlooked in the dehumanization literature (Demoulin et al., 2021). It was only in the late 2010s that scholars started to focus on the victims' perceptions of being dehumanized among sexually objectified women (e.g., Chevallereau et al., 2021), patients with severe alcohol-use disorders (e.g., Fontesse et al., 2020), and in employees within organizations (e.g., Caesens et al., 2017).

Specifically, researchers started to examine employees' perceptions of being denied the main tenets of humanness by their organization. Even though it has been suggested that the two forms of dehumanization—animalistic and mechanistic—may occur in organizational contexts (e.g., Bell & Khoury, 2011; Christoff, 2014), it is commonly argued that the mechanistic form of dehumanization is more pervasive in work settings (e.g., Bell & Khoury, 2011; Christoff, 2014). Therefore, research on organizational dehumanization has mainly focused on the mechanistic form of dehumanization. In line with the research body that seeks to consider the victims' perspective, organizational dehumanization focuses on employees' perceptions of being treated like interchangeable tools by their organization. As such, the concept of organizational dehumanization encompasses the violation of the core characteristics of humanity by the organization, including fungibility, subjectivity, and instrumentality.

Drawing on this conceptualization, scholars developed scales to measure organizational dehumanization. The first scale was created by Bell and Khoury (2011) to assess the extent to which employees feel dehumanized by their organization via eight questions targeting specific aspects of dehumanization perceptions in work settings. A sample item is "Does the [target organization] respond to your concerns, or does it focus on efficiency with [organization members] treated like robots or numbers?" Responses range from −3 (Focus on efficiency, treating [organization members] like robots or numbers) to +3 (Responds to personal concerns). However, one item of this scale (i.e., "Are you free to make decisions in important matters or does the [target organization] control everything with lots of formal rules and

1462 • ORGANIZATIONAL DEHUMANIZATION

Table 1. Eleven-Item Scale Measuring Organizational Dehumanization

1. My organization makes me feel that one worker is easily as good as any other
2. My organization would not hesitate to replace me if it enabled the company to make more profit
3. If my job could be done by a machine or a robot, my organization would not hesitate to replace me by this new technology
4. My organization considers me as a tool to use for its own ends
5. My organization considers me as a tool devoted to its own success
6. My organization makes me feel that my only importance is my performance at work
7. My organization is only interested in me when it needs me
8. The only thing that counts for my organization is what I can contribute to it
9. My organization treats me as if I were a robot
10. My organization considers me as a number
11. My organization treats me as if I were an object

Note: Scale anchors are 1 = *strongly disagree* to 7 = *strongly agree*.
Source: Caesens et al. (2017, p. 532).

bureaucracy?") appears to better capture job autonomy, which has been shown to be a distinct construct that predicts employees' organizational dehumanization perceptions (Caesens et al., 2019; Demoulin et al., 2020). Similarly, some items of Bell and Khoury's scale (2011) show conceptual overlap with the construct of perceived organizational support, which is distinct from organizational dehumanization (Caesens et al., 2017) (e.g., "Does the [target organization] care about and value you based on who you are as a person, or based on your performance?").

Therefore, another 11-item scale, which is the most widely used, was developed in order to assess organizational dehumanization perceptions on a Likert scale ranging from 1 (strongly disagree) to 7 (strongly agree) (Caesens et al., 2017) (see Table 1). The items were developed based on the main components of denied humanness (e.g., instrumentality, fungibility, subjectivity) (Nussbaum, 1995) as well as on the core characteristics of mechanistic dehumanization (e.g., being reduced to the status of a machine or robot) (Haslam, 2006). This scale shows good psychometric properties (Caesens et al., 2017) and is thus at the core of most studies in the field of organizational dehumanization. Specifically, analyses reveal that the scale developed by Caesens and her collaborators (2017) measures the unidimensional construct of organizational dehumanization that is distinct from other related concepts (e.g., perceived organizational support). However, the first item (i.e., "My organization makes me feel that one worker is easily as good as any other") has slightly weaker loadings (Caesens et al., 2017), suggesting that it may be less representative of the organizational dehumanization construct.

OVERLAP AND DIFFERENCES WITH RELATED CONSTRUCTS

Alongside the growing research body focusing on organizational dehumanization, other related constructs have been examined. Although some of these concepts target employees' perceptions of being exploited and treated with cruelty or, conversely, particularly cared for as human beings by their organization, there is evidence showing that they are distinct constructs.

Additionally, discrepancies with working objectification and work alienation are also discussed. The section "Perceived Organizational Support" aims at clarifying the conceptual similarities and differences with these related constructs.

Perceived Organizational Support.   Perceived organizational support (POS), defined as employees' general perceptions regarding "the extent to which their organization values their contribution and cares about their well-being" (Eisenberger et al., 1986, p. 501), has been at the core of an extended research body on the employee–organization relationship. Similar to organizational dehumanization, POS considers the targets' perspective by focusing on employees' perceptions of the relationship they hold with their organization. Yet it comes out from its definition that POS depicts the positive side of this relationship whereas organizational dehumanization captures its negative side. It is thus not surprising that these two concepts are strongly correlated (Caesens et al., 2017). However, there is empirical evidence showing that they are distinct constructs (Caesens et al., 2017). Accordingly, these findings suggest that POS and organizational dehumanization are not the ends of a single conceptual continuum. Corroborating this claim, scholars argue that employees' perceptions of their organization's failure to support its employees (i.e., low levels of POS) is conceptually distinct from employees' perceptions of being actively harmed by their organization (Gibney et al., 2009), for instance through an instrument-like treatment. Hence, POS is unable to assess the extent to which employees believe that their organization is being detrimental to them. This assertion leaves room for constructs that target the negative side of the employee–organization relationship such as organizational dehumanization.

Perceived Organizational Obstruction.   Given the inability of the POS construct to assess the negative side of the employee–organization relationship (Gibney et al., 2009), scholars have examined the latter through other concepts including perceived organizational obstruction (POO). POO is referred to as the "employees' belief that the organization obstructs, hinders, or interferes with the accomplishment of their goals and is a detriment to their well-being" (Gibney et al., 2009, p. 667). Both POO and organizational dehumanization capture employees' perceptions that their organization prioritizes the achievement of organizational objectives over workers' personal goals (Bell & Khoury, 2011; Gibney et al., 2009). Yet POO and organizational dehumanization show conceptual discrepancies. Supporting this view, Bell and Khoury (2011) suggest that organizational dehumanization encompasses employees' perceptions that they are being considered as mere tools rather than human beings in order to achieve organizational goals. In other words, the prioritization of organizational goals over employees' personal development is perceived to occur through a specific mechanism, namely employees' perceived reduction to the status of instruments, which implies the denial of workers' human features. Conversely, POO only focuses on the perceived hindering role of the organization in the achievement of employees' personal goals (Gibney et al., 2009), regardless of the kind of treatment they receive from the organization, which thus may not necessarily be dehumanizing.

Perceived Exploitation.   Along the same lines, the dark side of the employee–organization relationship has been explored through the concept of perceived exploitation, defined as the "employees' perceptions that they have been purposefully taken advantage of in their relationship with the organization, to the benefit of the organization itself" (Livne-Ofer et al., 2019, p. 1998). This definition spotlights some conceptual overlap between perceived exploitation and organizational dehumanization. First, both constructs consider employees' perceptions of the negative aspects of their relationship with their employing organization (Caesens et al., 2017; Livne-Ofer et al., 2019). Second, scholars argue that the emphasis placed on organizational aims at the expense of employees' personal goals is a key feature of perceived exploitation (Livne-Ofer et al., 2019) as well as of organizational dehumanization (Bell & Khoury, 2011). However, perceived exploitation encompasses perceived intentionality behind the organization's actions, whereas this is not necessarily the case of other constructs that target the negative aspects of the employee–organization relationship (Livne-Ofer et al., 2019) such as organizational dehumanization. In addition, perceived exploitation focuses on the extent to which employees perceive that their relationship with their organization is voluntarily imbalanced (e.g., in terms of financial reward) (Livne-Ofer et al., 2019). Conversely, the core characteristic of organizational dehumanization lies in employees' perceptions that they are being denied their humanness in order to act as cold and rigid tools, regardless of any possible imbalances. For instance, an employee may feel dehumanized because of specific job tasks while being totally satisfied with their salary.

Perceived Organizational Cruelty. Another construct aimed at capturing the negative dimension of the employee–organization relationship is perceived organizational cruelty (POC), defined as an "employee's perception that the organization holds him or her in contempt, has no respect for him or her personally, and treats him or her in a manner that is intentionally inhumane" (Shore & Coyle-Shapiro, 2012, p. 141). This definition highlights that POC and organizational dehumanization both focus on employees' perceptions regarding the extent to which their organization treats them with a clear lack of humanity. Yet unlike organizational dehumanization, POC may include a wide range of perceived malevolent actions that are not necessarily aimed at serving organizational purposes (Shore & Coyle-Shapiro, 2012). In other words, POC involves a personified conception of the organization as a harmful and cruel entity for unspecified reasons (Shore & Coyle-Shapiro, 2012) and not primarily for the maximization of the organization's profits. Conversely, organizational dehumanization focuses on employees' perceived denial of their humanness at work in order to achieve organizational goals.

Working Objectification. Drawing on Nussbaum's (1995) theorization of objectification, scholars have investigated the concept of working objectification, referred to as the object-like perception and treatment of individuals in the workplace (Andrighetto et al., 2017). In light of this definition, it appears that both working objectification and organizational dehumanization refer to the instrumentalization of workers who are considered as tools (Andrighetto et al., 2017; Bell & Khoury, 2011) devoted to serving organizational purposes (Volpato et al., 2017). Yet scholars posit that objectification involves the perception of individuals or social groups as mere objects (e.g., Andrighetto et al., 2017). As a consequence, in contrast to organizational dehumanization, most empirical investigations involving working objectification focus on the perpetrators' perspective. For instance, it has been shown that, compared with nonwork contexts, work contexts lead third parties to objectify targets to a greater extent (Belmi & Schroeder, 2021). Specifically, work environments are likely to promote strategic and calculative mindsets among third parties who, in turn, objectify others (Belmi & Schroeder, 2021). More precisely, specific categories of workers have been shown to be objectified by third parties (e.g., factory workers, subordinates, garbage collectors) (Andrighetto et al., 2017; Baldissarri, Valtorta et al., 2017; Gruenfeld et al., 2008; Valtorta et al., 2019a, 2019b). In addition, specific characteristics of the work itself such as repetitiveness of the movements, fragmentation of activities, and dependence on the machine lead laypeople to perceive target workers as objects rather than human beings (Andrighetto et al., 2017).

Although past research on working objectification mainly considered the perpetrators' perspective, a handful of studies on working objectification have focused on the victims' point of view (Andrighetto et al., 2018; Baldissarri & Andrighetto, 2021; Baldissarri, Andrighetto et al., 2017; Baldissarri et al., 2014, 2019). Yet these few studies on working objectification considering the employees' perspective do not focus on the employee–organization relationship. Instead, these studies consider objectification arising from a specific person (i.e., the supervisor) (Baldissarri et al., 2014, 2019) or from specific types of tasks that are supposed to elicit objectification perceptions (Baldissarri & Andrighetto, 2021; Baldissarri, Andrighetto et al., 2017; Baldissarri et al., 2019) mainly among undergraduate students in laboratory settings (Baldissarri & Andrighetto, 2021; Baldissarri, Andrighetto et al., 2017). Conversely, empirical work on organizational dehumanization investigates employees' perceptions of being treated like mere objects by their organization (e.g., Bell & Khoury, 2011; Caesens et al., 2017), which is considered the entity responsible for the employees' perceptions of being dehumanized (Ahmed & Khan, 2016; Bell & Khoury, 2011). In sum, working objectification literature mainly focuses on the social perception of workers or on objectification perceptions arising from concrete sources, whereas organizational dehumanization embodies the negative side of the employee–organization relationship from the employees' point of view.

Work Alienation.   Built upon a sociological theoretical framework, work alienation is defined as employees' "estrangement, or disconnection from work, the context, or self" (Nair & Vohra, 2009, p. 296). Conceptual overlap between work alienation and organizational dehumanization may be found in sociological work on the dehumanization of workers (Bell & Khoury, 2011). According to Marx (1961 as cited in Bell & Khoury, 2011), the feelings of estrangement that are at the core of alienation go hand in hand with the dehumanizing capitalistic system where human labor is commodified. Indeed, as the products of workers' labor belong to the owner of the company they are working for, employees tend to consider their work as a means to survive instead of as a component of their self-concept as human beings (Shantz et al., 2015). This process results in employees experiencing a disconnection from their work (Shantz et al., 2015). Since organizational dehumanization and work alienation are related constructs (Bell & Khoury, 2011), some job characteristics that have been found to predict organizational dehumanization (e.g., job autonomy, professional isolation) also appear to be antecedents of work alienation (Chiaburu et al., 2014). Yet, although both organizational dehumanization and work alienation consider the victims' (i.e., employees) perceptions and feelings, they are conceptually distinct from each other (Bell & Khoury, 2011). For instance, unlike work alienation, organizational dehumanization perceptions are embedded in the employee–organization relationship literature and imply holding the organization responsible for this instrument-like treatment (Ahmed & Khan, 2016; Bell & Khoury, 2011). More precisely, organizational dehumanization refers to employees' perceptions of being treated in a dehumanizing way by their organization. Conversely, work alienation refers to employees' feelings of being disconnected from their work, regardless of the treatment they receive from their organization.

THE NOMOLOGICAL NETWORK OF ORGANIZATIONAL DEHUMANIZATION

Prior empirical investigations on organizational dehumanization have enabled the elaboration of its nomological network by providing insight into its consequences as well as their underlying mechanisms, its antecedents, and its moderators (see Figure 1).

Consequences of Organizational Dehumanization. Since dehumanization is described as a harmful everyday phenomenon (Christoff, 2014), a considerable body of empirical work has investigated the consequences of organizational dehumanization for both employees and organizations. To date, it is widely assumed that the negative consequences of organizational dehumanization fall into three main outcome categories, namely employees' well-being, employees' attitudes toward their organization and their work, and employees' behaviors (Taskin et al., 2019) (see Figure 1).[1]

Employees' Well-Being. A significant number of studies have highlighted that organizational dehumanization tends to impair employees' well-being. Specifically, organizational dehumanization has been found to be deleterious for employees' mental health. Indeed, organizational dehumanization positively relates to employees' emotional exhaustion (Caesens

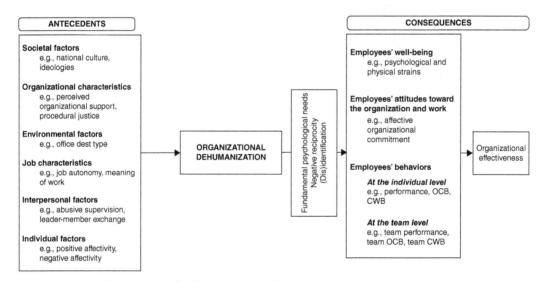

Figure 1. Nomological network of organizational dehumanization.
Note: OCB = organizational citizenship behaviors; CWB = counterproductive work behaviors.

& Stinglhamber, 2019; Caesens et al., 2017; Nguyen, Besson et al., 2021; Nguyen & Stinglhamber, 2020; Nguyen et al., in press; Stinglhamber et al., 2021), psychological strains at work (i.e., anxiety, anger, tension, and nervousness at work) (Caesens & Stinglhamber, 2019; Lagios et al., 2021; Taskin et al., 2019), job stress (Sarwar et al., 2021), and negative emotions (e.g., "sad," "blameworthy," "angry") (Demoulin et al., 2020). In the same vein, organizational dehumanization also seems to harm employees' physical health as it is positively linked to various psychosomatic symptoms (i.e., trouble sleeping, headache, acid indigestion or heartburn, eye strain, loss of appetite, dizziness, and fatigue) (Caesens & Stinglhamber, 2019; Caesens et al., 2017). Moreover, organizational dehumanization impairs employees' self-perceptions by decreasing their organization-based self-esteem (Demoulin et al., 2020) as well as their core self-evaluations (i.e., "fundamental, subconscious conclusions individuals reach about themselves" including self-esteem, generalized self-efficacy, locus of control, and neuroticism; Judge et al., 1998, p. 18) (Nguyen & Stinglhamber, 2021). Taken together, these studies highlight that the deleterious impact of organizational dehumanization perceptions extends beyond the scope of professional life by severely impairing employees' health and self-perceptions.

Employees' Attitudes Toward the Organization and Work. In addition to impairing employees' well-being, employees' perceptions of being dehumanized by their organization are also thought to impede organizational functioning (Bell & Khoury, 2011). Corroborating this suggestion, organizational dehumanization has been shown to influence employees' attitudes toward their organization (Caesens et al., 2019; Stinglhamber et al., 2021; Taskin et al., 2019). More precisely, empirical research shows that organizational dehumanization is negatively linked to employees' affective commitment to their organization (Caesens et al., 2019; Lagios et al., 2021; Nguyen & Stinglhamber, 2020; Nguyen et al., in press; Stinglhamber et al., 2021; Taskin et al., 2019). In the same vein, organizational dehumanization decreases employees' positive attitudes toward their work as it negatively relates to employees' job satisfaction (Caesens et al., 2017, 2019; Lagios et al., 2021; Nguyen, Besson et al., 2021; Nguyen, Dao et al., 2021; Nguyen & Stinglhamber, 2020, 2021; Nguyen et al., in press; Taskin et al., 2019).[2]

Employees' Behaviors. More importantly, the negative consequences of organizational dehumanization go beyond employees' attitudes toward the organization as employees' perceptions of being dehumanized further affect their behavioral intentions and tendencies as well as their actual behaviors (e.g., Demoulin et al., 2020; Stinglhamber et al., 2021; Taskin et al., 2019). Specifically, employees' organizational dehumanization perceptions are negatively associated with their supervisor-rated in-role performance (Sarwar & Muhammad, 2020), their extra-role performance (Taskin et al., 2019), as well as their promotive voice behaviors (i.e., "expression of constructive challenge intended to improve work environment rather than merely criticizing it"; Van Dyne & LePine, 1998, p. 854) (Stinglhamber et al., 2021). Prior research has shown that organizational dehumanization positively relates to employees' absenteeism rate (Lagios et al., 2021) and intentions to leave the organization (Ahmed & Khan, 2016; Bell & Khoury, 2016; Caesens et al., 2019; Caesens & Stinglhamber, 2019; Lagios et al., 2021; Nguyen, Dao et al., 2021; Nguyen & Stinglhamber, 2020; Nguyen et al., in press; Taskin et al., 2019).[3] In addition, employees' perceptions of being dehumanized by their organization positively relate to their tendency to engage in counterproductive work behaviors directed toward the organization (i.e., organizational deviance) (Ahmed & Khan, 2016; Sarwar et al., 2021) as well as toward organizational members (i.e., interpersonal deviance) (Ahmed & Khan, 2016). Moreover, organizational dehumanization has been found to lead employees to adopt particular types of regulatory behavioral strategies. Specifically, there is empirical evidence highlighting positive relationships between organizational dehumanization perceptions and avoidance coping (i.e., "avoiding or engaging in active attempts to get away from the stressor"; Feifel & Strack, 1989, p. 27) (Demoulin et al., 2020) as well as employees' tendency to engage in surface acting (i.e., a subdimension of emotional labor defined as "the expression of unfelt emotions by faking, suppressing, or amplifying emotions"; Nguyen & Stinglhamber, 2020, p. 832) (Nguyen, Besson et al., 2021; Nguyen, Dao et al., 2021; Nguyen & Stinglhamber, 2020, 2021; Nguyen et al., in press).

The Processes That Link Organizational Dehumanization to Outcomes. There is considerable empirical evidence showing the negative consequences of organizational dehumanization for both employees and organizations (e.g., Stinglhamber et al., 2021). In light of three main theoretical frameworks, researchers have started to identify the underlying mechanisms through which organizational dehumanization perceptions lead to these negative consequences (see Figure 1).

First, scholars suggest that self-determination theory (Deci & Ryan, 2000) may provide insight into how organizational dehumanization leads to deleterious consequences for employees (Christoff, 2014; Lagios et al., 2021). At the theoretical level, it has been suggested that organizational dehumanization perceptions would threaten employees' fundamental psychological needs (i.e., autonomy, belonging, and competence), which in turn are thought to impair employees' well-being (Caesens et al., 2019; Christoff, 2014). Consistent with this reasoning, organizational dehumanization has been shown to decrease employees' sense of autonomy, belonging, and competence (Lagios et al., 2021). In line with self-determination theory (Deci & Ryan, 2000), this threat to their fundamental psychological needs has been linked to increased absenteeism rate, psychological strains, and turnover intentions as well as decreased job satisfaction and affective commitment toward the organization (Lagios et al., 2021).

Second, in an attempt to explain how organizational dehumanization impedes organizational functioning, it has been argued that social exchange theory (Cropanzano & Mitchell, 2005) may be insightful to understand how organizational dehumanization entails negative attitudinal and behavioral consequences (Ahmed & Khan, 2016; Stinglhamber et al., 2021). Indeed, according to social exchange theory (Cropanzano & Mitchell, 2005), employees who feel they have been treated badly by their organization may want to reciprocate this negative treatment. Accordingly, some scholars have proposed that employees' perceptions of being dehumanized by their organization may lead them to return negative attitudes and behaviors toward their organization (Ahmed & Khan, 2016; Stinglhamber et al., 2021). This suggests that negative reciprocity may be at stake in the relationship between organizational dehumanization and its negative attitudinal and behavioral outcomes.

Third, researchers in the field have also suggested that social identity theory could be another useful theoretical framework for understanding how organizational dehumanization is linked to deleterious outcomes (Stinglhamber et al., 2021). For instance, organizational dehumanization may result in negative attitudes and behaviors toward the organization because employees tend to dissociate themselves from their organization to escape a diminishing experience (Bell & Khoury, 2011). In other words, employees would no longer identify themselves with a dehumanizing organization, as it may be too harmful for them to incorporate their organizational membership into their self-concept. Moreover, degrading work conditions lead employees to ask themselves why they attend a demeaning workplace on a regular basis, which elicits a dissonance (Schaubroeck et al., 2018). Consequently, employees solve this dissonance by maintaining a greater psychological distance between themselves and their workplace (i.e., disidentification), which in turn leads them to adopt congruent negative attitudes and behaviors (Schaubroeck et al., 2018). This suggests that organizational identification or, more aptly, organizational disidentification could act as an underlying mechanism between organizational dehumanization and its consequences. However, despite these theoretical insights, these claims have never been investigated at the empirical level.

Antecedents of Organizational Dehumanization. Given the deleterious consequences of organizational dehumanization perceptions for both employees and organizations, it is of primary importance to advance theory regarding the factors that contribute to the development of such perceptions in employees (Stinglhamber et al., 2021). Accordingly, the antecedents of organizational dehumanization have received substantial empirical attention (e.g., Ahmed & Khan, 2016; Bell & Khoury, 2016; Caesens et al., 2019; Caesens et al., 2017; Demoulin et al., 2020; Stinglhamber et al., 2021; Taskin et al., 2019). Drawing on prior research, six categories of predictors can be identified (see Figure 1).

Societal Factors. First, organizational dehumanization perceptions may emerge from societal factors. Indeed, dehumanization in work settings may arise from the ideologies in which organizations are embedded. For instance, organizational dehumanization finds part of its roots in the Western working system ruled by capitalism (Bell & Khoury, 2011). Since many organizations seek to improve their profits, productivity prevails over consideration of employees' personal subjectivity and well-being (Bell & Khoury, 2011). Accordingly, dehumanization in organizational contexts may be considered a necessary and acceptable strategy in order to meet capitalistic requirements (Christoff, 2014). As a result, an economic context characterized by competitive strategies where the employee–organization relationship is instrumental and performance-based (e.g., liberal market economy) (Cristiani & Peiró, 2018) is thought to be an antecedent of organizational dehumanization perceptions. Consequently, the odds for dehumanization are higher in organizations that obey the rules of the liberal market economy. In addition, organizational dehumanization may arise in government agencies where bureaucracy is at stake. Since bureaucracy is impersonal and goes hand in hand with a formalized and rule-based division of labor (Olsen, 2006), it may be thought of as a dehumanizing iron cage that separates individuals from their own actions (Bell & Khoury, 2011). In addition, national culture predicts organizational dehumanization perceptions among employees (Nguyen, Dao et al., 2021). Specifically, compared with British employees, Vietnamese workers were found to feel less dehumanized by their organization (Nguyen, Dao et al., 2021). This finding can be understood in light of the different societal norms that are conveyed in both cultures. By promoting the idea that employees should be entirely devoted to their organization and help the latter to achieve its goals, Vietnamese culture encourages employees to be efficient at work and trivializes individual subjectivity (Nguyen, Dao et al., 2021).

Organizational Characteristics. Second, some organizational characteristics were found to elicit organizational dehumanization perceptions among employees. It is argued that the way in which organizations are perceived to treat their employees leads workers to make inferences regarding the extent to which they are considered in all their personal subjectivity (Caesens et al., 2017; Väyrynen & Laari-Salmela, 2018). Accordingly, the extent to which organizational values and practices are people-oriented influences the development of organizational dehumanization perceptions among employees. In line with this claim, procedural justice is negatively linked to organizational dehumanization (Ahmed & Khan, 2016; Bell & Khoury, 2016). Additionally, perceived organizational support negatively predicts organizational dehumanization (Caesens et al., 2017).

Environmental Factors. Third, past research has highlighted that specific environmental factors are strong determinants of organizational dehumanization. Indeed, some work environments do not fulfill workers' basic needs as human beings (Taskin et al., 2019), which has been found to elicit organizational dehumanization perceptions (Demoulin et al., 2020). For instance, since they are thought to threaten employees' need for distinctiveness, collective and shared workspaces—flex-desks—(Taskin et al., 2019) increase employees' perceptions of being dehumanized by their organization.

Job Characteristics. Fourth, specific job characteristics are also important predictors of organizational dehumanization. Since they are offered by the organization, job characteristics may influence employees' perceptions of the way they are treated by their organization. For instance, perceptions of dehumanization arise when individuals feel that their autonomy and agency are deliberately being denied by the dehumanizing entity (Bell & Khoury, 2011) and that their work is meaningless as it reduces them to the status of working tools (Väyrynen & Laari-Salmela, 2018). Corroborating these claims, job autonomy (Caesens et al., 2019; Demoulin et al., 2020) and meaning of work (Caesens et al., 2019) have been found to negatively predict organizational dehumanization. Conversely, prior research highlights that performing one's job under conditions of professional isolation (i.e., "state of mind or belief that one is out of touch with others in the workplace"; Diekema, 1992 as cited in Golden et al., 2008, p. 1412) is positively linked to organizational dehumanization (Caesens et al., 2019; Demoulin et al., 2020). In the same vein, qualitative data suggest that a lack of social connections due to social distance (e.g., remote working, geographically separated or large work sites) is associated with employees' perceptions of being dehumanized (Väyrynen & Laari-Salmela, 2018).

Interpersonal Factors. Fifth, since dehumanization perceptions arise from the feeling that one has been treated in a degrading or humiliating way by others (Bastian & Haslam, 2010), it also appears that interpersonal factors are responsible for the emergence of organizational dehumanization perceptions. Specifically, previous research shows that perceived interpersonal justice from the supervisor is negatively linked to organizational dehumanization (Bell & Khoury, 2016). In addition, abusive supervision (i.e., "subordinates' perceptions of the extent to which supervisors engage in the sustained display of hostile verbal and nonverbal behaviors, excluding physical contact"; Tepper, 2000, p. 178) increases employees' organizational dehumanization perceptions (Caesens et al., 2019). Conversely, high-quality leader–member exchange (LMX) (i.e., a high-quality relationship between a supervisor and a subordinate) is negatively associated with the subordinate's perceptions of organizational dehumanization (Stinglhamber et al., 2021). Explanations for these findings may be found in the fact that supervisors are considered as representative agents of the organization, which is thus held responsible for their abusive behaviors (Caesens et al., 2019). Although these studies focus on the supervisor–subordinate relationship, it has been suggested that interpersonal mistreatments emanating from other significant organizational entities (e.g., coworkers, clients) may also entail organizational dehumanization perceptions (Caesens & Stinglhamber, 2019).

Individual Factors. Organizational dehumanization perceptions have further been found to result from individual factors. Employees vary in terms of personality traits and this may lead them to make sense of their environment in light of different frameworks. For instance, individuals high in negative affectivity are more likely to perceive situations in a negative way (Watson & Clark, 1984). Accordingly, since those people have personal dispositions to detect negative clues within their environment, negative affectivity is positively linked to organizational dehumanization perceptions, whereas positive affectivity negatively relates to organizational dehumanization (Nguyen, Besson et al., 2021; Nguyen, Dao et al., 2021; Nguyen & Stinglhamber, 2020; Nguyen et al., in press).

Moderating Mechanisms.

Alongside examining the antecedents and consequences of organizational dehumanization, scholars have also identified moderating mechanisms that strengthen or weaken the relationships between organizational dehumanization and its predictors and outcomes (e.g., Ahmed & Khan, 2016; Bell & Khoury, 2016; Caesens et al., 2019; Nguyen, Dao et al., 2021; Sarwar et al., 2021; Sarwar & Muhammad, 2020; Stinglhamber et al., 2021).

First, earlier work on dehumanization in the workplace showed that demographic characteristics could exacerbate the influence of some predictors on organizational dehumanization. Accordingly, gender was found to moderate the negative relationship between procedural justice and organizational dehumanization, with stronger effects for women than for men that carry over to outcomes (Ahmed & Khan, 2016; Bell & Khoury, 2016). These results suggest that men and women do not make sense of organizational characteristics (i.e., organizational justice) in the same way, leading them to develop organizational dehumanization perceptions to varying extents.

Second, the extent to which some antecedents of organizational dehumanization lead employees to feel dehumanized by their organization also depends on specific contextual factors (Caesens et al., 2019; Stinglhamber et al., 2021). For instance, the relationship between abusive supervision and organizational dehumanization is stronger when employees perceive high coworker support than when they perceive low coworker support (Caesens et al., 2019). This interactive effect then carries over to outcomes (Caesens et al., 2019). These findings were unexpected as the authors instead hypothesized that perceived coworker support would buffer the negative impact of abusive supervision (Caesens et al., 2019). Consistent with previous findings (e.g., Wu & Hu, 2009), these surprising results suggest that employees who benefit from high coworker support are more likely to become aware, for instance through consolation and discussions, of the inappropriateness and the harmfulness of abusive supervision. As a result, this exacerbates its negative consequences (Caesens et al., 2019; Wu & Hu, 2009) such as increasing organizational dehumanization perceptions (Caesens et al., 2019). In addition, a supervisor's organizational embodiment (SOE) (i.e., "employees' perceptions concerning the extent of their supervisor's shared identity with the organization"; Eisenberger et al., 2010, p. 1086) moderates the relationship between LMX and organizational dehumanization (Stinglhamber et al., 2021). More precisely, the relationship between LMX and organizational dehumanization is stronger when SOE is high (Stinglhamber et al., 2021). These findings suggest that employees whose supervisor is perceived as highly representative of the organization are more likely to attribute the positive exchanges they have with their supervisor (i.e., high-quality LMX) to the organization (Stinglhamber et al., 2021). Accordingly, attributing these favorable supervisor–subordinate interactions to the organization reduces organizational dehumanization perceptions (Stinglhamber et al., 2021). As a whole, these studies show that the extent to which interpersonal factors (e.g., abusive supervision, high-quality LMX) entail or reduce organizational dehumanization perceptions depends on the professional context in which they take place.

Third, variables moderating the relationship between organizational dehumanization and its outcomes have also been identified (Nguyen, Dao et al., 2021; Sarwar et al., 2021; Sarwar & Muhammad, 2020). For instance, the relationship between organizational dehumanization and work-related outcomes (i.e., decreased job satisfaction and increased turnover intentions) has been found to be weaker in high power distance countries (e.g., Vietnam) (i.e., "indicator of a country's preference for authority and power inequality in the workplace"; Hofstede, 1980 as cited in Nguyen, Dao et al., 2021, p. 4) as compared with low power distance countries (e.g., the United Kingdom) (Nguyen, Dao et al., 2021). These findings suggest that power distance legitimates the instrumentalization of workers. Specifically, workers in high power distance countries are more likely to find it acceptable to be reduced to the status of a mere tool to serve the goals of a hierarchically superior entity (i.e., the organization). In turn, they experience fewer negative consequences as they see their situation as fair and normative. Additionally, scholars have demonstrated that individual factors may also moderate the relationship between organizational dehumanization and its deleterious consequences (Sarwar et al., 2021; Sarwar & Muhammad, 2020). Accordingly, psychological capital (i.e., "an individual's positive psychological state of development" characterized by self-efficacy, optimism, hope, and resilience; Luthans et al., 2007, p. 3) weakens the influence of organizational dehumanization on outcomes (Sarwar & Muhammad, 2020). Moreover, the relationship between organizational dehumanization and its consequences is weaker under higher levels of occupational coping self-efficacy (i.e., an individual's belief about their ability to cope with job-related stressors) (Pisanti et al., 2015) as compared with lower levels (Sarwar et al., 2021). Taken together, these findings highlight that not all employees are equally affected by organizational dehumanization. Employees vary in terms of individual characteristics and operate in different cultural contexts, which may lead them to suffer more or less from being dehumanized by their employing organization.

A FUTURE RESEARCH AGENDA

First, given the conceptual similarities and differences between organizational dehumanization and several other constructs, it is of primary importance that researchers in the field make informed decisions about which construct is most relevant to their research goals. Therefore, it is recommended that appropriate labels and measurement scales be used to avoid confusion between organizational dehumanization and its related constructs (in particular, with working objectification). Since the mechanistic form of dehumanization of Haslam's model (2006) is considered the most prevalent in work settings (Bell & Khoury, 2011), the majority of studies on organizational dehumanization have focused on victims'—that is, employees'—perceptions of being used as interchangeable tools or robots. However, it has been suggested that the animalistic form of dehumanization may also occur in the organizational world (Bell & Khoury, 2011; Caesens et al., 2017), particularly among employees working in specific industries such as housekeeping and cleaning (Nisim & Benjamin, 2010). Therefore, future research should consider exploring the antecedents and consequences of animalistic dehumanization within organizations in order to identify similarities and differences with mechanistic dehumanization (e.g., Caesens et al., 2017; Nguyen & Stinglhamber, 2021). Moreover, although seminal work on organizational dehumanization focuses on employees' individual perceptions of the dehumanizing aspects of their own employee–organization relationship, future research could broaden this conceptualization. For instance, organizational dehumanization may be conceptualized as a climate shared by all the employees and could therefore be studied at the organizational level (Nguyen et al., 2021). Supporting this claim, prior research has shown that the treatment received from the organization at one hierarchical level tends to percolate to lower levels, suggesting the existence of a common organizational climate (Stinglhamber & Caesens, 2020). Therefore, beyond individual perceptions, the extent to which a specific work environment is globally dehumanizing could be assessed via multilevel analyses (Nguyen et al., 2021).

Second, despite researchers' increasing interest in dehumanizing phenomena within workplaces, the organizational dehumanization literature is still in its infancy. Hence, insightful directions for future research would be to extend its nomological network. In accordance with this view, only a small number of studies have examined the attitudinal consequences of organizational dehumanization (e.g., Caesens et al., 2019; Caesens et al., 2017; Nguyen, Dao et al., 2021; Nguyen & Stinglhamber, 2021; Stinglhamber et al., 2021; Taskin et al., 2019) and most of them remain unknown. For instance, future studies could investigate how employees' organizational dehumanization perceptions affect their normative and continuance commitment to their organization and their work engagement. In addition, scholars call for the identification of innovative behavioral outcomes such as counterproductive work behaviors (Stinglhamber et al., 2021) and hostile behaviors directed toward the organization that may be held responsible for the dehumanizing treatment (Ahmed & Khan, 2016). These behaviors aimed at retaliating against the organization could be explored at the individual level as well as at the team level (e.g., collective actions such as striking). Besides, future research should also examine whether the negative behavioral consequences of organizational dehumanization expand beyond the organization itself and involve specific organizational stakeholders (e.g., supervisors, colleagues, customers) (Stinglhamber et al., 2021) or even external targets (e.g., family, friends). Based on the trickle effects (Wo et al., 2019), supervisors who feel dehumanized by their organization may act rudely toward their subordinates who, in turn, would act rudely within their families, as it is too costly to retaliate against their supervisors. Overall, while past research has extensively explored the consequences of organizational dehumanization for employees, little attention has been paid to the outcomes for the organization itself (e.g., organizational effectiveness). Since employees' performance is severely affected by organizational dehumanization, its impact on organizational functioning would be worth being quantified to warn practitioners that pushing employees to act like robots is not a golden avenue to greater profits.

Third, several scholars call for empirical investigations of the mechanisms underlying the relationship between organizational dehumanization and its consequences (e.g., Stinglhamber et al., 2021). As mentioned before, social exchange theory (e.g., negative reciprocity) and social identity theory (e.g., organizational disidentification) could be relevant theoretical frameworks to this end (Stinglhamber et al., 2021). Moreover, drawing on social psychological work on dehumanization (Demoulin et al., 2021), it may be that disidentification processes occur at the individual level through self-dehumanization as an underlying mechanism between organizational dehumanization and its negative consequences. Indeed, employees who feel dehumanized by an external entity (i.e., their organization) may integrate the idea that they are less than human and start considering themselves as such, leading to deleterious outcomes.

In the same vein, new predictors of organizational dehumanization could also be identified (e.g., Caesens et al., 2019). For instance, it may be of particular interest to identify clusters in which organizational dehumanization is most prevalent depending on the work domain, the sector (e.g., private or public sector), or the size of the organization. Specifically, future research should examine whether organizational dehumanization is more pervasive within informal work contexts (i.e., "activities that are not covered, or are insufficiently covered, by formal legal and political arrangements," p. 340) where indecent and degrading work conditions are common (Gloss et al., 2017). Additionally, the role of technological breakthroughs embedded in human resources practices (e.g., digitalization and automation of work processes) (Stinglhamber et al., 2021) and interpersonal mistreatment by organizational entities other than supervisors (e.g., coworkers or customers) in the rise of organizational dehumanization perceptions among employees would be worth exploring. Along similar lines, organizational dehumanization literature may benefit from studies examining what other job characteristics (e.g., task variety, task identity, feedback) and what individual factors affect dehumanization perceptions.

Fourth, the underlying mechanisms through which the antecedents of organizational dehumanization elicit these perceptions among employees remain unknown, which is a promising avenue for future research. For instance, drawing on self-determination theory (Deci & Ryan, 2000), future research should elucidate the theoretical controversy regarding the role of employees' fundamental psychological needs thwarting in the nomological network of organizational dehumanization. On the one hand, some scholars argue that organizational dehumanization undermines employees' basic needs (e.g., autonomy, belonging, competence), which in turn impairs their well-being (Christoff, 2014; Lagios et al., 2021). On the other hand, other researchers propose that organizational dehumanization perceptions arise when employees' fundamental psychological needs are thwarted (Demoulin et al., 2020). In sum, it remains unclear whether fundamental psychological needs thwarting is a process explaining both the development of organizational dehumanization and its effects. Future research should try to make sense of these seemingly adversarial views. For instance, it may be that a vicious circle is at play, according to which organizational dehumanization thwarts employees' needs, which in turn reinforces organizational dehumanization perceptions. Specifically, when feeling like robots or tools in the workplace rather than human beings, employees feel that their psychological needs are not being fulfilled. As a result, the fact that their fundamental needs as human beings are not met may exacerbate organizational dehumanization perceptions as their humanity is being threatened at work.

Finally, organizational dehumanization literature shows two main methodological limitations. First, most studies on organizational dehumanization are cross-sectional, which leaves room for cross-lagged panel and experimental designs in order to draw conclusions regarding causality (e.g., Lagios et al., 2021; Stinglhamber et al., 2021). Second, since most empirical investigations of the nomological network of organizational dehumanization rely on data samples derived from single-source measures, future research should replicate and extend current findings using alternative measurement methods (e.g., Caesens et al., 2019; Caesens & Stinglhamber, 2019; Caesens et al., 2017; Demoulin et al., 2020; Nguyen & Stinglhamber, 2021; Stinglhamber et al., 2021; Taskin et al., 2019). For instance, the dehumanizing aspects of a particular employee's work environment could be more objectively assessed using customers', coworkers', or supervisors' ratings of the construct. Similarly, the behavioral outcomes of organizational dehumanization could be peer-rated (e.g., job performance assessed by a direct supervisor, family undermining assessed by a family member) or rated objectively (e.g., real absenteeism rate), which would allow inferences regarding organizational effectiveness.

CONCLUSION

Twenty-first-century workplaces are facing various challenges that are likely to undermine workers' humanness such as technological breakthrough, indecent work conditions, or specific economic ideologies, to name a few. Consequently, workers may feel used as interchangeable tools aimed at serving organizational goals. In turn, organizational dehumanization perceptions impair workers' well-being and negatively affect their attitudes toward their work and organization as well as their behaviors at work. Accordingly, practitioners should bear in mind that organizational effectiveness rhymes with humanness.

REFERENCES

Ahmed, I., & Khan, M. K. (2016). Organizational justice, counterproductive work behavior and turnover intentions relation: Mediation by dehumanization and moderation by gender. *Paradigms, 10*(2), 120–131. https://search.proquest.com/scholarly-journals/organizational-justice-counterproductive-work/docview/1855832061/se-2?accountid=12156

Andrighetto, L., Baldissarri, C., Gabbiadini, A., Sacino, A., Valtorta, R. R., & Volpato, C. (2018). Objectified conformity: Working self-objectification increases conforming behavior. *Social Influence, 13*(2), 78–90. https://doi.org/10.1080/15534510.2018.1439769

Andrighetto, L., Baldissarri, C., & Volpato, C. (2017). (Still) modern times: Objectification at work. *European Journal of Social Psychology, 47*(1), 25–35. https://doi.org/10.1002/ejsp.2190

Baldissarri, C., & Andrighetto, L. (2021). Being treated as an instrument: Consequences of instrumental treatment and self-objectification on task engagement and performance. *Human Performance, 34*(2), 85–106. https://doi.org/10.1080/08959285.2021.1878182

Baldissarri, C., Andrighetto, L., Gabbiadini, A., & Volpato, C. (2017). Work and freedom? Working self-objectification and belief in personal free will. *British Journal of Social Psychology, 56*(2), 250–269. https://doi.org/10.1111/bjso.12172

Baldissarri, C., Andrighetto, L., & Volpato, C. (2014). When work does not ennoble man: Psychological consequences of working objectification. *Testing, Psychometrics, Methodology in Applied Psychology, 21*(3), 327–339. https://doi.org/10.4473/TPM21.3.7

Baldissarri, C., Andrighetto, L., & Volpato, C. (2019). Feeling like an object: A field study on working self-objectification and belief in personal free will. *Testing, Psychometrics, Methodology in Applied Psychology, 26*(2), 185–197. https://doi.org/10.4473/TPM26.2.1

Baldissarri, C., Valtorta, R. R., Andrighetto, L., & Volpato, C. (2017). Workers as objects: The nature of working objectification and the role of perceived alienation. *Testing, Psychometrics, Methodology in Applied Psychology, 24*(2), 153–166. https://doi.org/10.4473/TPM24.2.1

Bastian, B., & Haslam, N. (2010). Excluded from humanity: The dehumanizing effects of social ostracism. *Journal of Experimental Social Psychology, 46*(1), 107–113. https://doi.org/10.1016/j.jesp.2009.06.022

Bell, C. M., & Khoury, C. (2011). Organizational de/humanization, deindividuation, anomie, and in/justice. In S. Gilliland, D. Steiner, & D. Skarlicki (Eds.), *Emerging perspectives on organizational justice and ethics* (pp. 167–197). Information Age.

Bell, C. M., & Khoury, C. (2016). Organizational powerlessness, dehumanization, and gendered effects of procedural justice. *Journal of Managerial Psychology, 31*(2), 570–585. https://doi.org/10.1108/JMP-09-2014-0267

Belmi, P., & Schroeder, J. (2021). Human "resources"? Objectification at work. *Journal of Personality and Social Psychology, 120*(2), 384–417. https://doi.org/10.1037/pspi0000254

Caesens, G., Nguyen, N., & Stinglhamber, F. (2019). Abusive supervision and organizational dehumanization. *Journal of Business and Psychology, 34*(5), 709–728. https://doi.org/10.1007/s10869-018-9592-3

Caesens, G., & Stinglhamber, F. (2019). The relationship between organizational dehumanization and outcomes: The mediating role of emotional exhaustion. *Journal of Occupational and Environmental Medicine, 61*(9), 699–703. https://doi.org/10.1097/jom.0000000000001638

Caesens, G., Stinglhamber, F., Demoulin, S., & De Wilde, M. (2017). Perceived organizational support and employees' well-being: The mediating role of organizational dehumanization. *European Journal of Work and Organizational Psychology, 26*(4), 527–540. https://doi.org/10.1080/1359432X.2017.1319817

Chevallereau, T., Maurage, P., Stinglhamber, F., & Demoulin, S. (2021). Sex-based and beauty-based objectification: Metadehumanization and emotional consequences among victims. *British Journal of Social Psychology.* Advance online publication. https://doi.org/10.1111/bjso.12446

Chiaburu, D. S., Thundiyil, T., & Wang, J. (2014). Alienation and its correlates: A meta-analysis. *European Management Journal, 32*(1), 24–36. https://doi.org/10.1016/j.emj.2013.06.003

Christ, K. L., Burritt, R. L., & Schaltegger, S. (2020). Accounting for work conditions from modern slavery to decent work. *Accounting, Auditing and Accountability Journal, 33*(7), 1481–1504. https://doi.org/10.1108/AAAJ-05-2020-4587

Christoff, K. (2014). Dehumanization in organizational settings: Some scientific and ethical considerations. *Frontiers in Human Neuroscience, 8*, 1–5. https://doi.org/10.3389/fnhum.2014.00748

Cristiani, A., & Peiró, J. M. (2018). Human resource function, unions and varieties of capitalism: Exploring their impact on human resource management practices based on CRANET data. *Employee Relations, 40*(6), 1072–1098. https://doi.org/10.1108/ER-10-2016-0198

Cropanzano, R., & Mitchell, M. S. (2005). Social exchange theory: An interdisciplinary review. *Journal of Management, 31*, 874–900. https://doi.org/10.1177/0149206305279602

Deci, E. L., & Ryan, R. M. (2000). The "what" and "why" of goal pursuits: Human needs and the self-determination of behavior. *Psychological Inquiry, 11*(4), 227–268. https://doi.org/10.1207/S15327 965PLI1104_01

Demoulin, S., Maurage, P., & Stinglhamber, F. (2021). Exploring metadehumanization and self-dehumanization from a target perspective. In M. Kronfeldner (Ed.), *The Routledge handbook of dehumanization* (pp. 260–274). Routledge.

Demoulin, S., Nguyen, N., Chevallereau, T., Fontesse, S., Bastart, J., Stinglhamber, F., & Maurage, P. (2020). Examining the role of fundamental psychological needs in the development of metadehumanization: A multi-population approach. *British Journal of Social Psychology, 60*(1), 196–221. https://doi.org/10.1111 /bjso.12380

Diekema, D. A. (1992). Aloneness and social form. *Symbolic Interaction, 15*(4), 481–500. https://doi .org/10.1525/si.1992.15.4.481

Eisenberger, R., Huntington, R., Hutchison, S., & Sowa, D. (1986). Perceived organizational support. *Journal of Applied Psychology, 71*(3), 500–507. https://doi.org/10.1037//0021%369010.71.3.500

Eisenberger, R., Karagonlar, G., Stinglhamber, F., Neves, P., Becker, T. E., Gonzalez-Morales, M. G., & Steiger-Mueller, M. (2010). Leader–member exchange and affective organizational commitment: The contribution of supervisor's organizational embodiment. *Journal of Applied Psychology, 95*(6), 1085–1103. https://doi.org/10.1037/a0020858

Feifel, H., & Strack, S. (1989). Coping with conflict situations: Middle-aged and elderly men. *Psychology and Aging, 4*(1), 26–33. https://doi.org/10.1037/0882-7974.4.1.26

Fontesse, S., Stinglhamber, F., Demoulin, S., Chevallereau, T., de Timary, P., Cappeliez, B., Bon, F., Geus, C., Talent, J., Ayache, L., & Maurage, P. (2020). Metadehumanization in severe alcohol-use disorders: Links with fundamental needs and clinical outcomes. *Addictive Behaviors, 107*(106425), 1–7. https://doi .org/10.1016/j.addbeh.2020.106425

Gibney, R., Zagenczyk, T. J., & Masters, M. F. (2009). The negative aspects of social exchange: An introduction to perceived organizational obstruction. *Group and Organization Management, 34*(6), 665–697. https://doi.org/10.1177/1059601109350987

Gloss, A., Carr, S. C., Reichman, W., Abdul-Nasiru, I., & Oestereich, W. T. (2017). From handmaidens to POSH humanitarians: The case for making human capabilities the business of I-O psychology. *Industrial and Organizational Psychology, 10*(3), 329–369. https://doi.org/10.1017/iop.2017.27

Golden, T. D., Veiga, J. F., & Dino, R. N. (2008). The impact of professional isolation on teleworker job performance and turnover intentions: Does time spent teleworking, interacting face-to-face, or having access to communication-enhancing technology matter? *Journal of Applied Psychology, 93*(6), 1412–1421. https://doi.org/10.1037/a0012722

Gruenfeld, D. H., Inesi, M. E., Magee, J. C., & Galinsky, A. D. (2008). Power and the objectification of social targets. *Journal of Personality and Social Psychology, 95*(1), 111–127. https://doi.org/10.1037/0022 -3514.95.1.111

Haslam, N. (2006). Dehumanization: An integrative review. *Personality and Social Psychology Review, 10*(3), 252–264. https://doi.org/10.1207/s15327957pspr1003_4

Haslam, N., & Loughnan, S. (2014). Dehumanization and infrahumanization. *Annual Review of Psychology, 65*, 399–423. https://doi.org/10.1146/annurev-psych-010213-115045

Hofstede, G. H. (1980). *Culture's consequences: International differences in work-related values.* SAGE.

Judge, T. A., Locke, E. A., Durham, C. C., & Kluger, A. N. (1998). Dispositional effects on job and life satisfaction: The role of core evaluations. *Journal of Applied Psychology, 83*(1), 17–34. https://doi .org/10.1037/0021%369010.83.1.17

Kelman, H. C. (1973). Violence without restraint: Reflections on the dehumanization of victims and victimizers. *Journal of Social Issues, 29*(4), 25–61. https://scholar.harvard.edu/files/hckelman/files /Violence_1973.pdf

Lagios, C., Caesens, G., Nguyen, N., & Stinglhamber, F. (2021). Explaining the negative consequences of organizational dehumanization: The mediating role of psychological need thwarting. *Journal of Personnel Psychology.* Advance online publication. https://doi.org/10.1027/1866-5888/a000286

Livne-Ofer, E., Coyle-Shapiro, J. A., & Pearce, J. L. (2019). Eyes wide open: Perceived exploitation and its consequences. *Academy of Management Journal, 62*(6), 1989–2018. https://doi.org/10.5465/amj .2017.1421

Luthans, F., Youssef, C. M., & Avolio, B. J. (2007). *Psychological capital: Developing the human competitive edge.* Oxford University Press.

Martinez, A. G., Piff, P. K., Mendoza-Denton, R., & Hinshaw, S. P. (2011). The power of a label: Mental illness diagnoses, ascribed humanity and social rejection. *Journal of Social Clinical Psychology, 30*, 1–23. https://doi.org/10.1521/jscp.2011.30.1.1

Marx, K. (1961). *Economic and philosophic manuscripts of 1844* (M. Mulligan, Trans.). Foreign Languages Publishing House.

Nair, N., & Vohra, N. (2009). Developing a new measure of work alienation. *Journal of Workplace Rights, 14*(3), 293–309. https://doi.org/10.2190/WR.14.3.c

Nguyen, N., Besson, T., & Stinglhamber, F. (2021). Emotional labor: The role of organizational dehumanization. *Journal of Organizational Health Psychology.* Advance online publication. https://doi.org /10.1037/ocp0000289

Nguyen, N., Cheung, F., & Stinglhamber, F. (in press). Emotional labor: A two-wave longitudinal person-centered approach. *International Journal of Stress Management.* https://doi.org/10.3390/health-care4040089

Nguyen, N., Dao, Q. A., Nhan, T. L. A., & Stinglhamber, F. (2021). Organizational dehumanization and emotional labor: A cross-cultural comparison between Vietnam and the United Kingdom. *Journal of Cross-Cultural Psychology, 52*(1), 43–60. https://doi.org/10.1177/0022022120972183

Nguyen, N., & Stinglhamber, F. (2020). Workplace mistreatment and emotional labor: A latent profile analysis. *Motivation and Emotion, 44*, 474–490. https://doi.org/10.1007/s11031-019-09803-8

Nguyen, N., & Stinglhamber, F. (2021). Emotional labor and core self-evaluations as mediators between organizational dehumanization and job satisfaction. *Current Psychology, 40*, 831–839. https://doi.org /10.1007/s12144-018-9988-2

Nisim, S., & Benjamin, O. (2010). The speech of services procurement: The negotiated order of commodification and dehumanization of cleaning employees. *Human Organization, 69*(3), 221–232. https://doi .org/10.17730/humo.69.3.g34840781k802q56

Nussbaum, M. C. (1995). Objectification. *Philosophy and Public Affairs, 24*, 249–291. https://doi.org /10.1111/j.1088-4963.1995.tb00032.x

O'Brien, G. V. (1999). Protecting the social body: Use of the organism metaphor in fighting the "menace of the feebleminded". *Mental Retardation, 37*(3), 188–200. https://doi.org/10.1352/0047%366765 (1999)037%3C;0188:PTSBUO%3E;2.0.CO;2

Olsen, J. P. (2006). Maybe it is time to rediscover bureaucracy. *Journal of Public Administration Research and Theory, 16*(1), 1–24. https://doi.org/10.1093/jopart/mui027

Pisanti, R., van der Doef, M., Maes, S., Lombardo, C., Lazzari, D., & Violani, C. (2015). Occupational coping self-efficacy explains distress and well-being in nurses beyond psychosocial job characteristics. *Frontiers in Psychology, 6*(1143), 1–14. https://doi.org/10.3389/fpsyg.2015.01143

Sarwar, A., Khan, J., Muhammad, L., Mubarak, N., & Jaafar, M. (2021). Relationship between organizational dehumanization and nurses' deviant behaviors: A moderated mediation model. *Journal of Nursing Management*. Advance online publication. https://doi.org/10.1111/JONM.13241

Sarwar, A., & Muhammad, L. (2020). Impact of organizational mistreatment on employee performance in the hotel industry. *International Journal of Contemporary Hospitality Management, 33*(2), 513–533. https://doi.org/10.1108/IJCHM-01-2020-0051

Schaubroeck, J. M., Lam, L. W., Lai, J. Y. M., Lennard, A. C., Peng, A. C., & Chan, K. W. (2018). Changing experiences of work dirtiness, occupational disidentification, and employee withdrawal. *Journal of Applied Psychology, 103*(10), 1086–1100. https://doi.org/10.1037/apl0000330

Shantz, A., Alfes, K., Bailey, C., & Soane, E. (2015). Drivers and outcomes of work alienation: Reviving a concept. *Journal of Management Inquiry, 24*(4), 382–393. https://doi.org/10.1177/1056492615573325

Shore, L. M., & Coyle-Shapiro, J. A.-M. (2012). Perceived organizational cruelty: An expansion of the negative employee–organization relationship domain. In L. M. Shore, J. A.-M. Coyle-Shapiro, & L. E. Tetrick (Eds.), *The employee–organization relationship: Applications for the 21st century* (pp. 139–157). Routledge.

Stinglhamber, F., & Caesens, G. (2020). Perceived organizational support. In V. I. Sessa & N. A. Bowling (Eds.), *Essentials of job attitudes and other workplace psychological constructs* (pp. 71–98). Taylor & Francis.

Stinglhamber, F., Caesens, G., Chalmagne, B., Demoulin, S., & Maurage, P. (2021). Leader–member exchange and organizational dehumanization: The role of supervisor's organizational embodiment. *European Management Journal*. Advance online publication. https://doi.org/10.1016/j.emj.2021.01.006

Taskin, L., Parmentier, M., & Stinglhamber, F. (2019). The dark side of office designs: Towards de-humanization. *New Technology, Work and Employment, 34*, 262–284. https://doi.org/10.1111/ntwe.12150

Tepper, B. J. (2000). Consequences of abusive supervision. *Academy of Management Journal, 43*(2), 178–190. https://doi.org/10.5465/1556375

Vaes, J., & Muratore, M. (2013). Defensive dehumanization in the medical practice: A cross-sectional study from a health care worker's perspective. *British Journal of Social Psychology, 52*(1), 180–190. https://doi.org/10.1111/bjso.12008

Vaes, J., Paladino, M. P., & Puvia, E. (2011). Are sexualized females complete human beings? Why males and females dehumanize sexually objectified women. *European Journal of Social Psychology, 41*(6), 774–785. https://doi.org/10.1002/ejsp.824

Valtorta, R. R., Baldissarri, C., Andrighetto, L., & Volpato, C. (2019a). Dirty jobs and dehumanization of workers. *British Journal of Social Psychology, 58*(4), 955–970. https://doi.org/10.1111/bjso.12315

Valtorta, R. R., Baldissarri, C., Andrighetto, L., & Volpato, C. (2019b). The dirty side of work: Biologization of physically tainted workers. *International Review of Social Psychology, 32*(1), 1–13. https://doi.org/10.5334/irsp.213

Van Dyne, L., & LePine, J. A. (1998). Helping and voice extra-role behaviors: Evidence of construct and predictive validity. *Academy of Management Journal, 41*(1), 108–119. https://doi.org/10.5465/256902

Väyrynen, T., & Laari-Salmela, S. (2018). Men, mammals, or machines? Dehumanization embedded in organizational practices. *Journal of Business Ethics, 147*(1), 95–113. https://doi.org/10.1007/s10551-015-2947-z

Volpato, C., Andrighetto, L., & Baldissarri, C. (2017). Perceptions of low-status workers and the maintenance of the social class status quo. *Journal of Social Issues, 73*(1), 192–210. https://doi.org/10.1111/josi.12211

Watson, D., & Clark, L. A. (1984). Negative affectivity: The disposition to experience aversive emotional states. *Psychological Bulletin, 96*(3), 465–490. https://doi.org/10.1037/0033-2909.96.3.465

Wo, D. X., Schminke, M., & Ambrose, M. L. (2019). Trickle-down, trickle-out, trickle-up, trickle-in, and trickle-around effects: An integrative perspective on indirect social influence phenomena. *Journal of Management, 45*(6), 2263–2292. https://doi.org/10.1177/0149206318812951

Wu, T. Y., & Hu, C. (2009). Abusive supervision and employee emotional exhaustion: Dispositional antecedents and boundaries. *Group & Organization Management, 34*(2), 143–169. https://doi.org/10.1177/1059601108331217

NOTES

1. For the sake of clarity, we present these three categories of consequences as independent of each other. A handful of studies, however, show that they may be interrelated and influence each other (Caesens & Stinglhamber, 2019; Nguyen & Stinglhamber, 2020; Nguyen, Dao et al., 2021; Sarwar et al., 2021).
2. Some scholars suggest that job satisfaction can also be considered as representative of employees' well-being rather than of their attitudes toward work (e.g., Caesens et al., 2017; Lagios et al., 2021; Nguyen & Stinglhamber, 2020).
3. Some scholars propose that employees' turnover intentions better embody a negative attitude toward the organization (e.g., Nguyen, Dao et al., 2021).

Noémie Brison, Florence Stinglhamber, and Gaëtane Caesens

SAFETY AT WORK

INTRODUCTION

This article focuses on how individuals, teams, and organizations deal with hazards that affect people's health and well-being at work and beyond. In their review of 100 years of safety research in applied psychology, Hofmann, Burke, and Zohar (2017) give an impressive account of how workplace safety has improved in many countries due to legislative action, technological improvements, and organizational measures, but how it also remains a major concern with an estimated 150 daily deaths in the United States alone still being related to exposure to hazards at work (AFL-CIO, 2015; cited in Hofmann et al., 2017). Workers may face such hazards directly, for instance by working with poisonous substances or heavy machinery, and/or they may be involved in work processes which also or even predominantly entail risks for others, such as performing surgery. The first kind of situation concerns what has been called personal safety, while the second situation concerns process safety (Grote, 2012; Hopkins, 2009). Causal mechanisms involved in personal versus process safety most likely differ due to differences in the visibility and complexity of risks, required competence for risk handling, available incentives for safe behavior, and conflicts between safety and production requirements. To date, however, research has not systematically addressed these differences (Thomas, 2012).

One tragic example of the significance of paying attention to both personal and process safety is the explosion at the BP refinery in Texas City in 2005 (Baker, 2007). At that refinery, safety programs had focused on personal safety by aiming to prevent slips, trips, falls, and vehicle accidents, which they successfully did. However, process safety was not attended to; several warnings and recommendations from external audits, regarding, for instance, necessary improvements in preventive maintenance and worker training, were left unheeded. Monitoring personal safety is generally easier because small incidents that may keep people from work for a few days—measured in recordable injury rates—are more frequent and can serve as a useful indicator for assessing the effectiveness of safety measures. Also, regulators often focus on recordable injury rates, which makes this a very popular metric in many industries. Monitoring process safety is much harder because—luckily—work processes rarely derail to an extent that results in major accidents such as airplane crashes, plant explosions, or train collisions.

Studies on process safety are thus confronted with the fundamental difficulty resulting from safety being a "dynamic non-event" (Weick, 1987). When, later in this article, data are presented on what factors predict safety, this difficulty needs to be acknowledged. Frequently, indirect measures are used to assess an organization's level of safety, such as rule-following behavior or positive perceptions of an organization's safety-related norms and values; these are considered leading indicators for safety, compared to lagging indicators such as injuries and accidents (Hopkins, 2009). How valid these indirect measures are is a matter of ongoing debate in safety research (Beus, McCord, & Zohar, 2016; Casey, Griffin, Flatau Harrison, & Neal, 2017), as the underlying problem of theoretical and empirical models hinging on rare events remains an unresolvable fundamental characteristic of safety research.

The article will concentrate on psychological research related to safety at work—which has primarily addressed personal safety—following the basic framework presented in Figure 1. Specifically, it will summarize findings concerning personal, team, and organizational antecedents, safety-related individual and team processes, and safety-related individual and team behaviors. It will introduce crucial concepts such as safety compliance and participation, adaptive team coordination, safety leadership, and safety climate and culture and discuss relevant research. There is sufficient evidence to strongly support the claim that the described linkages between antecedents and safety-related processes and behaviors are indeed causal (Beus et al., 2016). Also, safety research is quite international; as an example, studies reported in the journal *Safety Science* come from countries all around the globe, increasing the generalizability of the findings. Organizational research on risk and safety will be briefly summarized in order to illustrate benefits for a more integrative approach to safety at work, focusing on basic tensions stemming from contradictory requirements of both minimizing and coping with uncertainty, which have been explored most prominently in the high-reliability organizations (HRO) stream of research.

Figure 1. Basic framework for psychological research on safety at work.

SAFETY-RELATED BEHAVIOR

Safety-related behavior can be many different things, such as learning how to operate a new machine safely, giving others feedback on their safety performance, or discussing a new safety standard. Early research emphasized rule-compliance as the main desired safety-related behavior, and many studies have investigated the conditions under which workers may or may not follow safety rules. Deliberate rule violations—knowingly breaking rules designed to protect workers—were distinguished from errors where workers deviated from what would be safe behavior due to inattention or lack of knowledge (Reason, 1990). Violations may happen habitually as in the case of "cutting corners," enjoying unsafe behavior such as speeding, or handling conflicting demands in the work situation such as wearing ear protection and listening to warning signals (Reason, Parker, & Lawton, 1998). Hansez and Chmiel (2010) studied these habitual violations and found that job strain was positively related to cutting-corners type routine violations, while work engagement was negatively related to these violations as well as to violations related to conflicted situational demands. Violations may also happen exceptionally due to specific conditions that require other than the prescribed behavior (Reason et al., 1998). These violations may be life-saving as in the case of fire-fighters dropping their tools and lighting a fire in their escape path during the Mann Gulch fire (Weick, 1993).

A general concern with strict rule-following not being the one way to safety (e.g., Dekker, 2003; Grote, Weichbrodt, Günter, Zala-Mezö, & Künzle, 2009; Hale & Borys, 2013a, 2013b) is mirrored in the distinction between safety compliance and safety participation, two frequently studied individual behaviors (Neal, Griffin, & Hart, 2000). Safety compliance refers to following safety procedures and carrying out work in a safe manner, whereas safety participation is discretionary behavior aimed at proactively promoting safety, for instance by making suggestions during safety meetings or helping co-workers. Safety participation has also been captured as a special type of organizational citizenship behavior, including helping, voice, stewardship, whistleblowing, civic virtue, and initiating change (Hofmann, Morgeson, & Gerras, 2003).

Both safety compliance and safety participation have been found to be related to safety outcomes, such as injuries and accidents (Christian, Bradley, Wallace, & Burke, 2009; Cornelissen, Van Hoof, & De Jong, 2017). Frequently, studies have also taken safety compliance and participation as outcome variables, for instance in analyses on the impact of leadership style or safety climate.

SAFETY-RELATED PROCESSES

Individual processes. Individual processes have chiefly been studied with respect to individuals' perceptions of team and organizational characteristics that are considered important resources for safe behavior, foremost safety climate—perceptions of an organization's safety-related practices (Nahrgang, Morgeson, & Hofmann, 2011). Beus, Dhanani, and McCord (2015) found in a meta-analysis that safety climate perceptions and three personality characteristics (agreeableness, conscientiousness, neuroticism) together accounted for more than 40% of the variance in safety behaviors, with safety climate perceptions being more relevant as indicated by a two-thirds share in the explained variance. However, Beus, Munoz, and Arthur

(2015) have also shown that safety perceptions are directly influenced by personality characteristics, specifically neuroticism and locus of control.

Safety motivation, defined as "an individual's willingness to exert effort to enact safety behaviors and the valence associated with those behaviors" (Neal & Griffin, 2006, p. 947), as another safety-related individual process has also received some attention in the literature. In Christian et al.'s (2009) meta-analysis, safety motivation was strongly related to safety behaviors. Cognitive processes have been analyzed in relation to errors, where skill- and rule-based errors have been found to be related to automatic processing and knowledge-based errors to controlled processing within the constraints of bounded rationality (Reason, 1990). Also, more intricate relationships have been studied, as for instance by Wallace and Vodanovich (2003) who found that cognitive failure moderated the relationship between conscientiousness and unsafe work behaviors and accidents. Especially knowledge-based errors can be directly linked to the amount of safety knowledge, which has generally be found to be positively related to safety behavior and outcomes (Christian et al., 2009).

Team Processes. A long-standing topic in the team safety literature is the study of shared perceptions of safety-related policies, procedures, and practices—that is, a team's perception of safety climate (Zohar, 1980). While some climate measures focus on shared perceptions of managers' behaviors and attitudes (e.g., Zohar & Luria, 2010), others are based on a more generic set of individual safety-related perceptions concerning also aspects such as communication and support in the team, human resource management practices, or organizational safety systems (Flin, Mearns, O'Connor, & Bryden, 2000; Neal & Griffin, 2004). Generally, strong relationships between safety climate perceptions and safety outcomes are found, which appear to be stronger than the relationships between person-related characteristics and safety (Christian et al., 2009).

Besides research on shared safety-related perceptions in teams there is also a strong research stream that directly addresses specific team processes in high-risk teams. In particular, there have been several studies on coordination, that is the management of task interdependencies, in view of adaptively using different coordination mechanisms in accordance with changing task and situational requirements (e.g., Burtscher et al., 2011; Grote, Kolbe, Zala-Mezö, Bienefeld-Seall, & Künzle, 2010; Riethmüller, Fernandez Castelao, Eberhardt, Timmermann, & Boos, 2012; Uitdewilligen, Rico, & Waller, 2018; Valentine & Edmondson, 2015; Vashdi, Bamberger, & Erez, 2013; Waller, 1999). Two coordination mechanisms that have received much attention in this respect are explicit versus implicit coordination (Entin & Serfaty, 1999; Rico, Sánchez-Manzanares, Gil, & Gibson, 2008). Explicit coordination is the deliberate and resource-intensive establishment of common ground and subsequent decision-making based on the information acquired and evaluated in the team. Implicit coordination, on the other hand, relies on shared assumptions and knowledge about the team, the task, and the context, enabling team members to coordinate their action in an effortless manner with few demands on information acquisition and assessment. As implicit coordination is less resource-intensive it is considered especially suited for very demanding tasks. However, if these tasks entail unexpected elements, explicit coordination may become necessary (Grote et al., 2010). Of particular importance, therefore, is helping teams realize the need to switch between coordination mechanisms for which both speaking up (Kolbe et al., 2012) and more effortless behaviors such as talking to the room and monitoring team behavior (Kolbe et al., 2014) have been found to be effective.

ANTECEDENTS OF SAFETY-RELATED PROCESSES AND BEHAVIORS

Job Characteristics. An obvious job characteristic that will influence safety-related processes and behaviors is the amount and kind of risk inherent in the job. However, there is little comparative research on this, except for some studies that have examined the relationship between personality and preferences for low-risk versus high-risk jobs (e.g., Soane & Chmiel, 2005) and an analysis of safety climate and accidents across all occupations in Denmark (Ajslev et al., 2017), singling out workers in transport, construction, manufacturing, and service industries with the lowest safety climate perceptions. A meta-analysis examining the impact of job demands on employee health and safety more generally has shown that job demands created by risks and hazards at the workplace are related to both burnout and adverse safety outcomes (Nahrgang et al., 2011).

Another perspective on job demands, which is pervasive especially in practice-oriented safety research, is the requirement to manage the fundamental production-safety trade-off stemming from conflicting demands for doing a job efficiently and doing it safely (e.g., Cowing, Paté-Cornell, & Glynn, 2004; Reason, 1997). Predominantly, this conflict has been studied in terms of workers "cutting corners" (Reason et al., 1998) and as a basic indicator of individual, team, and organizational safety-related norms and values, expressed in management commitment to a "Safety First" principle, which is core to many safety climate measures (Beus, Payne, Bergman, & Arthur, 2010; Casey et al., 2017).

Discussions of job design for promoting safe behavior often feature contrasting views on the role of job control—or job autonomy as this construct is also frequently called—in line with general considerations of the importance of rule compliance. Job control is considered one of the main resources for dealing with job demands (Karasek, 1979). Older research on self-managing teams seems to indicate that job control is positively related to safety outcomes (Turner & Parker, 2003). In their meta-analysis, Nahrgang et al. (2011) found that autonomy had a positive impact on safety through work engagement. A study by Turner, Stride, Carter, and McCaughey (2012) indicates that job control is more beneficial for safety participation and less so for safety compliance, such as rule-following. Much research has addressed questions of job demands and job control in the context of highly automated work systems. The basic concern here, coined as "ironies of automation" (Bainbridge, 1983), is that people are put in charge of increasingly complex and non-transparent technical systems with decreasing opportunities for actively controlling these systems. This dilemma continues to be the root cause of many accidents, and research remains very active into means to overcome it (Grote, Weyer, & Stanton, 2014).

Personal Characteristics. Stemming from an old idea in safety research that some people are more "accident-prone" than others, many studies have addressed personal dispositions as antecedents of individual safety-related processes and behaviors. The notion of accident proneness was first introduced based on the observation that a small group of workers in a munitions factory appeared to have much higher accident rates than everyone else (Greenwood & Woods, 1919).

Ever since, this notion has been hotly debated, pointing for instance to statistical explanations for unequal distributions of accidents and differential exposure to hazardous situations as alternative explanations (Chmiel & Grote, 2017; Visser, Pijl, Stolk, Neelman, & Rosmalen, 2007). However, there is some evidence that certain personality characteristics predict involvement in accidents. In two meta-analyses (Christian et al., 2009; Clarke & Robertson, 2005), some support was found that agreeableness, conscientiousness, and internal locus of control were negatively related to accident involvement and injuries at work, whereas neuroticism was positively related to accidents and injuries. No relationship was found for extraversion and risk taking. Furthermore, personality characteristics may impact exposure to hazards in that people select certain work environments that best fit their dispositions, attitudes, and values (Edwards, 2008). Findings from Soane and Chmiel (2005), for instance, indicate that extraverted individuals prefer more, and conscientious individuals less, risky work environments.

Substantial research has addressed the more proximal relationship between individual characteristics and safety-related behaviors. In their meta-analysis, Beus et al. (2015) found that more agreeable and conscientious workers engaged less in unsafe behaviors. Moreover, extraversion and neuroticism were associated with more unsafe behaviors, and openness to experience was unrelated to (un)safe behavior. Hogan and Foster (2013) developed personality scales that matched presumed safety requirements more directly (e.g., scales for compliant and cautious personality) and, as could be expected, reported significant relationships, with safety outcomes mediated by safety-related behaviors. Zhang, Li, and Wu (2013) studied general mental ability in nuclear power plant operators and showed relationships with both safety compliance and safety participation.

Other research has looked into attitudes as less fundamental and stable individual characteristics. In their meta-analysis, Christian et al. (2009) found that general job-related attitudes such as job satisfaction and organizational commitment were positively related to safe behaviors. Based on the theory of planned behavior, Fugas, Silva, and Meliá (2013) showed that perceived behavioral control predicted compliant safety behavior, whereas positive safety attitudes and co-workers' safety norms in addition to behavioral control were relevant for proactive safety behaviors. Fogarty and Shaw (2010) reported that attitudes and norms favoring non-compliant behavior predicted intentions to violate rules and actual rule violations.

Team Characteristics. Research has established social support as an important driver for promoting safety (Nahrgang et al., 2011; Turner et al., 2012). A key aspect of social support is psychological safety, which has been defined as the perception that a team is safe for taking interpersonal risks involved in, for instance, questioning others' behavior or admitting to mistakes (Edmondson, 1999). Psychological safety has been studied especially as a prerequisite for speaking up, which in turn has been shown to be related to safety performance (Kolbe et al., 2012).

A second crucial factor for safety is leadership (Christian et al., 2009; Nahrgang et al., 2011). As in the leadership literature more generally, much of the research on safety has been concerned with identifying effective leadership styles (Donovan, Salmon, & Lenné, 2016). In particular, transformational leadership—that is leadership aimed at motivating employees through inspiration and charisma—has been found to be positively related to safety outcomes. However, in a meta-analysis by Clarke (2013) transactional leadership—the counterpart of transformational leadership, aimed at an exchange of rewards for fulfilling expectations—seems to support both safety participation and compliance, whereas transformational leadership supports mainly safety participation. Zohar and Luria (2010) have shown that transformational leadership is particularly important for promoting safe behavior when the priority of safety is not sufficiently embedded in company values. In a series of studies in nuclear power plants, Martínez-Córcoles and colleagues (2012, 2013, 2014) investigated the relationship between empowering leadership and safety-related behaviors, finding positive relationships with both safety compliance (mediated by role clarity) and safety participation (mediated by collaborative team learning). The requirement to adapt leadership styles to situational requirements more generally has been demonstrated by Yun, Faraj, and Sims (2005) who found that directive leadership in medical emergency teams was more successful in complex cases and with less experienced team members, while an empowering style was effective in less complex cases and with more experienced teams.

Another approach to leadership is to define it in functional terms as exerting influence on others in order to determine and achieve objectives. The tasks and processes involved in leadership are emphasized rather than the formal leadership role (Yukl, 2006). Thus, specific leadership behaviors can be related to safety behaviors and outcomes, as in the study by Griffin and Hu (2013) who found that safety-inspiring behavior was associated with safety participation and safety monitoring with safety compliance. Also, training specific behaviors, such as communicating safety as a priority, has been shown to improve safety behaviors (Zohar, 2002; Zohar & Polachek, 2014). The functional perspective on leadership also provides the foundation for the concept of shared leadership, which argues that leadership functions can be fulfilled not only by the formal leader, but by any team member. In high-risk teams, shared leadership has been shown to promote safety, for instance in shock trauma teams (Klein, Ziegert, Knight, & Xiao, 2006) and anesthesia teams (Künzle, Zala-Mezö, Wacker, Kolbe, & Grote, 2010). Bienefeld and Grote (2014) analyzed shared leadership within and across cockpit and cabin crews while handling a simulated emergency. Overall, successful aircrews were characterized by more shared leadership in the cabin, but not in the cockpit. Furthermore, more leadership of pursers, that is, the formal leaders of the cabin crew, toward the cockpit crew was evident in successful aircrews. The authors discuss their findings in view of the pursers' crucial role as boundary-spanners for achieving overall success and the support for this role through shared leadership in the cabin crew. More generally, the study indicates that some caution is needed in judging the benefits of shared leadership. It appears that shared leadership needs to be carefully balanced with leadership by the formal leader. Sharing should concern only delegation of specific leadership tasks, while the overall responsibility should remain with the formal leader, thereby creating some stability and orientation for team members (Grote, 2015b).

Finally, there may be situations where personal leadership is overall less important due to substitutes being in place, for instance standards that prescribe work processes in great detail or very experienced employees who know what to do without a leader telling them. In cockpit crews, it was indeed found that better performance in a simulated non-routine situation was linked to coordination patterns with little leadership and much implicit coordination in highly standardized work phases and more leadership during the less standardized work phases (Grote et al., 2010). Moreover, substitution may affect different leadership functions differently.

For instance, in anesthesia teams consisting of more experienced nurses and less experienced, but formally responsible residents, successful performance was linked to residents primarily initiating information search and structuring, while nurses took the lead in problem-solving (Künzle et al., 2010).

Organizational Characteristics.   Culture and climate are probably the most discussed organizational characteristic in the safety literature (Casey et al., 2017; Guldenmund, 2000). Generally, organizational culture concerns shared norms and assumptions guiding behavior while organizational climate refers to shared perceptions of organizational reality. Applying this distinction to safety culture and safety climate, safety culture can be defined as "the sum of all safety-related assumptions and norms that are shared by the majority of an organisation's members, and which find their expression in the way safety is actually dealt with in all areas of the organisation" (Müller, Brauner, Grote, & Künzler, 1998, p. 25), while safety climate reflects employees' shared perceptions of how safety is managed in the workplace (Zohar, 1980). Given the difficulties inherent in measuring safety culture, much more research has been devoted to studying organizational safety climate, usually measured in terms of the shared perception of organizational aspects such as management commitment to safety, adequate safety management tools and procedures, appropriate risk perception, priority of safety concerns over production pressures, and sufficient knowledge and skills (Flin et al., 2000). Overall, there is ample evidence that organizations which place high importance on safety as measured by safety climate questionnaires have better safety performance and outcomes than those that do not (Christian et al., 2009; Griffin & Curcuruto, 2016; Nahrgang et al., 2011). Research has also begun to consider the reverse relationship: that is, perceptions of a positive safety climate being the consequence of safe behavior and low accident rates (Bergman, Payne, Taylor, & Beus, 2014; Stride et al., 2013). Next to safety climate, safety culture remains a hotly debated topic, but frequently with a sense of frustration because culture tends to be assessed only through climate, it is abused as a catch-all category in accident investigations, and its potential for a deeper systemic understanding of the processes involved in (un)successful safety interventions is not taken advantage of (Grote, 2007; Silbey, 2009; Strauch, 2015).

Another crucial organizational characteristic is the level of formalization and standardization. As mentioned earlier already, there has been a shift in the safety literature toward acknowledging the need to flexibly respond to unexpected events rather than stress rule compliance alone (Dekker, 2003; Hale & Borys, 2013a; Weick, Sutcliffe, & Obstfeld, 1999). This raises the question of what constitutes effective safety rules, given that they should provide sufficient guidance but also leeway for adaptive action. Grote et al. (2009) have introduced the construct of flexible rules as a response to this question, which draws on the distinction suggested by Hale and Swuste (1998) between goal, process, and action rules. Goal rules only define the goal to be achieved, leaving open how this is accomplished by the actors concerned. Process rules provide guidance for deciding on the right course of action for achieving certain goals. Finally, action rules prescribe detailed courses of action, possibly without even mentioning the goal to be achieved. Goal and process rules and also those action rules that entail some decision latitude constitute flexible rules. As a rule of thumb on good rule-making, action rules are adequate when conditions are stable; goal and process rules should be used when high degrees of flexibility are required. Also, there are a number of important prerequisites

ORGANIZATIONAL RESEARCH ON RISK AND SAFETY

How organizations manage risk and safety has been a long-standing concern in the organizational literature as well. In the 1980s a fundamental debate was initiated by Perrow's (1984) postulate that in certain types of organizations, such as nuclear power plants or chemical plants, accidents cannot be prevented irrespective of how hard everyone in these organizations tries to do just that. His argument was that the demands placed on organizations due to complex interactions among system components, which require decentralized decision-making and action, and the demands due to tight coupling, that is, high interdependence among system components with little slack, which have to be managed via centralization, are irreconcilable. This so-called normal accident theory was challenged by a group of researchers who found in their empirical analyses in various such organizations that they do seem to manage these contradictions well. They termed their approach "high-reliability organizations (HRO)" theory and argued that these organizations are characterized by three overarching features (Roberts, 1990; Weick, Sutcliffe, & Obstfeld, 1999):

1. HROs are able to switch between more centralized and more decentralized modes of operation (LaPorte & Consolini, 1991),
2. HROs have systems in place that very deliberately manage the balance between stability and flexibility (e.g., Bigley & Roberts, 2001),
3. HROs are characterized by strong organizational cultures that serve as a centralization mechanism in an otherwise decentralized organization (Weick, 1987).

A number of conceptual developments in safety research have aimed to better understand and manage the fundamental tension between stability and flexibility. This tension results from the requirements to both minimize and cope with uncertainty (Grote, 2009, 2015b), and may even entail momentary increases in uncertainty, such as when individuals speak up to push for a change in course of action (Grote, 2015a). Resilience, originally discussed in biology (Holling, 1973), but also in sociology (Wildavsky, 1988), is one such concept. It has been defined as a system's ability to "bounce back" after disturbances, and, through learning from those situations, to "bounce forward" and increase the system's adaptive capacity for handling surprises (Woods, 2015), thus incorporating reactive and proactive responses to uncertainty (Pettersen & Schulman, 2016). Much of what has been written about resilience focuses on organizations' defining general characteristics that enable resilience, such as the necessity to continuously monitor, anticipate, respond, and learn (Hollnagel, Pariès, Woods, & Wreathall, 2011) or to manage trade-offs in the face of challenged system boundaries, which Woods (2016) has termed *graceful extensibility*.

Another important concept introduced into safety research is that of dynamic capabilities, originally stemming from the organizational strategy literature (Teece, Pisano, & Shuen, 1997). Dynamic safety capability is defined as "a set of higher order, future-oriented activities through which an organization systematically makes changes to its operational routines in pursuit of improved safety performance" (Griffin, Cordery, & Soo, 2015, p. 249). Dynamic safety capability is needed in particular due to increasing levels of external uncertainty organizations have to proactively deal with in order to maintain good safety performance. It entails abilities to detect opportunities and threats to safety in the environment, to manage tensions stemming from competing goals, and to transform the organization through second-order change. Casey et al. (2017) further spell out strategies that organizations use when trying to maintain control in highly dynamic environments, which they term *defend, adapt, leverage,* and *energize*. They also define specific characteristics of safety climate and safety culture that underpin these different strategies, thereby emphasizing that there is not necessarily just one right kind of climate and culture that fits all organizations. Similarly, Amalberti (2013) introduced three models of safety that fit the requirements of different industries which vary in the amount of uncertainty they have to handle.

These newer developments indicate a growing awareness that much can be gained from approaching safety at work with a broader and more integrative set of concepts, drawn from various disciplines, that address both personal and process safety (Hofmann et al., 2017). The fundamental requirements stemming from having to manage uncertainty, which all organizations face, may constitute a useful conceptual framework within which general organizational and psychological literatures and safety research can be integrated in order to develop a fuller understanding of what it takes to manage safety well (Grote, 2015b). The basic tensions inherent in safety management, such as stability versus flexibility, system versus local goals, or short versus long time frames (Reiman, Rollenhagen, Pietikäinen, & Heikkilä, 2015), can be found in all organizations, and this may lead to the realization that, at least in part, managing safety is not so different from good management more generally. This assumption is supported by research that found high-performance human resource management practices, characterized for instance by employee empowerment, broad information sharing, and employment security, accounting for 8% of the variance in lost-time injury rates across 138 organizations in Canada (Zacharatos, Barling, & Iverson, 2005).

SAFETY IN PRACTICE: RESEARCH ON SAFETY MANAGEMENT

Safety management concerns all organizational activities that aim at controlling risk and keeping it at an acceptable level (Grote, 2012). Individual safety management practices should be aligned within a safety management system to promote an integral approach to managing safety (Grote, 2017). Many components of safety management concern fundamental organizational functions, such as devising a safety policy, defining safety resources and responsibilities, developing safety standards and procedures, organizing internal and external audits of safety practices, ensuring processes for continuous improvement, and designing organizational systems for emergency management and management of change. Others mainly involve system engineering, such as risk identification, system design, and continuous measurement and assessment of indicators of safety performance. Though all these components also benefit from consideration of psychological processes, the two safety-management instruments that probably are most closely tied to psychological research are safety training and incident reporting and investigation. Both will be briefly reviewed here to give some indication of how interventions based on psychological safety research can directly benefit safety-management practices in organizations and strengthen perceptions of a positive safety climate.

Safety Training. Individual safety training, concerned primarily with building knowledge for personal safety, is common practice in most industries (Burke et al., 2006; Hofmann et al., 2017). Many companies, in high-risk industries in particular, have started to invest in team training in order to build up the skills needed for effective coordination, especially in emergency situations. This has happened in response to many accident analyses that convincingly showed malfunctioning coordination to be a significant precursor to accidents (Salas, Wilson, Burke, & Wightman, 2006). The aviation industry was the first to develop special training programs for so-called crew resource management in the cockpit (Helmreich, Merritt, & Wilhelm, 1999), focusing on leadership, decision-making, and communication skills. Over the last decade, similar programs have been introduced in many other domains, most prominently in medicine (Baker, Gustafson, Beaubien, Salas, & Barach, 2005).

Training methods range from classical lectures to behavior training in full-scale simulators. The first experimental evaluation of accident simulation as a training method was undertaken by Rubinsky and Smith (1973) who found that accident simulation in using a power tool reduced unsafe behavior significantly more than training by means of written instructions and demonstrations. Training often focuses on drills in order to ensure the correct execution of a predefined action path. Especially for technical simulator training in aviation or process industries, this has long been the dominant form of training because the main concern was to support people in performing certain tasks even under very high levels of stress during emergencies. Increasingly, more open forms of training aimed at adaptive decision-making and problem-solving have been introduced, which conform with the general idea that safety often has to be achieved in uncertain and unpredictable situations (e.g., Salas, Nichols, & Driskell, 2007). There is general agreement that the more engaging the teaching methods, the more profound the learning (Burke et al., 2006, 2011). Other issues are still debated, such as cross-cultural influences on learning and the measures best used to evaluate the effectiveness of training (Burke & Sockbeson, 2015; Salas et al., 2006).

Incident Reporting and Investigation. Incident reporting and investigation has long been a crucial element in safety management systems to ensure learning from errors and continuous improvement (van der Schaaf, Lukas, & Hale, 1991). The objective is to support systematic learning from experience and to specifically exploit minor events as opportunities for improving safety. There is much literature available on both the usefulness of incident reporting and investigation and the difficulties associated with introducing and properly employing it. Problems described concern general under-reporting, differential reporting by different occupational groups, lack of systematic analyses of incident reports, inadequate sharing, storing and retrieving of lessons learned, failure to implement concrete measures identified from incident analyses, and the consequences for the individuals involved in the reported incidents in terms of blame and punitive action (e.g., Carroll, 1998; Dekker, 2007; Pfeiffer, Manser, & Wehner, 2010; Ramanujam & Goodman, 2011). Especially in view of the last point, there is agreement that incident reporting can only work when blame and punitive action is avoided and confidentiality guaranteed (Dekker, 2007). However, this leaves the difficult issue of handling severe cases of misconduct which should be—and legally even have to be—followed up with measures addressed at the individual level. Regulatory agencies often require public reporting of incidents, which creates problems with potentially distorted information in order to avoid blame.

Another general recommendation is to keep incident reporting voluntary and to encourage reports not only on incidents in which the person was involved him- or herself, but also incidents that were observed without own personal involvement (Leape, 2002). Under those conditions usually the number of reported incidents increases substantially, which can raise new problems regarding the analysis of the reports and definition and implementation of concrete measures (Macrae, 2016). Furthermore, in several high-risk industries incident reporting is mandatory and reports are to be submitted to the regulator, for example, in aviation and in the nuclear industry, which constrains voluntary reporting schemes.

Regarding actual learning from incidents, an important concern is whether sufficient openness, for instance by fostering psychological safety (Edmondson, 1999), can be achieved that allows the creation of doubt needed to expand understanding beyond the already known. In his study of airline flight safety investigators, Macrae (2009) found that creating doubt was crucial in order to identify new risks from analyses of incidents and accidents. Without the willingness to admit to the limits and fallibility of one's own and others' knowledge, incident investigations will just reproduce existing assumptions about causes of unsafe behaviors and outcomes.

CONCLUSION

The results of safety research, most of it psychological, reviewed in this article show that there is a sound body of knowledge concerning the processes involved in achieving personal safety at work. Especially with respect to safety climate, there is also a growing understanding of how effects cut across levels of analysis from the individual to the team and the organizational level (e.g., Zohar & Luria, 2010). However, cross-level effects still constitute a challenge for future research.

Translating knowledge from safety research into effective safety interventions also remains demanding (Robson et al., 2007), not least because organizations place insufficient priority on workplace safety. Process safety, due to the potential for major accidents that not only harm workers but the larger population, and put the financial viability and reputation of the respective company at risk, should be a very immediate concern for organizations. However, interventions aimed at improving process safety are very costly and their effect much more difficult to trace compared to personal safety. Integrating psychological and organizational safety research and combining it with insights from the broader management literature is a promising way forward that expands actionable knowledge on both personal and process safety, making it harder for organizations to ignore.

FURTHER READING

Amalberti, R. (2013). *Navigating safety*. Dordrecht: Springer.
Beus, J. M., McCord, M. A., & Zohar, D. (2016). Workplace safety: A review and research synthesis. *Organizational Psychology Review, 6*, 352–381. https://doi.org/10.1177%2F2041386615626243

Clarke, S., Probst, T. M., Guldenmund, F., & Passmore, F. (Eds.) (2015). *The Wiley-Blackwell handbook of the psychology of occupational safety and workplace health*. Chichester, U.K.: John Wiley & Sons.

Griffin, M. A. & Curcuruto, M. (2016). Safety climate in organizations. *Annual Review of Organizational Psychology and Organizational Behavior*, 3, 191–212. https://doi.org/10.1146/annurev-orgpsych-041015-062414

Grote, G. (2012). Safety management in different high-risk domains—all the same? *Safety Science, 50*, 1983–1992. https://www.annualreviews.org/doi/abs/10.1146/annurev-orgpsych-041015-062414

REFERENCES

Ajslev, J., Dastjerdi, E. L., Dyreborg, J., Kines, P., Jeschke, K. C., Sundstrup, E., . . . Andersen, L. L. (2017). Safety climate and accidents at work: Cross-sectional study among 15,000 workers of the general working population. *Safety Science, 91*, 320–325. https://doi.org/10.1016/j.ssci.2016.08.029

Amalberti, R. (2013). *Navigating safety*. Dordrecht, Netherlands: Springer.

Bainbridge, L. (1983). Ironies of automation. *Automatica, 19*, 775–779. https://doi.org/10.1016/0005-1098(83)90046-8

Baker, J. (2007). The report of the BP U.S. Refineries Independent Safety Review Panel. http://sunnyday.mit.edu/Baker-panel-report.pdf

Baker, D. P., Gustafson, S., Beaubien, J. M., Salas, E., & Barach, P. (2005). Medical team training programs in health care. In K. Henriksen, J. B. Battles, & E. S. Marks (Eds.), *Advances in patient safety: From research to implementation*, Vol. 4: *Programs, tools, and products* (pp. 253–267). Rockville, MD: Agency for Healthcare Research and Quality. https://www.ncbi.nlm.nih.gov/books/NBK20580/pdf/Bookshelf_NBK20580.pdf

Bergman, M. E., Payne, S. C., Taylor, A. B., & Beus, J. M. (2014). The shelf life of a safety climate assessment: How long until the relationship with safety-critical incidents expires? *Journal of Business and Psychology, 29*, 519–540. https://doi.org/10.1007/s10869-013-9337-2

Beus, J. M., Dhanani, L. Y., & McCord, A. (2015). A meta-analysis of personality and workplace safety: Addressing unanswered questions. *Journal of Applied Psychology, 100*, 481–498. https://doi.org/10.1037/a0037916

Beus, J. M., McCord, M. A., & Zohar, D. (2016). Workplace safety: A review and research synthesis. *Organizational Psychology Review, 6*, 352–381. https://doi.org/10.1177/2041386615626243

Beus, J. M., Munoz, G. J., & Arthur, W. (2015). Personality as a multilevel predictor of climate: An examination in the domain of workplace safety. *Group & Organization Management, 40*, 625–656. https://doi.org/10.1177%2F1059601115576597

Beus, J. M., Payne, S. C., Bergman, M. E., & Arthur, W., Jr. (2010). Safety climate and injuries: An examination of theoretical and empirical relationships. *Journal of Applied Psychology, 95*, 713–727. https://doi.org/10.1037/a0019164

Bienefeld, N., & Grote, G. (2014). Shared leadership in multiteam systems: How cockpit and cabin crews lead each other to safety. *Human Factors, 56*, 270–286. https://doi.org/10.1177/0018720813488137

Bigley, G., & Roberts, K. H. (2001). The incident command system: High-reliability organizing for complex and volatile environments. *Academy of Management Journal, 44*, 1281–1299. https://doi.org/10.5465/3069401

Burke, M. J., Sarpy, S. A., Smith-Crowe, K., Chan-Serafin, S., Salvador, R. O., & Islam, G. (2006). Relative effectiveness of worker safety and health training methods. *American Journal of Public Health, 96*, 315–324. https://doi.org/10.2105/AJPH.2004.059840

Burke, M. J., Salvador, R. O., Smith-Crowe, K., Chan-Serafin, S., Smith, A., & Sonesh, S. (2011). The dread factor: How hazards and safety training influence learning and performance. *Journal of Applied Psychology, 96*, 46–70. https://doi.org/10.1037/a0021838

Burke, M. J., & Sockbeson, C. E. S. (2015). Safety training. In S. Clarke, T. M. Probst, F. Guldenmund, & J. Passmore (Eds.), *The Wiley-Blackwell handbook of the psychology of occupational safety and workplace health* (pp. 327–356). Chichester, U.K.: John Wiley & Sons.

Burtscher, M. J., Manser, T., Kolbe, M., Grote, G., Grande, B., Spahn, D. R., & Wacker, J. (2011). Adaptation in anaesthesia team coordination in response to a simulated critical event and its relationship to clinical performance. *British Journal of Anaesthesia, 106*, 801–806. https://doi.org/10.1093/bja/aer039

Carroll, J. S. (1998). Organizational learning activities in high-hazard industries: The logics underlying self-analysis. *Journal of Management Studies, 35*, 699–717. https://doi.org/10.1111/1467-6486.00116

Casey, T., Griffin, M. A., Flatau Harrison, H., & Neal, A. (2017). Safety climate and culture: Integrating psychological and systems perspectives. *Journal of Occupational Health Psychology, 22*, 341–353. https://doi.org/10.1037/ocp0000072

Chmiel, N., & Grote, G. (2017). Why do I put myself and others in danger or help increase safety? Person- and situation-related causes of safety behaviours. In N. Chmiel, F. Fraccaroli, & M. Sverke (Eds.), *An introduction to work and organizational psychology: An international perspective* (pp. 388–409). Chichester, U.K.: Wiley.

Christian, M. S., Bradley, J. C., Wallace, J. C., & Burke, M. J. (2009). Workplace safety: A meta-analysis of the roles of person and situation factors. *Journal of Applied Psychology, 94*, 1103–1127. https://psycnet.apa.org/doi/10.1037/a0016172

Clarke, S. (2013). Safety leadership: A meta-analytic review of transformational and transactional leadership styles as antecedents of safety behaviours. *Journal of Occupational and Organizational Psychology, 86*, 22–49. https://doi.org/10.1111/j.2044-8325.2012.02064.x

Clarke, S. & Robertson, I. T. (2005). A meta-analytic review of the Big Five personality factors and accident involvement in occupational and non-occupational settings. *Journal of Occupational and Organizational Psychology, 78*, 355–376. https://doi.org/10.1348/096317905X26183

Cornelissen, P. A., Van Hoof, J. J., & De Jong, M. D. T. (2017). Determinants of safety outcomes and performance: A systematic literature review of research in four high-risk industries. *Journal of Safety Research, 62*, 127–141. https://doi.org/10.1016/j.jsr.2017.06.009

Cowing, M. M., Paté-Cornell, M. E., & Glynn, P. W. (2004). Dynamic modeling of the tradeoff between productivity and safety in critical engineering systems. *Reliability Engineering & System Safety, 86*, 269–284. https://doi.org/10.1016/j.ress.2004.02.003

Dekker, S. (2003). Failure to adapt or adaptations that fail: Contrasting models on procedures and safety. *Applied Ergonomics, 34*, 233–238. https://doi.org/10.1016/S0003-6870(03)00031-0

Dekker, S. (2007). *Just culture—Balancing safety and accountability*. Aldershot, U.K.: Ashgate.

Donovan, S.-L., Salmon, P. M., & Lenné, M. G. (2016). Leading with style: A literature review of the influence of safety leadership on performance and outcomes. *Theoretical Issues in Ergonomics Science, 17*, 423–442. https://doi.org/10.1080/1463922X.2016.1143986

Edmondson, A. (1999). Psychological safety and learning behavior in work teams. *Administrative Science Quarterly, 44*, 350–383. https://doi.org/10.2307/2666999

Edwards, J. R. 2008. Person–environment fit in organizations: An assessment of theoretical progress. *Academy of Management Annals, 2*, 167–230. https://doi.org/10.1080/19416520802211503

Entin, E. E., & Serfaty, D. (1999). Adaptive team coordination. *Human Factors, 41*, 312–325. https://doi.org/10.1518%2F001872099779591196

Faraj, S., & Xiao, X. (2006). Coordination in fast-response organizations. *Management Science, 52*, 1155–1169. https://doi.org/10.1287/mnsc.1060.0526

Flin, R., Mearns, K., O'Connor, P., & Bryden, R. (2000). Measuring safety climate: Identifying the common features. *Safety Science, 34*, 177–192. https://doi.org/10.1016/S0925-7535(00)00012-6

Fogarty, G. J., & Shaw, A. (2010). Safety climate and the theory of planned behavior: Towards the prediction of unsafe behavior. *Accident Analysis, 42,* 1455–1459. https://doi.org/10.1016/j.aap.2009.08.008

Fugas, C. S., Silva, S. A., & Meliá, J. L. (2013). Profiling safety behaviors: Exploration of the sociocognitive variables that best discriminate between different behavioral patterns. *Risk Analysis, 33,* 838–850. https://doi.org/10.1111/j.1539-6924.2012.01913.x

Greenwood, M., & Woods, H. M. (1919). The incidence of industrial accidents upon individuals with special reference to multiple accidents. Industrial Fatigue Research Board, Medical Research Committee, Report No. 4. London, U.K.: Her Majesty's Stationery Office. https://archive.org/details/incidenceofindus00grea/page/n4

Griffin, M. A., Cordery, J., & Soo, C. (2015). Dynamic safety capability: How organizations proactively change core safety systems. *Organizational Psychology Review, 6,* 248–272. https://doi.org/10.1177/2041386615590679

Griffin, M. A., & Curcuruto, M. (2016). Safety climate in organizations. *Annual Review of Organizational Psychology and Organizational Behavior, 3,* 191–212. https://doi.org/10.1146/annurev-orgpsych-041015-062414

Griffin, M. A. & Hu, X. (2013). How leaders differentially motivate safety compliance and safety participation: The role of monitoring, inspiring, and learning. *Safety Science, 60,* 196–202. https://doi.org/10.1016/j.ssci.2013.07.019

Grote, G. (2007). Understanding and assessing safety culture through the lens of organizational management of uncertainty. *Safety Science, 45,* 637–652. https://doi.org/10.1016/j.ssci.2007.04.002

Grote, G. (2009). *Management of uncertainty—Theory and application in the design of systems and organizations.* Berlin, Germany: Springer.

Grote, G. (2012). Safety management in different high-risk domains—All the same? *Safety Science, 50,* 1983–1992. https://doi.org/10.1016/j.ssci.2011.07.017

Grote, G. (2015a). Promoting safety by increasing uncertainty—Implications for risk management. *Safety Science, 71,* 71–79. https://doi.org/10.1016/j.ssci.2014.02.010

Grote, G. (2015b). Managing uncertainty in high-risk environments. In S. Clarke, T. M. Probst, F. Guldenmund, & J. Passmore (Eds.), *The Wiley Blackwell handbook of the psychology of occupational safety and workplace health* (pp. 485–505). Chichester, U.K.: John Wiley & Sons.

Grote, G. (2017). Safety management principles. In N. Möller, S. O. Hansson, J.-E. Holmberg, & C. Rollenhagen (Eds.), *Handbook of safety principles* (pp. 625–646). Hoboken, NJ: John Wiley & Sons. https://doi.org/10.1002/9781119443070.ch27

Grote, G., Kolbe, M., Zala-Mezö, E., Bienefeld-Seall, N., & Künzle, B. (2010). Adaptive coordination and heedfulness make better cockpit crews. *Ergonomics, 52,* 211–228. https://doi.org/10.1080/00140130903248819

Grote, G., Weichbrodt, J. C., Günter, H., Zala-Mezö, E. & Künzle, B. (2009). Coordination in high-risk organizations: The need for flexible routines. *Cognition, Technology & Work, 11,* 17–27. https://doi.org/10.1007/s10111-008-0119-y

Grote, G., Weyer, J., & Stanton, N. (2014). Beyond human-centred automation—Concepts for human–machine interaction in multilayered networks. *Ergonomics, 57,* 289–294. https://doi.org/10.1080/00140139.2014.890748

Guldenmund, F. W. (2000). The nature of safety culture: A review of theory and research. *Safety Science, 34,* 215–257. https://doi.org/10.1016/S0925-7535(00)00014-X

Hale, A. R. & Borys, D. (2013a). Working to rule or working safely? Part 1: A state of the art review. *Safety Science, 55,* 207–221. https://doi.org/10.1016/j.ssci.2012.05.011

Hale, A. R. & Borys, D. (2013b). Working to rule or working safely? Part 2: The management of safety rules and procedures. *Safety Science, 55,* 222–231. https://doi.org/10.1016/j.ssci.2012.05.013

Hale, A. R., & Swuste, P. (1998). Safety rules: Procedural freedom or action constraint? *Safety Science, 29,* 163–177. https://doi.org/10.1016/S0925-7535(98)00020-4

Hansez, I., & Chmiel, N. (2010). Safety behavior: Job demands, job resources and perceived management commitment to safety. *Journal of Occupational Health Psychology, 15*, 267–278. https://psycnet.apa.org/doi/10.1037/a0019528

Helmreich, R. L., Merritt, A. C., & Wilhelm, J. A. (1999). The evolution of crew resource management training in commercial aviation. *International Journal of Aviation Psychology, 9*, 19–32. https://doi.org/10.1207/s15327108ijap0901_2

Hofmann, D. A., Burke, M. J., & Zohar, D. (2017). 100 years of occupational safety research: From basic protections and work analysis to a multilevel view of workplace safety and risk. *Journal of Applied Psychology, 102*, 375–388. https://doi.org/10.1037/apl0000114

Hofmann, D. A., Morgeson, F. P., & Gerras, S. J. (2003). Climate as a moderator of the relationship between leader-member exchange and content specific citizenship: Safety climate as an exemplar. *Journal of Applied Psychology, 88*, 170–178. https://doi.org/10.1037/0021-9010.88.1.170

Hogan, J., & Foster, J. (2013). Multifaceted personality predictors of workplace safety performance: More than conscientiousness. *Human Performance, 26*, 20–43. https://doi.org/10.1080/08959285.2012.736899

Holling, C. S. (1973). Resilience and stability of ecological systems. *Annual Review of Ecology and Systematics, 4*, 1–23. https://doi.org/10.1146/annurev.es.04.110173.000245

Hollnagel, E., Pariès, J., Woods, D. D., & Wreathall, J. (2011). *Resilience engineering in practice: A guidebook.* Aldershot, U.K.: Ashgate.

Hopkins, A. (2009). Thinking about process safety indicators. *Safety Science, 47*, 460–465. https://doi.org/10.1016/j.ssci.2007.12.006

Karasek, R. (1979). Job demands, job decision latitude and mental strain: Implications for job design. *Administrative Science Quarterly, 24*, 285–308. https://doi.org/10.2307/2392498

Klein, K. J., Ziegert, J. C., Knight, A. P., & Xiao, Y. (2006). Dynamic delegation: Shared, hierarchical, and deindividualized leadership in extreme action teams. *Administrative Science Quarterly, 51*, 590–621. https://doi.org/10.2189/asqu.51.4.590

Kolbe, M., Burtscher, M. J., Wacker, J., Grande, B., Nohynkova, R., Manser, T., Spahn, D., & Grote, G. (2012). Speaking-up is related to better team performance in simulated anesthesia inductions: An observational study. *Anesthesia & Analgesia, 115*, 1099–1108. https://journals.lww.com/anesthesia-analgesia/fulltext/2012/11000/Speaking_Up_Is_Related_to_Better_Team:Performance.16.aspx

Kolbe, M., Grote, G., Waller, M. J., Wacker, J., Grande, B., Burtscher, M. J., & Spahn, D. R. (2014). Monitoring and talking to the room: Autochthonous coordination patterns in team interaction and performance. *Journal of Applied Psychology, 99*, 1254–1267. https://doi.org/10.1037/a0037877

Künzle, B., Zala-Mezö, E., Wacker, J., Kolbe, M., & Grote, G. (2010). Leadership in anaesthesia teams: The most effective leadership is shared. *Quality and Safety in Health Care, 19*, 1–6. https://doi.org/10.1136/qshc.2008.030262

LaPorte, T., & Consolini, P. M. (1991). Working in practice but not in theory: Theoretical challenge of "High Reliability Organizations." *Journal of Public Administration Research and Theory, 1*, 19–47. https://doi.org/10.1093/oxfordjournals.jpart.a037070

Leape, L. L. (2002). Reporting of adverse events. *New England Journal of Medicine, 347*, 1633–1638. https://doi.org/10.1056/NEJMNEJMhpr011493

Macrae, C. (2009). Making risks visible: Identifying and interpreting threats to airline flight safety. *Journal of Occupational and Organizational Psychology, 82*, 273–293. https://doi.org/10.1348/096317908X314045

Macrae, C. (2016). The problem with incident reporting. *BMJ Quality & Safety, 25*(2). http://dx.doi.org/10.1136/bmjqs-2015-004732

Martínez-Córcoles, M., Schöbel, M., Gracia, F., Tomás, I., & Peiró, J. M. (2012). Linking empowering leadership to safety participation in nuclear power plants: A structural equation model. *Journal of Safety Research, 43*, 215–221. https://doi.org/10.1016/j.jsr.2012.07.002

Martínez-Córcoles, M., Gracia, F., Tomás, I., Peiró, J. M., & Schöbel, M. (2013). Empowering team leadership and safety performance in nuclear power plants: A multilevel approach. *Safety Science, 51*, 293–301. https://doi.org/10.1016/j.ssci.2012.08.001

Martínez-Córcoles, M., Gracia, F., Tomás, I., Peiró, J. M. (2014). Strengthening safety compliance in nuclear power operations: A role-based approach. *Risk Analysis, 34*, 1257–1269. https://doi.org/10.1111/risa.12173

Müller, S., Brauner, C., Grote, G., & Künzler, C. (1998). *Safety culture: A reflection of risk awareness.* Zurich, Switzerland: Swiss Re.

Nahrgang, J. D., Morgeson, F. P., & Hofmann, D. A. (2011). Safety at work: A meta-analytic investigation of the link between job demands, job resources, burnout, engagement, and safety outcomes. *Journal of Applied Psychology, 96*, 71–94. https://doi.org/10.1037/a0021484

Neal, A., & Griffin, M. A. (2004). Safety climate and safety at work. In J. Barling & M. R. Frone (Eds.), *The psychology of workplace safety* (pp. 15–34). Washington, DC: American Psychological Association.

Neal, A., & Griffin, M. A. (2006). A study of the lagged relationships among safety climate, safety motivation, safety behavior, and accidents at the individual and group levels. *Journal of Applied Psychology, 91*, 946–953. https://doi.org/10.1037/0021-9010.91.4.946

Neal, A., Griffin, M. A., & Hart, P. M. (2000). The impact of organizational climate on safety climate and individual behavior. *Safety Science, 34*, 99–109. https://doi.org/10.1016/S0925-7535(00)00008-4

Perrow, C. (1984). *Normal accidents—Living with high-risk technologies.* New York, NY: Basic Books.

Pettersen, K. & Schulman, P. (2016). Drift, adaptation, resilience and reliability: Toward an empirical clarification. *Safety Science.* https://doi.org/10.1016/j.ssci.2016.03.004

Pfeiffer, Y., Manser, T. & Wehner, T. (2010). Conceptualising barriers to incident reporting: A psychological framework. *BMJ Quality & Safety, 19*(e60), 1–10. https://doi.org/10.1136/qshc.2008.030445

Ramanujam, R. & Goodman, P. S. (2011). The challenge of collective learning from event analysis. *Safety Science, 49*, 83–89. https://doi.org/10.1016/j.ssci.2010.03.019

Reason, J. T. (1990). *Human error.* Cambridge, U.K.: Cambridge University Press.

Reason, J. T. (1997). *Managing the risks of organizational accidents.* Aldershot, U.K.: Ashgate.

Reason, J. T., Parker, D., & Lawton, R. (1998). Organizational controls and safety: The varieties of rule-related behaviour. *Journal of Occupational and Organizational Psychology, 71*, 289–304. https://doi.org/10.1111/j.2044-8325.1998.tb00678.x

Reiman, T., Rollenhagen, C., Pietikäinen, E., & Heikkilä, J. (2015). Principles of adaptive management in complex safety-critical organizations. *Safety Science, 71*, 80–92. https://doi.org/10.1016/j.ssci.2014.07.021

Rico, R., Sánchez-Manzanares, M., Gil, F., & Gibson, C. (2008). Team implicit coordination processes: A team knowledge-based approach. *Academy of Management Review, 33*, 163–184. https://doi.org/10.5465/AMR.2008.27751276

Riethmüller, M., Fernandez Castelao, E., Eberhardt, D., Timmermann, A., & Boos, M. (2012). Adaptive coordination development in student anaesthesia teams: A longitudinal study. *Ergonomics, 55*, 55–68. https://doi.org/10.1080/00140139.2011.636455

Roberts, K. H. (1990). Some characteristics of one type of high reliability organization. *Organization Science, 1*, 160–176. https://doi.org/10.1287/orsc.1.2.160

Robson, L. S., Clarke, J. A., Cullen, K., Bielecky, A., Severin, C., Bigelow, P. L. . . . Mahooda, Q. (2007). The effectiveness of occupational health and safety management system interventions: A systematic review. *Safety Science, 45*, 329–353. https://doi.org/10.1016/j.ssci.2006.07.003

Rubinsky, S., & Smith, N. (1973). Safety training by accident stimulation. *Journal of Applied Psychology, 57*, 68–73. https://doi.org/10.1037/h0034199

Salas, E., Nichols, D. R., & Driskell, J. E. (2007). Testing three team training strategies in intact teams. A meta-analysis. *Small Group Research, 38*, 471–488. https://doi.org/10.1177%2F1046496407304332

Salas, E., Wilson, K. A., Burke, C. S., & Wightman, D. C. (2006). Does crew resource management training work? An update, an extension, and some critical needs. *Human Factors, 48*, 392–412. https://doi.org/10.1518%2F001872006777724444

Silbey, S. S. (2009). Taming Prometheus: Talk about safety and culture. *Annual Review of Sociology, 35*, 341–369. https://doi.org/10.1146/annurev.soc.34.040507.134707

Soane, E., & Chmiel, N. (2005). Are risk preferences consistent? The influence of decision domain and personality. *Personality & Individual Differences, 38*, 1781–1791. https://doi.org/10.1016/j.paid.2004.10.005

Strauch, B. (2015). Can we examine safety culture in accident investigations, or should we? *Safety Science, 77*, 102–111. https://doi.org/10.1016/j.ssci.2015.03.020

Stride, C. B., Turner, N., Hershcovis, M. S., Reich, T. C., Clegg, C. W., & Murphy, P. (2013). Negative safety events as correlates of work-safety tension. *Safety Science, 53*, 45–50, https://doi.org/10.1016/j.ssci.2012.09.003

Teece, D. J., Pisano, G., & Shuen, A. (1997). Dynamic capabilities and strategic management. *Strategic Management Journal, 18*, 509–533. https://doi.org/10.1002/(SICI)1097-0266(199708)18:7%3C509::AID-SMJ882%3E3.0.CO;2-Z

Thomas, J. W. (2012). *A systematic review of the effectiveness of safety management systems.* Canberra, Australia: Australian Transport Safety Bureau.

Turner, N., & Parker, S. K. (2003). The effect of teamwork on safety processes and outcomes. In J. Barling & M. R. Frone (Eds.), *The psychology of workplace safety* (pp. 35–62). Washington, DC: American Psychological Association.

Turner, N., Stride, C. B., Carter, A. J., & McCaughey, D. (2012). Job demands–control–support model and employee safety performance. *Accident Analysis and Prevention, 45*, 811–817. https://doi.org/10.1016/j.aap.2011.07.005

Uitdewilligen, S., Rico, R., & Waller, M. J. (2018). Fluid and stable: Dynamics of team action patterns and adaptive outcomes. *Journal of Organizational Behavior, 39*, 1113–1128. https://doi.org/10.1002/job.2267

Valentine, M. A., & Edmondson, A. C. (2015). Team scaffolds: How meso-level structures enable role-based coordination in temporary groups. *Organization Science, 26*, 405–422. https://doi.org/10.1287/orsc.2014.0947

Van der Schaaf, T. W., Lucas, D. A., & Hale, A. R. (Eds.) (1991). *Near miss reporting as a safety tool.* Oxford, U.K.: Butterworth-Heinemann.

Vashdi, D. R., Bamberger, P. A., & Erez, M. (2013). Can surgical teams ever learn? The role of coordination, complexity, and transitivity in action team learning. *Academy of Management Journal, 56*, 945–971. https://doi.org/10.5465/amj.2010.0501

Visser, E., Pijl, Y. J., Stolk, R. P., Neelman, J., & Rosmalen, J. G. M. (2007). Accident proneness, does it exist? A review and meta-analysis. *Accident Analysis & Prevention, 39*, 556–564. https://www.ncbi.nlm.nih.gov/pubmed/17094932

Wallace, J. C., & Vodanovich, S. J. (2003). Workplace safety performance: Conscientiousness, cognitive failure, and their interaction. *Journal of Occupational Health Psychology, 8*, 316–327. https://psycnet.apa.org/doi/10.1037/1076-8998.8.4.316

Waller, M. J., 1999. The timing of adaptive group responses to nonroutine events. *Academy of Management Journal, 42*, 127–137. https://psycnet.apa.org/doi/10.2307/257088

Weick, K. E. (1987). Organizational culture as a source of high-reliability. *California Management Review, 29*, 112–127. https://doi.org/10.2307%2F41165243

Weick, K. E. (1993). The collapse of sensemaking in organizations: The Mann Gulch disaster. *Administrative Science Quarterly, 38*, 628–652. https://psycnet.apa.org/doi/10.2307/2393339

Weick, K. E., Sutcliffe, K. M., & Obstfeld, D. (1999). Organizing for high reliability: Processes of collective mindfulness. In R. I. Sutton & B. M. Staw (Eds.), *Research in organizational behavior* (Vol. 21, pp. 81–123). Amsterdam, The Netherlands: Elsevier Science/ JAI Press.

Wildavsky, A. (1988). *Searching for safety*. New Brunswick, NJ: Transaction Books.

Woods, D. D. (2015). Four concepts for resilience and the implications for the future of resilience engineering. *Reliability Engineering and System Safety, 141*, 5–9. https://doi.org/10.1016/j.ress.2015.03.018

Woods, D. D. (2016). Resilience as graceful extensibility to overcome brittleness. In IRGC, *Resource guide on resilience*. Lausanne, Switzerland: EPFL International Risk Governance Center.

Yukl, G. (2006). *Leadership in organizations* (6th ed.). Upper Saddle River, NJ: Pearson Prentice-Hall.

Yun, S., Faraj, S., & Sims Jr., H. P. (2005). Contingent leadership and effectiveness of trauma resuscitation teams. *Journal of Applied Psychology, 90*, 1288–1296. https://doi.org/10.1037/0021-9010.90.6.1288

Zacharatos, A., Barling, J., & Iverson, R. D. (2005). High-performance work systems and occupational safety. *Journal of Applied Psychology, 90*, 77–93. https://doi.org/10.1037/0021-9010.90.1.77

Zhang, L., Li, Y., & Wu, C. (2013). The influence of individual and team cognitive ability on operators' task and safety performance: A multilevel field study in nuclear power plants. *PLoS ONE, 8*, e84528. https://doi.org/10.1371/journal.pone.0084528

Zohar, D. (1980). Safety climate in industrial organizations—Theoretical and applied implications. *Journal of Applied Psychology, 65*, 96–102. https://doi.org/10.1037/0021-9010.65.1.96

Zohar, D. (2002). Modifying supervisory practices to improve subunit safety: A leadership-based intervention model. *Journal of Applied Psychology, 87*, 156–163. https://psycnet.apa.org/doi/10.1037/0021-9010.87.1.156

Zohar, D., & Luria, G. (2010). Group leaders as gatekeepers: Testing safety climate variations across levels of analysis. *Applied Psychology: An International Review, 59*, 647–673. https://doi.org/10.1111/j.1464-0597.2010.00421.x

Zohar, D., & Polachek, T. (2014). Discourse-based intervention for modifying supervisory communication as leverage for safety climate and performance improvement: A randomized field study. *Journal of Applied Psychology, 99*, 113–124. https://doi.org/10.1037/a0034096

Gudela Grote

QUALITY OF WORKING LIFE

INTRODUCTION

What is a good quality of working life? What experiences make up a good quality of work? What policies and practices need to be implemented to create the potential for a good quality of work? These are some of the questions being addressed by scholars with an interest in the quality of working life (QWL). The breadth of these questions surrounding QWL has attracted scholars from different disciplines and indicates the need for an interdisciplinary perspective. In addition, there are moral and ethical overtones to the topic that are allied to a further question—why should we be interested in the quality of work? Such questions are of interest to work and organizational (w/o) psychologists who are well placed to provide both conceptual and empirical input into the analysis of the subject. This article will explore their contribution, as well as that of other social scientists, and set those contributions within the wider economic and social context that has helped to shape the impact of attempts to ensure a good quality of working life.

The article starts with a brief introductory definition of quality of working life and then traces the empirical and contextual factors that led to widespread interest in and application of QWL in what will be termed Phase 1, which reached a peak in the 1970s. Thereafter, despite the growing body of relevant research, interest in the concept of QWL markedly declined. More recently, however, there has been a resurgence of interest, and in the early 2020s, QWL is emerging once again, in what can be described as Phase 2, as a topic of research and potential policy application. The article will trace this process, highlighting the contribution of w/o psychology.

WHAT IS QUALITY OF WORKING LIFE? A PRELIMINARY VIEW

When interest in QWL was at its highest during Phase 1, a major international conference was held (Davis & Cherns, 1975a) at which several leading scholars offered definitions of QWL. The most-cited definition was provided by Walton (1975; see also Walton, 1973). He offered eight criteria with which to determine the QWL, accepting that the emphasis within them is likely to vary across individuals and organizations. He acknowledges that these criteria are based on "personal observations, experiences, values, and assumptions about human nature" (Walton, 1975, p. 100) and suggests they could be confirmed, adapted, or supplemented by research. The eight criteria include the following:

- Adequate and fair compensation
- Safe and healthy working conditions
- Immediate opportunity to use and develop human capacities (i.e., job design)
- Opportunity for continued growth and security
- Social integration in the work organization
- Constitutionalism in the work organization (i.e., participation)
- Work and the total life space (i.e., work–life balance)
- The social relevance of work life

Walton cites the ideas of Maslow (1943) and Erikson (1963) as offering a theoretical basis for developing this set of QWL criteria. While the list contains topics that fall clearly within the domain of w/o psychology, some items such as constitutionalism—indicating a role for systems of worker participation and representation—imply a wider social science perspective. Embedded in the list are assumptions about the goals of QWL which extend beyond concepts such as job satisfaction to ideas about growth, security, fairness and equality, and work–life balance. Walton's list provides a preliminary indication of the possible features of QWL, but his acknowledgment that it is based on his own experience and values suggests that it needs a stronger conceptual and empirical grounding. This article will return to the definition of QWL in a later section. Since the aims of QWL focus mainly on improving the experience of work and on the well-being of workers, there are questions about why employers might be interested in pursuing policies and practices designed to promote QWL. With these questions in mind, the section on "The Origins of the Quality of Working Life Concept" addresses the emergence of the empirical basis for advocacy of QWL and this is followed by a section outlining "External Influences on Interest in Quality of Working Life" which analyses the factors that led to the initial interest of employers and governments.

THE ORIGINS OF THE QUALITY OF WORKING LIFE CONCEPT

The intellectual roots of QWL can be traced to the emergence and development of the concept of socio-technical systems by psychologists at the U.K. Tavistock Institute (Emery & Trist, 1965; Trist & Bamforth, 1951; Trist et al., 1963). It emerged in the early 1950s out of a background in which scientific management (Taylor, 1947) vied with human relations (Likert, 1967; Mayo, 1933) as approaches to manage the workforce. Whereas scientific management gave prominence to the technical system and often viewed the worker as an extension of the machine, human relations gave prominence to the social system. A core contribution of the socio-technical approach was to argue that there were costs in prioritizing one over the other and that the aim should be to optimize both. Three other features of the initial socio-technical approach are noteworthy. First, it emphasized the work team as the primary unit of analysis and the importance of task autonomy for workers and, more particularly, groups of workers in what came to be known as autonomous work groups. Second, it highlighted the importance of an open-systems perspective that recognized the influence on organizations of a potentially turbulent and fluid external system, implying that internal flexibility was required. Third, it advocated the implementation of autonomous work groups through a participative approach, involving the workers likely to be affected, albeit with the help of an external expert.

A series of research studies in coal mining (Trist et al., 1963), weaving (Rice, 1958), and manufacturing (Emery & Thorsrud, 1976) revealed the promise of the approach, as well as some of its challenges (for a fuller account, see Guest, 2022). As it evolved, advocates of the socio-technical approach developed a set of broader principles (Cherns, 1976). Emery and Thorsrud (1976) also incorporated ideas about human needs at work into their approach to socio-technical work design. They included the need for jobs designed to provide autonomy, challenge, ongoing learning and development, support, meaningfulness, and some sort of desirable future; in addition, they included the need to relate life at work to life outside work. These needs overlap with several of the criteria for QWL outlined by Walton.

A second relevant stream of theory and research addressed the role of motivation at work through the design of jobs. Whereas scientific management had sought to simplify tasks and human relations had focused on social relations to the neglect of tasks, Herzberg (1966) viewed task design as central and argued that workers were motivated by enriched jobs that provided challenging, responsible work. He provided evidence that job enrichment resulted in both higher satisfaction and performance (Herzberg, 1966, 1968; Paul et al., 1969). He differed in important respects, however, from the socio-technical approach by viewing social relations, groups, and participation as hygiene factors—important to get right to avoid dissatisfaction but unlikely to motivate. Herzberg's approach proved highly controversial, but his message had an appeal to managers since it left them in control of job design while promising higher performance. Over the years, other approaches have emerged that draw on motivation theory to address the redesign of jobs (see, for example, Hackman & Oldham, 1975); these approaches have proved more enduring and have been shown to have a positive impact on workers' motivation, satisfaction, and well-being, as well as on performance (for reviews, see Knight & Parker, 2021; Van den Broeck & Parker, 2017).

A third influence on the development of QWL was the evolution of industrial relations. Trade unions had become well established in all advanced economies by the mid-20th century, but industrial relations were often adversarial. Indeed, the initial coal-mining study (Trist

& Bamforth, 1951) that stimulated the socio-technical approach arose partly out of concern about poor industrial relations, as reflected in strikes and high levels of absenteeism alongside the failure of new technology to provide the expected increase in productivity. The search for better ways to manage employment relations led to an interest in worker participation. While this focus never garnered much enthusiasm in the United States, it became a major interest in Europe, with Germany and Scandinavia providing distinctive models (Ferner & Hyman, 1992). Germany had developed a formal system with worker directors and specified arrangements for negotiation, consultation, and communication. Norway had tested the role of worker directors, but an evaluation (Emery & Thorsrud, 1970) found that their presence had little or no influence on the shop floor. This led to the view that direct participation at shop-floor level would have more impact, a conclusion resulting in a series of studies that applied the socio-technical approach as a means of enhancing industrial democracy (Emery & Thorsrud, 1976). It is important to note that this initiative was not undertaken at the expense of representative participation. At the national level, Norwegian trade unions endorsed the research, while at the local level unions were involved in negotiating aspects of the proposed changes. The important assumptions behind advocacy of worker participation/industrial democracy at all levels of the enterprise was that it would help to address sources of worker discontent, leading to mutual benefits for employers and employees, and a growing body of evidence suggested that in appropriate circumstances, this was the case (Heller et al., 1998). As such, this approach is reflected in Walton's QWL dimension of "constitutionalism in the work organization."

EXTERNAL INFLUENCES ON INTEREST IN QUALITY OF WORKING LIFE

The aims of QWL are directed toward the well-being of the workforce. Why, therefore, might organizations be interested in adopting practices that might enhance QWL? The main answer lies in its potential to improve worker performance. To take the example of the initial coal-mining study that gave rise to the socio-technical approach (Trist & Bamforth, 1951), the introduction of new technology had failed to produce the expected improvements in productivity, and industrial relations were poor. The application of the socio-technical approach led to improvements in performance and local industrial relations (Trist et al., 1963). The Norwegian studies reported by Emery and Thorsrud (1976) also demonstrated performance improvements.

At the time of the initial interest in QWL, it became apparent that the challenges to performance improvement were more deeply rooted in the organization of work and in wider societal changes. Blauner (1964) had written about alienation arising from the workers' relation to technology and from the division of labor, providing what was, in effect, a compelling critique of scientific management. He characterizes the experience of factory work, particularly in mass production and in tightly controlled settings, in terms of the dimensions of alienation—powerlessness, meaninglessness, self-estrangement, and social alienation. The consequences are dissatisfaction, anxiety, demotivation, and psychological withdrawal that can extend into life outside work. Blauner also described the opposite case of "freedom" at work, citing examples of craftsmen and of controllers of automated systems. He advocates work redesign, citing the approach of Davis (1957), who became a leading advocate of both the socio-technical approach and QWL.

By the 1960s, improvements in education, the growth of mass communication, and rising expectations—including expectations about equal opportunities among women and ethnic minorities—compounded the problems of worker alienation, resulting in an increasing reluctance among many workers to undertake tightly controlled work. For industry, this alienation presented problems of high absenteeism and labor turnover, as well as low motivation and often poor quality of work. It became increasingly difficult to attract and retain workers. This was a problem that affected industries in many countries. For example, its impact was particularly marked in Scandinavia, where Volvo experienced increasing difficulty in persuading Swedes to work on its car production lines (Lindblom & Norstedt, 1975). In the United States, the federal government set up a task force to explore the quality of work and its relation to the quality of life and to the health of the nation. The report (United States Department of Health, Education, and Welfare, & W. E. Upjohn Institute for Employment Research, 1973) confirmed the problems of alienation and its extension to white-collar jobs, the challenge of rising expectations, and the need to improve the QWL. In seeking remedies, the authors asserted,

> "The redesign of jobs is the keystone of this report. Not only does it hold out some promise to decrease mental and physical health costs, increase productivity, and improve the quality of life for millions of Americans at all occupational levels, it would give, for the first time, a voice to many workers in an important decision-making process" (United States Department of Health, Education, and Welfare, & W. E. Upjohn Institute for Employment Research, 1973, pp. xii–xiii).

The report goes on to argue that while job redesign provides a cornerstone, more is needed in areas such as training and development in order to promote an improved QWL.

The call for improvements in QWL was heard in most advanced economies that were facing similar problems, and it resulted in a range of initiatives, including organizational innovations in job design, government sponsorship of research centers, and much research activity within universities. It seemed for a while that the evidence accumulated by w/o psychologists and other social scientists was being heeded. In a mood of optimism, a major international conference was held in 1972 to review progress, celebrate achievements, and discuss the way ahead (Davis & Cherns, 1975a). Many case studies illustrating improvements in QWL were presented (Davis & Cherns, 1975b), and in the section "Evidence About Improvements in Quality of Working Life" we review some of these and other examples of specific QWL initiatives.

EVIDENCE ABOUT IMPROVEMENTS IN QUALITY OF WORKING LIFE

Research exploring attempts to improve the QWL falls into two main categories. First, there is an extensive body of predominantly qualitative case-study material which describes a specific context, a program change program, and some outcomes. These studies can be highly insightful but lack the rigor associated with much contemporary research in w/o psychology. Second, there are quantitative studies that vary in rigor, from post hoc evaluations of changes to quasi-experimental research designs. A feature of the case studies is that they can address the organizational context, the central actors, and different levels of analysis. In contrast, many of the quantitative studies collect data at the level of the individual worker and are sometimes largely context-free. In what follows, this article will illustrate both.

Some of the early case studies were provided by researchers based at the U.K. Tavistock Institute of Human Relations seeking to apply the socio-technical approach. These included the coal-mining cases (Trist et al., 1963) and a series of interventions in Indian textile mills (Rice, 1958). Examples from Scandinavia have provided some of the most influential and widely cited cases of QWL initiatives. As noted in the section "External Influences on Interest in Quality of Working Life", Emery and Thorsrud (1976) applied the socio-technical principles in four companies in Norway. However, their studies had a wider focus beyond socio-technical thinking since they were also an exercise in industrial democracy that involved workers and union representatives, alongside action researchers, in agreeing to and implementing the design of new work arrangements. Reflecting the socio-technical principles, these invariably included the development of autonomous work groups that provided greater control and responsibility to the group members. The evaluations revealed that while one of the early interventions ended in failure, the other three demonstrated improvements in worker satisfaction and organizational performance.

The Norwegian studies had been strongly influenced by a psychological perspective and were based on assumptions about human needs. In contrast, initiatives at Volvo in Sweden were influenced more by engineers who were supported by an inspirational chief executive and a desire to address the difficulty of attracting and retaining workers on car production lines. Volvo engineers designing new plants, first at Kalmar and then at Uddevalla, and with the involvement of unions, abandoned the traditional production line in favor of autonomous work groups, eventually creating the opportunity for workers to build a complete car. The result was that productivity was at least as high as in the traditional car plants, problems of recruitment eased, and worker satisfaction and well-being increased, as reflected, among other things, in reduced labor turnover and absenteeism (Sandberg, 1993).

Two of the challenges that emerged from several of the early QWL case studies concerned sustainability and diffusion. Regarding sustainability, for example, despite the success of Volvo's innovative car plants, when demand for their cars fell back a little, the company chose to close these smaller plants and retain the larger plant that operated a traditional assembly line. In another example, one of the early Tavistock initiatives, the Ahmedabad study in Indian weaving mills, was reported as a success (Rice, 1958), but a follow-up by Miller (1975), a few years later, revealed that all but one of the mills that had introduced group working had reverted to more traditional production systems.

Diffusion, the challenge of encouraging other organizations or units to build on examples of success and adopt QWL initiatives, proved even more of a problem. Trist et al. (1963) report how despite clear evidence of improvements in performance and in QWL resulting from the introduction of autonomous work groups in U.K. coal mining, both management and unions, for different reasons, were unwilling to support diffusion to other mines. Trist et al. (1977) report the successful introduction of group working in a U.S. coal mine, but attempts to extend it were blocked by the union members, and the whole project collapsed as a result. Philips, a leading Dutch firm, had taken early initiatives to introduce what was termed *work structuring* with some success, but the underlying principle of organizing from the bottom up ran into opposition from junior and middle management and, as a result, often failed to spread more widely. In the United Kingdom, Shell's refinery division involved Tavistock Institute consultants to help with the development of a new philosophy of management (Hill, 1971) based on QWL principles. After a considerable investment in communicating and seeking commitment to the philosophy, the aim was to stimulate initiatives to improve the QWL throughout the organization. Despite some examples of success (Burden, 1975), the number of initiatives was very limited, leading Blackler and Brown (1980), in their highly critical analysis, to title their book *Whatever Happened to Shell's New Philosophy of Management?* Despite the limited impact in Shell UK, Trist (1981) notes that the approach underpinning the philosophy was more positively received in Canada and Australia. The limited diffusion was perhaps most surprising in Norway, where there had been strong endorsement of the initiatives reported by Emery and Thorsrud (1976), with support from national-level industry and trade union representatives. Bolweg (1976) notes that despite this support, there were very few new company initiatives, and, with one or two notable exceptions, most had limited impact or were abandoned.

Reflecting concerns about diffusion, research centers designed to spread the word about QWL were set up by a number of countries and, more particularly in the United States, by some universities. Their typical aims, reflecting the strategy in Norway, were to encourage or conduct demonstration cases to illustrate what could be achieved and then to spread the word about the benefits through various communication channels and short training courses. Examples include the Work Research Unit in the United Kingdom; L'Agence Nationale pour l'Amelioration des Conditions du Travail in France; and the Quality of Working Life Committee in Japan. Sweden had a well-established National Institute for Working Life. The German government sponsored a Humanization of Work program which developed some impressive cases but never received strong support from many companies, while unions were often unenthusiastic, and the program evolved into a focus on "work and technology" (Fricke, 2000). One outcome of the 1972 conference (Davis & Cherns, 1975b) was the International Council for the Quality of Working Life, whose membership included many of the leading advocates for and researchers on the QWL. This council eventually collapsed when the early champions of QWL stepped back but almost no one came forward to take their place. Most of the other national and university research centers also disappeared over time. On a more positive note, in 1975, the European Union set up the European Foundation for the Improvement of Living and Working Conditions, which continues to provide valuable survey data monitoring Europe-wide development in QWL.

In the United States, there were a number of initiatives in organizations to improve the QWL. Some involved the unions in a participative approach, such as the Saturn plant of General Motors (Rubinstein & Kochan, 2001), Cummings Engines (Bryan, 1975), and the Pennsylvania coal mine (Trist et al., 1977); other widely cited cases were in non-union settings such as Donnelly Mirrors (Iman, 1975) and the Topeka plant of General Foods (Walton, 1977). Taking a longer-term perspective, O'Toole and Lawler (2006) produced a follow-up to the 1972 task force report, *Work in America*. Drawing on commissioned reports, interviews, and a survey of Fortune 1000 companies, they reported little evidence of progress toward improved QWL in the United States since the original report. They divided companies into three categories, which they described as low-cost, global competitive, and high involvement. Low- cost companies had little interest in QWL; global companies displayed a divide between executives and professionals, who did well on some aspects of QWL, and other workers, often on insecure contracts, who fared much less well. Finally, the small group of high involvement companies offered scope for an enhanced QWL.

The second type of study often associated with QWL, more particularly in the United States, typically reported quantitative analysis of changes in work redesign to develop greater worker autonomy through either job enrichment or autonomous work groups. These were usually management-initiated innovations in work redesign and had as their primary aim to improve performance, with the possible side effect of improving the QWL by enhancing worker job autonomy. By 1982, Pasmore et al. (1982) were able to report 134 experimental interventions, 53% of which involved some form of autonomous work group. These were sometimes initiated and often evaluated by w/o psychologists, and it is notable that the technology was usually taken as given, so that changes involved only the social system. Indeed, only 16% of studies cited any changes in the technical system. The outcomes typically included productivity, cost-savings, quality control, attitudes, absence, and turnover. Evaluations reported success in more than 85% of cases on all performance-related criteria but fell to 54% for improvements in attitudes. It is notable that those few cases involving changes in technology were among the less successful. Another evaluation of published studies, by Cummings et al. (1977), was critical of the methodology of both the type of intervention and the evaluations, raising questions about whether these studies did amount to convincing evidence about the impact of management-initiated work redesign on QWL.

By the 1980s, interest in QWL had declined. Following the first major oil crisis in 1974, which provoked economic recession and reduced pressures in the labor market, the factors that had led organizations and governments to display an interest in QWL had largely disappeared. Most of the various QWL research centers either went into decline, closed down, or changed their focus. The symbolic closure of the Volvo car plants at Kalmar and Uddevalla, in the early 1990s, were viewed by some as signaling the end of an era (Buchanan, 1997) and reflecting the end of what this article has described as Phase 1 of the QWL movement.

REVITALIZING THE INTEREST IN QUALITY OF WORKING LIFE

Grote and Guest (2017) have argued that although the discourse had changed after the 1980s, greatly reducing explicit reference to QWL, relevant research on the various dimensions of QWL had continued, helping to build a stronger evidence base about its potential benefit for workers. They also noted that this research had become increasingly specialized, addressing topics such as work-life balance, employability, and job redesign rather than taking a wider view about the experience of work. A revived focus on QWL, they argued, offered the potential for an integrated approach to improvements in the quality of work that was now more strongly evidence-based. The growing strength of the evidence about the features of "good work" and the potential to integrate these under the umbrella of QWL provide the first component of the case for a renewed contemporary interest in QWL.

One area in which there has been a considerable advance is evidence about the impact of working life on employee well-being. The longstanding World Health Organization (WHO) definition of well-being is "a state of complete physical, mental and social well-being, not merely absence of disease or infirmity" (WHO, 1946). Considering well-being in work settings, Grant et al. (2007) define well-being as "the overall quality of an employer's experience and functioning at work" (p. 52). They suggest that work-related well-being has three facets of psychological, physical, and social functioning. The job demands-resources model (Bakker &

Demerouti, 2017) has helped to integrate research demonstrating the problems of stress and burnout from excessive demands and the benefits in terms of higher well-being from matching demands and resources. Findings across all dimensions of QWL confirm that work arrangements for a significant proportion of the working population fail to ensure acceptable levels of well-being. However, promoting well-being through the quality of work can have wider societal benefits. Kivimaki et al. (2012) presented evidence from meta-analysis of Europe-wide data of an association between job strain and incidence of coronary heart disease. The longitudinal U.K. Whitehall studies have revealed a link between the quality of work, reflected in levels of autonomy and control, and various indicators of health, even including longevity (Marmot et al., 2020). This research indicates that there is a wider economic and social benefit beyond the workplace to improvements in QWL.

Job design has provided the core of most activities to improve QWL. Systematic reviews of intervention studies confirm that job redesign is associated with, and usually predictive of, improvements in well-being (Daniels et al., 2017) and performance (Knight & Parker, 2021), but both reviews add an important caveat. The impact of interventions is invariably greater when they are integrated into the wider organizational system. This will include the sociotechnical system and also the human resource system. For example, training of workers to involve them in job redesign can reinforce its impact. Worker involvement and management support are also confirmed as contributory factors to successful outcomes. These findings have echoes of earlier research and indicate that while job redesign is central to QWL, we need to look beyond it both to improve the process of its implementation and to incorporate additional elements of QWL. One of these elements is the human resource management system.

Theory and research about human resource management (HRM) has widely adopted a systems approach that recognizes that a range of contextual factors can influence HRM strategy and HR practices and impact (Beer et al., 1984; Boxall & Purcell, 2016). It also recognizes that HR practices can be viewed as an interrelated system whereby the different practices mutually reinforce each other (Delery, 1998). This is reflected, for example, in the ability-motivation-opportunity (AMO) model (Appelbaum et al., 2000; Jiang et al., 2012), which advocates a combination of HR practices that promote workers' ability, motivation, and opportunity to contribute as intermediate goals for HRM. It is these elements in combination that are essential to influence workers' attitudes and performance. In this sense, more is better in order to provide a critical mass, and much of the early research on HRM indicated that the use of more HR practices was associated with higher performance (Boselie et al., 2005; Combs et al., 2006). The meta-analyses by Jiang et al. (2012) and Subramony (2009) that have focused on the AMO model confirm an association between AMO-focused HR practices and consequent higher levels of reported ability, motivation, and opportunity, and organizational performance. In the present context, the points to note are that it is a combination of practices that has the stronger impact and that many of the relevant HR practices also have the potential to improve the QWL. However, the major body of research has focused on the HRM–performance link, restricting the focus to those practices believed most likely to lead to enhanced performance. A more limited number of studies have explored performance and well-being outcomes together (Peccei & Van de Voorde, 2019; Van de Voorde et al., 2016) and indicate that adoption of more HR practices is often associated with both higher performance and higher well-being, although the relationship is not always straightforward (Ho & Kuvaas,

2020). A caveat is that measures of well-being are typically job satisfaction and organizational commitment, reflecting hedonic well-being; there is less convincing evidence about eudemonic well-being, including indicators such as mental and physical health. Nevertheless, the lesson from the research on HRM is that a systems approach is essential. For example, job redesign is associated primarily with opportunity to contribute but is only likely to have a positive impact if workers have received the relevant training and have the motivation to contribute.

As a counter to the dominant emphasis in HRM research on performance outcomes, Guest (2017) has proposed an approach to HRM that adopts an employees' perspective, highlighting HR practices that serve as antecedents to well-being. The sets of HR practices he outlines are very close to those associated with advocacy of QWL, suggesting that an integrated approach to well-being-oriented HRM provides a path to improvements in QWL. He argues that improving well-being also offers a path to higher organizational performance through its impact on worker motivation, higher skill utilization, and reduced absence and labor turnover. The growing body of research on HRM suggests that it has the potential to provide mutual gains for organizations and their employees and reinforces the evidence base highlighted by Grote and Guest (2017) in favor of a renewed interest in QWL.

A second reason for a renewed interest in QWL is the changing nature of employment and concern about the consequences of these changes for worker well-being. This concern is highlighted by Warhurst and Knox (2022), who note that when the original QWL movement was underway, the existence of a standard, full-time, and reasonably secure job was largely taken for granted. Since then, there has been the marked growth in temporary, fixed-term, and part-time employment, as well as self-employment. While these trends have been underway for some decades (Standing, 2011), the growth of the platform-based gig economy has accelerated the development of precarious employment. Warhurst and Knox cite extensive evidence from, for example, Quinlan (2021) and De Witte et al. (2016), showing that there is a link between the kind of job insecurity that flows from involuntary non-standard employment and lower work-related well-being. They argue, in line with Marmot et al. (2020), that this can have wider damaging consequences for the quality of life of these workers and their families. The growth of what Standing (2011) describes as "the precariat" and the associated growth in insecurity, poor well-being, and growing inequality is a concern for governments (e.g., Taylor et al., 2017) and international organizations (Organisation for Economic Co-operation and Development [OECD], 2018) and a further reason for a renewed interest in QWL.

A third factor provoking current interest in QWL is advances in technology and, in particular, the impact of digitalization. This is reflected both in the development of the platform economy, with its impact on the employment relationship described in the previous paragraph, and in the digitalization of "production" through use of artificial intelligence (AI), automation, robotics, and smart warehouses. An early analysis by Frey and Osborne (2013) predicted that these developments would lead to a major loss of jobs, although subsequent analysis reveals that their analysis overstated likely employment consequences partly because digitalization also helped to create some new jobs. Nevertheless, there is wide agreement that the consequences for work and employment are likely to be considerable, with a potential for jobs to be simplified and for work to become dehumanized. These developments in technology, known as Industry 4, have some parallels with the concerns about the dehumanizing impact of scientific management that heralded developments in socio-technical thinking (Trist & Bamforth, 1951) and early consideration of the QWL. Indeed, there has been a call for a swift move to Industry 5 (Xu et al., 2021) and for the re-adoption of a socio-technical approach to the design of work (Bednar & Welch, 2020; Parker & Grote, 2020) to counter the potentially damaging impact of developments that prioritize technology and which harm QWL. Concerns about the potential impact of digital technologies on the quality of work have stimulated interest in Industry 5 among international organizations such as the European Commission (Breque et al., 2021). A likely consequence of these concerns is a renewed emphasis on a socio-technical perspective, balancing the needs of technology and the workforce. Part of the argument for industry is that this could also have a positive impact on productivity, which has become a concern as growth in productivity has slowed across many advanced industrial economies.

A further, albeit unanticipated influence on the growing interest in QWL has been the impact of the Covid epidemic. The experience of working from home or under very different circumstances from those previously experienced has had a marked effect on attitudes to employment and to wider issues of work-life balance. It appears that many people are reluctant to return to the traditional 5-day week in an office, preferring more hybrid arrangements. A further impact of the Covid experience is that many people have rethought their attitude to work, and among older workers, in particular, some have opted out of the labor market while others have altered their expectations about what they want from the experience of work. The result in many countries has been a severe shortage of labor. This, in turn, has forced organizations to reconsider what they need to do to attract and retain workers. There is past evidence from surveys of the best companies to work for that those who offer a high QWL are more likely to attract and retain staff (Dineen & Allen, 2016).

The combination of factors from the increasingly impressive evidence base, to concerns about Industry 4, the impact of Covid, and labor shortages all point to a strong case for a re-kindled interest in QWL—what can be termed Phase 2 of the QWL movement—across all sectors of employment. Not surprisingly, interest in QWL has resurfaced among both academics and policy-makers. On the basis of these contemporary challenges, it is timely to reconsider what is now meant by QWL.

A CONTEMPORARY VIEW OF QUALITY OF WORKING LIFE

A relatively simple and pragmatic approach to rethinking QWL is offered by O'Toole and Lawler (2006) in their follow-up to the original, influential *Work in America* report (United States Department of Health, Education, and Welfare, & W. E. Upjohn Institute for Employment Research, 1973). They advocate the concept of "good work," which they view as comprising three main elements: meaningful work and an opportunity to grow and develop; economic resources and the security to live a good life; and supportive social relations. Their emphasis on economic resources rather than on physical functioning reflects their concern with growing inequality and insecurity in American workplaces. Inequalities in economic resources and in job quality have grown in many other advanced economies. Evidence in recent years in the United Kingdom and beyond (Felstead et al., 2015; Green, 2006; O'Toole & Lawler, 2006) has shown that levels of skill requirements and of autonomy have tended on average to decline and have reinforced greater inequality within organizations and in society at large. This finding suggests that among workers in low skill jobs, priorities for improved QWL may be limited without radical change, and this is reflected in the sometimes limited aspirations of these workers. For example, Jones et al. (2017) interviewed a cross-section of blue-collar workers such as bus drivers, machine operatives, and cleaners about their view of good work. For these workers, job security, personal safety, and enough pay to meet their family needs were the priorities. For some, autonomy and good social relationships were also important, but this varied depending on factors such as family commitments, life stage, and personal preferences. Given the association between poor quality jobs and indicators of general health identified by Marmot et al. (2020), this research suggests that contemporary QWL should be looking to a wider agenda, including the challenge of economic insecurity.

Grote and Guest (2017) have advocated a more elaborate approach to QWL that builds on Walton's early model. Their starting point is a concern that the growing body of relevant research potentially supporting advocacy of QWL has become too fragmented and needs to be reintegrated. At the same time, developments since the initial QWL movement have led them to expand Walton's original list of dimensions. They endorse the eight dimensions that Walton listed: adequate and fair compensation; a safe and healthy working environment; opportunity to use and develop human capacities; opportunities for growth and security; social integration; constitutionalism; consideration of total life space; and social relevance. However, they add two more, reflecting contemporary developments as well as advances in research that reveal influences on well-being. These additional dimensions are flexible working and individual proactivity. Flexibility reflects the importance of exercising choice, where possible, about when, where, and how to work. Individual proactivity concerns workers' motivation to initiate action (Parker et al., 2010) that is also reflected in the growing interest in job crafting (Wrzesniewski & Dutton, 2001) and I-deals (Rousseau, 2005), all reflecting the desire for a degree of autonomy and control. The greater focus on individual initiative also reflects the absence or decline of organized labor in many sectors of employment. Grote and Guest argue that an integrated approach across the dimensions of QWL is required since a deficit in any one factor, whether it is fair pay or work-life balance, can harm well-being even if other elements are present at work. Another way they consider integration of the different components of QWL is to distinguish levels of analysis within QWL—namely, the job (job redesign, proactivity, personal growth/development); the organization (compensation, healthy environment, social integration, constitutionalism); and the relationship between work and life outside work (work-life balance, flexibility, social relevance).

Warhurst and Knox (2022) in their "manifesto" for QWL suggest that the emphasis needs to shift from a focus on job redesign to an emphasis on employment. While not wishing to underplay the importance of job redesign, they argue that the major shift since the early interest in QWL has been the decline of the standard employment contract based on permanent full-time jobs, resulting in various forms of insecure work. They identify seven elements of what they refer to as "job quality": terms of employment; pay and benefits; job design and the nature of work; social support and cohesion; health, safety, and psychological well-being; work-life balance; and voice and representation. This list overlaps considerably with the list provided by Grote and Guest (2017), though it omits scope for growth and development, as well as social relevance. They argue that an important next step is to establish standards of employment. It is notable that over the years, the European Union has issued directives that set standards in areas such as health and safety, working hours, worker representation, equal pay, and equal opportunity. The growth of the platform-based gig economy, which has helped to provoke the increase in precarious work, is also stimulating discussion within Europe about setting standards for the terms of employment. While the idea of setting standards for employment may be feasible, it is difficult to see how this can be extended to the design of jobs. Recent interest in QWL in the European Union and the OECD indicates that the message about the need to improve the QWL is being taken up in international policy forums.

CONCLUSION

This article has traced the emergence, nature, and application of QWL over several decades, highlighting the contribution made by w/o psychologists through advances in theory and research to what is essentially an interdisciplinary approach to the application of evidence-based research. The integration and application of this knowledge evidence base is likely to require an interdisciplinary perspective, although there is no reason why w/o psychologists should not sit at the tables where QWL-related policy is formulated. In highlighting the importance of an integrated approach to QWL, there are lessons from the experience of HRM, where ability and motivation and opportunity to contribute are all essential. In the case of QWL, it is the combination of, for example, good job design, secure employment, and work-life balance that reflects high overall quality of working life. There will, of course, be payoffs and differences in preferences. We learned long ago that people have different orientations to work (Goldthorpe et al., 1967) and that work is more of a central life interest to some than to others. For some people, part-time employment or even temporary employment will be suitable; the important element is that there is choice. Legislation in a number of countries has been edging toward provision of that choice. Looking to the future, the challenge for social scientists is, first, to present a coherent approach to QWL for industry, governments, and international bodies and, second, to offer a convincing strategy of change. With respect to the former, this article has argued that the evidence base that makes the case for implementing QWL policy and practice already exists and is getting stronger. The lessons about the strategy of change from Phase 1 of the QWL movement is that action research, the preferred strategy at the time, can rarely offer sustained success. As Warhurst and Knox suggest, it may be time for standards, supported where necessary by legislation and effective monitoring to support implementation.

If standards are to be set and interest in QWL is to be reinvigorated, then the national context and the extent to which it is sympathetic to promoting QWL is likely to be important. This is reinforced in research exploring the relation between employment regimes (Gallie, 2007) and job quality. For example, a comprehensive study by Holman (2013) of the relation between job types, job quality, and employment regimes in Europe reveals an association between type of employment regime and job quality. His measure of job quality is close to QWL and includes job content and organization, pay, security and flexibility, skills and development, and forms of voice. Scandinavian countries, with their social democratic traditions, score most highly on job quality, followed by core European countries such as France and Germany, then by liberal economies such as the United Kingdom. Countries in the east and south of Europe report lower quality of work. Higher quality of work is associated with higher job satisfaction and higher psychological and physical well-being. The two features of social democratic countries that seem to have the greatest influence are employment policies and well-organized labor unions. While Holman based his study on the 2005 European Working Conditions Survey, Heyes and Tomlinson (2021) analyzed the 2015 survey to explore the relation between underemployment and well-being. Underemployment is concerned with fewer than desired working hours and low skill utilization. Using a much more limited set of countries for comparison, they also found that the social-democratic, or what they termed inclusive countries, reported the best employment conditions and higher well-being, while the liberal economies and, in particular, the United Kingdom, had the poorest results. Across the countries, low motivation and poor prospects had a particularly strong negative association with well-being. The importance of this type of analysis is that it confirms that the national institutional regimes have a strong influence on the QWL within a country and on well-being.

In summary, QWL is an umbrella concept that embraces a range of practices that are of considerable interest to w/o psychologists while also reflecting an interdisciplinary perspective within the social sciences. It is a concept that has been influenced by external factors so that its prominence has waxed and waned according to the pressure from these influences. Part of the argument in this analysis has been that the factors that provoked the growth of Phase 1 of the QWL movement in the 1960s—the problems of the application of scientific management; rising expectations among the workforce; and the linked problems of attracting, motivating, and retaining workers—are being repeated in Phase 2 in the 2020s, with the challenge of the digitalization of Industry 4, the changing employment contract, and shortages of labor. In both contexts, there has also been the challenge of limited productivity growth, more pronounced in some countries than others. Moreover, in both cases, there was an advance in relevant knowledge: in the 1950s and 1960s, this was socio-technical systems thinking; in the 2020s, it is the richer body of knowledge about the impact of work on well-being and about the range of practices that combine to promote work-related well-being, an improved QWL, and a positive spillover into life beyond work. A major reason why Phase 1 of the QWL movement declined was the advent in 1974 of the first major oil crisis, which distracted the attention of industrialists and governments. It would be a sad irony if external factors, including an energy crisis, had a similar impact in the 2020s, at a time when there is a resurgence of interest in QWL.

FURTHER READING

Bozkurt, O., & Cohen, R. (2018). Repair work as good work: Craft and love in classic car restoration training. *Human Relations*, 72(6), 1105–1128.

Cooke, G., Donaghey, J., & Zeytinoglu, I. (2013). The nuanced nature of job quality: Evidence from rural Newfoundland and Ireland. *Human Relations*, 66(4), 503–527.

Gallie, D. (2003). The quality of working life: Is Scandinavia different? *European Sociological Review*, 19(1), 61–79.

Greenan, N., Kalugina, E., & Walkowiak, E. (2014). Has the quality of working life improved in the EU-15 between 1995 and 2005? *Industrial and Corporate Change*, 23(2), 399–428.

Katz, H., Kochan, T., & Weber, M. (1985). Assessing the effects of industrial relations systems and efforts to improve the quality of working life on organizational effectiveness. *Academy of Management Journal*, 28(3), 509–526.

Pirsig, R. (1999). *Zen and the art of motorcycle maintenance: An inquiry into values.* Random House.

Sandberg, A. (1995). *Enriching production: Perspectives on Volvo's Uddevalla plant as an alternative to lean production.* Avebury.

Sennett, R. (2008). *The craftsman.* Penguin Books.

REFERENCES

Appelbaum, E., Bailey, T., Berg, P., & Kalleberg, A. (2000). *Manufacturing advantage: Why high-performance systems pay off.* ILR Press.

Bakker, A., & Demerouti, E. (2017). The job demands-resources theory: Taking stock and looking forward. *Journal of Occupational Health Psychology, 22* (3), 273–285.

Bednar, P., &. Welch, C. (2020). Socio-technical perspectives on smart working: Creating meaningful and sustainable systems. *Information Systems Frontiers, 22,* 281–298.

Beer, M., Spector, P., Lawrence, D., Mills, D., & Walton, R. (1984). *Human resource management: A general manager's perspective.* Free Press.

Blackler, F., & Brown, C. (1980). *Whatever happened to Shell's new philosophy of management?* Saxon House.

Blauner, R. (1964). *Alienation and freedom.* University of Chicago Press.

Bolweg, J. (1976). *Job design and industrial democracy.* Martinus Nijhoff.

Boselie, P., Dietz, G., & Boon, C. (2005). Commonalities and contradictions in HRM and performance research. *Human Resource Management Journal,15*(3), 67–94.

Boxall, P., & Purcell, J. (2016). *Strategy and human resource management* (4th ed.). Palgrave.

Breque, M., De Nul, L., & Petridis, A. (2021). *Industry 5.0: Towards a sustainable human-centric and resilient European industry.* European Director-General for Research and Innovation.

Bryan, J. (1975). Work improvement and job enrichment: The case of Cummins Engine Company. In L. Davis & A. Cherns (Eds.), *The quality of working life* (Vol. 2, pp. 315–329). Free Press.

Buchanan, D. (1997). Review of E. Sandberg (Ed). Enriching production: Perspectives on Volvo's Uddevalla plant as an alternative to lean production. *Human Resource Management Journal, 7*(4), 89.

Burden, D. (1975). Participative management as a basis for improved quality of jobs: The case of the micro-wax department Shell UK Ltd. In L. Davis & A Cherns (Eds.), *The quality of working life* (Vol. 2, pp. 201–215). Free Press.

Cherns, A. (1976). The principles of socio-technical design. *Human Relations, 29*(8), 783–792.

Combs, J., Yongmei, I., Hall, A., & Ketchen, D. (2006). How much do high-performance work practices matter? A meta-analysis of their effects on organizational performance. *Personnel Psychology, 59*(3), 501–528.

Cummings, T., Molloy, E., & Glen, R. (1977). A methodological critique of 58 selected work experiments. *Human Relations, 30*(8), 675–708.

Daniels, K., Gedikli, C., Watson, D., Semkina, A., & Vaughn, O. (2017). Job design, employment practices and well-being: A systematic review of intervention studies. *Ergonomics, 60*(9), 1177–1196.

Davis, L. (1957). Toward a theory of job design. *Journal of Industrial Engineering, 8,* 305–309.

Davis, L., & Cherns, A. (Eds.). (1975a). *The quality of working life* (Vol. 1). Free Press.

Davis, L., & Cherns, A. (Eds.). (1975b). *The quality of working life* (Vol. 2). Free Press.

Delery, J. (1998). Issues of fit in strategic human resource management: Implications for research. *Human Resource Management Review, 8*(3), 289–310.

De Witte, H., Pienaar, J., & De Cuyper, N. (2016). Review of 30 years of longitudinal research on the association between job insecurity and health and well-being: Is there causal evidence? *Australian Psychologist, 51*(1), 18–31.

Dineen, B., & Allen, D. (2016). Third party employment branding: Human capital inflows and outflows following "best places to work" certifications. *Academy of Management Journal, 59*(1): 90–112.

Emery, F., & Thorsrud, E. (1970). *Form and content in industrial democracy*. Tavistock.

Emery, F., & Thorsrud, E. (1976). *Democracy at work: The report of the Norwegian industrial democracy program*. Martinus Nijhoff.

Emery, F., & Trist, E. (1965). The causal texture of organizational environments. *Human Relations, 18*(1), 21–32.

Erikson, E. (1963). *Childhood and society* (2nd ed.). Norton.

Felstead, A., Gallie, D., & Green, F. (Eds.). (2015). *Unequal Britain at work*. Oxford University Press.

Ferner, A., & Hyman, R. (Eds.). (1992). *Industrial relations in the new Europe*. Blackwell.

Frey, C., & Osborne, M. (2013). *The future of employment: How susceptible are jobs to computerization?* [Oxford Martin Program on Technology and Employment]. University of Oxford.

Fricke, W. (2000). Twenty-five years of German research and development programs "Humanization of work/work and technology." *Concepts and Transformation, 5*(1), 133–138.

Gallie, D. (Ed.). (2007). *Employment regimes and the quality of work*. Oxford University Press.

Goldthorpe, J., Lockwood, D., Beckhofer, F., & Platt, J. (1967). *The affluent worker: Industrial attitudes and behavior*. Cambridge University Press.

Grant, A., Christianson, M., & Price, R. (2007). Happiness, health or relationships? Managerial practices and employee well-being tradeoffs. *Academy of Management Executive, 21*(1), 51–63.

Green, F. (2006). *Demanding work: The paradox of job quality in the affluent economy*. Princeton University Press.

Grote, G., & Guest, D. (2017). The case for reinvigorating quality of working life research. *Human Relations, 70*(2), 149–167.

Guest, D. (2017). Human resource management and employee well-being: Towards a new analytic framework. *Human Resource Management Journal, 27*(1), 22–38.

Guest, D. (2022). Socio-technical systems. *Oxford Research Encyclopedia of Psychology*.

Hackman, R., & Oldham, G. (1975). Development of the job diagnostic survey. *Journal of Applied Psychology, 60*(2), 159–170.

Heller, F., Pusic, E., Strauss, G., & Wilpert, B. (1998). *Organizational participation: Myth and reality*. Oxford University Press.

Herzberg, F. (1966). *Work and the nature of man*. Staples.

Herzberg, F. (1968). One more time, how do you motivate employees? *Harvard Business Review, 48*(1), 53–62.

Heyes, J., & Tomlinson, M. (2021). Underemployment and well-being in Europe. *Human Relations, 74*(8), 1240–1266.

Hill, P. (1971). *Towards a new philosophy of management*. Gower.

Ho, H., & Kuvaas, B. (2020). Human resource management systems, employee well-being and firm performance from mutual gains and critical perspectives: The well-being paradox. *Human Resource Management, 59*(3), 235–253.

Holman, D. (2013). Job types and job quality in Europe. *Human Relations, 66*(4), 475–502.

Iman, S. (1975). The development of participation by semiautonomous work teams: The case of Donnelly Mirrors. In L. Davis & A. Cherns (Eds.), *The quality of working life* (Vol. 2, pp. 216–231). Free Press.

Jiang, K., Lepak, D., Hu, J., & Baer, J. (2012). How does human resource management influence organizational outcomes? A meta-analytic investigation of mediating mechanisms. *Academy of Management Journal, 55*(6), 1264–1294.

Jones, W., Haslam, R., & Haslam, C. (2017). What is a "good" job? Modelling job quality for blue collar workers. *Ergonomics, 60*(1), 138–194.

Kivimaki, M., Nyberg, S., Batty, D., Fransson, E., Heikilla, K., Alredsson, L., Bjoner, J., Borritz, H., Burr, H., Casini, A., & Clays, E. (2012). Job strain as a risk factor for coronary disease: A collaborative meta-analysis of individual participant data. *The Lancet, 380*(9852), 1491–1497.

Knight, C., & Parker, S. (2021). How job design interventions affect performance: An evidence-based model from a systematic review. *Human Relations, 74*(1), 69–104.

Likert, R. (1967). *The human organization: Its management and value.* McGraw-Hill.

Lindblom, R., & Norstedt, J. (1975). *The Volvo report.* Swedish Employers' Federation.

Marmot, M., Allen, J., Boyce, T., Goldblatt, P., & Morrison, J. (2020). *Health equity in England: The Marmot review 10 years on.* Institute of Health Equity.

Maslow, A. (1943). A theory of human motivation. *Psychological Review, 50*(4), 370–396.

Mayo, E. (1933). *Human problems of an industrial civilization.* Macmillan.

Miller, E. (1975). Socio-technical systems in weaving, 1953–1970: A follow-up study. *Human Relations, 28*(4), 349–386.

Organisation for Economic Co-operation and Development. (2018). *Good jobs for all in a changing world of work: The OECD jobs strategy.*

O'Toole, J., & Lawler, E. (2006). *The new American workplace.* Palgrave Macmillan.

Parker, S., Bindl, U., & Strauss, K. (2010). Making things happen: A model of proactive motivation. *Journal of Management, 36*(4), 827–856.

Parker, S., & Grote, G. (2020). Automation, algorithms, and beyond: Why work design matters more than ever in a digital world. *Applied Psychology: An International Review.* Virtual Issue. https://doi.org/10.1111/apps.12241

Pasmore, W., Francis, C., Haldeman, J., & Shani, A. (1982). Socio-technical systems: A North American reflection of empirical studies of the seventies. *Human Relations, 35*(12), 1179–1204.

Paul, W., Robertson, K., & Herzberg, F. (1969). Job enrichment pays off. *Harvard Business Review, 47*(2), 61–78.

Peccei, R., & Van de Voorde, K. (2019). Human resource management–well-being–performance research revisited: Past, present and future. *Human Resource Management Journal, 29*(3), 539–568.

Quinlan, M. (2021). COVID-19, health and vulnerable societies. *Annals of Work Exposures and Health, 65*(3), 239–243.

Rice, A. K. (1958). *Productivity and social organization: The Ahmedabad experiment.* Tavistock Publications.

Rousseau, D. (2005). *I-deals: Idiosyncratic deals employees bargain for themselves.* M.E. Sharpe.

Rubinstein, S., & Kochan, T. (2001). *Learning from Saturn: Possibilities for corporate governance and employee relations.* Cornell University Press.

Sandberg, E. (1993). Volvo human-centred work organization—The end of the road? *New Technology, Work & Employment, 8*(2), 83–87.

Standing, G. (2011). *The precariat: The new dangerous class.* Bloomsbury.

Subramony, M. (2009). A meta-analytic investigation of the relationship between HRM bundles and firm performance. *Human Resource Management, 48*(5), 745–768.

Taylor, F. (1947). *Scientific management.* Harper.

Taylor, M., Marsh, G., Nicol, D., & Broadbent, P. (2017). *Good work: The Taylor review of modern working practices.* UK Government.

Trist, E. (1981). *The evolution of socio-technical systems.* Ontario Quality of Working Life Centre.

Trist, E., & Bamforth, K. (1951). Some social and psychological consequences of the Longwall method of coal-getting. *Human Relations, 4*(1), 3–38.

Trist, E., Higgin, G., Murray, H., & Pollock, B. (1963). *Organizational choice.* Tavistock Publications.

Trist, E., Susman, G., & Brown, G. (1977). An experiment in autonomous working in an American underground coal mine. *Human Relations, 30*(3), 201–236.

United States Department of Health, Education, and Welfare, & W. E. Upjohn Institute for Employment Research. (1973). *Work in America: Report of a special task force (1974).* MIT Press.

Van den Broeck, A., & Parker, S. (2017). Job and work design. *Oxford Research Encyclopedia in Psychology.*

Van de Voorde, K., Paauwe, J., & Van Veldhoven, M. (2016). Employee well-being and the HRM–organizational performance relationship: A review of quantitative studies. *International Journal of Management Reviews*, *14*(4), 391–407.

Walton, R. (1973). Quality of working life: What is it? *Sloan Management Review*, *15*(1), 11–21.

Walton, R. (1975). Criteria for quality of working life. In L. David. & A. Cherns (Eds.), *The quality of working life* (Vol. 1, pp. 91–104). Free Press.

Walton, R. (1977). Work innovations at Topeka: After six years. *Journal of Applied Behavioural Science*, *13*(3), 422–433.

Warhurst, C., & Knox, A. (2022). Manifesto for a new quality of working life. *Human Relations* 75(2), 304–321.

World Health Organization. (1946). *Preamble to the constitution of the World Health Organization.*

Wrzesniewski, A., & Dutton, J. (2001). Crafting a job: Revisioning employees as active crafters of their work. *Academy of Management Review*, *26*(2), 179–201.

Xu, X., Lu, Y., Vogel-Heuser, B., & Wang, L. (2021). Industry 4.0 and Industry 5.0—Inception, conception and perception. *Journal of Manufacturing Systems*, *61*, 530–535.

David E. Guest

WELL-BEING AT WORK

INTRODUCTION

Well-being is one of the most basic aspirations of human beings. Since its inception, psychology has focused on this issue, not just to better understand the phenomenon and processes related to it, but also to provide intervention strategies for its enhancement, improvement, and sustainability at the individual and collective levels. Important contributions to this endeavor have also come from work and organizational psychology. This article aims to offer a comprehensive view of the study of well-being at work. First, we focus on its conceptualization, paying special attention to its hedonic and eudaimonic types. Second, the main theoretical models are reviewed and their key antecedents and consequences are presented, with attention paid to cross-level relations. Finally, intervention strategies to improve well-being at work are discussed, considering strategies oriented toward the physical versus psychosocial, prevention versus promotion, and organizational versus individual. The relevant success factors of these interventions are examined. Figure 1 offers a summary of the well-being constructs, antecedents, outcomes, and interventions discussed in this article, for the purpose of providing an organizing framework for this work.

WELL-BEING AT WORK

Well-being at work refers to employees' experience of feeling good and having a sense of fulfillment and purpose (Sonnentag, 2015). It has been conceptualized from two distinct perspectives based in different philosophical traditions. On the one hand, the hedonic view of pleasure, also referred to as subjective well-being, reflected in employees' positive evaluations of their work, includes positive emotion, engagement, satisfaction, and the experience of

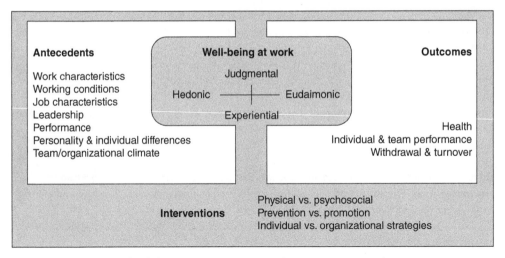

Figure 1. Summary of well-being constructs, antecedents, outcomes, and interventions.

positive affect (e.g., Diener, 2000). On the other hand, the eudaimonic view, also referred to as psychological well-being, encompasses personal growth and the sense of meaning (Ryff, 1995). Thus, well-being can be understood as having both pleasurable components and meaningful and functional components (Dolan, 2014; Ryan & Deci, 2001; Warr, 2019).

HEDONIC WELL-BEING

Hedonic or subjective well-being (SWB) refers to a subjective evaluation of people's lives and aspects of life (e.g., work), and it is generally defined as "how people evaluate their lives—both at the moment and for long periods such as the last year" (Diener et al., 2003, p. 404). In this regard, SWB shares the aspect of preference satisfaction, in that it allows people to decide how well their life is going without someone else determining their well-being (Graham, 2010).

Hedonism is one the oldest philosophical doctrines, and it is still studied today (Heathwood, 2014). From this perspective, SWB is understood in terms of the presence of pleasure and the absence of pain (Angner, 2010), and so it consists of a person's balance between pleasant and unpleasant experiences (Eid & Larsen, 2008). Pleasure or enjoyment is what ultimately makes life worth living (Heathwood, 2014). At work, hedonic well-being is defined in terms of what people think or feel about specific components of work (Robertson & Cooper, 2011), such as the work environment or the salary. From the hedonic perspective, SWB can refer to satisfaction or positive cognitions and affect about relevant factors of work, such as comfort in the workspace (e.g., temperature, air quality, the sound level), or about positive relationships with the supervisor or coworkers. It includes both cognitive judgments (such as life or job satisfaction) and affective experiences (such as positive emotions or positive or negative affectivity; Diener et al., 2018).

Cognitive Judgments of Hedonic Well-being. Job satisfaction has been defined as a "positive evaluative judgment one makes about one's job or job situation" (Weiss, 2002,

p. 175). Although some researchers view satisfaction as a multicomponent construct that contains both cognitive and affective components (e.g., Brief, 1998), Judge et al. (2017) pointed out that the cognitive aspects have been the predominant focus in the theory and measurement of job satisfaction. Work- or job-related satisfaction has been conceptualized as overall satisfaction (e.g., Quinn et al., 1974) or as a multidimensional construct that comprises satisfaction with several work facets, such as pay, promotion opportunities, tasks, supervision, or coworkers (Smith et al., 1969). Researchers frequently distinguish intrinsic and extrinsic types of job satisfaction (e.g., Sardžoska & Tang, 2015). Extrinsic job satisfaction refers to how people feel about aspects of the job (Ayala et al., 2017) related to external factors such as working conditions or coworkers, competitive pay and promotions, a flexible schedule and continuing education, or the job's social status (Judge, Parker et al., 2001). Intrinsic job satisfaction focuses on how people feel about the nature of the tasks or the work itself. It includes features such as variety, skill utilization, autonomy, group cohesion, and organizational characteristics (Ayala et al., 2017).

Life satisfaction is a broader construct related to work satisfaction, and it has been used as an indicator to assess workers' well-being. It refers to a cognitive-judgmental process (Diener et al., 1985) that consists of the assessment of one's satisfaction with life circumstances (Linley et al., 2009). It has been conceptualized as the result of satisfaction with life domains such as work, family, health, and so forth (Rode, 2004). Diener et al. (1985) pointed out that the judgment of how satisfied an individual is with his or her present state is based on a comparison with a standard that each individual sets for himself or herself (not externally imposed). Thus, life satisfaction is a key indicator of hedonic well-being (Linley et al., 2009) that is based on the person's own judgment (Diener et al., 1985).

Affective Experiences of Hedonic Well-being.

An important part of the study of well-being has focused on the study of affect (Kaplan et al., 2009). Affect refers to the phenomenological experience of "feeling" (Watson, 2000). In this regard, hedonic well-being has also been conceptualized as the experience of positive affect (e.g., Diener, 2000).

Positive emotions at work are forms of transient or state affect (e.g., Kaplan et al., 2009). In fact, affective well-being (Warr, 2007), which considers the experience of pleasure (e.g., state positive emotions) while performing different work activities (Dolan et al., 2011; White & Dolan, 2009), is generally thought to represent the core of well-being and mental health (Diener et al., 2011).

Affective well-being at work is often measured by asking the respondents to indicate how they have been feeling at work in the last couple of hours (e.g., White & Dolan, 2009). Given the dynamic and changing nature of emotions in response to the dynamic and changing contexts where workers have to operate, the level of well-being and happiness experienced by workers might vary from day to day and differ from their general or more trait-like level (Bakker & Daniels, 2013). These oscillations in positive emotions can trigger—and be triggered by—important work outcomes (Xanthopoulou et al., 2009).

Negative affectivity (NA) and positive affectivity (PA) refer to traits or more stable affective dispositions that reflect people's general tendencies to experience certain kinds of emotional states (i.e., personality characteristics; e.g., Kaplan et al., 2009; Watson & Clark, 1984). According to the prevalent approach in organizational research (e.g., Nelis et al., 2016), trait affectivity is formed by two independent factors, namely, positive affect and negative affect. On the one hand, trait PA is a component of temperament that is defined as "individual differences in the tendency to experience positive emotions and feeling states" (e.g., Stanton & Watson, 2014, p. 556). High trait PA persons are expected to be joyful, lively, confident, daring, attentive, and determined (Stanton & Watson, 2014). Along these lines, studies carried out in the work context provide evidence of the relationship between PA and work success (King et al., 2015). On the other hand, it can be expected that people higher in NA will probably experience negative feelings such as fear, hostility, guilt, and sadness (Stanton & Watson, 2014). These people tend to focus on the negative side of the world, hold a more negative view of themselves, experience distress and dissatisfaction, and get upset in any given situation (Watson & Clark, 1984). In contrast, people lower in NA would be expected to experience feelings such as serenity, calmness, relative contentment, security, and satisfaction with themselves (Watson & Clark, 1984).

EUDAIMONIC WELL-BEING

Well-being also refers to the eudaimonic experience of meaning, purpose, and growth at work (Rosso et al., 2010). In ancient Greek philosophy, Aristotle "considered hedonic happiness to be a vulgar ideal, making humans slavish followers of desires [and] posited, instead, that true happiness is found in the expression of virtue—that is, in doing what is worth doing" (Ryan & Deci, 2001, p. 145). Thus, eudaimonia has been defined as "the feelings accompanying behavior in the direction of, and consistent with, one's true potential" (Waterman, 1984, p. 16). Daimon, the "true self" (Norton, 1976), is an ideal in the sense of excellence toward which one strives, giving meaning to one's life. This approach to well-being consists of evaluating and reporting on how much meaning one's life has (Ryff & Keyes, 1995). To reflect these advances, there have been improvements in the measures of well-being (Organisation for Economic Co-operation and Development [OECD], 2013). Both activities that people find "pleasurable" and the "worthwhileness" associated with these activities (Dolan et al., 2011; Muric et al., 2022; White & Dolan, 2009), as well as purpose in life, personal growth, and a sense of meaning (Ryff, 1995), have been considered for several years.

Cognitive Judgments of Eudaimonic Well-being. Purpose and meaning at work are mainly understood as general values and attitudes about work, as well as the personal experience and significance of work (see Rosso et al., 2010 for a review). Meaning refers to the individual interpretation of what work signifies or the role work plays in the worker's life (Yeoman et al., 2019). Different kinds of meaning of work (i.e., contributing to the economic maintenance of one's family, the job as allowing one to have a positive impact on the organization, work as self-expression and self-fulfillment; Colby et al., 2001) have been distinguished. The individual doing the work defines whether his or her work is meaningful and contributes to making the world a better place (Wrzesniewski, 2003).

The perception of work's meaningfulness can stem from different sources. The first is the self or the individual's values, motivations, and beliefs about work. Specifically, what individuals envision as the desired end states they would like to attain through working will have an influence on their experience of meaningfulness (Rosso et al., 2010). Moreover, being intrinsically motivated at work will probably make them see congruence between their work activities and their self-concepts, which, in turn, will enhance the experience of meaningfulness (Rosso et al., 2010). Finally, the core beliefs people have about work, such as work orientations, will shape the meaning they give to work (Wrzesniewski et al., 1997). Accordingly, individuals who see their work as a job (i.e., a necessity to support life) will give a different meaning to work compared to those who see it as a career (i.e., an opportunity for personal growth) or as a calling (i.e., fulfillment of higher values in life; Wrzesniewski et al., 1997). Other important determinants of the meaning or meaningfulness of work are the interactions and relationships with others at work (e.g., coworkers, leaders) and outside the workplace (e.g., communities, family), as well as the context where individuals carry out their work (e.g., design of job tasks, organizational mission, financial circumstances, nonwork domains, and the national culture; see Rosso et al., 2010 for a review).

Experiences of Eudaimonic Well-being. In the area of eudaimonic well-being, research has predominantly focused on general individual dispositions or overall evaluations (Xanthopoulou et al., 2009) that capture general levels of meaning, but the dynamics of eudaimonic well-being at work largely remain unexplored (Sonnentag, 2015). Huta and Waterman (2013) explained that individuals can experience states of eudaimonic well-being (or meaningfulness at work), and that these states refer to individual momentary subjective feelings, emotions, and cognitive-affective appraisals. To capture these experiences, researchers recognize activity worthwhileness as a key component (Dolan et al., 2011). It can be defined as individuals' evaluation of the activities they perform as meaningful, important to others, and helpful in attaining important personal goals (White & Dolan, 2009). Indeed, some recent findings show that employees' experienced "worthwhileness" of their activities fluctuates (Kozusznik et al., 2019). In the research on "worthwhileness" associated with activities, White and Dolan (2009) found some discrepancies between activities that people find "pleasurable" and those considered "rewarding." In this way, time spent on a difficult but meaningful task for one's career would be considered relatively more rewarding than pleasurable, whereas time spent working in a comfortable and modern office would be relatively more pleasurable than "rewarding." From a theoretical point of view, in his Pleasure-Purpose Principle (the "PPP"), Dolan (2014) suggested that, in order to be truly happy, a person needs to have daily experiences of both purpose and pleasure. In this way, a happy life is one that contains many positive daily sentiments of pleasure and purpose, and a miserable life contains a preponderance of negative sentiments of pain (e.g., anger, worry, stress) and pointlessness (e.g., boredom, futility).

Activities that are considered "rewarding" can produce a state of flow, another construct that shows oscillations over time. The majority of the research on flow was developed during the 1980s and 1990s by Csikszentmihalyi and colleagues (e.g., Csikszentmihalyi & Csikszentmihalyi, 1988). Flow has been defined as a subjective state that is intrinsically rewarding and characterized by an intense and focused concentration on what one is doing in the present moment. When their attention is wholly invested, individuals lose the awareness of themselves as social actors and have a sense of control over their actions that is accompanied by a distortion of the temporal experience (the impression that time has passed more quickly than normal). Flow refers to an intrinsically motivated, or autotelic, activity that is rewarding in and of itself (auto = self, telos = goal), independently of its end product or any extrinsic reward for carrying out the activity (Nakamura & Csikszentmihalyi, 2013). When in a state of flow, the individual operates at full capacity (Deci, 1975). Indeed, people "in flow" describe their experience as being engaged in "just-manageable challenges by tackling a series of goals, continuously processing feedback about progress, and adjusting action based on this feedback" (Nakamura & Csikszentmihalyi, 2013, p. 240). This suggests that experiences of flow at work can be facilitated by activities (e.g., optimum task difficulty), and that there can be certain psychological preconditions, such as personal energetic resources (e.g., state of recovery; Debus et al., 2014), that facilitate the flow experience (Nakamura & Csikszentmihalyi, 2003).

Even though some authors, especially from the emotional and/or motivational domains, describe flow as an experience close to positive affect (Fredrickson, 1998), flow has also been described in terms of eudaimonic well-being, drawing attention to aspects such as vitality, absorption, and intrinsic motivation (Kashdan et al., 2008). Indeed, recent literature seems to conceptualize flow as a facet of eudaimonic well-being (Roysamb & Nes, 2016), given that it has been observed that individuals can experience flow even without describing the experience as pleasurable (Csikszentmihalyi, 1999). Although flow at work can be considered an ephemeral and transitory state (Fullagar & Kelloway, 2009) when "everything comes together for the performer" (Jackson & Eklund, 2002, p. 133), there may also be individual differences in the tendency to experience flow, regardless of the situation, which makes it possible to refer to a trait-like "autotelic personality," understood as a set of dispositional attributes that facilitate engagement in activities (Fullagar & Kelloway, 2009).

The issue of the main types of well-being and happiness is still open, and a number of researchers have pointed to the need for additional constructs, such as a "psychologically rich life" (Oishi & Westgate, 2022), or they have searched for finer grained constructs (Ruggeri et al., 2020) in order to improve the understanding of these concepts and interventions.

MAIN THEORIES ABOUT WELL-BEING AT WORK

Since the work of ancient Greek philosophers such as Epicurus or Aristotle, a number of well-being theories have developed. Some focus on the hedonic conception (Diener et al., 2002) and others on the eudaimonic. For instance, the top-down and bottom-up processes approach of Diener (1984) is based on the idea that there are basic and universal human needs that, when fulfilled, allow a person to be happy. Needs theorists argue that subjective well-being will change as individuals approach their goals, whereas trait theories suggest that subjective well-being is strongly influenced by stable personality dispositions (Diener et al., 2002). In this regard, it has been argued that, although life events can influence subjective well-being, people eventually adapt to these changes and return to biologically determined "set-points" or "adaptation-levels" (e.g., Headey & Wearing, 1992).

Theories dealing with well-being at work have paid attention to its relationship with performance, as in the Happy-Productive Worker Thesis. Additionally, the view that positive emotions play a role in generating and amplifying mental functions and behaviors has also received attention (Broaden-and-Build Theory). Furthermore, other theories have paid attention to the dynamic "micro" perspective, shedding light on the affective experiences and their outcomes at work (Adaptation Theory and Affective Events Theory). In theories dealing with eudaimonic well-being (Sonnentag, 2015), engagement has been considered an activity that, in itself, provides happiness (Diener et al., 2002; Peiró et al., 2021). In fact, Csikszentmihalyi (1975) suggested that people are happiest when they are engaged (flow) in interesting activities that match their skill level. Self-determination Theory (Ryan & Deci, 2000) has paid attention to the eudaimonic approach to well-being. Finally, multilevel analysis has highlighted that affective experiences can emerge as a collective phenomenon (Gamero et al., 2008) that may influence the collective performance of teams and organizations.

The Happy-Productive Worker Thesis. The Happy-Productive Worker Thesis (HPWT) assumes that, in general, well-being is an antecedent of performance, so that "happy" workers perform better than "unhappy" ones (Wright & Cropanzano, 2007). However, empirical evidence is not conclusive: some meta-analyses report weak (0.17; Iaffaldano & Muchinsky, 1985) or modest (0.30; Judge, Thoresen et al., 2001) correlations between job satisfaction and job performance. Additionally, Bowling (2007) showed spurious associations between satisfaction and performance, and Judge et al. (2017) questioned the causal structure of this relationship because attitudes can be either the cause or the consequence of performance. Other authors argued that, even if satisfaction does not cause task performance directly, it benefits the organization by increasing organizational citizenship behaviors (LePine et al., 2002). To explain these unclear results, scholars have revisited the HPWT on various occasions (Wright & Cropanzano, 2007; Zelenski et al., 2008) and raised several issues. First, in general, happy people are productive people, both when happiness is analyzed at a trait level and at a state level (e.g., happy mood). Second, the extent of support for the happy-productive worker thesis may depend on what is meant by "happiness." Specifically, of the many ways to conceptualize happiness, hedonic well-being has consistently been the one most strongly linked to productivity (Peiró et al., 2021). Finally, the relationship between well-being and performance should be analyzed through an experience-sampling method that participants assess at repeated moments over time while functioning in their natural setting, making it possible to draw conclusions about causality. Experience Sampling Method (ESM) is a method of data collection in which participants are assessed at repeated moments over the course of time while functioning in their natural settings.

Along these lines, there are studies showing that moderator variables may affect the strength of the relationship between workers' well-being and performance (Fogaça & Coelho, 2016; Warr, 2007). Moreover, the traditional approach of the HPWT has considered only a linear relationship between well-being (typically tested as job satisfaction) and performance. Analyzing the profiles of these relationships, Peiró et al. (2019) identified "synergistic patterns" ("happy-productive" and "unhappy-unproductive"), but also patterns with "antagonic" relations ("unhappy-productive" and "happy-unproductive"). A profile analysis of the relationships between these two variables indicated that over 50% of the respondents are either unhappy and productive or happy and unproductive workers. This is not unlikely. At times, job dissatisfaction (Zhou & George, 2001) or negative affect and moods (Bledow et al., 2013) can foster creative performance (understood as coming up with new ideas for products, services, and/or processes in order to better achieve the organization's goals; Amabile et al., 2005). Moreover, demographic covariates such as sector, seniority, and type of work are related to the allocation of individuals to one pattern or another in organizations (Peiró et al., 2019). In the case of hedonic well-being, the probability of belonging to the "medium low well-being, medium high performance" profile is greater in the production sector, in people with more than 5 years of seniority, and in technical/administrative work. To further explore these anomalous patterns where happiness hinders performance (i.e., creative performance; George & Zhou, 2007) or unhappiness enhances it (Bledow et al., 2013), Peiró et al. (2019) studied different operationalizations of well-being and their relationships with different performance measures. These authors found that the patterns are not only obtained for hedonic well-being (e.g., job satisfaction), but they also occur with operationalizations of eudaimonic well-being. Warr and Nielsen (2018), based on Ayala et al. (2017), highlighted that more needs to be learned about individuals who are outside the hypothesized pattern (happy-productive). The importance of these alternative configurations is reflected in the number of employees who are included within the antagonistic patterns (over 50%; Peiró et al., 2019). Uncovering these profiles is relevant in further understanding the complex relationship between well-being and performance.

Broaden-and-Build Theory.   One interesting challenge is to identify the mediating variables in the complex relationships between well-being and performance. A well-being construct (e.g., positive emotions) can mediate the relationship between another well-being construct (e.g., job satisfaction) and performance. This is the main tenet of the broaden-and-build theory, which emphasizes either the mediating or the moderating role of positive and negative emotions between well-being and performance. Positive emotions may induce different aspects of performance at work, and they may also amplify the impact of hedonic well-being (e.g., job satisfaction) on performance.

The Broaden-and-Build Theory (Fredrickson, 1998, 2001) has been developed in response to the inadequacy of traditional models that "did not do justice to positive emotions" (Fredrickson, 2003, p. 165) such as joy, interest, contentment, or love (Fredrickson, 1998, 2001). It highlights that positive emotions *broaden* an individual's momentary thought–action repertoires through play, exploration, savoring, or similar activities (Fredrickson, 2004). These broadened mindsets can be contrasted with the narrowed mindsets triggered by negative emotions (Fredrickson, 2004). Due to the broadened thought–action repertoires, positive emotions will promote the discovery of novel and creative actions, ideas, and social bonds, which will, in turn, build up the individual's physical, intellectual, social, or psychological resources (Fredrickson, 2004). Consequently, these new resources can serve as reserves that can be used in the future to cope with problems (Fredrickson, 2004). Therefore, positive emotions produce a "broad, flexible cognitive organization and ability to integrate diverse material" (Isen, 1990, p. 89), thus improving cognitive performance. In this regard, the broaden-and-build theory highlights the valuable role that positive emotions can play in the workplace (Vacharkulksemsuk & Fredrickson, 2013). Individuals who experience positive affect tend to think in a flexible, inclusive, and integrative way (Isen et al., 1991). They are open to information (Estrada et al., 1997) and show higher creative performance (Amabile et al., 2005), which positively influences their personal resources of optimism, self-efficacy, and self-esteem (Xanthopoulou et al., 2012) and unlocks beneficial ways of thinking that can build relational capacity in the workplace (Vacharkulksemsuk & Fredrickson, 2013). This process can spiral outward to a higher level that comprises the whole organization (Vacharkulksemsuk et al., 2011).

Despite this promising evidence, the study of positive emotions in the work context is relatively recent, and research still has to demonstrate its benefits (Vacharkulksemsuk & Fredrickson, 2013). It remains unclear how (and whether) broadened thought-action repertoires are translated into decisions and actions in organizations (Fredrickson, 2001; Vacharkulksemsuk & Fredrickson, 2013). There is also a need to further clarify whether the effects of positive emotions are additive or multiplicative, and what the tipping point is for "too many" positive emotions. Finally, scholars need to test the short- and long-term effects of positive emotions and study the mechanisms and moderators that explain these benefits for people's thoughts and behaviors at work (Vacharkulksemsuk & Fredrickson, 2013). In sum, the broaden-and-build theory provides an initial theoretical base from which to understand how workers who are in a positive state-of-mind have a greater ability to broaden their horizons (in terms of thought processes), which would make them engage in favorable actions resulting in beneficial work outcomes (Lussier et al., 2017).

Adaptation-Level Theory.   Although the analysis of differences in well-being across individuals has been fruitful, intraindividual variations in well-being are also relevant in theory and practice. From a theoretical perspective, the Adaptation-Level Theory (Brickman & Campbell, 1971) focuses on a dynamic "micro" perspective, shedding light on affective experiences and their outcomes at work. This theory offers an interesting perspective from which to understand fluctuations over time. According to Adaptation-Level Theory, exposure to earlier stimuli serves as a frame of reference for judging later stimuli (Helson, 1964). Consequently, the strength of a stimulus is compared to the central point of reference (the adaptation level or set point), and so the greater the distance between the adaptation level and the stimulus, the stronger the stimulus is (Lauterbach, 1979). Thus, this theory suggests that when a change in the external situation occurs, people will react with a change in their well-being as well. However, over time, individuals adapt to the modified external situation and return to their initial well-being set point. For example, Brickman et al. (1978) showed that state lottery winners reported only slightly higher levels of life satisfaction than a control group. In the same vein, Oswald and Powdthavee (2008) provided longitudinal evidence that people who become disabled exhibit a 30%–50% recovery in terms of mental well-being.

To explain this phenomenon, Brickman and Campbell (1971) proposed the hedonic adaptation hypothesis, suggesting that positive and negative hedonic states are costly (i.e., generating feelings is a waste of energy for the brain); thus, to minimize these fitness costs, humans adapt their hedonic states, quickly returning to "normal levels" or the set point. Despite all the empirical support received (Brickman et al., 1978; Mancini et al., 2011), studies have reported limitations, such as the assumption that all individuals have a similar way of adapting (Diener et al., 2010).

Some studies have highlighted the contributions of adaptation-level theory (e.g., Bowling et al., 2005; Ritter et al., 2016), although it has received limited attention, especially because it is not very supportive of the effectiveness of interventions to improve well-being in the workplace. Nevertheless, it furthers the understanding of well-being adaptation processes at work (Sonnentag, 2015), as well as the processes that underlie changes in well-being (Lucas, 2007).

Affective Events Theory. The Affective Events Theory (AET) was developed by Weiss and Cropanzano (1996), and it addresses the streams of affective events at work and their effects on affective and emotional experiences and on workers' behavior and attitudes. It "focuses on the structure, causes and consequences of affective experiences at work" (Weiss & Cropanzano, 1996, p. 11) by proposing that different events can have immediate affective consequences that make them "affective events." These events generate emotional reactions and changes in momentary affective states (Weiss & Cropanzano, 1996). In turn, momentary affect may have an impact on employees' behavior and the creation of work attitudes, drawing "much needed attention to streams of events that can unfold in workplaces" (Brief & Weiss, 2002, p. 284) and to the importance of the intra-individual variation and dynamics of different relevant constructs for employees' well-being (Ilies et al., 2007). According to AET, different characteristics of the work environment may elicit different encounters at work that, in turn, lead to specific affective reactions (Mitchell et al., 2014).

AET focuses on momentary events that cause concurrent positive or negative affective reactions, and it suggests that features of a stable work environment lead to the occurrence of different types of events (Fisher, 2002). According to AET, momentary affect may influence momentary behaviors in real time, producing what Weiss and Cropanzano (1996) referred to as "affect-driven behaviors" (Fisher, 2002). Mitchell et al. (2014) incorporated into AET the transactional theories of emotions (Lazarus & Folkman, 1984), which conceptualize affective responses as resulting from the dynamic interplay between characteristics of the person and the environment. The authors followed AET's recognition of individual and environmental factors as causes of work events; however, they proposed that individual and environmental factors have interactive effects on the occurrence of work events and the appraisals of these events (Mitchell et al., 2014).

Self-Determination Theory. Self-determination Theory suggests that the satisfaction of the essential human needs of competence, autonomy, and relatedness promotes motivation, high-quality performance, and well-being (Deci et al., 2017). It also highlights that the organizational context may foster the internalization and integration of the organizational values in its employees. As a consequence, employees will increase their commitment, behavioral effort and effectiveness, and volitional persistence, which will increase their well-being and performance (Manganelli et al., 2018). If individuals perceive their work activities as personally meaningful, or if they make them congruent with their other values and needs through integration, they are likely to be intrinsically motivated (Ryan & Deci, 2000, 2017) and become more engaged in these activities (Deci et al., 2017). Finally, empirical evidence supports the idea that workers who pursue intrinsic goals and values and see their activities as meaningful and motivational behave in more prosocial ways than those who do not (Ryan et al., 2008).

COLLECTIVE WELL-BEING AT WORK

In recent decades, more attention has been paid to the multilevel analysis of occupational well-being, which reflects the growing interest in well-being as both an individual and a collective phenomenon (Kozlowski & Klein, 2000). This is especially true in the case of team affective climate. There are a variety of other climate constructs, such as justice, safety, or violence climate, that do not refer to well-being per se and, therefore, will be omitted. There are also some types of climate (e.g., team stress climate, organizational well-being climate, or psychological safety climate) that can have potential implications for well-being. These will be elaborated on in the section "Antecedents of Well-being at Work."

Team Affective Climate. Although most of the research on affect has been carried out at the individual level, affective experiences are also collective phenomena, and different authors have pointed out that groups can develop shared affect (Barsade et al., 2000; Gamero et al., 2008; George, 1990). George (1990) researched the group affective tone and defined it as "consistent or homogeneous affective reactions within a group" (p. 77). A similar concept, "shared emotions," was referred to by Barsade et al. (2000). Other authors have studied "group moods" (Bartel & Saavedra, 2000) and "emotional climate" (De Rivera, 1992). González-Romá et al. (2000) provided empirical support for the validity of the "affective work team climate," described as "shared affective responses by a work team's members" (González-Romá et al., 2000, p. 98). According to George (1990), the existence of an affective work team climate can be justified by the attraction-selection-attrition framework (Schneider & Reichers, 1983). This framework posits that "people make the place," and that the formation of an organization can be determined by the individual attributes (i.e., personalities, goals, and values) of its workers (Oh et al., 2018), which, after being shaped by the organization's culture, make the workforce homogeneous (Schneider, 1987). Moreover, individual affective experiences of the group members can be communicated to other group members and form group affect, or it may be produced by similar contextual factors (e.g., leadership; see Korek et al., 2010). There is theoretical and empirical support for aggregating unit members' affective responses to the team level (George, 1990; González-Romá et al., 2000), resulting in different team climates.

ANTECEDENTS OF WELL-BEING AT WORK

Theories on well-being at work have pointed out several relevant antecedents that influence the level and changes in well-being. The study of these antecedents, both environmental and personal, has often been approached from the conceptualization of occupational stress.

Antecedents of Hedonic Well-being. Several theories have assumed that sources of stress or stressors are clear antecedents of hedonic well-being. These antecedents have been conceptualized as objective elements of threat and loss (Conservation of Resources Theory; Hobfoll, 2011), highlighting their objective nature and the circumstances where clear stressors occur. Other theories have conceptualized the antecedents of stress and well-being as resources and demands (Bakker & Demerouti, 2017) or control and demands (Karasek, 1979), whereas some have focused on the imbalance between efforts or contributions and the rewards received (Siegrist, 2010). From a transactional approach, Lazarus and Folkman (1984) highlighted that the appraisal of a situation is an essential process in the stress experience, and the nature of any particular stressor depends on the way the individual interprets it and the appraisal of the strategies to cope with it. Given the key role of the appraisal, the situation, and even individual demands, can be appraised as threats and/or challenges. When the demands are appraised as threats (i.e., the appraisal of distress) and coping strategies are poor, negative effects can occur, such as poor well-being (Jamal, 1999), leading to increasing negative affect, work dissatisfaction, and burnout (Cavanaugh et al., 2000). When the demands are appraised as challenges and opportunities, they may have positive outcomes for well-being. Positive stress experiences might trigger beneficial consequences such as well-being, work satisfaction, and organizational affective commitment (Scheck et al., 1997). Some researchers interpret stressors as either a challenge or a hindrance (Abbas & Raja, 2019; Cavanaugh et al., 2000); however, there is increasing evidence that they can coexist and occur simultaneously in response to the same stressor, but with different degrees of intensity (Folkman, 1997; Rodríguez et al., 2013).

Work Characteristics and Working Conditions. Job-related stressors can have an impact on employees' well-being (Cooper et al., 2001). In fact, 42% of U.S. employees have purposefully changed jobs due to stressful work environments (Reina & Reina, 2016). Stressors can be categorized in two broad categories (MacDonald et al., 2001): psychosocial and physical. Psychosocial stressors comprise characteristics of work activities and social relationships. Lack of autonomy or stressors related to role accomplishment have been widely studied and are defined as psychosocial demands, constraints, or opportunities that individuals perceive in their work roles (Beehr & Glazer, 2005). In a meta-analysis, Schmidt et al. (2014) showed that work stressors such as role ambiguity and role conflict are associated with negative well-being outcomes. Other important psychosocial work stressors, such as workload, poor relationships at work, personal accountability, and home–work balance, can be appraised both as a challenge and as a threat (e.g., Rodríguez et al., 2013). Specifically, lack of social support (Smith et al., 2004), poor social climate or interpersonal conflicts (Agervold & Mikkelsen, 2004), or situations characterized by prejudice and discrimination (Stuber et al., 2008) often impair well-being and may lead to undesired situations such as bullying at work (Agervold & Mikkelsen, 2004).

Physical stressors can include stimuli from the physical environment, such as temperature, noise, or lack of space or privacy (Mayo et al., 2012). Various physical conditions can hamper health and well-being at work, including tiring and painful positions, repetitive movements, carrying heavy loads, noise and vibrations, and breathing in smoke, dust, or vapor (Eurofound, 2010). For example, Rashid and Zimring (2008), in their review, suggested that physical stressors may negatively impact employees' well-being by increasing negative emotions or dissatisfaction. Additionally, they showed that ventilation, air quality, work area temperature, and ratings of the work area environment had a positive relationship with job satisfaction and satisfaction with the work environment (Rashid & Zimring, 2008). Finally, excessively hot or cold temperatures are associated with unsolicited complaints and low satisfaction with the workplace, and they may worsen psychosocial stressors by making it difficult to think and concentrate and producing poor social relationships (e.g., Rashid & Zimring, 2008).

Leadership. There is growing evidence of the impact of leadership on employee well-being (Taris & Nielsen, 2019). Leaders play an important role in the process of creating supportive conditions and cultures (Peiró, 2017). In this regard, previous studies have shown that different styles differ in their capacity to promote employee well-being (Samad et al., 2015). On the one hand, ineffective leadership practices and behaviors can seriously damage employees' well-being. Tepper (2000) pointed out that employees who perceive their supervisors as abusive experience low levels of job and life satisfaction and affective commitment. On the other hand, leaders who go beyond basic exchange relationships (e.g., using inspirational motivation and individual consideration or creating conditions that reduce or buffer stress) promote their employees' job satisfaction (Peiró & Rodriguez, 2008). Therefore, leadership styles and employee well-being are significantly linked (Samad et al., 2015). Additionally, leaders' behaviors play a moderator role in many relationships between stressors and individuals' well-being, given that supervisors are a privileged source of support to mitigate stressful work demands (Taris & Nielsen, 2019).

Personality and Individual Differences. Individuals' stable characteristics have been shown to predict individual well-being. Some studies have associated genetics (Røysamb & Nes, 2016), general personality dispositions such as positive affectivity (Danna & Griffin, 1999), or personality traits such as extraversion (Lucas & Fujita, 2000) with well-being experiences. According to Diener et al. (2003), personality is one of the strongest and most consistent predictors of well-being; it accounts for more variance in well-being than individual and demographic factors such as income, educational background, or marital status. There is considerable empirical evidence about the relationship between personality dimensions operationalized as the Big Five personality traits and well-being (e.g., Higgs & Dulewicz, 2014). Furnham and Petrides (2003) showed that all the Big Five factors, except neuroticism, showed a positive relationship with subjective well-being. DeNeve and Cooper (1998) reported that personality traits were significant predictors of life satisfaction, happiness, and positive affect, although they were less predictive of negative affect. More recent studies highlight that, in addition to extroversion and neuroticism, other traits such as conscientiousness, agreeableness, and openness/intellect are meaningfully associated with multiple well-being indicators (Sun et al., 2018).

Core self-evaluations are stable personality traits that involve people's fundamental evaluations of themselves (Judge, 2009). They refer to individuals' perceptions of their own ability and value. Research on core self-evaluations has received considerable attention in the organizational context in recent years (Peng et al., 2016). It posits a conceptual and empirical relationship between these traits and job satisfaction, suggesting that self-evaluation traits affect the way people act and react in various settings, predicting meaningful outcomes (Judge et al., 1998). In the same vein, it has been shown that psychological capital, a concept that combines four personality characteristics (self-efficacy, optimism, hope, and resiliency; Luthans, 2002), has been associated with employee well-being outcomes such as job satisfaction or organizational commitment (Mäkikangas et al., 2013).

ANTECEDENTS OF EUDAIMONIC WELL-BEING

Job Characteristics. Studies that explore the antecedents of eudaimonic well-being (EWB) at work focus mainly on the antecedents of engagement. In fact, in a review of the

Happy-Productive Worker Thesis, over three-quarters of the EWB–performance relationships reviewed referred to work engagement as vigor, dedication, and absorption (Peiró et al., 2021). The Job Demands-Resources (JD-R) model (Demerouti, 2007) states that engagement is promoted by the availability of external and personal resources at work. Job resources have motivational power that leads to work engagement and, consequently, to performance. Chung and Angeline (2010) also referred to these arguments, and Li and Qi (2015) used the JD-R and conservation of resources theories to hypothesize the mediating role of engagement in the relationship between supervisors' knowledge-sharing and task performance.

Leadership. Tepper (2000) pointed out that employees who perceive their supervisors as abusive experience higher psychological distress. However, Bae et al. (2013) argued that transformational leadership fosters engagement and, consequently, teachers' creativity and knowledge-creation behavior. In this regard, leaders who go beyond basic exchange relationships (e.g., employing inspirational motivation and individual consideration) promote their employees' job engagement and psychological well-being. Employees need to feel psychologically safe and confident, and leaders' empowering behaviors play a significant role in boosting their followers' psychological safety (Park et al., 2017).

Personality and Individual Differences. There is some evidence showing that the Big Five personality traits are related to both the presence of and the search for meaning (Steger et al., 2006). Specifically, neuroticism has been negatively associated with meaning in life. In turn, extraversion, conscientiousness, and agreeableness have been significantly and positively related to meaning in life (Steger et al., 2006). Additionally, psychological capital (i.e., self-efficacy, optimism, hope, and resiliency; Luthans, 2002) has been associated with psychological well-being (Mäkikangas et al., 2013).

PERFORMANCE AS AN ANTECEDENT OF HEDONIC AND EUDAIMONIC WELL-BEING

Although most of the research on the relationships between well-being and performance has studied performance as an outcome variable, it is important to consider that performance can influence well-being, and there are theoretical grounds for this causal relationship. Control theory, social cognitive theory, and goal setting theory all suggest that perceived performance is causally related to affect (Bandura, 1986). These models state that individuals monitor their performance levels against goals or standards. When their perception of their performance is below the standard, they experience negative affect. In contrast, when they perceive that their performance meets a goal, they experience positive affect. Empirical data support these theoretical considerations for both hedonic and eudaimonic well-being. With regard to the antecedents of hedonic performance (Akkermans et al., 2013; Fisher, 2002; Gabriel et al., 2011; Glomb et al., 2011; Harris et al., 2003; Seo & Ilies, 2009; Sonnentag, 2015), when considering the impact of performance on hedonic well-being, Fisher (2002) showed that most individuals felt more positive and experienced greater task satisfaction than usual when they were performing better than they usually did. Moreover, individuals who were more satisfied with their task accomplishment experienced more positive affective states (Gabriel et al., 2011). Furthermore, longitudinal studies have shown that self-rated performance is a predictor of increased dedication and decreased emotional exhaustion over time (Akkermans et al., 2013). Moreover, some research on the dynamics of well-being and performance has suggested that performance fluctuations can affect fluctuations in well-being at work (Sonnentag, 2015). Specifically, studies have found that performance (e.g., Seo & Ilies, 2009) and the experience of making progress toward one's goals at work (e.g., Harris et al., 2003) are predictors of positive affective states. Finally, there is also evidence that extra-role behaviors, such as altruistic and courtesy behaviors, are predictors of positive affective states, except for courtesy behaviors, which were associated with an increase in negative affect (Glomb et al., 2011).

CROSS-LEVEL AND MULTILEVEL ANTECEDENTS OF WELL-BEING

Some research has approached the issue from a cross-level perspective, showing that some collective phenomena in teams and whole organizations (e.g., work-unit stress climate, organizational well-being climate, psychosocial safety climate) may have an impact on individual-level well-being (D'Alleo & Santangelo, 2011).

Team Stress Climate. Teams' stress climate is a relevant concept to explain individual behavior and the consequences stemming from it (Peiró & González-Romá, 2013). It emerges when stress experiences are widely shared by the members of the same team, unit, or organization. In this way, organizational stress climate is likely to appear when there is a mismatch between demands and resources or an imbalance between contributions and compensations and the appraisal of these situations becomes shared by all or most of the members of the organization (Peiró & González-Romá, 2013). Team members' constant interactions with their physical and social setting lead to the development of "distinctive patterns of collective feeling and beliefs" (Katz & Kahn, 1978, p. 50), based on the individual descriptions (Rousseau, 1988) of their context. Thus, individual stress appraisals can be spread within the group and operationalized using composite aggregation models (Chan, 1998).

Stress climate can be produced through several processes (Peiró, 2008), such as group members' exposure to the same stressor, the culture and shared "rules of appraisal" (Averill, 1986), leadership qualities such as sense-making and charisma, team selection processes based on the Attraction-Selection-Attrition model (Schneider, 1987), or group socialization and leadership.

A study with army units (Tucker et al., 2005) analyzed the consequences of stress climate and showed that it intensifies the effects of individual perceptions of stressors on morale, commitment, and depression. Sora et al. (2009) showed that a stress climate due to job insecurity is negatively associated with individual job satisfaction and organizational commitment in Spanish workers (but not in their Belgian counterparts), beyond individual perceptions of job insecurity. Finally, there is also research showing the importance of specific configurations of distress and eustress appraisals shared by the members of a team in the study of stress climate. Kozusznik et al. (2015), in a study with 535 social service employees in 78 work units, identified the impact of different types of stress climate at work (i.e., distress climate, eustress climate, and balanced climate) on individual well-being (i.e., burnout and engagement) over time. Their main results showed that emotional exhaustion significantly decreased in teams where the climate changed over time from distressed to eustressed. Moreover, there was a significant increase in the level of inefficacy and a significant decrease in the level of vigor in teams in which the stress climate changed from balanced to distressed.

Organizational Well-Being Climate. A positive organizational well-being climate is a prerequisite for a healthy organization in which employees are able to flourish (cf., Ashkanasy & Härtel, 2014; Vacharkulksemsuk et al., 2011) in a friendly environment that nourishes their personal well-being (Ashkanasy & Härtel, 2014). Organizational climate has an affective component (Patterson et al., 2004). The emotions and affect that saturate an organization (Ashforth & Humphrey, 1995) manifest as an organization-wide phenomenon (Ashkanasy, 2003) that can be "palpably sensed" (De Rivera, 1992, p. 197). This is referred to as a positive affective organizational climate (cf., Ashkanasy & Härtel, 2014). Different organizations can have distinct affective climates, and the extent to which these climates are healthy or toxic depends on the affective and emotional states experienced by the employees (Härtel, 2008).

Research shows that a positive organizational affective climate is associated with job satisfaction, organizational commitment (Shadur et al., 1999), and positive employee affect (Schulte et al., 2009). Likewise, employees' shared perceptions of the extent to which the organization values and cares for employee welfare (Patterson et al., 2005) are positively related to individual commitment and negatively related to the need for recovery (Veld & Alfes, 2017).

Psychosocial Safety Climate. Moreover, research shows that a positive social climate, and specifically psychosocial safety climate (i.e., shared perceptions of organizational policies, practices, and procedures about psychological health and safety), also fosters individual well-being. In a study with Australian teachers and administrators, Dollard and Bakker (2010) showed that psychosocial safety climate predicted changes in individual distress and emotional exhaustion through their relationship with individual job demands. Furthermore, psychosocial safety climate was associated with changes in individual employee engagement through its relationship with skill discretion. Second, in a different two-wave study carried out in the Malaysian private sector (Idris & Dollard, 2014), psychosocial safety climate was found to have a cross-level lagged effect on individual employee exhaustion. Finally, in a similar vein, in a diary study in Australian schools, Garrick et al. (2014) investigated the impact of general psychosocial safety climate on the link between teachers' daily job demands and well-being. They found that psychosocial safety climate acted as a buffer of the impact of daily job demands on fatigue and boosted the impact of daily job demands on work engagement. In addition, psychosocial safety climate had a negative main effect on fatigue and a positive main effect on engagement.

OUTPUTS AND CONSEQUENCES OF WELL-BEING AT WORK

Work Performance. Well-being has often been studied as an important antecedent of employee performance, and this relationship has been the core focus of the Happy-Productive

Worker Thesis (Wright & Cropanzano, 2007). There is evidence showing that hedonic well-being predicts performance (Alessandri et al., 2017; Lyubomirsky et al., 2005; Wright & Cropanzano, 2000). In fact, when people are more satisfied with their jobs, they show higher performance (Fogaça & Coelho, 2016) and productivity (Böckerman & Ilmakunnas, 2010). Moreover, employees' positive emotions predicted the variance in supervisory ratings of employees' performance (Wright & Cropanzano, 2000), and higher positive affect predicted performance quality (Hosie et al., 2012). Finally, people who feel better than usual at work have been found to put more effort into their tasks and achieve a higher level of task performance (Zelenski et al., 2008). In this regard, feeling active and enthusiastic in the morning has been shown to increase levels of creative performance during the day (Binnewies & Wörnlein, 2011).

In terms of eudaimonic well-being, there is also evidence suggesting that work engagement enhances organizational outcomes, including productivity, task performance, and organizational citizenship behaviors (Rich et al., 2010). Additionally, a high sense of purpose or meaning is related to positive work attitudes such as organizational citizenship behavior (Schlechter & Engelbrecht, 2006).

Withdrawal and Turnover.   Organizations pay special attention to employee retention because of the costs of replacing valued employees (Holtom et al., 2005). Therefore, scholars have conducted research to examine the criteria associated with retention, such as intentions to quit, withdrawal behavior, and voluntary turnover (Griffeth et al., 2000). Accordingly, employees' well-being has been identified as an important antecedent of these organizational outcomes (Wright & Bonett, 2007). On the one hand, with regard to hedonic well-being, the literature suggests that job satisfaction is negatively related to the intention to be absent, which is a predictor of absence behavior related to lower levels of absenteeism (Soriano et al., 2018). On the other hand, employees who display higher levels of psychological well-being are less prone to turnover (Wright & Bonett, 2007).

Physical Health.   Physical health is another important outcome of well-being that is often identified in research (Diener et al., 2019). Indeed, hedonic well-being has been shown to be associated with increased self-reported health, lower morbidity, less pain, and longevity (Diener & Chan, 2011). Avey et al. (2010) described empirical evidence for a relationship between positive moods, happiness, life satisfaction, and physical and mental health outcomes. In this regard, a meta-analysis (Lyubomirsky et al., 2005) and recent theoretical reviews on this relationship (Ryff & Boylan, 2016) support the idea that happy people achieve better physical and mental health outcomes than unhappy people. Eudaimonic well-being also matters here (Ryff, 2013). Longitudinal studies have shown that a high level of psychological well-being is a protective factor against illnesses (Lamers et al., 2015). Therefore, psychological well-being has been recognized as playing a role in reducing disease or disability via optimal regulation of neurological and physiological systems (Ryff, 2013).

Cross-Level and Multilevel Outcomes of Well-Being.   Even though most of the research on the outcomes of well-being has been conducted at the individual level (Barrick et al., 2015; Judge, Thoresen, et al., 2001), there is growing evidence supporting the relationship between well-being and performance at the collective level of analysis (e.g., Kozlowski & Klein, 2000). García-Buades et al. (2020) conducted a systematic review of existing research on different collective well-being constructs (i.e., team satisfaction, group affect, and team engagement) with operationalizations of collective performance (i.e., self-rated team performance, leader-rated team performance, customers' satisfaction, and objective indicators). They showed that, in a variety of samples, organizational sectors, countries, conceptualizations, and operationalizations of well-being and performance, well-being at the collective level of analysis was positively associated with performance at the team, group, or unit level (García-Buades et al., 2020). Researchers have presented some time-lagged evidence that suggests a causal relationship between collective well-being and team performance. For example, González-Romá and Gamero (2012) showed that a team climate of support from the organization was positively related to positive team mood, which in turn was positively related to team members' ratings of team performance. In addition, in a time-lagged study in a sample of 119 public service departments in Wales, Messersmith et al. (2011) showed that high-performance work systems were an antecedent of departmental job satisfaction, which subsequently improved department performance.

In sum, a cross-level approach to antecedents and consequences of well-being shows that the relationship between well-being and its antecedents and consequences occurs at (and across) different levels of analysis. The most relevant collective antecedent of well-being seems to be organizational or work-unit climate (e.g., stress climate, well-being climate, psychosocial safety climate), which has been consistently associated with morale, commitment, depression, job satisfaction, burnout, and engagement. Furthermore, from a multilevel perspective of the consequences of well-being, the growing research points to the impact of collective well-being on team performance, thus mirroring the individual-level relationship between these two variables.

INTERVENTIONS TO IMPROVE WELL-BEING AT WORK

In recent decades, an important array of interventions has been developed to improve well-being at work, and some research has been conducted to test their effectiveness. These interventions are presented in the following sections: (a) physical versus psychosocial; (b) prevention versus protection; and (c) individual versus organizational strategies.

Physical- Versus Psychosocial-Oriented Strategies

Physical-Oriented Strategies. Psychological well-being at work is produced not only by psychological factors; it can also be influenced by physical work conditions. Classic ergonomic or "human factor" interventions are designed to decrease the amount of bending, stretching, leaning, or pushing workers do when performing a task, in order to protect their health and promote their safety and productivity (Larson, 1998). These interventions may also consist of introducing physical changes in office buildings, such as changes in ventilation systems or reduced space sharing (Danna & Griffin, 1999), which can have positive consequences for workers (Danna & Griffin, 1999; Fisk, 2000). To ensure optimal functioning, these strategies should contemplate training in workplace safety and security issues (American Psychology Association [APA], 2017). Meta-analyses show, however, that the research on the effects of ergonomic interventions is still inconclusive. On the one hand, sickness absences seem to be reduced by activities that promote ergonomics (Kuoppala et al., 2008). On the other hand, another more recent meta-analysis reveals inconsistent research findings that show either positive or negative consequences of ergonomic interventions for well-being (Sakuraya et al., 2020). One possible reason for this inconsistency is that, until now, research has mainly focused on associating environmental aspects with physical well-being, at the expense of psychological well-being (Colenberg et al., 2021), both its hedonic and eudaimonic components.

Psychosocial-Oriented Strategies. According to the European Working Conditions Survey (Eurofound, 2010) findings on risk factors in the workplace, the main psychosocial threats to well-being and health include work intensity, emotional demands, lack of autonomy, poor social relationships, and job insecurity. Solutions designed to ensure a psychologically healthy workplace consist of different types of interventions (see APA, 2017) that include the following: (a) increasing employee involvement and autonomy and empowering workers by promoting self-managed work teams, employee committees or task forces, continuous improvement teams, participative decision making, and employee suggestion forums; (b) facilitating work-life balance through flexible work arrangements (e.g., flextime, telecommuting, job sharing) and benefits such as assistance with childcare, eldercare benefits, benefits for family members and domestic partners, leave/time off, education, health, and housing assistance, which meet the needs not only of parents with children, but also those of singles and childless couples (Rife & Hall, 2015); (c) promoting employees' growth and development through continuing education and training courses, tuition reimbursement, career development or counseling services, opportunities for promotion, mentoring, leadership development programs, or coaching; (d) proposing health and safety initiatives to help employees develop a healthy lifestyle (e.g., stress management, smoking cessation), offering adequate health insurance, health screenings, resources to help employees address life problems, or Employee Assistance Programs (EAPs); and (e) offering employee recognition strategies such as fair monetary compensation, competitive benefits packages, acknowledgment of milestones, or performance-based bonuses and pay increases.

The review by Goldgruber and Ahrens (2010) suggested that psychosocial-oriented strategies may be more effective than physical (e.g., ergonomic) strategies. Specifically, they indicated that 91% of the stress-related interventions, compared to 48% of the ergonomics and back pain interventions, included in their review showed evidence supporting them (Goldgruber & Ahrens, 2010). These authors suggested that the efficacy of these interventions could be increased by designing combined, comprehensive, and multimodal interventions oriented toward helping both the individual and the organizational workforce as a whole (Goldgruber & Ahrens, 2010).

In 2011, the National Institute for Occupational Safety and Health launched a new program called Total Worker Health (TWH) and defined this new term as policies, programs, and practices that integrate protection from work-related safety and health hazards with promotion of injury and illness prevention efforts to advance worker well-being (National Institute for Occupational Safety and Health, 2018). Integrating organizational and individual strategies to reduce stress and injury at work has also been advocated by occupational health psychology (Tetrick & Peiró, 2016).

Regarding health promotion programs (also referred to as wellness programs), their aims are to improve employees' health and control healthcare costs. Studies show that well-designed and well-executed evidence-based programs (i.e., those that adopt best-practices principles and create cultures of health) achieve positive health and financial outcomes (Goetzel et al., 2012). In their meta-analysis, Baicker et al. (2010) reported that every $1 spent on workplace health promotion programs can decrease medical expenditures by about $3.27 and absenteeism costs by about $2.73. Additionally, reviews suggest that well-designed programs can improve health behaviors (e.g., smoking, diet, physical activity) and biometric measures (Soler et al., 2010) and decrease medical and absenteeism expenditures by 25% (Chapman, 2012).

Some studies also report mixed impacts of workplace health promotion programs on health-related behaviors and costs, suggesting that there is insufficient evidence about the effects on absenteeism and mental health (Osilla et al., 2012) and pointing to potential ethical risks associated with the implementation of these programs (e.g., Horwitz et al., 2013; Hull & Pasquale, 2017; Lewis et al., 2015; McIntyre et al., 2017). For example, the authors argued that: (a) wellness programs may result in classifying disabled or chronically ill workers in a way that adversely affects their opportunities or status (McIntyre et al., 2017); (b) unhealthy employees might be punished instead of being helped by such programs (Horwitz et al., 2013); and (c) employers could be provided with an opportunity to exercise increasing control over their employees (Hull & Pasquale, 2017). In a similar vein, other authors argued that corporations should disband or significantly modify wellness programs that tackle delicate topics such as weight-oriented issues (Lewis et al., 2015). With this in mind, future research should consider the organizational context (e.g., organizational culture) and other relevant moderators, with a special focus on ethical issues, in order to shed light on the effectiveness of workplace wellness programs and the challenges related to their implementation.

Finally, the use of large-scale wellness programs in some enterprises may not be possible due to the high initial investment involved. In this case, there are also smaller-scale microinterventions to increase well-being that consist of daily activities over several days. Generally, there is growing evidence of the effectiveness of these microinterventions in work settings (e.g., Clauss et al., 2018). However, a recent meta-analysis (Davis et al., 2016) showed that the positive promise of some specific types of microinterventions (i.e., expressing gratitude) can be limited, and enthusiasm should be tempered until more powerful and efficient interventions have been developed.

Well-Being Protection Versus Promotion Strategies

Well-Being Protection Strategies. The biopsychosocial healthy workplace protects workers' well-being by preventing injuries (Tetrick & Peiró, 2016), diseases, and stress (Conrad, 1988). Prevention-oriented interventions can eliminate or reduce stressors that are intrinsic to the job by: (a) introducing physical or ergonomic solutions (e.g., rearranging physical office layout); (b) modifying leadership and human resources practices (e.g., using more delegation, clearly defining and/or negotiating roles, offering regular appraisals, retraining opportunities, sabbaticals, career counseling, outplacement facilities, introducing flexible working arrangements and "family friendly" policies; Danna & Griffin, 1999) and carrying out task redesign and recruitment to alleviate work overload/underload; (c) offering training and education; and (d) promoting organizational activities (e.g., organization-based subsidized physical exercise programs, providing healthy lunches, offering counseling services; Danna & Griffin, 1999). For example, research shows that ensuring role clarity and reasonable workloads, offering leadership training that encourages supportive leadership styles, and generating policies to ensure fair and just treatment, decisions, and outcomes can all prevent workplace aggression and bullying (Hershcovis et al., 2015).

Well-being Promotion Strategies. Employee health and well-being can be promoted by implementing worksite wellness programs focused on risk factors, such as weight loss, fitness levels, or smoking cessation. These programs can include combinations of educational, organizational, and environmental activities (Danna & Griffin, 1999), and they can be provided using health risk assessments, self-help education materials, individual counseling, on-site fitness centers, seminars, and incentives for participation (Harris, 2016). These programs have several benefits, such as improving employee health and well-being, fitness, mental alertness, morale, and job satisfaction and enhancing the corporate image (Conrad, 1988; Danna & Griffin, 1999).

The investment in wellness programs can be maximized by: (a) providing a carefully executed incentive program (e.g., paid time to exercise at work, healthy vending machine or cafeteria food choices); (b) using goal-setting to facilitate program adherence (Sheeran & Silverman, 2003); (c) providing necessary tools and resources by individually tailoring programs; (d) marketing the program; and (e) evaluating program outcomes (Harris, 2016).

Positive psychology interventions, consisting of promotion intervention strategies, have been shown in meta-analyses (Sin & Lyubomirsky, 2009) to generally be beneficial. In their study, Seligman et al. (2005) showed that these interventions can enhance well-being, suggesting that "positive interventions can supplement traditional interventions that relieve suffering and may someday be the practical legacy of positive psychology" (p. 410). A meta-analysis by Sin and Lyubomirsky (2009) indicated that older, highly motivated to improve, and depressed people can particularly benefit from such interventions. In line with these ideas, the Mental Health Foundation of New Zealand (Mental Health Foundation, 2016) designed the Well-being Game, a free online game that draws on aspects of primary psychosocial interventions to reflect on the positive aspects of the players' lives. This tool has been recognized as an effective well-being intervention in an organizational context, given that employees who participated in this intervention reported lower stress levels and higher well-being levels (Keeman et al., 2017).

Individual Versus Organizational Strategies

Individual Strategies. Some strategies to prevent and improve well-being can be successfully adopted by individual employees. These strategies can include: (a) taking time to detach psychologically from work (e.g., turning off work-related email on one's personal phone, using out-of-office response during vacation, using separate computers for work and nonwork activities); (b) doing relaxing and recovery-promoting activities such as meditation, going for a walk, or reading a book; (c) doing challenging nonwork activities (e.g., engaging in challenging exercise, taking classes to learn a new skill) to replenish psychological resources; (d) establishing routines around recovery from work (e.g., regular meetings with friends, going to bed at the same time every night); (e) communicating to significant others one's need to recover and seeking opportunities for recovery in one's support network (Fritz & Ellis, 2015); and (f) engaging in emotion regulation, which is an important strategy employees can use to manage their emotions in difficult work situations (Hershcovis et al., 2015). In their review, Awa et al. (2010) found that about 82% of all individual-oriented interventions resulted in a significant reduction in burnout or an improvement in associated risk factors, whereas they found the evidence about organization-directed interventions to be inconclusive. These authors suggested that combined interventions are more beneficial than either individual- or organization-oriented interventions alone (Awa et al., 2010), and they indicated that refresher courses are important to ensure long-lasting positive effects of interventions. Similarly, in their review, Goldgruber and Ahrens (2010) showed that well-being interventions in the workplace designed to help individual workers reported greater effects than interventions for the workforce as a whole. A more recent review and meta-analysis in a sample of physicians suggested that both individual-focused and organizational interventions can reduce physician burnout (West et al., 2016). The authors did not indicate that any specific intervention was superior to others, and they suggested that both types of strategies are necessary.

Organizational Strategies.   Organizational interventions to increase or maintain well-being have already been broadly described. They often aim to avoid or reduce stressors at work or, when this is impossible, offer ways to deal with or recover from these demands (Fritz & Ellis, 2015). To successfully implement these interventions, organizational support (e.g., strategies, organizational policies, cultural norms, supervisors, and surrounding coworkers) is a key factor. For example, work-life balance strategies, such as workplace flexible scheduling, can help employees to recover and increase their control over their schedule and, in turn, their well-being (Fritz & Ellis, 2015). Moreover, organizational policies and norms on work-related technology use should limit the frequency of work-related phone calls or emails during evenings, weekends, and vacations, in order to encourage employees to recharge during nonwork time. Simultaneously, leaders should reinforce the norms for recovery because they can role model successful recovery by refraining from work during nonwork time. Finally, organizations should demonstrate their support for a balance between work and other life spheres, which include "family," but also leisure, social, and community (Kossek et al., 2011).

FUTURE RESEARCH

In the previous sections, the advances and limitations in the study of occupational well-being were presented. These limitations suggest directions for future research.

First, although well-being can be understood as having both pleasurable (or hedonic) and meaningful (or eudaimonic) components (Dolan, 2014; Ryan & Deci, 2001), the majority of the research has approached well-being at work from the hedonic perspective, conceptualizing it as judgments and evaluations of satisfaction with some work facets. Therefore, there is a need for future research along these lines, to study other types of well-being and their role in the occupational context. In this regard, it would be necessary to expand the limits of the research when developing well-being interventions at work, by also focusing on ways to stimulate both eudaimonic and hedonic well-being. Additionally, given the widespread use of technology in today's jobs (e.g., information and communication technology, robotization, artificial intelligence, cooperative platforms, etc.), well-being research and interventions should also consider the virtual facet of both hedonic and eudaimonic well-being at work (Rudolph et al., 2021) in order to help organizations make better job design choices.

Second, to overcome the limitations of the current knowledge about the relationship between well-being and performance (e.g., the research on HPWT), it is necessary to consider both the hedonic and eudaimonic components of well-being, as well as different aspects of job performance. Thus, knowledge about the role of different facets of well-being in individual performance and organizational productivity may contribute to the development of sustainable human resources practices by generating synergies between employees' hedonic and eudaimonic well-being and performance (Villajos et al., 2019).

Third, although emerging research is studying the possible trade-offs between well-being and performance, in general, the existing research ignores possible negative effects of high levels of well-being on performance and vice versa (Tenney et al., 2016). Therefore, it would be beneficial to simultaneously study both synergistic (e.g., happy-productive) and antagonistic (e.g., happy-unproductive) patterns and identify moderator and mediator variables, as well as contextual and personal features associated with membership in each pattern (Warr & Nielsen, 2018).

Finally, a desirable research development is the study of the dynamics of the relationship between well-being and its outcomes, combining an inter and intra approach to see how these phenomena unfold over time in people's work. This would provide answers to new research questions about the potential existence of an optimal zone of experiential well-being, beyond which more positivity predicts decreases in performance. To do so, it is necessary to select an adequate "temporal lens" (Ancona et al., 2001). Deciding on a timeframe for the research is especially important because it conditions the results and limits the possibilities for observation (Roe, 2014). Therefore, when studying well-being and its outcomes, it is important to keep in mind that, on the one hand, well-being may fluctuate within shorter periods of time (e.g., weeks, days, or even hours; Sonnentag, 2015), suggesting that a shorter time frame, such as a work week, can be sufficient to study it. On the other hand, as demonstrated in a systematic review by Mäkikangas et al. (2017), changes in the levels of well-being over longer periods of time are also typical, and the stability of well-being is relatively low. In particular, younger employees and job changers tend to display greater changes in their levels of well-being across time in comparison with older employees and job stayers. These advances should guide researchers when choosing proper research designs and methods to investigate specific time-related aspects of well-being. For example, researchers could employ a multilevel design and an experience-sampling method with short questionnaires and several data collection points during the day when examining the relationship between individual performance and perceived activity worthwhileness during specific types of tasks. In contrast, researchers who want to study the relationship between individual performance and more stable phenomena such as mood, which may fluctuate over longer periods of time, would not need to measure them several times a day. These more accurate assessments of well-being may provide an opportunity to answer emerging research questions, including some of the challenges raised in the previous paragraphs, such as measuring the dynamics of both hedonic and eudaimonic well-being, either in a virtual work setting or in collaboration with a robot, considering both their short- and long-term features.

CONCLUDING REMARKS

The aim of this article was to discuss the concept of well-being at work, which can be understood as workers' experience of feeling good, being fulfilled, and having a purpose over time. In this article, the two main components of well-being at work (hedonic and eudaimonic) were presented. In addition, the most relevant theoretical frameworks in the study of well-being at work were described. The first model, the Happy-Productive Worker Thesis, focuses on the antecedent role of well-being in performance. The second, Broaden-and-Build Theory, indicates that different types of well-being may play different roles as antecedents of different indicators of performance and other work outcomes, and it highlights the role of positive emotions as amplifiers and generators of positive outcomes related to performance. Third, the Adaption Level Theory focuses on a dynamic "micro" perspective, shedding light on affective experiences and their outcomes at work. The fourth model, the Affective Events Theory, uses a dynamic perspective to analyze the streams of affective events at work and their effects on workers' affective and emotional experiences, behaviors, and attitudes. Fifth, Self-determination Theory states that the satisfaction of needs promotes employees' well-being. Finally, the collective perspective on well-being at work incorporates a multilevel consideration into the analysis of occupational well-being by including collective concepts such as team affective climate and stress climate in teams. Furthermore, the antecedents and consequences of well-being at work were discussed, considering relationships at the same level and cross-level relationships. Finally, strategies and actions undertaken by organizations to improve well-being at work were described.

FURTHER READING

Bakker, A. B., & Daniels, K. (Eds.). (2012). *A day in the life of a happy worker*. Psychology Press.

Diener, E., Lucas, R. E., & Oishi, S. (2002). Subjective well-being: The science of happiness and life satisfaction. In C. R. Snyder & S. J. Lopez (Eds.), *Handbook of positive psychology* (pp. 463–473). Oxford University Press.

Dolan, P. (2014). *Happiness by design*. Hudson Street Press.

Huta, V. (2017). An overview of hedonic and eudaimonic well-being concepts. In L. Reinecke & M. B. Oliver (Eds.), *The Routledge handbook of media use and well-being: International perspectives on theory and research on positive media effects* (pp. 14–33). Routledge/Taylor & Francis Group.

Lyubomirsky, S. (2012). Hedonic adaptation to positive and negative experiences. In S. Folkman (Ed.), *The Oxford handbook of stress, health, and coping* (pp. 200–224). Oxford University Press.

Ryan, R. M., & Deci, E. L. (2001). On happiness and human potentials: A review of research on hedonic and eudaimonic wellbeing. *Annual Review of Psychology, 52*, 141–166.

Sonnentag, S. (2015). Dynamics of wellbeing. *Annual Review of Organizational Psychology and Organizational Behavior, 2*, 261–293. https://doi.org/10.1146/annurev-orgpsych-032414-111347

Sonnentag, S., Tay, L., & Nesher Shoshan, H. (2023). A review on health and well-being at work: More than stressors and strains. *Personnel Psychology, 76*(2), 473–510.

REFERENCES

Abbas, M., & Raja, U. (2019). Challenge-hindrance stressors and job outcomes: The moderating role of conscientiousness. *Journal of Business and Psychology, 34*(2), 189–201.

Agervold, M., & Mikkelsen, E. G. (2004). Relationships between bullying, psychosocial work environment and individual stress reactions. *Work and Stress, 18*(4), 336–351.

Akkermans, J., Brenninkmeijer, V., van den Bossche, S. N. J., Blonk, R. W. B., & Schaufeli, W. B. (2013). Young and going strong? A longitudinal study on occupational health among young employees of different educational levels. *Career Development International, 18*(4), 416–435.

Alessandri, G., Borgogni, L., & Latham, G. P. (2017). A dynamic model of the longitudinal relationship between job satisfaction and supervisor-rated job performance. *Applied Psychology, 66*(2), 207–232.

Amabile, T. M., Barsade, S. G., Mueller, J. S., & Staw, B. M. (2005). Affect and creativity at work. *Administrative Science Quarterly, 50*(3), 367–403.

American Psychology Association. (2017). *Creating a psychologically healthy workplace.*

Ancona, D. G., Goodman, P. S., Lawrence, B. S., & Tushman, M. L. (2001). Time: A new research lens. *Academy of Management Review, 26*(4), 645–663.

Angner, E. (2010). Subjective well-being. *The Journal of Socio-Economics, 39*(3), 361–368.

Ashforth, B. E., & Humphrey, R. H. (1995). Emotion in the workplace: A reappraisal. *Human Relations, 48,* 97–125.

Ashkanasy, N. M. (2003). Emotions in organizations: A multi-level perspective. In F. J. Yammarino & F. Dansereau (Eds.), *Research in multi-level issues* (Vol. 2, pp. 9–54). Elsevier Science.

Ashkanasy, N. M., & Härtel, C. E. J. (2014). Positive and negative affective climate and culture: The good, the bad, and the ugly. In B. Schneider & K. M. Barbera (Eds.), *The Oxford handbook of organizational climate and culture* (pp. 136–152). Oxford University Press.

Averill, J. R. (1986). The acquisition of emotions during adulthood. In R. Harre (Ed.), *The social construction of emotions* (pp. 98–118). Basil Blackwell.

Avey, J. B., Luthans, F., Smith, R. M., & Palmer, N. F. (2010). Impact of positive psychological capital on employee wellbeing over time. *Journal of Occupational Health Psychology, 15*(1), 17–28.

Awa, W. L., Plaumann, M., & Walter, U. (2010). Burnout prevention: A review of intervention programs. *Patient Education and Counseling, 78*(2), 184–190.

Ayala, Y., Peiró, J. M., Tordera, N., Lorente, L., & Yeves, J. (2017). Job satisfaction and innovative performance in young Spanish employees: Testing new patterns in the happy-productive worker thesis— Discriminant study. *Journal of Happiness Studies, 18*(5), 1377–1401.

Bae, S. H., Song, J. H., Park, S., & Kim, H. K. (2013). Influential factors for teachers' creativity: Mutual impacts of leadership, work engagement, and knowledge creation practices. *Performance Improvement Quarterly, 26,* 33–58.

Baicker, K., Cutler, D., & Song, Z. (2010). Workplace wellness programs can generate savings. *Health Affairs, 29*(2), 304–311.

Bakker, A. B., & Daniels, K. (2013). A day in the life of a happy worker: Introduction. In A. B. Bakker & K. Daniels (Eds.), *A day in the life of a happy worker* (pp. 1–7). Psychology Press.

Bakker, A. B., & Demerouti, E. (2017). Job demands–resources theory: Taking stock and looking forward. *Journal of Occupational Health Psychology, 22*(3), 273.

Bandura, A. (1986). *Social foundation of thought and action: A social cognitive theory.* Prentice Hall.

Barrick, M. R., Thurgood, G. R., Smith, T. A., & Courtright, S. H. (2015). Collective organizational engagement: Linking motivational antecedents, strategic implementation, and firm performance. *Academy of Management Annals, 58*(1), 111–135.

Barsade, S. G., Ward, A. J., Turner, J. D. F., & Sonnenfeld, J. A. (2000). To your heart's content: A model of affective diversity in top management teams. *Administrative Science Quarterly, 45,* 802–836.

Bartel, C., & Saavedra, R. (2000). The collective construction of work group moods. *Administrative Science Quarterly, 45*, 197–231.

Beehr, T. A., & Glazer, S. (2005). Organizational role stress. In J. Barling, E. K. Kelloway, & M. R. Frone (Eds.), *Handbook of work stress* (pp. 7–34). SAGE.

Binnewies, C., & Wörnlein, S. C. (2011). What makes a creative day? A diary study on the interplay between affect, job stressors, and job control. *Journal of Organizational Behavior, 32*, 589–607.

Bledow, R., Rosing, K., & Frese, M. (2013). A dynamic perspective on affect and creativity. *The Academy of Management Annals, 56*(2), 432–450.

Böckerman, P., & Ilmakunnas, P. (2010). The job satisfaction-productivity nexus: A study using matched survey and register data. *Industrial & Labor Relations Review, 65*(2), 244–262.

Bowling, N. A. (2007). Is the job satisfaction–job performance relationship spurious? A meta-analytic examination. *Journal of Vocational Behavior, 71*(2), 167–185.

Bowling, N. A., Beehr, T. A., Wagner, S. H., & Libkuman, T. M. (2005). Adaptation-level theory, opponent process theory, and dispositions: An integrated approach to the stability of job satisfaction. *The Journal of Applied Psychology, 90*(6), 1044.

Brickman, P., & Campbell, D. T. (1971). Hedonic relativism and planning the good society. In M. H. Appley (Ed.), *Adaptation level theory: A symposium* (pp. 287–302). Academic Press.

Brickman, P., Coates, D., & Janoff-Bulman, R. (1978). Lottery winners and accident victims: Is happiness relative? *Journal of Personality and Social Psychology, 36*(8), 917.

Brief, A. P. (1998). *Attitudes in and around organizations.* SAGE.

Brief, A. P., & Weiss, H. M. (2002). Organizational behavior: Affect in the workplace. *Annual Review of Psychology, 53*, 279–307.

Cavanaugh, M. A., Boswell, W. R., Roehling, M. V., & Boudreau, J. W. (2000). An empirical examination of self-reported work stress among U.S. managers. *The Journal of Applied Psychology, 85*(1), 65–74.

Chan, D. (1998). Functional relations among constructs in the same content domain at different levels of analysis: A typology of composition models. *The Journal of Applied Psychology, 83*(2), 234–246.

Chapman, L. S. (2012). Meta-evaluation of worksite health promotion economic return studies: 2012 update. *American Journal of Health Promotion, 26*(4), 1–12.

Chung, N. G., & Angeline, T. (2010). Does work engagement mediate the relationship between job resources and job performance of employees? *African Journal of Business Management, 4*, 1837–1843.

Clauss, E., Hoppe, A., O'Shea, D., González Morales, M. G., Steidle, A., & Michel, A. (2018). Promoting personal resources and reducing exhaustion through positive work reflection among caregivers. *Journal of Occupational Health Psychology, 23*(1), 127.

Colby, A., Sippola, L., & Phelps, E. (2001). Social responsibility and paid work in contemporary American life. In A. Rossi (Ed.), *Caring and doing for others: Social responsibility in the domains of family, work, and community* (pp. 349–399). University of Chicago Press.

Colenberg, S., Jylhä, T., & Arkesteijn, M. (2021). The relationship between interior office space and employee health and well-being—A literature review. *Building Research & Information, 49*(3), 352–366.

Conrad, P. (1988). Worksite health promotion: The social context. *Social Science & Medicine, 26*, 485–489.

Cooper, C. L., Dewe, P. J., & O'Driscoll, M. P. (2001). *Organizational stress: A review and critique of theory research and applications.* SAGE.

Csikszentmihalyi, M. (1975). *Beyond boredom and anxiety: The experience of play in work and games.* Jossey-Bass.

Csikszentmihalyi, M. (1999). If we are so rich, why aren't we happy? *The American Psychologist, 54*(10), 821.

Csikszentmihalyi, M., & Csikszentmihalyi, I. (1988). *Optimal experience.* Cambridge University Press.

D'Alleo, G., & Santangelo, A. (2011). Organizational climate and burnout in call-center operators. *Procedia – Social and Behavioral Sciences, 30*, 1608–1615.

Danna, K., & Griffin, R. W. (1999). Health and wellbeing in the workplace: A review and synthesis of the literature. *Journal of Management, 25*(3), 357–384.

Davis, D. E., Choe, E., Meyers, J., Wade, N., Varjas, K., Gifford, A., Quinn, A., Hook, J. N., van Tongeren, D. R., Griffin, B. J., & Worthington, E. L., Jr. (2016). Thankful for the little things: A meta-analysis of gratitude interventions. *Journal of Counseling Psychology, 63*(1), 20.

De Rivera, J. (1992). Emotional climate: Social structure and emotional dynamics. In K. T. Strongman (Ed.), *International review of studies on emotion* (Vol. 2, pp. 197–248). John Wiley & Sons.

Debus, M. E., Sonnentag, S., Deutsch, W., & Nussbeck, F. W. (2014). Making flow happen: The effects of being recovered on work-related flow between and within days. *The Journal of Applied Psychology, 99*(4), 713.

Deci, E. (1975). *Intrinsic motivation.* Plenum.

Deci, E. L., Olafsen, A. H., & Ryan, R. M. (2017). Self-determination theory in work organizations: The state of a science. *Annual Review of Organizational Psychology, 4,* 19–43.

Demerouti, E. (2007). The job demands-resources model: State of the art. *Journal of Managerial Psychology, 22,* 309–328.

DeNeve, K. M., & Cooper, H. (1998). The happy personality: A meta-analysis of 137 personality traits and subjective well-being studies. *Psychological Bulletin, 124,* 197–229.

Diener, E. (2000). Subjective well-being: The science of happiness and a proposal for a national index. *The American Psychologist, 55*(1), 34–43.

Diener, E., & Chan, M. Y. (2011). Happy people live longer: Subjective well-being contributes to health and longevity. *Applied Psychology: Health and Well-being, 3*(1), 1–43.

Diener, E., Lucas, R. E., & Oishi, S. (2002). Subjective well-being: The science of happiness and life satisfaction. In C. R. Snyder & S. J. Lopez (Eds.), *Handbook of positive psychology* (Vol. 2, pp. 63–73). Oxford University Press.

Diener, E., Lucas, R. E., & Scollon, C. N. (2006). Beyond the hedonic treadmill: Revising the adaptation theory of well-being. *The American Psychologist, 61*(4), 305–314.

Diener, E., Lucas, R. E., & Scollon, C. N. (2009). Beyond the hedonic treadmill: Revising the adaptation theory of well-being. In E. Diener (Ed.), *The science of well-being* (Vol. 37, pp. 103–118). Springer.

Diener, E., Ng, W., Harter, J., & Arora, R. (2010). Wealth and happiness across the world: Material prosperity predicts life evaluation, whereas psychosocial prosperity predicts positive feeling. *Journal of Personality and Social Psychology, 99*(1), 52–61.

Diener, E., Oishi, S., & Lucas, R. E. (2003). Personality, culture, and subjective well-being: Emotional and cognitive evaluations of life. *Annual Review of Psychology, 54*(1), 403–425.

Diener, E., Oishi, S., & Tay, L. (2018). Advances in subjective well-being research. *Nature Human Behaviour, 2*(4), 253–260.

Diener, E., Thapa, S., & Tay, L. (2019). Positive emotions at work. *Annual Review of Organizational Psychology and Organizational Behavior, 7,* 451–477.

Diener, E., Wirtz, D., Biswas-Diener, R., Tov, W., Kim-Prieto, C., Choi, D., & Oishi, S. (2009). New measures of well-being. In *Social indicators research series* (Vol. 39, pp. 247–266). Springer.

Diener, E. D., Emmons, R. A., Larsen, R. J., & Griffin, S. (1985). The satisfaction with life scale. *Journal of Personality Assessment, 49*(1), 71–75.

Diener, F. (1984). Subjective well-being. *Psychological Bulletin, 95,* 542–575.

Dolan, P. (2014). *Happiness by design.* Hudson Street Press.

Dolan, P., Layard, R., & Metcalfe, R. (2011, February). *Measuring subjective well-being for public policy.* Office for National Statistics.

Dollard, M. F., & Bakker, A. B. (2010). Psychosocial safety climate as a precursor to conducive work environments, psychological health problems, and employee engagement. *Journal of Occupational and Organizational Psychology, 83*(3), 579–599.

Eid, M., & Larsen, R. J. (Eds.). (2008). *The science of subjective well-being*. Guilford Press.

Estrada, C. A., Isen, A. M., & Young, M. J. (1997). Positive affect facilitates integration of information and decreases anchoring in reasoning among physicians. *Organizational Behavior and Human Decision Processes, 72*, 117–135.

Eurofound. (2010). *European working conditions survey 2010*.

Fisher, C. D. (2002). Real time affect at work: A neglected phenomenon in organisational behaviour. *Australian Journal of Management, 27*, 1–10.

Fisk, W. J. (2000). Health and productivity gains from better indoor environments and their relationship with building energy efficiency. *Annual Review of Environment and Resources, 25*(1), 537–566.

Fogaça, N., & Coelho, F. A. (2016). Is "happy worker" more productive. *Journal of Management Studies, 4*(4), 149–160.

Folkman, S. (1997). Positive psychological states and coping with severe stress. *Social Science & Medicine, 45*(8), 1207–1221.

Fredrickson, B. L. (1998). What good are positive emotions? *Review of General Psychology, 2*(3), 300–319.

Fredrickson, B. L. (2001). The role of positive emotions in positive psychology: The broaden-and-build theory of positive emotions. *The American Psychologist, 56*(3), 218–226.

Fredrickson, B. L. (2003). Positive emotions and upward spirals in organizations. In K. S. Cameron, J. E. Dutton, & R. E. Quinn (Eds.), *Positive organizational scholarship* (pp. 163–175). Berrett-Koehler.

Fredrickson, B. L. (2004). The broaden-and-build theory of positive emotions. *Philosophical Transactions of the Royal Society of London: Series B, Biological Sciences, 359*(1449), 1367–1378.

Fritz, C., & Ellis, A. M. (2015). *A marathon, not a sprint: The benefits of taking time to recover from work demands* (SIOP White Paper Series). Society for Industrial and Organizational Psychology.

Fullagar, C. J., & Kelloway, E. K. (2009). Flow at work: An experience sampling approach. *Journal of Occupational and Organizational Psychology, 82*(3), 595–615.

Furnham, A., & Petrides, K. V. (2003). Trait emotional intelligence and happiness. *Social Behavior and Personality, 31*(8), 815–823.

Gabriel, A. S., Diefendorff, J. M., & Erickson, R. J. (2011). The relations of daily task accomplishment satisfaction with changes in affect: A multilevel study in nurses. *The Journal of Applied Psychology, 96*, 1095–1104.

Gamero, N., González-Romá, V., & Peiró, J. M. (2008). The influence of intra-team conflict on work teams' affective climate: A longitudinal study. *Journal of Occupational and Organizational Psychology, 81*, 47–69.

García-Buades, M. E., Peiró, J. M., Montañez-Juan, M. I., Kozusznik, M. W., & Ortiz-Bonnín, S. (2020). Happy-productive teams and work units: A systematic review of the "happy-productive worker thesis." *International Journal of Environmental Research and Public Health, 17*(1), 69.

Garrick, A., Mak, A. S., Cathcart, S., Winwood, P. C., Bakker, A. B., & Lushington, K. (2014). Psychosocial safety climate moderating the effects of daily job demands and recovery on fatigue and work engagement. *Journal of Occupational and Organizational Psychology, 87*(4), 694–714.

George, J. (1990). Personality, affect, and behavior in groups. *The Journal of Applied Psychology, 75*, 107–116.

George, J. M., & Zhou, J. (2007). Dual tuning in a supportive context: Joint contributions of positive mood, negative mood, and supervisory behaviors to employee creativity. *The Academy of Management Annals, 50*(3), 605–622.

Glomb, T. M., Bhave, D. P., Miner, A. G., & Wall, M. (2011). Doing good, feeling good: Examining the role of organizational citizenship behavior in changing mood. *Personnel Psychology, 64*, 191–223.

Goetzel, R. Z., Pei, X., Tabrizi, M. J., Henke, R. M., Kowlessar, N., Nelson, C. F., & Metz, R. D. (2012). Ten modifiable health risk factors are linked to more than one-fifth of employer-employee health care spending. *Health Affairs, 31*(11), 2474–2484.

Goldgruber, J., & Ahrens, D. (2010). Effectiveness of workplace health promotion and primary prevention interventions: A review. *Journal of Public Health, 18*(1), 75–88.

González-Romá, V., & Gamero, N. (2012). Does positive team mood mediate the relationship between team climate and team performance? *Psicothema, 24*(1), 94–99.

González-Romá, V., Peiró, J. M., Subirats, M., & Mañas, M. A. (2000). The validity of affective work team climates. In M. Vartiainen, F. Avallone, & N. Anderson (Eds.), *Innovative theories, tools, and practices in work and organizational psychology* (pp. 97–109). Hogrefe & Huber.

Graham, C. (2010). *The challenges of incorporating empowerment into the HDI: Some lessons from happiness economics and quality of life research* (United Nations Development Programme Human Development Reports Research Paper 2010/13).

Griffeth, R. W., Hom, P. W., & Gaertner, S. (2000). A meta-analysis of antecedents and correlates of employee turnover: Update, moderator tests, and research implications for the next millennium. *Journal of Management, 26*(3), 463–488.

Harris, C., Daniels, K., & Briner, R. B. (2003). A daily diary study of goals and affective well-being at work. *Journal of Occupational and Organizational Psychology, 76*(3), 401–410.

Harris, M. M. (2016). *The business case for employee health and wellness programs* (SIOP White Paper Series). Society for Industrial and Organizational Psychology.

Härtel, C. E. J. (2008). How to build a healthy emotional culture and avoid a toxic culture. In C. L. Cooper & N. M. Ashkanasy (Eds.), *Research companion to emotion in organizations* (pp. 575–588). Edward Elgar.

Headey, B., & Wearing, A. J. (1992). *Understanding happiness: A theory of subjective well-being*. Longman Cheshire.

Heathwood, C. (2014). Subjective theories of well-being. In B. Eggleston & D.Miller (Eds.), *The Cambridge companion to utilitarianism* (pp. 199–219). Cambridge University Press.

Helson, H. (1964). Current trends and issues in adaptation-level theory. *The American Psychologist, 19*, 26–38.

Hershcovis, M. S., Reich, T. C., & Niven, K. (2015). *Workplace bullying: Causes, consequences, and intervention strategies* (SIOP White Paper Series). Society for Industrial and Organizational Psychology.

Higgs, M., & Dulewicz, V. (2014). Antecedents of well-being: A study to examine the extent to which personality and emotional intelligence contribute to well-being. *Journal of Human Resource Management, 25*(5), 718–735.

Hobfoll, S. E. (2011). Conservation of resources theory: Its implication for stress, health, and resilience. In S. Folkman (Ed.), *The Oxford handbook of stress, health, and coping* (pp. 127–147). Oxford University Press.

Holtom, B. C., Mitchell, T. R., Lee, T. W., & Inderrieden, E. J. (2005). Shocks as causes of turnover: What they are and how organizations can manage them. *Human Resource Management, 44*(3), 337–352.

Horwitz, J. R., Kelly, B. D., & DiNardo, J. E. (2013). Wellness incentives in the workplace: Cost savings through cost shifting to unhealthy workers. *Health Affairs, 32*(3), 468–476.

Hosie, P., Willemyns, M., & Sevastos, P. (2012). The impact of happiness on managers' contextual and task performance. *Asia-Pacific Journal of Human Resources, 50*(3), 268–287.

Hull, G., & Pasquale, F. (2017). Toward a critical theory of corporate wellness. *BioSocieties, 13*(1), 190–212.

Huta, V., & Waterman, A. S. (2013). Eudaimonia and its distinction from hedonia: Developing a classification and terminology for understanding conceptual and operational definitions. *Journal of Happiness Studies, 15*(6), 1425–1456.

Iaffaldano, M. T., & Muchinsky, P. M. (1985). Job satisfaction and job performance: A meta-analysis. *Psychological Bulletin, 97*(2), 251–273.

Idris, M. A., & Dollard, M. F. (2014). Psychosocial safety climate, emotional demands, burnout, and depression: A longitudinal multilevel study in the Malaysian private sector. *Journal of Occupational Health Psychology, 19*(3), 291.

Ilies, R., Schwind, K. M., & Heller, D. (2007). Employee well-being: A multilevel model linking work and nonwork domains. *European Journal of Work and Organizational Psychology, 16*(3), 326–341.

Isen, A. M., Rosenzweig, A. S., & Young, M. J. (1991). The influence of positive affect on clinical problem solving. *Medical Decision Making, 11,* 221–227.

Isen, M. A. (1990). The influence of positive and negative affect on cognitive organization: Some implications for development. In N. L. Stein, B. Leventhal, & T. Trabasso (Eds.), *Psychological and biological approaches to emotion* (pp. 75–94). Lawrence Erlbaum Associates.

Jackson, S. A., & Eklund, R. C. (2002). Assessing flow in physical activity: The flow state scale-2 and dispositional flow scale-2. *International Journal of Sport Psychology, 24*(2), 133–150.

Jamal, M. (1999). Job stress and employee well-being: A cross-cultural empirical study. *Stress Medicine, 15,* 153–158.

Judge, T., Parker, S., Colbert, A., Heller, D., & Ilies, R. (2001). Job satisfaction: A cross-cultural review. In N. Anderson, D. S. Ones, H. K. Sinangil, & C. Viswesvaran (Eds.), *Handbook of industrial, work and organizational psychology* (Vol. 2, pp. 25–52). SAGE.

Judge, T. A. (2009). Core self-evaluations and work success. *Current Directions in Psychological Science, 18*(1), 58–62.

Judge, T. A., Locke, E. A., Durham, C. C., & Kluger, A. N. (1998). Dispositional effects on job and life satisfaction: The role of core evaluations. *The Journal of Applied Psychology, 83*(1), 17.

Judge, T. A., Thoresen, C. J., Bono, J. E., & Patton, G. K. (2001). The job satisfaction–job performance relationship: A qualitative and quantitative review. *Psychological Bulletin, 127*(3), 376–407.

Judge, T. A., Weiss, H. M., Kammeyer-Mueller, J. D., & Hulin, C. L. (2017). Job attitudes, job satisfaction, and job affect: A century of continuity and of change. *The Journal of Applied Psychology, 102*(3), 356.

Kaplan, S., Bradley, J. C., Luchman, J. N., & Haynes, D. (2009). On the role of positive and negative affectivity in job performance: A meta-analytic investigation. *The Journal of Applied Psychology, 94*(1), 162–176.

Karasek, R. A. (1979). Job demands, job decision latitude, and mental strain: Implications for job redesign. *Administrative Science Quarterly, 24*(2), 285–308.

Kashdan, T. B., Biswas-Diener, R., & King, L. A. (2008). Reconsidering happiness: The costs of distinguishing between hedonics and eudaimonia. *The Journal of Positive Psychology, 3*(4), 219–233.

Katz, D., & Kahn, R. L. (1978). *The social psychology of organizations.* Wiley.

Keeman, A., Näswall, K., Malinen, S., & Kuntz, J. (2017). Employee well-being: Evaluating a well-being intervention in two settings. *Frontiers in Psychology, 8,* 505.

King, R. B., McInerney, D. M., Ganotice, F. A., Jr., & Villarosa, J. B. (2015). Positive affect catalyzes academic engagement: Cross-sectional, longitudinal, and experimental evidence. *Learning and Individual Differences, 39,* 64–72.

Korek, S., Felfe, J., & Zaepernick-Rothe, U. (2010). Transformational leadership and commitment: A multilevel analysis of group-level influences and mediating processes. *European Journal of Work and Organizational Psychology, 19,* 364–387.

Kossek, E. E., Baltes, B. B., & Matthews, R. A. (2011). How work-family research can finally have an impact in organizations. *Industrial and Organizational Psychology, 4,* 352–369.

Kozlowski, S. W. J., & Klein, K. J. (2000). Multilevel theory, research, and methods in organizations: Contextual, temporal, and emergent processes. In K. J. Klein & S. W. J. Kozlowski (Eds.), *Multilevel theory, research and methods in organizations: Foundations, extensions, and new directions.* Jossey-Bass.

Kożusznik, M. W., Peiró, J. M., & Soriano, A. (2019). Daily eudaimonic well-being as a predictor of daily performance: A dynamic lens. *PLOS ONE, 14*(4), e0215564.

Kozusznik, M. W., Rodríguez, I., & Peiró, J. M. (2015). Eustress and distress climates in teams: Patterns and outcomes. *International Journal of Stress Management, 22*(1), 1–23.

Kuoppala, J., Lamminpää, A., & Husman, P. (2008). Work health promotion, job well-being, and sickness absences—A systematic review and meta-analysis. *Journal of Occupational and Environmental Medicine, 50*(11), 1216–1227.

Lamers, S. M., Westerhof, G. J., Glas, C. A., & Bohlmeijer, E. T. (2015). The bidirectional relation between positive mental health and psychopathology in a longitudinal representative panel study. *The Journal of Positive Psychology, 10*(6), 553–560.

Larson, M. (1998). Worklife quality: Ergonomic workstations boost productivity. *Quality, 37*, 44–47.

Lauterbach, W. (1979). Learning plus: Towards a multifactorial theory of phobias—I: Adaptation level of phobic stimuli. *Journal of Behavior Therapy and Experimental Psychiatry, 10*(1), 25–28.

Lazarus, R. S., & Folkman, S. (1984). *Stress, appraisal, and coping*. Springer.

LePine, J. A., Erez, A., & Johnson, D. E. (2002). The nature and dimensionality of organizational citizenship behavior: A critical review and meta-analysis. *The Journal of Applied Psychology, 87*(1), 52.

Lewis, J. D. A., Khanna, V., & Montrose, S. (2015). Employers should disband employee weight control programs. *The American Journal of Managed Care, 21*(2), e91–e94.

Li, S. L., & Qi, J. (2015). Power sharing and task performance: The role of work engagement and traditionality. *Social Behavior and Personality, 43*, 767–776.

Linley, P. A., Maltby, J., Wood, A. M., Osborne, G., & Hurling, R. (2009). Measuring happiness: The higher order factor structure of subjective and psychological well-being measures. *Personality & Individual Differences, 47*(8), 878–884.

Lucas, R. E. (2007). Adaptation and the set-point model of subjective well-being: Does happiness change after major life events? *Current Directions in Psychological Science, 16*(2), 75–79.

Lucas, R. E., & Fujita, F. (2000). Factors influencing the relation between extraversion and pleasant affect. *Journal of Personality and Social Psychology, 79*, 1039–1056.

Lussier, B., Grégoire, Y., & Vachon, M. A. (2017). The role of humor usage on creativity, trust and performance in business relationships: An analysis of the salesperson-customer dyad. *Industrial Marketing Management, 65*, 168–181.

Luthans, F. (2002). Positive organizational behavior: Developing and managing psychological strengths. *Academy of Management Perspectives, 16*(1), 57–72.

Lyubomirsky, S., King, L., & Diener, E. (2005). The benefits of frequent positive affect: Does happiness lead to success? *Psychological Bulletin, 131*(6), 803–855.

MacDonald, L. A., Karasek, R. A., Punnett, L., & Scharf, T. (2001). Covariation between workplace physical and psychosocial stressors: Evidence and implications for occupational health research and prevention. *Ergonomics, 44*(7), 696–718.

Mäkikangas, A., Feldt, T., Kinnunen, U., & Mauno, S. (2013). Does personality matter? A review of individual differences in occupational well-being. In A. B. Bakker (Ed.), *Advances in positive organizational psychology* (Vol. 1, pp. 107–143). Emerald Group.

Mäkikangas, A., Kinnunen, U., Feldt, T., & Schaufeli, W. (2017). The longitudinal development of employee well-being: A systematic review. *Work and Stress, 30*(1), 46–70.

Mancini, A. D., Bonanno, G. A., & Clark, A. E. (2011). Stepping off the hedonic treadmill: Individual differences in response to major life events. *Journal of Individual Differences, 32*(3), 144.

Manganelli, L., Thibault-Landry, A., Forest, J., & Carpentier, J. (2018). Self-determination theory can help you generate performance and well-being in the workplace: A review of the literature. *Advances in Developing Human Resources, 20*(2), 227–240.

Mayo, M., Sanchez, J. I., Pastor, J. C., & Rodriguez, A. (2012). Supervisor and coworker support: A source congruence approach to buffering role conflict and physical stressors. *International Journal of Human Resource Management, 23*(18), 3872–3889.

McIntyre, A., Bagley, N., Frakt, A., & Carroll, A. (2017). The dubious empirical and legal foundations of workplace wellness programs. *Health Matrix, 27*, 59.

Mental Health Foundation. (2016). *Well-being game*.

Messersmith, J. G., Patel, P. C., Lepak, D. P., & Gould-Williams, J. S. (2011). Unlocking the black box: Exploring the link between high-performance work systems and performance. *The Journal of Applied Psychology, 96*(6), 1105.

Mitchell, M. E., Eby, L. T., & Lorys, A. (2014). Feeling work at home: A transactional model of women and men's negative affective spillover from work to family. In M. J. Mills (Ed.), *Gender and the work-family experience* (pp. 121–140). Springer.

Muric, A., Soriano, A., Zappala, S., & Peiró, J. M. (2022). Can activity worthwhileness explain OCB-I change? The mediating role of positive emotions. *Journal of Occupational and Organizational Psychology, 38*(2), 93–100.

Nakamura, J., & Csikszentmihalyi, M. (2003). Creativity in later life. In R. K. Sawyer (Ed.), *Creativity and development* (pp. 186–216). Oxford University Press.

Nakamura, J., & Csikszentmihalyi, M. (2013). The concept of flow. In M. Csikszentmihalyi (Ed.), *Flow and the foundations of positive psychology*. Springer.

National Institute for Occupational Safety and Health. (2018). *NIOSH Total Worker Health Program*.

Nelis, S., Bastin, M., Raes, F., Mezulis, A., & Bijttebier, P. (2016). Trait affectivity and response styles to positive affect: Negative affectivity relates to dampening and positive affectivity relates to enhancing. *Personality & Individual Differences, 96*, 148–154.

Norton, D. L. (1976). *Personal destinies*. Princeton University Press.

Oh, I. S., Han, J. H., Holtz, B., Kim, Y. J., & Kim, S. (2018). Do birds of a feather flock, fly, and continue to fly together? The differential and cumulative effects of attraction, selection, and attrition on personality-based within-organization homogeneity and between-organization heterogeneity progression over time. *Journal of Organizational Behavior, 39*(10), 1347–1366.

Oishi, S., & Westgate, E. C. (2022). A psychologically rich life: Beyond happiness and meaning. *Psychological Review, 129*(4), 790–811.

Organisation for Economic Co-operation and Development. (2013). *OECD guidelines on measuring subjective well-being*.

Osilla, K. C., Van Busum, K., Schnyer, C., Larkin, J. W., Eibner, C., & Mattke, S. (2012). Systematic review of the impact of worksite wellness programs. *The American Journal of Managed Care, 18*(2), e68–e81.

Oswald, A. J., & Powdthavee, N. (2008). Does happiness adapt? A longitudinal study of disability with implications for economists and judges. *Journal of Public Economics, 92*(5–6), 1061–1077.

Park, J. G., Kim, J. S., Yoon, S. W., & Joo, B. K. (2017). The effects of empowering leadership on psychological well-being and job engagement: The mediating role of psychological capital. *Leadership and Organization Development Journal, 38*(3), 350–367.

Patterson, M. G., Warr, P. B., & West, M. A. (2004). Organizational climate and company performance: The role of employee affect and employee level. *Journal of Occupational and Organizational Psychology, 77*, 193–216.

Patterson, M. G., West, M. A., Shackleton, V. J., Dawson, J. F., Lawthom, R., Maitlis, S., & Wallace, A. M. (2005). Validating the organizational climate measure: Links to managerial practices, productivity and innovation. *Journal of Organizational Behavior, 26*(4), 379–408.

Peiró, J. M. (2008). Stress and coping at work: New research trends and their implications for practice. In K. Naswall, J. Hellgren, & M. Sverke (Eds.), *The individual in the changing working life*. Cambridge University Press.

Peiró, J. M. (2017). Liderazgo y salud laboral. In L. En Garcia-Izquierdo (dir.), *Ergonomía y Psicosociología aplicada a la prevención de Riesgos Laborales* (pp. 545–572). Cátedra Asturias de Prevención. Universidad de Oviedo.

Peiró, J. M., & González-Romá, V. (2013). El clima organizacional de estrés: Componentes, procesos de aparición, fuerza y efectos. In C. Alchieri & J. Barreiros (Eds.), *Proceedings of the Conferencias del XXXIV Congreso Interamericano de Psicología* (pp. 131–150). Sociedad Brasileira de Psicologia das Organisaçoes e do Trabalho.

Peiró, J. M., Kozusznik, M. W., Rodríguez, I., & Tordera, N. (2019). The happy-productive worker model and beyond: Patterns of well-being and performance at work. *IJERPH, 16*(3), 479.

Peiró, J. M., Montesa, D., Soriano, A., Kozusznik, M. W., Villajos, E., Magdaleno, J., Djourova, N. P., & Ayala, Y. (2021). Revisiting the happy-productive worker thesis from a eudaimonic perspective: A systematic review. *Sustainability*, *13*, 3174.

Peiró, J. M., & Rodríguez, I. (2008). Work stress, leadership and organizational health. *Papeles del Psicólogo*, *29*(1), 68–82.

Peng, J., Li, D., Zhang, Z., Tian, Y. U., Miao, D., Xiao, W. E. I., & Zhang, J. (2016). How can core self-evaluations influence job burnout? The key roles of organizational commitment and job satisfaction. *Journal of Health Psychology*, *21*(1), 50–59.

Quinn, R. P., Staines, G. L., & McCullough, M. R. (1974). *Job satisfaction: Is there a trend?* U.S. Department of Labor.

Rashid, M., & Zimring, C. (2008). A review of the empirical literature on the relationships between indoor environment and stress in health care and office settings: Problems and prospects of sharing evidence. *Environment and Behavior*, *40*(2), 151–190.

Reina, D., & Reina, M. (2016). *The truth behind workplace stress*. American Management Association.

Rich, B. L., Lepine, J. A., & Crawford, E. R. (2010). Job engagement: Antecedents and effects on job performance. *The Academy of Management Annals*, *53*(3), 617–635.

Rife, A. A., & Hall, R. J. (2015). *Work-life balance* (SIOP White Paper Series). Society for Industrial and Organizational Psychology.

Ritter, K. J., Matthews, R. A., Ford, M. T., & Henderson, A. A. (2016). Understanding role stressors and job satisfaction over time using adaptation theory. *The Journal of Applied Psychology*, *101*(12), 1655.

Robertson, I., & Cooper, C. L. (2011). *Well-being: Productivity and happiness at work*. Palgrave Macmillan.

Rode, J. C. (2004). Job satisfaction and life satisfaction revisited: A longitudinal test of an integrated model. *Human Relations*, *57*(9), 1205–1230.

Rodríguez, I., Kozusznik, M. W., & Peiró, J. M. (2013). Development and validation of the Valencia eustress-distress appraisal scale. *International Journal of Stress Management*, *20*(4), 279–308.

Roe, R. A. (2014). Performance, motivation and time. In A. Shipp & Y. Fried (Eds.), *Time and work: Volume 1—How time impacts individuals* (pp. 63–110). Routledge/Taylor & Francis.

Rosso, B. D., Dekas, K. H., & Wrzesniewski, A. (2010). On the meaning of work: A theoretical integration and review. *Research in Organizational Behavior*, *30*(C), 91–127.

Rousseau, D. M. (1988). The construction of climate in organizational research. In C. L. Cooper & I. T. Robertson (Eds.), *International review of industrial and organizational psychology* (pp. 139–158). Wiley.

Røysamb, E., & Nes, R. B. (2016). Genes, environments and core features of eudaimonic wellbeing. In J. Vittersø (Ed.), *Handbook of eudaimonic well-being* (pp. 233–252). Springer.

Rudolph, C. W., Allan, B., Clark, M., Hertel, G., Hirschi, A., Kunze, F., & Zacher, H. (2021). Pandemics: Implications for research and practice in industrial and organizational psychology. *Industrial and Organizational Psychology*, *14*(1–2), 1–35.

Ruggeri, K., Garcia-Garzon, E., & Maguire, Á. (2020). Well-being is more than happiness and life satisfaction: A multidimensional analysis of 21 countries. *Health and Quality of Life Outcomes*, *18*, 192.

Ryan, R., & Deci, E. L. (2000). La teoría de la autodeterminación y la facilitación de la motivación intrínseca, el desarrollo social, y el bienestar. *The American Psychologist*, *55*(1), 68–78.

Ryan, R. M., & Deci, E. L. (2001). On happiness and human potentials: A review of research on hedonic and eudaimonic wellbeing. *Annual Review of Psychology*, *52*, 141–166.

Ryan, R. M., & Deci, E. L. (2017). *Self-determination theory: Basic psychological needs in motivation, development, and wellness*. Guilford.

Ryan, R. M., Huta, V., & Deci, E. L. (2008). Living well: A self-determination theory perspective on eudaimonia. *Journal of Happiness Studies*, *9*(1), 139–170.

Ryff, C. D. (1995). Psychological wellbeing in adult life. *Current Directions in Psychological Science*, *4*(4), 99–104.

Ryff, C. D. (2013). Eudaimonic well-being and health: Mapping consequences of self-realization. In A. S. Waterman (Ed.), *The best within us: Positive psychology perspectives on eudaimonia* (pp. 77–98). American Psychological Association.

Ryff, C. D., & Boylan, J. M. (2016). Linking happiness to health: Comparisons between hedonic and eudaimonic well-being. In L. Bruni & P. L. Porta (Eds.), *Handbook of research methods and applications in happiness and quality of life* (pp. 53–70). Edward Elgar.

Ryff, C. D., & Keyes, C. L. (1995). The structure of psychological wellbeing revisited. *Journal of Personality and Social Psychology, 69*(4), 719–727.

Sakuraya, A., Imamura, K., Watanabe, K., Asai, Y., Ando, E., Eguchi, H., Nishida, N., Kobayashi, Y., Arima, H., Iwanaga, M., Otsuka, Y., Sasaki, N., Inoue, A., Inoue, R., Tsuno, K., Hino, A., Shimazu, A., Tsutsumi, A., & Kawakami, N. (2020). What kind of intervention is effective for improving subjective well-being among workers? A systematic review and meta-analysis of randomized controlled trials. *Frontiers in Psychology, 11*, 528656.

Samad, A., Reaburn, P., Davis, H., & Ahmed, E. (2015, April 13–14). *An empirical study on the effect of leadership styles on employee wellbeing and organizational outcomes within an Australian regional university* [Conference session]. Proceedings of the Australasian Conference on Business and Social Sciences, University of Central Queensland, Sydney, Australia, 984–999.

Sardžoska, E. G., & Tang, T. L. P. (2015). Monetary intelligence: Money attitudes—Unethical intentions, intrinsic and extrinsic job satisfaction, and coping strategies across public and private sectors in Macedonia. *Journal of Business Ethics, 130*(1), 93–115.

Scheck, C. L., Kinicki, A. J., & Davy, J. A. (1997). Testing the mediating processes between work stressors and subjective wellbeing. *Journal of Vocational Behavior, 50*, 96–123.

Schlechter, A. F., & Engelbrecht, A. S. (2006). The relationship between transformational leadership, meaning and organisational citizenship behaviour. *Management Dynamics: Journal of the Southern African Institute for Management Scientists, 15*(4), 2–16.

Schmidt, S., Roesler, U., Kusserow, T., & Rau, R. (2014). Uncertainty in the workplace: Examining role ambiguity and role conflict, and their link to depression—A meta-analysis. *European Journal of Work and Organizational Psychology, 23*, 91–106.

Schneider, B. (1987). The people make the place. *Personnel Psychology, 40*, 437–453.

Schneider, B., & Reichers, A. E. (1983). On the etiology of climate. *Personnel Psychology, 36*, 19–39.

Schulte, M., Ostroff, C., Shmulyian, S., & Kinicki, A. (2009). Organizational climate configurations: Relationships to collective attitudes, customer satisfaction, and financial performance. *The Journal of Applied Psychology, 94*, 618–634.

Seligman, M. E., Steen, T. A., Park, N., & Peterson, C. (2005). Positive psychology progress: Empirical validation of interventions. *The American Psychologist, 60*(5), 410.

Seo, M., & Ilies, R. (2009). Organizational behavior and human decision processes the role of self-efficacy, goal, and affect in dynamic motivational self-regulation. *Organizational Behavior and Human Decision Processes, 109*, 120–133.

Shadur, M. A., Kienzle, R., & Rodwell, J. J. (1999). The relationship between organizational climate and employee perceptions of involvement: The importance of support. *Group & Organization Management, 24*, 479–503.

Sheeran, P., & Silverman, M. (2003). Evaluation of three interventions to promote workplace health and safety: Evidence for the utility of implementation intentions. *Social Science & Medicine, 56*(10), 2153–2163.

Siegrist, J. (2010). Effort-reward imbalance at work and cardiovascular diseases. *International Journal of Occupational Medicine and Environmental Health, 23*(3), 279.

Sin, N. L., & Lyubomirsky, S. (2009). Enhancing well-being and alleviating depressive symptoms with positive psychology interventions: A practice-friendly meta-analysis. *Journal of Clinical Psychology, 65*(5), 467–487.

Smith, D. R., Wei, N., Zhao, L., & Wang, R. S. (2004). Musculoskeletal complaints and psychosocial risk factors among Chinese hospital nurses. *Occupational Medicine, 54*(8), 579–582.

Smith, P. C., Kendall, L. M., & Hulin, C. L. (1969). *The measurement of satisfaction in work and retirement.* Rand McNally.

Soler, R. E., Leeks, K. D., Razi, S., Hopkins, D. P., Griffith, M., & Aten, A. (2010). A systematic review of selected interventions for worksite health promotion: The assessment of health risks with feedback. *American Journal of Preventive Medicine, 38*(2), S237–S262.

Sonnentag, S. (2015). Dynamics of wellbeing. *Annual Review of Organizational Psychology, 2,* 261–293.

Sora, B., Caballer, A., Peiro, J. M., & De Witte, H. (2009). Job insecurity climate's influence on employees' job attitudes: Evidence from two European countries. *European Journal of Work & Organisational Psychology, 18*(2), 125–147.

Soriano, A., Kozusznik, M. W., Peiró, J. M., & Mateo, C. (2018). Mediating role of job satisfaction, affective well-being, and health in the relationship between indoor environment and absenteeism: Work patterns matter! *Work, 61*(2), 313–325.

Stanton, K., & Watson, D. (2014). Positive and negative affective dysfunction in psychopathology. *Social and Personality Psychology Compass, 8*(9), 555–567.

Steger, M. F., Frazier, P., Oishi, S., & Kaler, M. (2006). The meaning in life questionnaire: Assessing the presence of and search for meaning in life. *Journal of Counseling Psychology, 53*(1), 80–93.

Stuber, J., Meyer, I., & Link, B. (2008). Stigma, prejudice, discrimination and health. *Social Science & Medicine, 67*(3), 351.

Sun, J., Kaufman, S. B., & Smillie, L. D. (2018). Unique associations between big five personality aspects and multiple dimensions of well-being. *Journal of Personality, 86*(2), 158–172.

Taris, T. W., & Nielsen, K. (2019). Leadership in occupational health psychology. *Work and Stress, 33*(2), 105–106.

Tenney, E. R., Poole, J. M., & Diener, E. (2016). Does positivity enhance work performance? Why, when, and what we don't know. *Research in Organizational Behavior, 36,* 27–46.

Tepper, B. J. (2000). Consequences of abusive supervision. *Academy of Management Journal, 43*(2), 178–190.

Tetrick, L. E., & Peiró, J. M. (2016). Health and safety: Prevention and promotion. In M. J. Grawitch & D. W. Ballard (Eds.), *The psychologically healthy workplace: Building a win-win environment for organizations and employees* (pp. 199–229). American Psychological Association.

Tucker, J. S., Sinclair, R. R., & Thomas, J. L. (2005). The multilevel effects of occupational stressors on soldiers' well-being, organizational attachment, and readiness. *Journal of Occupational Health Psychology, 10*(3), 276.

Vacharkulksemsuk, T., & Fredrickson, B. L. (2013). Looking back and glimpsing forward: The broaden-and-build theory of positive emotions as applied to organizations. In A. B. Bakker (Ed.), *Advances in positive organizational psychology* (Vol. 1, pp. 45–60). Emerald Group.

Vacharkulksemsuk, T., Sekerka, L. E., & Fredrickson, B. L. (2011). Establishing a positive emotional climate to create 21st-century organizational change. In N. M. Ashkanasy, C. P. M. Wilderom, & M. F. Peterson (Eds.), *The handbook of organizational culture and climate* (Vol. 2, pp. 101–118). SAGE.

Veld, M., & Alfes, K. (2017). HRM, climate and employee well-being: Comparing an optimistic and critical perspective. *International Journal of Human Resource Management, 28*(16), 2299–2318.

Villajos, E., Tordera, N., & Peiró, J. M. (2019). Human resource practices, eudaimonic well-being, and creative performance: The mediating role of idiosyncratic deals for sustainable human resource management. *Sustainability, 11*(24), 6933.

Warr, P. (2007). *Work, happiness, and unhappiness.* Lawrence Erlbaum Associates.

Warr, P. (2019). *The psychology of happiness.* Routledge.

Warr, P., & Nielsen, K. (2018). Wellbeing and work performance. In E. Diener, S. Oishi, & L. Tay (Eds.), *Handbook of well-being* (pp. 1–22). DEF.

Waterman, A. S. (1984). *The psychology of individualism*. Praeger.

Watson, D. (2000). *Mood and temperament*. Guilford Press.

Watson, D., & Clark, L. A. (1984). Negative affectivity: The disposition to experience aversive emotional states. *Psychological Bulletin, 96*(3), 465–490.

Weiss, H. M. (2002). Deconstructing job satisfaction separating evaluations, beliefs and affective experiences. *Human Resource Management Review, 12*, 173–194.

Weiss, H. M., & Cropanzano, R. (1996). Affective events theory: A theoretical discussion of the structure, causes, and consequences of affective experiences at work. *Research in Organizational Behavior, 18*, 1–74.

West, C. P., Dyrbye, L. N., Erwin, P. J., & Shanafelt, T. D. (2016). Interventions to prevent and reduce physician burnout: A systematic review and meta-analysis. *Lancet, 388*(10057), 2272–2281.

White, M. P., & Dolan, P. (2009). Accounting for the richness of daily activities. *Psychological Science, 20*(8), 1000–1008.

Wright, T., & Cropanzano, R. (2000). Psychological well-being and job satisfaction as predictors of performance. *Journal of Occupational Health Psychology, 5*(1), 84–94.

Wright, T. A., & Bonett, D. G. (2007). Job satisfaction and psychological well-being as nonadditive predictors of workplace turnover. *Journal of Management, 33*(2), 141–160.

Wright, T. A., & Cropanzano, R. (2007). The happy/productive worker thesis revisited. In J. J. Martocchio (Ed.), *Research in personnel and human resources management* (pp. 269–307). Bingley.

Wrzesniewski, A. (2003). Finding positive meaning in work. In K. S. Cameron, J. E. Dutton, & R. E. Quinn (Eds.), *Positive organizational scholarship: Foundations of a new discipline* (pp. 296–308). Berrett-Koehler.

Wrzesniewski, A., McCauley, C., Rozin, P., & Schwartz, B. (1997). Jobs, careers, and callings: People's relations to their work. *Journal of Research in Personality, 31*(1), 21–33.

Xanthopoulou, D., Bakker, A. B., Demerouti, E., & Schaufeli, W. B. (2009). Work engagement and financial returns: A diary study on the role of job and personal resources. *Journal of Occupational and Organizational Psychology, 82*, 183–200.

Xanthopoulou, D., Bakker, A. B., Demerouti, E., & Schaufeli, W. B. (2012). A diary study on the happy worker: How job resources relate to positive emotions and personal resources. *European Journal of Work and Organizational Psychology, 21*(4), 489–517.

Yeoman, R., Bailey, C., Madden, A., & Thompson, M. (Eds.). (2019). *The Oxford handbook of meaningful work*. Oxford University Press.

Zelenski, J. M., Murphy, S. A., & Jenkins, D. A. (2008). The happy-productive worker thesis revisited. *Journal of Happiness Studies, 9*(4), 521–537.

Zhou, J., & George, J. M. (2001). When job dissatisfaction leads to creativity: Encouraging the expression of voice. *The Academy of Management Journal, 44*(4), 682–696.

Małgorzata W. Kożusznik, Aida Soriano, and José M. Peiró

Organizational Change

ORGANIZATION CHANGE

ORGANIZATIONS

To understand organizational change, it is necessary to understand organizations. Thus this article begins with a discussion of the foundational characteristics of organizations and related enterprises, and then moves to the discussion of organizational change.

Following conventional usage, here the term *organization* is used to refer to a *purposeful hierarchical human system* whose members contribute their efforts or other resources to the system in order to acquire valued resources, such as their livelihood. Some organizations, such as fraternities and other clubs, might be designed and maintained to serve no purpose other than providing their members with emotional satisfaction. Other organizations, such as police forces, hospitals, legislatures, and schools are created by society to fulfill its needs for safety, governance, and education. Business organizations are created by entrepreneurs or by other organizations for the purpose of generating wealth for their creators.

The organization theory and organization design literatures attribute the following characteristics to organizations: *socially constructed* (human entities interact in shaping and changing them), *goal directed* (although components may have varied goals, each component has at least one assigned activity that contributes to one of the organization's focal goals), *boundary maintaining* (routinely distinguishes between members and nonmembers), *hierarchically differentiated* (one or more components has the authority to assign tasks to one or more subordinates) (Aldrich, 1979, 2008; Huber, 2011, pp. 118–119). Additionally, organizations are characterized as *open systems* (they interact with their environment) (Scott & Davis, 2007, pp. 87–106). Galbraith (2014) provides an exemplar of the normative organizational design literature that assumes and incorporates these characteristics. The living systems literature (Miller, 1972, 1978) asserts that the hierarchical structure of an organization contains at least two levels of decision-makers with the authority to make decisions for lower-level organizational members to enact (Miller, 1972, p. 5, 1978, p. 595). Therefore, for a human system to be referred to as an organization, it must have at least three levels. Although not as grounded in theory, in an update of his classic work Morgan (2006) provides rich, provocative, and credible descriptions of organizations as machines, organisms, brains, cultures, political systems, and psychic prisons.

Authority and Other Influences as Determinants of Changes in Organizations and Other Enterprises.

Authority to create and implement change varies with the specific responsibilities that society directs the organization to fulfill, with the values to which society requires the organization to adhere, with the organization's circumstances, and with the degree of resistance and/or acceptance from the organization's members, especially its highly-valued members.

Limitations of Top Management's Authority to Make Changes to the Organization's Structure or Actions.

Two factors strongly influence the extent of the aggregate of authority, power, and influence that the organization's top managers and other leaders have to make changes in the organization's features or the actions of its members. One is the importance to society of the function that society has assigned to the organization. The other is the bargaining power and influence of its key members, those members who are most critical to the functioning of the core purpose of the organization. Thus leaders of *military organizations* have more authority over the organization's features and the actions of its members, and thus more power to make changes in the organization's structure or actions, than do the leaders of other types of organizations. This high level of authority follows from the criticality of the responsibility assigned by society to the organization—to reliably and effectively protect society, and to the lack of bargaining power of those many of its members whose departure from the organization is determined by schedules and regulations.

Next in its possession and use of authority to make changes to the organization's features is the top management of large *religious organizations in the Western world*, religions such as Sunni and Shiite Muslims, Judaism, the Roman Catholic Church, the Greek and Russian Orthodox churches, and the large Protestant Christian churches. However, in the second decade of the 21st century, the top management of the Roman Catholic Church in America became "divided" and "polarized" ("A Widening Schism," 2018). Because not all members of most nations are religious, or adhere to the same religion, the responsibility of a religious organization, "to reliably and effectively protect society," is not a cultural feature of most countries. Relatedly, the upper-level managers of religious organizations cannot control the actions of their mid- to lower-level managers as effectively as can the upper-level managers of military organizations.

The top managers of *business organizations* are primarily responsible for providing wealth to the organization's owners. They generally have a high level of authority, even to the point of selling or dismembering the organization and thereby possibly harming organizational stakeholders. Society is accordingly watchful over its business organizations and creates governmental agencies to serve as overseers. The extent of the power that an organization's top managers have to make changes in the organization's features, or in the actions of its members, is sometimes curtailed by the threat that many dissatisfied organizational members would engage in a walkout or strike, or that highly valued members would abandon the organization.

Burke (2018a, pp. 13–19) provides a basis for reasoning about the limitations on authority that confront top managers seeking to change organizations that serve multiple constituencies. For example, *government agencies, non-university schools,* and some *non-profit organizations* are responsible for reliably and effectively performing specified functions for specific societal components. Top managers of these entities have a moderate to high level of authority over their employees, curtailed somewhat by governmental regulations and societal norms. Top-level managers of *universities, medical-care institutions,* and other *organizations facing tight labor markets for highly trained employees* have only a modest level of control over the actions of those employees who provide the organization's focal service. This situation follows from two circumstances: (a) the professional norms of many of these employees often compete with economic concerns and (b) the labor market demand for the talents of such employees provides them with negotiating strength to engage in what they see as appropriate actions.

Circumstance-Based Variations in Power Versus Non-Hierarchical Influence. An organization's chief executive officer (CEO) and top management team (TMT) have considerable authority and influence over their organization's members, subject to social norms and legal constraints. Whether they are initiating an organizational change or the organization is confronted with a changing situation, these top managers typically generate an interpretation of the situation and choose the response actions the organization is to take. In either of two circumstances these top managers are influenced by organizational members with non-hierarchical influence over the organization change.

Consider first the circumstances where the top management decision-makers are choosing organizational responses to threats or opportunities, or are otherwise considering initiating significant changes. In such situations, these decision-makers often become aware that certain members of the organization (e.g., technical experts or boundary spanning personnel) have expertise that these top management decision-makers need, but do not have. These expertise-possessing members have a scarce and needed resource, information, and therefore, from *strategic-contingency theory* (Salancik & Pfeffer, 1977), they are likely to influence top management's choices.

A second form of non-hierarchical influence surfaces when the organization is involved in a circumstance-induced major change. In the context of such a change, all of the organization's members potentially have some degree of unspoken influence. This influence follows from the fact that, when confronted with circumstance-induced change, such as the loss of an important market or a governmental directive to make a change in the organization's practices, a significant proportion of the organization's members are likely to feel threatened or otherwise dissatisfied and may consider either abandoning the organization or making other adjustments to previously anticipated futures with the organization (Fugate, Prussia, & Kinicki, 2012; Oreg, Bartunek, Lee, & Do, 2018; Oreg, Vakola, & Armenakis, 2011). If any of these actions begins to evolve and is considerably adverse to the interests of the organization, the organization's top management will be motivated to consider which of its preferred actions must be modified, and how, if the concerns of the threatened members are to be alleviated and the organization's adversity is to be avoided.

BUSINESS STRUCTURES DIFFERENT FROM ORGANIZATION STRUCTURES

Late in the 20th century, businesses with network structures began to appear. One such structure is a network of generally unrelated subcontractors organized by an entrepreneur or prime contractor in order to produce goods or services without investing a great deal of its capital. Another network version is a *value chain*, a company's network of linked processes (each process is generally associated with an independent organization and adds value in the form of components—broadly defined—until a product for end-users is created). A third version is a network organized by a business that seeks to focus on a few management functions and subcontract out all other functions. For example, Nike, the sneaker and athletic wear company, focuses on design and marketing and contracts out its other functions (cf., Davis, 2016a). Prime contractors change their network by adding or deleting subcontractors.

At the beginning of the 21st century, businesses began to exploit advances in communication and transportation technology to create *platforms*. A platform is a nexus of rules and software which enables enterprises to link entities that seek information, goods, or services with other entities that will provide other information, goods, services, or funds (Davis, 2016a; Parker, Van Alstyne, & Choudary, 2016; Spulber, 2019; Van Alstyne, Parker, & Choudary, 2016). As of this writing, prominent examples of platforms are eBay, Amazon's online retail sales of products, and Uber's matching of customers who need transportation with drivers who provide transportation. Currently less well known is Airbnb's temporary housing platform that links seekers of short-term housing with owners of rooms available for short-term rentals. Less well known than its retail sales business is Amazon's labor platform, which enables Amazon to obtain work from the lowest-wage-bidding work seekers. Having explored (a) the organization construct, (b) the effects of variations on top management's ability to change the organization, and (c) the structures of businesses not using the typical organization structure, the article turns now to examining the organization change construct, the circumstances that lead to organization change, and the changes associated with specific circumstances.

ORGANIZATION CHANGE AND ITS EXTERNAL IMPETUSES

A "change" is a difference in an entity's state, condition, or property that occurs across an interval of time. In the organization change literature, "organization change" refers not only to changes at the organization level of analysis; it often refers to changes at other levels of analysis, ranging from individuals such as the organization's chief executive officer (CEO) to populations of organizations. The organization change literature, especially in the global west, which is our primary focus, deals with business organizations more than it does with any other particular type of organization. Accordingly, this article deals with changes in business organizations more than with changes in any other type of organization. Nevertheless, changes in other types of organizations and in non-organizational business enterprises are also examined. Organizational changes prompted by sources of change in the organization's external environment are examined first; then examined are organizational changes prompted by sources in the organization's internal environment. For each locus of change, a variety of organizational responses is described. It is worth noting that, even though something is changing in almost all organizations almost all of the time, organizations do have strong inertial tendencies.

Sources of Change in External Organizational Environments. The external environments of organizations have long been changing rapidly (Bell, 1976; Gates, 1996; Huber, 1984). A driving force in these changes has been the ongoing advances in technology, particularly communication, manufacturing, and transportation technologies, and especially the advances in information processing technologies (Kelly, 2016). To note that external organizational environments have been changing rapidly actually describes the phenomenon inadequately; the rate of change in the technology-related environments of organizations has not just been changing rapidly, it has been accelerating (Huber, 2004; Powell & Snellman, 2004). There are good reasons to believe that these environments will change even more rapidly in the future (Kelly, 2016).

This acceleration in the rate of environmental change is primarily a consequence of the following reciprocal relationship:

1. Advances in technology are likely to continue their accelerating rate of change because *an underlying driver of these technological advances* (i.e., advances *in science), continues to progress and to prompt and facilitate advances in technology*, and
2. These advances in science are likely to continue their accelerating rate of change because three *underlying drivers of these scientific advances (e.g., advances in computing technologies, scientific measurement technologies*, and *communication technologies*), serve as tools in the conduct of science and thus enable scientists to be more productive (Huber, 2004, pp. 31–34).

Organizational Responses to Changes in External Environments. Changes in markets or government policy or strategic changes by competitors are changes in the organization's external environment that generally require organization change and that can be threats and/or opportunities. In recent decades, attempts to control the adverse effects of using fossil fuels or to employ sources of renewable energy have been sources of change in business environments. Changes in human populations (such as migrations, changes in birth rates, and changes in societal norms) are sources of change in the natural world that occur infrequently and sometimes slowly, but which can frequently affect the circumstances of business organizations. Many sources of change in the external environment prompt decision-makers to consider changing the organization's strategy, such as initiating changes in product lines, pricing, or market image. The choices and characteristics of these possible changes generally lead to further searches for information about the environment. An example of such a search is March's (1991) description of an organization's exploration of its environment (a search to identify new opportunities) versus exploitation of its current strategic practices (a search for ways to capitalize on the organization's current features and practices). Other sources of change in the external environment, such as changes in the economy or in the availability of relevant employees, might not require changes in strategy but rather may require only changes in the organization's form or features, such as downsizing, eliminating layers of hierarchy, or changing the organization's compensation system. In practice, in order to avoid taking costly or risky actions, organizational decision-makers often choose a "wait and see" tactic, either to gather information or to see if the threat regresses (Arrow, 1974, p. 49; Gilbert, 2005, p. 746, 2006, p. 153).

Threat-rigidity (T-R) theory (Staw, Sandelands, & Dutton, 1981) describes a common organizational response to an adverse change in the organization's external. This theory predicts that an external threat to the vital interests of an individual, group, or organization, will lead to forms of rigidity in which the threatened entity will continue enacting, or even intensifying, existing actions—rather than searching for different actions that might reduce or eliminate the potential harm associated with the threat. Associated with continuing their ongoing actions, threatened organizations tend also to adapt to threats by intensifying three features of their structure. They increase centralization of authority, increase formalization, and increase the scope or intensity of efficiency-enhancing practices (Staw et al., 1981). Staw et al. do not explain this centralization of authority, but gathering and using power follows from executives' disposition to fulfill their social role of protecting the viability of their organization and the interests of its stakeholders (Fiske & Taylor, 1991, pp. 119–121). Although, as Staw et al. (1981) observed, adverse changes in an organization's external environment prompt the organization to modify its structure and communication practices, favorable changes might also prompt such changes. For example, newly available advances in information technologies might enable an organization to make performance-enhancing changes in its structure or decision processes (cf., Huber, 1990).

From their review of empirical works that dealt with organizational responses to *threatening situations* and also from their use of upward extrapolation, Staw et al. (1981) induced hypotheses to the effect that, when faced with threats to their vital interests, organizations are highly likely to undertake any or all of three *actions* that *change* their structure. They tend to (a) increase centralization of authority, (b) increase formalization, and (c) increase the scope or intensity of efficiency-enhancing practices. Each of these three actions contributes to *rigidity*. Staw et al. (1981) explain how outcomes of these changes can have either dysfunctional or functional effects—dysfunctional effects if the threatening situation is unfamiliar to the organization or functional effects if the threatening situation is familiar. Using this same database, the researchers also induced the hypotheses that seriously threatened organizations tend to generate and exhibit three information-processing *behaviors* to an extent greater than that manifested before they encountered the threatening situation. They (a) generate communications that tend to be simplified rather than complex, (b) rely on prior knowledge rather than searching for new interpretations of the situation or new coping actions, and (c) exhibit symptoms of dysfunctional communication or information overload. Staw et al. (1981, pp. 512–513) argue that these behaviors can also contribute to rigidity and can be dysfunctional. These six hypotheses, three concerning *actions* and three concerning *behaviors*, exemplify *rigidity* in the context of T-R theory at the organizational level and are the essence of the theory at the organizational level. (Here and elsewhere, let us view *actions* as those *behaviors* that are intentional.)

POPULATION-LEVEL ORGANIZATION CHANGE

In its early formulation (Hannan & Freeman, 1977, p. 939), population ecology theory posited that (a) the diversity of organizational forms in a population of organizations is isomorphic to the diversity of environments in the population, (b) that isomorphism can result either because non-optimal organizational forms are selected out or because organizational decision-makers learn optimal responses and adjust organizational behavior accordingly, and (c) that as a population's environment changed, in circumstances such as the availability of a needed resource, those organizations which were unable to adapt would disappear, causing a change in the content of the population. The theory has been substantially altered or substantially modified in response to contrary theorizing (Child, 1972, 1997) and research findings (Barnett & Carroll, 1995; Dobrev, Kim, & Carroll, 2002) and the incorporation into the model of ideas from other theories, particularly neo-institutional theory (DiMaggio & Powell, 1983; Meyer & Rowan, 1977).

Population-Level Learning as a Form of Change and Homogenization. Miner and Haunschild (1995) define population-level learning as "systematic change in the nature and mix of organizational action routines in a population of organizations, arising from experience" (1995, p. 118). They conceptualize population-level learning as "the result of repeated variation-selection-retention processes. *Variation* occurs when different types of routines are enacted by different firms (either individually or in clusters), or by the population as a whole. *Selection* occurs when one routine, cluster, or stable menu of routines (Suchman, 1994) persist while others drop out. *Retention* processes include the ongoing mechanism and factors that sustain the presence and execution of routines once they have become widespread in the population" (Miner & Haunschild, 1995, pp. 119–122). What has just been described is a homogenizing process. Another homogenizing process occurs when organizations of the same type change to adopt the current or evolving "dominant logic" (Bettis & Prahalad, 1995), the current belief about an organizational property such as structure or a practice (Prahalad, 2004; Westphal, Gulati, & Shortell, 1997). This adoption process is referred to as "mimetic isomorphism" by Aldrich and Ruef (2006, p. 176), who note that "mimetic isomorphism implies that firms will adopt the practice, regardless of its efficacy" (2006, p. 176).

Changes in the Distribution of Size, Power, and Number of Business Organizations. In the last few years of the second decade of this century, the media and the scholarly community addressed the adverse effects of the domination of giant companies on the economies and policies of the United States and, to a lesser extent, the world. A giant problem; the superstar company (2016) noted that "The giants ... deploy huge armies of lobbyists. ... superstar firms are gaining control of entire markets and finding new ways to entrench themselves." (See also Mayer, Wright, & Phan, 2017). These phenomena are interpretable as instances of population level learning (Miner & Haunschild, 1995), via either copying or experience. Davis (2016a, 2016b) also described changes in business organizations, but looked at different variables—focusing not on growth in size and power of already huge organizations, but on decreases in the number and size of business organizations caused by changes in technology (e.g., platform enterprises) and decreases in number caused by the acquisition activities of the corporate giants.

SOURCES, TYPES, AND EFFECTS OF COMMON CHANGES IN INTERNAL ENVIRONMENTS

Many changes in an organization's internal environment are adaptations to changes in the organization's external environment. Many others are associated with the facts that upper-level managers are motivated to improve their organization's performance or circumstances, that middle-level managers often "sell" ideas for change to top management (Dutton et al., 1997; Dutton, Ashford, O'Neil, & Lawrence, 2001), and that organizations are living systems that are continuously evolving.

Changes Initiated by Middle Managers. Everyday observation makes clear that middle managers are often more aware of issues of interest to customers, suppliers, employees, and other stakeholders than are upper-level managers. In order to call attention to these issues, and thereby enhance the circumstances of the organization's stakeholders, middle managers often engage in *issue selling*, "an interpersonal process involving individuals of different status" (Dutton et al., 1997) and "an early part of a more general change process" (Dutton et al., 2001). The issue-selling perspective directs attention to managers not part of the top management team as potential change agents and portrays organization change as a more pluralistic process than is portrayed in the upper echelons perspective (Finkelstein, Hambrick, & Cannella, 2009; Hambrick, 2007).

It is not unusual for top managers to initiate change whose implementation must be led by middle managers (Huy, 2002). Thus, middle managers' judgments of the legitimacy of a particular organizational change at various times during a change process has considerable impact on the success of the organizational change (Huy, Corley, & Kraatz, 2014). So do the emotional reactions of the middle managers not only to a change itself, but also to the top managers who initiated it (Balogun, Bartunek, & Do, 2015; Vuori & Huy, 2016). When their emotional responses are negative the likelihood of the success of the change will be decreased.

Intentional and Unintentional Organizational Learning. Organizations experience events in their ecosystems. Those events that are significant or strange provoke attempts to learn about, understand, and learn from them, and such learning is a form of change. It is often and simplistically assumed that organizational performance must be enhanced in order to claim that organizational learning has occurred. However, to the contrary, learning does not always lead to veridical knowledge that could enhance performance, as sample data may be misinterpreted or misrepresentative (e.g., Levitt & March, 1988). Thus learners can incorrectly learn (by misinterpreting information) and can correctly learn that which is incorrect (by correctly interpreting incorrect or otherwise misrepresentative data). In view of these observations, Huber (1991, p. 89) concluded that "An entity learns if, through its processing of information, the range of its potential behaviors is changed."

Senge (1990) advocated the importance of organizations becoming learning organizations in which "employees excel at creating, acquiring, and transferring knowledge" (Garvin, Edmondson, & Gino, 2008, p. 110). However, Garvin et al. acknowledge that it is difficult to create effective learning organizations, due to frequent lacks of supportive learning environments, concrete learning activities, and leadership behavior that fosters rather than impedes effective learning. Edmondson (2002), focusing on learning within teams within organizations, found that team members' perceptions of how power is distributed within the organization and how safe it is to take risks also affects their learning.

Organizational Forgetting and Intentional Unlearning. "Organizational forgetting refers to 'the loss, voluntary or otherwise, of organizational knowledge' (Martin de Holan & Phillips, 2004, p. 1606)" (Mariano, Casey, & Olivera, 2018, p. 169). Accidental or inadvertent forgetting encompasses both knowledge loss and knowledge depreciation, where knowledge loss refers to failure to maintain knowledge and knowledge depreciation refers to the gradual decay of organizational knowledge (Mariano et al., 2018, p. 169). Organizational unlearning has been viewed as including (a) changing acquisition processes and possible retrieval processes in the organization memory, (b) disruption or recreations of the organization's memory, (c) purposely eliminating memories, and (d) disintegrating the community's collective infrastructure of routines (Akgun, Byrne, Lynn, & Halit, 2007, p. 797; see also Fiol & O'Connor, 2017a, 2017b).

Change Effects of Immigration or Emigration on Organizational Members' Values or Competencies. Changes in the organization's membership as a result of immigration or emigration can lead to a change in the post-change membership's values or competencies in two ways. One way is that the post-change membership will reflect values or competencies in accord with the post-change proportions of members who possess these values or competencies (March, 1981, p. 565). The other way that a change in the membership's values or competencies occurs is that new members may influence the values or competencies of the organization's pre-immigrant members (Levitt & March, 1988, pp. 319–340).

Stakeholder-Forced Turnover of Top Management. That stakeholders force replacement of top managers who do not cause the organization to perform well is common knowledge. Occasionally poor organizational performance follows from executives taking aberrant actions to advance their personal circumstances rather than the organization's circumstances, a phenomenon that is explained by agency theory (Emirbayer & Mische, 1998; Eisenhardt, 1989; Wowak, Gomez-Mejia, & Steinbach, 2017). Somewhat less frequently executives engage in narcissistic behavior (Chatterjee & Hambrick, 2007) or other behaviors that reflect extremely high levels of core self-evaluations (Hiller & Hambrick, 2005) and which disgrace or otherwise stain the organization's image or reputation. These violations of adherence to the executive's organizational and social roles (Fiske & Taylor, 1991) constitute a significant departure from the expectations of owners and boards of directors, and provoke these entities to replace the executive. These matters have received no noticeable attention by scholars regarding organization change. Further, the turnover of such top managers likely causes organizational change in itself and may affect the implementation of already planned changes (e.g., Ginsberg & Abrahamson, 1991; Wiersema & Bantel, 1993).

PLANNED ORGANIZATIONAL CHANGE

Many changes come about in organizations as a result of ongoing evolution in external or internal characteristics. Sometimes, however, there are planned efforts whose intent is to create change in organizations. Many of these aim, at least in part, to transform an organization's culture. This section of the article thus includes a discussion of cultural change; organization development (OD), which has been a primary means of achieving such change; and participant responses to change. All of these changes are receiving considerable contemporary attention.

Changes in Organizational Culture. Aside from external stimuli that affect their culture, organizations may become cultural characterizations of themselves; organizations become less culturally flexible as members who are prone to deviate from the cultural norm in terms of beliefs or actions leave the organization, either of their own accord or under duress. This pattern intensifies the organization's culture, an organization change that leads to further departures of cultural deviants and reinforces the organization's cultural homogenization. On the other hand, new members may potentially foster cultural heterogeneity if they are able influence the values of the organization's prior members (Levitt & March, 1988, pp. 328–320).

It is common to speak of the need to change an organization's culture whenever there are problems with organizational functioning. Thus, organizational culture has often been the primary focus of organizational change attempts, even though the term "culture" has sometimes been used very sketchily and loosely when such attempts are undertaken.

The most influential definition has been Schein's (2010) tripartite one of culture as including artifacts; values; and, at root, unconscious assumptions. Schein's model treats culture as a given throughout an organization, developed out of early, especially founding, experiences in the organization. Given this, it is difficult to change an organization's culture.

Recently, however, Swidler's (1986) conceptualization of culture as a toolkit that provides resources on which individuals and organizations can draw when formulating change has become more influential (Hatch, Schultz, & Skov, 2015) in organizational circles. Swidler's approach suggests that organizational culture reflects a social construction process in which organizational members draw on cultural tools in order construct their understandings of themselves. Culture change largely means constructing new understandings. Thus, culture is not a given, but something quite malleable.

Organization Development and Its Forms. The term *organization development* (OD) has been used since the 1960s as a means to intervene in organization processes in order to increase their effectiveness (cf. Burke, 2018a; Cummings & Worley, 2015). It originally was defined as an organization-wide effort that was managed from the top and aimed at increasing organizational effectiveness and health through planned interventions into an organization's processes, based on behavioral science knowledge (Beckhard, 1969). Its initial planned interventions were intended to improve work practices, especially in work teams, and they were based on action research approaches that involved consultants and participants jointly diagnosing problems and then determining together how to address them (e.g., Pasmore & Friedlander, 1982).

Planned organizational change efforts based on the general rubric of OD have expanded in scope considerably since their beginnings (cf. Bartunek & Woodman, 2015). Starting in the 1970s, OD developed greater attention to socio-technical systems approaches, which focused in particular on the recognition that an organization is simultaneously a social and technical system (Pasmore, 1988). This was reflected in studies of the quality of work life interventions (Macy & Izumi, 1993); in high-involvement workplaces (Lawler, 1986); and, more recently, in discussions of the importance of employee engagement at work (Axelrod, 2010).

Beginning in the 1980s (Bunker & Alban, 1997), OD started to include what came to be called, first, large-group interventions and then system-wide interventions, in which members of a "whole system" (Holman, Devane, & Cady, 2007)—top decision-makers, other leaders, and stakeholders in the organization—came together in short bursts of time (usually two to three days interspersed between extensive planning and implementation times) to create their "desired future." Among the most popular methods for accomplishing this are open space, future search, and world café (all of which are described in Holman et al., 2007).

Over the course of the years, the philosophy of OD has evolved considerably. It has moved away from an emphasis on diagnosing problems toward a more social constructionist approach and a growing emphasis on narrative approaches to knowledge. This approach has come to be called "dialogic OD." Bushe and Marshak (2009, p. 361) summarized the new perspective, arguing that "dialogic OD practice is a conscious intent to engage the whole system in dialog and synergistic relationships in such a way that: mental models are surfaced; new knowledge, structures, processes, practices, and stories are collaboratively created and shared; and diverse stakeholder voices and perspectives are heard."

The dialogic OD approach overlaps considerably with positive organization studies (Cameron, Dutton, & Quinn, 2003; Cameron, Mora, Leutscher, & Calarco, 2011), which turns research and practice attention to how organizations create positive, value-based processes and outcomes. This is particularly true of its signature initiative, Appreciative Inquiry (Cooperrider & Whitney, 1999). This method starts by discovering the positive and life-giving aspects in even dire organizational situations, under the assumption that exploring what is positive is more likely to give life to a system than is exploring what is negative. It then progresses through phases of creating results-oriented vision, designing possible ways of accomplishing it, and then strengthening the capacity of a system to accomplish its desires. Among the places where Appreciative Inquiry has been implemented was a 2004 Global Leaders Summit, at a meeting involving then UN secretary-general Kofi Annan and nearly 500 business leaders from around the world.

There have been some differences of opinion regarding the contemporary success of OD. Some, such as Burke (2018), believe that it is not keeping up with changes in the world, so might not endure. Others (e.g., Bartunek & Woodman, 2012) suggest that the kinds of organizational issues OD addresses are so crucial that it will continue to evolve and exist. Still others (Stouten, Rousseau, & De Cremer, 2018) suggest that OD has considerable potential but that its evidence base has not been adequate. Stouten et al. summarize evidence that can foster its ongoing improvement.

RESISTANCE AND OTHER RESPONSES TO ORGANIZATION CHANGE

It is often taken for granted that resistance to change will be the response of recipients to planned change initiatives undertaken by change agents and other organizational leaders (e.g., Battilana & Casciaro, 2013; Hon, Bloom, & Crant, 2014; Oreg & Bergson, 2019). Further, it is assumed that resistance contributes considerably to the failure of change. However, in recent years it has become clear that recipients of change do not automatically reject it, that there are multiple types of recipient responses to change. Thus, it is important to attend to the variety of emotional and behavioral responses to change exhibited by recipients of change.

Recently, Oreg et al. (2018), building on the circumplex of emotions originally developed by Russell (1980), suggested that recipients' affective and behavioral responses to change may be both positive and negative, and activated or non-activated. They may take the form of resistance, but they may also take forms of proactivity, disengagement, or passive acceptance. Further, these various responses will depend at least in part on how relevant the goals of the change are to change recipients, as well as the congruence of the goals with their own aspirations.

IMPORTANCE OF TEMPORAL DIMENSIONS OF PLANNED CHANGE

Although this is usually not recognized, a number of temporal dimensions of change play important roles in its progress. The most common image used to describe temporal dimensions of planned organizational change over time has been Lewin's (1947) dictum that change unfolds in three steps that he labeled unfreezing, moving, and freezing. These steps give a sequential image of the process of organizational change, one that includes the ordering of events over time (e.g., Amis, Slack, & Hinings, 2004; Langley, 1999). In Lewin's depiction, the ordering of change is linear.

However, since Lewin's time there has been considerable development in understanding the complexities of time and temporal dimensions in and among organizations (e.g., Albert, 2013; Bartunek & Woodman, 2015; Bluedorn, 2002; Kunisch, Bartunek, Mueller, & Huy, 2017). This has led to the recognition of how organizational change is intertwined with multiple temporal dimensions in addition to sequence, and that these dimensions may affect how it takes place.

One temporal dimension that likely affects the course of change is timing (Ancona, Goodman, Lawrence, & Tushman, 2001; Langley, 1999), which is reflected in, among other things, the presence of deadlines, timetables, timing norms, and windows of opportunity, all of which suggest that some times are more appropriate than others to initiate particular actions. Another is pacing (Amis et al., 2004; Ancona & Chong, 1996), which refers to the speed of change at particular times in a change. Yet another is rhythms, the types of cycles that occur during change. Klarner and Raisch (2013, p. 168) note that organizational changes likely occur in one or more of four types of rhythms: focused (long periods of change and short periods of stability), punctuated (long periods of stability and short periods of change), temporarily switching (alternating stability and change), and regular (in which intervals between changes are relatively equal). Finally, an important temporal dimension is whether a change is monophonic (carried out by one actor or set of actors in one sequence) or polyphonic (Albert, 2013), carried out by multiple actors in multiple settings and involving differing sequences, rhythms, and pacing. How these different patterns mesh with each other often affects the course of change.

In other words, organizational change is highly unlikely to unfold along straightforward, linear pathways. Rather, how it unfolds will depend on its timing. Further, its pacing will likely shift during the course of change, and it will follow some type(s) of rhythmic pattern. Its success will depend at least in part on how well its timing, pacing, and rhythm mesh with those of others on whom it depends.

EMERGING DISTINCTIONS IN TYPES OF ORGANIZATIONAL CHANGE

Over the past decades there has been an increasing awareness of the multiple forms organization change might take. In particular, there has been increased recognition of radical and continuous change, dialectical and paradoxical change, emergence and decline, death and rebirth. These types of change extend considerably the recognition of the types of events and processes that characterize organizational change, and show why it cannot always be fully planned.

Radical Versus Continuous Change.   Starting in the 1980s, there began to be considerable discussion of organizational transformation, or radical change. Although the discussions have had a variety of meanings (e.g., Bartunek, 1984; Tushman & Romanelli, 1985), they have shared the general acknowledgement that radical change is not linear; the organization is not getting better at what it is already doing. Rather, there is a drastic shift in key components of the organization, sometimes in its mission, often in strategy, structure, power, and culture; and the change must be led from the top. Further, the assumption has sometimes been made that radical change must be accomplished in a short amount of time if it is to be accomplished at all (Romanelli & Tushman, 1994). However, results of a 12-year longitudinal study by Amis et al. (2004) made evident that radical change does not necessarily occur in short bursts.

Radical change has been contrasted with continuous change, (e.g., Brown & Eisenhardt, 1997), which describes ways that organizational change can take place more or less continuously through a number of sequenced steps or microprocesses (Reay, Golden-Biddle, & Germann, 2006). Those who emphasize continuous change also sometimes use a geological metaphor that indicates that organizations contain multiple layers of history, and even a radical change may shift only the top layers (Cooper, Hinings, Greenwood, & Brown 1996).

DIALECTICAL AND PARADOXICAL CHANGE

In recent years there has been increased attention to the roles of tensions and contradictions in organizational life (e.g., Hargrave & Van de Ven, 2017) and their importance for change. (Such awareness has always been more present in the Global East than the Global West, cf. Jing & Van de Ven, 2014; Marshak, 1993). Tensions and contradictions can be treated as dualisms in which the sides are in competition with each other and in which one side of the tension must "win" over the other. Or they may be treated as dualities in which the need for both sides of the tensions is acknowledged (e.g., Seo & Creed, 2002; Seo et al., 2004).

Dialectical change illustrates dualities. It occurs when the tensions are treated as equivalent to a thesis and antithesis, and allowed to inform each other through productive conflict in such a way that together they culminate in a new synthesis. Bartunek (1984) and Seo and Creed (2002) have shown that this kind of pattern may lead to organizational and institutional change associated with radically new understandings.

Paradoxical approaches to organizational life also focus on dualities. However, contrary to treating them as theses and antitheses to be resolved in some way, members of an organization may treat them as simultaneously valid; inherently interdependent; and, as such, the foundation of organizing (Smith & Lewis, 2011). Further, Smith and Lewis have identified four paradoxical tensions at the root of organizing. These are learning, belonging, organizing, and performing.

From a paradox perspective, change often takes the form of organizational members moving from seeing contradictions as dualisms—as fundamentally in competition with each other with one winning over the other—to recognizing their joint interdependence. This new view is considered to lead to considerable creative energy, in which organizational members are able to re-examine their assumptions, develop new and more complex visions for what they are about (Andriopoulos and Lewis, 2009), and lead more complexly.

Emergence. Most approaches to organizational change have been based on an implicit assumption that change is planned by and led from top management. However, advances in complexity theory, beginning with the work of Lorenz (1963), who showed ways that small changes in one area may generate large changes in others, have challenged that idea and led to new perceptions of how radical change may take place absent the initiation of top management.

Lorenz identified that novelty may emerge in living systems when small parts join together to create a whole that is more than the sum of the parts (Ablowitz, 1939). This type of pattern may occur in organizations when very small changes culminate in larger ones. Lichtenstein (2014), in particular, has described generative emergence in organizations as the creation of new social entities, such as new projects and social innovations, from their preexisting elements.

One example of this pattern in organizational settings comes from the creation of an emergent change in a church that was initiated by apparently small changes that together became radical over time (Plowman et al., 2007). Another is the creation of musical theatres in Branson, Missouri, over the course of a 100-year span that began with fluctuations in "a lake, a book, and a train" (Chiles, Meyer, & Hench, 2004, p. 503) that were amplified by self-reinforcing processes over time.

Decline, Death, and Rebirth. In early scholarly approaches to organizational change, the implicit, if not explicit, assumption was that organizations keep developing over time (e.g., Greiner, 1972). Since the 1980s, there has been increased recognition that this assumption does not correspond with the real situations of organizations. In fact, organizational decline is a common experience of organizations, especially in times of external economic scarcity (Whetten, 1980). Further, most organizations eventually die (Sutton, 1987).

However, organizations may be very resilient. Seasonal organizations, such as summer camps, may come back to life every year after months of dormancy (Birnholtz, Cohen, & Hoch, 2007). Some organizations that decline may experience a renaissance (Siggelkow, 2001). Some organizations that die may stimulate new organizations that carry out their legacy (Walsh & Bartunek, 2011). In other words, death may be a form of change in organizations, not solely an ending.

CONCLUSION

The scope and variety of organization changes described here make clear that organization change is a familiar and important feature of society's ecosystem. The scope and variety of the literature also elucidate that organization change is an area of considerable interest and importance to society and to the research community.

REFERENCES

A giant problem; The superstar company. (2016). *The Economist*, September 17. https://www.economist.com/leaders/2016/09/17/a-giant-problem

A widening schism; The Catholic church in America is as politically divided as the country. (2018). *The Economist*, September 6. https://www.economist.com/united-states/2018/09/06/the-catholic-church-in-america-is-as-politically-divided-as-the-country

Ablowitz, R. (1939). The theory of emergence. *Philosophy of Science, 6*(1), 1–16.

Akgun, A. E., Byrne, J. C., Lynn, G. S., & Halit, K. (2007). Organizational learning as changes in beliefs and routines in organizations. *Journal of Organizational Change Management, 20*(6), 794–812.

Albert, S. (2013). *When: The art of perfect timing*. San Francisco, CA: John Wiley.

Aldrich, H. E. (1979). *Organizations and environments*. Englewood Cliffs, NJ: Prentice-Hall.

Aldrich, H. E. (2008). *Organizations and environments: Population learning; Properties/characteristics of organizations*. Palo Alto, CA: Stanford Business Books.

Aldrich, H., & Ruef, M. (2006). *Organizations evolving*. London, U.K.: SAGE.

Amis, J., Slack, T., & Hinings, C. R. (2004). The pace, sequence, and linearity of radical change. *Academy of Management Journal, 47*(1), 15–39.

Ancona, D., & Chong, C. L. (1996). Entrainment: Pace, cycle, and rhythm in organizational behavior. *Research in Organizational Behavior, 18*, 251–284.

Ancona, D. G., Goodman, P. S., Lawrence, B. S., & Tushman, M. L. (2001). Time: A new research lens. *Academy of Management Review, 26*(4), 645–663.

Andriopoulos, C., & Lewis, M. W. (2009). Exploitation-exploration tensions and organizational ambidexterity: Managing paradoxes of innovation. *Organization Science, 20*(4), 696–717.

Arrow, K. D. (1974). Modelling internal organizational change. *Annual Review of Sociology, 21*, 217–236.

Axelrod, R. (2010). *Terms of engagement: New ways of leading and changing organizations*. Oakland, CA: Berrett-Koehler.

Balogun, J., Bartunek, J. M., & Do, B. (2015). Senior managers' sensemaking and responses to strategic change. *Organization Science, 26*, 960–979.

Barnett, W. P., & Carroll, G. R. (1995). Modeling internal organizational change. *Annual Review of Sociology, 21*(1), 217–236.

Bartunek, J. M. (1984). Changing interpretive schemes and organizational restructuring: The example of a religious order. *Administrative Science Quarterly, 29*(3), 355–372.

Bartunek, J. M., & Woodman, R. W. (2012). The spirits of organization development, or why OD lives despite its pronounced death. In K. Cameron & G. Spreitzer (Eds.), *Handbook of positive organizational scholarship* (pp. 727–736). New York. NY: Oxford University Press.

Bartunek, J. M., & Woodman, R. W. (2015). Beyond Lewin: Toward a temporal approximation of organization development and change. *Annual Review of Organizational Psychology and Organizational Behavior, 2*, 157–182.

Battilana, J., & Casciaro, T. (2013). Overcoming resistance to organizational change: Strong ties and affective cooptation. *Management Science, 59*, 819–836.

Beckhard, R. (1969). *Organization development: Strategies and models*. Reading, MA: Addison-Wesley.

Bell, D. (1976). *The coming of post-industrial society: A venture in social forecasting*. New York, NY: Basic Books.

Bettis, R. A., & Prahalad, C. K. (1995). The dominant logic: Retrospective and extension. *Strategic Management Journal, 16*, 5–14.

1568 • ORGANIZATION CHANGE

Birnholtz, J. P., Cohen, M. D., & Hoch, S. V. (2007). Organizational character: On the regeneration of camp poplar grove. *Organization Science, 18*(2), 315–332.

Bluedorn, A. C. (2002). *The human organization of time: Temporal realities and experience*. Stanford, CA: Stanford University Press.

Brown, S. L., & Eisenhardt, K. M. (1997). The art of continuous change: Linking complexity theory and time-paced evolution in relentlessly shifting organizations. *Administrative Science Quarterly, 42*, 1–34.

Bunker, B. B. & Alban, B. T. (1997). *Large group interventions: Engaging the whole system for rapid change*. San Francisco, CA: Jossey-Bass.

Burke, W. W. (2018a). *Organization change: Theory and practice*. Thousand Oaks: SAGE.

Burke, W. W. (2018b). The rise and fall of the growth of organizational development: What now? *Consulting Psychology Journal: Practice and Research, 70*(3), 186–206.

Bushe, G. R., & Marshak, R. J. (2009). Revisioning organization development: Diagnostic and dialogic premises and patterns of practice. *Journal of Applied Behavioral Science, 45*(3), 348–368.

Cameron, K. S., Dutton, J. E., & Quinn, R. E. (Eds.). (2003). *Positive organizational scholarship: Foundations of a new discipline*. San Francisco, CA: Berrett-Koehler.

Cameron, K. S., Mora, C., Leutscher, T., & Calarco, M. (2011). Effects of positive practices on organizational effectiveness. *Journal of Applied Behavioral Science, 47*(3), 266–308.

Cao, Q., Maruping, L. M., & Takeuchi, R. (2006). Disentangling the effects of CEO turnover and succession on organizational capabilities: A social network perspective. *Organization Science, 17*(5), 563–576.

Chatterjee, A., & Hambrick, D. D. (2007). It's all about me: Narcissistic chief executive officers and their effects on company strategy and performance. *Administrative Science Quarterly, 52*(3), 351–386.

Child, J. (1972). Organization structure, environment and performance: The role of strategic choice. *Sociology, 6*(1), 1–15.

Child, J. (1997). Strategic choice in the analysis of action, structure, organizations and environment: Retrospect and prospect. *Organization Studies, 18*(1), 43–77.

Chiles, T. H., Meyer, A. D., & Hench, T. J. (2004). Organizational emergence: The origin and transformation of Branson, Missouri's musical theaters. *Organization Science, 15*(5), 499–519.

Cooper, D. J., Hinings, B., Greenwood, R., & Brown, J. L. (1996). Sedimentation and transformation in organizational change: The case of Canadian law firms. *Organization Studies, 17*(4), 623–647.

Cooperrider, D., & Whitney, D. (1999). *Appreciative inquiry: A positive revolution in change*. San Francisco, CA: Berrett-Koehler.

Cummings, T. G., & Worley, C. G. (2015). *Organizational development and change*. Stanford, CT: Cengage Learning.

Davis, G. F. (2016a). *The vanishing American corporation: Navigating the hazards of a new economy*. Oakland, CA: Berrett-Koehler.

Davis, G. F. (2016b). Can an economy survive without corporations? Technology and robust organizational alternatives. *Academy of Management Perspectives, 30*(2), 129–140.

DiMaggio, P. J., & Powell, W. W. (1983). The iron cage revisited: Institutional isomorphism and collective rationality in organizational fields. *American Sociological Review, 48*(2), 147–160.

Dobrev, S. D., Kim, T.-Y., & Carroll, G. R. (2002). The evolution of organizational niches: U.S. automobile manufacturers, 1885–1981. *Administrative Science Quarterly, 47*(2), 233–264.

Dutton, J., Ashford, S., O'Neill, R., & Lawrence, K. (2001). Moves that matter: Issue selling and organizational change. *Academy of Management Journal, 44*(4), 716–736.

Dutton, J., Ashford, S., Wierba, L, O'Neill, R., & Hayes, E. (1997). Reading the wind: How middle managers read the context for issue selling. *Strategic Management Journal, 18*(5), 407–423.

Edmondson, A. (2002). The local and variegated nature of learning in organizations: A group-level perspective. *Organization Science, 13*(2), 128–146.

Eisenhardt, K. M. (1989). Agency theory: An assessment and review. *Academy of Management Review, 14*(1), 57–74.

Emirbayer, M., & Mische, A. (1998). What is agency? *American Journal of Sociology, 103*(4), 962–1023.

Finkelstein, S., Hambrick, D. C., & Cannella Jr., A. E. (2009). *Strategic leadership: Theory and research on executives, top management teams, and boards.* New York, NY: Oxford University Press.

Fiol, M., & O'Connor, E. (2017a). Unlearning established organizational routines—Part I. *The Learning Organization, 24*(1), 3–29.

Fiol, M., & O'Connor, E. (2017b). Unlearning established organizational routines—Part II. *The Learning Organization, 24*(2), 82–92.

Fiske, S. T., & Taylor, S. E. (1991). *Social cognition.* New York, NY: McGraw-Hill.

Fugate, M., Prussia, G. E., & Kinicki, A. M. (2012). Managing employee withdrawal during organizational change: The role of threat appraisal. *Journal of Management, 38*(3), 890–914.

Galbraith, J. R. (2014). *Designing organizations: Strategy, structure, and process at the business unit and enterprise levels.* San Francisco, CA: Jossey-Bass.

Garvin, D. A., Edmondson, A. C., & Gino, F. (2008). Is yours a learning organization? *Harvard Business Review, 86*(3), 109–116.

Gates, B. (1996). *The road ahead.* New York, NY: Penguin.

Gilbert, C. G. (2005). Unbundling the structure of inertia: Resource versus routine rigidity. *Academy of Management Journal, 48*(5), 741–763.

Gilbert, C. G. (2006). Change in the presence of residual fit: Can competing frames coexist? *Organization Science, 17*(1), 150–167.

Ginsberg, A., & Abrahamson, E. (1991). Champions of change and strategic shifts: The role of internal and external change advocates. *Journal of Management Studies, 28*(2), 173–190.

Greiner, L. (1972). Evolution and revolution as organizations grow. *Harvard Business Review, 76*(3), 3–11.

Hambrick, D. C. (2007). Upper echelons theory: An update. *Academy of Management Review, 32*(2), 334–343.

Hannan, M. T., & Freeman, J, (1977). The population ecology of organizations. *American Journal of Sociology, 82*(5), 929–964.

Hargrave, T. J., & Van de Ven, A. H. (2017). Integrating dialectical and paradox perspectives on managing contradictions in organizations. *Organization Studies, 38*(3–4), 319–339.

Hatch, M. J., Schultz, M., & Skov, A. M, (2015). Organizational identity and culture in the context of managed change: Transformation in the Carlsberg Group, 2009–2013. *Academy of Management Discoveries, 1*(1), 58–90.

Hiller, N. J., & Hambrick, D. C. (2005). Conceptualizing executive hubris: The role of (hyper-) core self-evaluations in strategic decision-making. *Strategic Management Journal, 26*(4), 297–319.

Holman, P., Devane, T., & Cady, S. (2007). *The change handbook: The definitive resource on today's best methods for engaging whole systems* (2nd ed.). San Francisco, CA: Berrett-Koehler.

Hon, A. H., Bloom, M., & Crant, J. M. (2014). Overcoming resistance to change and enhancing creative performance. *Journal of Management, 40*(3), 919–941.

Huber, G. P. (1984). The nature and design of post-industrial organizations. *Management Science, 30*(8), 928–951.

Huber, G. P. (1990). A theory of the effects of advanced information technologies on organization design, intelligence, and decision making. *Academy of Management Review, 15*(1), 47–71.

Huber, G. P. (1991). Organizational learning: The contributing processes and their literatures. *Organization Science, 2*(1), 88–115.

Huber, G. P. (2004). *The necessary nature of future firms: Attributes of survivors in a changing world.* London, U.K.: SAGE.

Huber, G. P. (2011). Organizations: Theory, design, future. In S. Zedeck (Ed.), *APA handbook of industrial and organizational psychology* (pp. 117–160). Washington, DC: American Psychological Association.

Huy, Q. N. (2002). Emotional balancing of organizational continuity and radical change: The contribution of middle managers. *Administrative Science Quarterly, 47*(1), 31–69.

Huy, Q. N., Corley, K. G., & Kraatz, M. S. (2014). From support to mutiny: Shifting legitimacy judgments and emotional reactions impacting the implementation of radical change. *Academy of Management Journal, 57*(6), 1650–1680.

Jing, R., & Van de Ven, A. H. (2014). A yin-yang model of organizational change: The case of the Chengdu Bus Group. *Management and Organization Review, 10*(1), 29–54.

Kelly, K. (2016). *The inevitable: Understanding the 12 technological forces that will shape our future.* New York, NY: Penguin Random House.

Klarner, P., & Raisch, S. (2013). Move to the beat—Rhythms of change and firm performance. *Academy of Management Journal, 56*(1), 160–184.

Kunisch, S., Bartunek, J. M., Mueller, J., & Huy, Q. N. (2017). Time in strategic change research. *Academy of Management Annals, 11*(2), 1005–1064.

Langley, A. (1999). Strategies for theorizing from process data. *Academy of Management Review, 24*(4), 691–710.

Lawler III, E. E. (1986). *High-involvement management. Participative strategies for improving organizational performance.* San Francisco, CA: Jossey-Bass.

Levitt, B., & March, J. G. (1988). Organizational learning. *Annual Review of Sociology, 14,* 319–340.

Lewin, K. (1947). Frontiers in group dynamics: Concept, method and reality in social science; social equilibria and social change. *Human Relations, 1*(1), 5–41.

Lichtenstein, B. (2014). *Generative emergence: A new discipline of organizational, entrepreneurial and social innovation.* New York, NY: Oxford University Press.

Lorenz, E. N. (1963). Deterministic nonperiodic flow. *Journal of the Atmospheric Sciences, 20,* 130–141.

Macy, B. A., & Izumi, H. (1993). Organizational change, design, and work innovation: A meta-analysis of 131 North American field studies—1961–1991. *Research in Organizational Change and Development, 7,* 235–313.

March, J. G. (1981). Footnotes to organizational change. *Administrative Science Quarterly, 26*(4), 563–577.

March, J. G. (1991). Exploration and exploitation in organizational learning. *Organization Science, 2*(1), 71–87.

Mariano, S., Casey, A., & Olivera, F. (2018). Managers and organizational forgetting: A synthesis. *The Learning Organization, 25*(3), 169–179.

Marshak, R. J. (1993). Lewin meets Confucius: A review of the OD model of change. *Journal of Applied Behavioral Science, 29*(4), 393–415.

Martin de Holan, P., & Phillips, N. (2004). Remembrance of things past: The dynamics of organizational forgetting. *Management Science, 50*(11), 1603–1613.

Mayer, C., Wright, M., & Phan, P. (2017). Management research and the future of the corporation: A new agenda. *Academy of Management Perspectives, 31*(3), 179–182.

Meyer, J. W., & Rowan, B. (1977). Institutionalized organizations: Formal structure as myth and ceremony. *American Journal of Sociology, 83*(2), 340–363.

Miller, J. G. (1972). Living systems: The organization. *Behavioral Science, 17*(1), 1–182.

Miller, J. G. (1978). *Living systems.* New York, NY: McGraw-Hill.

Miner, A. S., & Haunschild, P. R. (1995). Population level learning. *Research in Organization Behavior, 17,* 115–166.

Morgan, G. (2006). *Images of organizations* (updated ed.). Thousand Oaks, CA: SAGE.

Oreg, S, Bartunek, J. M., Lee, G., & Do, B. (2018). An affect-based model of recipients' responses to organizational change events. *Academy of Management Review, 43*(1), 65–86.

Oreg, S., & Berson, Y. (2019). Leaders' impact on organizational change: bridging theoretical and methodological chasms. *Academy of Management Annals, 13*(1), 272–307.

Oreg, S., Vakola, M., & Armenakis, A. (2011). Change recipients' reactions to organizational change: A 60-year review of quantitative studies. *Journal of Applied Behavioral Science, 47*(4), 461–524.

Parker, G. G., Van Alstyne, M. W., & Choudary, S. P. (2016). *Platform revolution: How networked markets are transforming the economy—And how to make them work for you.* New York, NY: Norton.

Pasmore, W. A. (1988). *Designing effective organizations: The sociotechnical systems perspective* (Vol. 6). John Wiley & Sons Inc.

Pasmore, W., & Friedlander, F. (1982). An action-research program for increasing employee involvement in problem solving. *Administrative Science Quarterly, 27*(3), 343–362.

Plowman, D. A., Baker, L. T., Beck, T. E., Kulkarni, M., Solansky, S. T., & Travis, D. V. (2007). Radical change accidentally: The emergence and amplification of small change. *Academy of Management Journal, 50*(3), 515–543.

Powell, W. W., & Snellman, K. (2004). The knowledge economy. *Annual Review of Sociology, 30*, 199–220.

Prahalad, C. K. (2004). The blinders of dominant logic. *Long Range Planning, 37*(2), 171–179.

Reay, T., Golden-Biddle, K., & Germann, K. (2006). Legitimizing a new role: Small wins and microprocesses of change. *Academy of Management Journal, 49*(5), 977–998.

Romanelli, E., & Tushman, M. L. (1994). Organizational transformation as punctuated equilibrium: An empirical test. *Academy of Management Journal, 37*(5), 1141–1166.

Russell, J. A. (1980). A circumplex model of affect. *Journal of Personality and Social Psychology, 39*(6), 1161–1178.

Salancik, G. R., & Pfeffer, J. (1977). Who gets power—and how they hold on to it: A strategic-contingency model of power. *Organizational Dynamics, 5*(3), 3–21.

Schein, E. H. (2010). *Organizational culture and leadership* (4th ed.). San Francisco, CA: Jossey-Bass.

Scott, W. R., & Davis, G. F. (2007). *Organizations and organizing: Rational, natural, and open systems perspectives.* Upper Saddle River, NJ: Prentice Hall.

Senge, P. (1990). *The fifth discipline: The art and science of the learning organization.* New York, NY: Currency Doubleday.

Seo, M. G. & Creed, W. D. (2002). Institutional contradictions, praxis, and institutional change: A dialectical perspective. *Academy of Management Review, 27*(2), 222–247.

Seo, M., Putnam, L., & Bartunek, J. M. (2004). Dualities and tensions of planned organizational change. In M. S. Poole & A. H. Van de Ven (Eds.), *Handbook of organizational change and innovation* (pp. 73–109). New York, NY: Oxford University Press.

Siggelkow, N. (2001). Change in the presence of fit: The rise, the fall, and the renaissance of Liz Claiborne. *Academy of Management Journal, 44*(4), 838–857.

Smith, W. K., & Lewis, M. W. (2011). Toward a theory of paradox: A dynamic equilibrium model of organizing. *Academy of Management Review, 36*(2), 381–403.

Spulber, D. F. (2019). The economics of markets and platforms. *Journal of Economics and Management Strategy, 28*(1), 159–172.

Staw, B. M., Sandelands, L. E., & Dutton, J. E. (1981). Threat-rigidity effects in organizational behavior: A multilevel analysis. *Administrative Science Quarterly, 26*(4), 501–524.

Stouten, J., Rousseau, D. M., & De Cremer, D. (2018). Successful organizational change: Integrating the management practice and scholarly literatures. *Academy of Management Annals, 12*(2), 752–788.

Suchman, M. (1994). *On advice of counsel: Law firms and venture capital funds as information intermediaries in the structuration of Silicon Valley.* Unpublished doctoral dissertation. Stanford University, Stanford, CA.

Sutton, R. I. (1987). The process of organizational death: Disbanding and reconnecting. *Administrative Science Quarterly, 32*(4), 542–569.

Swidler, A. (1986). Culture in action: Symbols and strategies. *American Sociological Review, 51*(2), 273–286.

Tushman, M. L., & Romanelli, E. (1985). Organizational evolution: A metamorphosis model of convergence and reorientation. *Research in Organizational Behavior, 7,* 171–222.

Van Alstyne, M. W., Parker, G. G., & Choudary, S. P. (2016). Pipes, platforms, and the new rules of strategy. *Harvard Business Review, 19*(4), 54–62.

Vuori, T. O., & Huy, Q. N. (2016). Distributed attention and shared emotions in the innovation process: How Nokia lost the smartphone battle. *Administrative Science Quarterly, 61*(1), 9–51.

Walsh, I. J., & Bartunek, J. M. (2011). Cheating the fates: Organizational foundings in the wake of demise. *Academy of Management Journal, 54*(5), 1017–1044.

Westphal, J. D., Gulati, R., & Shortell, S. M. (1997). Customization or conformity? An institutional and network perspective on the content and consequences of TQM adoption. *Administrative Science Quarterly, 42*(1), 366–394.

Whetten, D. A. (1980). Organizational decline: A neglected topic in organizational science. *Academy of Management Review, 5*(4), 577–588.

Wiersema, M. F., & Bantel, K. A. (1993). Top management team turnover as an adaptation mechanism: The role of the environment. *Strategic Management Journal, 14*(7), 485–504.

Wowak, A. J., Gomez-Mejia, L. R., & Steinbach, A. L. (2017). Inducements and motives at the top: A holistic perspective on the drivers of executive behavior. *Academy of Management Annals, 11*(2), 669–702.

George P. Huber and Jean M. Bartunek

GENERATIVE EMERGENCE: RESEARCH AND PRAXIS FOR SOCIAL INNOVATION

EMERGENCE AND GENERATIVE EMERGENCE

Emergence as a discipline has existed since the beginning of the 20th century, as philosophers and scientists have explored this ubiquitous phenomenon of order creation (e.g. Lewes, 1877; Pepper, 1926). In formal terms its research question is: How does a new entity form, whose properties (outcomes) increase the capacity of all of its elements? Answers to this question have formed a broad literature of emergence studies, with major contributions by philosophers (Bedau & Humphreys, 2008; Klee, 1984; Stephen, 1992), physicists and biologists (Bernard, 1901; Odum, 1988; Prigogine, 1955; Reid, 2007), evolutionists (Corning, 1983; Eigen, 1971; Jantsch, 1980; Lotka, 1922, 1945; Morgan, 1923), complexity scientists (Crutchfield, 1994a; Csanyi & Kampis, 1985; Goldstein, 2018), and many scholars in organization science (Anderson, Arrow, & Pines, 1988; Crawford & McKelvey, 2012; Dooley, 2019; Fulmer & Ostroff, 2015; Perkmann & Spicer, 2014), along with researchers in virtually every discipline of the natural and social sciences.

Emergence is extremely relevant because emergents are everywhere; we are immersed in them (Clayton & Davies, 2006; Goldstein, 2002; Scott, 2012). In terms of industrial and organizational psychology, examples of emergents include projects and initiatives (Bird,

1988; 1992; Saynisch, 2010), teams (DeRue, Nahrgang, & Ashford, 2015; Kozlowski & Chao, 2012; Plowman et al., 2007a; Smith & Gemmill, 1991), organizational resources (Grand, Braun, Kuljanin, Kozlowsli, & Chao, 2016; Ployhart & Moliterno, 2011), and the creation of organizations (Brush, Manolova, & Edelman, 2008; Lichtenstein, Dooley, & Lumpkin, 2006; Nonaka, 1988; Padgett & Powell, 2011). At a more macro level, researchers have examined emergent collaborations (Beck & Plowman, 2013; Browning, Beyer, & Shetler, 1995; Lawrence, Hardy, & Phillips, 2002), new technologies and innovation (Cheng & Van de Ven, 1996; Dougherty & Dunne, 2011; Garud, Kumaraswamy, & Karnøe, 2010; Garud, Simpson, Langley, & Tsoukas, 2015; Grodal, Gotsopoulos, & Suarez, 2015), and the emergence of new fields, industries, institutions, and social movements (Dew, Reed, Sarasvathy, & Wiltbank, 2011; Fiol & Romanelli, 2012; Maguire, Hardy, & Lawrence, 2004; Pacheco, York, & Hargrave, 2014; Roundy, Bradshaw, & Brockman, 2018; Sawyer, 2005; Zeleny, 1981). Overall this summary reflects emergence across eight systemic levels of analysis (from individual to social movements; Emmeche, Koppe, & Stjernfelt, 1997), and a science of emergence is uncovering their accompanying dynamics of order creation—the conditions and processes which ultimately lead to a tangible emergent.

Two simple examples from nature help emphasize the core qualities of emergence. The first is a simple drop of water, composed of millions of molecules yet holding an independent shape, and an unexpected outcome—wetness. Where does *wetness* come from (Corning, 2012)? In a similar manner, the V-shape of flying geese is a tangible form that transcends its elements, and in so doing it increases the capacity of each bird and the entire flock (Cutts & Speakman, 1994; Hainsworth, 1987).

Note that all emergents have tangible outcomes (as for example the V-shape flying across the sky), and yet every one of them is constantly emerging; in this way emergence is a *process* with material *outcomes* (Bertalanffy, 1950; Lichtenstein, 2016). One formal model for this order-creation process is generative emergence, which stipulates four sequential phases that lead to the emergence of a new entity (Lichtenstein, 2014).

Organizationally and socially, emergent outcomes have significant influence. Whether a new initiative (project or product), a new venture, or a social innovation, what emerges is a distinct entity with agency—the ability to act in the world, contributing to customers and their community. Like the previous exemplars, these effects are caused by, but go beyond, the interdependence of all their elements. To take an organizational example, consider a venture that replaces all of its employees; even though its core elements have totally changed, the company itself remains. In terms of outcomes, an emergent generates tremendous gains in capacity (Lotka, 1945; Swenson, 1989; Wicken, 1986). As Adam Smith surmised: The organization of labor in a pin factory allows each individual to make a hundredfold more pins than if they were making them on their own.

In sum, emergence is the instantiation of a new system (McKelvey, 2001). The most parsimonious definition for this dual potential is from Jeff Goldstein (1999), who explains that emergence leads to "coherent structures, patterns, and properties in . . . complex systems" (p. 49). Here, coherent structures refer to the creation of new entities, whereas patterns and properties refer to internal order which can transform a system from within. Both are due to dynamic processes that lead to new order creation. Identifying these dynamics is the essence of generative emergence.

Emergence in the Context of Change and Transformation. To be clear, emergence is only one of the many ways that psychologists and organization scientists have explained system change. For example, there is long-standing research into adaptation, whereby the agent (individual, organization, ecosystem) gains feedback from other agents, learns from these patterns, and alters its behavior to better adapt to the current conditions. In ecosystems, this ongoing adaptivity is theorized as *resilience* (Folke, 2006; Folke et al., 2010; Gunderson & Holling, 2001; Holling, 1973, 2001), which has both psychological and organizational correlates (Caza & Milton, 2011; Masten, 2013; Ortiz-de-Mandojana & Bansal, 2016; Sutcliffe & Vogus, 2003).

Likewise, there are many theories and approaches to understanding change and transformation. In organization science, change can be conceptualized as learning and innovation, interventions to improve structure or strategy, and a range of dynamics that can lead to large-scale alterations or transformations (Garud & Van de Ven, 2002; Girod & Whittington, 2015; Kuhn, 1970; Langley, Smallman, Tsoukas, & Van de Ven, 2013; Poole, Van de Ven, Dooley, & Holmes, 2000). Some scholars have emphasized how multiple levels of change can produce stronger systemic effects (Geels, 2010; Geels & Schott, 2007; Kozlowski, Chao, Grand, & Kuljanin, 2013; Kozlowski & Klein, 2000; Pacheco et al., 2014) leading to transformations of organizations and even institutions.

Emergence differentiates itself from change in one important aspect: Change is an alteration of resources and structures currently accessible to the system—the system shifts but retains its essential identity. In contrast, emergence is the creation of an entirely new entity—something that was not there before is instantiated as an agent in its ecology (Ashby, 1947; Clayton & Davies, 2006; Goldstein, 2018; Padget & Powell, 2011; Sawyer, 2004; Tsoukas & Chia, 2002). Clearly, the dynamics of this instantiation have captured the attention of many dozens of scientists.

Amid this panoply of theories—from adaptation to resilience to change and innovation to transformation to emergence—many causal dynamics have been proposed. One of these is based on the empirical findings from the thermodynamics of dissipative structures (Bernard, 1901; Prigogine, 1955; Prigogine, Nicolis, & Babloyantz, 1972), which shows how emergence—and its resulting increase in systemic capacity—can be reliably produced in far-from-equilibrium systems (Nicolis & Prigogine, 1989; Prigogine & Glansdorff, 1971). Given the potential of this theory, many researchers have made rigorous analogies between the science and various social phenomenon (Artigiani, 1987; McKelvey, 2004a; Schieve & Allen, 2014; Smith, 1986), including organizations and the leadership within them (Carr-Chellman, Kitchel, & Freeman, 2020; Leifer, 1989; McKelvey, 2004b; Smith & Gemmill, 1991). The next section (see "Theory of Generative Emergence") explains the originating science for this form of emergence, and its mapping onto organizations through the four-phase model of generative emergence (Lichtenstein, 2014).

THEORY OF GENERATIVE EMERGENCE

Empirical Foundation from the Science of Thermodynamics. Since generative emergence theory draws closely on empirical findings from thermodynamics, it is useful to start with a very brief description of the core experiment there. The empirical setup is a closed container of fluid, with heat energy being dissipated through it, sourced from the bottom and drawn out from the top (Barnard, 1901; Prigogine & Stengers, 1984)—this is a dissipative structure. The formal experiment begins when the researchers turn up the heat source, which increases the energy flux, producing a *disequilibrium state* in the system. As higher levels of energy flow through the container, normal molecular interactions (the current structures) are unable to keep up with their task of dissipating the incoming heat energy. This leads to turbulence in the fluid, inexorably producing *micro-experiments*, each of which is a spontaneous attempt (innovation) to maintain the system's structure amid this increasing energy flux. But as the entire dissipative structure reaches a limit, the systemic changes become *amplified* through nonlinear feedback loops; this pushes the entire system to a *threshold* of structural stability.

Beyond that tipping point is emergence. Specifically at this threshold one of the *micro-experiments* becomes the seed for a totally new macrostructure of the dissipative structure: Tornado-like vortexes spontaneously form ("self-organize") within the container, each of which has the capacity to dissipate "orders of magnitude" more heat from the source to the sink (Swenson, 1989; see also Crutchfield, 1994a; Robb, 1990; Wicken, 1988). Almost immediately these vortexes "stabilize" and retain their structure as long as there is a continued high level of energy through the system. This process and its outcomes have been repeated over nearly 100 years of equivalent tests (Bénard, 1901; Nicolis, 1989; Prigogine & Glansdorff, 1971; Swenson, 1989, 2000).

Applying the Dynamics of Emergence to Social Systems.

Rigorous analogies of this process have been developed in dozens of studies in organizational and institutional psychology (Baldwin, Murray, Winder, & Ridgway, 2004; Dyke, 1988; McKelvey, 2004b). In particular, in-depth longitudinal case studies have confirmed the presence of these emergence dynamics in psychology and leadership (Barton, 1994; Guastello, 1998, 2001; Lichtenstein & Plowman, 2009; Nowak, Tesser, Vallacher, & Borkowski, 2000), in entrepreneurial startups (Fuller, Warren, & Argyle, 2008; Gartner & Brush, 2007; Lichtenstein, 2000; McKelvey, 2004b), in organizational transformations (Gemmill & Smith, 1985; MacIntosh & MacLean, 1999; Nonaka, 1988), and in alliances and geographic regions (Artigiani, 1987; Browning et al., 1995; Chiles, Meyer, & Hench, 2004). A summary of these dynamics forms the analogy utilized by dozens of organization scientists; all of these applications have been carefully integrated into four consonant phases, which are direct analogies to the original experiments in thermodynamics (Prigogine & Stengers, 1984)—see Table 1.

Emergence begins when systems are pushed into *disequilibrium* (McKelvey, 2004a; Meyer, Gaba, & Colwell, 2005) due to an influx of new energy (e.g., opportunity, effort, dramatic external changes). As this influx continues, the system's structures are less and less able to manage the increased energy flux—as a result the system experiences *stress* and turbulence. The growing stress leads to *micro-experiments*, local innovations whose dynamics can become *amplified* rapidly (Arthur, 1990; Chiles & Meyer, 2001; Plowman et al., 2007a). These *nonlinear dynamics* build to a *threshold* of change—a tipping point beyond which the system cannot retain its current structure (Arthur, 1990; Gladwell, 2000; Granovetter, 1978). This tipping point inevitably catalyzes the *emergence* of a new order through a *recombination of components* in the system (Lichtenstein et al., 2006; Robb, 1990). This emergence of a new order can dramatically improve the system's functionality (McKelvey, 2004a; Sawyer, 2005; Smith, 1986).

Table 1. Documented Sequences of Reemergence

	Phase 1: Disequilibrium Organizing	Phase 2: Stress/ Experiments Amplify to a Threshold	Phase 3: New Order: Recombination	Phase 4: Stabilizing Feedback	Outcomes: New Level; Higher Capacity
Nonaka (1988)	**Creation Of Chaos**	**Amplification Of Fluctuation**	**The New Order Restructuring Knowledge**	**Cooperation for Resolving Discrepancies**	*More Knowledge, More Dissemination*
Leifer (1989)	**Far-from-equilibrium Conditions**	**Experimentation** Trigger Event	**Transformation Re-synthesis**	**Stability**	*More Adaptive, Flexible*
Smith and Gemmill (1991)	**Non-equilibrium State**	**Experimentation Symmetry Breaking**	**Self-referencing**	**Resonance, Reparation**	*More Adaptability*
Browning, Beyer, and Shetler (1995)	**Irreversible Disequilibrium**	**Self-organizing Processes**	**A New Order**	Unintended Consequences	*Saved The U.S. Industry; Major Growth*
MacIntosh and MacLean (1999)	**Creating Far-from-equilibrium Conditions**	**Conditioning**, Positive Feedback, Decision Point	The Organization…Formulate[s] A New Deep Structure	**Managing The Feedback Process**	*Positive Outcomes When Process Followed*
Lichtenstein (2000)	**Increased Organizing**	**Tension, Experiments, to a Threshold**	**Newly Emerging Configuration**	Continued organizing	*Outcomes from the Transition*
Chiles, Meyer, and Hench (2004)	**Fluctuation Dynamics**	**Fluctuations and Positive Feedback**	**Resource Re-combinations**	**Stabilization Dynamics**	*More Tourists, More Shows, Higher Reputation Of Area*
Plowman et al. (2007a)	**Far-from-equilibrium State**	**Actions Amplify Small Changes**	**Acquiring New And Rearranging Existing Resources**	**Negative Feedback**	*Rapid, New Growth Of The Congregation*

Note: **Bold** refers to authors' section headings; Title Case draws from their core argument.

Finally, once the new order is in place, the system produces balancing feedback loops that *stabilize* and strengthen the emergent structures (Goldstein, 1994; Smith, 1986).

In summary, the four distinct phases of emergence are directly applicable to social systems: (a) *Disequilibrium conditions* in a system cause an increase in *stress* and *turbulence*, (b) which leads to *experiments* that get *amplified* up to *a critical threshold*, (c) on the other side of which is *new order emergence*, through *a recombination of components*, and (d) finally this is followed by the *stabilization* of new structures through balancing feedback. The next sections more fully present these four phases of generative emergence (see "Mapping Emergence Dynamics in Entrepreneurial Ventures"), and how their operationalization leads to leadership tools for producing each phase (see "Praxis: Psychology and Leadership of Generative Emergence"), dramatically increasing the prospects of successful emergence of new systems.

MAPPING EMERGENCE DYNAMICS IN ENTREPRENEURIAL VENTURES

Phase 1: Disequilibrium Organizing, and Stress.
The first condition for emergence is high-intensity organizing that pushes the system into a *disequilibrium state* (MacIntosh & MacLean, 1999; Meyer et al., 2005). In entrepreneurial terms, these dynamics are caused by an aspiration to create value, termed *opportunity tension* (Chiles, Tuggle, McMullen, Bierman, & Greening, 2010; Lichtenstein, 2009). *Opportunity* refers to the potential for value creation (Lumpkin & Dess, 1996; McMullan, Plummer, & Acs, 2007), while *tension* reflects "creative tension" (Fritz, 1989)—the personal passion to bring the opportunity into fruition (Baron, 2008; Cardon, Wincent, Singh, & Drnovsek, 2009). Thus, opportunity tension is the proactive drive that sets the stage for emergence (Guastello, 1987).

This high level of organizing activity (Gartner & Brush, 2007; Gartner & Starr, 1993), which pushes the system away from its initial structure (Goldstein, 1988), also produces high levels of uncertainty, extremely long working days, and a great deal of *stress* in the entrepreneur and her support system (Huff, Huff, & Thomas, 1992; McKelvey, 2004a). If the team can maintain the organizing effort through this stress, they approach the second phase of the emergence process.

Phase 2: Experiments and Amplifications to a Critical Threshold.
Following the dissipative structures analogy, increased stress elicits *micro-experiments*—unique ways to deal with the turbulence of high-energy organizing. Experiments are happening all the time in organizations (Dooley, 1997; Leifer, 1989), but when the venture is pushed into disequilibrium these increase in rate and potential influence. Even though experiments may resolve local points of stress, overall they do not counter the growth of disequilibrium caused by determined entrepreneurial organizing. Instead, stress and experiments accumulate, producing nonproportional effects that *amplify* the system's dynamics (Arthur, 1990), up to a *critical threshold* (Granovetter, 1978; Leifer, 1989). On the other side of this tipping point is *emergence*—either the collapse of the whole system or the creation of a new order (Goldstein, 1988; Wicken, 1981).

Phase 3: Emergence Through a Recombination of System Components.
In the positive case, new structures emerge through a *recombination* of existing resources and properties, yielding a new system state (Baker & Nelson, 2005; Corning, 1995; Salthe, 1989; Ulrich

& Probst, 1984). In entrepreneurial terms, a new venture starts up and invokes a transformation in the learning and skills of the team (Gartner & Brush, 2007; McKelvey, 2004b), and a total reconfiguration (symbiotic integration) of designs, resources, and routines (Goldstein, 2018; Guastello, 1995; Lichtenstein, 2014). These nonlinear dynamics often create surprising outcomes, but once enacted the changes settle down to a "quiet roar."

Phase 4: Stabilization of the Newly Emerged State. This new dynamic state stabilizes when amplification dynamics are reduced due to the higher capability of the new structures. By integrating the most efficient aspects of the new order, entrepreneurial leaders legitimize—institutionalize and sustain—the new state (Artigiani, 1987; Chiles & Meyer, 2001).

A critical final detail is that the emergent system will remain stable only if the system remains in a far-from-equilibrium state (McKelvey, 2004a; Meyer et al., 2005; Prigogine & Glansdorff, 1971). Thus, this last phase does not imply a draw-down of inputs. Instead emergence builds on those increased flows, organizing them in far more effective ways. As such, the balancing feedbacks that arise in this phase serve to resist external perturbations, allowing the system to stay resilient over time.

Outcomes: Emergent Order Increases System Capacity. Positive outcomes from emergence are not assured; as any entrepreneur will attest, neither are they common. However, if the previous conditions are set, and the process unfolds in roughly the sequence identified, generative emergence predicts that new order creation is likely to generate increased capacity in the venture and in its agents (Lichtenstein, 2014). These capacity increases may extend beyond the focal system; for example, emergent partnerships and new collaborations might expand capabilities, and a creative solution might create new resources that can lead to a social innovation. In these ways, emergence can bring an expansion of the company's very identity, as expressed by the project manager of one newly reorganized fast-growth company: "I think it's even more than the beginning of a new stage. I think it's a redefinition of the [company] as we know it" (Lichtenstein, 2000). These outcomes and similar ones have been found in many empirical studies across multiple levels of analysis (Browning et al., 1995; Chiles et al., 2004; Leifer, 1989; MacIntosh & MacLean, 1999; Nonaka, 1988; Plowman et al., 2007b; Smith & Gemmill, 1991).

. . . Or, The Collapse of the System. However, moving through the four phases does not ensure a positive outcome; as my dissertation advisor once quipped, "A company can self-organize itself right over a cliff!" Essentially, emergence outcomes occur on a continuum, starting from dissolution and extending to the positive outcomes expressed above (Chalmers, 2006; Crutchfield, 1994b; Goldstein, 2002). There are at least two explanations for negative outcomes. First, (re)creating an entire system all at once is extremely challenging; it involves an unprecedented amount of internal processing that can—and often does—overwhelm the system (agents). The second reason refers to a theoretical claim, namely that the new order will stabilize itself *if it is creating value* (McKelvey, 2004a; Robb, 1990; Schieve & Allen, 2014). Thus, when a new venture is unable to re-leverage its resources to produce more capacity, the lack of positive effect may trigger the organization's demise—a situation faced by countless entrepreneurs as well as two of the four companies analyzed by Lichtenstein (2000).

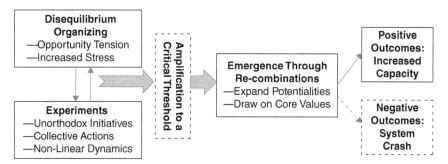

Figure 1. Sequences and outcome dynamics for generative emergence.

In sum, emergence can generate two types of outcomes: greater capacity, or an overall demise. In some ways these two potential outcomes are linked: "Following a bifurcation point, and old system may disintegrate [in order to] attain a more complex and appropriate ... new order" (Browning et al., 1995, p. 142). However, if the conditions are right, a recombination of elements, followed by a stabilization of the system, is likely to yield a new entity with greater capacity to accomplish its mission and goals (MacIntosh & MacLean, 1999).

Figure 1 provides an image of the sequence of these four phases and their outcomes.

Validating the Analogy in Multiple Levels of Social Systems.

How well does this analogy hold across a range of similar studies? Analyzing the parallels, or lack thereof, is the final step in validating the analogy between the science of dissipative structures and its applications (Tsoukas, 1989, 1991). This validation analysis is presented in Table 1, which draws on nine classic studies across multiple levels of analysis that are direct analogies to the emergence theory of dissipative structures. Perhaps the most convincing part of this examination is the fact that virtually all of the empirical examples are *inductive* theory-development studies, in which scholars collected longitudinal data from emergent endeavors, and searched for the best way to describe their dynamics. Surprisingly, even though the research teams operated independently without predefined constructs, their exploratory analyses identified the *same four processes* to describe their cases. The fact that these scholars, who were looking at emergence across very different contexts, found the same dynamics give rise to emergence, provides a high degree of empirical validity for the model.

PRAXIS: PSYCHOLOGY AND LEADERSHIP OF GENERATIVE EMERGENCE

Drawing on these studies and others, a number of leadership scholars have explored a range of case examples of emergence to help uncover a praxis for supporting the emergence of new systems. Much of this praxis derives from a developing literature on complexity leadership (Goldstein, Hazy, & Lichtenstein, 2010; Plowman et al., 2007b; Uhl-Bien, Marion, & McKelvey, 2007; Uhl-Bein & Arena, 2017). However, these approaches have correlates in other leadership theories as well. For example, distributed and shared leadership focus on the interchange between leaders and their followers, which help initiate substantive shifts "from the inside out" (Bolden, 2011; Denis, Langley, & Sergi, 2012; Pearce & Conger, 2003). Likewise, relational leadership emphasizes the interdependence within systems, which can also be used to spark transformative shifts (Anand, Vidyarthi, & Park, 2015; Gittell, Seidner, & Wimbush, 2010; Uhl-Bien & Arena, 2017). In addition, transformational leadership extends traditional notions of transactions into shared interventions that can spark wholesale system change (e.g., East, 2019; Montuori & Donnelly, 2017; Torbert & Associates, 2004).

Elements of all of these can be seen in the leadership of generative emergence; a summary of those theoretically grounded tools and exemplars can offer guidance for those seeking to enact generative emergence. The following subsections use case study examples to show how leaders have initiated the conditions or dynamics of emergence, through the four phases of generative emergence. To make the examples clearer, brief introductions of each of the main studies follow.

- ServiceCo, DevelopNet, and ApplySci are fast-growth emerging ventures, each seeking to establish themselves in a high-tech market (Lichtenstein, 2000).
- Mission Church is a large and long-standing institution, seeking to reinvent itself after years of steady decline in membership (Plowman et al., 2007a).
- SEMATECH is a prospective interorganizational collaboration, whose members hope to codevelop technology (software and hardware) for an emerging tech industry (Browning et al., 1995).
- Branson, Missouri, is a small town that unexpectedly emerged as a center for live musical theater (Chiles et al., 2004).

Phase 1: Encourage Aspiration, Conflict, Uncertainty, and Stress.   Creating and maintaining a disequilibrium state has been shown to drive emergence in larger organizations (Plowman et al., 2007a), in new market creation (Fiol & Romanelli, 2012; Tan, 2007), and in major shifts in industries and institutions (Baker & Nelson, 2005; Purdy & Gray, 2009). This is exemplified in Branson, Missouri, where a best-selling book and two 60-minute episodes heralded Branson's foray into musical theater. Here, entrepreneurial *aspiration* moved the quiet rural town far away from its previous culture, creating the space for unexpected inputs. The opening of Andy Williams's theater in 1992 marked a "'distinct break [that] went against the norm,' said his manager. . . . 'It changed the frame of reference, and broke the mindset of Branson as a country music venue, and ushered in a new regime of order'" (Chiles et al., 2004, p. 509).

Behind these acts of *creative tension* is an uncertainty that accrues when moving into the unknown. Successful cases show how *encouraging uncertainty* by *surfacing conflict* can facilitate the process. For example, the attempted turnaround at Mission Church—situated downtown in the middle of a large southwestern U.S. city—was sparked by a series of controversial actions by the two new pastors, which amplified a growing uncertainty about the church's viability (Plowman et al., 2007a). To begin, a series of open discussions were held to talk about the problems plaguing the failing church. Further sources of disequilibrium included welcoming homosexuals for the first time, inviting provocative speakers, and a new project providing meals and support to the neighborhood's homeless people (Plowman et al., 2007a). In leadership terms, these moves altered the assumptions of organizational members, moving them out of their comfort zone into a state of disequilibrium (Goldstein, 1988; Surie & Hazy, 2007).

In successful instances of generative emergence, entrepreneurial leaders do not take these challenges as a reason to back off on their vision, but continue to push the system farther away from its norm, *amplifying the internal stress*. For example, "organization building" activities at DevelopNet increased by more than 400% in this phase—and 500% at ApplySci. However, this rise was paralleled by extreme financial stress. As described by a senior scientist at ApplySci, "Can we stay alive? Not the way we're structured financially. The hourglass is running out. I don't know what the founder has up his sleeve." The only answer to this challenge is to encourage innovation (Lichtenstein, 2000).

Phase 2: Unorthodox Initiatives, Collective Actions, and Nonlinearity.

As stress increases, there is a concomitant increase in *experiments*—bottom-up organizing efforts aimed at reducing the rise in turbulence. As the following examples show, these come in many different forms, as agents across the system try to manage the amplified flow of energy they face. For example, when entrepreneurs at SEMATECH found that their planned business models were not accomplishing their collaborative goals, they tried *unconventional alternatives*. In particular they adopted practices from member companies and tried expanding them across the entire alliance, unexpectedly creating a new momentum (Browning et al., 1995, pp. 141–142). Similarly, emergence dynamics at Mission Church were catalyzed by *collective actions* by a group of young adults there, who self-funded an initiative to make and serve breakfast for homeless people in the immediate vicinity. This unorthodox idea became even more controversial (causing increased disequilibrium) when one of the pastors arrived at a city-wide event on homelessness with 12 of the best-known homeless customers from Café Corazon. This move amplified the issue of marginalized people in the city, and its unintended spotlight increased internal momentum for the organizational turnaround effort (Plowman et al., 2007a).

Collective action also played a significant role in the emergences at Branson. For example, Branson's first musical theater started as a collective organization; further, the Ozark Marketing Council attracted increasing waves of tourists to the area, accelerating the resources necessary for emergence. These activities were amplified by the collective organizing of entrepreneurs, financiers, and community leaders, who catalyzed further transformations of the region (Chiles et al., 2004).

Leaders can help spark these *amplification dynamics* by reinforcing them as they occur. Positive feedback from one action/event increases the likelihood that other similar events will occur (Anderson, 1999; Guastello, 2001, 2010). This practice of "deviation amplification" (Maruyama, 1963) helps intensify the nonlinear dynamics already occurring in the system. This practice was noted in many studies; for example at Mission Church, "the tension the organization was experiencing . . . made it all the more likely that a small change could emerge and be amplified into something much larger" (Plowman et al., 2007a, p. 537). These dynamics were exemplified by the seemingly innocuous idea to start Café Corazon which would normally have been quashed by the silk-and-stockings heritage of the church. However, in the context of disequilibrium conditions, the experiment took off, catalyzing the reemergence of the entire institution. Initially aiming to serve just one meal to about 75 marginalized citizens, within a few weeks Café Corazon was serving over 200 breakfasts a week. Then one day a doctor arrived with a small table for informal checkups; this became amplified into a large-scale free medical clinic at the church, as well as additional services which were funded through public grants. What initially was a unorthodox bottom-up initiative became the seed for an entirely new mission at the church to become a leader in social activism, and a concomitant growth of membership from a totally new demographic.

Phase 3: Draw on Core Values to Expand Potentiality. Leaders can have a powerful positive influence in how recombinations can *expand possibilities* to facilitate long-term success. Branson provides exemplars due to the rapid turnover of theater facilities, constantly providing avenues for upgrades and creative changes. Even more, entrepreneurs found that failures were themselves opportunities for recombinations—in the words of one founder: "We built the theater so that if it didn't work, we could put in boat storage for the lakes. That's why we built it with no slope, with a flat floor" (Chiles et al., 2004, p. 514). These ventures were literally designed to reconfigure themselves (Garud, Kumaraswamy, & Sambamurthy, 2006), as entrepreneurial leaders incorporated a range of ultimate uses that could leverage existing resources in creative ways.

Such recombinations can also *expand the pie for all the agents in the ecology*, increasing the effectiveness and adaptiveness of the system at multiple levels. For example, at SEMATECH, at least half of the consortium's resources were directed not to alliance members but to their suppliers, with the unintended outcome being greater commitment and cooperation among the consortium, and extending the collaboration well beyond its initial 5-year plan. Similarly at Mission Church, when Café Corazon became too large for the existing building, organizers requested the use of an unused, dilapidated wing of the church. In so doing the church was able to enlarge its scope from a Sunday morning ministry to a host of social services: a new homeless shelter open daily, space for more clinics, a large area for clothes to be given away, and the incorporation of showers and other facilities for marginalized neighbors. In both cases, an artful recombination of resources extends the viability and effectiveness of the emergence of the new order.

An organization's central values can be expressed through symbolic actions, especially in moments of extreme disequilibrium and reorientation (Marion & Uhl-Bien, 2001; Selden & Fletcher, 2015). When a reorganization is "correlated" to the *core values of the venture*, the new structures are more likely to be viable and accepted (Gehman, Trevino, & Garud, 2013; Perkman & Spicer, 2014). This correlation was well expressed at ServiceCo within a week of their reemergence, when it was clear that all the employees who had worked on the now-disbanded product line were superfluous in the newly designed venture. But rather than lay off half of its employees, the founders decided to base their reorganization decisions on core values they had long espoused in the company. Thus, the roles and structures of the emergent product were totally recombined, allowing this other half of the company to be integrated into newly formulated support and innovation activities (Lichtenstein, 2000). Other *values-based decisions* included a whole-office redesign that featured open cubicle spaces, small meeting rooms, and new labs for research and development activities. In addition to improving relationality and efficiency, these symbolic actions invoked a shared meaning about what was most important at the new ServiceCo. Further, this link between new structures and long-term values supported the stabilization of the emergence (see "Phase 4: Link New Order to Values, and Maintain the New Energy Flow").

Phase 4: Link New Order to Values, and Maintain the New Energy Flow. Two dynamics set the conditions for a stabilization of the nascent reorganization. First, as demonstrated at ServiceCo, the stabilization of the new order will be facilitated when the new design is *embedded in the system's core values,* or if draws on those values to determine which emergent initiatives to support and which should be a little less emphasized. Mission Church provides a revealing example of the latter. Café Corazon's expansion into a full-time shelter was met with resistance from local businesses, who complained about homeless people waiting in line for the center to open while employees and guests at the nearby hotel were arriving for the day. In response, the pastors adjusted the hours of the homeless shelter to minimize this conflict. On the other hand, when some congregational members wanted the mission of the organization to be centered solely on providing social services, the pastors decided to limit the growth of services into areas that they considered appropriate "ministry," thus distinguishing Mission Church from government agencies that serve the poor.

A stronger example was seen in Branson, where leaders sought to retain the integrity (stability) of the new era that had emerged. This was achieved through a collective influence behavior called *Bransonizing,* whereby "locals counseled newcomers on the importance of fully reflecting local cultural values in their performances, and maintaining the cultural consistency that had become central to Branson's national image" (Chiles et al., 2004, p. 512). That is, a new theater could be accepted in Branson only if it carefully honored the local culture by enacting the widely shared values of "wholesome community with traditional moral fiber and friendliness." In this way all theaters were constrained yet enabled by being more fully integrated into the local fabric of culture and beliefs that led to Branson's success.

A second critical dynamic is that the newly organized system will be retained only with the *continued flux of high energy into the system* (Fuller et al., 2008; Girod & Whittington, 2015; Meyer et al., 2005). Staying in this state is not easy, for it requires that the new, higher level of organizing and resources (customers, investments) be constantly renewed such that this overall flow is not diminished (Baldwin et al., 2004; Dooley, 1997; McKelvey, 2004a). However, maintaining this constant pace takes a tremendous amount of creativity, and the pursuit of additional organizing over time. The art of accomplishing this was well expressed in Branson. Following the emergence of the new theater industry there, collective organizations brought additional new resources to bear by leveraging a strong set of common values, a deepening commitment to pro-business policies, and a coordination of marketing efforts across member organizations. Ultimately this influx of additional energy maintained the increased level of organizing in the region, thus stabilizing the emergent order.

Leverage Outcomes Through Value Creation. Positive outcomes from emergence have been illustrated throughout the article; one of these is the creation of a new entity, which *transcends the elements (agents) within it.* Groups transcend their members, new ventures transcend their internal teams, transformed organizations redefine their mission, and new alliances extend the boundaries of previous organizing (Chiles & Meyer, 2001; Emmeche et al., 1997; Lawrence et al., 2002). In the literature of entrepreneurship as emergence, once the company starts up and gains its first customers, it simultaneously becomes a competitor in the market, a new source of advertising revenue, a link in the supply chain, and other tangible outcomes (Gartner, 1985, 1993; Gartner & Brush, 2007; Santos & Eisenhardt, 2009; Sarasson, Dean, & Hilliard, 2006; Sarasvathy & Dew, 2005).

The second outcome revolves around a central purpose of emergence, namely to *increase the system's capacity to create value*—for itself, and as a contribution to its customers/ecology (Lichtenstein et al., 2006; Nicholls-Nixon, 2005). However, the emergence and stabilization of a new entity will be retained to the degree that the venture focuses on value-creation activities. Although this was the case in most of the examples cited so far, a counterexample makes the opposite point clearly.

The emergence of ApplySci as a high-potential startup was met with enthusiasm by the board of directors (mainly investors), who quickly hired a chief executive officer (CEO) to stabilize the venture and start the next phase of growth. However, the new executive pursued a "blue sky" strategy that was rather disconnected from the venture's existing strengths; to pay for these she enacted a series of cost-cutting moves that severely limited the firm's capacity to respond to potential new orders. Worse, the CEO's strong decision-making style countered the original values of the firm, disenfranchising its remaining employees. "The result was a feeling of discouragement, frustration and chaos" (Lichtenstein, 2000, p. 136), as well as a financial shortfall which disrupted the stability of the emergence and sent the venture into rapid decline. Ultimately, the business had to undergo an abrupt acquisition, causing a loss of nearly US$8,000,000 in investments. In sum, although the reemergence at ApplySci appeared to be successful, the resulting drop in value-creation activities resulted in the dissolution of the organization. Here, reinforcing feedbacks can be the difference between positive emergence and catastrophic failure (Guastello, 1995).

All of these tools and dynamics in generative emergence—the actions that organizers can use to help generate emergence—are summarized in Table 2.

Table 2. Phases and Leadership Dynamics for Generative Emergence

---

Phase 1: Disequilibrium organizing, and stress
- aspiration and opportunity tension
- surfacing conflict, embracing uncertainty
- positive role of stress

Phase 2: Experiments and amplifications to a critical threshold
- encourage unorthodox initiatives and collective actions
- emphasize nonlinear dynamics

Phase 3: Emergence through a recombination of system resources
- recombine elements to expand possibilities
- reorganize based on core values

Phase 4: Stability of the newly emerged state
- link emergent order to existing values
- maintain the higher level of organizing

Outcomes: Emergent order increases capacity
- leverage outcomes by maintaining value creation

CONCLUSION: WHAT WE CAN LEARN FROM EMERGENCE

Propositions of Generative Emergence. This article has attempted to summarize the theory of generative emergence, using frameworks and examples relevant to organizational and industrial psychology. The four-phase process of generative emergence is based on a rigorous analogy from a classic experiment in thermodynamics that reveals the dynamics of order creation in far-from-equilibrium systems. These dynamics have been identified in multiple studies of emergence, and the four phases they reflect have been validated across a range of inductive case analyses. In addition to summarizing this research, the article identifies a set of leadership tools which have been shown to help catalyze each of the phases in turn.

Two formal propositions can be derived about generative emergence, based on its four phases: disequilibrium organizing, and stress; experiments and amplification to a critical threshold; emergence through a recombination of elements; and stabilization of the newly emergent state. The first proposition is that the combination of these dynamics is a necessary, but not necessarily sufficient, condition for the emergence of a new order. The second is a much stronger claim about the outcomes of emergence: The more closely these four dynamics are enacted in parallel to the experiments from dissipative structures—that is, that each phase follows the theoretical details described herein, and that the four phases occur in sequence—the more likely the order that emerges will have positive outcomes, such as higher system capacity and greater agency of the entity.

Admittedly these are strong claims, yet I believe they are warranted based on the past 25 years of emergence research (Corning, 2012; Goldstein, 2018; Prigogine & Stengers, 1984; Robb, 1990; Sawyer, 2004). However, until they are tested and confirmed in a rigorous experiment, they remain propositions at best. Verifying these propositions is a prescient goal of future research.

Contributions to a Science and Praxis of Emergence. Emergence has strong theoretical roots, which have been explored by scholars in nearly every discipline—an initial list was provided in the introduction (see "Emergence and Generative Emergence"). The range of emergence research is impressive; moreover, there is beginning to be a consensus on the core theoretical principles of emergence, developed by long-standing researchers including Bar-Yam (2004), Bedau and Humphreys (2008), Clayton (2006), Crutchfield (1994a), and Goldstein (1999, 2002). The essence of these theoretical foundations can be integrated into three principles, which appear to capture the central findings of emergence scholars (Lichtenstein, 2011a, 2018). With further collaboration, these may help initiate a more formal science of emergence.[1]

At the same time, it is less clear how such a science can extend current theories of management psychology, organization studies, and institutionalization. Each already has models of innovation, entrepreneurship, and system change, including theories of group formation, opportunity recognition, and the creation of "noncorporeal actors." Although emergence scholars have set out the conditions and principles for new order creation, these theoretical constructs have not been assimilated into organizational and institutional psychology, for two primary reasons.

First, many of the underlying theories of current emergence research are based in complexity science, which was the origin for much of the emergence work in organization studies and management—including Ulrich and Probst (1984), Guastello (1995), Brown and Eisenhardt (1997), Dooley (1997), Anderson (1999), MacIntosh and MacLean (1999), and extending through numerous papers by McKelvey (1997, 1999, 2004b). As Dooley (2019) points out, "The proliferation of research articles, empirical studies, practical applications, and institutions (specialized journals and professional societies) in the 1990's was suggestive of a significant change in theory and practice of organizational sciences – a paradigm shift." However, since its peak in the early 2000s, the prevalence of complexity scholarship has declined significantly (Dooley, 2019, p. 5). Currently very few complexity-based papers are being published in top management journals, suggesting that the interest in nonlinear dynamics and the sciences of order creation is on the wane.

Perhaps more importantly, Dooley found that in these academic articles, the terms *complexity* and *emergence* were often used in a "vernacular way" with complexity being interpreted as "many" and emergence as the "beginning of." For example, an unpublished analysis of top-tier journals in management identified 28 articles published between 2000 and 2016 in which the term *emergence* was in the title. However only one of these (published in *Management Information Systems Quarterly*) used principles from complexity science or emergence in their theory or methods. Thus, although emergence is used as a descriptor for creation and newness, the underlying principles of emergence are not much in use within academic research.

However, in contrast to the pursuit of academic theory, a more viable contribution of generative emergence is in supporting the practice of order creation, as a guide to encouraging the dynamics (steps and sequence) for creating innovations and new systems as a whole. Thus, rather than a purely theoretical tool, emergence may be more valuable as a catalyst for the organizing of emergents of all kinds. Examples include new projects, initiatives, teams, ventures, innovations, markets, and even social movements. A number of management scholars have taken this approach to explore the processes (actions) that can spark entrepreneurial startup (Gartner & Brush, 2007; Lichtenstein & Kurjanowicz, 2010; Perkmann & Spicer, 2014; Selden & Fletcher, 2015), the dynamics of innovation (Dew et al., 2011; Garud et al., 2006), and more recently for the emergence of sustainable ventures (Battilana & Dorado, 2010; Elkington, 1994; Neto & Almeida, 2018) and sustainability more broadly (Buenstorf, 2000; Chertow & Ehrenfeld, 2012; Lichtenstein, 2011b; Varga et al., 2009).

In part this conclusion reflects the wide variety of perspectives and disciplines that have been used to study emergence, each of which makes certain claims about its underlying dynamics. Notwithstanding the potential advances from a science of emergence, the diversity of approaches across levels of analysis make it hard to discern what exactly an emergence theory would contain. Even more, this emphasis on praxis over theory can be deduced from the propositions for generative emergence, which claim that the outcomes of emergence cannot be predicted with certainty.

Yet, these propositions also highlight the primary goal of this work; namely, to draw on a wide range of empirical research to identify the conditions and actions that are mostly likely to produce emergence, in ways that improve the capacity and viability of the new system. The vast majority of these insights have been derived from interviews with entrepreneurs and in close observation of contexts undergoing emergence. Thus, the findings—the four phases and the praxis of activating them—have a strong degree of face validity, and reliability in action. As individuals utilize these tools and provide feedback on their effectiveness, more robust versions of generative emergence will emerge.

REFERENCES

Anand, S., Vidyarthi, P. R., & Park, H. S. (2015). LMX differentiation: Understanding relational leadership at individual and group levels. In T. N. Bauer & B. Eddogan (Eds.), *The Oxford handbook of leader-member exchange*. Oxford, UK: Oxford University Press.

Anderson, P. (1999). Complexity theory and organization science. *Organization Science, 10*, 216–232.

Anderson, P., Arrow, K., & Pines, D. (1988). *The economy as an evolving complex system*. Redwood City, CA: Addison-Wesley.

Arthur, B. (1990, February). Positive feedbacks in the economy. *Scientific American, 262*(2), 92–99.

Artigiani, R. (1987). Revolution and evolution: Applying Prigogine's dissipative structures model. *Journal of Social and Psychological Structures, 10*, 249–264.

Ashby, R. (1947). Principles of the self-organizing dynamic system. *Journal of General Psychology, 37*, 125.

Baker, T., & Nelson, R. (2005). Creating something from nothing: Resource construction through entrepreneurial bricolage. *Administrative Science Quarterly, 50*, 232–366.

Baldwin, J., Murray, R., Winder, B., & Ridgway, K. (2004). A non-equilibrium thermodynamic model of industrial development: Analogy or homology. *Journal of Cleaner Production, 12*, 841–853.

Bar-Yam, Y. (2004). A mathematical theory of strong emergence using multiscale variety. *Complexity, 9*(6), 15–24.

Baron, R. (2008). The role of affect in the entrepreneurial process. *Academy of Management Review, 33*, 328–340.

Barton, S. (1994). Chaos, self-organization, and psychology. *American Psychologist, 49*, 5–14.

Battilana, J., & Dorado, S. (2010). Building sustainable hybrid organizations: The case of commercial microfinance organizations. *Academy of Management Journal, 53*(6), 1419–1440.

Beck, T. E., & Plowman, D. A. (2013). Temporary, emergent interorganizational collaboration in unexpected circumstances: A study of the Columbia space shuttle response effort. *Organization Science, 25*(4), 1234–1252. https://dx.doi.org/10.1287/orsc.2013.0888

Bedau, M., & Humphreys, P. (Eds.). (2008). *Emergence: Contemporary readings in philosophy and science*. Cambridge, MA: MIT Press.

Bénard, H. (1901). Les tourbillons cellulaires dans une nappe liquide transportant de la chaleur par convection en régime permanent. *Annales de Chimie et de Physique, 23*, 62–114.

Bertalanffy, L. von. (1950, January 13). The theory of open systems in physics and biology. *Science, 111*, 23–28.

Bird, B. (1988). Implementing entrepreneurial ideas: The case for intention. *Academy of Management Review, 13*, 442–453.

Bird, B. (1992). The operations of intentions in time: The emergence of new ventures. *Entrepreneurship Theory and Practice, 17*, 11–20.

Bolden, R. (2011). Distributed leadership in organizations: A review of theory and research. *International Journal of Management Reviews, 13*, 251–269.

Brown, S., & Eisenhardt, K. (1997). The art of continuous change: Linking complexity theory and time-based evolution in relentlessly shifting organizations. *Administrative Science Quarterly, 42*, 1–34.

Browning, L., Beyer, J., & Shetler, J. (1995). Building cooperation in a competitive industry: Sematech and the semiconductor industry. *Academy of Management Journal, 38*, 113–151.

Brush, C., Manolova, T., & Edelman, L. (2008). Properties of emerging organizations: An empirical test. *Journal of Business Venturing, 23*, 547–566.

Buenstorf, G. (2000). Self-organization and sustainability: Energetics of evolution and implications for ecological economics. *Ecological Economics, 33*, 119–134.

Cardon, M., Wincent, J., Singh, J., & Drnovsek, M. (2009). The nature and experience of entrepreneurial passion. *Academy of Management Review, 34*(3), 511–532.

Carr-Chellman, A., Kitchel, A., & Freeman, S. (2020). Negentropy: Energy creating tools for organizational development. *Tech Trends, 64*, 275–279.

Caza, B. B., & Milton, L. (2011). Resilience at work: Building capability in the face of adversity. In R. Cameron & G. Spreitzer (Eds.), *Oxford handbook of positive organizations* (pp. 895–908). New York, NY: Oxford University Press.

Chalmers, D. (2006). Strong and weak emergence. In P. Clayton & P. Davies (Eds.), *The re-emergence of emergence: The emergentist hypothesis from science to religion* (pp. 244–256). New York, NY: Oxford University Press.

Cheng, Y., & Van de Ven, A. (1996). The innovation journey: Order out of chaos? *Organization Science, 6*, 593–614.

Chertow, M. & Ehrenfeld, J. (2012). Organizing self-organizing systems: Toward a theory of industrial symbiosis. *Journal of Industrial Ecology, 16*(1), 13–27.

Chiles, T., & Meyer, A. (2001). Managing the emergence of clusters: An increasing returns approach to strategic change. *Emergence, 3*(3), 58–89.

Chiles, T., Meyer, A., & Hench, T. (2004). Organizational emergence: The origin and transformation of Branson, Missouri's musical theaters. *Organization Science, 15*(5), 499–520.

Chiles, T., Tuggle, C. S., McMullen, J., Bierman, L., & Greening, D. (2010). Dynamic creation: Elaborating a radical Austrian approach to entrepreneurship. *Organization Studies, 31*, 7–46.

Clayton, P. (2006). Conceptual foundations of emergence theory. In P. Clayton & P. Davies (Eds.), *The re-emergence of emergence: The emergentist hypothesis from science to religion* (pp. 1–34). New York, NY: Oxford University Press.

Clayton, P., & Davies, P. (2006). *The re-emergence of emergence: The emergentist hypothesis from science to religion.* New York, NY: Oxford University.

Corning, P. (1983). *The synergism hypothesis: A theory of progressive evolution.* New York, NY: McGraw-Hill.

Corning, P. (1995). Synergy and self-organization in the evolution of complex systems. *Systems Research, 12*(2), 89–121.

Corning, P. (2012). The re-emergence of emergence, and the causal role of synergy in emergent evolution. *Synthese, 185*(2), 295–317.

Crawford, G. C., & McKelvey, B. (2012). Strategic implications of power law distributions in the creation and emergence of new ventures: Power law analyses in three panel studies. *Frontiers of Entrepreneurship Research, 32*, 12–16.

Crutchfield, J. (1994a). The calculi of emergence: Computation, dynamics and induction. *Physica D, 75*(1–3), 11–54.

Crutchfield, J. (1994b). Is anything ever new? Considering emergence. In G. Cowan, D. Pines, & D. Meltzer (Eds.), *Complexity: Metaphors, models, and reality* (pp. 479–497). Reading, MA: Addison-Wesley.

Csanyi, V., & Kampis, G. (1985). Autogenesis: Evolution of replicative systems. *Journal of Theoretical Biology, 114*, 303–321.

Cutts, C., & Speakman, J. (1994). Energy savings in formation flight of pink-footed geese. *Journal of Experimental Biology, 189*, 251–261.

Denis, J.-L., Langley, A., & Sergi, V. (2012). Leadership in the plural. *Academy of Management Annals, 6*(1), 211–283.

DeRue, D. S., Nahrgang, J. D., & Ashford, S. J. (2015). Interpersonal perceptions and the emergence of leadership structures in groups: A network perspective. *Organization Science, 26*(4), 1192–1209. https://dx.doi.org/10.1287/orsc.2014.0963

Dew, N., Reed, S., Sarasvathy, S., & Wiltbank, R. (2011). On the entrepreneurial genesis of new markets: Effectual transformations versus causal search and selection. *Journal of Evolutionary Economics, 21,* 231–253.

Dooley, K. (1997). A complex adaptive systems model of organization change. *Nonlinear Dynamics, Psychology, and the Life Sciences, 1,* 69–97.

Dooley, K. (2019). Complexity science and the organization sciences: 1999–2018. In D. Kiel & E. Elliott (Eds.), *Chaos theory in the social sciences: Foundations and applications* (Vol. 4). Ann Arbor: University of Michigan Press (In Preparation).

Dougherty, D., & Dunne, D. (2011). Organizing ecologies of complex innovation. *Organization Science, 22*(5), 1214–1223.

Dyke, C. (1988). Cities as dissipative structures. In B. Weber, D. Depew, & J. Smith (Eds.), *Entropy, information and evolution: New perspectives on physical and biological evolution.* Cambridge, MA: MIT Press.

East, J. (2019). *Transformational leadership for the helping professions: Engaging head, heart, and soul.* New York, NY: Oxford University Press.

Eigen, M. (1971). Molecular self-organization and the early stages of evolution. *Quarterly Reviews of Biophysics, 4,* 149–212.

Elkington, J. (1994). Toward the sustainable corporation: Win-win-win business strategies for sustainable development. *California Management Review, 36*(3), 90–100.

Emmeche, C., Koppe, S., & Stjernfelt, F. (1997). Explaining emergence: Towards an ontology of levels. *Journal for General Philosophy of Science, 28*(1), 83–119.

Fiol, M., & Romanelli, E. (2012). Before identity: The emergence of new organizational forms. *Organization Science, 23*(3), 597–611.

Folke, C. (2006). Resilience: The emergence of a perspective for social-ecological systems analyses. *Global Environmental Change, 16*(3), 253–267.

Folke, C., Carpenter, S., Walker, B., Scheffer, M., Chapin, T., & Rockstrom, J. (2010). Resilience thinking: Integrating resilience, adaptability and transformability. *Ecology and Society, 15*(4), 20–28.

Fritz, R. (1989). *The path of least resistance.* New York, NY: Fawcett Columbine.

Fuller, T., Warren, L., & Argyle, P. (2008). Sustaining entrepreneurial business: A complexity perspective on processes that produce emergent practice. *International Entrepreneurship Management Journal, 4,* 1–17.

Fulmer, C. A., & Ostroff, C. (2015). Convergence and emergence in organizations: An integrative framework and review. *Journal of Organizational Behavior, 31*(S1), S122–S145. https://dx.doi.org/10.1002/job.1987

Gartner, B., & Starr, J. (1993). The nature of entrepreneurial work. In S. Birley & I. MacMillan (Eds.), *Entrepreneurship research: Global perspectives* (pp. 35–67). Amsterdam, Netherlands: North-Holland.

Gartner, W. (1985). A conceptual framework for describing the phenomenon of new venture creation. *Academy of Management Review, 10,* 696–706.

Gartner, W. (1993). Words lead to deeds: Towards an organizational emergence vocabulary. *Journal of Business Venturing, 8,* 231–239.

Gartner, W., Bird, B., & Starr, J. (1992). Acting as if: Differentiating entrepreneurial from organizational behavior. *Entrepreneurship Theory and Practice, 16*(3), 13–30.

Gartner, W., & Brush, C. (2007). Entrepreneurship as organizing: Emergence, newness and transformation. In M. Rice & T. G. Habbershon (Eds.), *Entrepreneurship: The engine of growth* (Praeger perspectives on entrepreneurship 3) (pp. 1–20). Westport, CT: Praeger Publishers.

Garud, R., Kumaraswamy, A., & Karnøe, P. (2010). Path dependence or path creation? *Journal of Management Studies, 47*(4), 760–774.

Garud, R., Kumaraswamy, A., & Sambamurthy, V. (2006). Emergent by design: Performance and transformation at Infosys Technologies. *Organization Science, 17,* 277–286.

Garud, R., Simpson, B., Langley, A., & Tsoukas, H. (Eds.). (2015). *The emergence of novelty in organizations.* Oxford, UK: Oxford University Press.

Garud, R., & Van de Ven, A. (2002). Strategic organizational change processes. In H. Pettigrew, H. Thomas, & R. Whittington (Eds.), *Handbook of strategy and management* (pp. 206–231). London: SAGE.

Geels, F. (2010). Ontologies, socio-technical transitions (to sustainability), and the multi-level perspective. *Research Policy, 39,* 495–510.

Geels, F., & Schott, J. (2007). Typology of sociotechnical transition pathways. *Research Policy, 36,* 399–417.

Gehman, J., Trevino, L., & Garud, R. (2013). Values work: A process study of the emergence and performance of organizational values practices *Academy of Management Journal, 56*(1), 84–112.

Gemmill, G., & Smith, C. (1985). A dissipative structure model of organization transformation. *Human Relations, 38*(8), 751–766.

Girod, S., & Whittington, R. (2015). Change escalation processes and complex adaptive systems: From incremental reconfigurations to discontinuous restructuring. *Organization Science, 26*(5), 1520–1535.

Gittell, J. H., Seidner, R., & Wimbush, J. (2010). A relational model of how high-performance work systems operate. *Organization Science, 21*(2), 490–506.

Gladwell, M. (2000). *The tipping point: How little things can make a big difference.* Boston, MA: Little, Brown & Co.

Goldstein, J. (1988). A far-from-equilibrium systems approach to resistance to change. *Organizational Dynamics, 15*(1), 5–20.

Goldstein, J. (1994). *The unshackled organization.* Portland, OR: Productivity Press.

Goldstein, J. (1999). Emergence as a construct: History and issues. *Emergence, 1*(1), 49–72.

Goldstein, J. (2000). Emergence: A concept amid a thicket of conceptual snares. *Emergence, 2*(1), 5–22.

Goldstein, J. (2002). The singular nature of emergent levels: Suggestions for a theory of emergence. *Nonlinear Dynamics, Psychology and Life Sciences, 6,* 293–309.

Goldstein, J. (2018). Emergence and radical novelty: From theory to methods. In E. Mitleton-Kelly, A. Paraskevas, & C. Day (Eds.), *Handbook of research methods in complexity science* (pp. 507–524): Northampton, MA: Edward Elgar.

Goldstein, J., Hazy, J., & Lichtenstein, B. (2010). *Complexity and the nexus of leadership: Leveraging nonlinear science to create ecologies of innovation.* New York, NY: Palgrave Macmillan.

Grand, J., Braun, M., Kuljanin, G., Kozlowsli, S., & Chao, G. (2016). The dynamics of team cognition: A process-oriented theory of knowledge emergence in teams. *Journal of Applied Psychology, 101*(10), 1353–1385.

Granovetter, M. (1978). Threshold models of collective behavior. *American Journal of Sociology, 83,* 1420–1443.

Grodal, S., Gotsopoulos, A., & Suarez, F. F. (2015). The coevolution of technologies and categories during industry emergence. *Academy of Management Review, 40*(3), 423–445. https://dx.doi.org/10.5465/amr.2013.0359

Guastello, S. (1987). A butterfly catastrophe model of motivation in organizations. *Journal of Applied Psychology, 72,* 165–182.

Guastello, S. (1995). *Chaos, catastrophe, and human affairs: Applications of nonlinear dynamics to work, organizations, and social evolution.* Mahwah, NJ: Erlbaum.

Guastello, S. (1998). Self-organization and leadership emergence. *Nonlinear Dynamics, Psychology, and Life Sciences, 2,* 301–315.

Guastello, S. (2001). Nonlinear dynamics in psychology. *Discrete Dynamics in Nature and Society, 6,* 11–29.

Guastello, S. (2010). Self-organization and leadership emergence in emergency response teams. *Nonlinear Dynamics, Psychology, and Life Sciences, 14*(2), 179–204.

Gunderson, L., & Holling, C. S. (Eds.). (2001). *Panarchy: Understanding transformations in human and natural systems.* Washington, DC: Island Press.

Hainsworth, F. R. (1987). Precision and dynamics of positioning by Canada geese flying in formation. *Journal of Experimental Biology, 128*, 445–462.

Holling, C. S. (1973). Resilience and stability of ecological systems. *Annual Review of Ecology and Systematics, 4*, 1–23.

Holling, C. S. (2001). Understanding the complexity of economic, ecological, and social systems. *Ecosystems, 4*, 390–405.

Huff, J., Huff, A., & Thomas, H. (1992). Strategic renewal and the interaction of cumulative stress and inertia. *Strategic Management Journal, 13*, 55–75.

Jantsch, E. (1980). *The self-organizing universe*. New York, NY: Pergamon Press.

Klee, R. (1984). Micro-determinism and concepts of emergence. *Philosophy of Science, 51*, 44–63.

Kozlowski, S. W. J., & Chao, G. T. (2012). The dynamics of emergence: Cognition and cohesion in work teams. *Managerial and Decision Economics, 33*(5–6), 335–354. https://dx.doi.org/10.1002/mde.2552

Kozlowski, S. W. J., Chao, G. T., Grand, M. T. B., & Kuljanin, G. (2013). Advancing multilevel research design: Capturing the dynamics of emergence. *Organizational Research Methods, 16*(4), 581–615.

Kozlowski, S. W. J., & Klein, K. J. (2000). A multi-level approach to theory and research in organizations: Contextual, temporal, and emergent processes. In K. Klein & S. W. J. Kozlowski (Eds.), *Multilevel theory, research, and methods in organizations: Foundations, extensions, and new directions*. San Francisco, CA: Jossey-Bass.

Kuhn, T., 1970. *The structure of scientific revolutions*. Chicago, IL: University of Chicago Press.

Langley, A., Smallman, C., Tsoukas, H., & Van de Ven, A. (2013). Process studies of change in organization and management: Unveiling temporality, activity, and flow. *Academy of Management Journal, 56*(1), 1–13.

Lawrence, T., Hardy, C., & Phillips, N. (2002). Institutional effects of interorganizational collaboration: The emergence of proto-institutions. *Academy of Management Journal, 45*, 281–290.

Leifer, R. (1989). Understanding organizational transformation using a dissipative structure model. *Human Relations, 42*, 899–916.

Lewes, G. H. (1877). *The physical basis of mind: Being the second series of problems of life and mind*. Boston, MA: J. R. Osgood.

Lichtenstein, B. (2000). Self-organized transitions: A pattern amid the "chaos" of transformative change. *Academy of Management Executive, 14*(4), 128–141.

Lichtenstein, B. (2009). Moving far from far-from-equilibrium: Opportunity tension as the catalyst of emergence. *Emergence: Complexity and Organization, 11*(4), 15–25.

Lichtenstein, B. (2011a). Levels and degrees of emergence: Toward a matrix of complexity in entrepreneurship. *International Journal of Complexity in Leadership and Management, 1*(3), 252–274.

Lichtenstein, B. (2011b). What should be the locus of activity for sustainability: Eight emerging ecologies of action for sustainable entrepreneurship. In T. Lumpkin & J. Katz (Eds.), *Social and sustainable entrepreneurship* (Vol. 13, pp. 235–278). Bingley, UK: Emerald.

Lichtenstein, B. (2014). *Generative emergence: A new discipline of organizational, entrepreneurial, and social innovation*. New York, NY: Oxford University Press.

Lichtenstein, B. (2016). Emergence and emergents in entrepreneurship: Complexity science insights into new venture creation. *Entrepreneurship Research Journal, 6*(1), 43–52.

Lichtenstein, B. (2018). Bringing complexity into social analysis: Three principles from emergence. *Annals of Social Science and Management Studies, 11*(5), 1–3.

Lichtenstein, B., Dooley, K., & Lumpkin, T. (2006). Measuring emergence in the dynamics of new venture creation. *Journal of Business Venturing, 21*, 153–175.

Lichtenstein, B., & Kurjanowicz, B. (2010). Tangibility, momentum, and the emergence of The Republic of Tea. *ENTER Journal, 1*, 125–148.

Lichtenstein, B., & Plowman, D. A. (2009). The leadership of emergence: A complex systems leadership theory of emergence at successive organizational levels. *The Leadership Quarterly, 20*, 617–630.

Lotka, A. (1922). Contribution to the energetics of evolution. *Proceedings of the National Academy of Sciences, 6,* 147–151.

Lotka, A. (1945). The law of evolution as a maximal principle. *Human Biology, 17,* 167–194.

Lumpkin, G. T., & Dess, G. (1996). Clarifying the entrepreneurial orientation construct and linking it to performance. *Academy of Management Review, 21,* 135–172.

MacIntosh, R., & MacLean, D. (1999). Conditioned emergence: A dissipative structures approach to transformation. *Strategic Management Journal, 20,* 297–316.

Maguire, S., Hardy, C., & Lawrence, T. (2004). Institutional entrepreneurship in emerging fields: HIV/AIDS treatment advocacy in Canada. *Academy of Management Journal, 47,* 657–680.

Marion, R., & Uhl-Bien, M. (2001). Leadership in complex organizations. *The Leadership Quarterly, 12,* 389–418.

Maruyama, M. (1963). The second cybernetics. *American Scientist, 51,* 164–179.

Masten, A. S. (2013). Risk and resilience in development. In P. D. Zelazo (Ed.), *The Oxford handbook of developmental psychology: Vol. 2. Self and other* (pp. 579–607). Oxford, UK: Oxford University Press.

McKelvey, B. (1997). Quasi-natural organization science. *Organization Science, 8,* 351–380.

McKelvey, B. (1999). Self-organization, complexity catastrophe, and microstate models at the edge of chaos. In J. Baum & B. McKelvey (Eds.), *Variations in organization science* (pp. 279–310). Thousand Oaks, CA: SAGE.

McKelvey, B. (2001). What is complexity science? It is really order creation science. *Emergence, 3*(1), 137–157.

McKelvey, B. (2004a). Toward a 0th Law of Thermodynamics: Order creation complexity dynamics from physics and biology to bioeconomics. *Bioeconomics, 6,* 65–96.

McKelvey, B. (2004b). Toward a complexity science of entrepreneurship. *Journal of Business Venturing, 19,* 313–342.

McMullan, J., Plummer, L., & Acs, Z. (2007). What is an entrepreneurial opportunity? *Small Business Economics, 28,* 273–283.

Meyer, A., Gaba, V., & Colwell, K. (2005). Organizing far from equilibrium: Nonlinear change in organizational fields. *Organization Science, 16,* 456–473.

Mihata, K. (1997). The persistence of emergence. In R. Eve, S. Horsfall, & M. Lee (Eds.), *Chaos, complexity, and sociology: Myths, models and theories* (pp. 30–38). Thousand Oaks, CA: SAGE.

Montuori, A., & Donnelly, G. (2017). Transformative leadership. In J. Neal (Ed.), *Handbook of personal and organizational transformation.* Cham, Switzerland: Springer International.

Morgan, C. L. (1923). *Emergent evolution.* London, UK: Williams & Norgate.

Neto, G., & Almeida, C. (2018). A framework of actions for strong sustainability. *Journal of Cleaner Production, 196,* 1629–1643.

Nicholls-Nixon, C. (2005). Rapid growth and high performance: The entrepreneur's "impossible dream?" *Academy of Management Executive, 19*(1), 77–89.

Nicolis, G. (1989). Physics of far-from-equilibrium systems and self-organization. In P. Davies (Ed.), *The new physics.* New York, NY: Cambridge University Press.

Nicolis, G., & Prigogine, I. (1989). *Exploring complexity.* New York, NY: W. H. Freeman.

Nonaka, I. (1988). Creating organizational order out of chaos: Self-renewal in Japanese firms. *California Management Review, 30*(Spring), 57–73.

Nowak, A., Tesser, A., Vallacher, R., & Borkowski, W. (2000). Society of self: The emergence of collective properties in self-structure. *Psychological Review, 107,* 39–61.

Odum, H. (1988). Self-organization, transformity, and information. *Science, 242,* 1132–1139.

Ortiz-de-Mandojana, N., & Bansal, P. (2016). The long-term benefits of organizational resilience through sustainable business practices. *Strategic Management Journal, 37*(8), 1615–1631.

Pacheco, D. F., York, J. G., & Hargrave, T. J. (2014). The coevolution of industries, social movements, and institutions: Wind power in the United States. *Organization Science, 25*(6), 1609–1632. https://dx.doi.org/10.1287/orsc.2014.0918

Padgett, J., & Powell, W. (2011). *The emergence of organizations and markets*. Princeton, NJ: Princeton University Press.

Pearce, C., & Conger, J. (Eds.). (2003). *Shared leadership: Reframing the hows and whys of leadership*. Thousand Oaks, CA: SAGE.

Pepper, S. (1926). Emergence. *Journal of Philosophy, 23*, 241–245.

Perkmann, M., & Spicer, A. (2014). How emerging organizations take form: The role of imprinting and values in organizational bricolage. *Organization Science, 25*(6), 1785–1806. https://dx.doi.org/10.1287/orsc.2014.0916

Plowman, D. A., Baker, L., Beck, T., Kulkarni, M., Solansky, S., & Travis, D. (2007a). Radical change accidentally: The emergence and amplification of small change. *Academy of Management Journal, 50*, 515–543.

Plowman, D. A., Solansky, S., Beck, T., Baker, L., Kulkarni, M., & Travis, D. (2007b). The role of leadership in emergent, self-organization. *The Leadership Quarterly, 18*(4), 341–356.

Ployhart, R., & Moliterno, T. (2011). Emergence of the human capital resource: A multilevel model. *Academy of Management Review, 36*(1), 127–150.

Poole, M. S., Van de Ven, A., Dooley, K., & Holmes, M. (2000). *Organizational change and innovation processes: Theory and methods for research*. New York, NY: Oxford University Press.

Prigogine, I. (1955). *Introduction to the thermodynamics of irreversible processes*. New York, NY: Wiley.

Prigogine, I., & Glansdorff, P. (1971). *Thermodynamic theory of structure, stability, and fluctuations*. New York: Wiley & Sons.

Prigogine, I., Nicolis, G., & Babloyantz, A. (1972). Thermodynamics of evolution. *Physics Today, 25*(11), 23–38.

Prigogine, I., & Stengers, I. (1984). *Order out of chaos*. New York, NY: Bantam Books.

Purdy, J., & Gray, B. (2009). Conflicting logics, mechanisms of diffusion, and multi-level dynamics of emergence in institutional fields. *Academy of Management Journal, 52*, 355–380.

Reid, R. (2007). *Biological emergences: Evolution by natural experiment*. Cambridge, MA: MIT Press.

Robb, F. (1990). On the application of the theory of emergence and of the law of maximum entropy production to social processes. *Systems Practice, 3*, 389–399.

Roundy, P., Bradshaw, M., & Brockman, B. (2018). The emergence of entrepreneurial ecosystems: A complex adaptive systems approach. *Journal of Business Research, 86*(May), 1–10.

Salthe, S. (1989). Self-organization of/in hierarchically structured systems. *Systems Research, 6*(3), 199–208.

Santos, F., & Eisenhardt, K. (2009). Constructing markets and shaping boundaries: Entrepreneurial power in nascent fields. *Academy of Management Journal, 52*, 643–671.

Sarasson, Y., Dean, T., & Hilliard, B. (2006). Entrepreneurship as the nexus of individual and opportunity: A structuration view. *Journal of Business Venturing, 21*, 286–305.

Sarasvathy, S., & Dew, N. (2005). New market creation through transformation. *Journal of Evolutionary Economics, 15*, 533–565.

Sawyer, K. (2004). The mechanisms of emergence. *Philosophy of the Social Sciences, 34*, 260–282.

Sawyer, K. (2005). *Social emergence: Societies as complex systems*. New York, NY: Cambridge University Press.

Saynisch, M. (2010). Beyond frontiers of traditional project management: An approach to evolutionary, self-organizational principles and the complexity theory; results of the research program. *Project Management Journal, 41*(2), 21–37. https://dx.doi.org/10.1002/pmj.20159

Schieve, W., & Allen, P. (2014). *Self-organization and dissipative structures: Applications in the physical and social sciences*. Austin, TX: University of Texas Press.

Scott, A. J. (2012). *A world in emergence: Cities and regions in the 21st century*. London, UK: Edward Elgar.

Selden, P., & Fletcher, D. (2015). The entrepreneurial journey as an emergent hierarchical system of artifact-creating processes. *Journal of Business Venturing, 30*(4), 603–613.

Smith, C. (1986). Transformation and regeneration in social systems: A dissipative structure perspective. *Systems Research, 3*, 203–213.

Smith, C., & Gemmill, G. (1991). Self-Organization in small groups: A study of group effectiveness within non-equilibrium conditions. *Human Relations, 44*, 697–716.

Stephen, A. (1992). Emergence: A systematic view on its historical facets. In A. Beckermann, H. Flohr, & J. Kim (Eds.), *Emergence or reduction? Essays on the prospects of nonreductive physicalism* (pp. 25–48). Berlin, Germany: Walter de Gruyter.

Surie, G. & Hazy, J. (2007). Generative leadership: Nurturing innovation in complex systems. In J. Hazy, J. Goldstein, & B. Lichtenstein (Eds.), *Complex systems leadership theory* (pp. 349–367). Mansfield, MA: ISCE Publishing.

Sutcliffe, K., & Vogus, T. (2003). Organizing for resilience. In K. Cameron, J. Dutton, & R. Quinn (Eds.), *Positive organizational scholarship* (pp. 95–110). San Francisco, CA: Berrett-Koehler.

Swenson, R. (1989). Emergent attractor and the law of maximum entropy production: Foundations to a theory of general evolution. *Systems Research, 6*(3), 187–197.

Swenson, R. (1992). Order, evolution, and natural law: Fundamental relations in complex system theory. In C. Negoita (Ed.), *Cybernetics and applied systems* (pp. 125–147). New York: Marcel Dekker.

Swenson, R. (2000). Spontaneous order, autocatakinetic closure, and the development of space time. *Annuls of New York Academy of Sciences, 901*, 311–319.

Tan, J. (2007). Phase transitions and emergence of entrepreneurship: The transformation of Chinese SOEs over time. *Journal of Business Venturing, 22*, 77–96.

Torbert, B. & Associates. (2004). *Action inquiry: The secret of timely and transforming leadership*. San Francisco: Berrett-Koehler.

Tsoukas, H. (1989). The validity of idiographic research explanations. *Academy of Management Review, 14*(4), 551–561.

Tsoukas, H. (1991). The missing link: A transformational view of metaphors in organizational science. *Academy of Management Review, 16*(3), 566–585.

Tsoukas, H., & Chia, R. (2002). On organizational becoming: Rethinking organizational change. *Organization Science, 13*, 567–583.

Uhl-Bien, M., & Arena, M. (2017). Complexity leadership: Enabling people and organizations for adaptability. *Organizational Dynamics, 46*(1), 9–20.

Uhl-Bien, M., Marion, R., & McKelvey, B. (2007). Complexity leadership theory: Shifting leadership from the industrial age to the information era. *The Leadership Quarterly, 18*, 298–318.

Ulrich, H., & Probst, J. B. (Eds.). (1984). *Self-organization and management of social systems*. Berlin, Germany: Springer-Verlag.

Varga, L., Allen, P., Strathern, M., Rose-Anderssen, C., Baldwin, J. & Ridgway, K. (2009). Sustainable supply networks: A complex systems perspective. *Emergence: Complexity and Organization, 11*(3), 16–36.

Wicken, J. (1981). Evolutionary self-organization and the entropy principle: Teleology and mechanism. *Nature and System, 3*, 129–141.

Wicken, J. (1986). Evolutionary self-organization and entropic dissipation in biological and socioeconomic systems. *Journal of Social and Biological Structures, 9*, 261–273.

Wicken, J. (1988). Thermodynamics, evolution, and emergence: Ingredients for a new synthesis. In B. Weber, D. Depew, & J. D. Smith (Eds.), *Entropy, information, and evolution: New perspectives on physical and biological evolution* (pp. 139–172). Cambridge, MA: MIT Press.

Zeleny, M. (Ed.). (1981). *Autopoiesis, dissipative structures, and spontaneous social orders*. Boulder, CO: Westview Press.

NOTE

1. In their briefest form these are as follows. *Principle 1: Emergence Is in Disequilibrium.* That is, systems that are emerging operate in far-from-equilibrium conditions, being pushed away from stability and equilibrium. This disequilibrium creates the conditions through which emergence can occur (Goldstein, 1994, 2002; Leifer, 1989; Lichtenstein, 2014; Mihata, 1997; Prigogine & Stengers, 1984; Robb, 1990; Swenson, 1989). *Principle 2: Emergence of Emergents.* That is, emergence is an unfolding process which yields a tangible emergent—an entity with perceptible boundaries and measurable outcomes (Fiol & Romanelli, 2012; Lichtenstein, 2016; Reid, 2007). As alluded to already, these two aspects are interdependent: emergence has both a continuous expression and a tangible outcome. *Principle 3: Emergence Increases Capacity.* This idea is central to the positive potential outcomes of emergence, namely that it yields an increase in systemic capacity, measured as greater efficiency and increased agency in the emergent (Dyke, 1988; Jantsch, 1980; Odum, 1988; Wicken, 1981). An important extension is the idea, first proposed by Goldstein (1999, 2000), that there is a continuum of emergence—increasing degrees of emergence (Lichtenstein, 2011a), where further iterations on the scale produce outcomes with more impact and greater potential. Further, this increasing potential is expressed as an increase in systemic capacity, measured as greater efficiency and increased agency in the emergent (Dyke, 1988; Jantsch, 1980; Odum, 1988; Wicken, 1981).

Benyamin Lichtenstein

ORGANIZATIONAL INTERVENTIONS

INTRODUCTION

Organizational interventions have been defined as "planned, behavioral, theory-based actions that aim to improve employee health and well-being through changing the way work is designed, organized, and managed" (Nielsen & Abildgaard, 2013, p. 278). A key component of such interventions is that they focus on changing work practices, policies, and procedures (Sørensen et al., 2021). Organizational interventions have been recommended as they address the causes of poor well-being rather than merely treating the symptoms (European Trade Union Confederation [ETUC], 2004; International Labor Office [ILO], 2001; World Health Organization [WHO] & Burton, 2010). Despite being the recommended method, meta-analyses comparing organizational interventions to interventions targeting the individual have found that organizational interventions are less effective in demonstrating improvements in well-being (Richardson & Rothstein, 2008; van der Klink et al., 2001).

Scholars have argued that such comparisons are inappropriate and that comparing individual-level interventions with organizational-level interventions is like comparing apples and oranges (Nielsen & Miraglia, 2017). Criticisms are that organizational-level interventions do not target individuals with problems but rather target a larger group of employees who may not all necessarily experience the same problem (Nielsen & Miraglia, 2017) and that there is no single intervention that works across all settings. Organizational interventions also need to be context-specific; in other words, they must target changes in the working conditions that have an adverse effect on employee well-being in the specific organization (e.g., conflicts with patients and relatives may be an issue in healthcare, but not in nonpatient-focused organizations; Di Tecco et al., 2020). Organizational intervention shows inconsistent findings and this may be due to implementation issues (Nielsen, 2013). Therefore the participatory interventions that tailor the intervention to the organizational context may be the way forward (Nielsen & Randall, 2015). This tailoring to the organizational context, however, means that intervention content—the activities aimed at changing work policies, practices, and procedures—is not predefined and little is known about what activities are developed in such interventions and which working conditions they aim to change. A state-of-the-art review of the implementation of participatory organizational intervention can be found in Nielsen (2023). These types of activities are outlined, which can be implemented in participatory organizational interventions to improve the way work is organized, designed, and managed. In this article, a review of the literature, the activities that have been implemented in previous studies, and which demands and resources they may address are outlined.

ORGANIZATIONAL INTERVENTIONS AND THE WORKING CONDITIONS THEY TARGET

In an attempt to understand which working conditions to target with organizational interventions, reviews have classified interventions according to these targets. Semmer (2006) classified working conditions that may be changed through organizational interventions into three different categories. The first category of organizational interventions targets task characteristics. These include improving task identity, enabling workers to understand how their tasks contribute to the end product, increasing autonomy over how to do the tasks, or using job rotation to increase skills variety. The second targets working conditions, including excessive workloads, ergonomics, and work scheduling. The third target's role clarification and social relationships, and activities may include peer-to-peer training to improve social support. Reviewing these types of interventions, Semmer (2006) found inconsistent results: all interventions showed promising results in improving some well-being outcomes but failed to show consistent improvements across all well-being outcomes measured. Furthermore, Semmer concluded that effects may be short-lived. Semmer did not discuss whether interventions reviewed used a participatory design, and little is therefore known about what the role of a participatory process would have been.

More recently, Fox et al. (2021) conducted a systematic review of group and organizational interventions employing a similar classification. First, upon reviewing interventions focused on flexible work and scheduling, they identified three subcategories: flexwork (control over where and when you work), self-scheduling (making requests for work scheduling), and shift changes (such as working longer shifts to get more time off between shifts). Across the three subcategories, in 21 interventions, they found overall positive effects on employee well-being and a few null effects. One shift change intervention reported two negative well-being outcomes and one self-scheduling intervention revealed a negative effect on well-being. Second, reviewing 18 job and task change interventions, they identified three subcategories: job redesign (targeting workplace processes, e.g., increasing frontline workers' control or autonomy), lean management practices (work groups identifying operational goals and formalizing or standardizing work processes), and resource addition (adding staff or material resources to support workers doing their job). As with flexwork interventions, outcomes on employee well-being were primarily positive; only a few studies showed null effects. One lean management study found only negative effects as did one intervention aimed at increasing staff and material resources. A third type of intervention focused on improving team dynamics (improving interpersonal and working relationships), in total 11 were reviewed. These types of interventions showed predominantly positive well-being effects, but many failed to find significant improvements across all well-being outcomes. No negative effects were reported. In a later review, Semmer (2011) drew similar conclusions on the inconsistent effects of organizational interventions but emphasized the challenge in separating intervention studies into these categories, as interventions often targeted multiple areas.

Fox et al. (2021) also reviewed 19 participatory organizational interventions, a type of intervention where employees and managers in collaboration decide on the design and implementation of the intervention process and the content of the intervention, thus addressing a mix of working conditions (Nielsen, 2013). In their review, Fox et al. (2021) did not consider which activities were implemented to improve working conditions and employee well-being (for example, activities to streamline task completion). Similar results of participatory organizational interventions were found such as interventions targeting team dynamics. Most studies on participatory organizational interventions found positive effects on some well-being outcomes, but null effects on others; six studies failed to find any effects at all. No participatory organizational intervention studies reported a negative effect on employee well-being.

In summary, the findings of these reviews of organizational interventions showed inconsistent results in terms of their ability to improve employee well-being; however, the literature reviewed suffers from two limitations: (a) the general organizational intervention literature does not address whether the intervention activities were tailored to fit the needs of the organization (Nielsen & Randall, 2015), which may account, at least in part, for disappointing results, and (b) upon reviewing participatory organizational interventions, specific activities implemented to improve working conditions have not been explored. The remainder of this article focuses on participatory organizational interventions which tailor intervention activities to the needs of the organization (Nielsen & Noblet, 2018) and reviews participatory intervention in light of a more fine-grained framework for classifying interventions. Participatory intervention studies that have explicitly described the intervention activities and which have made suggestions as to which working condition they target are reviewed. In many cases, it has not been clearly stated which demands or resources were targeted by the activities; however, attempts have been made to suggest which demand or resource may be improved by implementing a given activity.

PARTICIPATORY ORGANIZATIONAL INTERVENTIONS

Participatory organizational interventions are often implemented through five phases (Nielsen, 2023; Nielsen & Noblet, 2018; Nielsen et al., 2010). In the first phase, the intervention is prepared, a steering group is established, and key stakeholders in implementing the intervention are identified. A communication strategy is developed and the subsequent phases and their methods are planned (Nielsen, 2023). In the second phase, a systematic screening is conducted to identify and prioritize the changes that are needed to the way work is organized, designed, and managed. In the third phase, the action planning phase, detailed activities are planned to make the necessary changes identified in the second phrase. In the fourth phase, the activities are implemented and monitoring is undertaken to ensure this is done according to plan. Finally, in the fifth phase, the intervention process itself—as well as the extent to which implemented activities were successful in improving employee well-being—are evaluated (Nielsen, 2023; Nielsen & Noblet, 2018; Nielsen et al., 2010). In participatory organizational interventions, management and employees together with key stakeholders such as human resources and occupational health practitioners jointly decide what happens at each phase of the intervention, for example, what methods are chosen to screen or identify which working conditions employees perceive need to change and what activities and changes are needed to improve those working conditions and the well-being of employees (Nielsen, 2023).

Multiple advantages to participation in organizational interventions have been identified (Arneson & Ekberg, 2005). First, employees taking part in an organizational intervention reported their way of thinking had changed. Rather than focusing on the production and doing their jobs, participation in the intervention had raised self-awareness of the importance of their own well-being. Second, engaging in discussions had raised awareness of working conditions and insights into shared perceptions of these conditions, which created a sense of belonging. Third, the participatory process promoted proactivity: employees felt engaged and responsible for taking action to implement changes. Fourth, the participatory process promoted a sense of coherence and cohesion as employees felt they gained a better understanding of each other's perspectives. Fifth, the participatory process helped create a sense of community: employees felt they were not alone in making changes and felt supported by each in making changes happen. Finally, employees felt that the process helped develop and implement feasible and realistic actions (Arneson & Ekberg, 2005).

Key to participatory interventions is that they are not predefined (Nielsen & Miraglia, 2017); in other words, what activities are needed to improve working conditions and employee well-being are not determined up front but are identified and agreed upon through the screening and action planning phases of the intervention. Even within the same organization, departments may target different working conditions depending on the needs identified in the screening phase (Fox et al., 2021). A consequence of the lack of predefined intervention content has been that evaluation of participatory organizational interventions has focused on the role of the intervention process on the intervention's ability to improve employee well-being (Havermans et al., 2016). An increasing body of research has therefore focused on the "how to" of the organizational intervention process (Nielsen, 2023; Roodbari et al., 2021). Despite these important developments, it is nevertheless important to understand the type of activities, for example, what the content of participatory organizational interventions are and what working conditions activities may target.

A FRAMEWORK FOR CLASSIFYING PARTICIPATORY ORGANIZATIONAL INTERVENTIONS

The classification into three main categories of working conditions (Semmer, 2006) is somewhat restricted given the plethora of working conditions. For example, the Management Standards suggest changes may be made to six generic working conditions: demands, control, support, roles, relationships, and changes (Cousins et al., 2004). The different levels of intervention within each intervention makes it difficult for organizations and practitioners to identify which level they should focus their energy on. Based on the Individual, Group, Leader and Organizational IGLO framework (Nielsen et al., 2017) and the Job Demands-Resources (JD-R) model (Demerouti et al., 2001), Nielsen and Christensen (2021) suggested that intervention activities should address both the resources and the demands prevalent in employees' working conditions.

A central tenet of the JD-R model (Demerouti et al., 2001) is the balance between job demands (the working conditions and demands employees put on themselves, which require sustained effort or skills) and job resources (the working conditions and the individual's cognitions, emotions, and behaviors that enable employees to thrive in their jobs and promote their well-being). This dual perspective is important as well-being can be defined as "comprising the various life/non-work satisfactions enjoyed by individuals (i.e., satisfaction and/or dissatisfaction with social life, family life, recreation, spirituality, and so forth), work/job-related satisfactions (i.e., satisfaction and/or dissatisfaction with pay, promotion opportunities, the job itself, co-workers, and so forth), and general health" (Danna & Griffin, 1999, p. 359), and therefore does not just focus on the absence of well-being but also on the growth potential of individuals. Furthermore, building resources may buffer the demands of the job that cannot easily be addressed (Vignoli et al., 2017). As such, participatory organizational interventions should focus not only on preventing poor well-being, but also aim to create workplaces where people can thrive and develop as part of their jobs. An advantage of the JD-R model is its flexible approach to what working conditions are, as any aspect of the work, and more recently also of individuals in the workplace that may influence employee well-being (Demerouti et al., 2001).

ACTIVITIES TO REDUCE ADVERSE JOB DEMANDS AND INCREASE RESOURCES IN PARTICIPATORY ORGANIZATIONAL INTERVENTIONS

Nielsen and Christensen (2021) suggested that activities implemented as part of participatory organizational interventions should address both the demands and resources experienced by employees and at multiple levels, as prescribed by the IGLO framework (Day & Nielsen, 2017; Nielsen et al., 2017). According to this framework, activities aim to address demands and resources at the individual, group, leader, and organizational levels. At the individual level, activities can be developed to change the inherent demands people put on themselves (e.g., their expectations for career progression) and enhance individual resources such as self-efficacy (i.e., employees' beliefs they can overcome the challenges they face at work; Bandura, 1986). At the group level, activities can be developed that address group demands (e.g., group conflict; Løkling et al., submitted) or develop resources such as social support. At the leader or line manager level, activities may address the demands leaders put on employees, for example, reducing unrealistic performance targets or increasing leaders' resources such as enabling them to enact health-promoting leadership behaviors (Kelloway & Barling, 2010). Finally, at the organizational level, activities include changes to human resource policies and practices, for example, reducing job demands through introducing workload policies or introducing hybrid working policies that offer employees flexibility in where and when to do their jobs or designing jobs that enable employees to make decisions on how to best perform their jobs.

INDIVIDUAL-LEVEL ACTIVITIES

A range of studies of participatory organizational interventions have identified the activities planned at the individual level to either reduce work demands or increase resources. These activities fall broadly within the area of training, performance appraisals, and induction.

Increasing Individual Resources. The most common set of activities identified have been training to increase individuals' resources. These could be to increase person–environment fit as employees have been trained to improve their abilities to do their jobs, such as hospital staff getting training in care provision (Stab & Hacker, 2018). On-the-job training has also been introduced which may improve person–environment fit (Huijs et al., 2019). Training, coaching, and mentoring have been implemented with the aim to increase autonomy (Hasson et al., 2014). Also, Nielsen et al. (2007) reported employees received empowerment training to increase levels of autonomy. To increase job enrichment, Sorensen et al. (2021) adjusted and promoted an already existing feedback tool that shop floor employees and managers had not previously made use of. Other examples of training included appreciative dialogue training and feedback training which could improve social support and collaboration (Huijs et al., 2019). Job crafting training has been implemented to improve social support and increase autonomy (Huijs et al., 2019) or enhance job resources and recovery generally (Niks et al., 2018). Training has also been introduced to support changes at higher levels of activity, for example in a call center where teams were allocated greater responsibility and employees were trained in how to perform new tasks to ensure a person–environment fit (Holman & Axtell, 2016; Holman et al., 2010; Nielsen et al., 2007).

A second popular activity to increase individual resources has been to introduce or improve existing performance appraisal procedures. In a study where job insecurity was identified as a challenge due constant restructuring and changes to job roles, discussions were integrated into individual performance appraisals to make employees aware of the demands of the "future postal service employee" to reduce lack of role clarity (Abildgaard et al., 2018). In another study, templates for performance appraisals were refined to make assessment more transparent, thereby increasing role clarity and managing expectations (Holman & Axtell, 2016). Also, to ensure person–environment fit, Schelvis et al. (2016) reported that performance appraisals and personal competence plans were introduced. Performance appraisals have also been redefined to focus more on achievements with the aim to improve effort–reward balance (Holman et al., 2010).

Improving induction for new recruits has also been a target for activities at the individual level, for example, to ensure socialization (Biron et al., 2016; Hasson et al., 2014). Bakhuys Roozeboom et al. (2020) reported that a mentoring system was introduced to ensure socialization among new recruits. Furthermore, individual health profiling and access to massage and exercise have been introduced with the aim to improve physical health (Nielsen et al., 2007). Finally, Hasson et al. (2014) reported one activity focusing on return to work for employees who returned from long-term sick leave, which could potentially improve person–environment fit as work adjustments can be made to fit the employees' needs.

Reducing Adverse Job Demands at the Individual Level. Most training activities have been aimed at increasing resources; however, Nielsen et al. (2007) reported that employees

Table 1. Overview of Individual-Level Activities

Activities to reduce demands	Activities to increase resources
Reducing physical risks • Ergonomics training • Individual health profiling • Massage and exercise support	*Increasing person–environment fit* • Skills training in how to perform additional responsibilities • Training in care provision • On the job training • Personal development plans • Return to work support *Increasing autonomy* • Coaching, mentoring, and training • Job crafting training *Improving social support and collaboration* • Feedback training • Appreciative dialogue training • Job crafting training *Increasing role clarity and feedback* • Performance appraisals *Increasing effort–rewards balance* • Focus on achievements *Improving socialization* • Socialization of new employees *Promoting job enrichment* • Adjusting a coaching and feedback tool for use among shop floor workers

received ergonomics training to reduce physical demands, and the job crafting training mentioned by Huijs et al. (2019) also aimed at reducing adverse job demands. See Table 1 for an overview of activities at the individual level.

GROUP-LEVEL ACTIVITIES

At the group level, studies reported action plans aimed at reducing adverse job demands and increasing job resources. These activities fall broadly within the areas of social and collaboration activities, empowerment, and team development activities. See Table 2 for an overview of activities at the group level.

Increasing Group-Level Resources. Increasing social support as a job resource was a key focus in several studies. Hasson et al. (2014) and Nielsen et al. (2007) reported a range of informal activities such as lunches and informal get-togethers to increase social support, Biron et al. (2016) reported working time rescheduling, and Stab and Hacker (2018) reported the planning of breaks to enable employees to take breaks at the same time. Sørensen and Holman (2014) reported that activities to improve feedback between colleagues were introduced with the aim of increasing social support. To improve social support, Biron et al. (2016), Nielsen et al. (2007), and Niks et al. (2018) reported teambuilding activities were planned, and

Uchiyama et al. (2013) described the introduction of civility procedures (such as greetings and using colleagues' names). Additionally, Le Blanc et al. (2007) reported that some team members would be appointed "guardian angels" and were tasked with looking out for colleagues' well-being. Also, the physical environment was changed to encourage social interaction (Biron et al., 2016).

Another range of activities to improve collaboration revolved around team meetings. These included the scheduling of team meetings during the day shift (Uchiyama et al., 2013), team members taking turns to manage team meetings (Sørensen & Holman, 2014), and team meetings focused on discussing topics important to the team (Linzer et al., 2017).

Team development was also a popular target to improve collaboration. Team development activities included study groups for team tasks (Uchiyama et al., 2013) and Huijs et al. (2019) reported each team member was allocated two hours a week to keep their knowledge up-to-date. Finally, to improve collaboration, activities revolved around team restructuring and allocation of team tasks (Biron et al., 2016; Stab & Hacker, 2018; Uchiyama et al., 2013).

A range of activities have revolved around empowering teams and increasing autonomy. For example, jobs were redesigned to give teams more autonomy over administrative tasks such as organizing breaks, logging performance and working hours, and managing flextime (Holman & Axtell, 2016) or the distribution of work (Huijs et al., 2019). Schelvis et al. (2016) reported a move towards self-managing teamwork to increase autonomy, and Hasson et al. (2014) reported activities focused on improving autonomy by discussing problems and suggesting solutions at team meetings. Stab and Hacker (2018) reported activities revolved around enabling nurses to participate in decision-making around work processes and infrastructure in the team, creating opportunities for presenting ideas concerning work facilitation and a system for assessing issues in the team. Furthermore, in the Nielsen et al. (2007) study, teams received empowerment training to improve autonomy at the team level.

To increase role clarity, guidelines on team processes have been developed to improve role clarity for team members on loan from other teams, making it easier for incoming employees to complete their tasks (Abildgaard et al., 2018). Niks et al. (2018) reported the implementation of team workshops to help identify goals for improving working conditions and processes for communication and cooperation, with follow-up workshops to ensure progress and reflection.

Reducing Adverse Group-Level Job Demands. Fewer group-level activities have focused on reducing adverse job demands. Nielsen et al. (2014) provided an example of an activity aimed at reducing team conflict whereby colleagues could draw a red card to stop members of the team arguing, and the discussion would then be taken up again at a later team meeting when the arguing colleagues had calmed down. Another group-level activity was to communicate information about planned changes at team meetings to reduce job insecurity (Stab & Hacker, 2018) and discussions of problematic patients in unit meetings to reduce emotional demands (Uchiyama et al., 2013).

LEADER-LEVEL ACTIVITIES

Fewer activities of participatory interventions have focused on making changes to the way work is organized, designed, and managed at the leader line manager level. Most activities

Table 2. Overview of Group-Level Activities

Activities to reduce demands	Activities to increase resources
Reducing interpersonal conflict • Introduction of a time out "red card" *Reducing job insecurity* • Information about planned changes at team meetings *Reducing emotional demands* • Discussions of problematic patients	*Improving social support and collaboration activities* • Informal social activities • Feedback between employees • "Guardian angels" appointed to look out for team members' well-being • Team-building activities • Restructuring of teams, revision of work tasks and procedures • Civility protocol • Reorganization of team meetings (e.g., scheduling team meetings) during day shifts, taking turns organizing meetings, discussing "meaningful topics," team meeting management • Planning of activities and breaks • Team workshops focused on improving team goals *Increasing autonomy* • Devolvement of administrative tasks and running team briefings, devolvement of time planning and through self-managing teamwork • Team meetings used to analyze and improve problem solving • Group empowerment training *Increasing role clarity* • Guidelines on teamwork practices and procedures

focused on increasing leaders' resources, by either improving communication or making sure leaders were available. See Table 3 for an overview of leader-level activities.

Increasing Leader-Level Resources.

In one study, supervisor social support was the aim with activities focused on supervisors being more available, holding follow-up meetings, and going on informal office tours (Hasson et al., 2014). In another study, responsibility for managing repairs was devolved to station managers to increase their autonomy (Randall et al., 2005). In a study by Biron et al. (2016), a permanent committee of managers was established to discuss problems they encountered with the employees, which would have the potential to improve overall working conditions. A leader-level activity in the Niks et al. (2018) study involved coaching supervisors to build personal resources; however, which resources were not specified.

With the aim to reduce job insecurity, a communication charter was developed and implemented outlining the strategy for when, what, and who should communicate about planned changes (Abildgaard et al., 2018). To improve communication, activities reported by Linzer et al. (2017) included regular emails from leaders and meetings between leaders and clinicians.

As at the individual level, training may focus on equipping supervisors with the necessary skills for new ways of working. In a study by Sørensen et al. (2021), a webinar introduced a coaching and feedback tool to supervisors as a way to support them in coaching and mentoring shop floor employees.

Reducing Adverse Job Demands at the Leader Level.   At the leader level, only one study reported activities to reduce adverse job demands. To reduce conflicting demands, an activity reported by Dollard and Gordon (2014) focused on increasing managers' communication about unexpected tasks from other units.

ORGANIZATIONAL-LEVEL ACTIVITIES

Most activities to reduce adverse job demands and increase resources were identified at the organizational level. Activities revolved around changing work procedures, implementation of policies, improving collaboration and communication across units, and introducing direct participation in work changes. See Table 4 for an overview of organizational-level activities.

Increasing Organizational-Level Resources.   Changing work procedures is a much-implemented strategy to increase resources. As an example, Abildgaard et al. (2018) reported that a change in procedures was introduced to improve meaningfulness. In this study, customer orders had previously been piecemeal, but employees were given greater responsibility and were able to follow the product's pathway through the production system.

A range of activities have focused on increasing autonomy. Holman and Axtell (2016) reported how responsibility for minor customer queries was devolved to employees, and Stab and Hacker (2018) reported that empathetic psychosocial care and case conferences were introduced. In connection with organizational change, meetings were introduced where employees had the opportunity to influence new changes to work processes (Abildgaard et al.,

Table 3. Overview of Leader-Level Activities

Activities to reduce adverse job demands	Activities to increase resources
Reducing conflicting demands • Increasing managers' communication about unexpected tasks from other units	*Improving supervisor support* • Supervisors being more available, holding follow-up meetings, and conducting information office tours *Increasing supervisor autonomy* • Supervisors assuming responsibility for managing repairs *Reducing job insecurity* • Supervisors' consistent and coherent communication about changes *Improving communication* • Regular emails and meetings between staff and leaders • Management committee to discuss problems with employees with the potential to improve working conditions *Supervisor development* • Supervisor coaching to build personal resources • Webinar to build supervisors' skills to provide feedback and mentoring

2018; Hasson et al., 2014) and meetings were introduced to give employees a voice (Le Blanc et al., 2007).

Activities with the potential to improve communication and collaboration between groups have been recorded, either between day and night shifts (Abildgaard et al., 2019), between work teams (Sørensen & Holman, 2014), between different professional groups (Stab & Hacker, 2018), between departments (Biron et al., 2016), and between management and employees, through union–management committees (Hasson et al., 2014), or between employees and external providers (Linzer et al., 2017). Other activities reported have been promoting a culture of support and actively communicating the message of support (Uchiyama et al., 2013) or developing manuals formalizing work processes and cleaning procedures to improve communication (Tsutsumi et al., 2009). To improve communication, computers were installed in hospital wards allowing nurses to complete their administrative tasks (Randall et al., 2005), and restructuring the way work was implemented was done to promote collaboration and skills use across teams (Hasson et al., 2014).

A range of activities could have the potential to increase role clarity such as clearly defining which employees were responsible for which tasks (Stab & Hacker, 2018; Uchiyama et al., 2013), developing a manual for service procedures (Dollard & Gordon, 2014), introducing a dialogue about how core tasks should be completed, and forming alliances with partners outside the organization (Schelvis et al., 2016).

Activities at the organizational level also aimed to ensure clear pathways for career progression. For example, one activity involved Human Resources rolling out a formal plan for progression (Dollard & Gordon, 2014). Another activity identified to optimize task organization was to reclassify jobs to ensure the position reflected employee' job tasks, and administrative procedures were revised (Biron et al., 2016).

With the aim to improve effort–reward balance (i.e., the imbalance between efforts invested at work and reciprocity and recognition from the workplace; Siegrist, 2016), activities focused on celebrating at meetings and informal events (Dollard & Gordon, 2014; Hasson et al., 2014) and the introduction of a secret service where colleagues could anonymously acknowledge accomplishments (Huijs et al., 2019). A few studies have reported activities focused on improving quality of service. To increase quality of care, emphasis was put on psychosocial parts of the work process (Stab & Hacker, 2018), and to improve the quality of care for patients with chronic illnesses, a number of projects were initiated including a focus on depression and diabetes and the use of patient portals (Linzer et al., 2017).

Finally, to enhance work–life balance, flexible work time scheduling, time off in lieu, and overtime pay policies have been introduced (Hasson et al., 2014) as well as integrating nurses' wishes for which shifts to work, planning rosters to allow for recovery between shifts, and the implementation of long-term planning and predictable rota planning (Stab & Hacker, 2018).

Reducing Adverse Job Demands at the Organizational Level. Activities have been implemented to reduce adverse job demands with the vast majority focused on reducing quantitative work demands. These activities have revolved around prioritizing breaks and ensuring appropriate staffing levels (Biron et al., 2016; Niks et al., 2018; Sorensen et al., 2021), effective meeting management (Dollard & Gordon, 2014; Sørensen & Holman, 2014; Uchiyama et al., 2013), prioritization of projects (Sørensen & Holman, 2014), compliance to the workload policy (Schelvis et al., 2016), optimization of work processes (e.g., efficient reporting about patients and ordering supplies; Le Blanc et al., 2007), using stamps instead of handwriting (Tsutsumi et al., 2009), managing recall lists (Biron et al., 2016), the devolvement of responsibilities and time allocated to these tasks (Linzer et al., 2017), the introduction of an ideas register for how to improve work processes enabling employees to work more effectively (Bakhuys Roozeboom et al., 2020; Dollard & Gordon, 2014; Sørensen & Holman, 2014), procedures around the use of emails (Sørensen & Holman, 2014), the introduction of lean management (Niks et al., 2018), and staffing level increases (Hasson et al., 2014).

Reducing emotional demands could be achieved through activities such as debriefing and introducing study groups (Uchiyama et al., 2013). In a study by Abildgaard et al. (2019), video surveillance was installed to help employees gain a better overview of the production, potentially reducing cognitive demands. Randall et al. (2007) reported an activity was introduced to reduce role conflict, namely the development of guidelines for office hours enabling nurses to complete their administrative tasks.

Activities to reduce physical risks included the redesign of work layout (Tsutsumi et al., 2009), the establishment of physical facilities such as a staff room, extra walls and projectors in all classrooms, and to improve the services of the facilitation services office to ensure a good physical environment (Schelvis et al., 2016), regular cleaning of the staff room (Uchiyama et al., 2013), standardized cleaning and machine maintenance (Tsutsumi et al., 2009), and replacing defective and old equipment (Biron et al., 2016). To address safety and ergonomic issues in a food service company, an industrial hygienist conducted a walk through, and the results were shared with supervisors and senior management to prioritize activities to address equipment use, risks of slips and falls, and prolonged standing, lifting, and carrying (Sorensen et al., 2021). To reduce safety risks and to improve ergonomics, Tsutsumi et al. (2009) reported that in manufacturing, parts were clearly labelled, work-stations and work layouts were redesigned, and procedures for managing noise, dust clean-up, and material storage and handling were revised.

DISCUSSION

The focus has been on the changes that can be made to working conditions to improve employee well-being through organizational interventions. It has been argued that interventionists need to understand what types of activities are implemented as part of participatory organizational interventions. Reviews of organizational interventions have found inconsistent results (Fox et al., 2021) and scholars have argued that the way interventions are designed and implemented account at least in part for some of the variation in the effectiveness of such interventions (Nielsen & Noblet, 2018; Nielsen et al., 2010); however, interventionists also need to understand what activities are implemented to reduce adverse job demands and increase resources. Based on the IGLO framework (Day & Nielsen, 2017; Nielsen et al., 2017), these activities are classified according to whether they target the individuals, work groups, leaders and line managers, and/or organizational practices, policies and procedures, and job redesign (Nielsen & Christensen, 2021). It is important to note that many studies did not explicitly report *which* activities had been implemented, and many of those that did report such activities failed to report which working conditions were the target.

Table 4. Overview of Organizational-Level Activities

Activities to reduce adverse job demands	Activities to increase resources
Reducing quantitative demands • Prioritization of breaks and ensuring appropriate staffing levels • Effective meeting management • Compliance to the workload policy • Optimization of work processes • Prioritization of projects • Introduction of an ideas register for how to improve work processes, enabling employees to work more effectively • Introduction of lean management • Procedures around the use of emails • Increase of staffing levels *Reducing emotional demands* • Debriefing, study groups, and discussions of problematic patients *Reducing cognitive demands* • Video surveillance of production *Reducing role conflict* • Work processes planning *Reducing physical risks* • Changes to physical facilities • Old and defective equipment replaced • Safety and ergonomics assessment • Standardized cleaning procedures • Redesign of physical work environment and procedures • Formalization of cleaning times • Redesign of work layout • Regular machine maintenance	*Increasing autonomy* • Influence over changes to work procedures • Devolvement of customer management • Worktime planning • Weekly meetings to ensure employees a voice in working matters *Increasing meaningfulness* • Synthetization of client services *Increasing communication and collaboration* • Installation of computers • Communication of task responsibility • Promotion of a culture of support and actively communicating the message of support • Communication between shifts, work units, professions, and employees and management • Revision of work process manuals • Establishment of union–management committee to ensure collaboration on changes to work organization *Ensuring career progression* • Human Resources career succession plan *Improving work-life balance* • Identification of providers' "wishes" and communication among providers • Integration of nurses' wishes for shifts into rota planning • Introduction of policies concerning working time and overtime pay *Improving effort-reward balance* • Recognition of employee achievements at meetings and events • Anonymous acknowledgement of colleagues' achievements *Improving role clarity* • Reorganization of core task delivery • Formation of alliances with external partners *Improving workflow and task organization* • Introduction of changes to the allocation of tasks and time allocated • Job reclassification and revision of task and administrative procedures *Improving quality of care* • Initiation of specific projects and use of patient portal

A few important conclusions can be drawn from this review. First, it is clear that the participatory approach offers a flexible way to identify which changes are needed to improve working conditions and employee well-being; a large range of activities targeted both adverse job demands and resources. Most activities were implemented at the organizational level, mostly focusing on job redesign and aiming to improve communication and collaboration, reducing quantitative work demands, and increasing autonomy. At all levels of intervention, most activities focused on increasing resources. The fewest activities have been implemented at the leader level despite the evidence that supervisors have a profound impact on employee well-being (Skakon et al., 2010). Importantly, most studies employed a multilevel approach. Participatory organizational interventions enable the identification of activities at all levels of intervention, be it the individual, the group, the leader, or the organizational. All the studies reviewed here implemented activities on at least two levels of intervention. The same demands and resources can be addressed at multiple levels. For example, collaboration may be improved by training individuals on how to provide feedback, through introducing team-building activities, or, at the organizational level, through revision of work process protocols. Employees and managers should in collaboration determine which activity is appropriate in their organization. Second, the participatory approach has the potential to ensure that activities are tailored to the challenges faced by employees (Nielsen et al., 2010); this also means that psychosocial working conditions *and* physical working conditions have been addressed, and that activities focus on reducing safety and ergonomic risks. Third, few of the activities identified in this review addressed many of the emerging challenges faced by today's working population. The drastic increase in digitalization and teleworking has reduced social interaction and this poses challenges for teamwork and leadership (López Peláez et al., 2021). Furthermore, in today's diverse workforce (Le et al., 2021), activities may need to be developed that address the multicultural and language challenges diversity may present.

ESTABLISHING PROGRAM LOGIC

Many studies only provided brief descriptions of what activities were planned and only a few included which demands or resources the activities aim to change (c.f., Niks et al., 2018, who provided an extensive list of activities in an appendix). To date, there is little information about how activities are developed or why participants believe they may improve target demands and resources. This limitation calls for the formulation of program logic, or the explication of program logic.

Program logic refers to the theory of what causes change, and in practice can be defined as a diagram or model that sets out the components of an intervention and how they in combination lead to a specified outcome (Hawkins, 2020). Program logic is typically depicted in a series of boxes that contain propositions linked by arrows. Program logic outlines the theory of change, and these theories describe how the move from a problem to outputs and outcomes is expected to occur. A theory of change may describe the assumptions about a whole program (i.e., why the participatory organizational intervention may improve employee well-being), or a component of an intervention (i.e., why job crafting training may influence the outputs such as demands and resources and the outcomes of employee well-being; Wong et al., 2016). Program logic and the formulation of theories of change may be crucial in participatory organizational interventions as activities are not predefined but determined by employees and managers in collaboration. The formulation of program theories about the intervention and its activities may help ensure that activities that have a greater likelihood of bringing about the intended outcomes are prioritized. If it cannot be clearly established how an activity may reduce a demand or increase a resource, it should perhaps not be initiated. Clearly formulated program logic also facilitates evaluation as it becomes clear what should be evaluated. To date, program logic in participatory organizational intervention is only vaguely formulated. As an example, Sørensen and Holman (2014) formulated a program logic around meeting arrangements with the output of having "better meetings". For an IGLO level intervention, Gupta et al. (2018) formulated two program theories. The first stated that the implementation of action plans aimed to modify work demands and improve job resources would positively influence work ability and the need for recovery. The second stated that the empowerment of employees through the participatory approach combined with the learning acquired by line managers and union and safety representatives would improve the capability of the organization to maintain the intervention. There is a need for researchers of participatory organizational intervention to focus more on the development of program logic and theories of change.

As the context plays an important role in the extent to which activities are implemented according to plan (Nielsen & Miraglia, 2017), program logic theories should also include considerations of what contextual factors should be in place to ensure the activities are implemented according to plan (e.g., the resources necessary). It may be that contextual factors need to be changed before the main activity can be implemented, for example as in the Holman and Axtell (2016) study where employees were trained in how to perform new tasks before new responsibilities were formally devolved to them.

It is noteworthy that although participatory intervention research to date has only to a limited extent developed program logic, the activities that have been planned can easily be mapped onto existing work psychology theories. To develop theory-based program theories, facilitators should have a solid knowledge of such theories and supporting research. Developing guidelines for facilitators on how to develop activities based on clearly formulated program theories may ensure evidence-based activities are implemented thus increasing the likelihood of interventions achieving their intended outcomes.

EVALUATING THE EFFECTIVENESS OF ACTIVITIES

The impact of intervention activities on working conditions and employee well-being in participatory organizational interventions is rarely explored explicitly (Nielsen et al., 2022). In fact, evaluators of interventions lack agreed approaches and measures on how to measure activities (Nielsen et al., 2022). Abildgaard et al. (2018) included measures of the extent to which the four planned activities identified to reduce job insecurity had been implemented; however, they did not link these to intervention outcomes. Hasson et al. (2014) listed planned activities and asked participants about their perceptions of whether activities had been implemented according to plan and if they had, whether they had worsened or improved working conditions or had an effect at all. Participants could also state whether the activities were already in place. Furthermore, analyses were performed to link the extent to which activities had been implemented with intervention outcomes. These analyses supported that where activities had been implemented, they led to improvements in the working conditions targeted. Biron et al. (2016) developed a set of questions to test whether participants had been fully/frequently, partly/sometimes, or not at all/never exposed to the three groups of activities targeting relationships with colleagues, task organization, or working conditions generally. She and her colleagues conducted structural equation modeling and found that exposure to task organization and working conditions interventions reduced psychosocial constraints which in turn was related to reduced psychological distress (Biron et al., 2016) thus establishing a chain of effects as described by Nielsen and Abildgaard (2013). Stab and Hacker (2018) evaluated whether activities could not yet be assessed, had been implemented, and had (a) no outcome, (b) little improvement, (c) great improvement, or (d) had worsened the situation but failed to establish the extent to which activities were linked to outcomes.

There is therefore a need to consider how participatory organizational interventions are evaluated to determine which of the activities implemented lead to the intended outcomes. Such evaluation would involve listing planned activities in follow-up questionnaires, asking participants whether these had been implemented, and either asking whether they had led to intended outcomes or statistically analyzing whether implemented activities led to an improvement in intended outcomes by reducing adverse job demands or increasing resources. The role of the context should also be evaluated. Realist evaluation suggests this can be done in contextual–mechanism–outcome (CMO) configurations: determining the contextual factors that lead to the activities and the mechanisms being implemented according to plan and testing how the implementations of mechanisms or activities led to changes in the intended outcomes (i.e., reductions in adverse job demands, and increases in job resources and employee well-being; Nielsen & Miraglia, 2017).

CONCLUSION

Organizational interventions show inconsistent results in their ability to improve working conditions and employee well-being. Participatory organizational interventions are recommended as they offer a tailored approach to addressing adverse working conditions. Such interventions may either reduce adverse job demands or increase resources in the workplace targeting the individual, group, leader, and organizational policies, practices, and procedures (e.g., through job redesign). The present state-of-the-art review demonstrates that many activities have been implemented to improve employee well-being at multiple levels of intervention, aiming to reduce adverse job demands and increasing resources; however, the theory behind why these activities may bring about the intended outcomes (program logic) and the evaluation of whether activities are implemented according to plan and whether they do in fact bring about intended outcomes are in many cases lacking. A future challenge for the research of participatory organizational interventions is to develop an understanding of how to create and implement activities that may lead to intended outcomes.

REFERENCES

Abildgaard, J. S., Nielsen, K., & Sverke, M. (2018). Can job insecurity be managed? Evaluating an organizational-level intervention addressing the negative effects of restructuring. *Work & Stress*, 32(2), 105–123. https://doi.org/10.1080/02678373.2017.1367735

Abildgaard, J. S., Nielsen, K., Wåhlin-Jacobsen, C. D., Maltesen, T., Christensen, K. B., & Holtermann, A. (2019). "Same, but different": A mixed-methods realist evaluation of a cluster-randomized controlled participatory organizational intervention. *Human Relations, 73*(10), 1339–1365. https://journals.sagepub.com/doi/10.1177/0018726719866896

Arneson, H., & Ekberg, K. (2005). Evaluation of empowerment processes in a workplace health promotion intervention based on learning in Sweden. *Health Promotion International, 20*(4), 351–359. https://academic.oup.com/heapro/article/20/4/351/2182102

Bakhuys Roozeboom, M. C., Schelvis, R. M., Houtman, I. L., Wiezer, N. M., & Bongers, P. M. (2020). Decreasing employees' work stress by a participatory, organizational level work stress prevention approach: A multiple-case study in primary education. *BMC Public Health, 20*, 1–16. https://doi.org/10.1186/s12889-020-08698-2

Bandura, A. (1986). The explanatory and predictive scope of self-efficacy theory. *Journal of Social and Clinical Psychology, 4*(3), 359–373.

Biron, C., Ivers, H., & Brun, J. P. (2016). Capturing the active ingredients of multicomponent participatory organizational stress interventions using an adapted study design. *Stress and Health, 32*(4), 275–284. https://doi.org/10.1002/smi.2700

Cousins, R., Mackay, C. J., Clarke, S. D., Kelly, C., Kelly, P. J., & McCaig, R. H. (2004). "Management standards" work-related stress in the UK: Practical development. *Work & Stress, 18*(2), 113–136. https://doi.org/10.1080/02678370410001734322

Danna, K., & Griffin, R. W. (1999). Health and well-being in the workplace: A review and synthesis of the literature. *Journal of Management, 25*(3), 357–384. https://journals.sagepub.com/doi/10.1177/014920639902500305

Day, A., & Nielsen, K. (2017). What does our organization do to help our well-being? Creating healthy workplaces and workers. In N. Chmiel, F. Fraccaroli, & M. Sverke (Eds.), *An introduction to work and organizational psychology* (pp. 295–314). Wiley Blackwell.

Demerouti, E., Bakker, A. B., Nachreiner, F., & Schaufeli, W. B. (2001). The job demands-resources model of burnout. *Journal of Applied Psychology, 86*(3), 499–512.

Di Tecco, C., Nielsen, K., Ghelli, M., Ronchetti, M., Marzocchi, I., Persechino, B., & Iavicoli, S. (2020). Improving working conditions and job satisfaction in healthcare: A study concept design on a participatory organizational level intervention in psychosocial risk management. *International Journal of Environmental Research and Public Health, 17*(10), 3677. https://doi.org/10.3390/ijerph17103677

Dollard, M. F., & Gordon, J. A. (2014). *Evaluation of a participatory risk management work stress intervention* (Vol. 21, No. 1, p. 27). Educational Publishing Foundation. https://doi.org/10.1037/a0035795

European Trade Union Confederation. (2004). *Framework agreement on work-related stress.*

Fox, K. E., Johnson, S. T., Berkman, L. F., Sianoja, M., Soh, Y., Kubzansky, L. D., & Kelly, E. L. (2021). Organisational- and group-level workplace interventions and their effect on multiple domains of worker well-being: A systematic review. *Work & Stress, 36*(1), 30–59. https://doi.org/10.1080/02678373.2021.1969476

Gupta, N., Wåhlin-Jacobsen, C. D., Abildgaard, J. S., Henriksen, L. N., Nielsen, K., & Holtermann, A. (2018). Effectiveness of a participatory physical and psychosocial intervention to balance the demands and resources of industrial workers: A cluster-randomized controlled trial. *Scandinavian Journal of Work, Environment and Health, 44*(1), 58–68. https://doi.org/10.5271/sjweh.3689

Hasson, H., Brisson, C., Guérin, S., Gilbert-Ouimet, M., Baril-Gingras, G., Vézina, M., & Bourbonnais, R. (2014). An organizational-level occupational health intervention: Employee perceptions of exposure to changes, and psychosocial outcomes. *Work & Stress, 28*(2), 179–197. https://doi.org/10.1080/02678373.2014.907370

Havermans, B. M., Schelvis, R. M., Boot, C. R., Brouwers, E. P., Anema, J. R., & van der Beek, A. J. (2016). Process variables in organizational stress management intervention evaluation research: A systematic review. *Scandinavian Journal of Work, Environment & Health, 42*(5), 371–381.

Hawkins, A. J. (2020). Program logic foundations: Putting the logic back into program logic. *Journal of MultiDisciplinary Evaluation, 16*(37), 38–57.

Holman, D., & Axtell, C. (2016). Can job redesign interventions influence a broad range of employee outcomes by changing multiple job characteristics? A quasi-experimental study. *Journal of Occupational Health Psychology, 21*(3), 284–295. https://doi.org/10.1037/a0039962

Holman, D. J., Axtell, C. M., Sprigg, C. A., Totterdell, P., & Wall, T. D. (2010). The mediating role of job characteristics in job redesign interventions: A serendipitous quasi-experiment. *Journal of Organizational Behavior, 31*(1), 84–105. https://doi.org/10.1002/job.631

Huijs, J. J., Houtman, I. L., Taris, T. W., & Blonk, R. W. (2019). Effect of a participative action intervention program on reducing mental retirement. *BMC Public Health, 19*(1), 1–11. https://doi.org/10.1186/s12889-019-6522-x

International Labor Office. (2001). *Guidelines on occupational safety and health management systems.*

Kelloway, E. K., & Barling, J. (2010). Leadership development as an intervention in occupational health psychology. *Work & Stress, 24*(3), 260–279. https://doi.org/10.1080/02678373.2010.518441

Le, H., Nielsen, K., & Noblet, A. (2021). The well-being and voice of migrant workers in participatory organizational interventions. *International Migration 60*, 52–71. https://doi.org/10.1111/imig.12885

Le Blanc, P. M., Hox, J. J., Schaufeli, W. B., Taris, T. W., & Peeters, M. C. (2007). Take care! The evaluation of a team-based burnout intervention program for oncology care providers. *Journal of Applied Psychology, 92*(1), 213–227. https://doi.org/10.1037/0021-9010.92.1.213

Linzer, M., Poplau, S., Brown, R., Grossman, E., Varkey, A., Yale, S., Williams, E. S, Hicks, L., Wallock, J., Khonhost, D., & Barbouche, M. (2017). Do work condition interventions affect quality and errors in primary care? Results from the healthy work place study. *Journal of General Internal Medicine, 32*(1), 56–61. https://doi.org/10.1007/s11606-016-3856-2

Løkling, T., Nielsen, K., & Christensen, M. (submitted). Organizational interventions in light of workplace conflict: Integrating dynamical system theory as a foundation for handling complexity and intervention strategies. In A. Day & C. Cooper (Eds.), *Mental health at work.* Routledge.

López Peláez, A., Erro-Garcés, A., Pinilla García, F. J., & Kiriakou, D. (2021). Working in the 21st century. The coronavirus crisis: A driver of digitalisation, teleworking, and innovation, with unintended social consequences. *Information, 12*(9), 377.

Nielsen, K. (2013). How can we make organizational interventions work? Employees and line managers as actively crafting interventions. *Human Relations, 66*, 1029–1050. https://doi.org/10.1177/0018726713477164

Nielsen, K. (2023). Improving employee well-being through improving working conditions: A review on how we can make participatory organizational interventions work. In L. E. Tetrick, G. G. Fisher, M. T. Ford, & J. C. Quick (Eds.), *Handbook of occupational health psychology* (3rd ed.). American Psychological Association.

Nielsen, K., & Abildgaard, J. S. (2013). Organizational interventions: A research-based framework for the evaluation of both process and effects. *Work & Stress, 27*(3), 278–297. https://doi.org/10.1080/02678373.2013.812358

Nielsen, K., Abildgaard, J. S., & Daniels, K. (2014). Putting context into organizational intervention design: Using tailored questionnaires to measure initiatives for worker well-being. *Human Relations, 67*(12), 1537–1560. https://doi.org/10.1177/0018726714525974

Nielsen, K., & Christensen, M. (2021). Positive participatory organizational interventions: A multilevel approach for creating healthy workplaces. *Frontiers in Psychology, 12*, 696245. https://doi.org/10.3389/fpsyg.2021.696245

Nielsen, K., De Angelis, M., Innstrand, S. T., & Mazzetti, G. (2022). Quantitative process measures in interventions to improve employees' mental health: A systematic literature review and the IPEF framework. *Work & Stress.* https://doi.org/10.1080/02678373.2022.2080775

Nielsen, K., & Miraglia, M. (2017). What works for whom in which circumstances? On the need to move beyond the "what works?" question in organizational intervention research. *Human Relations*, 70(1), 40–62. https://doi.org/10.1177/0018726716670226

Nielsen, K., Nielsen, M. B., Ogbonnaya, C., Känsälä, M., Saari, E., & Isaksson, K. (2017). Workplace resources to improve both employee well-being and performance: A systematic review and meta-analysis. *Work & Stress*, 31(2), 101–120. https://doi.org/10.1080/02678373.2017.1304463

Nielsen, K., & Noblet, A. (2018). Introduction: Organizational interventions: Where we are, where we go from here? In K. Nielsen & A. Noblet (Eds.), *Organizational interventions for health and well-being: A handbook for evidence-based practice* (pp. 1–23). Routledge.

Nielsen, K., & Randall, R. (2015). Addressing the fit of planned interventions to the organizational context. In M. Karanika-Murray & C. Biron (Eds.), *Derailed organizational stress and well-being interventions: Confessions of failure and solutions for success* (pp. 107–118). Springer.

Nielsen, K., Randall, R., & Albertsen, K. (2007). Participants' appraisals of process issues and the effects of stress management interventions. *Journal of Organizational Behavior*, 28(6), 793–810. https://doi.org/10.1002/job.450

Nielsen, K., Randall, R., Holten, A. L., & González, E. R. (2010). Conducting organizational-level occupational health interventions: What works? *Work & Stress*, 24(3), 234–259.

Niks, I., De Jonge, J., Gevers, J., & Houtman, I. (2018). Work stress interventions in hospital care: Effectiveness of the DISCovery method. *International Journal of Environmental Research and Public Health*, 15(2), 332. https://doi.org/10.3390/ijerph15020332

Randall, R., Cox, T., & Griffiths, A. (2007). Participants' accounts of a stress management intervention. *Human Relations*, 60(8), 1181–1209. https://doi.org/10.1177/0018726707081660

Randall, R., Griffiths, A., & Cox, T. (2005). Evaluating organizational stress-management interventions using adapted study designs. *European Journal of Work and Organizational Psychology*, 14(1), 23–41. https://doi.org/10.1080/13594320444000209

Richardson, K. M., & Rothstein, H. R. (2008). Effects of occupational stress management intervention programs: A meta-analysis. *Journal of Occupational Health Psychology*, 13(1), 69–93. https://psycnet.apa.org/doiLanding?doi=10.1037%2F1076-8998.13.1.69

Roodbari, H., Axtell, C., Nielsen, K., & Sorensen, G. (2021). Organisational interventions to improve employees' health and wellbeing: A realist synthesis. *Applied Psychology: An International Review*, 71, 1058–1081. https://doi.org/10.1111/apps.12346

Schelvis, R. M., Wiezer, N. M., Blatter, B. M., van Genabeek, J. A., Hengel, K. M. O., Bohlmeijer, E. T., & van der Beek, A. J. (2016). Evaluating the implementation process of a participatory organizational level occupational health intervention in schools. *BMC Public Health*, 16(1), 1–20. https://doi.org/10.1186/s12889-016-3869-0

Semmer, N. K. (2006). Job stress interventions and the organization of work. *Scandinavian Journal of Work and Environmental Health*, 32, 515–527.

Semmer, N. K. (2011). Job stress interventions and organization of work. In J. C. Quick & L. E. Tetrick (Eds.), *Handbook of occupational health psychology* (2nd ed., pp. 299–318). American Psychological Association.

Siegrist, J. (2016). Effort-reward imbalance model. In G. Fink (Ed.), *Stress: Concepts, cognition, emotion, and behavior* (pp. 81–86). Academic Press.

Skakon, J., Nielsen, K., Borg, V., & Guzman, J. (2010). Are leaders' well-being, behaviours and style associated with the affective well-being of their employees? A systematic review of three decades of research. *Work & Stress*, 24(2), 107–139. https://doi.org/10.1080/02678373.2010.495262

Sorensen, G., Peters, S. E., Nielsen, K., Stelson, E., Wallace, L. M., Burke, L., Nagler, E. M., Roodbari, H., Karapanos, M., & Wagner, G. R. (2021). Implementation of an organizational intervention to improve low-wage food service workers' safety, health and wellbeing: Findings from the Workplace Organizational Health Study. *BMC Public Health*, 21(1), 1–16. https://doi.org/10.1186/s12889-021-11937-9

Sørensen, O. H., & Holman, D. (2014). A participative intervention to improve employee well-being in knowledge work jobs: A mixed-methods evaluation study. *Work & Stress, 28*(1), 67–86. https://doi.org/10.1080/02678373.2013.876124

Stab, N., & Hacker, W. (2018). Participatory redesign of work organisation in hospital nursing: A study of the implementation process. *Journal of Nursing Management, 26*(4), 382–392. https://doi.org/10.1111/jonm.12545

Tsutsumi, A., Nagami, M., Yoshikawa, T., Kogi, K., & Kawakami, N. (2009). Participatory intervention for workplace improvements on mental health and job performance among blue-collar workers: A cluster randomized controlled trial. *Journal of Occupational and Environmental Medicine, 51*(5), 554–563. https://doi.org/10.1097/JOM.0b013e3181a24d28

Uchiyama, A., Odagiri, Y., Ohya, Y., Takamiya, T., Inoue, S., & Shimomitsu, T. (2013). Effect on mental health of a participatory intervention to improve psychosocial work environment: A cluster randomized controlled trial among nurses. *Journal of Occupational Health, 55*(3), 173–183. https://doi.org/10.1539/joh.12-0228-OA

van der Klink, J. J., Blonk, R. W., Schene, A. H., & Van Dijk, F. J. (2001). The benefits of interventions for work-related stress. *American Journal of Public Health, 91*(2), 270–276. https://doi.org/10.2105/ajph.91.2.270

Vignoli, M., Nielsen, K., Guglielmi, D., Tabanelli, T. C., & Violante, F. S. (2017). The importance of context in screening in occupational health interventions in organizations: A mixed methods study. *Frontiers in Psychology: Organizational Psychology, 8*, 1347. https://doi.org/10.3389/fpsyg.2017.01347

Wong, G., Westhorp, G., Manzano, A., Greenhalgh, J., Jagosh, J., & Greenhalgh, T. (2016). RAMESES II reporting standards for realist evaluations. *BMC Medicine, 14*(1), 1–18. https://doi.org/10.1186/s12916-016-0643-1

World Health Organization, & Burton, J. (2010). *WHO healthy workplace framework and model: Background and supporting literature and practices.* https://apps.who.int/iris/handle/10665/113144

Karina Nielsen

ORGANIZATION DEVELOPMENT

OVERVIEW

Organization development (OD) refers to a process of planned change within an organization that particularly focuses on the organization's culture. It also focuses on the organization as a whole, not just its culture or its strategy, structure, or information technology. OD is grounded in system theory as well as in a set of human values such as respect for others regardless of race, gender, and other diversities that tend to drive people apart rather than bring them together. Its other primary values include honesty, collaboration, trust, and social justice.

While this article on OD is a part of the encyclopedia article on I/O psychology, it should be noted that while OD and I/O can operate together, their theoretical roots differ. Even though the *O* in I/O refers to *organization*, most I/O psychologists spend their time on issues related to the individual, such as selection, training, retention, and job–person fit. OD practitioners, on the other hand, work within a system-theory framework—focusing on the organization as a whole with an emphasis on the external environment, mission, strategy, culture, leadership, and performance.

Another difference between the two processes is that I/O psychologists place research front and center, whereas OD practitioners are guided more by theory. The latter consider the organization to be an open system and conduct their analysis largely on the basis of Kurt Lewin's concept of the environment as a field of forces that drive and restrain organizational members' behavior. This field-of-forces perspective comes from Lewin's applications of or derivations from theoretical physics. Whereas traditional I/O psychologists are driven by empiricism, experienced OD practitioners are driven by Lewinian theory. While the differences between I/O psychologists and OD practitioners do not render them exclusive practices, the distinctions do affect how each considers organizational data and practice.

The history of OD is steeped in the work that Lewin did in the fields of social and organizational psychology. His research, especially regarding leadership, was implemented largely by Alfred Marrow in his roles as a psychologist and CEO of the Harwood Manufacturing Corporation. OD in its nascent stage was largely concerned with training individuals to be participative in their roles as managers and supervisors. As OD evolved, the phases of organization began to change based on Lewin's work and systems thinking. In the 1960s, OD practitioners began to follow the three-phase model, wherein they first *unfroze* the organization, then performed a series of *change* interventions, and finally *refroze* the system in order to retain the new ways of conducting work of the organization. This three-phase approach expanded as OD efforts became more in demand such that the latest evidence-based model consists of 10 steps, beginning with diagnosis and ending with sustainability.

Does OD work? Any OD effort is only as good as the validity of the theory and models applied, combined with the skills and abilities of the practitioner—change leader—involved. Appropriate applications of OD can indeed lead to change that improves and sustains the work of the organization. A 1967 report (Marrow, Bowers, & Seashore, 1967) on changes at the Harwood Corporation as well as evidence over the years since has shown that OD, when conducted according to what is known about how change can be led and managed effectively, does indeed work.

In the West, death and taxes have traditionally been considered to be the inevitabilities of life. Recently, change has come to be considered the third inevitability. Change may be rapid for some of us and slower for others, but it is inevitable, nevertheless. Change occurs in all areas of our lives, from our personal lives, to our families, to our workplaces, to world climate. In this article, my objective is to gain a deeper understanding of change at the organizational level. But my focus is not on happenstance organizational changes that take place; rather, it is on what has been known since the 1950s as *organization development*, which focuses on changes that are planned, deliberate, focused on the goals to be attained, and values based.

The purposes of this article are to explain what OD is, where it comes from, how it is carried out, what the research about it indicates, what its underlying value system represents, and the trends for the future.

Two Cases. One of the best ways to explain anything is to use case studies to illustrate a point. To do this, I will review two relatively short examples of OD, one carried out in a manufacturing division of a business firm and the other carried out in a medical school. A definition and discussion of OD follow these two cases.

1616 • ORGANIZATION DEVELOPMENT

Case Example: A Manufacturing Division. A number of years ago, I served as consultant at a large U.S. manufacturing company. The division I worked in manufactured heavy electrical equipment in two different plants. I was called in because the division was in trouble. About a month prior to when the company got in touch with me, a senior vice president from corporate headquarters had told the division's top management that unless it turned things around within 6 months, he would see to it that the division was closed down. That meant the possibility of a job loss for approximately 1,000 people, including the division's top management group of six people. The problems the division was facing concerned complaints by two major utility companies that had been customers of theirs that their orders were invariably late in delivery, and when the products did arrive they were poor in quality or did not meet the product standards that were originally specified.

Within the division, everyone blamed everyone else for the problems. The marketing people complained that the design engineers took too long and designed things too much in "their own way" instead of according to what the customer wanted. The design engineers blamed the production people for not following the design specifications. The production people, in turn, complained that the engineers designed the products for tolerances entirely too close for the antiquated machinery they had to use in the manufacturing process. And both the design engineers and production people blamed the marketing and sales "hotshots" (as they frequently called them) for promising customers highly unrealistic delivery dates. And so the round robin of complaints went.

On my first consulting visit to the company, I spent several hours discussing the division's problems with its general manager. He also showed me the entire operation and focused on the manufacturing process. And we had a meeting with his subordinate managers at which I asked questions, they asked me questions, and we explored the issues. I proposed that the next step be that I conducted individual interviews with each of them, after which I would report back to them as a group what the interview data indicated, and finally we would plan the next steps together. They agreed to the proposal, and 2 weeks later I spent a day interviewing each of the six members of the division's top management team—the managers of marketing, finance, manufacturing, engineering, employee relations, and the overall division general manager. On the following day, we had a meeting in which we discussed my interview findings. Stated simply, it became clear that these people were not working well together, especially with respect to trying to determine the primary causes of their problems. The blame was not confined to the shop floor. Regardless of their level in the division, individual managers were certainly not "above" the mutual blaming process. We decided, therefore, to spend a few days off-site to explore in more depth the issues that existed among them in an attempt to "get their act together." In OD language, this activity is referred to as "team building."

As a result of the off-site meeting, the six managers became more cohesive as a group and achieved a greater clarity and sense of priority regarding the division's problems. The highest priority, which was the next step in the consultation, was addressing the conflict that existed between the design engineers and the manufacturing (production) group of managers and supervisors. To deal with the conflict some weeks later, I arranged for another 3-day off-site meeting of 12 people, consisting of the top six managers within manufacturing and the equivalent six from the engineering design department. Although there were a number of conflicts between the two groups, the main ones concerned the engineers' complaint that the manufacturing group did not follow their design specifications closely enough and the latter group's lament regarding the old and inadequate machines they had to work with. In other words, as the manufacturing managers put it, "Those design engineers just stay glued to their drafting boards and have absolutely no understanding or any concern about our problems on the shop floor."

In an attempt to bring to the surface as much of the conflict as possible and then gain some points of resolution, I used a technique that is considered a fairly standard practice in OD for dealing with a conflict between two groups in an organization who have to work together effectively for the ultimate success of the organization. The procedure for problem solving begins with the two groups exchanging their perceptions with each other—each group describing how it sees itself and the other group. After this exchange, again working separately, then identify what they consider the problems to be within the interface—that is, in the domain of information exchange and the general relations between the two groups. Next, a negotiation occurs regarding which problems both groups agree are most important to them. The final phase consists of forming cross-groups (in this case, three groups of four persons each—two employees from engineering and two from manufacturing), with each group taking on a different problem around which to plan action steps that the two dissenting groups can take to resolve the conflict. A number of problems were indeed handled effectively and progress was made.

The most significant issue that emerged as a consequence of this intergroup meeting is the belief that the manufacturing group was not consistent in what and how they communicated with the design engineers. About 2 months later, therefore, I helped to conduct a team-building session with the top group from manufacturing. This meeting helped the manufacturing employees to clarify as a unit what they needed from the design engineers (and other groups from within the division) and what their priorities were for dealing with some of their internal problems.

Summary. My consultative effort with this division lasted about 9 months. By the end of that time, the division had "turned around." The corporation's quarterly report for that period shows that the division, compared with all the other divisions, was no longer at the bottom of the heap with respect to net profit and customer complaints. From the perspective of OD, two primary interventions had been made—team building, for the top management team and for the manufacturing group, and an intergroup conflict-resolution session between manufacturing and design engineering. Each intervention occurred quite naturally as a result of the previous one since such activities always produce further diagnostic information. In fact, as I gathered and analyzed more and more information, I eventually came to the conclusion that a major cause of problems for the division lay within its reward system. There was no basis for positive reinforcement, no incentive system of any kind; therefore, because they had few resources besides their individual ability to be persuasive, first-line supervisors relied heavily on punitive techniques (e.g., threatening layoffs). The system of pay for the hourly workers was based on equality—that is, for a given set of jobs, all received the same pay except in the case of seniority—rather than equity, where people's pay level is based on their performance.

I recommended making a change in this regard to the division general manager. He responded, "No way!" This particular reward system was corporation-wide, and he explained that he did not have the power to change that. I further suggested that we take the matter to his boss. He politely said no, and with that my consulting effort ended. There was further work that could have been done, but I considered the effort to be one of continuing to "put out fires" rather than dealing with underlying systemic causes.

Case Example: A Medical School. For well over 3 years, an internal consultant within a medical school and I worked together in an organization development (OD) effort. We conducted team-building sessions (similar to the ones mentioned in the previous case) with a number of the academic and clinical departments, and we also held an intergroup conflict-resolution session that was in response to a three-way problem. The conflict was among three subunits within the clinical pathology department—that of the medical doctors, that of the PhD biologists and chemists, and that of the medical technicians. Although the procedure was more complicated, we followed essentially the same format I described in the previous case.

What made this OD effort different from the previous example is that it produced a major change in the school's internal structure. Prior to my arrival, a school curriculum-planning committee had been meeting on and off for 2 years. Its members believed that their plan for a new curriculum was excellent, but they couldn't seem to move toward implementing the change itself. When asked why there had been no movement toward implementation, the committee chair said the faculty were "not ready." In interviews with a variety of people and in discussions with the committee, I discovered that most of the faculty members were suspicious of the committee's work. Little or no communication outside the committee had occurred. The faculty may or may not have been ready to make the change, but they were definitely paranoid. What are those committee members doing? is a question they would pose to me. The members of the committee were enthusiastic about their plan, but they feared that if it came to a faculty vote, which eventually would be a necessity, they would lose. Our data confirmed their fear.

After quite an effort, the internal consultant and I persuaded the committee to run the risk of having its plan modified and involve a large number of other faculty in the planning process. We then organized a planned change process that eventually involved a hundred individuals, more than a third of the entire faculty. The original planning group became a steering committee, and numerous other committees were formed according to subject matter and the member's year of medical school, from first year through the fourth. A year later, the new plan was put before the entire faculty and was approved by a four-to-one vote. The dean was ecstatic. He had been hoping for a two-to-one vote and got much more than he had expected. Getting this approval moved us to the next stage—making it work. A structural change was required. The change involved was from having one main subunit of the school as the academic departmental structure to having two primary units—the departments and four teaching groups each formed according to student school year. The new structure was a matrix with most faculty having two "home bases," their academic department and their teaching unit. The heads of the four teaching units were accountable to the associate dean for education, and this structural entity within the school maintained a separate budget from the academic departments. Thus, the academic departments' mission was modified to that of exclusively graduate training and research, as opposed to the previous mission, which included these two functions plus classroom education for the 4-year medical students. Implementation of the change spanned 4 consecutive years, owing to the fact that it began with an entering freshman class and continued sequentially, rather than applying to the curriculum of all 4 years separately. Thus, the change was orderly and allowed plenty of time for "debugging" the new system.

I should point out that during this change effort my internal colleague and I regularly spent time with the dean and his immediate staff. We counseled the dean regarding his management strategy and style and we worked with him in his relationship with the staff, particularly with the associate dean for education. Trust between the dean and his associate was key to the success of the change. Also critical, of course, was the fact that a significant number of the faculty members were directly involved in planning the change, particularly those changes that each one of them would later be responsible for implementing.

Summary of the Cases.   These two cases represent many of the more common elements and practices of OD. They are (a) working collaboratively with the client rather than only serving as an expert adviser; (b) intervening only after information determining what the intervention will consist of has been collected; (c) using multiple interventions—team building, intergroup problem solving, structural modifications, training, coaching, and involvement techniques; and (d) in general, applying both evidence-based and theoretical knowledge from the behavioral sciences.

DEFINING ORGANIZATION DEVELOPMENT

The definition of organization development (OD) proposed by Beckhard (1969) remains the most popular and accepted one. He defined OD as "an effort (1) *planned*, (2) *organization-wide*, and (3) *managed* from the top, to (4) increase *organization effectiveness* and *health* through (5) *planned interventions* in the organization's 'process' using *behavioral-science knowledge*" (p. 9). He went on to explain further the italicized terms in his definition, suggesting that the emphasis is on the planned application of behavioral science knowledge for organizational improvement with top management remaining in charge.

While many scholars—for example, Beer (1980), Cummings and Worley (2005), and Huse (1980)—agree with most of Beckhard's definition, some take issue with the "managed from the top" aspect. They contend that OD can start anywhere in the organization—at the top, in the middle, or even with the rank and file. They agree that top management should not be opposed to an OD effort but think that too strong a commitment to change on its part, especially in the early stages, could cause resistance lower down in the organization.

It is true that OD can and has started at levels of an organization other than at the top. However, if the organization in question is a hierarchically structured one, which most are, certainly within the domains of business-industry and government, the following caveat applies: The OD effort must be managed from the top if it is to be implemented "organization-wide," to use Beckhard's term.

More importantly, the question really concerns *what* is managed from the top. In our case, the what that was managed from the top was the *process* of change, not necessarily the *content* of the new organizational state. If top management had defined the desired state—not only for the overall organization but for all the organizational units as well—resistance would no doubt have occurred. When the process is managed in a manner that involves the lower-level employees, the content (or the substantive aspects of change) will have less of a chance of being resisted since those directly affected are taking part in the decisions.

The emphasis in my definition of OD is on cultural change and the integration of the organization's goals with the needs of its members. OD necessarily involves change, but organizational change does not always involve OD. Three criteria determine whether an organizational change can be considered an effective OD intervention. If the intervention (a) responds to the actual needs for change as experienced by organizational members, (b) involves organizational members in the planning and implementing of the changes, and (c) leads to a change in the organization's culture, then the change is considered effective (Burke & Noumair, 2015). Not everyone in the field agrees with these criteria, particularly the third one—cultural change. Meeting this third criterion implies that the change is in a certain direction. And as I see it, most of the time it is.

Referring back to the case examples, the intervention at the medical school met all three of the criteria for an effective OD intervention, but the consultation with the manufacturing division did not lead to cultural change; that is, to a change in the organization's reward system. Even though OD techniques were used, the effort could not be considered, in the final analysis, effective OD. Adhering strictly to my three criteria, then, I consider the manufacturing division case to have been a short-term success, but for the purposes of OD, in the long run, it was a failure.

To be more specific about cultural change in an organization, the direction of change is typically toward developing an organizational culture where:

- Managers exercise their authority more participatively than unilaterally and arbitrarily.
- Cooperative and collaborative behavior is valued more highly than competitive behavior.
- The growth and development of organizational members is just as important as making a profit or meeting a budget.
- Organizational members at all levels periodically receive feedback on their performance.
- Equal opportunity and fairness for people abounds—in recruitment, promotion practices, and the organization's reward system.
- Organizational members are kept informed, especially concerning matters that directly affect their jobs or them personally.

I could go on with this list, but perhaps this short list gives you a sense of what the new organizational culture should approach after OD had been underway for a while, at least a couple of years.

In an attempt to provide more than just a sense of effective organization culture, however, I'll refer to other scholars' thinking about it. I'll first discuss the writing of Katz and Kahn (1966). These authors have contended that the culture of an organization is reflected in its (a) system of norms and values, (b) history of internal and external struggles, (c) types of people who seek to work there, (d) work processes and physical layout, (e) modes of communication, and (f) exercise of authority. In a previous entry, I used these six factors to compare three classical and traditional views of organizational culture (and the more prevailing culture of organizations today) with the desired organizational culture for the purposes of OD. The three views are taken from the writings of Argyris, Bennis, and Massie. Argyris uses the term "formal" to describe current organizational cultures; Bennis calls them "bureaucracies"; and Massie refers to the characteristics of the "classical" (and still prevailing) theory of organizational management. These three traditional descriptions are quite similar to one another and are in striking contrast to Beckhard's outline for what he calls a "healthy" organization and one that is aspired to in an OD effort. Using the six factors of Katz and Kahn as a basis for the comparisons, Table 1 summarizes the three traditional/classical views and compares them with that of an organization that is involved in OD.

Table 1. Comparison of Contemporary Organizational Cultures with Culture of Organization Involved in OD

Factors reflecting culture of an organization	Formal organizations	Culture of contemporary bureaucratic organizations	Classical organizations	Culture of organization involved in OD
Norms and values	Individuality is suppressed and no value placed on self-actualization.	Interpersonal relations are impersonal and conformity is rewarded.	Groups activities are viewed on an objective and impersonal basis; highest value placed on productivity; people do not value the freedom of determining their own approaches to problems.	Individuality is stressed by utilizing the maximum level of maximum human resources; feelings expressed as well as logical thoughts; collaborative efforts rewarded with less emphasis on competition; high value placed on democratic process of working together and interacting.
History of internal and external struggles: classical conflict	The organization's demands and the individual's need to self-actualize usually differ considerably.	Interpersonal and organizational, as it is common in a bureaucracy to have bosses without technical competence and workers with it.	Conflict between boss and worker since supervision is required to get work done.	No conflict; conflict among human beings is inevitable.
History of internal and external struggles: style of conflict resolution	Individual needs are suppressed since organizational demands come first.	Conflicts are ignored since it is assumed the boss will eventually retire or be "promoted."	Varies, but decisions are made by the boss, who handles them any way he or she sees fit, typically in an autocratic manner.	Conflicts are brought out into the open and managed creatively.
Work	Logical thinkers; highly rational people who suppress their feelings.	Conditioned "organization people" who desire order, structure, and stability in their lives.	Rational people who do not like to work; when they are required to, they prefer (a) the security of a definite task, (b) to be directed, and (c) to receive money as their primary incentive.	People with a strong need for self-actualization.

(Continued)

Table 1. Continued

Factors reflecting culture of an organization	Formal organizations	Culture of contemporary bureaucratic organizations	Classical organizations	Culture of organization involved in OD
Work processes and physical layout	Logical and systematic (i.e., functioning according to scientific management principles).	Division of labor based on functional specialization.	Clear-cut patterns of work predicted and established; simple tasks stressed because they are easier to master and lead to higher productivity.	Form of organizational structure follows function; self-renewing, viable systems that are organized in a variety of ways depending on the task.
Modes of communication	Conforms to what organizational charts and manuals prescribe.	Follows well-defined system based on rights and duties of employees.	Restricted to limits of the specific job and hierarchical channels; otherwise members will be confused and infringe on the domain of others.	Freedom of communication upward, downward, and laterally with an emphasis on openness and candor.
Exercise of authority	Authority-obedience principle	Follows well-defined system based on rights and duties of employees.	Authority has its source at the top of hierarchy and is delegated downward; coordination won't be achieved unless it is planned and directed from above; in a cooperative endeavor, members are unable to work out their individual roles without detailed guidance from their superiors.	Authority is a function of knowledge and competence as well as role; decision-making is on the basis of information source rather than organizational role.

Note: Concept of formal organizations (first column) taken from Argyris; concept of cultures of organization (second column) taken from Bennis; concept of classical organizations (third column) taken from Massie; cultures of organization of OD (fourth column) taken from Beckhard.

As stated earlier, complete agreement concerning a definition of what OD is or should be does not exist among professionals in the field. While most professionals would be willing to cite Beckhard's definition as perhaps the standard one, they would likely, at the same time, have their own version.

As an OD consultant, I take a normative approach and define *organization development* as a process of applying knowledge from the behavioral sciences to changes in an organization's culture, so that individual needs and organizational goals can be integrated more effectively.

Even though definitional differences remain, most people in the field would agree that OD (a) involves change; (b) is a continuing process, not a program or discrete event; (c) uses behavioral science technology; and (d) follows an action research model (to be explained in the following section).

Where Did OD Come From?   OD has the following three primary historical roots—all of which are associated with particular institutions:

1. **Sensitivity or t-group training**: associated with the National Training Laboratories Institute for Applied Behavioral Science
2. **Group relations and sociotechnical systems**: associated with the Tavistock Institute of London
3. **Survey feedback**: associated with the Institute for Social Research (ISR) at the University of Michigan

The functions can be described as follows. *Sensitivity or t-group training* involves the application of group dynamics for individual learning via interpersonal relations and feedback regarding the impact of one's behavior on others. It evolved from the work of Kurt Lewin and his associates during the late 1940s. For a comprehensive explanation of the methods and their beginnings, see Bradford et al. (1964). Briefly, sensitivity training involves the analysis of interpersonal relations in small groups, according to which the major source of information is the behavior and feelings of the group members themselves. Facilitated by a trainer, participants give feedback to one another on their behavior in the group, and this process becomes the learning source for individual growth and development. Group members also have the opportunity to learn about group behavior. During the latter part of the 1950s, sensitivity trainers began to apply this learning methodology within organizations, using the training as an attempt to change certain aspects of an organization, especially managerial style (see, for example, Shepard, 1960). Gradually, sensitivity training, or at least much of the methodology derived from it, was used to improve the interpersonal relationships among members of an organizational unit or team. This type of applicability was the forerunner of what are known today in OD as process consultation and team building. The current practice of OD encompasses much more than team building, but this important intervention remains popular and has its roots in sensitivity training.

Group relations and *sociotechnical systems* represent the two branches of the Tavistock Institute. Group relations, not unlike sensitivity training, consists of training at various levels of human interaction and is conducted in small and large groups and focuses more on unconscious processes than overt behavior. The theoretical father of group relations is Wilfred Bion, a contemporary of Kurt Lewin but a psychoanalyst rather than a social psychologist; therefore, he concentrated on the emotions and motives beneath the surface of conscious behavior. Sociotechnical systems involve change activities in an organization that account for both the technological requirements and the social relationships of the people directly involved. One of the early studies that provided the basis for what was later called the sociotechnical systems approach to organizational change was conducted by Trist and Bamforth (1951). Both researchers were staff members of the Tavistock Institute and involved in group relations training and organizational change. They were asked by a coal mining company in England to help with a technological change problem in which the company had introduced a new technique for mining coal, but following the change, absenteeism had increased and productivity had decreased. The researchers found that the company had ignored the social relationships of the miners and the importance of these relationships for morale and productivity. The technical change required a greater division of labor and thereby had broken up long-established work teams. They showed the company how it could, without returning to the old method, modify the technical change by making the work more composite and could, as a result, retain the social patterns so important to the miners. The conceptual framework guiding Trist and Bamforth, as well as their colleagues at Tavistock—Rice, Emery, Higgens, Bridger, and others—was built on the following belief: Any organization is simultaneously a technical *and* a social system, and to ignore either in a change process is to invite failure since the two systems are inextricably related. Current interventions in OD, such as job redesign, autonomous work groups, and structural design of organizations, especially manufacturing operations, have their roots in the sociotechnical way of thinking about and changing an organization.

Survey feedback, a method of diagnosing problems in an organization with the use of a questionnaire and intervening, was developed by Rensis Likert, Floyd Mann, and colleagues in the 1950s at the University of Michigan's ISR. Collecting information from organizational members via a questionnaire was not particularly unusual at the time. Surveying employees' attitudes and the state of their morale, while not pervasive among organizations of the day, was an established procedure. Using the survey results for effective organizational change was unusual, however. What these University of Michigan psychologists realized is that although organizational managers might find the survey results interesting and might even be concerned with the findings, rarely did anything change in the organization as a result of the surveys. Moreover, in some cases organizations would experience greater rather than fewer problems as a consequence of conducting them. The fact that a survey was conducted would raise employees' expectations that their opinions were important to management and that some action would be taken to resolve the problems expressed. When nothing different actually occurred, employee skepticism if not cynicism would increase. Mann (1957), in particular, developed a process whereby the survey results were summarized and reported back within "family" units of the organization; that is, to the people who worked together, often as a team. By carefully following certain steps of problem solving for groups, these family units would be able to (a) analyze the survey results in light of their own domain of work and (b) plan and later take steps for resolving problems identified via the survey. Thus, the technique got its name, *survey feedback*, as a result of questionnaire results "fed" back in a structured way to the persons who had generated the data in the first place, giving them the opportunity of doing something about the problems they had collectively identified. Survey feedback is a common practice in

OD today; the book *Feedback and Organization Development* by David Nadler (1977) is devoted entirely to this type of change methodology.

Although these three historical roots of OD differ, they have at least one common property—they are all based on an action research model of change—which has contributed the three methodologies all currently being used in OD. *Action research* literally means to take action as a result of research findings. Thus, action research is distinguished from "pure" research. Both types of research may contribute to some body of knowledge, but the outcome of the latter is far more significant than that of the former. The primary objective of action research is ultimately to take some form of action. Just as important in the process is to take the action based on what the data, objectively derived and interpreted, would indicate. Action research, as originally conceived, followed the scientific method quite closely during the research phase (Chein et al., 1948). As used in OD, however, the concept is interpreted more loosely. Working according to an action research model means that action is taken based on the data collected and that, in turn, the action taken generates further data to be collected and acted on. French (1969) has briefly clarified how OD should be conducted within the framework of action research. For a more comprehensive treatment of the relationship between action research and OD, see Frohman et al. (1976).

Burnes (2019) tells the story of how Lewin's thinking shaped the survey-feedback work conducted at the ISR at the University of Michigan based on Alfred Marrow's influence as a client, as the CEO of the Harwood Manufacturing Corporation and as the biographer of Lewin (Marrow, 1969).

Before concluding this section, I'd like to briefly clarify a point. At the outset of this article, I described two cases of OD in action. When conducting an OD effort, what does the practitioner, the change leader, actually do? Recall that, in the end, the cases differed from each other, in that in one, that of the medical school, effective OD actually occurred—that is, sustained change in the organization was established—whereas in the other case, that of the manufacturing organization, within the work units team dynamics were enhanced and relations between groups improved, yet no fundamental aspect of the organization's culture seems to have been affected all that much, if at all. In other words, a temporary fix to the problem of uncooperative behavior was provided, but no long-term change in the organization's culture, especially concerning the reward system, occurred. Even though I, as the consultant in both cases, followed a similar set of steps in each, the ultimate outcome was not the same. Similar steps can lead to different outcomes. The context matters. With these points in mind, let us review the primary steps that OD practitioners follow in most cases.

STEPS IN THE OD PROCESS

The six primary steps in any organization development (OD) process are entry, contract, data collection and diagnosis, feedback, intervention, and evaluation. I shall now proceed to explain each of these steps.

Entry.   Typically, the initial contact for an OD effort is initiated by the client. While "marketing one's services" is important for the survival of an OD consultant, whether internal to the organization or outside it, the consultant is more often than not asked by the client to discuss the possibilities of help. Also typically, the client calls for the assistance of an OD consultant because organizational members are having painful work experiences (see, e.g., the book *Organizational Diagnosis* by Harry Levinson [1972]). However, it is *not* typical for the client to identify the problem in any systemic fashion; that is, in terms that follow some model of how organizations function. According to Goodstein (1978), "The client system presents 'symptoms' that may suggest to the consultant some underlying problem in one or more of the organizational models" (p. 78). Thus, it is critical that the OD consultant is working according to at least one model of how organizations function—or are supposed to function for optimal efficiency and effectiveness.

Sometimes the OD consultant will be contacted by the client with a request to conduct a management development program, a negotiation skills workshop, or supervisory training. But even requests such as these should not necessarily be taken at face value. For example, Goodstein and Boyer (1972) report a case in which the initial request was for a "communications workshop," but the consultants quickly learned that their client organization was experiencing turmoil characterized by considerable anger and suspicion. They concluded that to conduct such a workshop would have led to open warfare. Eventually, the consultants moved with their client toward dealing with the underlying problems directly rather than attempting to "fix" the organization with a communications workshop.

Thus, in OD work this initial step, entry into the client organization, may be the most difficult one. The OD consultant is attempting to reach two objectives simultaneously: the establishment of a rapport with the client—having their interpersonal "chemistry" mix adequately—and the attainment of enough valid information to determine accurately the nature of the organization's problem(s) and whether OD is appropriate. With respect to the first objective, establishing a rapport, the most significant ingredient in this process is trust. Establishing some basis for interpersonal trust is important for any consultant-client relationship, but it is particularly important in the OD consultation. There are at least three reasons for this emphasis on trust:

1. Since OD is rather vaguely defined, the client must believe more in the expertise of the consultant as a person than in certain packages of the technique, or programs the client may already know about. Further, it is not always clear exactly *what* the client is buying. Moreover, a guaranteed outcome is typically not possible.

2. A client accepting a consultation frequently experiences defensive feelings. The acceptance of help can be perceived as a failure on the part of the client, whose defensive feelings can be especially keen in an OD situation since the consultation is largely in the "people" domain of organizational activities. Many client managers believe that while it is OK not to know about a particular technology—say, something concerning electronic data processing—somehow it is less acceptable not to know how to handle organizational behavior problems, such as how to help the client motivate his or her staff. In the initial process, it is therefore essential that the OD consultant be sensitive to what the client's feelings entail.

3. Both the consultant and client know that because of the nature of their potential work together in this OD process, it is highly likely that they will delve into sensitive areas. It is also likely that the top boss in the situation will hear some things that he or she would rather not. The client quite naturally wants some assurance that the consultant will treat

these potentially sensitive areas with care and discretion. It should be added here that differences related to culture (Steele, 1977), ethnicity, race, and even gender (Berg, 1977) between the client and consultant become magnified during entry. The greater the differences between client and consultant, the more potential distrust there will be to overcome.

The second objective during the initial phase is for the consultant to "get a fix" on the organization—that is, to obtain as quickly as possible enough information to determine whether an OD effort is warranted. Moreover, since OD involves change, the consultant must assess the client's "readiness" to undertake it. Pfeiffer and Jones (1978) have developed a readiness checklist for the consultant. Some examples of the 15 indicators that they deem important are (a) whether the organization is experiencing a crisis, (b) the nature of the organization's culture—how amenable is it to change? (c) the organization's resources—can it afford the cost involved in an OD effort? (d) structural flexibility—how easily can reporting relationships be changed? and (e) a presence of internal consultants—are they available or is there potential for development of certain people for this role?

Another way of considering an organization's readiness for change is to conceptualize the potential in terms of what the social and psychological costs would be. David Gleicher's formula (referred to by Beckhard & Harris, 1977) for determining these costs is:

$$C = (ABD) > X$$

where C = change, A = level of dissatisfaction with the status quo, B = clear desired state, D = practical first steps toward the desired state, and X = cost of change. In other words, someone has to have enough dissatisfaction with the current state of affairs (variable A) to have the motivation to be mobilized for the change. The various subsystems need to have clear-enough goals (variable B) for the "cost" (variable X) to be worthwhile. For each subsystem, there needs to be some awareness of practical first steps (variable D) for movement to take place (Beckhard & Harris, 1977, pp. 25–26).

Both clarity on the direction of change *and* motivation are necessary. Beckhard and Harris (1977) report a case where "we discovered and he [the client] discovered that although he had been dissatisfied with the status quo and had a clear picture of what he wanted to do and had instituted some practical first steps to carry out the change, he was not in fact *that* dissatisfied" (p. 27). They go on to state that when the client became aware of his relative lack of motivation, he changed some of his behavior and plans, so that eventually the change occurred satisfactorily.

To summarize: At entry, consultants have two objectives: (a) to determine the efficacy of the interpersonal "chemistry" between them and their clients and (b) to determine whether OD is appropriate. With respect to the latter objective, the consultant must (a) discriminate between problem symptoms and causes—or communicate to the client as quickly as possible a way of getting at the causes—and (b) discern the client's readiness for change.

Contract. There usually is a formal as well as an informal contract between the consultant and client. The formal contract may be a simple letter of agreement that states briefly and in general terms what the consultant will do, how frequently the client will be billed (if the consultant is an external one), and when the contract will terminate. Or the contract may be a formal document whereby the consultant agrees (perhaps even swears), among other things, not to divulge information obtained during the OD process. I once consulted with a company that contracted with the Department of Defense from time to time; not only did I have to sign a legal contractual document for the corporation but I had to meet standards for a "secret" clearance from the federal government as well.

In an OD consultation, the informal contract with the client is perhaps the more important one. Adhering to values that underlie—and, I might add, undergird—OD, the consultant establishes an agreement with the client whereby they will (a) keep each other informed as much as possible; (b) be open with each other in their communications, especially regarding concerns either party might have; (c) clarify what each expects to get from the relationship; and (d) in general, determine the ground rules of how they will operate with each other (Weisbord, 1973).

Data Collection and Diagnosis. There are four primary modes of collecting information about an organization:

1. **Observation**: In this basic mode, the consultant not only records what he or she sees and hears but attempts to "sense" the organization from a feeling perspective. Does he or she find that the organization "feels," for example, (a) warm or cold; (b) close or distant; (c) like a pleasant, fun place to work or uncomfortable; and (d) open or guarded?
2. **Documents**: The consultant may learn a lot by studying the typical records kept by the organization—such as data on absenteeism, the current annual report, the number of grievances (if the organization is unionized)—and by reading recent reports from important committees or task forces.
3. **Questionnaires**: Surveys of organizational members' perceptions and attitudes about a variety of factors may be conducted by using an outside standardized questionnaire or by designing one especially for the client organization. An example of the former type of questionnaire is the "Profile of Organizational Characteristics" by Likert (1967). This instrument surveys organizational members' attitudes about management practices from the standpoints of what they perceive the current state to be and of a more ideal state they desire. Questionnaire results are then "profiled" according to the differences between the perceived, actual, and ideal states and according to the degree of participative management practiced by the organization's manager. The degree of profiled participation ranges from autocratic—no participation—to consensual group decision-making—considerable participation.

    Likert's profile as well as other standardized questionnaires may not completely suit an organization's requirements, especially when information needs to be collected in areas other than management practices. In these cases, a specially tailored questionnaire may need to be constructed. Before actually composing such a questionnaire, it is usually best to conduct a number of interviews, selected but randomized within the organization, so that the more salient dimensions for questionnaire items can be determined.

    Time permitting, it is often wise to administer some combination of both an outside standardized questionnaire (so that useful comparisons may be made) and a tailor-made internal one. It is important, for example, to create a survey from a model such as Likert's or one based on the Burke-Litwin model (Burke & Litwin, 1992).

4. **Interviews**: Interviewing is the most popular mode of data collection among OD consultants. Interviews may be conducted with one person at a time or in small groups. When done in the privacy of a manager's office, a consultant can usually get more information than they would from a group interview, at least at the outset of an OD effort; but if time is limited, interviewing people in groups may indeed suffice. Unless I am attempting to gain information about a specific matter I normally ask the following four open-ended questions in an interview:

   a. What is going well in the organization; what are its strengths or positive qualities?
   b. What is not going well in the organization; what are the problems, weaknesses, issues that need attention?
   c. What is satisfying about your particular job; what is rewarding?
   d. What are the barriers, hindrances, or blocks that prevent you from doing the kind of job you would like to do or think you should be doing?

The first two questions concern organizational matters, and the third and fourth address the individual and his or her job. The first and third questions focus on the positive, while the second and fourth ask about problems, the negative side. Of course, these are not the only questions asked; additional, more specific questions are raised within each of the four categories. With the negative questions, the consultant is trying to find out areas in need of change, but with the positive questions, he or she is trying to find out areas that need strengthening and reinforcing, not necessarily changing. Also with the latter questions, the consultant is trying to demonstrate that OD is not a change activity done merely for the sake of change but, rather, an effort toward intervening in areas where people in the organization feel a need for change.

To help with diagnosis—and particularly to avoid as much as possible the consultant's bias about what *should* be "corrected" in an organization or what is "proper" regarding managerial practice—a model and a theoretical approach to analyzing and making sense out of the information collected are a must. Explicitly, and if not certainly implicitly, every consultant (whether in OD or not) has a "model" or particular way of looking at and analyzing an organization. It is probably true that anyone who has lived and/or worked in an organization for some length of time has notions about what makes an organization the way it is and what should be done to make it better. My own views are steeped in social psychology, the field of my graduate education. I pay particular attention to the norms and values that exist in the organization—what people conform to and what they feel is right and wrong about behavior in the organization. I am also interested in power and rewards—how decisions get made, how influence is exercised, and what behavior people *feel* rewarded and punished for doing in the organization. Other consultants have different views or pet areas for diagnosis. Thus, it is important to use a model for diagnosing an organization; and while the model may reflect one's bias, it should be comprehensive enough to ensure that significant domains of organizational life and functioning will not be overlooked (see, e.g., Burke & Litwin, 1992).

Feedback. The next part of the OD process is the consultant's provision of a summarized and analyzed version of data collected during the previous step. This reporting back to the client is termed "feedback" in OD, since the consultant, in a manner of speaking, is "holding a mirror before the client" and, consequently, the client organization is "viewing a reflection" of what members have said about *their* organization. This feedback may be extensive and fairly complicated (i.e., in need of interpretation) when it is a summary of a major survey. As noted earlier, Mann (1957) developed a process whereby considerable data may be "fed" back and handled in a participative way. His survey feedback method uses naturally existing "family" units in the organization. These units receive feedback regarding the overall organization, information with respect to their unit, and comparative data from other units that are comparable to them organizationally. For more detailed and current methods of dealing effectively with the feedback process of survey data, see Nadler (1977). Although the opinions of OD consultants differ slightly, for me, the feedback process has three parts:

1. A summary of the interviews is provided, organized according to the questions asked. As much as possible, verbatim phrases from the interview are used, with a preference for those that tend to summarize what others also said. A number follows each phrase indicating how many of the interviewees referred to that topic.
2. The interview data are then categorized and analyzed according to some model of organizational functioning. This analysis is discussed with the client group so that accuracy and agreement can be reached. An alternate step for this part of the feedback process is to present a model and then involve the client group themselves in the categorization and analysis. In any case, the objective of this part of the feedback is to provide a conceptual framework that uses systematic and organizational terminology so that a better understanding of the nature of the problems can be achieved and a priority for action planning can be established. The purpose of emphasizing organizational and systematic language here is to ensure that the change effort will be directed toward the organization as a system rather than toward individuals, per se.
3. As a final part of the feedback, I give the client a synthesis of my observations, impressions, and emotional reactions. I make sure that this part of the feedback process is distinct from the previous two parts so that greater clarity can be maintained between what they have said (the more objective part for consultative purposes) and my subjective impressions.

Intervention. In OD, intervention involves a planned response to a diagnosed need for change. Sequentially, then, the intervention proceeds as follows: data collection, then diagnosis, then feedback. It should, however, be clarified that while it is logical to explain the OD process as an orderly sequence of events, in reality an intervention is made the moment management decides to use a consultant. Interventions also occur thereafter, some even considerably before the feedback step. Generally, the interventions, or series of planned change activities, occur after and as a response to a thorough diagnosis. I might add that even though I use the adjective "thorough," no diagnosis can be complete since organizations are never quite the same from one day to the next. And the longer the consultant waits between data collection and feedback, the more out of date the diagnosis will be. Thus, it is imperative that action be taken as soon as feasible—a lapse of a month between data collection and feedback is a long time for fast-moving organizations like those dealing directly with consumers. Moreover, any intervention provides more information for diagnosis. Besides, as Kurt Lewin, the theoretical father of OD, has pointed out—to paraphrase—the best way to understand an organization is to try to change it.

To be effective, according to Argyris (1970), an intervention must meet three conditions: (a) it must generate valid information; (b) it must provide free, informed choices for the client; and (c) it must create an internal commitment on the part of the client to the choices made. These conditions are considered by Argyris (1970) to be "integral parts of any intervention activity, no matter what the substantive objectives are . . . for example, developing a management performance evaluation scheme, reducing intergroup rivalries, increasing the degree of trust among individuals, redesigning budgetary systems, or redesigning work" (p. 7). As Argyris indicates, an OD intervention may take a variety of forms as long as it meets certain conditions. As noted earlier, I would like to add one other condition: The intervention must lead to cultural change.

Thus, interventions in OD may come in all shapes and sizes. A number of years ago, Harvey Hornstein and I summarized all OD interventions into six categories:

- team building
- managing conflict
- survey feedback
- technostructural
- training
- miscellaneous

As might be apparent, we easily covered ourselves with the sixth category. Since that time, others have developed more comprehensive and sophisticated categories. After our rather simple scheme came the OD cube by Schmuck and Miles (1971). Their three classifiers are (a) the diagnosed problems (e.g., goals, communication, and the definition of the leadership role); (b) the focus of attention—from person, to dyad, to team, to intergroup, to total organization; and (c) the mode of intervention, such as training, process consultation, confrontation, and techno-structural activity. Blake and Mouton (1976) conceive of OD interventions and the consultative process as three sided. Their Consulcube, as they call it, is similar to the Schmuck and Miles cube but differs with respect to the nature of two of the dimensions: (a) the focal issues, which are social and psychological; and (b) the kinds of interventions, which range from "acceptant" to "prescriptive" and based on "theory and principles," which provide advice and direction for the client.

Bowers et al. (1975) also have a cube, which includes *precursor conditions* (problem causes), *problem behaviors* (symptom-like conditions), and *impingement modes* (types of intervention, e.g., survey feedback). So do Lippitt and Lippitt (1978), and it includes *client* (individual to total system), *change agent* (from "reflector" to "advocate"), and *intervention phase* (from entry to action taking). French and Bell (1978) have a scheme (not a cube) and so do White and Mitchell (1976), which *is*, alas, another cube. It is safe to say that the field of OD is not lacking for categories of interventions. One typology that has proved more useful than most is that of Harrison (1970), which specifies "depth" of intervention categories. His categories form a continuum of emotional involvement. The greater the depth of intervention, the more the focus of change is on areas of the personality or self; the less the depth, the more the focus of change is on areas external to the person—the more formal and public aspects of one's role. Huse (1980) categorizes most interventions in OD according to Roger Harrison's (1970) continuum, beginning with *system-wide approaches*, which fall at the "surface" end of the depth dimension. Interventions in this category include:

a change in the organization's structure

- survey feedback
- a confrontation meeting (see, e.g., Beckhard, 1967)
- quality of work-life programs
- grid organization development (see Blake & Mouton, 1968)

The next level concerns *individual-organizational interfaces*, such as:

- job design
- role analysis
- management by objectives

Concern with *personal work style* is the next level, representing greater depth, and involves:

- process consultation (see Schein, 1969)
- team building
- role negotiation
- intergroup conflict resolution

The final level, which is of the greatest depth, is *intra- and interpersonal*, and includes:

- life and career planning
- sensitivity training
- a group-relations conference
- personal consultation/counseling

Harrison (1970) suggests two criteria for choosing an intervention; that is, its degree of depth. He states that the consultant should not intervene at a deeper level than that

- "required to produce enduring solutions to the problems at hand" (p. 190); and
- "at which the energy and resources of the client can be committed to problem solving and to change" (p. 198).

Some of the interventions I have used with clients include the transition model of Beckhard and Harris (1977), which I have used as a format for managing the change effort, process consultation, and team building, especially with top management groups; a modified version of the confrontation meeting (Beckhard, 1967); the nominal group technique (Delbecq et al., 1975); and management training, which emphasizes the diagnosis of one's style and approach as an individual manager based on a multirater feedback system (Church et al., 2019).

As a way of summarizing this myriad of OD interventions, let us return to OD's history. As noted earlier, OD grew out of three origins, and most if not all interventions in use today came from these beginnings.

Its *sensitivity training* origin spawned interventions that deal with personal concerns and relationships, such as career development; team building; intergroup conflict resolution; and training, especially management development programs that emphasize superior-subordinate relationships and multirater feedback.

Its *survey feedback* origin is manifested in practice today in much the same way as it began. However, the contribution this approach has made to OD is considerably broader than the method itself. The emphasis on systematic data collection and diagnosis has influenced OD practice significantly. Furthermore, the fact that survey feedback is based largely on organizational members' perceptions has helped to put into perspective the importance of understanding that the organization's behavior is a function of how people *perceive* reality, not the reality itself.

Its *sociotechnical* origin has helped OD practitioners, who are typically people oriented, to be cognizant of the technology of an organization, whether it be in the manufacturing or service sector, and to better understand the relationship between the people and technological dimensions of the organization. A second, but no less important, contribution the sociotechnical origin has made is the result of the attention the sociotechnical professionals have given to structure both from the standpoint of the dimensions of a given job and the organization's overall design. It is only in recent years that OD professionals have finally become aware of the fact that the way jobs and organizations are designed and therefore structured, especially in the domain of authority, has pervasive effects on employees' behavior.

Space does not permit an explanation of how each of these interventions is actually done. For example, it might be further asked, What do you do when you serve as a process consultant? How is team building implemented? What is the design for an intergroup conflict resolution session? What is job enrichment and how do you do it? For answers to these particular questions, I can refer you, respectively, to Schein (1988), Dyer (1987), Burke (2006), and Hackman (1977).

Evaluation. The sixth, but not necessarily final, step in OD is evaluation. While last in the sequence, evaluation efforts will produce more information for diagnosis and allow the cyclical process to continue. In fact, it is prudent to begin evaluation at the data collection stage so that before and after the intervention(s) assessments can be made. If a survey has been conducted at the data collection stage, repeating the survey after one or more interventions have been made can provide useful, comparative information.

The major problem with OD evaluation, at least from a research standpoint, is the fact that it is practically impossible to arrange to have a proper control group. See the article by Blumberg and Pringle (1983) for an example of a failure in this regard. Rarely, if ever, are any two organizations comparable; similar maybe, but with distinct differences. These differences are difficult to control. Often the best one can do is to make two or more assessments within the client organization over time and make comparisons accordingly. Since so many factors cannot be controlled for optimal research purposes, it is wise to use multiple methods of assessment. A before-and-after survey is rarely sufficient. In addition, measures should be taken over time in such areas as rates of absenteeism, turnover, grievances, productivity, and related performance indices, such as the extent to which objectives are met.

These assessments, typically produced in numerical form, are necessary for a sound evaluation of OD. In the final analysis, however, the OD effort will stand or fall as a consequence of what the client, usually the organization's managers, thinks and feels. And these behavioral reactions may or may not jibe with the numbers. Managers are normally very pragmatic people, and if they "feel" like the OD effort is paying off, chances are that it is.

Summary. These six steps—(a) entry, (b) contracting, (c) data collection and diagnosis, (d) feedback, (e) intervention, and (f) evaluation—represent the primary phases of the OD process. Most OD efforts follow, in general, this sequence even though portions of the six steps often occur "out of phase."

Ultimately the nature of the OD process that occurs while following these six steps is very much an interaction between the OD practitioner and the client—the change recipient. Moreover, the client is the final decision-maker, not the OD practitioner. Following the same six steps, which can lead to sustained change, is a function of the *interaction* between the two parties—it is dependent on the degree to which the practitioner has understood the context, particularly (a) what the organization is attempting to deal with in its external environment (changing technology, competition, government regulations, etc.); and (b) the culture within which the client lives and its impact on organizational members. Often the practitioner is a psychologist, or at least educated in some aspect of the behavioral sciences. The client is most often an engineer, economist, or marketer—that is, someone who thinks differently about people and situations than does a psychologist. Common ground regarding language and meaning is always an underlying objective of the OD practitioner-client relationship.

And finally, the focal point for change is systemic, or within the organization itself, rather than among the individuals, per se. If an OD effort has been successful, organizational members' behavior will have changed, but these changes are not, as a rule, modifications in individuals' personalities. What has changed will be the "personality" or culture of the organization as reflected in such behavioral activities, to name only a few areas, as new conforming patterns; a modified reward system (not necessarily increases in pay but different criteria, for example, about how raises are determined); greater participation in decision making; and a more open communication process.

THE OD CONSULTANT/PRACTITIONER

Without outlining any unreachable ideals, I shall now provide a set of lists of the competencies in terms of knowledge and skills an organization development (OD) consultant should have, whether internal to an organization or external. (These lists are not in any particular order, nor are they exhaustive, but they do represent some of the more important areas.)

Knowledge. The OD consultant should be knowledgeable in the following areas:

- the behavioral sciences and their applicability
- the design and management of organizational change activities
- self-awareness of his or her own motives, strengths, limitations, biases, values, and the behavior used to manifest his or her feelings
- the nature and characteristics of organizations
- the nature of human behavior, especially personality, motivation, and principles of learning and development
- evaluation research

Skills. The OD consultant should have the ability to:

- listen actively and empathetically
- form relationships based on trust and honesty
- collaborate
- design and conduct learning activities
- perceive others' behavior accurately
- communicate articulately and avoid jargon
- work with groups in a variety of activities
- counsel and coach effectively, especially in a one-on-one situation
- diagnose problems, whether organizational or at the individual level

Since OD represents certain values, it is important that the consultant holds similar ones. On several different occasions, usually as part of a training program, I have conducted sessions on values for OD consultants. As we have wrestled with the difficult process of trying to understand and articulate the values we hold, I have found that most people in the field seem to be biased toward the individual rather than collectives (groups, organizations, etc.) by favoring such behaviors as freedom from coercion: having choice, opportunities to learn and grow, and a deep concern for human worth and dignity. These OD consultants (and my sample was certainly not random) expressed their similar values as those they hold for themselves and the ones they hope they can help others maintain in organizational life. I'm not certain, of course, but if these value statements are indeed representative, there doesn't appear to be much concern about helping organizations qua organizations. For me, at least since organizations are such a pervasive part of our lives, it is valuable to see that many survive and operate effectively enough that human needs can be met both individually and societally.

As noted several times earlier, there are both external consultants and those who are employees of the organization, or internal consultants. A word now about the latter. Internal OD practitioners are usually employed in staff positions that are within the personnel or human resource management area.

Ideally, OD should be conducted by a combination of external and internal consultants, especially at the outset. The external consultant can bring: (a) additional knowledge and skill to supplement or complement the internal consultant, and (b) a more objective viewpoint. On the other hand, the external consultant cannot know and understand the organization as thoroughly as the internal consultant can. The key role of the internal consultant is that of *sustaining* the OD effort once it has begun. A major objective of the external consultant, therefore, is to arrange for an internal counterpart if none exists.

THEORETICAL FOUNDATIONS OF ORGANIZATION DEVELOPMENT

As mentioned already, much of organization development (OD) practice is based on the thinking of Kurt Lewin. Both sensitivity training and survey feedback developed from Lewin's theoretical influence. He conceptualized change for a group or organization as a three-step process: unfreeze, move, and refreeze. Before an organization can change, it must be "unfrozen" from its present state. *Unfreezing* may occur as a result of any one of several activities or interventions. The most common one is the organization being confronted with information that is negative and arousing. To learn that we are not doing as well as we thought can have an unfreezing effect, reminding us we need to do something about our present conditions. Unfreezing can also occur as a result of some key managers being exposed to a different way of doing things. The second step must be taken while the organization is still in an unfrozen state. The *movement* step involves the act of changing something, such as the organization's strategy, structure, planning process, the way people work together in groups, and the like. Once movement has occurred and the new behavior is underway, the final step, *refreezing*, takes place. This step often becomes one of determining the appropriate reward system so that the new behavior will be reinforced and maintained.

Lippitt et al. (1958) extended Lewin's three steps into five:

1. Development of a need for change (unfreezing)
2. Establishment of a change relationship with the client
3. Work toward change (movement)
4. Generalization and stabilization of the change (refreezing)
5. Termination of the relationship

Most of the elaboration of Lewin's steps done by Lippitt and colleagues was on number 3, the change/movement step. They conceptualized this step as having three substeps or phases—diagnosis, examination of alternative change goals, and transformation of these goals into action.

There is no single all-encompassing theory of OD. Lewin's three steps come the closest. These steps are based on his original field theory in social psychology (see Deutsch, 1968; Burnes, 2020), but the steps themselves are nothing more than a model for OD consultants to follow. Most consultants know these steps and some of the principles behind them, but few have actually studied Lewin's field theory. Nevertheless, most consultants know how to conduct one of the frequently used techniques in OD that is based on Lewinian field theory, the "force field analysis" intervention. When conducting a force field analysis, one is considering both those forces within a larger field of forces that *push* toward change (e.g., management pressure) and those forces that *restrain* movement toward change (e.g., group norms regarding level of productivity). Using this technique, the consultant and client are in a better position to know how to deal with peoples' resistances to change. One of the earliest and best examples of this use is the classic study and change effort done at the Harwood Corporation by Coch and French (1948).

Lewin's theoretical influence on OD is no doubt the heaviest, but others have helped to shape the field as well. Theorists who have contributed to the predominantly individual-oriented approaches to organizational change and the areas they have worked in include:

- **Maslow**: motivational approaches, value orientations, and career development
- **Herzberg**: job enrichment
- **Skinner**: incentive systems and behavioral modification

Following are the theorists who have contributed mostly to group approaches to change and the subjects they have studied:

- **Bion**: diagnosing collusion (see Harvey, 1977); autonomous work groups; sociotechnical systems; and team building
- **Lewin**: group decision-making, managing change via groups, participation and involvement techniques using groups
- **Argyris**: sensitivity training and interpersonal competence (the theorist has helped to operationalize McGregor's theory *Y*)

Those theorists who have contributed more to total-system approaches and the areas in which they contributed are:

- **Likert**: survey methodology and feedback, group decision-making, and participative management
- **Lawrence and Lorsch; Galbraith**: organization design and structural change
- **H. Levinson**: diagnosis of an organization's history and current functioning, particularly with respect to psychoanalytic theory
- **Blake and Mouton**: grid organization development

From my three categories of theorists' approaches, it should be easy to see that OD has been influenced in diverse ways. There are a couple of things that most if not all of these theorists have in common, however: Their interests are or have been concerned with change, particularly organizational, and they have favored action research as a way of understanding what is appropriate to change.

Does OD Work?   Many scholar-practitioners have contributed to our understanding of the theoretical underpinnings and principles of practice regarding OD. But none have done so more thoroughly and clearly than Kurt Lewin. The most devoted chronicler and implementer of Lewin's ideas, theory, and research was Alfred Marrow (see, e.g., Marrow, 1969). And, more recently, a prominent chronicler of Marrow's life and work is the British scholar Bernard Burnes (see Burnes, 2007; Burnes, 2019). Marrow learned of Lewin in the 1930s when he was a graduate student in industrial-organizational psychology and followed Lewin's thinking for the rest of his life. Marrow's father was the founder and for many years the CEO of the Harwood Manufacturing Corporation. Alfred followed in his father's footsteps and during the 1940s became CEO himself. He soon began to transform the company's approach to management. What in particular caught Marrow's attention was Lewin's research on the managerial approach or style. Studies showed that a participative approach to management as compared with autocratic and laissez-faire styles is superior in terms of employee's work performance (see Lewin et al., 1939, which features one of the original studies by Lewin, Lippitt, and White). Based on Marrow's commitment to Lewin's scholarship and his position as CEO of Harwood, he proclaimed to all managers in the company at the time that in order to keep their jobs they must begin a transition to participative management. If a manager refused, he or she was given a severance package and forced to leave the company. In other words, Marrow *dictated* participative management. To be fair about this brief story, Marrow, knowing that managing participatively was difficult to do effectively, hired a number of social psychologists from the Institute of Social Research (ISR) at the University of Michigan, Lewinians one and all at the time (e.g., John R. P. French, Alex Bavelas, Rensis Likert, Ron Lippitt, and Dorwin

Cartwright and others) to conduct management training. In the process of this undertaking, the months rolled into years, but Marrow stayed the course and eventually showed significantly higher company performance than there had been in the past (Burnes, 2019). Furthermore, Hardwood became strong enough financially in the 1950s and early 1960s to acquire its primary competitor, the Weldon Manufacturing Company. With Weldon, Marrow started the participative management edict all over again and within a few years enjoyed similar financial and growth results as he had with Harwood.

Later in the 1960s, Marrow hired David Bowers and Stanley Seashore, also from the ISR at the University of Michigan, to conduct a longitudinal study of the Hardwood-Weldon experience. They consequently showed the empirical effectiveness of the changes made as a result of participative management, which would serve as the lodestar of the effort that became known as organization development. With considerable documentation as to its effectiveness, this change story is chronicled in *Management by Participation* (Marrow et al., 1967). Since that time, numerous studies have documented, with appropriate caveats, the efficacy of OD efforts (to name some of the prominent studies, Seashore & Bowers [1970], Beckhard & Lake [1971], White & Mitchell [1976], and Porras [1978]). In general, these studies have shown that OD, done right, pays off.

More recently, scholars have focused on key aspects of OD that exist on a smaller scale, such as case studies. An exception is the story of change at British Airways (see Kotter [1990], Goodstein & Burke [1991], and Burke [2018]). Studies focusing on components of organizations include articles by Oreg et al. (2011) considering recipients of change; Oreg and Berson (2019) on the impact of the leader; Suddaby and Foster (2017) on the importance of an organization's history; and the evidence-based article by Stouten et al. (2018) on the steps and sequences in practitioner models of change. An elaboration of the Stouten et al. article follows in the conclusion. And for an overview of organizational change efforts and their effectiveness, see Burke (2020).

TRENDS

Moving to the present and future, let us consider 10 trends in the larger world of organizational change that directly affect the field of organization development (OD) and will likely help to define the field for the future. The first 4 trends come from a recent award-winning article by Church and Burke (2017) and the remaining 6 are new.

Church and Burke begin their coverage by identifying three environmental changes that are driving organizational responses and change, whether planned or not: the changing nature of *work*, the changing nature of *data*, and the changing dynamics of the *workplace*. These drivers have produced four trends or shifts that are affecting OD and I/O psychology significantly.

Trend #1. A shift to platforms over products. Facebook is not a replica of General Motors. They have in common organizational hierarchical qualities, but that's about it. Social technology has given birth to new and different organizational structures that require OD practitioners to have an even stronger dependence on open system theory and the demand for new applications of that theory such as dealing with resistance to change.

Trend #2. A shift to digital over mechanical. As with the last trend, there is the need for system thinking to transform the ways of innovation and the workplace itself so that they can accommodate digital forms of processing data.

Trend #3. A shift to insights over data. Big data sets are here to stay, but interpretation lags. What does this mean? The work to be done is developing skills of interpretation and not becoming enthralled only by large amounts of data.

Trend #4. A shift to talent over employees. It is often discussed that there is a war for talent and it seems to be at all costs. This has generated a great divide in organizations between the haves and the have-nots. Companies now have large talent management functions and spend lots of money on search firms to find and bring them talent from all corners of the globe. This competition generates serious issues for OD practitioners and their values of social justice.

Trend #5. Lewin's third step of refreeze is now passé. With organizational change becoming a constant, the concept of refreeze in Lewin's three steps or phases is now being called into question. One change leads to another, and to refreeze is to slow the whole movement to a halt, so the argument goes. In the fast-moving world we live in, change, as I noted earlier, has joined the inevitable status of death and taxes. But Lewin's position, while appropriate to call into question, should not be entirely discarded. Perhaps one can think in terms of both refreezing and continuous change at the same time, such as by admonishing the refreezing of parts but not the whole. And the refreeze step is never considered to be permanent. It may be appropriate, for example, to change and refreeze an organization's reward system—say, its ways of providing incentives—but only for a few years, not forever. The point is that for organizational behavior change to take effect, it must be positively reinforced along with the rewarding of new norms. This would involve cultural change but not of the entire culture and not necessarily for years to come. For new behavior to stick, it must be reinforced. One can also think in terms of refreezing being reinforced as a way of organizational life, in general, and flexibly applied as a reinforcement of local changes. To see how this approach to refreezing (although the authors don't use the term) might be applied operationally and function on a large scale, see the book *Built to Change* by Lawler and Worley (Lawler & Worley, 2006).

Trend #6. New social technology. Even though not everyone agrees, I for one (see Burke, 2018) have been critical of the OD field for being dormant regarding new social technology since 1987, when appreciative inquiry emerged (Cooperrider & Srivastva, 1987). An exception to my criticism could be the work of Michael Beer and his colleagues (Beer et al., 1990). Based on change data, they showed that instead of the usual top-down approach, which had usually failed, a unit-by-unit approach that incorporates a top management model of planned change is more effective. Their work clearly showed that dependency on a top-down initiative alone led to failure. In other words, focusing on a unit-by-unit approach with top management support, rather than its direct involvement alone dictating the change, is more effective. Beer (2020) has elaborated on this earlier work with current views that he refers to as a "strategic fitness process." He uses a physical fitness metaphor for his approach and refers to such fitness examples as facing up to problems, telling the truth, and other similar interventions (or exercises).

Another innovation in the practice of OD is the application of positive psychology. Cameron (2020) suggests that the application of positive organizational scholarship to organizational change has been overlooked, and he has shown that new OD interventions based on a positive approach can contribute significantly to OD effectiveness. With work like Beer's and Cameron's continuing to be published, OD is not likely to become stagnant in the future.

Trend #7. The movement to large firms along with a new label—change management. Historically, the growth of OD was reflected in the membership of the OD network, particularly in the 1970s and 1980s. The membership included individuals primarily, but small firms began to emerge as the demand for OD services increased. This growth of membership was gradual, not explosive. When practiced competently, OD was proving to be accepted and helpful but without fanfare. In other words, OD was controversial. Its roots were in the sensitivity training movement of the 1950s and therefore perceived by many as too emotionally based, with more of a focus on people's feelings than logic and reason. Yet as the practice became more structured and used interventions such as feedback for managers incorporating a "360-degree" format, that is, managers receiving feedback from subordinates, peers, and bosses to compare with their personal ratings, (completing the circle) into the overall learning process, its acceptance grew more likely. Moreover, in the 1990s large consulting firms such as Accenture, PriceWaterhouseCoopers, and McKinsey began to offer OD services for their clients. Today most large firms provide OD for their clients, but the practice is not called OD. This label remains problematic for the original reasons such as too emotional. Now the services are promoted as "change management." I have taken issue with this name change (see Burke, 2021), arguing that the practice of change management is nothing more than facilitation of what executives want rather than the planned change of an organization's culture.

Trend #8. The importance of an organization's history. With the practice of OD rates remain high regarding change failure (as high as 70%), it has become clear that many organizations attempting to bring about change repeat past mistakes. At the outset of an organization's plans for change, it would be wise, therefore, to examine how the change has been conducted and managed in the past. The work of Suddaby and Foster (2017) provides useful perspectives regarding how executives conceive of their organization's change history. They identify four models that are usually implicit in an executive's memory rather than obvious: (a) *history-as-fact*—this conception of history involves an inexorable accumulation of events that limit choice and cause inertia (Kelly & Amburgey, 1991); (b) *history-as-power*—this involves the belief that change is the consolidation of power by the owners; (c) *history-as-sense-making*—this looks at how executives experience events, not the events themselves; and (d) *history-as-rhetoric*—in this conception of history, the past is cast as a narrative or story and is highly subjective. Suddaby and Foster's main point is that executives' implicit theories of change as well as their abilities to change are influenced by these particular models.

Trend #9. The practice of OD is becoming more evidence based. Having emerged in the late 1950s, the field of OD is over 70 years old. And it is only now that researchers are providing evidence that supports or questions how OD is practiced. Perhaps the best evidence so far regarding the efficacy of OD can be found in the 2018 article by Stouten, Rousseau, and

DeCreme (Stouten et al., 2018), mentioned already in this article and expounded on in the conclusion.

The researchers' scholarly work addresses the heart of the OD practice; that is, the elaboration and validity of conclusions. Lewin's three-step model—unfreeze, change, and refreeze. As noted earlier, these authors combed a large expanse of the literature and found, as might be expected, both evidence for and questions about Lewin's model. Elaboration of this important work will be provided later in the article. Work of this nature will no doubt be highly welcomed in the future.

Trend #10. The role, importance, and impact of change leadership. Oreg and Berson (2019) have provided an extensive review of leadership as it pertains to organizational change, and found, to their surprise, a large chasm between the impact of leadership and organizational change. According to their findings, this lack of a relationship had not been studied systematically. In their review, Oreg and Berson attempt to tackle this problem and reduce the chasm. These scholars specified two key roles or paths of influence for change leaders: (a) the strategic choices they make and (b) the leadership style they choose to enact. In other words, leaders influence organizational change primarily through their choices of strategy (see Drucker, 1994) and style (e.g., top down, participative and inclusive, collaborative). These scholars have provided considerable unreported evidence up until now to support their points.

CONCLUSION

Organization development (OD) is a skill-based practice largely reliant on how skillful the practitioner/consultant is. OD has not reached the levels of sophistication and respect exemplified by, say, the practice of medicine or law. Moreover, medicine and law are considered professions with codes of ethics and commonly accepted ways of conducting the practice, as taught in schools of medicine and law. For OD, there is a long and, no doubt, winding path to reaching professional status. The six steps of an OD project covered in this chapter—starting with *entry* and ending with *evaluation*—provide a path to follow and if skillfully implemented, can produce genuine change. Yet they are relatively generic and have been gleaned over time out of how respected people in the field of OD explain their consulting practice. When I used to be asked, How and where do I learn about OD? I would respond with "Go sit at the feet of Dick Beckhard." But Dick died a few years ago along with most of the first generation of OD leaders and practitioners. OD is therefore gradually being taught in a series of informal networks and in a decentralized, loosely coupled, and somewhat competitive set of graduate programs scattered at universities around the world. The viability of OD for the future rests largely with the success of these university programs. The potential good news is that OD will become more academically grounded and influenced by a more systematic application of evidence from the behavioral sciences. And perhaps we can benefit more than we have in the past from scholarly work such as the article by Stouten, Rousseau, and De Cremer (Stouten et al., 2018) on the literature of organizational change. These authors wanted to know what evidence existed to support (or not to support) models or steps required for successful organizational change, not unlike the six covered earlier in this article.

The authors begin with a discussion of two significant challenges, as they put it: (a) The scientific literature on organizational change is scattered and lacks focus regarding basic processes. This may be the reason, the authors contend, that practitioners rely more on the popular literature than on a science-based category of publications. (b) There is a difficulty of learning from experience. Organizational change is complex; takes time and considerable patience; and can require quite diverse approaches, from changing strategies to making a merger or acquisition work successfully, to relocations, to the introduction of new technology, to name only a few examples. With these challenges in mind, Stouten et al. (2018) nevertheless plunged ahead and reviewed seven popular models of change steps in an attempt to determine if evidence from the scientific literature supports these practitioners' models.

Stouten and his colleagues begin with descriptions of (a) Lewin's three phases of unfreeze, change, and refreeze; go on to discuss (b) Beer's six steps of diagnosis, vision, support, implementation, institutionalization, and making adjustments as required; then cover (c) the appreciative inquiry model that includes Cooperrider's four stages, discovery, dream, design, and destiny; proceed to describe (d) Judson's five steps; then review (e) Kanter, Stein, and Jick's 10 steps; after that look at (f) Kotter's eight steps; and finally discuss (g) Hiatt's five steps.

Suffice it to state that there is a considerable overlap across these seven models. After reviewing the models, Stouten and colleagues searched the scientific literature to determine whether and to what degree the evidence supported these models. As might be expected, they found some evidence to be supportive and some unsupportive. In summary, most of the models (a) assumed a top-down approach, (b) ignored history, (c) emphasized empowerment and learning, and (d) stressed the value of feedback. Yet there were many gaps among the models. The authors (Stouten et al., 2018) then synthesized the literature and concluded that there are 10 principles and steps of effective OD (or change management, to use their language). A summary of these evidence-based steps follows:

1. **Get facts regarding the nature of the problem(s) (first diagnostic step)**: Find out if the change is really needed. This is determined by two sets of facts: the degree of need and historical conditions or constraints that might affect a change effort.
2. **Assess and address the organization's readiness for change (second diagnostic step)**: Doing this is a matter of determining the organization's readiness for change. This assessment can be made by first finding out (a) the organization's history regarding change successes and failures, (b) the degree of success currently experienced by organizational members, and (c) the degree of capability of senior leadership to guide and manage the change.
3. **Implement evidence-based change interventions**: Three sources of evidence are needed to support appropriate actions to be taken. To gather them, (a) select a diverse group of people inside and outside the organization who have experience with the problem and can help; (b) identify key stakeholders to test ideas with; and (c) identify the benefits and risks of specific kinds of change. Helpful mechanisms along the way include facilitating learning activities for organizational members and providing rewards that motivate change.
4. **Develop effective change leadership throughout the organization**: Developing change-related skills for leaders is highly desirable.

5. **Develop and communicate a compelling change vision**: In the literature, there is strong agreement on the importance of this step, according to Stouten and his colleagues. Not apparent is the necessary content for a compelling vision statement. Useful criteria for an effective statement have been suggested (see Nanus, 1992), but evidence does not seem to exist that would show that vision content is associated with change performance.
6. **Work with social networks and tap their influence**: Models so far have ignored this step even though evidence suggests that (a) network relations augment individual skills, and (b) belonging to a professional group, like an OD network, can be useful.
7. **Use enabling practices to support implementation**: Employing goal setting, learning activities, participation, emphases on social justice, and transitional structures such as task forces have been shown to be helpful for change efforts.
8. **Promote microprocesses and experimentation**: This step includes creating pilot tests for identifying new interventions and multiple small interventions that support experiential learning.
9. **Assess change progress and outcomes over time**: Answering the question "Are we making any progress?" is absolutely necessary.
10. **Deploy multiple methods for answering this critical question and institutionalize the changes to sustain its effectiveness**: Ensure that changes, such as implementation of governance, use of technology, and human relations practices, are integrated into the larger system.

Even though the original six steps (entry, contract, data gathering and diagnosis, feedback, intervention, and evaluation) discussed earlier in this article have been useful, they are not sufficiently comprehensive. They, perhaps, need to be melded into the latest, evidence-based 10-step version. Besides, OD practitioners today need to follow, as much as possible, evidence-based practice in all that we do. Following the 10 steps synthesized by Stouten and colleagues is indeed recommended. Doing so puts the OD practitioners on the right path, but there is no guarantee that an organizational change effort will succeed. The OD process is, after all, a function of the effectiveness of two primary *interactions*, one between the OD practitioners and the client, and the other between the change skills of the practitioner and the appropriate application of the skills to the situation; that is, based on relevant knowledge and action research (see Burnes's article [Burnes, 2020] explaining Lewin's applicable theory and methods).

And finally, while the practice of OD is still in a process of development, growing evidence regarding organizational change from organizational psychology such as the Stouten et al. (2018) article and related studies will help to pave the way for a bright and encouraging future.

REFERENCES

Argyris, C. (1957). *Personality and organization: The conflict between system and the individual.* Harper & Row.
Argyris, C. (1962). *Interpersonal competence and organizational effectiveness.* Dorsey Press.
Argyris, C. (1964). *Integrating the individual and the organization.* Wiley.
Argyris, C. (1970). *Intervention theory and method.* Addison-Wesley.
Beckhard, R. (1967). The confrontation meeting. *Harvard Business Review, 45*(2), 149–155.
Beckhard, R. (1969). *Organization development: Strategies and models.* Addison-Wesley.

Beckhard, R., & Harris, R. T. (1977). *Organizational transitions: Managing complex change.* Addison-Wesley.

Beckhard, R., & Lake, D. G. (1971). Short and long-range effects of a team development effort. In H. A. Hornsetin, B. B. Bunker, W. W. Burke, M. Gindes, & R. J. Lewicki (Eds.), *Social intervention: A behavioral science approach* (pp. 421–439). Free Press.

Beer, M. (1980). *Organization change and development.* Goodyear.

Beer, M. (2020). Making a difference: Developing actionable knowledge for practice and theory. *Journal of Applied Behavioral Science, 56,* 506–520.

Beer, M., Eisenstat, R. A., & Spector, B. (1990). *The critical path to corporate renewal.* Harvard Business School Press.

Bennis, W. G. (1966). *Changing organizations.* McGraw Hill.

Berg, D. N. (1977). Failure at entry. In D. N. Berg & P. H. Mirvis (Eds.), *Failures in organization development and change* (pp. 33–55). Wiley.

Blake, R. R., & Mouton, J. S. (1968). *Corporate excellence through grid organization development.* Gulf.

Blake, R. R., & Mouton, J. S. (1976). *Consultation.* Addison-Wesley.

Blumberg, M., & Pringle, C. D. (1983). How control groups can cause loss of control in action research: The case of Rushton Coal Mine. *Journal of Applied Behavioral Science, 19,* 409–425.

Bowers, D. G., Franklin, J. L., & Pecorella, P. (1975). Matching problems, precursors, and interventions in OD: A systematic approach. *Journal of Applied Behavioral Science, 11,* 391–410.

Bradford, L. P., Gibb, J. R., & Benne, K. D. (1964). *T-group theory and laboratory method.* Wiley.

Burke, W. W. (2006). Conflict in organizations. In M. Deutsch, P. T. Coleman, & E. C. Marcus (Eds.), *The handbook of conflict resolution* (2nd ed., pp. 781–804). Jossey-Bass.

Burke, W. W. (2018). *Organization change: Theory & practice* (5th ed.). SAGE.

Burke, W. W. (2020). Historical currents in scholarship of organization change. In M. S. Poole & A. Van de Van (Eds.), *The Oxford handbook of organization change* (pp. 23–49). Oxford University Press.

Burke, W. W. (2021). Reflection: Change management is NOT organization development. In A. B. Shani & D. A. Noumair (Eds.), *Research in organizational change and development* (Vol. 29; pp. 261–274). Emerald.

Burke, W. W., & Hornstein, H. A. (Eds.). (1972). *The social technology of organization development.* University Associates.

Burke, W. W., & Litwin, G. H. (1992). A casual model of organizational performance and change. *Journal of Management, 18,* 532–545.

Burke, W. W., & Noumair, D. A. (2015). *Organization development: A process of learning and changing* (3rd ed.). Pearson Education.

Burnes, B. (2007). Kurt Lewin and the Harwood Studies: The foundations of OD. *Journal of Applied Behavioral Science, 43,* 213–231.

Burnes, B. (2019). The role of Alfred J. Marrow and the Harwood Manufacturing Corporation in the advancement of OD. *Journal of Applied Behavioral Science, 55,* 397–427.

Burnes, B. (2020). The origins of Lewin's three-step model of change. *Journal of Applied Behavioral Science, 56,* 32–59.

Cameron, K. (2020). Responses to the problem of OD stagnation: A tribute to Warner Burke. *Journal of Applied Behavioral Science, 56,* 462–481.

Chein, I., Cook, S., & Harding, J. (1948). The field of action research. *American Psychologist, 3,* 43–50.

Church, A. H., Bracken, D. W., Fleenor, J. W., & Rose, D. S. (Eds.). (2019). *The handbook of strategic 360 feedback.* Oxford University Press.

Church, A. H., & Burke, W. W. (2017). Four trends shaping the future of organizations and organization development. *OD Practitioner, 49*(3), 14–22.

Coch, L., & French, J. R. P. (1948). Overcoming resistance to change. *Human Relations, 1,* 512–532.

Cooperrider, D. L., & Srivastva, S. (1987). Appreciative inquiry in organizational life. In W. A. Pasmore & Woodman, R. W. (Eds.), *Research in organizational change and development* (Vol. 1). JAI Press.

Cummings, T., & Worley, C. G. (2005). *Organization development and change* (8th ed.). Southwestern College Publishing.

Delbecq, A. L., Van de Ven, A. H., & Gustafson, D.H. (1975). *Group techniques for program planning: A guide to nominal group and Delphi processes*. Scott Foresman.

Deutsch, M. (1968). Field theory in social psychology. In G. Lindzey & E. Aronson (Eds.), *The handbook of social psychology* (Vol. 1, 2nd ed., pp. 412–487). Addison-Wesley.

Drucker, P. F. (1994). The theory of the business. *Harvard Business Review, 72*(5), 95–104.

Dyer, W. G. (1987). *Team building: Issues and alternatives* (2nd ed.). Addison-Wesley.

French, W. L. (1969). Organization development: Objectives, assumptions, and strategies. *California Management Review, 12,* 23–34.

French, W. L., & Bell, C. H., Jr. (1978). *Organization development: Behavioral science interventions for organization improvement* (2nd ed.). Prentice-Hall.

Frohman, M. A., Sashkin, M., & Kavanagh, M. J. (1976). Action research as applied to organization development. *Organization and Administrative Science, 7*(1,2), 129–142.

Goodstein, L. D. (1978). *Consulting with human service systems*. Addison-Wesley.

Goodstein, L. D., & Boyer, R. K. (1972). Crisis intervention is a municipal agency: A conceptual case analysis. *Journal of Applied Behavioral Science, 8,* 318–340.

Goodstein, L. D., & Burke, W. W. (1991). Creating successful organizational change. *Organizational Dynamics, 19*(4), 5–17.

Hackman, J. R. (1977). Work design. In J. R. Hackman & J. L. Suttle (Eds.), *Improving life at work* (pp. 96–162). Goodyear.

Harrison, R. (1970). Choosing the depth of organizational intervention. *Journal of Applied Behavioral Science, 6,* 181–202.

Harvey, J. B. (1977). Consulting during crises of agreement. In W. W. Burke (Ed.), *Current issues and strategies in organization development* (pp. 160–186). Human Sciences Press.

Hornstein, H. A., Bunker, B. B., Burke, W. W., Gindes, M., & Lewicki, R. J. (1971). *Social intervention: A behavioral science approach*. Free Press.

Huse, E. F. (1980). *Organization development and change* (Rev. ed.). West.

Katz, D., & Kahn, R. L. (1966). *The social psychology of organizations*. Wiley.

Katz, D., & Kahn, R. L (1978). *The social psychology of organizations* (2nd ed.). Wiley.

Kelly, P., & Amburgey, T. (1991). Organizational inertia and momentum: A dynamic model of strategic change. *Academy of Management Journal, 34,* 591–612.

Kotter, J. P. (1990). *Changing the culture at British Airways*. Harvard Business School Case 491–009.

Kotter, J. P. (1996). *Leading change*. Harvard Business School Press.

Lawler, E. E., III, & Worley, C. G. (2006). *Built to change: How to achieve sustained organizational effectiveness*. Jossey-Bass.

Levinson, H. (1972). *Organizational diagnosis*. Harvard University Press.

Lewin, K., Lippitt, R., & White, R. K. (1939). Patterns of aggressive behavior in experimentally created "social climates." *Journal of Social Psychology, 10,* 271–299.

Likert, R. (1967). *The human organization*. McGraw Hill.

Lippitt, G., & Lippitt, R. (1978). *The consulting process in action*. University Associates.

Lippitt, R., Watson, J., & Westley, B. (1958). *Dynamics of planned change*. Harcourt, Brace.

Mann, F. C. (1957). Studying and creating change: A means to understanding social organization. In C. M. Arensburg *et al.* (Eds.) *Research in industrial human relations*. Harper.

Marrow, A. J. (1969). *The practical theorist*. Basic Books.

Marrow, A. J., Bowers, D. G., & Seashore, S. E. (1967). *Management by participation*. Harper & Row.

Massie, J. L. (1965). In J. G. March (Ed.), *Handbook of organizations*. Rand McNally.

Nadler, D. A. (1977). *Feedback and organization development: Using data-based methods*. Addison-Wesley.

Nanus, B. (1992). *Visionary leadership: Creating a compelling sense of direction for your organization.* Jossey-Bass.

Oreg, S., & Berson, Y. (2019). Leaders' impact on organizational change: Bridging theoretical and methodological chasms. *Academy of Management Annals, 13,* 272–307.

Oreg, S., Vakola, M., & Armenakis, A. (2011). Change recipients' reactions to organizational change. *Journal of Applied Behavioral Science, 47,* 461–524.

Pfeiffer, J. W., & Jones, J. E. (1978). OD readiness. In W. W. Burke (Ed.), *The cutting edge: Current theory and practice in organization development* (pp. 179–185). University Associates.

Porras, J. I. (1978). The impact of organization development: Research findings. *Academy of Management Review, 3*(2), 249–266.

Schein, E. H. (1969). *Process consultation.* Addison-Westley.

Schein, E. H. (1988). *Process consultation: Its role in organization development* (Vol. 1). Addison-Wesley.

Schmuck, R. A., & Miles, M. B. (Eds.). (1971). *Organization development in schools.* National Press Books.

Seashore, S., & Bowers, D. (1963). *Changing the structure and functioning of an organization: Report of a field experiment* (Monograph No. 33). Institute for Social Research.

Seashore, S. E., & Bowers, D. G. (1970). Durability of organizational change. *American Psychologist, 25,* 227–233.

Shepard, H. A. (1960). Three management programs and the theory behind them. In *An action research program for organization improvement.* Foundation for Research on Human Behavior.

Steele, F. (1977). Is the culture hostile to organization development? The U.K. example. In D. N. Berg & P. H. Mirvis (Eds.), *Failures in organization development and change* (pp. 23–31). Wiley.

Stouten, J., Rousseau, D. M., & De Cremer, D. (2018). Successful organizational change: Integrating the management practice and scholarly literatures. *Academy of Management Annals, 12*(2), 752–788.

Suddaby, R., & Foster, W. M. (2017). History and organizational change. *Journal of Management, 43,* 19–38.

Trist, E., & Bamforth, K. (1951). Some social and psychological consequences of the long wall method of goal setting. *Human Relations, 4,* 1–8.

Weisbord, M. (1973). The organization development contract. *OD Practitioner, 5*(2), 1–4.

White, S., & Mitchell, T. (1976). Organization development: A review of research content and research design. *Academy of Management Review, 1,* 57–73.

W. Warner Burke

Directory of Contributors

Kari Wik Ågotnes
University of Bergen
Bullying and Harassment in the
Workplace

Jos Akkermans
Vrije Universiteit Amsterdam
Careers and Career Development

Valeria Alterman
University of Miami
Retirement

Neil Anderson
University of Valencia
Creativity at Work

Conny H. Antoni
Trier University
Virtual Teams and Digital
Collaboration

Ann M. Arthur
ACT, Inc.
Moderator Variables

Neal M. Ashkanasy
University of Queensland
Emotions at Work;
Organizational Behavior

Sherry Aw
James Cook University
Employee Work Experiences,
Feelings, and Morality

Jean M. Bartunek
Boston College
Organization Change

Tayla N. Bauer
Portland State University
Overqualification in the Workplace

• 1647

Regine Bendl
Vienna University of Economics and Business
Diversity in the Workplace

Agata Bialkowski
University of Queensland
Emotions at Work

Tiffany M. Bisbey
George Washington University
Team Dynamics and Processes in the Workplace

Ryan S. Bisel
University of Oklahoma
Communication in Organizations

Gerhard Blickle
University of Bonn
Political Skill at Work and in Careers

Susanne Braun
Durham University
Dark Personalities in the Workplace

Noémie Brison
Université catholique de Louvain
Organizational Dehumanization

W. Warner Burke
Columbia University
Organization Development

Abraham P. Buunk
University of Groningen
Social Comparison in Organizations

David M. Cadiz
Portland State University
Ageism in the Workplace

Gaëtane Caesens
Université catholique de Louvain
Organizational Dehumanization

Alessandra Capezio
Australian National University
Evidence-Based Decision-Making and Practice in Organizations

Helio Carpintero
Universidad a Distancia de Madrid
History of Organizational Psychology

Stuart C. Carr
Massey University
Humanitarian Work and Organizational Psychology

Sharon Clarke
University of Manchester
Occupational Health Psychology

Karyssa A. Courey
Rice University
Gender in Organizations

Nele De Cuyper & Hans De Witte
KU Leuven
Job Insecurity

Edward L. Deci
University of Rochester
Self-Determination Theory and Its Relation to Organizations

Patrick L'Espoir Decosta
Australian National University
Evidence-Based Decision-Making and Practice in Organizations

James M. Diefendorff
University of Akron
Work Motivation

Alana B. Dorris
University of Queensland
Organizational Behavior

DIRECTORY OF CONTRIBUTORS · 1649

Mark G. Ehrhart
University of Central Florida
  Organizational Climate and
  Culture

Stale Einarsen
University of Bergen
  Bullying and Harassment in the
  Workplace

Patricia Elgoibar
University of Barcelona
  Conflict Management

Berrin Erdogan
Portland State University
  Overqualification in the Workplace

Martin Euwema
Katholieke Universiteit LeuvenConflict
  Management

Nadya Fouad
University of Wisconsin-Milwaukee
  Careers and Career Development

Franco Fraccaroli
University of Trento
  Aging Workforce Issues From a
  Multilevel Approach

Matthew S. Fritz
University of Nebraska-Lincoln
  Mediator Variables;
  Moderator Variables

Adrian Furnham
Norwegian Business School
  Individual Differences at Work

Ante Glavas
University of Vermont
  Corporate Social Responsibility: An
  Overview From an Organizational and
  Psychological Perspective

Sharon Glazer
University of Baltimore
  Cross-Cultural Issues in Industrial, Work,
  and Organizational Psychology; Work,
  Stress, Coping, and Stress Management

Vicente González-Romá
University of Valencia
  Multilevel Modeling Methods

Katrina A. Graham
Suffolk University
  The Psychology of Abusive Supervision

Yannick Griep
Radboud University Nijmegen
  Temporal Dynamics in Organizational
  Psychology

Gudela Grote
ETH Zurich
  Safety at Work

David E. Guest
King's College London
  The Sociotechnical Approach to Work
  Organization; Human Resource
  Management and Organizational
  Psychology; Quality of Working Life

Astrid Hainzl
Vienna University of Economics and Business
  Diversity in the Workplace

Leslie B. Hammer
Portland State University
  Work and Family

Mikki Hebl
Rice University
  Gender in Organizations

Ana Hernández
University of Valencia
  Multilevel Modeling Methods

Chengquan Huang
University of Florida
Industrial and Organizational
Psychology From a Global Perspective

Zhefan Huang
University of Florida
Industrial and Organizational
Psychology From a Global Perspective

George P. Huber
University of Texas at Austin
Organization Change

Remus Ilies
Bocconi University
Employee Work Experiences, Feelings,
and Morality

Kerstin Isaksson
Mälardalen University
Psychological Contracts and the
Employment Relationship

Robert G. Jones
Missouri State University
An Applied Approach to Psychology of
Sustainability

Aysegul Karaeminogullari
Pontificia Universidad Javeriana
Overqualification in the Workplace

Sabreen Kaur
Monash University
Job Crafting

Megan E. Kenworthy
University of Akron
Work Motivation

Eden King
Rice University
Gender in Organizations

Małgorzata W. KożusznikGhent University
Well-Being at Work

Kurt Kraiger
University of Memphis
Training From an Organizational
Psychology Perspective

Iris Kranefeld
University of Bonn
Political Skill at Work and in Careers

Emma K. Kristal
Suffolk University
The Psychology of Abusive
Supervision

Ravi S. Kudesia
Temple University
Organizational Sensemaking

Chatherine Kwantes
University of Windsor
Cross-Cultural Issues in Industrial,
Work, and Organizational Psychology

Richard P. Larrick
Duke University
Judgment and Decision-Making
Processes

Gary P. Latham
University of Toronto
Goal Setting Theory: Causal
Relationships, Mediators, and
Moderators

M. Asher Lawson
INSEAD
Judgment and Decision-Making
Processes

Faith C. Lee
University of Akron
Work Motivation

Joel Lefkowitz
Baruch College and the Graduate Center, CUNY
Ethics in Work and Organizational
Psychology

DIRECTORY OF CONTRIBUTORS · 1651

Michael P. Leiter
Acadia University
The Psychology of Work Engagement;
Burnout in Organizations

Houston F. Lester
University of Mississippi
Mediator Variables

Benyamin Lichtenstein
University of Massachusetts Boston
Generative Emergence: Research and
Praxis for Social Innovation

Cong Liu
Hofstra University
Work, Stress, Coping, and Stress
Management

David M. Long
College of William and Mary
Impression Management

Vicente Martínez-Tur
University of Valencia
Justice in Teams

Yanran Mei
Rice University
Gender in Organizations

Heike Mensi-Klarbach
Vienna University of Economics and Business
Diversity in the Workplace

James A. Meurs
Kennesaw State University
Political Skill at Work and in
Careers

Carolina Moliner
IDOCAL-University of Valencia
Justice in Teams

Lucas Monzani
University of Western Ontario
Positive Leadership in Organizations

Rose Mueller-Hanson
Community Interface Services
Work Performance Management and
Assessment

Henny Mulders
Maastricht University
Disabilities at Work

Lourdes Munduate
University of Seville
Conflict Management

Linh K. Nguyen
University of Akron
Work Motivation

Karina Nielsen
University of Sheffield
Organizational Interventions

Belgin Okay-Somerville
University of Glasgow
Work and Organizational Issues
Affecting Young Workers

Anja H. Olafsen
University of South-Eastern Norway
Self-Determination Theory and Its
Relation to Organizations

Sharon K. Parker
Curtin University
Job and Work Design;
Job Crafting

Cedric Patterson
Rice University
Gender in Organizations

José M. Peiró
University of Valencia
Well-Being at Work

MacKenna L. Perry
Portland State University
Work and Family

Kristina Potočnik
University of Edinburgh
Creativity at Work

Michael G. Pratt
Boston College
General Coding and Analysis in Qualitative Research

Amy C. Pytlovany
Portland State University
Ageism in the Workplace

Mislav Radic
Bocconi University
Corporate Social Responsibility: An Overview From an Organizational and Psychological Perspective

Amon Rapp
University of Torino
Human-Computer Interaction

Makai A. Ruffin
Rice University
Gender in Organizations

Katherine Ann Rush
University of Oklahoma
Communication in Organizations

Eduardo Salas
Rice University
Team Dynamics and Processes in the Workplace

Jesús F. Salgado
University of Santiago de Compostela
Personnel Selection

Mahima Saxena
University of Nebraska Omaha
Informal Work

Benjamin Schneider
University of Maryland
Organizational Climate and Culture

Sandra Schruijer
Utrecht University
The Group Dynamics of Interorganizational Collaboration

Birgit Schyns
NEOMA Business School
Dark Personalities in the Workplace

Rosalind H. Searle
University of Glasgow
Work and Organizational Issues Affecting Young Workers; Counterproductive Work Behaviors

Leilani Seged
Rice University
Gender in Organizations

Tomoki Sekiguchi
Kyoto University
Person-Environment Fit From an Organizational Psychology Perspective

Eva Selenko
Loughborough University
Work and Organizational Issues Affecting Young Workers

Aida Soriano
University of Valencia
Well-Being at Work

Daniel Spurk
University of Bern
Careers and Career Development

Dirk D. Steiner
Université Côte d'Azur
Organizational Justice

Dillon Stewart
Rice University
Gender in Organizations

Florence Stinglhamber
Université catholique de Louvain
Organizational Dehumanization

DIRECTORY OF CONTRIBUTORS · 1653

Meridith Townsend
Rice University
Gender in Organizations

Raymond Trau
Macquarie University
Sexual Orientation (LGBTQ+) Issues in
Industrial and Organizational Psychology

Donald M. Truxillo
Portland State University
Aging Workforce Issues From a Multilevel
Approach; Ageism in the Workplace

Anaja Van den Broeck
KU Leuven
Job and Work Design

Rolf Van Dick
Goethe University Frankfurt
Positive Leadership in Organizations

Suzanne van Gils
BI Norwegian Business School
Ethical Leadership

Niels Van Quaquebeke
Kühne Logistics University
Ethical Leadership

Matti Vartiainen
Aalto University
Telework and Remote Work

Mo Wang
University of Florida
Industrial and Organizational Psychology
From a Global Perspective; Retirement

Peter Warr
University of Sheffield
Individual Differences in the Vitamin
Model of Well-Being

Jennica Webster
Marquette University
Sexual Orientation (LGBTQ+) Issues in
Industrial and Organizational Psychology

Jordyn Williams
Rice University
Gender in Organizations

Jo Wintle
Deakin University
Burnout in Organizations

Barbara Wisse
University of Groningen
Dark Personalities in the Workplace

Lale M. Yaldiz
Portland State University
Aging Workforce Issues From a
Multilevel Approach

Junhui Yang
University of Florida
Industrial and Organizational
Psychology From a Global
Perspective

Yunyue Yang
Yokohama National University
Person–Environment Fit From
an Organizational Psychology
Perspective

Gahyun Yoo
Boston University
The Psychology of Abusive
Supervision

Hannes Zacher
Leipzig University
Action Regulation Theory; Temporal
Dynamics in Organizational
Psychology

Fangfang Zhang
Curtin University
Job Crafting

Fred Zijlstra
Maastricht University
Disabilities at Work

Index

Notes: Page numbers printed in boldface indicate a major discussion, while those followed by "*f*" indicate figures and illustrations and those followed by "*t*" indicate tables. For the benefit of digital users, indexed terms and table entries that span two pages (e.g., 52–53) may, on occasion, appear on only one of those pages.

AA (affirmative action), 541
AAAP (American Association of Applied Psychology), 20–21
Aan 't Goor, J., 822
a priori codes, 303
ABC (authenticity, balance, challenge) model, 1226
Abildgaard, J. S., 1609–1610
ability
    general cognitive, 1144–1146, 1145*t*, 1151–1153, 1152*t*
    in goal setting theory, 110–111, 113–114
    as individual difference at work, 550
    networking, 486–487, 1233
ability, motivation, opportunity (AMO) bundles, 1109–1110, 1112, 1115, 1506–1507
absenteeism, overqualification and, 1209
abusive leadership, 968
abusive supervision. *See also* workplace harassment
    benefits in spite of, 927–928

consequences of, 925–928
emotions and cognitive processes in, 924
employee effects of, 925–926
employee factors in, 924–925
individual differences causing, 924
individual intervention tactics and coping with, 929
international differences in interventions for, 929–930
Machiavellianism and, 511
measuring, 922
OCB and CWB impact of, 944
organizational dehumanization and, 1471–1472
organizational interventions for, 928–929
overview of, 920–921
past experiences contributing to, 923
perception's role in, 920 n.1, 921–922
retaliation toward, 929
self-regulation failure causing, 923–924
social exchange theory and, 923

• 1655

abusive supervision (*continued*)
  social learning theory and, 923
  supervisors reacting to own, 926–927
  team impact of, 927
  witness experiences of, 927
Academy of Management (AOM), 529
  Careers Division, 1218
  Code of Ethics, 50
Accelerated Bias-Corrected Bootstrap Test, 216
Accenture, 1640
acceptance and commitment therapy (ACT), 1454
accident proneness
  personality and, 1352–1353
  safety and, 1484–1485
accommodating conflict behavior, 1029
accommodative HRM, 1117
accounts, sense-making and, 1006
accuracy
  in procedural justice, 1066
  in ratings, 1281–1283
Acker, J., 537
ACM SIGCHI (Association for Computing Machinery
    Special Interest Group on Computer–Human
    Interaction), 741
ACM Transactions on Computer-Human Interaction, 728
acquiring, in EDMP, 29, 37f, 38
acquisition integration, culture and, 339
ACT (acceptance and commitment therapy), 1454
action
  bias, 32f, 33
  central characteristics of, 99
  complete tasks and, 103–105
  definition of, 99
  learning, 1181
  in personality development, 104
  psychology of sustainability and taking, 179
action-oriented mental model of action regulation, 103–104
action processes, in teamwork, 842
action regulation across the adult lifespan (ARAL), 105–106
action regulation theory
  action-oriented mental model of, 103–104
  central characteristics of action and, 99
  complete tasks and action in, 103–105
  execution monitoring in, 101
  feedback processing in, 101–102
  flexible action patterns of, 102–103
  foci of, 103–104
  goal development and selection in, 100–101
  hierarchical structure of, 102–103
  history of, 98–99
  intellectual level of, 103
  for learning and training, 105

life-span developmental theories and, 105–106
  mapping environment or orientation in, 100–101
  meta-cognitive heuristics of, 103
  overview of, 97–98
  sensorimotor or skill level of, 102
  sequential structure of, 99–102
  theoretical and practical implications of, 104–106
  work design in, 104–105
action research
  multi-organizational group dynamics and, 382–383
  OD and, 1625
  in sociotechnical approach to work organization, 80
  systems-psychodynamics approach to, 378–379
action theory, in Causal Steps Test, 209, 210f
active influence, political skill and, 488–489, 489t
active learning, 1179–1180
actors, in impression management, 805
AD (additional decrement), in Vitamin Model of
    well-being, 143f, 144, 146
Adams, John Stacey, 881–882, 1064
adaptability. *See* career adaptability
adaptation
  bilateral, 1130
  carrying capacity and species, 172–173
  change continuum, 178, 178t
  mental, 173
  mutual, 1130
  psychological criteria for, 173
  unilateral, 1130
  virtual teams and, 868
  well-being and degree of, 150–151
Adaptation-Level Theory, 1523
adaptation theory, work and family and, 1373–1374
adaptation training, 1179
adapting, in career construction theory, 1223
adaptive sense-making, 1009–1010
adaptivity
  in career construction theory, 1223
  job design and, 697
additional decrement (AD), in Vitamin Model of
    well-being, 143f, 144, 146
additive spillover, 1377
adjustment, retirement, 1254–1255, 1263–1265
administrators, WOP, 66
adult mobbing, 1426
advancement, age discrimination and, 640–641
advantageous comparison, 1325
adversarial behavior, 1028–1029
advice-seeking, 808
advocacy, for SGMs, 657
AET. *See* affective events theory
affability, political skill and, 488, 489t

affect
  circumplex model of, 448
  decision-making and, 960–961
  organizational behavior and, 958–959
affect-based emergent states, 842–844, 871
affect-driven behaviors, 450–451
affective disposition, well-being and, 148, 1517–1518
affective events theory (AET), 440, 450f
  moral behavior and, 430–431
  well-being and, 1523–1524
  on within-person variations of emotions, 450–451
  on work and family, 1373–1374
Affective Revolution, 430, 446–447
"affect spin," 282
affirmative action (AA), 541
Affordable Care Act, 2010, 1369–1370
AGCT (Army General Classification Test), 10
age. *See also* older workers; retirement; young workers
  defining categories of, 642
  gender in organizations and, 575
  generational differences and, 601–603
  of global population, 633
  group faultlines related to, 623, 641
  knowledge transfer and, 624
  leadership and, 624
  overqualification and, 1202–1203
  retirement and, 1252
  well-being and, 148
age bias, 634t. *See also* ageism in workplace;
    age prejudice
age discrimination, 638–642. *See also* ageism in
    workplace
  advancement and, 640–641
  age stereotypes and, 638
  context in, 638–639
  definition of, 621, 634t
  interpersonal interactions and, 641–642
  older workers and, 623–624
  outcomes associated with, 639–642
  performance appraisals and, 641
  personnel selection and, 640
  training and development and, 641
age diversity
  climate, 624–625
  in workplace, 624
ageism in workplace
  definition of, 633
  discrimination and, 641–642
  future research on, 643–644
  intervention for, 643–644
  metastereotypes and, 642–643
  overview of, 633

prejudice and, 637–638
  stereotypes and, 635–636
  terms and definitions for, 634t
  tripartite approach to, 634
age metastereotypes, 642–643
agency, gender in organizations and, 571–572
age prejudice, 636–638
  definition of, 634t
  theoretical frameworks relating to, 637
  work outcomes associated with, 637–638
age stereotypes, 634–636
  age discrimination and, 638
  definition of, 621, 634t
  explicit, 622
  implicit, 622, 643
  older workers and, 621–623
  positive, 636
  prescriptive compared to descriptive, 643
  theoretical frameworks relating to, 634–635
  work outcomes associated with, 635–636
  for young workers, 598, 636
aggregated job crafting score, 715–716
aggregation
  in EDMP, 29, 39–40, 37f, 39f
  JDM and, 402
aggression, agreeableness and, 559
aging workers. *See* older workers
agreeableness
  evolutionary perspective on, 553–554
  high, average, low levels of, 554t
  as job performance predictor, 1146
  overview of, 558–559
  positive and negative consequences of, 555t
  work outcomes and, 556, 557t
Aguilera, R. V., 1093
Aguinis, H., 261, 906, 1079, 1083–1084, 1086, 1093, 1282
Ahmedabad experiment, 84
AI (artificial intelligence), 741
  in digital workforce, 331–332, 342
  HRM using, 331
AIP (International Association of Psychotechnology),
    17–19, 21
Airbnb, 1556
Ajzen, I., 288–289
Akkermans, J., 1233
Alba-Ramirez, A., 1200
alienation. *See* work alienation
Alliance for Organizational Psychology (AOP), 21,
    353–354
allyship, for SGMs, 657
ALS (average leadership style), 980
alternative psychological approaches to HCI, 733–734

alternative work arrangements, 786. *See also* informal work
Alvesson, M., 912
Amabile, T. M., 1305–1307
Amazon, 1556
Amazon Alexa, 744
ambiguity, in environment, 997–998. *See also* role ambiguity
ambivalence, well-being and, 141
ambivalent sexism theory, 573–574
Ambrose, M. L., 883, 1068–1069
American Association of Applied Psychology (AAAP), 20–21
American Psychological Association (APA), 8, 20–21, 353–354
American Society for Mechanical Engineers, 5–6
The American Soldier (Stouffer), 11–12
American Soldier studies, 813–814
Americans with Disabilities Act, 668
AMO (ability, motivation, opportunity) bundles, 1109–1110, 1112, 1115, 1506–1507
amplification dynamics, in generative emergence, 1581–1582
analysis in qualitative research
    artifacts created from, 318
    axial coding and, 313–315
    coding compared to, 309–310
    componential, 311–312, 312*f*, 314*t*
    concrete and abstract, 319
    contact summary forms for, 317
    cultivating doubt for, 317–318
    data gathering and, 303–304, 304*f*
    data structure for, 316, 316*f*
    domain, 310–311, 310*f*
    ethnographic approach to, 310–313
    grounded theory and, 312–317, 316*f*
    how to think about, 318–320
    member check in, 316
    memoing and, 313–315, 317
    overview of, 302
    parts and wholes in, 319
    pitfalls in, 319–320
    reflexive documents for, 317
    study design and, 303, 304*f*
    taxonomic, 311, 311*f*
    theoretical description and, 319–320
    theoretical model example of, 312, 313*f*
    translation compared to, 302, 320
    writing up findings and, 303–304, 304*f*
analysis of variance (ANOVA) models
    main effect contrast and, 232–233
    more than three variables in, 247–248
    one-way, 256–258

    post hoc tests and, 233
    simple main effects in, 230
    3×3, 232–233
    2×2, 229–230, 231*f*, 232
anchoring bias, 960
Anderson, Hans Christian, 983–984
animalistic dehumanization, 1461, 1473
Annual Review of Psychology, 10–11
ANOVA models. *See* analysis of variance models
Anscombe, G. E. M., 54
antecedents, 207, 228–229
anti-categorical complexity, 536–537
antisocial personality disorder, 566*t*
anxiety, burnout and, 1452
AOM. *See* Academy of Management
AOP (Alliance for Organizational Psychology), 21, 353–354
APA (American Psychological Association), 8, 20–21, 353–354
APA Code (Ethical Code of American Psychological Association), 50
    on caring-nonmaleficence, 51
    on education and WOP, 62–63
    on moral virtues, 51
    on practitioners working with organizations, 65–66
    specificity in, 56
    on values, 55
apparent sincerity, 486
applying, in EDMP, 29, 37*f*, 40
ApplySci, 1581, 1584
appraisal-centered approach, for emotions at work, 449
appraising, in EDMP, 29, 37*f*, 38–39
Appreciative Inquiry, 1563
approach crafting, 710–711, 715, 717
approach goals, 100–101
approach motivation, 416–418
aptitude by treatment interaction, 246
ARAL (action regulation across the adult lifespan), 105–106
arbitration, for conflict resolution, 1037
aretaic (virtue) theory, 54
Argentina, telework/remote work in, 719
Argyris, Chris, 10–11, 13, 983, 1125–1126, 1631, 1637
Aristotle, 74 n.1, 141, 1518
Arkin, R. M., 798*t*, 801*t*, 802
Army General Classification Test (AGCT), 10
army units, team stress climate and, 1529–1530
Arnett, J. J., 600
artificial intelligence. *See* AI
ASA (attraction-selection-attrition) model, 465–466, 886–887, 1050–1051, 1142–1143
Ashford, S. J., 907

Ashkanasy, N. M. *See also* five-level model of emotions at work
  on emotional intelligence, 456–457
  on emotional spectrum, 446–447
  five-level model of emotions at work by, 449–455, 450f
  on historical studies of emotions, 447
Ashton-James, C. E., 447
asking, in EDMP, 29, 37–38, 37f
aspirations
  employee, 129–130
  generative emergence and, 1580
assessing, in EDMP, 29, 37f, 40
assessment center method, 1149–1150
Association for Computing Machinery Special Interest Group on Computer–Human Interaction (ACM SIGCHI), 741
associative-memory processes, in JDM, 393–394
"As We May Think" (Bush), 729
Atchley, R. C., 1259
attention deployment, in emotion regulation, 151–152
attitudes. *See* job attitudes
attraction-selection-attrition (ASA) model, 465–466, 886–887, 1050–1051, 1142–1143
attractiveness, social comparison and, 822–823
attribution of blame, 1325
attribution theory
  CSR and, 1090
  HRM impact and, 1115–1116
Australia, 956
  telework/remote work in, 719
authenticity, balance, challenge (ABC) model, 1226
authenticity, qualitative research standards for, 321t
authentic leadership, 163
  ethical leadership compared to, 942–943
authority, organizational change and, 1555–1556
automation, 195
  young workers and, 603
autonomous motivation, 121–122, 127–128, 130, 419, 969
autonomy
  home-based telework/remote work and, 764
  individual training for, 1600
  informal work and, 785
  motivation and, 420–421
  need for, 123, 420
  organizational activities for, 1604–1605
  orientation, 122
  paradox, 764
  respect and, 1453
  teams and, 1602
autoregressive mediation models, 219, 220f
availability, mobile telework/remote work and, 767–768
availability bias, 960

average causal effects, 220–221
average deviation indices, 880–881
average leadership style (ALS), 980
aviation psychology, 8–9
avoidance crafting, 710–711, 715, 717
avoidance goals, 100–101
avoidance motivation, 416–418
avoidant personality disorder, 566t
avoiding
  conflict behavior, 1029
  in identity management, 653–654
axial coding, 313–315

Babbage, Charles, 5, 673–674
Babiak, P., 517
backhanded compliments, 807
Baer, M. D., 289–291
Bakker, A. B., 690–691, 709–710, 1300. *See also* job demands-resources model
balance effectiveness, 1377
balance satisfaction, 1377
Baldes, J. J., 116
Baldwin, T. T., 1178
BAM (British Academy of Management), 529
Bamforth, K., 78, 1623–1624
Bandura, A., 422–423, 437–438, 571, 599, 1223–1224, 1324–1327
Barends, E., 29–30, 35, 37–38
Bargh, J. A., 116
Barnard, Chester, 13–14
Baron, R. M., 208–210
Barr, P. S., 1008
Barrick, M. R., 1146
Baruch, Y., 1234
BAS (behavioral activation system), 417–418
baseline by treatment interaction, 246
baseline model with random intercepts, 256–258
basic psychological needs theory (BPNT), 123–124
"battered child syndrome," 1005
Bauer, D. J., 263
Baum, M., 719–720
Baumeister, R. F., 798t
Baxter, G., 92–93
Bayesian statistics, mediator variables and, 216–217
Bayes's Theorem, 39–40
Beach, S. R., 813
Beckhard, R., 1619–1623, 1627, 1632, 1641
Bednar, P., 93–94
Beehr, T. A., 1349
Beer, Michael, 1639
behavior. *See* moral behavior; organizational behavior
behavioral activation system (BAS), 417–418

behavioral career competencies, 1233
behavioral crafting, 710–711
behavioral decision theory, 26–27
behavioral economics, 401
behavioral experience approach, to workplace bullying, 1430
behavioral inhibition system (BIS), 417–418
behavioral modification, 14–15
behavioral performance, teamwork and, 845
behavioral standards, 1276, 1278
behavioral structured interviews, 1148
behavior change technologies, 743
Belgium, OP in, 19
Bell, C. M., 1461–1463
beneficence, ethics of care and, 51
benevolence, qualitative research standards for, 321*t*
benevolent sexism, 573–574
benign envy, 821
Bennett, N., 885–887, 889
Bentham, Jeremy, 53
Berson, Y., 1641
best available evidence, 27, 29, 31
"best practice" logic, EDMP compared to, 26
Beyer, J., 1576*t*
Bias-Corrected Bootstrap Test, 216
biases
    action, 32*f*, 33
    age, 634*t*
    anchoring, 960
    availability, 960
    class, 599
    confirmation, 960
    consultant authority, 32*f*, 33
    in decision-making, 960
    evaluation, 341
    hindsight, 960
    implicit-bias training, 26
    meta-cognitive, 32*f*, 35
    overconfidence, 960
    personnel selection procedures and, 1153–1154
    related to diversity, 340–341
    social, 32*f*, 34–35
bias-suppression, in procedural justice, 1066
Bies, R. J., 882–883
Big Five Traits of personality, 554*t*, 544*f*, 555*t*, 560–561, 957. *See also* agreeableness; conscientiousness; extraversion; neuroticism; openness to experience
bilateral adaptation, 1130
Bindl, U. K., 712*t*
Binet, Alfred, 8, 19
Bingham, Walter V. D., 8–9
Binomial Effect Size Display, 1179

biodata, 1150
biofeedback, 1412
Bion, Wilfred R., 12, 375–376, 1637
Biron, C., 1609–1610
birthrate declines, 625
BIS (behavioral inhibition system), 417–418
bisexual workers. *See* sexual and gender minorities
Bizzi, L., 712*t*
Blackler, F., 1503–1504
Black–Scholes formula, 1005
Blake, R. R., 1631, 1637
Blauner, R., 1501
blinding, 406
Blount, S., 289–291
The Body Shop, 1080–1081
Boehnlein, P., 719–720
Bolino, M. C., 802–806
Bolweg, J., 86
Bonferroni corrections, 233
Bonnardel, Raymond, 19
bootstrapping, 215–216
borderline personality disorder, 566*t*
border theory, on work and family, 1372
Bostock v. Clayton County, 660
Boston Vocation Bureau, 7
boundaryless career theory, 1218–1219, 1221–1222
boundaryless mindset (psychological mobility), 1221–1222
boundaryless organization, 969
boundary management
    in career self-management, 1232
    work-family conflict and, 1378
boundary theory, on work and family, 1372
Bowen, D., 1115–1118
Bowen, Howard R., 1079–1080
Bowers, David, 1631–1632, 1638
Bowling, N. A., 1349
Boyer, R. K., 1626
BPNT (basic psychological needs theory), 123–124
BP refinery explosion, Texas City, 1480–1481
bracketing and noticing, in sense-making, 1003–1004
Branson, Missouri, 1580–1583
"Bransonizing," 1583
Brenninkmeijer, V., 1233
bridge employment, 1256–1257, 1264
Briggs, C., 331
Briscoe, J. P., 1219–1221
British Academy of Management (BAM), 529
British Airways, 1638
British Workplace Employment Relations surveys, 1113
broaden-and-build theory, 1522–1523
Brodsky, Carroll M., 1426, 1433

Brown, C., 1503–1504
Brown, M. E., 938
Brown, S. D., 1224–1225, 1229
Browning, L., 1576t
Bruning, P. F., 710, 712t
Buchanan, D., 91
Budworth, M. H., 115–116
buffering interactions, 237–238
bullying. *See* abusive supervision; workplace bullying
"bully-victims," 1435
bundles, HRM and, 1109–1110
bureaucratic managerial model, 6–7
Burgi-Tian, J., 1282
Burke, W. W., 1638
Burnes, Bernard, 1637–1638
Burnford, J., 585–586
burnout, 166, 358–359
    analytical approaches to, 1449–1451
    anxiety and, 1452
    conceptual framework of, 1448–1449
    contrasting definitions of, 1448
    cynicism and, 1453
    definition of, 1447–1448
    depression and, 1448
    emotional demands and, 1348–1349
    exhaustion and, 1448
    future research on, 1455–1457
    interventions for, 1454–1455
    JD-R model on, 1451
    job crafting for, 1455
    job demands, job resources and, 690
    Maslach Burnout Inventory and, 1292–1295,
        1447–1449
    measuring, 1294
    from occupational stress, 1342–1343
    Oldenburg Burnout Inventory and, 1297
    organizational interventions for, 1454–1455
    overview of, 1447
    poor emotional intelligence and, 1452
    as relationship problem, 1451–1453
    resource loss and, 1345–1346
    social comparison and, 823–824
    social relationships and, 1453
    as three-part syndrome, 1447
    work engagement and, 1293
    worklife profile, 1449–1451
Burnout Measure, 1448
Burris, V., 1199, 1208–1209
Bush, Vannevar, 729
business case for CSR, 167, 1080–1081, 1086
business organizations, authority for change in, 1555
business strategy, HRM and, 1106–1107

business structures, organization structures compared to, 1556
Buunk, A. P., 815–821, 823–824
bystanders and observers, of workplace bullying, 1437

Café Corazon, 1581–1583
Calico Mills, Ahmedabad experiment, 84
Caligiuri, P., 358
callings
    career, 1238
    positive psychology and, 1354–1355
Cameron, K., 1640
Campbell, W. K., 508–509
Campion, M. A., 691, 693–694, 710, 712t
Camus, Jean, 8–9
Canada, telework/remote work in, 719–720
Canadian Psychological Association Code of Ethics for
        Psychologists. *See* CPA Code
Canadian Society for Industrial/Organizational
        Psychology (C-SIOP), 353–354
candidate evaluation, JDM for, 405–406
Cannon-Bowers, J. A., 1178
CAQDAS (Computer Aided Qualitative Data Analysis
        Software), 326 n.5
career adaptability
    as career resource, 1233
    definition of, 1222
    outcomes associated with, 1223
    for self-management, 1223
    sustainable careers and, 1225–1226
career construction theory, 1222–1223, 1233
careerism, 1253
career mobility theory, overqualification and, 1208
career(s)
    calling, 1238
    choice across life span, 1228–1229
    competencies, dimensions of, 1233
    competencies, young workers and, 597–601
    crafting, 1233
    customization, 1234–1235
    definition of, 1218
    exploration, 1229
    global, 1234
    identity, young workers and, 600
    job insecurity spillover to, 1168–1169
    kaleidoscope, 1226
    outcomes, political skill and, 490–495
    resources, 1232–1233
    self-management, 1224–1225, 1232–1233
    shocks, 1237
    success, 1229–1230
    timetables, 639
    transitions, 1235–1237

career studies
- boundaryless career theory in, 1218–1219, 1221–1222
- on career calling, 1238
- on career choice across life span, 1228–1229
- career construction theory in, 1222–1223, 1233
- on career exploration, 1229
- on career resources, 1232–1233
- on career self-management, 1224–1225, 1232–1233
- on career shocks, 1237
- on career success, 1229–1230
- on career transitions, 1235–1237
- on changing employment relations, 1234–1235
- conservation of resources theory and, 1227
- definition and history of, 1218–1219
- on employability, 1230–1233
- human capital and, 1227
- on kaleidoscope careers, 1226
- on organizational career management, 1234–1235
- protean career theory in, 1218–1221
- psychology of working theory and, 1226–1227
- social cognitive career theory in, 654, 1218–1219, 1223–1225
- social exchange theory and, 1227–1228
- on sustainable careers, 1225–1226
- vocational development theory and, 1228
- on work-nonwork interface, 1237–1238

caregiving responsibilities, gender differences in, 582–583
Carmona, C., 815–818
Carnegie Mellon University, 8–9
carriers, 757
Carroll, A. B., 67, 1082
carrying capacity, species adaptation and, 172–173
Castro-Solano, A., 822
categorical by categorical (2x2) interaction models, 229–232, 231f
categorical by categorical (3x3) interaction models, 232–233
categorical mediator variables, 217
CATs (critically appraised topics), 39
Cattell, James McKeen, 8–9
causality orientations theory (COT), 122, 124, 129
causal mediation, 220–221
Causal Steps Test, 208–212, 210f
caution, conscientiousness and, 560
CBT. See cognitive behavioral therapy
CC (corporate citizenship), 1083
CCB (conglomerate conflict behavior), 1030–1031
CCO (communication constitutes organizing) theory, 977, 987
CDE (controlled direct effect), 221

CE (constant effect), in Vitamin Model of well-being, 143f, 144
CEB (Corporate Executive Board), 1273–1274
CEBM (Center for Evidence-Based Management), 29
CED (Committee for Economic Development), 1080
Center for Evidence-Based Management (CEBM), 29
centering at grand mean (CGM), 258–259
centering within cluster method (CWC), 258–259
centralization, 968
Centre of Expertise for Inclusive Organisations (CIAO), 674–676
CEO narcissism, 509–510
certainty, in environments, 997–998
CET (cognitive evaluation theory), 121–122, 124, 419
CGM (centering at grand mean), 258–259
chain of command, 968
challenge-hindrance model, on occupational stress, 1347
challenge stressors, 1347, 1396, 1401, 1417
Chandler, A. D., 5–6
change management, OD as, 1640
change-oriented leadership, 938–939
change process fairness climate, 889
change score mediation model, 218–219
changing employment relations, 1234–1235
channel expansion theory, 864–865
Charmaz, K., 313–315
check-ins, 1279–1281
Checkland, P., 92
Cheng, H., 552, 564
Cherns, A., 82
Chetty, Raj, 404–405
CHI (Conference on Human Factors in Computing Systems), 728–730
Chicago Board Options Exchange, 992–993
childcare, gender and responsibilities with, 582
Chiles, T., 1576t
Chinese Culture Connection, 355
CHI PLAY (Computer-Human Interaction in Play), 741
chocolate cake model of narcissism, 508–509
choice, in goal setting theory, 110
Christiania Spigerverk, Norway, 85
Church, A. H., 1638
Cialdini, R. B., 798t, 801t, 802, 804–805
circumplex model of affect, 448
Civil Rights Act, 1964, 15, 67, 660
civil rights movement, 14, 541
Claparède, Edouard, 21
class
- bias, 599
- "doing difference" and, 535–537, 536f
- intersectionality and, 536–537

Clegg, C., 92–93

climate. *See* organizational climate
climates and cultural ecology, 32*f*, 33
climate strength, 1046
"climcult framework," 1054–1055
clocks, adoption of, 1368
cluster analysis, 1449
CMO (contextual-mechanism-outcome) configurations, 1610
coaching. *See also* leadership
  conflict, 1036–1037
  for performance management, 1280–1281
  in teamwork, 834
coalition, 966
coal mining studies, sociotechnical approach to work organization and, 78, 83
"coasting," 415
Coch, L., 79–80
coding in qualitative research
  a priori, 303
  amount of data in, 305, 308
  analysis compared to, 309–310
  axial, 313–315
  CAQDAS for, 326 n.5
  data gathering and, 303–304, 304*f*
  dummy, 234–235
  emergent, 303
  "first cycle" and "second cycle," 308
  focused, 313–315
  functions of, 309
  granularity level in, 305–308, 306*t*
  "how to" knowledge of, 304–309
  how to think about, 309–310
  line-by-line, 305–307
  by "meaningful chunks" of data, 307
  open, 313, 318
  overview of, 302
  selective, 315
  study design and, 303, 304*f*
  translation compared to, 302, 320
  when to begin, 305
  writing up findings and, 303–304, 304*f*
The Coding Manual for Qualitative Researchers (Saldaña), 304
coercion
  coercive isomorphism, 1084
  definition of, 59*t*
  examples of, 59–61*t*
  power and, 965–966
cognition/cognitive
  ability tests, in personnel selection, 1144–1146, 1145*t*
  appraisal, 1343
  biases, 32*f*, 34–35

cognitive-based emergent states, 844
collective, 995
crafting, 709–711
frames, 1004
job design and, 696
means of sense-making, 1004–1005
miser, 635
models of HCI, 732–733
oligopoly, 1012
overqualification, 1198
performance in teamwork, 845
planning for retirement, 1254
processes and abusive supervision, 924
processes of decision-making, 13–14
psychology and CSR, 1092
resources for retirement, 1258
sciences and HCI, 732–733
scripts, 1004
in teamwork, 834
cognitive behavioral therapy (CBT), 1357–1358, 1454
  mediator variables and, 207–208, 228–229
cognitive evaluation theory (CET), 121–122, 124, 419
Cognitive Reflection Task (CRT), 398–399
cognitivism, 14
cohesion, teamwork and, 843
Cole, D. A., 213
collaboration. *See also* multi-organizational group dynamics
  behavior, 1030
  concept of, 372
  digital, 860–862
  diversity in, 372–373
  multi-organizational group dynamics and, 371–372
  shared problem definition for, 372–373
  team improvements for, 1602
collective
  actions in generative emergence, 1581
  cognition, 995
  efficacy and teamwork, 843
  orientation and teamwork, 843
  well-being, 1524–1525
collectivism
  job crafting and, 720
  receptivity to mindset of, 1009
Colombia, telework/remote work in, 719
Colquitt, A. L., 1275–1276, 1286–1287
Colquitt, J. A., 289–291, 883–884
Committee for Economic Development (CED), 1080
Commonwealth Disability Discrimination Act of 1992, Australia, 956
communality, gender in organizations and, 571–572
communication constitutes organizing (CCO) theory, 977, 987

communication in organizations. *See also* downward communication; lateral communication in organizations; upward communication
  conduit compared to constitutive perspective of, 977–978
  downward, 978–982, 987
  fairness and, 1284–1285
  grapevine, 985
  intercultural, 340
  KSAOs, 866–867
  lateral, 985–986, 988–989
  network perspectives on, 986
  person-centered, 979
  position-centered, 979
  teamwork and, 833–834, 964–965
  telework and, 986–989
  upward, 982–984, 988
communicative career competencies, 1233
commuting, telework/remote work impacts on, 770
comparative feeling, law of, 152
comparative HRM, 1118
compassion and empathy, moral emotions and, 432–433, 438–439
compensation
  contingent pay, 127
  evaluation biases and, 341
  gender pay disparities and, 578–579
  managerial, 336–337
  non-contingent pay, 128–129
  overqualification and, 1206–1207
  pay-for-performance, 1283–1284
  rewards and, 128
  in SDT research in workplace, 128–129
  wage intervals in humanitarian work and organizational psychology, 191–193
  wage precarity and informal work, 782–783
competence
  need for, 123, 420
  organizational change and, 1561
  qualitative research standards for, 321*t*
  in SCM, 574, 621–622
  in stereotype content model, 621–622
competence-based approach to employability, 1230–1231
competitive behavior, 1028–1029
competitiveness
  agreeableness and, 559
  in conflict, 1031–1032, 1033*t*
  overqualification and, 1208–1209
complementary fit, 465, 467
complete mediation, 210
complete tasks and action, 103–105

componential analysis, 311–312, 312*f*, 314*t*
componential theory of creativity, 1310
componential theory of organizational creativity, 1306–1307
compounding, 400
compromising conflict behavior, 1030
computationally intensive tests, mediator variables and, 216–217
Computer Aided Qualitative Data Analysis Software (CAQDAS), 326 n.5
Computer-Human Interaction in Play (CHI PLAY), 741
computers. *See* human-computer interaction
Computer-Supported Cooperative Work and Social Computing (CSCW), 741
conceptual theory, in Causal Steps Test, 209, 210*f*
concern, in career construction theory, 1222
conditional process models, 218, 244–245
conduit perspective of communication in organizations, 977–978
Conference on Human Factors in Computing Systems (CHI), 728–730
confidence, in career construction theory, 1222
configural invariance, 243–244
confirmability, qualitative research standards for, 321*t*
confirmation bias, 960
conflict
  characteristics of, 1026–1027
  coaching, 1036–1037
  constructive and destructive, 1031–1032
  cooperative or competitive orientation in, 1031–1032, 1033*t*
  definition of, 1025–1027
  in generative emergence, 1580
  process, 965, 1027
  relationship, 965, 1027
  resolution, agreeableness and, 559
  task, 965, 1027
  teamwork and, 833, 965
  workplace bullying and interpersonal, 1432–1433
conflict behavior
  accommodating, 1029
  avoiding, 1029
  compromising, 1030
  conglomerate, 1030–1031
  definition of, 1028–1031
  dual-concern model of, 1028–1030, 1029*f*
  forcing, 1028–1029
  problem solving, 1030
conflict management
  conflict resolution compared to, 1035–1036
  constructive, 1033–1035
  constructive controversy and, 1034

cooperative conflict-resolution skills in, 1035
cooperative or competitive orientation in, 1031–1032, 1033t
definition of, 1025, 1031
group process and decision-making in, 1035
KSAOs, 866–867
rapport-building skills for, 1034
teamwork and, 833
trust development in, 1033–1034
conflict resolution
arbitration for, 1037
coaching for, 1036–1037
concept of, 1035–1037
conflict management compared to, 1035–1036
cooperative skills for, 1035
decision-making by authorities for, 1037
mediation in, 1036
negotiation for, 1036
confounder variables
definition of, 208, 228–229
path model diagram of, 209f, 229f
conglomerate conflict behavior (CCB), 1030–1031
connectivity paradox, mobile telework/remote work and, 767–768
conscientiousness
elements of, 560–561
evolutionary perspective on, 553–554
high, average, low levels of, 554t
as job performance predictor, 1146
overview on, 560–561
positive and negative consequences of, 555t
work outcomes and, 556, 557t
work success and, 562
consequent, 207
consequentialism, 53–54
conservation of resources (COR) theory
career studies and, 1227
goal setting theory and, 962
job design and, 698–699
job insecurity and, 1162
on occupational stress, 1345–1346
on stress, 1401
on work and family, 1371
conservation psychology, 174–175
consistency, in procedural justice, 1066
consistent mediation, 211
constant comparative method, in grounded theory, 313
constant effect (CE), in Vitamin Model of well-being, 143f, 144
constitutive perspective of communication in organizations, 977–978
constructionist perspective on diversity, 534

constructive controversy, 1034
construct validity, qualitative research standards for, 321t
consultant authority bias, 32f, 33
consultation, 966
contact summary forms, 317
contending behavior, 1028–1029
context-free well-being, 143, 143f, 145–146
contextualist approach to organizations, sense-making in, 994–995
contextual-mechanism-outcome (CMO) configurations, 1610
contextual moderators, in teamwork, 846–847
contextual performance, 1141–1142, 1142f, 1145t, 1151–1153, 1153t
contingency theory, 15
contingent labor, 786
contingent pay, 127
continuity theory, on retirement, 1259
continuous by categorical interaction models, 233–236, 234f
continuous by continuous interaction models, 236–238, 237f
continuous organizational change, 1565
continuum model, 635
contract, in OD, 1627–1634
contract labor, 786
contrast, in social comparison, 819–821
contrast by contrast interaction, 232–233
control
in career construction theory, 1222
political skill and, 488, 489t
problem-focused coping and, 1408
social comparison and, 820–821
controlled direct effect (CDE), 221
controlled motivation, 121
controlled orientation, 122
controlling rewards, 121–122
control preference, conscientiousness and, 560
control theory, 98, 416
conventional structured interviews, 1148
Convention on the Rights of Persons with a Disability (CRPD), United Nations, 668
conversational agents, in HCI, 744–745
Conway, N., 289–291
cookbook approach to ethical dilemmas, 67
Cooke, F. L., 336
Cooke, R. A., 356–357
cooperation
agreeableness and, 559
behavior, 1030
in conflict, 1031–1032, 1033t
conflict-resolution skills, 1035
in teamwork, 833

coordination, in teamwork, 832–833
coping, 1343–1344
  across cultures, 1409
  definition of, 1406–1407
  emotion-focused, 1408–1409
  overview of, 1394–1396
  problem-focused, 1408
  stress management and, 1406–1410
COPS (criterion-oriented personality scales), 1146–1147
Corbin, Juliet, 313–316
Cordery, J., 89
core capabilities, in EDMP, 37f, 43–44
core self-evaluation (CSE) theory, 961
core values, generative emergence and, 1582
corporate citizenship (CC), 1083
Corporate Executive Board (CEB), 1273–1274
corporate giving, 1080–1081
corporate responsibility (CR), 1083
corporate social performance (CSP), 1079, 1082
corporate social responsibility (CSR)
  attribution theory and, 1090
  business case for, 167, 1080–1081, 1086
  cognitive psychology and, 1092
  concept and history of, 1079–1081
  CR/CC and, 1083
  CS and, 1082–1083
  CSP and, 1079, 1082
  dark side of, 1089–1090
  definitions of, 1079–1080
  developmental psychology and, 1092
  in education, 1091
  future research on, 1092–1093
  humanitarian work and organizational psychology
    and, 194–195
  individual level of analysis on, 1087–1089
  institutional level of analysis on, 1084–1086
  internal and external, 1091–1093
  isomorphism and, 1084
  measurement issues in, 1091
  micro, 1087–1089
  micro-political, 1091
  motivation for, 1085–1086
  multilevel models for, 1093
  organizational identity/identification and, 1090
  organizational level of analysis on, 1086–1087
  overview of, 1078–1079
  perceptions of, 1091
  philanthropy and, 1092–1093
  political, 1084–1085
  positive organizational leadership and, 909
  psychological availability and, 1088–1089
  psychological safety and, 1088–1089

  purpose and, 1088–1089
  reputation of firms and, 1084–1085
  for shared value, 1086–1087
  social identity theory and, 1086–1087
  stakeholder salience and, 1084–1085
  stakeholder theory and, 1082
  strategic sponsorship and, 1092–1093
  third-party mechanisms of, 1090
  values congruence and, 1088–1089
corporate sustainability (CS), 1082–1083
correctability, in procedural justice, 1066
corrective feedback, downward communication and, 982
correspondence interference theory, 806
corruption, 57
  definition of, 59t
  examples of, 59–61t
COR theory. See conservation of resources theory
COT (causality orientations theory), 122, 124, 129
Council on Scientific Organization of Labor, 6
counterculture subcultures, 1052–1053
counterfeiting, in identity management, 653–654
counterproductive performance, 1141–1142,
    1142f, 1145t, 1151, 1152t
  emotions linked to, 1323–1324
counterproductive work behaviors (CWBs)
  abusive supervision impact on, 944
  costs of, 1319–1320
  dark personalities and, 1322–1323
  definition of, 1320
  environment and, 1326–1327
  ethical leadership and, 942
  Machiavellianism and, 511–512, 1322–1323
  measurement of, 1321
  moral behavior and, 435
  moral licensing and, 1327–1329
  narcissism and, 1322–1323
  OCB and, 1320, 1327–1329
  organizational culture impact on, 1322
  overqualification and, 1208
  overview of, 1319–1320
  production deviance and, 1320–1321
  psychopathy and, 515, 1322–1323
  situational perspective on, 1323–1324
  social cognitive theory on, 1324–1327
  stress and, 1323–1324
  type and structure of, 1320–1321
COVID-19 pandemic, 185, 189, 581
  global uncertainty and, 333
  performance management impact of, 1286–1287
  quality of working life and, 1508
  telework/remote work and impact of, 719, 762,
    771–773

underemployment of young workers and, 603
universal basic income and, 196
as work disrupter, 779
Cox, T. H., 538
CPA Code (Canadian Psychological Association Code of Ethics for Psychologists), 50
on moral virtues, 51
rule-deontology and, 53
specificity in, 56
CR (corporate responsibility), 1083
craft model of management, 31, 32f, 44
Crain, T. L., 1379
created environment, 1327
creative self-efficacy, 1310
creative tension, generative emergence and, 1580
creative thinking, 1306–1307
creativity at work
antecedents of, 1309–1313
componential theory of, 1310
componential theory of organizational creativity, 1306–1307
contextual factors of, 1311–1313
definition of, 1305–1306
emotions at work and, 1311
future research avenues for, 1313–1315
individual creative action theory, 1308
as individual difference, 550
individual factors in, 1309–1311
interactionist theory of organizational creativity, 1307
leadership fostering, 1312
motivation and, 1310–1311
overqualification and, 1207–1208
overview of, 1305
peer relationships influencing, 1312
personality and, 1309
process models of, 1308–1309
self-efficacy and, 1310
teams and, 1313–1314
theoretical frameworks of, 1306–1309, 1313–1314
creativity-relevant skills, 1310
credibility, qualitative research standards for, 321t
Crenshaw, K., 536–537
criteria, in personnel selection, 1140–1141
criterion-oriented personality scales (COPS), 1146–1147
criterion problem, psychology of sustainability and, 176
critical and analytical thinking, in EDMP, 37f, 41–42
critical appraisal, 42
critical design, in HCI, 740
critical diversity research, 543–545, 544t
criticality, qualitative research standards for, 321t

critically appraised topics (CATs), 39
Cropanzano, R., 891–892, 1068–1069, 1071–1072
Cross-Cultural Collaboration on Contemporary Careers (5C), 1229–1230
cross-cultural competence, 334–335
cross-cultural differences
enhancing cooperation with, 343
measuring and analyzing, 342–343
cross-cultural IWOP
cultural competence and intelligence and, 358
cultural values and, 354–355
diversity, equity, and inclusion and, 362–363
flexible work arrangements and, 359
future of, 362–364
globalization and, 356–362
global mindsets and, 358
GLOBE project and, 355–358
historical development of, 353–356
leadership and, 357–358
occupational safety, stress, and health and, 358–360
organizational culture and, 356–357
overview of, 352–353
precarious and decent work and, 360
remote work and, 363
social axioms and, 355–356
trust and, 360–362
work-nonwork conflict and, 359
cross-cultural training, 335
cross-level interaction
moderator variables and, 242
in 1-1-1 mediation models, 268–269
cross-training, team, 848, 1179
crowdwork, 786
CRPD (Convention on the Rights of Persons with a Disability), United Nations, 668
CRT (Cognitive Reflection Task), 398–399
crystallized intelligence, 615
CS (corporate sustainability), 1082–1083
CSCW (Computer-Supported Cooperative Work and Social Computing), 741
CSE (core self-evaluation) theory, 961
C-SIOP (Canadian Society for Industrial/Organizational Psychology), 353–354
CSP (corporate social performance), 1079, 1082
CSR. See corporate social responsibility
Culbertson, S. S., 1177–1178, 1187
Culpepper, S. A., 261
cultural competence, 358
cultural intelligence, 358
cultural relativism, 52
cultural tightness and looseness, 355–358
cultural values, 354–355

culture. *See also* cross-cultural IWOP; organizational culture
  acquisition integration and, 339
  as boundary condition, 338–339
  competence across, 334–335
  coping across, 1409
  emotional, 454–455
  generalizability of management practices across, 338–339
  globalization and, 337
  GLOBE project and, 338
  individual differences at work and, 551
  intercultural communication, 340
  interfirm relationships in intercultural settings, 339
  job crafting and differences of, 719–720
  measuring and analyzing differences in, 342–343
  motivation and, 424
  PE fit differences by, 471
  training across, 335
  work in intercultural settings, 339–340
CultureAmp, 362
Cummings, T., 88–89
curiosity, in career construction theory, 1222
Curran, P. J., 263
Curry, Stephen, 406
curvilinear change, 239–240, 239f
curvilinear relationships, 695
CWBs. *See* counterproductive work behaviors
CWC (centering within cluster method), 258–259
cyberslacking, 765–766
cybervetting, employer, 485
cynicism, 1294, 1296
  burnout and, 1453

DA (demands-abilities) fit, 473, 475
Damasio, A. R., 448
dampening interactions, 237–238
dark personalities (Dark Triad). *See also* Machiavellianism; narcissism; psychopathy
  CWB and, 1322–1323
  dealing with, 516–517
  definitions of, 506–508
  future research on, 517–518
  Machiavellianism and, 512–513
  narcissism and, 508–510
  overview of, 506
  political skill and, 495–496
  psychopathy and, 515–516
Dasborough, M. T., 448, 455
data
  decision-making driven by, 32f, 33–34
  OD and collection and diagnosis of, 1628–1629

qualitative research gathering of, 303–304, 304f
  shifts to insights from, 1639
data-frame theory of sense-making, 1004–1005
Daus, C. S., 456–457
Davis, K. E., 806
Davis, L., 90
Davis, M., 94
Dawson, J., 1298–1299
DC (demands-control) model, 1344–1345, 1345t
DCS (demands-control-support) model, 1344–1345, 1345t
decentralization, 968
decent work, 1226
  globalization and, 360
  informal work and deficits of, 784
Decent Work Agenda, 188
decision-making. *See also* ethical decision-making; evidence-based decision-making and practice; judgment and decision-making
  affect and, 960–961
  by authorities for conflict resolution, 1037
  biases in, 960
  bounded rationality of, 13–14
  cognitive processes of, 13–14
  data-driven compared to hypothesis-led, 32f, 33–34
  errors in, 960
  with ethics, 66–70
  group, 963–964
  Lefkowitz's model for, 68–69
  naturalistic, 403
  participative, 115
  perception and, 960
  retirement, 1254, 1262–1263
  values in, 14
decision neglect in organizations, 35
decreasing hindering job demands, 709
DeCremer, D., 1641
deduction, in theory development, 111
deep acting, 452–453, 1348–1349
deep breathing, 1412
deep-level diversity, 531, 533t
defensive avoidance, 378
dehumanization, 1325. *See also* organizational dehumanization
  animalistic and mechanistic, 1461, 1473
  genocide and, 1461
  process of, 1460–1461
deliberative processing, 178
Demand-Induced Strain Compensation model (DISC model), 691–692
demands-abilities (DA) fit, 473, 475
demands-control (DC) model, 1344–1345, 1345t

demands-control-support (DCS) model, 1344–1345, 1345t
Dember, W. N., 115
Demerouti, E., 690–691, 1299, 1354. *See also* job demands-resources model
Deming, W. Edwards, 354
demographic factors, as individual differences at work, 551
demographic transitions, older workers and, 625–626
Denton, F. T., 1252–1253
deontic model of justice, 927, 1071–1072
deontology, 52–53
departmentalization, 968–969
dependability, qualitative research standards for, 321t
dependent personality disorder, 566t
dependent variables, 207, 228
depression, burnout and, 1448
De Rivera, J., 454
DeRue, D. S., 907
descriptive age stereotypes, 643
design fictions, in HCI, 740
Designing Interactive Systems (DIS), 741
Desirable Difficulties, 1181
desires and needs, JDM and, 397
Deutsch, M., 1025–1026, 1032
development
    age discrimination and, 641
    job crafting and, 716
    systems approach to, 614–615
developmental experiences, political skill and, 488–490, 489t
developmental HRM, 1117
developmental psychology, CSR and, 1092
DevelopNet, 1581
deviation amplification, 1581–1582
De Vos, A., 1225–1226
Diagnostic and Statistical Manual of Mental Disorders (DSM), 565, 566t
dialectical change, 1565–1566
dialogic OD, 1563
Dickson, William J., 9
differential overqualification theory, 1202
differentiation, in identity management, 654
diffusing responsibility, 1325
diffusion, QWL and, 1503–1504
digital, shift from mechanical to, 1639
digital collaboration, 860–862. *See also* virtual teams
digital economy, 786
digital fluency, 331
digital literacy, of young workers, 598, 603
digital online telework, 755t, 758–762, 759f, 769. *See also* telework

digital platform-based economy, 332, 1638
digital workforce, globalization and, 331–332, 342
dignity, 55–56
dimensional emotions, 449
dimensional invariance, 243–244
diminishing marginal utility, 395
diminishing sensitivity, JDM and, 396
direct effect, 210
direct self-assessment, 1196–1197
Dirty Dozen, 517
DIS (Designing Interactive Systems), 741
disabilities at work
    accommodations for, 670–676
    disability definition, 667–668
    disclosure of, 670
    gender and, 575
    job application process and, 668–670
    job crafting and carving and, 672–673
    legislation on, 668
    open hiring and, 670
    overview of, 667–668
    redesign of work and, 673–676
    sheltered employment and, 671–672
    stereotypes and, 669–670
disappointment and regret, 397
disclosure
    of disabilities at work, 670
    SGMs and identity, 654–656
DISC model (Demand-Induced Strain Compensation model), 691–692
discrepancy testing, 177
discrete emotions, 449
discrimination
    age, 634t, 641–642
    gender, 573, 956
    gender-based hiring, 577–578
    SGMs and, 649–653
    against young workers, 642
discrimination, related to diversity, 340–341
discursive means of sense-making, 1005–1007
disengaged worklife profile, 1449–1450
disequilibrium state, 1574–1577, 1595 n.1
disordinal interaction, 230–231, 231f
disparity, diversity and, 537–538
dispersion, justice in teams and, 891
displacing responsibility, 1325
dispositional approach to employability, 1230–1231
dispute-related bullying, 1432
disruptions, in mobile telework/remote work, 767
dissatisfaction, 686
dissent, upward communication and, 984
distinctive features of identity, 1009

distortion, upward communication and, 983–984
distributed cognition theory, 733–734
Distribution of the Product Test, 215
distributive justice, 881–883, 1063–1065, 1150–1151
distributive negotiation, 1036
diversity. *See also* gender in organizations; race; sexual
    and gender minorities
  age, 624–625
  biases and discrimination related to, 340–341
  climate, 658
  in collaboration, 372–373
  constructionist perspective on, 534
  critical research on, 543–545, 544t
  cross-cultural IWOP and, 362–363
  deep-level, 531, 533t
  definitions of, 531–534, 537–538
  disparity and, 537–538
  dividend, 538
  "doing difference" and, 535–537, 536f
  "doing gender" and, 535
  economic value of, 541–542
  essentialist perspective on, 533–534
  EU anti-discrimination legislation on, 532, 533t
  four layers of, 531, 532f, 533t
  gender and initiatives for, 585
  globalization and challenges of, 337–341
  in HRM, 1108
  inclusion and, 341
  interfirm relationships in intercultural settings
    and, 339
  intersectionality and, 536–537
  justice in teams and member, 891
  mainstream literature on, 542–545, 544t
  management generalizability in cross-cultural settings
    and, 338–339
  organizational behavior and, 956
  overview on, 529–530
  primary and secondary dimensions of, 531–532, 533t
  research perspectives on, 542–545, 544t
  separation and, 537–538
  social constructionism and, 534–535
  surface-level, 531, 533t
  in teams, 837–838
  training, 540–541
  value in, 538–539
  variety and, 537–538
  work in intercultural settings and, 339–340
  in workplace, 537–538, 545
diversity management
  AA and, 541
  business compared to moral rationale for, 541–542
  criticisms of, 541–542

definition of, 538–539
equal opportunity compared to, 539
future challenges to, 545
to inclusion, 540–541
value in diversity and, 538–539
diversity programs, for stress management, 1415
Dobrow, S. R., 1238
documents, for data collection, 1628
"doing difference," 535–537, 536f
"doing gender," 535
Doldor, E., 495
Dollard, M. F., 1350–1351
domain analysis, 310–311, 310f
domain-specific expertise, in JDM, 403–404
domain-specific well-being, 141–142, 145
double randomization, 214
doubt raisers, in letters of recommendation, 578
downward communication
  concept of, 978–982
  corrective feedback and, 982
  employee productivity and, 978–979
  employee turnover and, 979–980
  framing and sense-giving in, 981–982
  job satisfaction and, 979
  leader-member exchange and, 980–981
  "mum effect" in, 982
  telework and, 987
Dragow, F., 553
drive theory, 416
Drucker, Peter, 11, 1080
DSM (*Diagnostic and Statistical Manual of Mental
  Disorders*), 565, 566t
dual-concern model of conflict behavior, 1028–1030,
  1029f
dual conflict, 372–373, 380
dual goal expectancy, 413
dual-salary systems, 192–193
Duffy, R. D., 1238
dummy codes, 234–235
dummy variables, 234
Dunnett corrections, 233
Dunnette, Marvin D., 15
Dutch Test of Conflict Handling, 1031
Dutton, J. E., 709–713, 715
dynamic safety capability, 1488–1489

Eagly, A. H., 571–572
EAGR approach, 982
EAOHP (European Association for Occupational Health
  Psychology), 1339–1340
EAPs (employee assistance programs), 187, 1411
Earley, Chris, 354

early retirement, 1255
Eason, K., 92
EAWOP (European Association of Work and Organizational Psychology), 18–19, 21, 353–354
eBay, 1556
ecological psychology, 733
economic insecurity, quality of working life and, 1508–1509
economic justice, 50
economic tenuousness, informal work and, 784–785
economy, globalization and new forms of, 332
Edmondson, D., 94
EDMP. *See* evidence-based decision-making and practice
educational psychology, 5
education and educators
    CSR in, 1091
    in EDMP, 45
    gender and gaps in, 576–577
    job insecurity and level of, 1164–1165
    overeducation and, 1196–1197, 1199–1201
    overqualification from, 1200–1201
    values and, 63
    WOP and, 62–63
    young workers and level of, 598
EEC (European Economic Community), 10–11
efficacy. *See also* self-efficacy
    in psychological capital, 161
    teamwork and collective, 843
    in work engagement measurement, 1294–1295
effort
    in goal setting theory, 110
    in training, 1181
effort-recovery theory, 1347–1348
    on work and family, 1373
Effort-Reward Imbalance (ERI) model, 1402
egalitarianism, gender in organizations and, 586
ego depletion, 923–926
EGOS (European Group of Organization Studies), 529
Einola, K., 912
Eisenberg, E. M., 977
Eisenhardt method, 325 n.3
elapsed time, 286
elder care, gender and responsibilities with, 583
electronic job crafting intervention, 722–723
ELIZA, 744
Elliott, V., 308
Elsbach, K. D., 1008
embodied interaction, 735–736
embodied means of sense-making, 1007–1008
emergence. *See also* generative emergence
    change and transformation context of, 1574

complexity science and, 1586
continuum of, 1595 n.1
in disequilibrium, 1595 n.1
of emergents, 1595 n.1
learning from, 1585–1587
in nature, 1573
of organizational change, 1566, 1574
overview of, 1572–1574
science and praxis of, 1585–1587
social systems and dynamics of, 1575–1577
in systemic capacity, 1595 n.1
emergent codes, 303
emergent states
    in teamwork, 842–844
    in virtual teams, 869–871
emerging adulthood, 600
emerging markets, globalization and, 330
Emery, F., 80–81, 84, 86, 92, 94
emic leadership, 357–358
emigration, change effects of, 1561
emotional climate, 454–455, 1525
    teams and, 965
emotional contagion, 453–454
emotional co-regulation, 452–453
emotional culture, 454–455
emotional intelligence, 452, 455–457
    burnout and poor, 1452
    organizational behavior and, 959
Emotional Intelligence (Goleman), 452
emotional labor, 452–453
    occupational stress and, 1348–1349
    organizational behavior and, 959
emotional resources, for retirement, 1258
emotional stability, as job performance predictor, 1146
emotion-focused coping, 1343–1344, 1408–1409
emotion regulation
    attention deployment in, 151–152
    interpersonal, 452–453
    reappraisal in, 153
    situation selection and modification in, 151
    subsequent behavior in, 153
    well-being and, 151–153
emotion-rule dissonance, 1348–1349
emotions at work. *See also* moral emotions
    abusive supervision and, 924
    appraisal-centered approach for, 449
    between-person differences of, 451–452
    burnout and demands of, 1348–1349
    conceptualizing, 447–449
    creativity at work and, 1311
    CWBs linked to, 1323–1324
    defining, 447–448

1672 • **INDEX**

emotions at work (*continued*)
  dimensional compared to discrete, 449
  emotional intelligence and, 452, 455–457
  feelings compared to, 429–430
  five-level model of, 449–455, 450f
  in groups and teams, 453–454
  historical study of, 447
  integrating five-levels of, 455–457, 456f
  interpersonal/dyadic interactions and, 452–453
  in JDM, 396–397
  leadership and, 453–454
  measuring, 448–449
  mood compared to, 448
  multilevel theory of, 446–447
  multiple goals and, 413
  organizational behavior and, 958–959
  organization-wide, 454–455
  overview of, 446–447
  primary and secondary, 448
  regret and disappointment, 397
  shared, 1525
  spectrum of, 446–447
  as state or trait, 447–448
  surface acting and deep acting in, 452–453, 1348–1349
  trait affectivity and, 452
  within-person variations of, 450–451
empathy and compassion, moral emotions and, 432–433,
    438–439
The Emperor's New Clothes (Anderson), 983–984
employability
  career studies on, 1230–1233
  job insecurity and, 1169
employee assistance programs (EAPs), 187, 1411
employees
  abusive supervision and behaviors of, 924–925
  abusive supervision effects on, 925–926
  creativity at work and motivation of, 1310–1311
  downward communication and job satisfaction of, 979
  downward communication and productivity of, 978–979
  downward communication and turnover of, 979–980
  ethical leadership and identification of, 941
  ethical leadership and performance of, 942
  goals and input of, 422–423
  HRM impact and attributions of, 1115–1116
  justice predicting behavior of, 879–880
  Machiavellianism and, 512–513
  narcissism and, 510
  organizational behavior and values of, 957–958
  orientations and aspirations of, 129–130
  psychopathy and, 515–516
  shift to talent over, 1639
  workers compared to, 781

employer branding, 668–669
employer cybervetting, 485
employment interviews, 1147–1149
employment-organization relationship (EOR), 1135
employment relationships
  as exchange relationships, 1125–1126
  overview of, 1125
employment stages, gender and, 576–583
employment standards, quality of working life and,
    1509–1511
empowerment, overqualification and sense of, 1210
enacted values, 1054–1055
enactive mastery, 422–423
enactment, sense-making and, 1009–1012
enactment-selection-retention process in organizations,
    998f, 999–1000, 1002
Enders, C. K., 258
engaged worklife profile, 1449–1450
engagement. *See* work engagement
Engelbart, Douglas, 729
enhancement hypothesis, 1370–1371
enhancing psychological states, 422–423
enhancing subcultures, 1052–1053
ENIAC, 729
Enron, 938
Entrepreneurial Finance Lab, 189–190
entry, in OD, 1625–1627
environment. *See also* person-environment fit
  ambiguity and equivocality in, 997–998
  created, 1327
  CWBs and, 1326–1327
  imposed, 1326
  job insecurity sources in, 1166
  mapping or orientation of, 100–101
  mobile telework/remote work and changing, 767
  organizational dehumanization factors from, 1470
  physical, of work, 969
  risk, certainty, and uncertainty in, 997–998
  selecting, 1326–1327
  sense-making perspective on, 997–998
  stress management and physical, 1405–1406
  well-being sources in, 142–147, 142t, 143f
environmental psychology, 174–175
envy, social comparison and, 821–823
EOR (employment-organization relationship), 1135
EPP (Eysenck Personality Profiler), 558
Equal Employment Opportunity Commission, 580
equality, 50
Equality Act, United Kingdom, 668
equal opportunity
  diversity management compared to, 539
  gender in organizations and, 584–585

Equiframe, 191
equipment mental models, 870
equity, 50
    cross-cultural IWOP and, 362–363
equity theory
    distributive justice and, 1064–1065
    motivation and, 962
equivocality, in environment, 997–998
equivocation, upward communication and, 983–984
Erez, Miriam, 352, 354
ergonomics, sociotechnical approach for, 92–93
"Ergonomics for a Computer" (Shackel), 729
"Ergonomics in the Design of a Large Digital Computer
        Console" (Shackel), 729
ERI (Effort-Reward Imbalance) model, 1402
error invariance, 243–244
escalation of commitment, 960
ESM (Experience Sampling Method), 1521
espoused values, organizational culture and, 1050,
        1054–1055
essentialist perspective on diversity, 533–534
essential multicollinearity, 247
ethical climate, 1045–1046
Ethical Code of American Psychological Association.
        See APA Code
ethical decision-making
    following through in, 70
    information gathering in, 69
    Lefkowitz's model of, 68–69
    problem analysis and choice in, 69–70
    problem identification in, 69
ethical dilemmas
    cookbook approach to, 67
    definition of, 57
    examples of, 59–61t
    forms of, 58, 59t
    intuitive approach to, 67–68
    legalistic approach to, 66–67
    solving, 66–70
    virtuous approach to, 67
ethical dimensions
    caring-beneficence, 51
    caring-nonmaleficence, 51
    definition of, 50–51
    fairness and justice, 50
    moral virtue/character, 51
    respect for people, 50
ethicality, in procedural justice, 1066
ethical leadership, 163, 358
    antecedents of, 939–940
    authentic leadership compared to, 942–943
    current directions on, 945

CWBs and, 942
definition of, 938
empirical complexity and research on, 944–945
employee identification and, 941
employee performance and, 942
incentive systems and, 939–940
leader and follower moral disengagement and, 940
leader-follower relationships shaped by, 942
leader-member exchange and, 940–941
leader moral identity and, 940
operationalization and dimensionality of, 938–939
organizational citizenship behavior and, 941–942
overview of, 937–938
respectful leadership compared to, 943
servant leadership compared to, 942–943
social exchange theory and, 940–941
social learning theory and, 940–941
unethical leadership compared to, 943–944
Ethical Leadership at Work Questionnaire, 938–939
Ethical Leadership Scale, 938–939
ethical reasoning, 49, 52
    moral hygiene and, 68
ethical relativism, 52
ethical situations/problems
    conceptual foundations of, 49–50
    definition of, 50
ethics. See also moral behavior
    additional guidelines for, 51–52
    conceptual foundations of, 49–50
    decision-making with, 66–70
    definition of, 49
    deontological approaches to, 52–53
    of humanitarian work and organizational psychology,
        185–186
    meta-issues in, 50–52
    moral disengagement theory and behavioral, 437
    normative models of, 54–55
    organizational politics and, 966–967
    professional relations and, 62–63
    research, 63
    of science, 64
    survey data from WOP, 58–62
    teleological approaches to, 53–54
    universalism in, 51–52
    universalizability in, 52
    values and, 55–56
    virtue (aretaic) theory of, 54
    in WOP, 49–70
ethics of care
    beneficence and, 51
    definition of, 50
    nonmaleficence, 51

ethnography
 analysis in qualitative research and, 310–313
 in HCI, 738
ethnomethodology, HCI and, 734–735
etic leadership, 357–358
eudaimonia, 1518
eudaimonic well-being, 141
 antecedents of, 1527–1528
 cognitive judgments of, 1518–1519
 definition of, 1518
 experiences of, 1519–1520
 job characteristics and, 1527–1528
 job performance and, 1528–1529
 leadership and, 1527–1528
 overview of, 1518–1520
 personality and, 1528
euphemistic labeling, 1325
European Academy of Management (EURAM), 529
European Association for Occupational Health
  Psychology (EAOHP), 1339–1340
European Association of Work and Organizational
  Psychology (EAWOP), 18–19, 21, 353–354
European Economic Community (EEC), 10–11
European Foundation for the Improvement of Living and
  Working Conditions, 1504
European Group of Organization Studies
  (EGOS), 529
European Union (EU), 10–11
 anti-discrimination legislation, 532, 533t
 telework/remote work in, 718–720
European Workplace Innovation Network (EUWIN),
  93–94
evaluation
 biases, 341
 candidate, JDM for, 405–406
 in OD, 1633
 performance, 1281–1283
 self, 817, 1324–1325
 in TNA, 1183–1184
 training, 1188–1189
evidence-based decision-making and practice
  (EDMP)
 acquiring in, 29, 37f, 38
 aggregating in, 29, 37f, 39–40
 applying in, 29, 37f, 40
 appraising in, 29, 37f, 38–39
 asking in, 29, 37–38, 37f
 assessing in, 29, 37f, 40
 best available evidence in, 27, 29, 31
 "best practice" logic compared to, 26
 core capabilities in, 37f, 43–44
 critical and analytical thinking in, 37f, 41–42

education in, 45
functional capabilities in, 37–40, 37f
future directions for, 44–45
history of, 27
implementation of, 42–43
knowledge generation and translation in, 37f, 42–43
in leadership development, 25–26, 37f, 43–44
logic model for, 39–40, 39f
in management, 27–28
in medicine, 25, 27
meta-cognitive skills in, 37f, 41
methodological pluralism and, 30
misconceptions about, 29–30
organizational norms and socialization processes as
  barrier to, 31–34, 32f
in organizations, definition and key features, 27–29
in organizations capabilities framework, 26–27,
  36–44, 37f
overview of, 24–27
six skills in, 29, 37–40, 37f
sources of evidence in, 28–29
triangulating multiple sources of evidence in,
  27–28, 30
unaided individual/group decision and judgment
  processes as barrier to, 32f, 34–36
EVLN (exit-voice-loyalty-neglect) model, 1132
exacerbating interactions, 237–238
exact inference, 216–217
The Examination of Men's Wits (Huarte), 19
exchange, 966
exchange relationships, 1125–1126
exclusion, in multi-organizational groups, 381
execution monitoring, 101
Executive Order 10450, 660
exemplary role modeling, positive dyadic leadership and,
  906
exhaustion, 1294, 1296
 burnout and, 1448
exit-voice-loyalty-neglect (EVLN) model, 1132
exosystems, 1371
expatriates, performance management systems for,
  336–337
expectancy theory, 15, 414, 1109–1110
 motivation and, 962–963
expectations, performance management and setting,
  1276–1278
expected utility theory, 395
experience
 overqualification from, 1201–1202
 personnel selection criterion of, 1147
Experience Sampling Method (ESM), 1521
experiment wise Type I error rate, 233

expertise, JDM and, 400–401
explicit age stereotypes, 622
explicit coordination, 1483–1484
exploitation, perceived, 1463–1464
external continuity, 1259
external CSR, 1091–1093
external dimensions, in four layers of diversity, 531, 532f
external environments, organizational change and, 1557–1558
external feedback, 1228
external regulation, 122, 419–420
external validity, qualitative research standards for, 321t
extraversion
  disadvantages of, 556
  high, average, low levels of, 554t
  introverts compared to, 556
  overview of, 556
  positive and negative consequences of, 555t
  work outcomes and, 556, 557t
extrinsic aspirations, 123
extrinsic job satisfaction, 1516–1517
extrinsic motivation, 122, 419–420, 422
Eysenck Personality Profiler (EPP), 558

fabrication, 64, 65t
Factor 2 psychopathy, 517–518
factorial invariance testing, 243–244
factor (co)variance invariance, 243–244
faint praise, in letters of recommendation, 578
Fair Labor Standards Act, 1938, 1368
fairness
  communication in organizations and, 1284–1285
  as ethical dimension, 50
  judgments, 1063
fairness heuristic theory (FHT), 885–886
fair treatment
  importance of, 1071–1072
  relational model of, 1071–1072
  self-interest model of, 1071–1072
  sources of, 1071
falsification, 64, 65t
family, job insecurity spillover to, 1168–1169
Family and Medical Leave Act (FMLA), 1369–1370
family policies, gender in organizations and, 585
family-supportive supervisor behaviors (FSSB), 1382–1383
family-to-work conflict (FTWC), 1377–1381
family-to-work enrichment (FTWE), 1379, 1381–1382
family-work interference (FIW), 1355–1356, 1398–1399
Fang, Y., 341
fast thinking, in JDM, 398
"fatigue curve," 7

faultlines
  of age in groups and teams, 623, 641
  justice in teams and, 890–891
Fay, D., 1354
fearless dominance (FD), 514–515
feature-specific well-being, 145
feedback
  downward communication and corrective, 982
  effective, 1279–1280
  external, 1228
  from job, 420–421
  managers and, 1279, 1281
  in OD, 1629–1630
  in performance management, 1278–1281
  survey, 1623–1625, 1633
  for teamwork, 848
  three parts in, 1630
  in training, 1182
  virtual teams and, 868–869
Feedback and Organization Development (Nadler), 1624–1625
feedback processing
  action regulation and, 101–102
  in goal setting theory, 110–111, 113
  psychology of sustainability and, 179–180, 180t
feedforward, 1280
feelings
  Affective Revolution and, 430
  definition of, 429–430
  emotions compared to, 429–430
  moral behavior and, 430
Feldman, D. C., 1204–1205
Feldman, Martha, 317
Fenstermaker, S., 535
Ferguson, M. W., 261
Ferris, G. R., 801t, 802–803
Festinger, L., 813, 815, 817–818
FHT (fairness heuristic theory), 885–886
Fiedler, Fred E., 15
field theory, 1636
  Lewin and, 465–466, 1400
  on stress, 1399–1400
financial planning, for retirement, 1254
financial resources, for retirement, 1258
financial well-being, 1261
Fine, S., 1198, 1207, 1212
"first cycle" codes, 308
First-Order Standard Error Test (Sobel Test), 211, 214–215
Fischer, K. W., 447–448
Fisher, C. D., 449
Fisher, D. M., 339

1676 · INDEX

Fiske, S. T., 635–636, 801*t*, 802
5C (Cross-Cultural Collaboration on Contemporary Careers), 1229–1230
five-level model of emotions at work, 449–455, 450*f*
　between-person differences level of, 451–452
　groups and teams level of, 453–454
　integrating, 455–457, 456*f*
　interpersonal/dyadic interactions level of, 452–453
　organization-wide level of, 454–455
　within-person temporal variations level of, 450–451
FIW (family-work interference), 1355–1356, 1398–1399
fixed-mindset theory, 561
"fix the women" framing, 583–584
flattery, 806
flexibility paradigm, 771–772
flexible action patterns, of action regulation, 102–103
flexible rules, 1487–1488
flexible work arrangements (FWAs)
　cross-cultural IWOP and, 359
　future research on, 1417
　occupational health psychology and, 1356–1357
　organizational interventions for, 1596–1597
　for stress management, 1414–1415
flextime, work and family and, 1383
flourishing well-being, 141
flow, well-being and, 1519–1520
fluid intelligence, 615
FMLA (Family and Medical Leave Act), 1369–1370
focused climate, 1044–1046
focused coding, 313–315
focused rhythms, planned organizational change and, 1564
Folkman, S., 448
Follett, Parker, 1025–1026
forced ranking and rating, 1282–1283
forced remote work, 771–772
force field analysis intervention, 1402–1403, 1636
forcing conflict behavior, 1028–1029
Ford, C. M., 1305, 1308
Ford, Henry, 675–676
Ford, J. K., 1177–1178
formal discrimination, SGMs and, 650–651
formalization, 968
formal organizational work-family policy, 1382
formal organization of enterprises, study of, 6
formal overqualification, 1198
formal power, 965–966
formal sectors, humanitarian work and organizational psychology in, 193
founder's influence, on organizational culture, 1050–1051
four layers of diversity, 531, 532*f*, 533*t*
Fox, K. E., 1596–1597
France, OP in, 19

Frayne, C. A., 115–116
Fredrickson, B. L., 451
freelance, 786
Freeman, Edward, 1082
Frei, C., 1200
French, J., 79–80
frequent statistics, 216
Frese, Michael, 15–16
Fried, Y. E., 281, 283–284, 289–291
Friedman, Milton, 66, 1082
friendship, agreeableness and, 559
Frijda, N. H., 150, 152, 448
Fritz, J. M., 985–986
Frontiers in Psychology, 1092
FSSB (family-supportive supervisor behaviors), 1382–1383
FTWC (family-to-work conflict), 1377–1381
FTWE (family-to-work enrichment), 1379, 1381–1382
Fugate, M., 1230–1231
Fullerton, J., 538
Full Range of Leadership Model, 514
functional capabilities, in EDMP, 37–40, 37*f*
The Functions of the Executive (Barnard), 13–14
Fundamental Problem of Causal Inference, 220–221
Furnham, A., 552, 564–565
future time prediction, 284–288
FWAs. *See* flexible work arrangements

Gadke, D., 558
gain-loss framing, JDM and, 395
Galanter, E., 98
Galbraith, J., 14, 1637
Galton, Francis, 5
gameful interaction, in HCI, 742
gamification, 742
Gardenswartz, L., 531–532, 532*f*, 533*t*
Gardner, W., 801*t*, 803
Garfinkel, Harold, 734
Garvin, D. A., 1560–1561
Gattig, A., 175–176
"gay advantage," 651
gay workers. *See* sexual and gender minorities
GCA (general cognitive ability), 1144–1146, 1145*t*, 1151–1153, 1152*t*
GCT (goal contents theory), 123–124, 129–130
GECo (Geneva Emotional Competence Test), 456
Geels, F., 94
Gelfand, M. J., 352
Gemelli, Agostino, 8–9
Gemmill, G., 1576*t*
gender in organizations. *See also* sexual and gender minorities
　AA and, 541
　age and, 575

agency and, 571–572
ambivalent sexism theory on, 573–574
caregiving responsibilities and, 582–583
challenges in securing employment, 576–579
communality and, 571–572
disabilities and, 575
discrimination by, 573, 956
diversity and inclusion initiatives for, 585
"doing difference" and, 535–537, 536f
"doing gender," 535
educational gaps and, 576–577
egalitarianism and, 586
employment stages and, 576–583
equal opportunity and, 584–585
family policies and, 585
"fix the women" framing and, 583–584
glass ceiling and, 572, 579–580
glass escalator and, 573
hiring discrimination and, 577–578
intersectionality and, 536–537, 574–575
job navigation and, 579–583
kaleidoscope careers and, 1226
lack of fit theory on, 573
leadership perceptions and, 580
leaky pipeline and, 579–580
letters of recommendation and, 578
marital status and, 1202
menstruation, maternity, menopause and, 581
mentor access and, 580–581
negotiation differences and, 579
non-binary experiences in, 525 n.1
occupational health and, 581–582
on-the-job support and, 585
organizational culture and, 585–586
organizational dehumanization and, 1471
overqualification and, 1202
pay disparities and, 578–579
race and, 574–575
remedies for inequities of, 583–586
"revise work culture" frame for, 585–586
role congruity theory on, 572
SCM on, 574
self-promotion and, 577
similarity, 815–816
social comparison by, 815–816
social learning theory on, 571
social role theory on, 571–572
telework and, 765
theories of, 571–576
"value the feminine" strategy and, 584
well-being and, 148
work and family and, 1368–1369, 1377

gender policing, 652
general cognitive ability (GCA), 1144–1146, 1145t,
    1151–1153, 1152t
generalized anxiety disorder, 558
General Work and Engineering Psychology (Hacker), 98
generational differences, young workers and, 601–603
generative emergence
    amplification dynamics in, 1581–1582
    aspiration and, 1580
    collective actions in, 1581
    conflict in, 1580
    core values and, 1582
    creative tension and, 1580
    disequilibrium organizing in, 1574–1577, 1595 n.1
    documented sequences of, 1576t, 1579
    energy flow maintenance in, 1583
    expanding possibilities through, 1582
    leadership of, 1583–1585, 1584t
    micro-experiments in, 1574–1577
    new order linked to values in, 1583
    overview of, 1572–1574
    phases and outcomes of, 1577–1579, 1579f, 1585
    positive outcomes through, 1583–1585
    propositions of, 1585
    recombination of system components in, 1577–1578
    social systems and dynamics of, 1575–1577
    stabilization of newly emerged state in, 1578
    stress in, 1577, 1581
    theory of, 1575–1577
    thermodynamics and, 1574–1575
    uncertainty and, 1580
    unconventional alternatives in, 1581
generically subjective of organizations, 1000
Geneva Emotional Competence Test (GECo), 456
genocide, dehumanization and, 1461
George, J. M., 289–291, 1300
Germain, Jose, 19
Germany, OP in, 18–19
Gibbons, F. X., 823
Gibson, D. E., 449
gig economy, 332. *See also* informal work
    job crafting and, 719
    terminology of, 786
gig work, 786
Glacier Metal Co., 12
glass ceiling phenomenon, 572, 579–580
glass cliff phenomenon, 572
glass escalator phenomenon, 573
Glavas, A., 1079, 1086, 1088–1089, 1092–1093
Glazer, S., 352
Gleicher, David, 1627
global careers, 1234

globalization, 14
  biases and discrimination related to diversity and, 340–341
  cross-cultural IWOP and, 356–362
  culture and, 337
  definition of, 329–330
  digital workforce and, 331–332, 342
  diversity, equity, and inclusion and, 362
  diversity-related challenges of, 337–341
  emerging markets and, 330
  enhancing cooperation in, 343
  HRM and, 333–337
  intercultural communication and, 340
  interfirm relationships in intercultural settings and, 339
  IWOP from perspective of, 329–330, 342–343
  labor supply and, 330
  leadership and, 357–358
  management generalizability in cross-cultural settings and, 338–339
  measuring and analyzing cross-cultural differences and, 342–343
  new forms of economy and, 332
  occupational safety, stress, and health and, 358–360
  organizational culture and, 356–357
  pace of, 331, 363
  performance management and, 335–337
  personnel selection, training and, 334–335
  precarious and decent work and, 360
  recruitment and, 334
  trust and, 360–362
  workers, managers and uncertainty of, 333
  work in intercultural settings and, 339–340
Global Leadership and Organizational Behavior Effectiveness (GLOBE) project, 338, 355–358, 719, 910
global mindsets, 358
Global Organization for Humanitarian Work Psychology (GOHWP), 187, 192, 194, 360
global positive leadership, 909–910
GLOBE (Global Leadership and Organizational Behavior Effectiveness) project, 338, 355–358, 719, 910
goal contents theory (GCT), 123–124, 129–130
goal gradient hypothesis, 406–407
goal rules, 1487–1488
goals
  approach, 100–101
  avoidance, 100–101
  commitment, 110–111
  definition of, 99, 412
  development and selection of, 100–101

  difficulty of, 421–422
  employee input for, 422–423
  hierarchical structure of, 100
  as motivation's central organizing structure, 412–416
  multiple, 413
  phases of, 413–416
  priming, in subconscious, 116–117
  proximal, 113
  setting/choice of, 406–407, 414, 421–422
  specific, high, 110–111
  striving for, 414–416
Goals, Operators, Methods, and Selection rules (GOMS), 739
goal setting theory, 98, 280–281, 415
  ability in, 110–111, 113–114
  conservation of resources theory and, 962
  cultural differences in, 354
  economic benefits of, 116
  empirical research and, 111–113
  feedback processing in, 110–111, 113
  ignoring moderators in, 113–114
  induction in, 111
  job performance and, 112
  learning in, 114
  methods in, 114–116
  overview of, 110–111
  participative decision-making and, 115
  resources in, 110–111, 114
  self-efficacy and, 115–116
  specific, high goals in, 110–111
  in subconscious, 116–117
Goffman, Erving, 799–800, 805
GOHWP (Global Organization for Humanitarian Work Psychology), 187, 192, 194, 360
Goldberg, E., 1275–1276, 1286–1287
Goldstein, I. L., 1177
Goldstein, Jeff, 1573, 1595 n.1
Goleman, D., 452
GOMS (Goals, Operators, Methods, and Selection rules), 739
González-Romá, V., 264, 269–271
Gooding, R. Z., 115
Goodstein, L. D., 1625–1626
Google Scholar, 94
Gottfredson, L., 552–553
Gottfredson, R. K., 261, 906
government agencies, authority for change in, 1555
grandiose narcissism, 509
grapevine communication, sense-making and, 985
gratitude, moral emotions and, 434
Greenberg, J., 882–883

"green cape" interventions, 1417–1418
Green Five taxonomy, 175–176
Greenhalgh, L., 1160
gregariousness, positive leadership and, 904
Greyston Bakery, 670
Griep, Y., 283–284, 289–291
Griffin, M., 89, 1352
Griffioen, C., 824
Grodal, S., 309, 320–323
Gross, J. J., 151, 153, 452–453
Grote, G., 93–94, 1505, 1507, 1509
grounded theory, 303
    analysis and, 312–317, 316f
    axial coding and, 313–315
    concept building in, 315
    constant comparative method in, 313
    data structure for, 316, 316f
    focused coding and, 313–315
    HCI and, 736–737
    memoing in, 313–315, 317
    open coding and, 313, 318
    refining models in, 315
    selective coding and, 315
group-mean centering, 258
groups. See also multi-organizational group dynamics
    adverse job demand reductions for, 1602
    age-related faultlines in, 623, 641
    conflict management processes in, 1035
    decision-making in, 963–964
    dynamics of, 11–12
    emotions at work in, 453–454
    mentality of, 12
    moods of, 1525
    OD and relations in, 1623–1624, 1633
    overqualification effects on, 1211
    participatory organizational interventions for, 1601–1602, 1603t
    resources increased for, 1601–1602
    safety climate in, 1352
groupthink, 374
Grudin, J., 729–730
Gruys, M. L., 1320–1321
Guarana, C. L., 289–291
Guest, David, 1126–1127, 1505, 1507, 1509
guilt and shame, moral emotions and, 431–432, 439
Gulf of Evaluation, 732–733
Gulf of Execution, 732–733

Hacker, W., 98–99, 102, 673–674, 1609–1610
Hackman, J. R., 420–421, 673–674, 695
    JCM of, 687–688, 698–700
Hagedoorn, M., 1344–1345

Haleblian, J., 338
Hall, D. T., 1219–1220
Hammer, L. B., 1379
Handbook of Industrial and Organizational Psychology (Dunnette), 15
Handbook on the Temporal Dynamics of Organizational Behavior (Griep and Hansen), 283–284
Hansen, S. D., 283–284, 289–291
happiness
    productivity and, 1521
    sustainable careers and, 1225–1226
    well-being compared to, 141
happy-productive worker thesis (HPWT), 1521–1522
The Harassed Worker (Brodsky), 1426
harassment. See workplace harassment
Hare, R. D., 517
Hargadon, A. B., 1008
Harris, R. T., 1627
Harrison, D. A., 531, 533t, 537–538
Harrison, Roger, 1631–1632
Haslam, N., 1460–1461
Hasson, H., 1609–1610
Hatha yoga, 1454
HATs (human-agent teams), 862–863, 872–873
Haunschild, P. R., 1559
Hawthorne Studies, 79
HCI. See human-computer interaction
HCs (Health Circles), 1404–1405
HDS (Hogan Development Survey), 565
HDS Bold scale, 509
health. See also occupational health psychology
    job design and, 695–696
    justice perceptions and, 1069
    occupational, 358–360
    occupational, gender differences in, 581–582
    occupational stress impact on, 1340–1343, 1341t
    older workers and, 621
    organizational-level interventions for occupational, 1413–1414
    overqualification and, 1205–1206
    retirement decision-making and, 1262
    sustainable careers and, 1225–1226
    well-being and, 1531
    workplace health promotion programs, 1534
healthcare management policies, for stress management, 1415–1416
Health Circles (HCs), 1404–1405
health insurance, retirement and, 1264
healthy organizations
    emotional climate and, 455
    pledge of, 1417–1418
Heath, C., 406–407

hedging, in letters of recommendation, 578
hedonic calculus, 53
hedonic well-being, 141
   affective experiences of, 1517–1518
   antecedents of, 1526–1527
   cognitive judgments of, 1516–1517
   definition of, 1516
   job characteristics and, 1525–1526
   job performance and, 1528–1529
   leadership and, 1526–1527
   overview of, 1516–1518
   personality and, 1526–1527
   working conditions and, 1525–1526
hedonism, 1516
Heilman, M. E., 573
helping, agreeableness and, 559
Hench, T., 1576t
Hendrickx, L., 175–176
Henri, Victor, 8
Hernández, A., 264, 269–271
Hernandez, M., 289–291
Hersch, J., 1197, 1208
Herzberg, Frederick, 12, 961, 1500, 1636
   two-factor theory of, 686–687
heterosexist harassment, 652
heterosexuality, 573–574
Hewlin, P. F., 539–540
HEXACO model, 558
HF&E (human factors and ergonomics), 728
hierarchical linear models, 240–241
high commitment HRM, 1109
"high-flyers," 562–564
Highhouse, Scott, 402, 404
high-performance work practices (HPWPs), 1222
High Potential Traits Indicator (HPTI), 564–565
high-reliability organizations (HRO) theory, 1488
highway project, as multi-organizational group dynamics
   example, 377–379
HILDA (Household Income Labour Dynamics in
   Australia), 581–582
hindrance stressors, 1347, 1395, 1397–1398, 1401, 1417
hindsight bias, 960
hiring discrimination
   gender-based, 577–578
   SGMs and, 649–650
Hirschi, A., 1232–1233
history-as-fact, 1640
history-as-power, 1640
history-as-rhetoric, 1640
history-as-sense-making, 1640
histrionic personality disorder, 566t
Hochschild, A. R., 447, 452, 457–458

Hofstede, G., 337, 354–356
Hogan Development Survey (HDS), 565
Hogarth, Robin, 400
Holland, J. L., 466–467, 1219
Hollenbeck, J. R., 414
Hollingworth, Harry, 7
home-based remote work, 755t, 756, 764–766
home-based telework, 755t, 756, 764–766
homogeneity, in teams, 837–838
hope, in psychological capital, 161
hostile sexism, 573–574
Hough, L. M, 1146
Household Income Labour Dynamics in Australia
   (HILDA), 581–582
HPTI (High Potential Traits Indicator), 564–565
HPWPs (high-performance work practices), 1222
HPWT (happy-productive worker thesis), 1521–1522
HRM. *See* human resource management
HRO (high-reliability organizations) theory, 1488
Huang, K., 336
Huarte, Juan, 19
Hull, C. A., 416
Hülsheger, U. R., 1349
Hultin, H., 1203, 1205–1206
human-agent teams (HATs), 862–863, 872–873
human-autonomy teams, 862, 872–873
human capital, 333–334
   career studies and, 1227
   HRM and, 1110, 1117
   retirement and theory of, 1259–1260
   strategic managing of, 1234
   younger workers and, 597–598
human-computer interaction (HCI)
   alternative psychological approaches to, 733–734
   cognitive models of, 732–733
   cognitive science theories of, 732–733
   conversational agents in, 744–745
   ethnography in, 738
   ethnomethodology and, 734–735
   first-wave, 730–733
   gameful interaction in, 742
   grounded theory and, 736–737
   history of, 729–730
   Internet, mobile phones and, 730
   keystroke-level model and, 737
   lines of research in, 741–745
   methods for designing interaction, 738–739
   methods for evaluating interaction, 739–740
   methods for understanding user behavior, 737–738
   overview of, 728
   participatory design in, 738–739
   Personas in, 738–739

phenomenology and, 735–736
research through design methods of, 740
scenario-based design in, 738–739
second-wave, 730–731, 734–735
self-tracking in, 742–744
social practices and, 736
storyboards in, 738
task analysis and, 737
theories of, 731–737
third-wave, 730–731, 736–737
ubiquitous computing and, 730, 739
usability in, 739
user experience in, 739–740
Wizard of Oz technique and, 738
human factors and ergonomics (HF&E), 728
humanistic psychology, 12–13
humanitarian work and organizational psychology
conceptual foundations of, 187–188
corporate social responsibility and, 194–195
ethical foundations of, 185–186
in formal and informal sectors, 193
historical foundations of, 186–187
individual level of, 189–190
organizational level of, 190
overview of, 184–185
planet protection and, 196
political foundations of, 188–189
psychology field and, 197
societal level of, 190–191
sustainable livelihood in, 188
unemployment and underemployment in, 194
universal basic income and, 196
wage intervals in, 191–193
humanitarian work psychology (HWP), 187
humanization of work, 15
human nature, 1460–1461
humanness, 1460–1461
Human Relations, 78, 88–89
human relations model, 9–10
Human Relations Movement, 673–674
human resource management (HRM)
accommodative, 1117
aggregating practices of, 1112
AI-based tools in, 331
alternative rationales for content of, 1108–1109
bundles and, 1109–1110
business strategy and, 1106–1107
comparative, 1118
definition of, 1105
detail in practices of, 1111
developmental, 1117
diversity in, 1108

employee attributions to impact of, 1115–1116
globalization and, 333–337
high commitment, 1109
human capital and, 1110, 1117
identifying and measuring practices of, 1112
implementation of, 1116–1117
individual differences and, 1117
industrial relations and, 1106
influences on development of, 1106–1108
internal fit and, 1109–1110
international assignment of employees in, 330
longitudinal research on, 1118–1119
multilevel modeling methods for, 1117–1118
nature of, 1108–1112
OB and, 1107
organizational performance outcomes and, 1112–1119
overview of, 1105–1108
performance management and, 335–337, 1286–1288
personnel selection, training and, 334–335, 1109
quality of working life and, 1506–1507
recruitment and, 334
response categories for practices of, 1111
signaling theory and, 1115–1116
sources of information on practices in, 1111
WOP and, 1105–1107
Human Rights Council, United Nations, 659–660
human subject at work, 7–8
human uniqueness, 1460–1461
humblebragging, 807
Humphrey, S. E., 691, 694
Hunsfos paper mill, Norway, 85
Hutchins, E., 732–734
Hüttges, A., 1354
HWP (humanitarian work psychology), 187
hypothesis-led decision-making, 32f, 33–34

IA (impulsive antisociality), 514–515
IAAP (International Association of Applied Psychology), 21, 353–354
iatrogenic effect, 246
IATs (implicit association tests), 622
IBM Watson Developer Cloud, 744
ICF (International Classification of Functioning, Disability and Health), 668
ICTs. *See* information and communication technologies
i-deals (idiosyncratic deals), 1234, 1300, 1382–1383
identification
ethical leadership and employee, 941
organizational, CSR and, 1090
positive dyadic leadership and followers', 906
in social comparison, 819–821
identified regulation, 122, 419

identity
  career, young workers and, 600
  centrality, 655
  disclosure, SGMs and, 654–656
  distinctive features of, 1009
  leadership, 907–908
  management, SGMs and, 653–654
  organizational, CSR and, 1090
IDEO, 1314–1315
ideological psychological contracts, 1128–1129
idiosyncratic deals (i-deals), 1234, 1300, 1382–1383
IGLO (Individual, Group, Leader and Organizational)
    framework, 1598–1599, 1608–1609
"I like my leader" effect, 910–911
ILO (International Labour Organization), 659–660,
    779–780, 787–788, 1395
imagery, 1412
imitation game, of Turing, 744
immigration, change effects of, 1561
IMOI (Inputs→Mediators→Outputs→Inputs)
    framework
  contextual moderators in, 846–847
  emergent states in, 842–844, 869–871
  ICTs and, 863–866, 864f
  inputs, 840–841, 859 n.1
  mediators, 842–844, 850t
  member characteristics in, 836–837
  outputs, 845–846, 850t
  overview of, 834–847, 835f
  situational demands in, 867
  summary of, 850t
  task characteristics in, 840–841
  team characteristics in, 837–840
  team leadership in, 868–869
  team learning and adaptation in, 868
  team members' KSAOs in, 866–867
  team processes in, 841–842, 868–869
  team tasks in, 866
  for virtual team effectiveness, 863–871, 864f
implementation intentions, 415, 422–423
implicit age stereotypes, 622, 643
implicit association tests (IATs), 622
implicit-bias training, 26
implicit career timelines, 639
implicit coordination, 1483–1484
implicit evidence hierarchies, managers', 32f, 35–36
implicit leadership theories, 639
implicit performance theories, 639
imposed environment, 1326
impression management
  actors compared to targets in, 805
  advice-seeking and, 808

correspondence interference theory and, 806
definitions of, 797–798, 798t
disagreements about, 803–805
future research on, 808–809
individual strategies for, 800
influence tactics and, 799
measurement of, 804
missed opportunities for, 807–808
origins of research on, 799–800
overview of, 797–799
political skill and, 492
question-asking and, 807–808
self-presentation and, 799
target as judge in, 806
targets as source of information and, 805–806
taxonomies of, 800–803, 801t
unsolicited touching and, 808
impression mismanagement, 806–807
impulsive antisociality (IA), 514–515
incentive systems, ethical leadership and, 939–940
incident reporting and investigation, in safety
    management, 1490–1491
incivility. See also workplace bullying
  definition of, 59t, 1428–1429
  examples of, 59–61t
  focus of, 1427–1428
  moral behavior and, 435–436
  unethical behavior compared to, 57–58
inclusion
  business compared to moral rationale for, 541–542
  cross-cultural IWOP and, 362–363
  definition of, 539
  diversity and framework for, 341
  diversity management to, 540–541
  framework of, 539, 540t
  gender and initiatives for, 585
  individual perception of, 539–540
Inclusive Redesign of Work, 674–676
income inequality, 184. See also compensation
  job insecurity and, 195–196
incomplete mediation, 210
inconsistent mediation, 211
increasing challenging job demands, 709
increasing social job resources, 709
increasing structural job resources, 709
independent variables, 207, 228–229
India, telework/remote work in, 719
indirect effect, 211, 213
indirect self-assessment, 1196–1197
indirect tactics, 802
Individual, Group, Leader and Organizational (IGLO)
    framework, 1598–1599, 1608–1609

individual causal effects, 220–221
individual creative action theory, 1308
individual differences at work. *See also* personality
  analyzing variables in, 552
  Big Five Traits of personality and, 554*f*, 555*t*, 560–561
  change over time, 561–562
  culture and, 551
  "high-flyers" and, 562–564
  importance of, 568
  overview of, 550–551
  success and, 562–564
  types of, 550–551
individual-focused stress management, 1411–1413
individual job crafting, 709–711
induction, in goal setting theory, 111
industrial, work, and organizational psychology (IWOP).
    See also cross-cultural IWOP
  as culturally impacted discipline, 354–356
  future role of culture in, 362–364
  globalization and, 356–362
  from global perspective, 329–330, 342–343
  initial inclusion of culture in, 353–354
industrial and organizational psychology.
    See organizational psychology
industrial psychology. *See* organizational psychology
industrial relations
  HRM and, 1106
  QWL concept influenced by, 1500–1501
Industrielle Psychotechnik, 9
industriousness, conscientiousness and, 560
Industry 4, 1507–1508
ineffective worklife profile, 1449–1450
inequality regimes, 537
influence behaviors, in career self-management, 1232
influence tactics. *See also* impression management
  definition of, 797–798
  impression management and, 799
  types of, 966
informal organizational work-family policy, 1382–1383
informal sectors, humanitarian work and organizational
    psychology in, 193
informal work
  autonomy and, 785
  characteristics of, 783–786
  decent work deficits and, 784
  definition of, 779–780
  downside of, 782
  economic tenuousness, poverty and, 784–785
  global presence of, 785
  names and labels of, 785–786
  organizational dehumanization and, 1474
  overview of, 779–783

precarious work and, 783–784
purpose of studying, 787–788
scheduling in, 781
skill upgrading in, 783
stereotypes of, 787–788
wage precarity and, 782–783
work in the informal economy compared to, 786–787
informational justice, 882–883
informational rewards, 121–122
information and communication technologies (ICTs),
    331–332, 755. *See also* virtual teams
  collaborative, 860–861
  media naturalness and, 865
  media richness and, 864–865
  media synchronicity and, 865–866
  social presence and, 863–864
  team learning and, 868
  team processes and, 867–868
  telework and, 986–989
  in virtual teams, 863–866, 864*f*
information richness, 864
information systems, sociotechnical approach for, 92–93
informative prior distribution, 216
ingratiation, 802, 966
inheritance of well-being, 147–148
inputs, in teamwork, 840–841, 850*t*, 859 n.1
Inputs→Mediators→Outputs→Inputs framework.
    See IMOI framework
In Search of Excellence (Peters and Waterman), 996
insights, shifts from data to, 1639
inspirational appeal, 966
Institute of Professional Orientation, 8–9
Institute of Social Research (ISR), 1637–1638
institutional theory, sense-making and, 1013–1014
Integral Organizational Renewal (IOR), 91–92
integrated regulation, 122
integrating, in identity management, 653–654
integration/segmentation preferences, for work and
    family, 1372–1373
integrative negotiation, 1036
integrative work design (IWD) model, 692–695, 693*f*
integrative work-family systems model, 1371
integrity, qualitative research standards for, 321*t*
intellectual level, of action regulation, 103
intelligence
  debate over change in, 561–562
  as individual difference at work, 551
  openness to experience and, 560
  in workplace, 552–553
Intelligence Quotient (I.Q.), 8, 552–553
intelligent personal assistants (IPAs), 744
intelligent user interfaces (IUI), 741

intent, in workplace bullying, 1428–1429
intentional organizational learning, 1560–1561
intentional unethical behavior, 57
intentional unlearning, 1561
interactional justice, 882–883, 1066–1067
interactionist theory of behavior, 465–466
interactionist theory of organizational creativity, 1307
interaction mental models, 870
interaction models
    categorical by categorical (2x2), 229–232, 231f
    categorical by categorical (3x3), 232–233
    continuous by categorical, 233–236, 234f
    continuous by continuous, 236–238, 237f
    curvilinear change and, 239–240, 239f
    moderator variables and, 229–240
    software for, 248–249
    standardized interaction coefficients and, 238
    three-way, 239–240
inter-categorical complexity, 536–537
intercepts-and-slopes-as-outcomes model, 263–264
intercepts-as-outcomes model, 261–263
intercultural communication, 340
intercultural KSAOs, 866–867
interdependence, in teams, 840
interests crafting, 716–717
interfirm relationships in intercultural settings, 339
inter-group justice, 891–893
intergroup relations, 373–374
intergroup stereotyping, 380
internal continuity, 1259
internal CSR, 1091–1093
internal dimensions, in four layers of diversity, 531, 532f
internal environments, organizational change and,
    1560–1561
internal fit, HRM and, 1109–1110
internal validity, qualitative research standards for, 321t
international assignment of employees, in HRM, 330
International Association of Applied Psychology (IAAP),
    21, 353–354
International Association of Psychotechnology (AIP),
    17–19, 21
International Classification of Functioning, Disability
    and Health (ICF), 668
International Council for the Quality of Working Life,
    1504
International Labour Organization (ILO), 659–660,
    779–780, 787–788, 1395
International Workingmen's Association, 5
Internet, HCI and, 730
interpersonal climate, SDT research in workplace and,
    125–126
interpersonal discrimination, SGMs and, 651–653

interpersonal emotion regulation, 452–453
interpersonal influence, 486
interpersonal justice, 882–883
interpersonal OCB (OCB-I), 436
interpersonal processes, in teamwork, 842
interpersonal relationships, overqualification and,
    1208–1209, 1211
interpersonal skill training, 1454
interpretive products of sense-making, 1008–1009
interrater agreement index, 880–881
interruptions, in mobile telework/remote work, 767
intersectional invisibility, 340–341
intersectionality
    definition of, 574–575
    diversity and, 536–537
    gender in organizations and, 574–575
    SGMs and, 650
intersection point, 236
intersex workers. *See* sexual and gender minorities
intersubjective level of organizations, 1000
interventions. *See also* organizational interventions;
        participatory organizational interventions
    for abusive supervision, 928–930
    for ageism in workplace, 643–644
    for burnout, 1454–1455
    criteria for choosing, 1632
    effective conditions of, 1631
    force field analysis, 1402–1403, 1636
    "green cape," 1417–1418
    JDM and external, 401–402
    JDM and internal, 402–404
    job crafting, 721–723, 1358
    in OD, 1630–1633
    for organizational climate improvements, 1048–1049
    organizational-level occupational health, 1413–1414
    for psychology of sustainability, 179–180, 180t
    "red cape," 1417–1418
    stress management, 1357–1358, 1415–1416
    for teamwork, 847–848
    types of, 1631
    for well-being at work, 1535–1536
    for work engagement improvement, 1298–1300
    work-family, 1383–1384
interviews
    for data collection, 1629
    employment, 1147–1149
    Kahneman on challenges of, 405
intra-categorical complexity, 536–537
intraclass correlation coefficient, 240–241
intrinsic aspirations, 123
intrinsic job satisfaction, 1516–1517
intrinsic motivation, 121, 419, 422, 1306–1307

introjected regulation, 122, 419–420
introverts, extraverts compared to, 556
intuitive approach to ethical dilemmas, 67–68
invariance testing, SEM and, 243–244
investment theory, 559
I-O psychology. *See* organizational psychology
IOR (Integral Organizational Renewal), 91–92
Ioteyko, Iosefa, 19
IPAs (intelligent personal assistants), 744
I.Q. (Intelligence Quotient), 8, 552–553
irrelevancy, in letters of recommendation, 578
isomorphism, CSR and, 1084
ISR (Institute of Social Research), 1637–1638
issue selling, 1560
IUI (intelligent user interfaces), 741
IWD (integrative work design) model, 692–695, 693*f*
IWOP. *See* industrial, work, and organizational psychology

James, L. R., 885
Janssen, P. P. M., 819
Japan
 OP in, 20
 telework/remote work in, 719
Jaques, Elliott, 12
JCE (Michigan Job Crafting Exercise), 722
JCM (job characteristics model), 687–688, 698–700
JD-C/S (job demands-control/support) model, 1400–1401
JDM. *See* judgment and decision-making
JD-R model. *See* job demands-resources model
JDS (job diagnostics survey), 1404–1405
jealous, social comparison and, 821–823
Jehn, K. A., 965
Jellison, J. M., 798*t*
Jepsen, D. M., 25
Jiang, K., 1112–1113
Jiang, Z., 1229
job-age stereotypes, 622–623
job analysis, in training needs assessment, 1183
job analysis method, 1196–1197
job application process, disabilities and, 668–670
job attitudes
 job design and, 696
 job insecurity and, 1167–1168
 older workers and, 619–620
 organizational dehumanization's impact on, 1467
 overqualification and, 1204
 SDT research outcomes on, 131
 teamwork and, 845
job candidate evaluation, JDM for, 405–406
job carving, disabilities and, 672–673

job characteristics
 as antecedents, 693–695
 eudaimonic well-being and, 1527–1528
 hedonic well-being and, 1525–1526
 motivation and, 420–421, 673–674
 overqualification and, 1203
 relations with outcomes of, 695
 safety-related, 1484
job characteristics model (JCM), 687–688, 698–700
job control, safety and, 1484
job crafting
 aggregated score for, 715–716
 for burnout, 1455
 collectivism and, 720
 coworker reactions to, 718
 cultural differences and, 719–720
 defining, 708–711
 development and, 716
 in different populations and contexts, 718–720
 disabilities and, 672–673
 empirically testing relationships of constructs of, 714–716
 gig economy and, 719
 individual, 709–711
 interventions, 721–723, 1358
 JD-R model on, 709
 managers and, 718
 meta-analyses and reviews on, 717
 motivation and, 716–717
 new forms of, 716–717
 older workers and, 718–719
 overview of, 708
 person-job fit and, 719
 positive psychology and, 1354
 reflective compared to formative constructs of, 714–715
 scales for measuring, 711–714, 712*t*
 social context influences on, 717–718
 strengths and interests in, 716–717
 team, 711, 720–721
 types of, 709–711
 work engagement and, 1299–1300
job demand control model, Karasek's, 688
job demands
 burnout and, 690
 definition of, 690, 709
 group-level reduction of adverse, 1602
 leader-level reduction of adverse, 1604
 organizational-level reduction of adverse, 1605–1606
 participatory organizational interventions reducing, 1600–1601
 political skill and, 492–493
 safety impact of, 1484

job demands-control/support (JD-C/S) model, 1400–1401
job demands-resources (JD-R) model
  balance in, 1599
  on burnout, 1451
  on job crafting, 709
  job design and, 690–691
  on occupational stress, 1346–1347
  participatory organizational interventions and, 1599
  resources in, 126–127
  on stress, 1400–1401
  well-being in, 690
  work engagement and, 1297–1298, 1527–1528
job design. *See also* job crafting
  adaptivity and, 697
  behavioral outcomes of, 697–698
  cognition and, 696
  contemporary models of, 691–692
  COR theory and, 698–699
  definition of, 683–684, 708
  different outcomes of, 697–698
  DISC model and, 691–692
  Hackman and Oldham's JCM and, 687–688, 698–700
  health, well-being and, 695–696
  Herzberg's two-factor theory and, 686–687
  history of models on, 684–691
  IWD model and, 692–695, 693*f*
  JD-R model and, 690–691
  job attitudes and, 696
  job characteristics as antecedents for, 693–695
  Karasek's job demand control model and, 688
  learning promoted in, 692, 696
  overview of, 683–684
  personal resources in, 698–700
  proactivity and, 697–698
  quality of working life and, 1506
  role ambiguity and role conflict in, 692
  scientific management and, 685
  social approaches to, 685–686
  sociotechnical systems theory and, 686
  Taylorism and, 685
  Theory X and Theory Y on, 686
  Vitamin Model of well-being and, 689–690
job diagnostics survey (JDS), 1404–1405
job embeddedness, 1131–1132
job engagement. *See* work engagement
job enlargement, 686–687, 969
job enrichment, 686–687, 1500
job experience. *See* experience
job insecurity
  attitudes and, 1167–1168
  causes of, 1166–1167
  consequences of, 1169–1170

  COR theory and, 1162
  definition of, 1160–1161
  education level and, 1164–1165
  employability and, 1169
  environmental sources of, 1166
  as hindrance, 1171–1172
  income inequality and, 195–196
  individual sources of, 1164–1166
  involuntary nature of, 1161
  job preservation and, 1168
  job-related sources of, 1166
  justice and, 1163
  labor unions and, 1167–1168
  latent deprivation theory and, 1162
  moderator variables and, 1170–1171
  organizational behavior and, 1163
  organizational sources of, 1166
  outcomes associated with, 1170*t*
  problematic aspects of, 1161–1164
  psychological contracts and, 1163
  relevance of, 1160
  SDT and, 1162
  SIT and, 1163–1164
  social attitudes and, 1163–1164
  spillover to family, society, and career, 1168–1169
  strain and, 1162–1163, 1167
  subjectivity of, 1161
  theoretical frameworks of, 1165*t*
  transactional stress theory and, 1162–1163
  turnover and, 1167
  voting behavior and, 1169
job knowledge tests, 1149
job market size, overqualification and, 1203–1204
job navigation, gender and, 579–583
job performance. *See also* performance management
  agreeableness as predictor of, 1146
  conscientiousness as predictor of, 1146
  dimensions of, 1141–1142, 1142*f*
  elements of, 1319–1320
  emotional stability as predictor of, 1146
  goal setting theory and, 112
  older workers and, 620–621
  overqualification and, 1207
  personnel selection and measurement of, 1141–1143, 1151–1153, 1152*t*
  political skill as predictor of, 490–491, 490*f*
  team job crafting and, 721
  telework/remote work impacts on, 770–771
  well-being and, 1521–1522, 1528–1531
job preservation, job insecurity and, 1168
job redesign, 1358, 1509–1510
  stress management and, 1404–1405

job resources. *See also* job demands-resources model;
resources
  burnout and, 690
  definition of, 690, 709
Jobs, Steve, 927–928
job satisfaction
  definition of, 1516–1517
  downward communication and, 979
  home-based telework/remote work and, 766
  intrinsic and extrinsic, 1516–1517
  organizational behavior and, 956–957
  overqualification and, 1204
job search, overqualification and, 1202
job security, overqualification and, 1204–1205
job skill training, 1454
job stereotype content, 639
Johnson, G. J., 1204–1205, 1209
Johnson, W. R., 1204–1205, 1209
Johnston, W., 541
joint optimization, 80
joint reviewing, multi-organizational groups and,
  381–382
Jones, A. P., 885
Jones, E. E., 798*t*, 799–803, 801*t*, 806
Jones, G. R., 289–291
Jones, J. E., 1627
Journal of Applied Psychology, 9, 16–17, 287–288
Journal of Personality and Social Psychology, 208–209
Journal of Personnel Research, 9
judgment and decision-making (JDM)
  aggregation and, 402
  associative-memory processes in, 393–394
  CRT and, 398–399
  diminishing sensitivity and, 396
  domain-specific expertise in, 403–404
  dual system theories of, 398–400
  emotional and motivational processes in, 396–397
  external interventions for improving, 401–402
  fast and slow thinking in, 398
  focus of, 392
  gain-loss framing and, 395
  for goal setting, 406–407
  improving, 401–404
  internal interventions for improving, 402–404
  for job candidate evaluation, 405–406
  learning environments and expertise in, 400–401
  loss aversion and, 395–396
  naturalistic, 403
  needs and desires and, 397
  in OP, 404
  overview of, 391
  prospect theory and, 395–396, 395*f*

  psychological processes in, 393–398
  psychophysical processes in, 394–397
  quantitative models for, 402
  rational models of, 391–393
  representativeness and, 392–393
  for retirement savings, 404–405
  risk aversion and, 394–395
  rule-based processes in, 397–399
  search in, 394
  workplace applications of, 404–407
judgment-driven behaviors, 450–451
justice. *See also* organizational justice
  climate, 884–888, 1045–1046
  climate strength, 889–891
  dark side of, 1066
  definition of, 50
  deontic model of, 927, 1071–1072
  distributive, 881–883, 1063–1065, 1150–1151
  employee behavior predicted by, 879–880
  as ethical dimension, 50
  at individual level, 881–884
  informational, 882–883
  interactional, 882–883, 1066–1067
  inter-group, 891–893
  interpersonal, 882–883
  job insecurity and, 1163
  orientation, 1069–1070
  overall, 883–884
  parallelism between justice in teams and individual,
    888–889
  peer, 891–893
  perceptions, 1068–1070
  proactive, 1068–1069
  procedural, 882–884, 1065–1066, 1150–1151
  rewards and, 128
  uncertainty reduced by, 1072
justice in teams
  ASA model and, 886–887
  birth and early stages of, 884–888
  change process fairness climate and, 889
  dispersion and, 891
  expansion of scientific knowledge and, 880
  faultlines, subgroups and, 890–891
  future research on, 889–893
  inter-group justice and, 891–893
  justice climate strength and outcomes of, 889–891
  LMX and, 891
  member diversity and, 891
  organizational climate and, 885–888
  overview of, 879–881
  parallelism between individual justice and, 888–889
  peer justice and, 891–893

justice in teams (*continued*)
    research technique development and, 880–881
    sense-making and, 885–886
    shift towards, 880
    structuralist approach for, 887
    symbolic interaction approach for, 885–886
just-in-time workforce, 786

Kahn, R. L., 1620
Kahn, W. A., 1294, 1300–1301
Kahneman, Daniel, 399
    on associative-memory processes in JDM, 394
    on diminishing marginal utility, 395
    on dual system theories of JDM, 398
    on interviews, 405
    on limited rationality, 14
    on prospect theory, 395–396
    on rational models of JDM, 392–393
    on System 1 and System 2 thinking, 34–35
    on theory-induced blindness, 111
kaleidoscope careers, 1226
Kalleberg, A. L., 1136–1137
Kandola, R., 538
Kant, Immanuel, 943
Kantrowitz, T., 1275
Karasek, R. A., 688
Kässi, O., 762
Kassing, Jeffrey, 984
Katz, D., 1620
Keats, John, 376
Keeney, Ralph, 403–404
Kelcey, B., 270
Kelly, J., 88
Kelman, H. C., 63
Kenny, D. A., 208–210
Key Performance Indicators (KPIs), 1276–1278
keystroke-level model, HCI and, 737
Khoury, C., 1461–1463
Kiersztyn, A., 1200
Killman, R. H., 1031
King, Martin Luther, Jr., 14
King, Z., 1232
Kirkpatrick, D. L., 1188
Klein, Gary, 403
Klein, K. J., 537–538
Knight, Bobby, 927–928
Knight, C., 1298–1299
know-how, young workers and, 597–598
knowledge, skills, and abilities (KSAs), 26, 832, 847
knowledge, skills, attitudes, and other characteristics
    (KSAOs), 866–867
knowledge economy, 332

knowledge generation and translation, EDMP, 37f, 42–43
knowledge transfer, age and, 624
know-whom, young workers and, 598–600
know-why, young workers and, 600–601
Koen, J., 1233
Kondratieff cycles, 94
Kooij, D. T., 716
Koppess Bryan, L. L., 1140
Korsgaard, S., 309
Kotter, J. P., 1125–1126
Kowalski, R. M., 798t, 801t, 802
Kozlowski, S. W., 287–288
KPIs (Key Performance Indicators), 1276–1278
Kraepelin, Emil, 7, 18–19
Kraiger, K., 1177–1178, 1182, 1187–1188
KSAOs (knowledge, skills, attitudes, and other
    characteristics), 866–867
KSAs (knowledge, skills, and abilities), 26, 832, 847

labels, sense-making and, 1005
Laboratory for Industrial Psychotechnology, 8–9
labor supply, globalization and, 330
labor unions, job insecurity and, 1167–1168
lack of fit theory, 573
LaHuis, D. M., 261
Lahy, Jean Maurice, 7, 19
laissez-faire leadership, 1434
language, sense-making and, 1005–1007
Larson, Wilhoit, 987
late career norms, older workers and changing, 626–627
latent change score (LCS) models, 219
latent class analysis, 244
latent deprivation theory, 1162
latent growth curve mediation models, 219
latent mean invariance, 243–244
latent profile analysis (LPA), 342–343, 1449
latent transition analysis, 244
lateral communication in organizations
    concept of, 984–986
    sense-making and grapevine communication in, 985
    telework and, 988–989
    troublesome peers and, 985–986
Latham, Gary P., 115–117, 288–289, 354, 406
Lau, D. C., 890
"Lavender Scare," 660
Lawler, E., 1109–1110, 1508–1509
law of comparative feeling, 152
Lawrence, B. S., 639
Lawrence, J. W., 1637
Lawson, M. A., 399–400
Lazarus, R. S., 448–449
LCS (latent change score) models, 219

leader and follower moral disengagement, 940
leader bullying, 921. *See also* abusive supervision
leader-follower relationships
    ethical leadership shaping, 942
    respect in, 943
leader-leader exchange (LLX), 721
leader-member exchange (LMX), 967
    downward communication and, 980–981
    ethical leadership and, 940–941
    justice in teams and, 891
    partnerships of, 980–981
    positive dyadic leadership and, 906
    workplace safety and, 1353
leader moral identity, 940
leadership. *See also* abusive supervision; ethical
    leadership; positive leadership
    abusive, 968
    adverse job demand reductions for, 1604
    age and, 624
    authentic, 163, 942–943
    change-oriented, 938–939
    contingency theory and development of, 15
    creativity at work fostered by, 1312
    cross-cultural IWOP, globalization and, 357–358
    definition of, 525 n.1
    development of, 967
    EDMP in development of, 25–26, 37f, 43–44
    emotions at work and, 453–454
    etic and emic, 357–358
    eudaimonic well-being and, 1527–1528
    framing, 981–982
    gendered perceptions and, 580
    of generative emergence, 1583–1585, 1584t
    hedonic well-being and, 1526–1527
    humility, 163
    identity, 907–908
    implicit theories of, 639
    laissez-faire, 1434
    Machiavellianism and, 510–512
    managerial leadership development, 1179
    narcissism and, 508–509, 516
    organizational change and, 1641
    organizational climate and, 1047–1048
    participative, 79
    participatory organizational interventions for,
      1602–1604, 1604t
    passive-avoidant, 1434–1435
    person-oriented, 937–938
    political skill in, 494–495
    psychopathy and, 513–515
    in PWO studies, 163
    resources increased for, 1603

respectful, 943
role congruity theory and, 572
romance of, 910–911
safety, 1353, 1485–1486
SDT research in workplace and, 126
servant, 942–943
SGM discrimination in promotions to, 650–651
shared, 1486
social identity model of, 907–908
task-oriented, 937–939
team job crafting and, 720–721
teams and, 840, 868–869, 967–968
telework/remote work and, 765, 772–773
time in organizational psychology and, 285–286
"tough love," 921
transformational compared to transactional, 126, 580,
    1485–1486
unethical, 943–944
virtual teams and, 868–869
workplace bullying and, 1434–1435
leaky pipeline, 579–580
Leana, C., 712t, 721
Lean In (Sandberg, S.), 583–584
learning
    action, 1181
    action regulation for, 105
    active, 1179–1180
    definition of, 1177–1178
    from emergence, 1585–1587
    in goal setting theory, 114
    intentional and unintentional organizational,
      1560–1561
    JDM and, 400–401
    job design promoting, 692, 696
    motivation for, 1184–1185
    population-level, 1559
    training and, 1177–1179
    variability in, 1181
    vicarious, 422–423
    virtual teams and, 868
Leary, M. R., 798t, 801t, 802–806
Leboyer, Claude Levy, 19
Lee, S. J., 798t
Lefkowitz, J., 57
    ethical decision-making model of, 68–69
    on values in education, 63
legalistic approach to ethical dilemmas, 66–67
legislation
    on disabilities at work, 668
    EU anti-discrimination, 532
    SGMs and employment, 659–660
legitimate power, 965–966

legitimating, 966
Lehdonvirta, V., 762
Leifer, R., 1576t
Leiter, M. P., 1292–1293, 1296, 1451
Lent, R. W., 1224–1225, 1229
Leroy, S., 289–291
lesbian workers. *See* sexual and gender minorities
letters of recommendation, gender differences in, 578
Leventhal, G. S., 882, 1065–1066
Levinson, Harry, 1625–1626, 1637
Lewin, Kurt, 10
    on conflict, 1025–1026
    field theory and, 465–466, 1400
    force field analysis and, 1402–1403
    on justice in teams and organizational climate, 885
    on OD, 1615, 1623–1625, 1635–1639
    on sociotechnical perspective, 11
    on temporal dimensions of planned change, 1564
    on T-groups, 12
Leymann, H., 1429, 1432–1433
Leymann Inventory of Psychological Terror, 1430
LGBTIQ workers. *See* sexual and gender minorities
Li, C., 338
Li, X. H., 338
Liang, X., 338
Liao, C., 1300
Licht, J. G., 289–291
Lichtenstein, B., 1566, 1576t
Licklider, Joseph Carl Robnett, 729
life-course perspective, on retirement, 1258–1259
life expectancy increases, 625
life satisfaction, 1517
life-span developmental theories
    action regulation and, 105–106
    motivation and, 601
    older workers and, 616–617
    selection-optimization-compensation, 616
    socioemotional selectivity, 616–617
    young workers and, 597
life stages, 1228
lifestyle, personality and, 563
Likert, Rensis, 13, 1624–1625, 1628, 1637
Lindholm, R., 90
line-by-line coding, 305–307
Linnenberg, M. S., 309
Lipmann, O., 18–19
Lippitt, G., 1631–1632
Lippitt, R., 11, 1631–1632, 1636
Litvin, D. R., 531–532, 533t
livelihood insecurity, 195
living wage, 191–192
LLX (leader-leader exchange), 721

LMX. *See* leader-member exchange
loading invariance, 243–244
Locke, Ed A., 116, 288–289, 354, 406
Locke, K., 309, 313–315, 317–318
logic model for EDMP, 39–40, 39f
logrolling behavior, 1031
Lomov, Boris F., 18
longitudinal data, qualitative research standards for, 321t
longitudinal mediation, 218–220
longitudinal research, on HRM, 1118–1119
Lorenz, E. N., 1566
Lorsch, P. R., 1637
loss aversion, JDM and, 395–396
Low, J. O., 9–10
Lowery, M., 541–542
LPA (latent profile analysis), 342–343, 1449

Macey, W. H., 1293–1294
MacGregor, Douglas, 13
Machiavelli, Niccolo, 510–511
Machiavellianism, 957
    abusive supervision and, 511
    CWBs and, 511–512, 1322–1323
    definition of, 506–507
    employees and, 512–513
    leadership and, 510–512
    moral behavior and, 511
    organizational citizenship behavior challenged by, 512–513
    in workplace, 510–513
MacIntosh, R., 1576t
MacLean, D., 1576t
MacRae, I., 564–565
macrosystems, 1371
main comparison, 232
main effect contrast, moderator variables and, 232–233
mainstream diversity literature, 542–545, 544t
main workplace, 757
Makice, K., 331
Mäkikangas, A., 1300
making codes, 309
malicious envy, 821
The Managed Heart (Hochschild), 447, 457–458
management and managers. *See also* boundary
    management; diversity management; human
    resource management; impression management;
    performance management; stress management
    in absence of EDMP, 31–36
    change, OD as, 1640
    compensation and, 336–337
    consultant authority bias, 32f, 33
    craft model of, 31, 32f, 44
    EDMP in, 27–28

epistemic beliefs of, 35–36
expertise fallacy, 32*f*, 35
feedback and, 1279, 1281
generalizability in cross-cultural settings, 338–339
globalization, uncertainty and, 333
implicit evidence hierarchies of, 32*f*, 35–36
job crafting and, 718
leadership development of, 1179
middle managers initiating change, 1560
need support, 125–126
non-probabilistic reasoning of, 32*f*, 36
organizational career, 1234–1235
of PCS, 1135–1137
performance, 335–337
political skill for, 493
safety, 1490–1491
stakeholder-forced turnover of top, 1561
symbolic, 32*f*, 33
telework/remote work and, 765, 772–773
time, 1403–1404
training of, 1179
workplace bullying and, 1434–1435
Management by Participation (Marrow), 1638
Management Information Systems Quarterly, 1586
Management of Differences Exercise (MODE), 1031
Management Standards, 1598–1599
"man-computer symbiosis," 729
mandatory retirement, 1255
man-machine interfaces, 729
Mann, Floyd, 1624–1625, 1629–1630
Manstead, A. S., 798*t*
March, J. G., 10–11, 1557–1558
Marcuse, Herbert, 15
Margolis, J. D., 167
marital status, gender and, 1202
Marrow, Alfred, 1615, 1625, 1637–1638
Martin, J., 453
Martinko, M. J., 801*t*, 803
Marx, Karl, 5, 1465–1466
Maslach, C., 1292–1293, 1296, 1451
Maslach Burnout Inventory (MBI), 1292–1295,
    1447–1449
Maslach Burnout Inventory-General Scale (MBI-GS),
    1294, 1447
Maslow, Abraham, 12, 961, 1636
maternity, gender in organizations and, 581
"Matthew effect," 1231–1232
Mauno, S., 1168–1169
MAV (mindfulness-, acceptance-, and value-based
    intervention), 1454
Maxwell, S. E., 213
Mayer, J., 447, 452, 456

Mayer-Salovey-Caruso Emotional Intelligence Test
    (MSCEIT), 456
Maynard, D. C., 1197–1198, 1209, 1211–1212
Mayo, George Elton, 9, 685
MBI (Maslach Burnout Inventory), 1292–1295,
    1447–1449
MBI-GS (Maslach Burnout Inventory-General Scale),
    1294, 1447
MBTI (Myers-Brigg Type Inventory), 553
McCall, L., 536–537
McGregor, D. M., 686, 961, 978
McKinsey, 1640
McNeish, D., 270–271
MDGs (millennium development goals), 185, 187
meaning at work, 1518–1519
meaningfulness, stress management and, 1410
measurement errors, in multilevel modeling methods,
    270–271
measurement model, in SEM, 242–243
mechanical, shift to digital over, 1639
mechanistic dehumanization, 1461, 1473
media naturalness, ICTs and, 865
media richness, ICTs and, 864–865
media synchronicity, ICTs and, 865–866
mediated effect, 211, 213
mediated moderation, 244–245
mediation
    analysis, 207–208
    in conflict resolution, 1036
    postphenomenology and, 735–736
mediator variables
    autoregressive models and, 219, 220*f*
    Bayesian statistics and, 216–217
    bootstrapping and, 215–216
    categorical, 217
    causal, 220–221
    Causal Steps Test and, 208–212, 210*f*
    CBT and, 207–208, 228–229
    challenges with, 221–223
    change score models and, 218–219
    complete/incomplete mediation and, 210
    computationally intensive tests and, 216–217
    conditional process model and, 218, 244–245
    consistent/inconsistent mediation and, 211
    definition of, 207–208
    direct effect and, 210
    Distribution of the Product Test and, 215
    double randomization and, 214
    First-Order Standard Error Test and, 211, 214–215
    latent growth curve models and, 219
    LCS models and, 219
    longitudinal, 218–220

1692 • INDEX

mediator variables (*continued*)
  measurement challenges with, 222
  mediated effect and, 211, 213
  moderator variables compared to, 208–209, 228–229
  multilevel, 217–218
  multiple studies and designs of, 223
  of overqualification, 1210
  parallel mediator model and, 212–213, 212f
  parallel process models and, 219–220
  path model diagram of, 209f, 229f
  sensitivity analysis and, 222–223
  serial mediator model and, 211–212, 212f
  single-mediator model and, 208–211
  in teamwork, 842–844, 850t
  temporal design and, 213–214, 222
  temporal precedence and, 213
  trajectory growth curve models and, 219
medical-care institutions, authority for change in, 1555
Medicare, 1262–1263
medicine, EDMP in, 25, 27
meditation, 1412, 1454
Melburg, V., 801–803, 801t
member characteristics, teamwork, 836–837
member check, in analysis, 316
member diversity, justice in teams and, 891
MEMEX, 729
memoing, 313–315, 317
men. *See* gender in organizations
menopause, gender in organizations and, 581
menstruation, gender in organizations and, 581
mental health, workplace bullying and, 1431
mental illness, gender and, 581–582
mentors, 1600
  gender differences in access to, 580–581
mesosystems, 1371
meta-cognitive bias, 32f, 35
meta-cognitive heuristics, 103
meta-cognitive skills, in EDMP, 37f, 41
metaknowledge, 870
metaphors, sense-making and, 1005–1006
metastereotypes, age, 642–643
Metcalfe, Henry, 5
methodological appropriateness, 38–39
methodological pluralism, 30
#MeToo Movement, 581
Meyer, A., 1576t
Meyer, J. P., 212
Michigan Job Crafting Exercise (JCE), 722
Michigan Model, 688
microaggressions, 651–653
micro-CSR, 1087–1089
micro-experiments, in generative emergence, 1574–1577

micro-political CSR, 1091
Microsoft, 1080–1081
microsystems, 1371
middle managers, organizational change and, 1560
Midvale Steel plant, 685
migrant status
  change effects of, 1561
  overqualification from, 1201
Miles, M. B., 1631
military organizations, authority for change in, 1554
military psychology, 10
Mill, John Stuart, 53–54
millennium development goals (MDGs), 185, 187
Miller, E., 84
Miller, G. A., 98
Millman, Z., 115–116
mimetic isomorphism, 1084
mindfulness, 1357–1358, 1454
  for stress management, 1412
mindfulness-, acceptance-, and value-based intervention
    (MAV), 1454
mindful organizing, sense-making and, 1010–1012, 1011f
Miner, A. S., 1559
minimum wage, 191–192
minority stress model, 652
Mira-y-Lopez, Emilio, 19
Mission Church, 1580–1583
mixed models, 240–241
Moag, J. S., 882–883
mobile phones, HCI and, 730
mobile telework and remote work, 756–757, 766–769
mobile virtual teams, 758–759
MODE (Management of Differences Exercise), 1031
moderated mediation, 244–245
moderator variables
  categorical by categorical (2x2) interaction models
      and, 229–232, 231f
  categorical by categorical (3x3) interaction models
      and, 232–233
  challenges with, 245–248
  conditional process model and, 218, 244–245
  continuous by categorical interaction models and,
      233–236, 234f
  continuous by continuous interaction models and,
      236–238, 237f
  cross-level interaction and, 242
  curvilinear change and, 239–240, 239f
  definition of, 208, 228–229
  in experimental psychology, 228
  in interaction models, 229–240
  job insecurity and, 1170–1171
  main effect contrast and, 232–233

mediator variables compared to, 208–209, 228–229
multicollinearity and, 247
multilevel, 240–242
of overqualification, 1210–1211
path model diagram of, 209f, 229f
post hoc tests and, 233
in SEM, 244–245
simple main effects and, 230–231
standardized interaction coefficients and, 238
statistical power and, 246–247
three-way interaction models and, 239–240
too many, 247–248
treatment interaction and, 246
Moede, Walter, 7, 18–19
molar climate, 1044, 1047–1048
Monk, Andrew, 732
monophonic change, 1564
Monte Carlo confidence intervals, 264–266, 269–270
mood, emotion compared to, 448
Moore, G. E., 53
moral behavior. *See also* ethical leadership
AET and, 430–431
CWBs and, 435
feelings and, 430
future research on, 440–441
incivility and, 435–436
leader and follower moral disengagement, 940
leader moral identity, 940
Machiavellianism and, 511
moral credentials, 1328
moral credits, 1328
moral emotions and outcomes of, 434–437, 440f
moral foundations theory, 943
moral hygiene and ethical reasoning, 68
moral justification, 1325
moral licensing, 437–440, 1327–1329
moral maturity, 939
moral philosophy, 49–50
moral psychology, 49–50, 67
moral realism, 52
moral virtue/character, 51
organizational citizenship behavior, 430, 436, 439–440
self-regulatory system of, 437–438
unethical pro-organizational behaviors, 436
moral disengagement, 437–440
behavioral ethics and, 437
future research on, 440
leader and follower, 940
moral emotions and, 437–439
strategies, 437–438
unethical leadership and, 944
unethical pro-organizational behaviors and, 436

moral emotions
behavioral outcomes of, 434–437, 440f
compassion and empathy, 432–433, 438–439
definition of, 431
future research on, 440–441
gratitude, 434
guilt and shame, 431–432, 439
moral disengagement and, 437–439
"Robin Hood Effect" and, 438
Morewedge, Carey, 403
Morgeson, F. P., 691, 694
Morrison, E. W., 1131
motivation. *See also* self-determination theory
approach and avoidance, 416–418
autonomous, 121–122, 127–128, 130, 419, 969
contemporary theories of, 961
controlled, 121
control theory and, 416
creativity at work and, 1310–1311
for CSR, 1085–1086
culture and, 424
defining, 411–412
discrepancies stimulating, 416
equity theory and, 962
expectancy theory and, 15, 414, 962–963
extrinsic, 122, 419–420, 422
goal setting/choice and, 414, 421–422
goal striving and, 414–416
implementation intentions for, 415, 422–423
as individual difference at work, 551
intrinsic, 121, 419, 422, 1306–1307
in JDM, 396–397
job characteristics and, 420–421, 673–674
job crafting and, 716–717
for learning, 1184–1185
life-span developmental theories and, 601
multiple goals and, 413
older workers and, 616–619
organizational behavior and, 960–963
phases of, 413–416
practices for influencing, 421–423
prosocial, 1310–1311
qualitative view on, 132–133
QWL concept influenced by theory of, 1500
resource replenishment for, 423
safety, 1483
SDT on workplace and, 123–125, 124f
self-efficacy and, 422–423, 962–963
for social comparison, 817–818
social factors and, 421
social learning theory and, 962
for telework, 762

motivation (*continued*)
 training, older workers and, 618–619
 for training, 1184–1185
 two-factor theory of, 686–687, 961
 virtual teams and, 871
 X-Y theory of, 961
 of young workers, 601–603
motivational resources, for retirement, 1258
motivation-hygiene theory, 12
Mount, M. K., 1146
Mouton, J. S., 1631, 1637
moving places, 757
MSCEIT (Mayer-Salovey-Caruso Emotional Intelligence
 Test), 456
MSEM (multilevel structural equation modeling), 270–271
MTSs (multi-team systems), 847
Mueller-Hanson, R. A., 1275–1276, 1278–1280
multicollinearity, moderator variables and, 247
multilevel mediation, 217–218
multilevel modeling methods
 baseline model with random intercepts, 256–258
 complex, 264–269
 cross-level moderation in 1-1-1 mediation, 268–269
 for CSR, 1093
 for HRM, 1117–1118
 for identity management, 654
 intercepts-and-slopes-as-outcomes model, 263–264
 intercepts-as-outcomes model, 261–263
 limitations of, 270–271
 logic underlying, 254–256, 254f, 255f
 measurement and sampling errors in, 270–271
 Monte Carlo confidence intervals and, 264–266,
  269–270
 OLS regression and, 253
 1-1-1 mediation, 265f, 267t, 268–269
 one-way ANCOVA model with random effects,
  258–260
 overview of, 253–254
 for positive leadership, 902–904, 903f
 random coefficients and, 256
 random-coefficients regression model, 260–261
 random effects and, 256
 research opportunities with, 271–272
 sample sizes for, 264
 sample sizes for complex, 269–270
 SPSS syntax to estimate, 272
 2-1-1 mediation, 265f, 266–268, 267t
 2-2-1 mediation, 265f, 266, 267t
 variance-covariance components of, 256
multilevel moderation, 240–242
multilevel structural equation modeling (MSEM),
 270–271

multi-organizational group dynamics
 action research and, 382–383
 collaboration and, 371–372
 defensive avoidance and, 378
 dual conflict in, 372–373, 380
 exclusion in, 381
 groupthink and, 374
 highway project example of, 377–379
 intergroup relations and, 373–374
 intergroup stereotyping in, 380
 joint reviewing and, 381–382
 multi-teams and, 374
 narcissism and, 381
 in network society, 371
 overview of, 371, 382–383
 in practice, 377–382
 public authority and, 381
 scapegoating in, 377–378
 shared problem definition in, 372–373, 380
 social psychological perspective on, 373–375
 systems levels of, 372
 systems-psychodynamic perspective on, 375–379
 table convening representatives from, 372, 372f
 Yacht Club simulation for, 379–382
multiple goals, 413
multiple-group analysis, SEM and, 243
multiplicative spillover, 1377
multi-teams, 374
multi-team systems (MTSs), 847
"mum effect," 982
Mumford, E., 92
Mumford, M. D., 1308–1309
Münsterberg, Hugo, 7–8, 18–19, 353
Murnighan, J. K., 890
mutual adaptation, 1130
mutual investment, 1136
mutual trust, 1033
Myers, Charles S., 8–9
Myers-Brigg Type Inventory (MBTI), 553
Myokinetic Apperception Test, 19

NA (negative affectivity), 1517–1518
Nadkarni, S., 289–291
Nadler, David, 1624–1625, 1629–1630
name-calling, 1426
NAQ-R/NAQ (Negative Acts Questionnaire), 1430
narcissism, 957
 CEO, 509–510
 chocolate cake model of, 508–509
 CWBs and, 1322–1323
 definition of, 506–507
 employee behavior and, 510

grandiose, 509
leadership and, 508–509, 516
multi-organizational groups and, 381
overqualification and, 1203
research into, 517–518
vulnerable, 509, 517–518
in workplace, 508–510
narcissistic personality disorder, 566t
narratives, sense-making and, 1006
National Bureau of Economic Research, 577
National Institute for Occupational Safety and Health, 1384–1385, 1533–1534
National Institute of Industrial Psychology, 8–9
nationalism, 15–16
naturalistic decision making, 403
Naumann, S. E., 885–887, 889
Neal, A., 1352
need frustration, 131–133
needs and desires, JDM and, 397
need satisfaction, 131
profiles of, 133
well-being and, 131–132
Needs Identification Phase, in TNA, 1183–1184
Needs Specification Phase, in TNA, 1183–1184
needs-supplies (NS) fit, 472–473, 475
need support, 125–126
Negative Acts Questionnaire (NAQ-R/NAQ), 1430
negative affectivity (NA), 1517–1518
negative capability, 376
negative time aspects, 284–285
negativity, in letters of recommendation, 578
negotiation
for conflict resolution, 1036
distributive, 1036
gendered differences in, 579
integrative, 1036
Nepper, Henri, 8–9
Netherlands, IOR and, 91–92
Netherlands Institute for the Improvement of the Quality of Work and Organization (NKWO), 92
net promoter score (NPS), 1282
Nettle, D., 553–554
networking ability, 486–487, 1233
network perspectives, on communication in organizations, 986
network society, 371
neurosciences, OP and, 16
neuroticism
disorders associated with, 558
EPP labeling facets of, 558
evolutionary perspective on, 553–554
HEXACO model for, 558

high, average, low levels of, 554t
overview of, 558
positive and negative consequences of, 555t
work outcomes and, 556, 557t
work success and, 562
Neutral Objects Satisfaction Questionnaire, 148
Nevo, B., 1198, 1207, 1212
Nielsen, K., 1600
Niessen, C., 712t
Niles, F. S., 424
Nilles, J. M., 754–756, 762–763
Nisbett, Richard, 403
Nixon, A. E., 1341
NKWO (Netherlands Institute for the Improvement of the Quality of Work and Organization), 92
Nobo, Norway, 85
Noe, R. A., 1178
No Grow dimension, of overqualification, 1197–1198
nomads, 757
Nonaka, I., 1576t
non-contingent pay, 128–129
nonessential multicollinearity, 247
nonmaleficence
ethics of care and, 51
universalism and, 51–52
nonparticipation in labor force, 1252–1253
non-probabilistic reasoning, 32f, 36
non-profit organizations, authority for change in, 1555
nonstandard employment, of young workers, 596
nontraditional work/employment, 785. *See also* informal work
non-university schools, authority for change in, 1555
normalizing, in identity management, 654
Norman, Donald, 732–733
normative ethical models, 54–55
normative isomorphism, 1084
Norsk Hydro fertilizer company, Norway, 85–86
Norsk Medisinaldepot, 86
Norstedt, J., 90
Norway, female CEOs in, 585
Norwegian studies on sociotechnical approach, 84–86, 1503
noticing and bracketing, in sense-making, 1003–1004
NPS (net promoter score), 1282
NS (needs-supplies) fit, 472–473, 475
null model, 256–258

OAR (overall assessment rating), 1149–1150
OB. *See* organizational behavior
Obergefell v Hodges, 660
objective career success, 1229–1230
objective overqualification, 1198
objective PE fit, 467–468, 470

objective time, 281, 285–286, 293
objectivism, 52
observations
  for data collection, 1628
  in systems-psychodynamics, 376
obsessive-compulsive personality disorder, 566t
OCB. *See* organizational citizenship behavior
OCB-I (interpersonal OCB), 436
occasional teleworkers, 756
occupational future time perspective, 284–285
occupational health, 358–360
  gender differences in, 581–582
  organizational-level interventions for, 1413–1414
occupational health psychology (OHP)
  definition of, 1339–1340
  flexible work arrangements and, 1356–1357
  occupational stress in, 1350–1351
  organizational interventions for, 1357–1358
  positive psychology on, 1353–1355
  work-family conflict and, 1355–1356
  work-family enrichment and, 1356
  workplace safety and, 1351–1353
occupational stress
  burnout from, 1342–1343
  challenge-hindrance model on, 1347
  COR theory on, 1345–1346
  DC and DCS models of, 1344–1345, 1345t
  effort-recovery theory on, 1347–1348
  emotional labor and, 1348–1349
  globalization and, 358–360
  health, well-being and impact of, 1340–1343, 1341t
  job demands-resources model on, 1346–1347
  overview of, 1340–1351
  as process, 1340
  psychosocial safety climate and, 1350–1351
  role theory on, 1344
  sources of, 1340
  theories of, 1343–1348
  transactional model of, 1343–1344
  workplace harassment and, 1349–1350
OD. *See* organization development
OECD Guidelines to Multinational Enterprises, 188
"office buzz," 985
Office of Research Integrity, 64
OHP. *See* occupational health psychology
OIT (organismic integration theory), 122, 124
OLBI (Oldenburg Burnout Inventory), 1297
old age dependency ratio, 626
Oldenburg Burnout Inventory (OLBI), 1297
older workers. *See also* retirement
  age discrimination and, 623–624
  age diversity climate and, 624–625

age diversity in workplace and, 624
age stereotypes and, 621–623
bridge employment and, 1256–1257, 1264
changing perceptions on, 627
cognitive changes of, 615
definitions of, 614
demographic transitions and, 625–626
health and, 621
individual context for, 615–617
job attitude changes of, 619–620
job crafting and, 718–719
job performance and, 620–621
knowledge transfer and, 624
late career and retirement norm changes and, 626–627
life-span developmental theories and, 616–617
motivation and, 616–619
multilevel context for, 614–615
organizational context for, 617–625
overqualification and, 1203
overview of, 613–614
pension system changes and, 626
personality changes of, 615–616
physical changes of, 615
psychological contracts and, 627–628
shiftwork and, 621
societal context for, 625–628
systems approach to development and, 614–615
training motivation and, 618–619
in work and family issues, 1369
Oldham, G. R., 420–421, 673–674, 695
  JCM of, 687–688, 698–700
"old wine in new bottles" argument, 911–912
OLI (Online Labour Index), 762
OLOH (organizational-level occupational health)
  interventions, 1413–1414
OLS (ordinary least squares) regression, 253
on-demand work, 786
1-1-1 multilevel mediation model, 265f, 267t, 268–269
One Dimensional Man (Marcuse), 15
one-way ANCOVA model with random effects, 258–260
one-way ANOVA model, 256–258
ongoing progress monitoring, 1278–1279
Online Labour Index (OLI), 762
on-site movers, 757
on-the-job support, gender and, 585
ontological oscillation, sense-making and, 1000
OP. *See* organizational psychology
open coding, 313, 318
open-ended future time perspective, 284–285
open hiring, disabilities and, 670
openness to experience
  evolutionary perspective on, 553–554

high, average, low levels of, 554*t*
intelligence and, 560
investment theory and, 559
literature on, 559–560
overview of, 559–560
positive and negative consequences of, 555*t*
work outcomes and, 556, 557*t*
opportunity to perform, 1186
opportunity to prevent harm, 59–61*t*
optimism, in psychological capital, 161
option attractiveness, 1009
ordinal interaction, 230–231, 231*f*
ordinary least squares (OLS) regression, 253
Oreg, S., 1641
organismic integration theory (OIT), 122, 124
organizational assessment, in training needs assessment, 1183
organizational behavior (OB). *See also* organizational citizenship behavior
  affect and, 958–959
  affect and decision-making in, 960–961
  diversity and, 956
  emotional intelligence, emotional labor and, 959
  emotions and, 958–959
  employee values and, 957–958
  group decision-making and, 963–964
  HRM and, 1107
  job insecurity and, 1163
  job satisfaction and, 956–957
  macro (organizational) level of, 968–971
  meso (group) level of, 963–968
  micro (individual) level of, 956–963
  motivation and, 960–963
  organizational change and, 970–971
  in organizational climate and culture, 969–970
  organizational structure and, 968–969
  overview of, 879–881
  perception and, 959–960
  personality and, 957
  physical environment of work and, 969
  team performance and, 964–968
  work engagement and, 956–957
organizational career management, 1234–1235
organizational change
  authority and, 1555–1556
  behavior and, 970–971
  circumstance-based variations in power and, 1555–1556
  competence and, 1561
  continuous, 1565
  decline, death, rebirth as, 1566
  dialectical, 1565–1566

emergence of, 1566, 1574
emerging distinctions in types of, 1565
evidence supporting successful, 1641–1643
external environments and, 1557–1558
external impetuses for, 1556–1558
immigration and, 1561
intentional and unintentional organizational learning and, 1560–1561
internal environments and, 1560–1561
leadership and, 1641
middle managers and, 1560
non-hierarchical influence on, 1555–1556
OD and, 1562–1563, 1619–1620, 1621–1622*t*
organizational culture and, 1053–1054, 1562
organizational forgetting, intentional unlearning and, 1561
paradoxical, 1565–1566
planned, 1562–1564
population-level, 1559
radical, 1565
resistance and other responses to, 1563–1564
stakeholder-forced turnover of top management and, 1561
temporal dimensions of planned, 1564
threat-rigidity theory and, 1558
values and, 1561
organizational character, 909
organizational choice, 79–80
Organizational Choice (Trist), 79–80
organizational citizenship behavior (OCB). *See also* organizational behavior
  abusive supervision impact on, 944
  CWB and, 1320, 1327–1329
  ethical leadership impact on, 941–942
  interpersonal, 436
  Machiavellianism challenging, 512–513
  moral behavior and, 430, 436, 439–440
  moral licensing and, 439
  PE fit and, 470, 472
  positive dyadic leadership and, 906
organizational climate
  behavior and, 969–970
  boundary conditions and, 1046–1047
  climate strength and, 1046
  "climcult framework" for, 1054–1055
  definition of, 1044
  foundation issues in, 1047–1048
  interventions for improving, 1048–1049
  justice in teams and, 885–888
  leadership and, 1047–1048
  measurement of, 1044–1045
  moderation effects and, 1047

organizational climate (*continued*)
  multiple, simultaneous climates in, 1048–1049
  organizational culture and, 970, 1054–1055
  organizational dehumanization as, 1473
  organizational effectiveness and, 1047–1048
  overview of, 1044
  psychological climate compared to, 1044
  safety and, 1487
  well-being and, 1529–1530
organizational constraints, 1397–1398
organizational creativity
  componential theory of, 1306–1307
  interactionist theory of, 1307
organizational culture, 15–16
  ASA model and, 1050–1051
  behavior and, 969–970
  categories of, 1049–1050
  "climcult framework" for, 1054–1055
  cross-cultural IWOP, globalization and, 356–357
  CWBs and impact of, 1322
  definition of, 1049
  espoused values and, 1050, 1054–1055
  factors of, 1620
  founder's influence on, 1050–1051
  gender and, 585–586
  levels of, 1050
  OD and, 1620, 1621t
  organizational change and, 1053–1054, 1562
  organizational climate and, 970, 1054–1055
  organizational effectiveness and, 1052
  overview of, 1044
  positive organizational leadership and, 908–909
  safety and, 1487
  socialization and, 1051–1052
  subcultures and, 1052–1053
organizational death, 1566
organizational decline, 1566
organizational dehumanization
  abusive supervision and, 1471–1472
  animalistic and mechanistic, 1461, 1473
  antecedents of, 1469–1471
  behavioral impact of, 1467–1468
  conceptualization and operationalization of,
    1460–1462
  consequences of, 1467–1468
  environmental factors causing, 1470
  future research agenda on, 1473–1475
  gender and, 1471
  historical background of, 1460–1462
  individual factors causing, 1471
  informal work and, 1474
  interpersonal factors causing, 1470–1471

job attitudes and impact of, 1467
job characteristics causing, 1470
moderating mechanisms for, 1471–1473
nomological network of, 1466–1473, 1466f
organizational characteristics causing, 1470
as organizational climate, 1473
overview of, 1459–1460
perceived exploitation compared to, 1463–1464
POC compared to, 1464
POO compared to, 1463
POS compared to, 1463
processes linking outcomes to, 1468–1469
psychological capital and, 1472–1473
related constructs compared to, 1465–1466
scales measuring, 1461–1462, 1462t
self-determination theory and, 1468, 1474–1475
social exchange theory and, 1468, 1474
social identity theory and, 1468–1469, 1474
societal factors causing, 1469–1470
supervisor's organizational embodiment and,
    1471–1472
well-being impact of, 1466–1467
work alienation compared to, 1465–1466
working objectification compared to, 1464–1465
organizational demography, 639
Organizational Diagnosis (Levinson), 1625–1626
organizational dimensions, in four layers of diversity,
    531, 532f
organizational effectiveness
  organizational climate and, 1047–1048
  organizational culture and, 1052
organizational forgetting, 1561
organizational goals, talent strategies aligned to, 1287t
organizational health psychology, 16
organizational interventions. *See also* interventions;
    participatory organizational interventions
  for burnout, 1454–1455
  definition of, 1595
  evaluating effectiveness of, 1609–1610
  for flexible work arrangements, 1596–1597
  for occupational health psychology, 1357–1358
  overview of, 1595–1596
  program logic for, 1608–1609
  reviews of, 1606–1608
  for role clarification, 1596
  for self-scheduling, 1596–1597
  for shift changes, 1596–1597
  for social relationships, 1596
  for task characteristics, 1596
  working conditions targeted by, 1596–1597
organizational justice
  dimensionality of, 1067–1068

distributive justice and, 1063–1065
fairness judgments and, 1063
fair treatment's importance in, 1071–1072
fair treatment sources and, 1071
future directions of, 1072–1073
interactional justice and, 1066–1067
overview of, 1063
perceptions of, 1068–1070, 1328
principles of, 1067–1068
proactive, 1068–1069
procedural justice and, 1065–1066
processes linking outcomes to, 1069–1071
organizational learning, intentional and unintentional, 1560–1561
organizational-level occupational health (OLOH) interventions, 1413–1414
organizational mobility preference (physical mobility), 1221–1222
organizational performance
    HRM and outcomes of, 1112–1119
    overqualification and, 1209–1210
    telework/remote work impacts on, 770–771
organizational politics
    ethics and, 966–967
    political skill and, 966
    power and, 965–967
organizational psychology (OP). *See also* humanitarian work and organizational psychology; industrial, work, and organizational psychology; time in organizational psychology
    in Belgium, 19
    bureaucratic managerial model and, 6–7
    cognitive processes of decision-making and, 13–14
    consolidation period in, 14–15
    early uses of, 3–4
    expansion period of, 10–14
    in France, 19
    in Germany, 18–19
    handbooks on, 17
    humanistic psychology and, 12–13
    humanitarian work and, 184–197
    humanization of work in, 15
    human relations model and, 9–10
    human subject at work and, 7–8
    impact of, 15–16
    in Japan, 20
    JDM in, 404
    networks of researchers in, 20–21
    neurosciences and, 16
    OD and, 1614–1615
    overview of, 3–4
    recent developments in, 15–17

sociotechnical perspective of, 11–12
in Spain, 19
on stress at work, 1395–1396
study of formal organization of enterprises and, 6
study of scientific organization of work and, 5–6
in USSR/Russia, 17–18
World War I and, 8–9
World War II and, 10
Organizational Psychology (Schein), 10–11
organizational rebirth, 1566
organizational resilience, 774
organizational silence, upward communication and, 983
organizational structure, behavior and, 968–969
organizational subcultures, 1052–1053
organizational virtue, in PWO studies, 161–162
organization development (OD), 970–971
    action research and, 1625
    as change management, 1640
    consultant/practitioner competencies, 1634–1635
    contract in, 1627–1634
    data collection and diagnosis in, 1628–1629
    defining, 1614, 1619–1625
    dialogic, 1563
    effectiveness of, 1615, 1637–1638
    entry in, 1625–1627
    evaluation in, 1633
    evidence-based, 1640–1641
    evolution of, 1615
    feedback in, 1629–1630
    group relations, sociotechnical systems and, 1623–1624, 1633
    historical roots of, 1623–1625
    interventions in, 1630–1633
    knowledge for, 1634
    manufacturing case example of, 1616–1617
    medical school case example of, 1618–1620
    OP and, 1614–1615
    organizational change and, 1562–1563, 1619–1620
    organization history and, 1640
    overview of, 1614–1619
    positive psychology and, 1640
    readiness checklist in, 1627
    sensitivity training and, 1623
    skills for, 1635
    steps in, 1625–1634
    stress at work and frameworks of, 1396, 1397f
    survey feedback and, 1623–1625, 1633
    theoretical foundations of, 1635–1638
    trends in, 1638–1641
    trust in, 1626–1627
organization-focused stress management, 1415–1416
organization history, OD and, 1640

The Organization Man (Whyte, W. H., Jr.), 14–15
organizations. *See also* gender in organizations
    adverse job demand reductions for, 1605–1606
    autonomy activities for, 1604–1605
    business structures compared to, 1556
    characteristics of, 1553–1554
    decision neglect in, 35
    definition of, 3, 1553
    EDMP in, definition and key features, 27–29
    EDMP in capabilities framework of, 26–27, 36–44, 37*f*
    enactment-selection-retention process in, 998*f*,
        999–1000, 1002
    generically subjective of, 1000
    healthy, emotional climate and, 455
    intersubjective level of, 1000
    job insecurity sources in, 1166
    as open systems, 80
    participatory organizational interventions for,
        1605–1606, 1607*t*
    "refreezing," 1635–1636, 1639
    resources increased for, 1604–1605
    as role systems, 3–4
    seasonal, 1566
    sense-making perspective on, 998–1000
    systems, capabilities, and context of, 32*f*, 34
    "unfreezing," 1635–1636
Organizations (March and Simon), 10–11
organization-wide level of emotion, 454–455
organizing to code, 309
orientations, employee, 129–130
Orne, M. T., 63
orthogonal subcultures, 1052–1053
Ostroff, C., 1115–1118
other workplaces, 757
O'Toole, J., 1508–1509
Ouchi, W. G., 20
outcome expectations, in social cognitive career theory,
    1223–1225
outcome variables, 207, 228
Outlaw, R., 289–291
outputs, in teamwork, 845–846, 850*t*
overall assessment rating (OAR), 1149–1150
overall effect, in Causal Steps Test, 209, 210*f*
overall indirect effects, 213
overall justice, 883–884
overall regression models, 234
overconfidence bias, 960
overeducation, 1196–1197, 1199–1201
overextended worklife profile, 1449–1450
over-investment, 1136
overqualification
    absenteeism and, 1209

age and, 1202–1203
career mobility theory and, 1208
causes of, 1200–1204
cognitive, 1198
compensation and, 1206–1207
competitiveness and, 1208–1209
creativity and, 1207–1208
CWBs and, 1208
from education, 1200–1201
from experience, 1201–1202
forms of, 1196–1198
future research directions for, 1211–1213
gender and, 1202
group-level effects of, 1211
health, well-being and, 1205–1206
interpersonal relationships and, 1208–1209, 1211
job attitudes and, 1204
job characteristics and, 1203
job market size and, 1203–1204
job performance and, 1207
job satisfaction and, 1204
job search and, 1202
job security and, 1204–1205
measurement inconsistency of, 1212
measures of, 1196–1198
mediators of, 1210
micro and macro levels of investigation on, 1212–1213
from migrant status, 1201
moderators of, 1210–1211
national context and, 1204
No Grow dimension of, 1197–1198
objective, 1198
organizational performance and, 1209–1210
overeducation and, 1196–1197, 1199–1201
overview of, 1195–1196
past employment history and, 1203
peers' feelings of, 1210–1211
perceived, 1198, 1207–1208, 1210
personality and, 1203, 1211
proactivity and, 1207–1208
real and formal, 1198
recruitment and, 1211–1212
relative deprivation theory and, 1198–1199
sense of empowerment and, 1210
skill compensation theory and, 1201
status inconsistency theory and, 1199
as temporary or permanent, 1199–1200
theoretical foundations of, 1198–1199
training performance and, 1207
turnover and, 1209
as underemployment, 1195–1196
upward mobility and, 1208

over-qualification, PE misfit and, 474
Ozark Marketing Council, 1581

PA (positive affectivity), 1517–1518
pacing, planned organizational change and, 1564
Packer, A., 541
Pager, D., 341
panic disorder, 558
PAR (participatory action research), 1404–1405
paradoxical change, 1565–1566
parallel (stacked) mediator model, 212–213, 212*f*
parallel process mediation models, 219–220
paranoid cognition, 653
paranoid personality disorder, 566*t*
Parfyonova, N. M., 1209, 1211
Pariguin, Boris, 17–18
Parker, S., 93–94, 692, 710–711, 714–716
PARRY, 744
Parsons, Frank, 7, 1229
Parsons, Talcott, 734
partially latent variables, 243
participative decision-making (PDM), 115
participative leadership, 79
participatory action research (PAR), 1404–1405
participatory design, in HCI, 738–739
participatory organizational interventions
    advantages of, 1598
    evaluating effectiveness of, 1609–1610
    framework for classifying, 1598–1599
    group-level activities in, 1601–1602, 1603*t*
    individual-level activities in, 1600–1601, 1601*t*
    job demands-resources model and, 1599
    leader-level activities in, 1602–1604, 1604*t*
    organizational-level activities in, 1605–1606, 1607*t*
    phases of, 1597–1598
    program logic for, 1608–1609
    reviews of, 1606–1608
Pasmore, W., 88–89
passive-aggressive personality disorder, 566*t*
passive-avoidant leadership, 1434–1435
past employment history, overqualification and, 1203
Patagonia, 1080–1081
paternalism, 573–574
Patterson, M., 1298–1299
pay disparities, gender differences in, 578–579
pay-for-performance, 1283–1284
PCC (protean career concept), 1219–1220
PCO (protean career orientation), 1219–1221
PCP (protean career path), 1219–1220
PCs. *See* psychological contracts
PDM (participative decision-making), 115
Peace Corps, 186

peer justice, 891–893
peer relationships
    creativity at work influenced by, 1312
    feelings of overqualification in, 1210–1211
    lateral communication and, 985–986
PE fit. *See* person-environment fit
Peiró, José M., 19
PE (person-environment) misfit, 473–475
pendulums, 757
Peng, H., 1252–1253
pension systems
    international variations in, 1252–1253
    older workers and changes in, 626
people with disabilities. *See* disabilities at work
perceived employability, 1230–1231
perceived exploitation, 1463–1464
perceived organizational cruelty (POC), 1464
perceived organizational obstruction (POO), 1463
perceived organizational support (POS), 1463
perceived overqualification, 474, 1198, 1207–1208, 1210
Percentile Bootstrap Test, 215–216
perception
    in abusive supervision, 920 n.1, 921–922
    decision-making and, 960
    justice, 1068–1070
    organizational behavior and, 959–960
perceptiveness, political skill and, 488, 489*t*
perfectionism, conscientiousness and, 560
performance. *See* job performance
performance appraisals
    age discrimination and, 641
    to increase individual resources, 1600
performance goals, 1276–1278
performance management. *See also* job performance
    coaching for, 1280–1281
    COVID-19 pandemic impact on, 1286–1287
    critique of, 1273–1274
    definition of, 1273
    evaluation in, 1281–1283
    feedback in, 1278–1281
    flaws of, 1275–1276, 1286–1287
    future of, 1286–1288
    globalization and, 335–337
    goals of, 1274
    human resource management and, 335–337,
        1285–1286
    implementing, 1285–1286
    outcomes of, 1275
    process of, 1276–1285
    progress monitoring in, 1278–1281
    rewards in, 1283–1285
    setting expectations in, 1276–1278

performance management (*continued*)
    talent strategies aligned to organizational goals for,
      1287t
    time spent on, 1273–1274
performance promotor score, 1282–1283
performance theories, implicit, 639
periodic progress monitoring, 1278–1279
permanent teleworkers, 756
perseverance, conscientiousness and, 561
persistence, in goal setting theory, 110
personal appeal, 966
personal informatics, 743
personality. See also *specific traits*
    accident proneness and, 1352–1353
    Big Five Traits of, 554f, 555t, 560–561, 957
    change over time, 561–562
    creativity at work and, 1309
    development, action in, 104
    eudaimonic well-being and, 1528
    in four layers of diversity, 531, 532f
    hedonic well-being and, 1526–1527
    "high-flyers" and, 562–564
    as individual difference at work, 551
    lifestyle and, 563
    models of, 553, 554f
    organizational behavior and, 957
    overqualification and, 1203, 1211
    personnel selection and inventories of, 1145t,
      1146–1147
    risk-taking and, 563, 957
    social support and, 563
    stress and, 563
    taxonomy of, 553–561
    teams and, 839
    well-being and, 149–150
    workplace bullying and, 1435–1436
    work success and, 562–564
Personality and Organization (Argyris), 10–11
personality disorders at work, 565–568, 566t
personal power, 965–966
personal resources, in job design, 698–700
person analysis, in training needs assessment, 1183
Personas, in HCI, 738–739
person-centered communication, 979
person-environment (PE) fit
    acronyms for, 466t
    attraction-selection-attrition theory and, 465–466
    culture and differences of, 471
    dimensions of, 467
    direct and indirect assessments of, 468
    dynamic perspective of, 472–473
    field theory and, 465–466

forms of, 467
individual outcomes influenced by, 468–470, 469f
interactionist theory of behavior and, 465–466
misfit and, 473–475
objective and subjective, 467–468, 470
organizational practices and, 476–477
outcomes of different dimensions of, 470–471
overview of, 465
personnel selection and, 475–476
recruitment and, 475
simultaneous effects of multiple dimensions of, 471–472
socialization and, 476–477
on stress, 1400
theoretical foundations of, 465–467
theory of work adjustment and, 466–467
vocational fit theory and, 466–467
work and family and, 1373
person-environment (PE) misfit, 473–475
person-group (PG) fit
    definition of, 467
    outcomes of, 471
    separate effects of, 472
person-in-job prototypes, 639
person-job (PJ) fit, 465
    definition of, 467
    job crafting and, 719
    outcomes of, 470
    personnel selection and, 475–476, 1142–1143
    PO fit influencing, 472–473
    recruitment and, 475
    separate effects of, 472
Personnel Psychology, 16–17
personnel selection
    age discrimination and, 640
    applicant perceptions and reactions to, 1150–1151
    approaches to, 1141–1143
    assessment center method in, 1149–1150
    biodata in, 1150
    criteria in, 1140–1141
    disabilities and, 668–670
    employment interviews in, 1147–1149
    experience criterion in, 1147
    formative procedures' operational validity for,
      1147–1150, 1148t
    general cognitive ability tests in, 1144–1146, 1145t,
      1151–1153, 1152t
    globalization and, 334–335
    HRM and, 334–335, 1109
    job knowledge tests in, 1149
    job performance measurement and, 1141–1143,
      1151–1153, 1152t
    overview of, 1140–1141

PE fit and, 475–476
personality inventories in, 1145t, 1146–1147
person-job fit in, 475–476, 1142–1143
person-organization fit in, 475–476, 1142–1143
predictors in, 1140–1141
procedures, 1143–1150
race and bias in procedures for, 1153–1154
reference check in, 1150
reflective procedures' operational validity for, 1144–1147, 1145t
selection fairness model for, 1150–1151
situational judgment tests in, 1149
team-organization fit in, 1142–1143
work and family issues and, 1385–1386
work sample tests in, 1149
person-organization (PO) fit, 465
outcomes of, 470
personnel selection and, 475–476, 1142–1143
PJ fit influencing, 472–473
recruitment and, 475
separate effects of, 472
socialization and, 476–477
stress management and, 1404
person-oriented leadership, 937–938
person perception, 806
person-person (PP) fit, 467
person-supervisor (PS) fit
outcomes of, 471
separate effects of, 472
socialization and, 477
person-vocation (PV) fit
definition of, 467
outcomes of, 470–471
Peru, telework/remote work in, 719
Peters, T. J., 996
Petrou, P., 712t, 1299, 1354
Pettigrew, A. M., 1049
Pfeffer, J., 115, 486, 966
Pfeiffer, J. W., 1627
PG fit. *See* person-group fit
phased retirement, 1256
phenomenology, HCI and, 735–736
philanthropy, CSR and, 1092–1093
phobias, 558
physical abuse, 1426
physical environment of work. *See also* environment
organizational behavior and, 969
stress management and, 1405–1406
physical hazards, workplace safety and, 1351
physical mobility (organizational mobility preference), 1221–1222
physical resources, for retirement, 1258

physical stressors, 1526
physical well-being, 1261
physiological functional capacity, 668
Piccolo, R. F., 117
Piéron, Henri, 19
Pinillos, J. L., 19
Piorkowski, Curt, 7, 18–19
Pittman, T. S., 798t, 800–803, 801t
PJ fit. *See* person-job fit
plagiarism, 64, 65t
planned organizational change, 1562–1564
planning, time management and, 1403–1404
plans
development and selection of, 101
retirement, 1254, 1261–1262
for tasks, conscientiousness and, 560
Plans and Situated Action (Suchman), 734–735
Plans and the Structure of Behavior (Miller, G. A., Galanter, and Pribram), 98
plaster hypothesis, 561
plasticity hypothesis, 561
platforms, 1556, 1638
Plato, 533–534
plausibility, qualitative research standards for, 321t
pleasure, purpose and, 1519
Plowman, D. A., 1576t
PNDE (pure natural direct effect), 221
PNIE (pure natural indirect effect), 221
POB (positive organizational behavior), 160
POC (perceived organizational cruelty), 1464
PO fit. *See* person-organization fit
political behavior, 486
political CSR, 1084–1085
political skill
active influence and, 488–489, 489t
affability and, 488, 489t
antecedents of, 488–490, 489t
control and, 488, 489t
dark personalities and, 495–496
definition of, 486–487
developmental experiences and, 488–490, 489t
dimensions of, 486
emerging research areas in, 495–497
implications for practice of, 497
impression management and, 492
job demands and, 492–493
as job performance predictor, 490–491, 490f
in leadership, 494–495
for managers, 493
measurement of, 487–488, 497
mediating variables and, 493
as moderator, 491–492

political skill (*continued*)
    organizational politics and, 966
    overview of, 485–486
    perceptiveness and, 488, 489t
    self-rated, 487–488, 497
    social media, reputation formation and, 496–497
    stress management and, 493–494
    training in, 497
    in workplace and career outcomes, 490–495
political skill inventory (PSI), 487–488, 497
politics. *See* organizational politics
polyphonic change, 1564
POO (perceived organizational obstruction), 1463
population ecology, 996, 1559
population-level learning, 1559
population-level organizational change, 1559
POS (perceived organizational support), 1463
POS (positive organizational scholarship), 160
position-centered communication, 979
positioning behaviors, in career self-management, 1232
positive affective organizational climate, 1530
positive affectivity (PA), 1517–1518
positive dyadic leadership, 905–907
positive leadership
    concept of, 901–904
    core assumptions across theories, models, and
      frameworks of, 904
    critiques to, 910–912
    dyadic leadership, 905–907
    global, 909–910
    gregariousness and, 904
    implications for future and practice of, 912–913
    integrative multilevel model of, 902–904, 903f
    as "naïve," 912
    nature of organizations and, 904
    organizational leadership, 908–909
    organizational stakeholders and, 902
    "The Self" and, 904
    self-leadership, 904–905
    team leadership, 907–908
positive organizational behavior (POB), 160
positive organizational leadership, 908–909
positive organizational scholarship (POS), 160
positive psychology, 16, 902
    callings and, 1354–1355
    job crafting and, 1354
    on occupational health psychology, 1353–1355
    OD and, 1640
    proactivity and, 1354
    thriving at work and, 1355
positive relationships, in PWO studies, 162
positive self-leadership, 904–905

positive team leadership, 907–908
positive work and organization (PWO) studies
    applications and practices of, 163–164
    concerns and future directions of, 164–167
    construct clarity and proliferation in, 165–166
    co-optation or misuse, 166–167
    definition of, 161
    leadership in, 163
    organizational virtue in, 161–162
    overview of, 160–161
    "positive" definition challenges in, 164–165
    positive relationships in, 162
    positive work-identity in, 163
    psychological capital in, 161, 166–167
    states and outcomes in, 163
    thriving in, 163
positive work-identity, 163
positivity, defining, 164–165
"positivity ratio," 166
posterior distribution, 216
post hoc tests, 233
postphenomenology, 735–736
post-structuralism, 534–535
poverty, informal work and, 784–785
power, organizational politics and, 965–967
power imbalance, in workplace bullying, 1428
PP (person-person) fit, 467
practicality, psychology of sustainability and, 179
practical utility, 7
The Practice of Management (Drucker), 11
practitioners, WOP, 64–66
Preacher, K. J., 263
precarious work
    globalization and, 360
    informal work and, 783–784
predatory bullying, 1432
predictors, in personnel selection, 1140–1141
predictor variables, 207, 228
preference utilitarianism, 53–54
preferred comparison direction, 817–818
prejudice, agreeableness in reaction to, 559. *See also* age
    prejudice
prescriptive age stereotypes, 643
pressure. *See* work pressure
preventative stress management, 1405–1406
prevention focus, 417, 1299
Pribram, K. H., 98
PriceWaterhouseCoopers, 1640
primary appraisal, 1343
primary diversity dimensions, 531–532, 533t
primary emotions, 448
primary work roles, 62

priming goals, in subconscious, 116–117
The Prince (Machiavelli), 510–511
Principles of Scientific Management (Taylor, F. W.), 6
privacy, mobile telework/remote work and, 768–769
proactive justice, 1068–1069
proactivity
    job design and, 697–698
    overqualification and, 1207–1208
    positive psychology and, 1354
    sustainable careers and, 1225–1226
probabilistic reasoning, 42
problem-focused coping, 1408
problem solving conflict behavior, 1030
problem-solving coping, 1343–1344
problem understandings, 1009
procedural justice, 882–884, 1065–1066, 1150–1151
process conflict, 965, 1027
process models of creativity, 1308–1309
process rules, 1487–1488
procrastination
    conscientiousness and refrainment from, 560
    goal striving and, 415
PRODCLIN, 215
production deviance, 1320–1321
productivity
    happiness and, 1521
    sustainable careers and, 1225–1226
products, trends away from, 1638
professional relations, ethics and, 62–63
"Profile of Organizational Characteristics" (Likert), 1628
program logic, for participatory organizational
    interventions, 1608–1609
progress monitoring, in performance management,
    1278–1281
Project Global Living Organizational Wage (Project
    GLOW), 192
project-management KSAOs, 866–867
promise-based beliefs, of PCs, 1126–1127
promotions
    age discrimination and, 640–641
    focus, 417, 1299
    SGM discrimination and, 650–651
prosocial motivation, 1310–1311
prospect theory, JDM and, 395–396, 395*f*
protean career concept (PCC), 1219–1220
protean career orientation (PCO), 1219–1221
protean career path (PCP), 1219–1220
protean career theory
    in career studies, 1218–1221
    on retirement, 1260–1261
prototype matching, 639
prototypes, person-in-job, 639

provocative victim, 1435
proximal goals, 113
PSC. *See* psychosocial safety climate
PS fit. *See* person-supervisor fit
PSI (political skill inventory), 487–488, 497
PsyCap (psychological capital), 161, 166–167, 1472–1473
psychoanalysis, 375
psychological availability, CSR and, 1088–1089
psychological capital (PsyCap), 161, 166–167, 1472–1473
psychological change, 178–179, 178*t*
psychological climate, organizational climate compared
    to, 1044
psychological connections, with work engagement,
    1295–1296
psychological contracts (PCs)
    antecedents of, 1129–1130
    breach of, 1131–1132, 1134, 1163
    content of, 1127–1129
    creation and development of, 1130–1131
    EVLN model and, 1132
    fulfillment and positive deviations from, 1134
    history, definitions, and debates of, 1125–1127
    ideological, 1128–1129
    job insecurity and, 1163
    maintenance of, 1133–1134
    measurement and methods of investigating, 1132–1133
    older workers and, 627–628
    overview of, 1125
    perceptions of two interacting parties in, 1135
    practical management perspective on, 1135–1137
    promise-based beliefs of, 1126–1127
    relational, 1128–1129, 1163
    research issues and emerging topics in, 1133–1135
    state of, 1127
    transactional, 627–628, 1128–1129
    violation of, 1131–1132, 1134
The Psychological Corporation, 8–9
psychological detachment, 1347–1348
psychological mobility (boundaryless mindset),
    1221–1222
psychological need satisfaction, in SDT, 420
psychological safety
    CSR and, 1088–1089
    social support and, 1485
    teamwork and, 843
psychology of sustainability
    applied approach to, 173–175
    criterion problem and, 176
    deliberative processing and, 178
    discrepancy testing and, 177
    feedback processing and, 179–180, 180*t*
    five criteria for, 176–179

psychology of sustainability (*continued*)
  fundamental assumptions of, 175–176
  intervention for, 179–180, 180*t*
  overview of, 172–173
  practicality and, 179
  psychological change and, 178–179, 178*t*
  taking action and, 179
psychology of working theory (PWT), 1226–1227
psychopathy
  CWBs and, 515, 1322–1323
  definition of, 506–508
  dimensions of, 513
  employees and, 515–516
  Factor 2, 517–518
  leadership and, 513–515
  in workplace, 513–516
psychophysical processes, in JDM, 394–397
psychosocial safety climate (PSC), 1435
  occupational stress and, 1350–1351
  well-being and, 1530
psychosocial stressors, 1526
psychosocial well-being, 1261
psychotechnology, 7–9, 17–18. *See also* organizational
    psychology
PSYCONES project, 1125, 1129
public authority, multi-organizational groups and, 381
Pulakos, E. D., 1275–1276, 1278–1280
punctuated rhythms, planned organizational change and,
    1564
pure natural direct effect (PNDE), 221
pure natural indirect effect (PNIE), 221
purpose
  CSR and, 1088–1089
  pleasure and, 1519
  at work, 1518–1519
putting patterns together, 309
PV fit. *See* person-vocation fit
PWO studies. *See* positive work and organization studies
PWT (psychology of working theory), 1226–1227

QRPs (questionable research practices), 64
Quaker Oats, 1314–1315
qualitative research. *See also* analysis in qualitative
    research; coding in qualitative research
  data gathering in, 303–304, 304*f*
  standards for, 320–323, 321*t*
  study design in, 303, 304*f*
  writing up findings in, 303–304, 304*f*
Quality Control Handbook (Deming), 354
quality of working life (QWL)
  conceptual origins of, 1500–1501
  contemporary view of, 1508–1510

  COVID-19 pandemic and, 1508
  definition and criteria of, 1499
  diffusion and, 1503–1504
  economic insecurity and, 1508–1509
  employment standards and, 1509–1511
  evidence for improvements in, 1502–1505
  external influences on interest in, 1501–1502
  human resource management and, 1506–1507
  Industry 4 and, 1507–1508
  job design and, 1506
  job redesign and, 1509–1510
  overview of, 1498–1499
  revitalizing interest in, 1505–1508
  sustainability and, 1503
  well-being and, 1505–1507
  work alienation and, 1502
quantitative fallacy, 33–34
quantitative models, for JDM, 402
quasi-spot investment, 1136
queer workers. *See* sexual and gender minorities
questionable research practices (QRPs), 64
question-asking, impression management and, 807–808
questionnaires
  on content of PCs, 1128
  for data collection, 1628–1629
Qvale, T., 86
QWL. *See* quality of working life

race
  AA and, 541
  coping by, 1409
  "doing difference" and, 535–537, 536*f*
  gender in organizations and, 574–575
  intersectionality and, 536–537
  microaggressions targeting, 651–652
  personnel selection procedures and, 1153–1154
radical commerce, 193
radical organizational change, 1565
Rahim's Organizational Conflict Inventory (ROCI),
    1031
random coefficients, 241, 256
random-coefficients regression model, 260–261
random effects, 240–241, 256
  one-way ANCOVA model with, 258–260
rapid appraisals of evidence (REAs), 39
rapport-building skills, 1034
ratings, 1281–1283
rationality, sense-making and, 996–997
rational models of JDM, 391–393
rational persuasion, 966
RCR (responsible conduct of research), 63
readiness checklist, in OD, 1627

Reagan, Ronald, 541
realized matches approach, 1196–1197
real overqualification, 1198
reappraisal, in emotion regulation, 153
REAs (rapid appraisals of evidence), 39
Reciprocity Ring, 163
recombination of system components, in generative
    emergence, 1577–1578
recruitment
    disabilities and, 668–670
    globalization and, 334
    overqualification and, 1211–1212
    PE fit and, 475
    talent and, 668–669
"red cape" interventions, 1417–1418
redesign of work, disabilities and, 673–676
reductionist approach to organizations, sense-making
    in, 994
reference check, 1150
referent-shift consensus model, 1044–1045
Reflected Best-Self Exercise, 163
reflective career competencies, 1233
reflective design, in HCI, 740
reflexive documents, 317
"refreezing" organizations, 1635–1636, 1639
regions of significance, 236
regret and disappointment, 397
regular rhythms, planned organizational change and,
    1564
regular teleworkers, 756
regulatory focus theory, 417
reinforcement theory, 962
relatedness, need for, 123, 420
relational contracts, 627–628
Relational Coordination Collaborative, 163
relational crafting, 709
relational demography, 623, 639, 641
relational model of fair treatment, 1071–1072
relational models theory, 943
relational psychological contracts, 1128–1129, 1163
relationship conflict, 965, 1027
relationships motivation theory (RMT), 123
relative deprivation theory
    overqualification and, 1198–1199
    social comparison and, 819
relaxation, 1357–1358, 1454
reliability, qualitative research standards for, 321t
Religious Freedom Restoration Act, 1993, 660
religious organizations, authority for change in, 1554
remote work. See also telework; virtual teams
    challenges measuring, 717
    commuting impacts of, 770

company benefits of, 771
costs and savings of, 770
COVID-19 pandemic impact on, 719, 762, 771–773
coworkers and, 768–769
cross-cultural IWOP and, 363
cyberslacking and, 765–766
definitions of, 755–759, 755t
drivers of, 762–763
in Europe, 718–720
forced, 771–772
home-based, 755t, 756, 764–766
impacts of, 769–771
individual and organizational performance and,
    770–771
leadership, managers and, 765, 772–773
mobile, 756–757, 766–769
prevalence of, 761–762
resilience and future of, 773–775
technology enabling, 772
in United States and Canada, 719–720
representativeness
    JDM and, 392–393
    in procedural justice, 1066
reputation formation, political skill, social media and,
    496–497
reputation of firms, CSR and, 1084–1085
research and researchers
    justice in teams and development of, 880–881
    misconduct, 64, 65t
    questionable research practices, 64
    scientific integrity and, 64
    social nature of, 63–64
    WOP and, 63–64
research ethics, 63
research record, 65t
research through design, in HCI, 740
Resick, C. J., 358
resilience
    definition of, 774
    in psychological capital, 161
    stress management and, 1410
    teams and organizational, 774
    telework/remote work and, 773–775
    training, 186
    uncertainty and, 1488
resilient individuals, 774
resource(s)
    caravans, 699
    career, 1232–1233
    dependence, 996
    gain spiral, 1345–1346
    in goal setting theory, 110–111, 114

resource(s) (*continued*)
increasing for groups, 1601–1602
increasing for individuals, 1600
increasing for leaders, 1603
increasing for organizations, 1604–1605
in job demands-resources model, 126–127
loss, 1345–1346
replenishment of, 423
retirement perspective based on, 1258
respect
autonomy and, 1453
for people, 50
respectful leadership, 943
response generalization, 49–50
responsible conduct of research (RCR), 63
rest/respite, for stress management, 1412–1413
Results Only Work Environment (ROWE), 1384
retention, in population-level learning, 1559
retirement
age and, 1252
bridge employment and, 1256–1257, 1264
categories of, 1252–1253
continuity theory on, 1259
decision-making, 1254, 1262–1263
definition, measurement, and concepts of, 1252–1257
early, 1255
empirical findings on temporal process of, 1261–1265
health and, 1262
health insurance and, 1264
human capital theory on, 1259–1260
life-course perspective on, 1258–1259
mandatory, 1255
norms, older workers and changing, 626–627
overview of, 1251–1252
phased, 1256
planning, 1254, 1261–1262
protean career theory on, 1260–1261
resource-based perspective on, 1258
role theory on, 1257
savings, JDM for, 404–405
self-assessment of, 1253
theoretical frameworks for research on, 1257–1261
transition and adjustment, 1254–1255, 1263–1265
well-being during, 1261
work-to-retirement transitions, 1236–1237
"revise work culture" frame, 585–586
rewarding activities, well-being and, 1519–1520
reward power, 965–966
rewards, 121–122
compensation and, 128
justice and, 128

in performance management, 1283–1285
teamwork and, 846
rhythms, planned organizational change and, 1564
Rice, A. K., 84
Richardson, K. D., 798*t*
Richter, A. W., 289–291
Rickley, M., 335
Riess, M., 798*t*
risk
in environments, 997–998
JDM and aversion to, 394–395
organizational research on safety and, 1488–1489
risk-taking, personality and, 563, 957
Rivera, Lauren, 405
RMT (relationships motivation theory), 123
Roberson, Q. M., 884–886, 891
"Robin Hood Effect," 438
Robinson, S., 1131
ROCI (Rahim's Organizational Conflict Inventory), 1031
Rock, David, 1279
Roe, R., 1133–1134
Roe, Robert, 21, 280, 673–674
Roethlisberger, Fritz, 9
Rogers Commission, 1013
Rognes, J., 1136–1137
role ambiguity, 1344
in job design, 692
workplace bullying and, 1433–1434
role analysis, for stress management, 1413
role clarification, organizational interventions for, 1596
role conflict, 692, 1344
definition of, 59*t*
examples of, 59–61*t*
political skill for stress management and, 493–494
workplace bullying and, 1433–1434
role congruity theory, 572
role exit, 1257
role overload, 493–494, 1344
role stressors, 1398
role theory, 638–639
on occupational stress, 1344
on retirement, 1257
on stress, 1400
on work and family, 1370–1371
role transition, 1257
romance of leadership, 910–911
Rosenblatt, Z., 1160
Rosenfeld, P., 798*t*
Rousseau, Denise M., 25, 27–28, 35, 289–291, 1126, 1300
Rousseau, D. M., 1641
ROWE (Results Only Work Environment), 1384

Rowe, A., 531–532, 532f, 533t
rudeness
  definition of, 59t
  examples of, 59–61t
  unethical behavior compared to, 57–58
Rudolph, C. W., 293
rule-based processes, in JDM, 397–399
rule-deontology, 53
Rupp, D. E., 637–638, 1068–1069, 1071–1072
Russia, OP in, 17–18

Sackett, P. R., 1320–1321
Sackmann, S. A., 1052
safety. *See also* workplace safety
  accident proneness and, 1484–1485
  behavior related to, 1482
  climate, 1352–1353
  compliance, 185
  dynamic safety capability, 1488–1489
  incident reporting and investigation and, 1490–1491
  individual processes related to, 186–187
  job characteristics influencing, 1484
  job control and, 1484
  job demands and, 1484
  leadership, 1353, 1485–1486
  management, 1490–1491
  motivation, 1483
  occupational, 358–360
  organizational characteristics related to, 1487–1488
  organizational research on risk and, 1488–1489
  participation, 185
  personal characteristics influencing, 1484–1485
  priority, 1352
  psychological, CSR and, 1088–1089
  psychological, social support and, 1485
  psychological, teamwork and, 843
  team characteristics influencing, 1485–1487
  team processes related to, 187–188
  training, 1490
  work-family conflict and, 1380–1381
safety climate, 1044–1046. *See also* psychosocial safety
    climate
Salancik, G. R., 115, 966
Salas, E., 1178–1179, 1188
Saldaña, J., 303–304
Salovey, P., 447, 452, 456
sampling errors, in multilevel modeling methods, 270–271
Sandberg, J., 1002
Sandberg, Sheryl, 583–584
satisfaction, 686
Saxena, M., 781–782
scapegoating, 377–378, 1426

Scarborough, H., 88–89
scarcity hypothesis, 1370–1371
SCARF theory, 1279
SCCT (social cognitive career theory), 654, 1218–1219,
    1223–1225
scenario-based design, in HCI, 738–739
Schadenfreude, 821
Schalk, R., 1133–1134
Schaufeli, W. B., 690–691, 1294–1297, 1299–1300, 1354.
    See also job demands-resources model
scheduling, in informal work, 781
Scheffé corrections, 233
Schein, E. H., 10–11, 455, 909, 1050–1051, 1126
Schewe, A. F., 1349
schizoid personality disorder, 566t
schizotypal personality disorder, 566t
Schlenker, B. R., 798t, 804–805
Schmidt, F. L., 116
Schminke, M., 883, 1068–1069
Schmitt, F. L., 1153
Schmuck, R. A., 1631
Schneider, B., 1050–1051, 1293–1294
Schneider, D. J., 798t
school-to-work transitions, 596, 1235–1236
science, technology, engineering, and mathematics
    (STEM) fields, 576–577
scientific integrity, 64
scientific knowledge, expansion of, 880
scientific management, 685
scientific organization of work, study of, 5–6
scientist-practitioner model, 173–174, 179
SCM. *See* stereotype content model
SCO (social comparison orientation), 823–824
Scott, Walter Dill, 7–9, 353
Scott Company, 8–9
scripts, cognitive, 1004
SCT (social categorization theory), 623, 634–635
SDGs (sustainable development goals), 185, 188
SDT. *See* self-determination theory
SDT research in workplace
  advancements of, 132–135
  compensation in, 128–129
  contingent pay in, 127
  employee orientations and aspirations in, 129–130
  general methodology advances in, 134–135
  interpersonal climate and, 125–126
  job and organizational characteristics in, 126–127
  job attitude outcomes of, 131
  leadership and, 126
  longitudinal approaches to, 133–134
  non-contingent pay in, 128–129
  outcomes of, 131–132

SDT research in workplace (*continued*)
  person-centered approaches to, 132–133
  well-being and functioning outcomes of, 131–132
  work behavior outcomes of, 130–131
search, in JDM, 394
Seashore, Stanley, 1638
seasonal organizations, 1566
seasonal work, 781–782
secondary appraisal, 1343
secondary diversity dimensions, 531–532, 533*t*
secondary emotions, 448
secondary interventions. *See* coping
secondary work roles, 62
"second cycle" codes, 308
second-order sense-making, 1013
segmentation/integration preferences, for work and
    family, 1372–1373
selecting environments, 1326–1327
selection, in population-level learning, 1559. *See also*
    personnel selection
selection fairness model, 1150–1151
selection-optimization-compensation (SOC) theory,
    616, 1117
selective coding, 315
"The Self," positive leadership and, 904
self-assessment of retirement, 1253
self-concept, 1228
self-determination, 55–56
self-determination theory (SDT), 961. *See also* SDT
    research in workplace
  on autonomous motivation compared to controlled
      motivation, 121
  BPNT and, 123–124
  CET and, 121–122, 124
  COT and, 122, 124, 129
  definition of, 121
  extrinsic motivation in, 419–420
  GCT and, 123–124, 129–130
  job insecurity and, 1162
  OIT and, 122, 124
  organizational dehumanization and, 1468, 1474–1475
  overview of, 121–123
  positive self-leadership and, 905
  psychological need satisfaction in, 420
  research in workplace, 134–135
  RMT and, 123
  well-being and, 1524
  on workplace motivation, 123–125, 124*f*
self-direction, 1219–1221
self-efficacy
  creative, 1310
  goal setting theory and, 115–116, 415

motivation and, 422–423, 962–963
  social cognitive career theory and, 1223–1225
  young workers and, 599
self-enhancement, social comparison and, 817
self-evaluation
  deviant behavior and, 1324–1325
  social comparison and, 817
self focus, in action regulation, 104
self-improvement, social comparison and, 817
self-interest model of fair treatment, 1071–1072
self-labeling approach, to workplace bullying, 1429–1430
self-management, 41
  career, 1224–1225, 1232–1233
  career adaptability for, 1223
  training, 422–423
self-presentation. *See also* impression management
  definitions of, 797–798, 798*t*
  impression management and, 799
self-promotion, gender differences in, 577
self-rated political skill, 487–488, 497
self-reflectiveness, 1324–1325
self-regulation, 41, 98–99
  abusive supervision from failure of, 923–924
  in effective training, 1180
  theory, 280–281
Self-Report Psychopathy Scale-Revised, 514
self-scheduling, organizational interventions for,
    1596–1597
self-tracking, in HCI, 742–744
Seligman, Martin, 160
SEM. *See* structural equation modeling
SEMATECH, 1581–1582
Senge, P., 1560–1561
"sensebreaking" process, 1003
sense-giving, downward communication and, 981–982
sense-making
  accounts and, 1006
  adaptive, 1009–1010
  building blocks of, 995–996
  Chicago Board Options Exchange example of,
      992–993
  cognitive means of, 1004–1005
  consequences of perspective of, 996–997
  contextual influences on, 1012–1014
  in contextualist approach to organizations, 994–995
  data-frame theory of, 1004–1005
  discursive means of, 1005–1007
  distinctive features of identity and, 1009
  embodied means of, 1007–1008
  enactment and, 1009–1012
  enactment-selection-retention process in
      organizations and, 998*f*, 999–1000, 1002

environment and perspective of, 997–998
formative historical context of, 996
future directions of, 1013–1014
grapevine communication and, 985
institutional theory and, 1013–1014
interpretive products of, 1008–1009
justice in teams and, 885–886
labels and, 1005
language and, 1005–1007
metaphors and, 1005–1006
mindful organizing and, 1010–1012, 1011*f*
multiple parties in, 1013
narratives and, 1006
noticing and bracketing in, 1003–1004
ontological oscillation and, 1000
option attractiveness and, 1009
organizations from perspective of, 998–1000
in organizing context, 1001–1002
overview of, 993–994
as perspective, 993–994, 998–1000
problem understandings and, 1009
as process, 993–994, 1012–1014
properties of process of, 1000–1001
rationality and, 996–997
receptivity to collectivist mindset and, 1009
in reductionist approach to organizations, 994
second-order, 1013
triggers of, 1002–1003
sense of empowerment, overqualification and, 1210
sensitivity analysis, 222–223
sensitivity training, 1623, 1632–1633
sensorimotor or skill level, of action regulation, 102
separation, diversity and, 537–538
serial (sequential) mediator model, 211–212, 212*f*
servant leadership, 942–943
service climate, 1044–1047
ServiceCo, 1582–1583
SEs (standard errors), 264
Sessions, H., 289–291
SET. *See* social exchange theory
sexual and gender minorities (SGMs)
advocacy for, 657
allyship for, 657
diversity climate and, 658
employment-related legislation on, 659–660
formal discrimination and, 650–651
"gay advantage" and, 651
hiring discrimination and, 649–650
identity centrality and, 655
identity disclosure and, 654–656
identity management and, 653–654
individual mitigation strategies for, 653

interpersonal discrimination and, 651–653
interpersonal mitigation strategies for, 656–657
intersectionality and, 650
"Lavender Scare" and, 660
leadership and promotion discrimination and, 650–651
microaggressions targeting, 651–653
organizational mitigation strategies for, 658
paranoid cognition and, 653
social support for, 656
societal attitudes towards, 659
societal mitigation strategies for, 659–660
stereotypes and, 650
stigma consciousness and, 655
terminology of, 649
sexual harassment, 1426
SGMs. *See* sexual and gender minorities
Shackel, Brian, 729
Shalley, C. E., 1305–1306
shame and guilt, moral emotions and, 431–432, 439
SHARE (Survey of Health Ageing and Retirement in Europe), 1262
shared emotions, 1525
shared leadership, 1486
shared mental models (SMMs), 844, 870–871
shared value, CSR for, 1086–1087
sharing economy, 332
Sheffield studies on sociotechnical approach, 87–88
Shell demonstration projects, 86–87, 1503–1504
sheltered employment, disabilities and, 671–672
Shetler, J., 1576*t*
Shi, J., 1261
shift changes, organizational interventions for, 1596–1597
shiftwork, older workers and, 621
Shipp, A. J., 281, 283–284, 289–291
Short Dark Triad, 517
Shoss, M. K., 1171
SHRM (Society for Human Resource Management), 406
signaling, in identity management, 654
Siguan, M., 19
Sillito-Walker, S. D., 1068
similarity
gender, 815–816
similarity-attraction paradigm, 637
social comparison and, 814–816
Simon, Herbert, 10–11, 13–14, 392
simple effect contrast, 232–233
simple main effects, moderator variables and, 230–231
simple regression equation, 235
Sin, H., 537–538

single-mediator model, 208–211
SIOP (Society for Industrial and Organizational Psychology), 20–21, 55–56, 58, 187, 192
SIP (social information processing), 885–886
Siri, 744
SIT. *See* social identity theory
situational demands, in virtual teams, 867
situational judgment tests, 1149
situation awareness, teamwork and, 844
situation selection and modification, in emotion regulation, 151
skill compensation theory, 1201
skill upgrading, in informal work, 783
skill variety, 420–421
Skinner, B. F., 14–15, 1636
sleep, for stress management, 1412–1413
Slemp, G. R., 712*t*
Sloman, S. A., 399
Slowik, L. H., 289–291
slow thinking, in JDM, 398
Small, M. L., 341
SMART (Specific, Measurable, Achievable, Relevant, and Time-bound) goals, 1276
smartphone technology, for stress management, 1412
Smith, Adam, 673–674, 684–685, 1573
Smith, C., 1576*t*
SMMs (shared mental models), 844, 870–871
Snakes in Suits (Babiak and Hare), 517
SNAQ, 1430
Sobel Test (First-Order Standard Error Test), 211, 214–215
social astuteness, 486–487
social attitudes, job insecurity and, 1163–1164
social axioms, 355–356
social biases, 32*f*, 34–35
social capital, 598–599
social categorization theory (SCT), 623, 634–635
social climate, social comparison and, 820–821
social cognitive career theory (SCCT), 654, 1218–1219, 1223–1225
social cognitive theory, 599, 1324–1327
social comparison
    American Soldier studies and, 813–814
    attractiveness and, 822–823
    burnout and, 823–824
    control and, 820–821
    definition of, 813
    dimensions of, 818
    effects of, 818–819
    envy and, 821–823
    by gender, 815–816
    identification and contrast in, 819–821
    jealousy and, 821–823

motivations for, 817–818
overview of, 813–814
preferred direction of, 817–818
relative deprivation and, 819
self-evaluation, self-improvement, self-enhancement and, 817
social climate and, 820–821
stress and, 820–821
taboo of, 814
uncertainty, similarity and, 814–816
upward-and-downward, 818–819
social comparison orientation (SCO), 823–824
social constructionism, diversity and, 534–535
social context
    in action regulation, 104
    as job crafting influence, 717–718
social dominance orientation, 924
social effectiveness constructs, 485–486
social exchange theory (SET), 436
    abusive supervision and, 923
    career studies and, 1227–1228
    ethical leadership and, 940–941
    organizational dehumanization and, 1468, 1474
    trust and, 1034
    on work and family, 1373
social factors, motivation and, 421
social identity model of leadership, 907–908
social identity theory (SIT), 623, 634–635
    CSR and, 1086–1087
    job insecurity and, 1163–1164
    organizational dehumanization and, 1468–1469, 1474
social information processing (SIP), 885–886
social isolation, 765
Socialist International, 5
socialization
    as EDMP barrier, 31–34, 32*f*
    organizational culture and, 1051–1052
    PE fit and, 476–477
social justice, 50
social learning theory
    abusive supervision and, 923
    ethical leadership and, 940–941
    gender in organizations and, 571
    motivation and, 962
social media, political skill, reputation formation and, 496–497
social practices, HCI and, 736
social presence, ICTs and, 863–864
social psychology, multi-organizational group dynamics and, 373–375
The Social Psychology of Organizing (Weick), 996

social relationships
  burnout and, 1453
  home-based telework/remote work and, 765
  mobile telework/remote work and, 768
  organizational interventions for, 1596
social resources, for retirement, 1258
Social Responsibilities of Business Corporations, 1080
Social Responsibilities of the Businessman (Bowen, H. R.),
    1079–1080
social responsibility (SR), 1079–1080. *See also* corporate
    social responsibility
social role theory, 638–639
  on gender in organizations, 571–572
social skill, 485
social support
  personality and, 563
  psychological safety and, 1485
  for SGMs, 656
  stress management and, 1409–1410
  for training, 1184–1187
"societal power-knowledge complex," 534–535
society, job insecurity spillover to, 1168–1169
Society for Human Resource Management (SHRM),
    406
Society for Industrial and Organizational Psychology
    (SIOP), 20–21, 55–56, 58, 187, 192
socioemotional selectivity theory (SST), 616–617
sociotechnical approach to work organization, 11–12
  action research in, 80
  Ahmedabad experiment and, 84
  background to, 78–79
  coal mining studies and, 78, 83
  commitment challenges of, 86
  design of jobs and work groups in, 80–82
  evolution of, 80–82
  future of, 93–94
  general principles of, 79–80
  for information systems and ergonomics, 92–93
  IOR in Netherlands and, 91–92
  joint optimization in, 80
  Norwegian studies on, 84–86, 1503
  OD and, 1623–1624, 1633
  organizational choice in, 79–80
  organizations as open systems in, 80
  origins of, 78–79
  outcomes of, 88–89
  overview of, 77
  preliminary assessment of, 88–89
  QWL concept influenced by, 1500
  Sheffield studies on, 87–88
  Shell demonstration projects and, 86–87, 1503–1504
  Trist and Bamforth's coal mining study and, 78

Volvo case and, 90–91, 1503
  work groups in, 80–82
sociotechnical systems theory, 686
SOC (selection-optimization-compensation) theory,
    616, 1117
SOE (supervisor's organizational embodiment), 1471–1472
SOHP (US Society for Occupational Health
    Psychology), 1339–1340
Sollier, Paul, 19
solutioneering, 32*f*, 33
Somerville, I., 92–93
Sonnentag, S., 1301
Sousa-Poza, A., 1200
space, mobile workers and, 757
Spain, OP in, 19
spatial flexibility hypothesis, 1203–1204
Spearman, Charles, 8
Specific, Measurable, Achievable, Relevant, and
    Time-bound (SMART) goals, 1276
specific indirect effects, 213
speech-based intelligent personal assistants, 744
Spence, M., 1199–1200
Spencer, B. G., 1252–1253
Spielrein, Isaak, 17–18
spiritual leadership, 163
spousal care, gender and responsibilities with, 583
Spradley, J. P., 310
Spreitzer, G. M., 167
SPSS syntax to estimate multilevel models, 272
SR (social responsibility), 1079–1080. *See also* corporate
    social responsibility
SST (socioemotional selectivity theory), 616–617
Stab, N., 1609–1610
stabilization of newly emerged state, in generative
    emergence, 1578
stacked (parallel) mediator model, 212–213, 212*f*
stakeholder salience, CSR and, 1084–1085
stakeholder theory, 1082
standard errors (SEs), 264
standardized interaction coefficients, 238
starting problem, 406–407
states and outcomes, in PWO studies, 163
statistical power, moderator variables and, 246–247
status inconsistency, 1199
Staw, B. M., 1558
STEM (science, technology, engineering, and
    mathematics) fields, 576–577
STEP (Student Training for Entrepreneurial
    Promotion), 190
stereotype content model (SCM)
  ageism in workplace and, 635–636
  age prejudice and, 637

stereotype content model (SCM) (*continued*)
  competence and warmth in, 574, 621–622
  on gender in organizations, 574
stereotypes, 341. *See also* age stereotypes
  disabilities at work and, 669–670
  of informal work, 787–788
  job-age, 622–623
  job stereotype content, 639
  SGMs and, 650
Stern, William, 7–9, 18–19
stigma consciousness, 655
stimulus generalization, 49–50
Stimulus Organism Response model, 208
storyboards, in HCI, 738
Stouffer, Samuel A., 11–12
Stouten, J., 1641–1643
strains
  definition of, 1398–1399
  job insecurity and, 1162–1163, 1167
strategic-assertive tactics, 801–802
strategic-contingency theory, 1555
strategic-defensive tactics, 801–802
strategic fitness process, 1639
strategic sponsorship, CSR and, 1092–1093
Strauss, Anselm, 313–316
Strauss, K., 1354
strengths crafting, 716–717
stress. *See also* occupational stress
  conservation of resources theory on, 1401
  CWBs and, 1323–1324
  ERI model on, 1402
  field theory on, 1399–1400
  future research on, 1416–1418
  in generative emergence, 1577, 1581
  job demands-control/support model on, 1400–1401
  job demands-resources model on, 1400–1401
  leading frameworks on work-related, 1399–1402
  organizational psychology on work-related, 1395–1396
  organization development frameworks for, 1396, 1397f
  overview of work-related, 1394–1396
  personality and, 563
  person-environment fit on, 1400
  physical stressors, 1526
  political skill and management of, 493–494
  psychosocial stressors, 1526
  role theory on, 1400
  social comparison and, 820–821
  transactional framework on, 1401–1402
  transactional model of, 1343–1344
stress climate, well-being and team, 1529–1530

stress management
  biofeedback for, 1412
  coping and, 1406–1410
  diversity programs for, 1415
  EAPs and, 1411
  emotion-focused coping and, 1408–1409
  flexible work arrangements for, 1414–1415
  future research on, 1416–1418
  healthcare management policies for, 1415–1416
  individual-focused, 1411–1413
  interventions, 1357–1358, 1415–1416
  job redesign and, 1404–1405
  long-term benefits of, 1411
  meaningfulness and, 1410
  mindfulness for, 1412
  organizational-level occupational health interventions for, 1413–1414
  organization-focused, 1415–1416
  overview of, 1394–1396
  participatory action research and, 1404–1405
  person-organization fit and, 1404
  physical environment for, 1405–1406
  planning, time management and, 1403–1404
  preventative, 1405–1406
  problem-focused coping and, 1408
  resilience and, 1410
  role analysis for, 1413
  sleep/rest/respite for, 1412–1413
  smartphone technology for, 1412
  social support and, 1409–1410
  wellness programs and, 1417–1418
stressor-detachment model, 1347–1348
stressors
  challenge, 1347, 1396, 1401, 1417
  defining, 1398–1399
  hindrance, 1347, 1395, 1397–1398, 1401, 1417
  organizational constraints and, 1397–1398
  physical, 1526
  psychosocial, 1526
  role, 1398
  work-family conflict and, 1398–1399
  workload as, 1398
  workplace mistreatment and, 1397–1398
strict invariance, 243–244
structural equation modeling (SEM)
  conditional process models and, 244–245
  invariance testing and, 243–244
  measurement model in, 242–243
  moderator variables in, 244–245
  multiple-group analysis and, 243
  structural model in, 242–243
structural invariance, 244

structuralist approach, for justice in teams, 887
structural model, in SEM, 242–243
Student Training for Entrepreneurial Promotion (STEP), 190
study design in qualitative research, 303, 304f
style, as individual difference at work, 551
subconscious, priming goals in, 116–117
subcultures, organizational, 1052–1053
subgroups, justice in teams, faultlines and, 890–891
subjective career success, 1229–1230
subjective PE fit, 467–468, 470
subjective time, 281, 284–285, 293
subjective well-being (SWB), 1516
subjectivism, 52
subsequent behavior, in emotion regulation, 153
success, career, 1229–1230
Suchman, Lucy, 734–735
Suls, J., 813
Sunstein, C. R., 401–402
Super, D. E., 1219, 1228, 1237–1238
supervision. See abusive supervision
supervisor's organizational embodiment (SOE), 1471–1472
superworkers, 101, 105
supplementary fit, 465, 467
supplementary teleworkers, 756
surface acting, 452–453, 1348–1349
surface-level diversity, 531, 533t
survey feedback, OD and, 1623–1625, 1633
Survey of Health Ageing and Retirement in Europe (SHARE), 1262
sustainability, QWL and, 1503. See also psychology of sustainability
sustainable careers, 1225–1226
sustainable development goals (SDGs), 185, 188, 363–364, 787
sustainable livelihood
    definition of, 188
    in humanitarian work and organizational psychology, 188
    United Nations Global Compact for, 189
SWB (subjective well-being), 1516
symbolic interaction approach, for justice in teams, 885–886
symbolic management, 32f, 33
synchrony preference, 289–291
synergistic interactions, 237–238
System 1 and System 2 thinking, 34–35
systemic capacity, emergence in, 1595 n.1
systemic reviews meta-analysis, 39
systemic uncritical emulation, 31
systems approach to development, older workers and, 614–615

systems-psychodynamics
    for action research approach, 378–379
    key concepts in, 375–376
    multi-organizational group dynamics and, 375–379
    observations in, 376
systems theory, 375
    on work and family, 1371
Szumal, J. L., 356–357

tactical-assertive tactics, 801–802
tactical-defensive tactics, 801–802
taking action, psychology of sustainability and, 179
talent
    recruitment and, 668–669
    shift from employees to, 1639
    strategies aligned to organizational goals, 1287t
Tang, S., 289–291
Tangible, Embedded, and Embodied Interaction (TEI), 741
targets
    in impression management, 805
    as judge, 806
    as source of information, 805–806
    of workplace bullying, 1427–1428
Tarique, I., 358
task analysis
    HCI and, 737
    in training needs assessment, 1183
task characteristics, organizational interventions for, 1596
task crafting, 709
tasks
    complete, 103–104
    conscientiousness and planning, 560
    focus on, in action regulation, 104
    identity of, 420–421
    significance of, 420–421
    task characteristics, teamwork, 840–841
    task conflict, 965, 1027
    task mental models, 870
    task-oriented leadership, 937–939
    task performance, 1141–1142, 1142f, 1145t, 1151, 1152t
    of virtual teams, 866
Tavistock Institute, 12, 80–81, 84, 87–88, 1500, 1503, 1623–1624
Tavistock Institute of Human Relations, 78
taxonomic analysis, 311, 311f
Taylor, Frederick Winslow, 6, 78–79, 673–674, 685
Taylor, S., 635
Taylorism, 685, 1368
Taylor Society, 6
Taylor System, 6
Tchagneno, C., 193

team affective climate, 1524–1525
team mental models, 870
team-organization fit, 1142–1143
team perceived virtuality, 862
teams. *See also* groups; justice in teams; virtual teams
  abusive supervision impact on, 927
  adaptation in, 868
  age diversity in, 624
  age-related faultlines in, 623, 641
  autonomy and, 1602
  building, 848
  characteristics of, 837–840
  collaboration improvement in, 1602
  coordination of, 1179
  creativity at work and, 1313–1314
  cross-training, 848, 1179
  defining, 831
  digital collaboration in, 860–862
  effectiveness of, 831–832, 965
  emotional climate and, 965
  emotions at work in, 453–454
  homogeneity and diversity in, 837–838
  human-agent, 862–863, 872–873
  human-autonomy, 862, 872–873
  interdependence in, 840
  job crafting in, 711, 720–721
  leadership and, 840, 868–869, 967–968
  learning and, 868
  location of, 840
  microdynamics in, 838
  optimal size of, 839
  organizational politics and power in, 965–967
  overview of, 830–834
  performance elements in, 964–968
  personality and, 839
  positive team leadership, 907–908
  processes of, 841–842, 868–869
  resilience among, 774
  roster changes in, 838–839
  safety processes of, 187–188
  safety-related characteristics of, 1485–1487
  shift towards, 880
  sociotechnical systems theory and, 686
  tasks of, in virtual teams, 866
  training, 847–848, 1179
  well-being and stress climate of, 1529–1530
teamwork
  action processes in, 842
  behavioral performance and, 845
  coaching in, 834
  cognition in, 834
  cognitive performance and, 845

  cohesion and, 843
  collective efficacy and, 843
  collective orientation and, 843
  communication and, 833–834, 964–965
  conflict in, 833, 965
  conflict management in, 833
  contextual moderators in, 846–847
  cooperation in, 833
  coordination in, 832–833
  definition of, 832–834
  emergent states in, 842–844
  encouraging, 849
  feedback for, 848
  IMOI framework for, 835*f*, 846–847, 850*t*
  inputs, 840–841, 850*t*, 859 n.1
  interpersonal processes in, 842
  interventions for, 847–848
  job attitudes and, 845
  measuring, 848–849
  mediators in, 842–844, 850*t*
  member characteristics in, 836–837
  multi-team systems and, 847
  outputs, 845–846, 850*t*
  psychological safety and, 843
  as recursive process, 845–846
  rewards and, 846
  shared mental models and, 844
  situation awareness and, 844
  task characteristics in, 840–841
  team characteristics in, 837–840
  team processes in, 841–842
  transactive memory system and, 844
  transition processes in, 841–842
  trust and, 843
  uncertainty and, 847
technological affordances, in mobile telework/remote
  work, 767–768
Tedeschi, J. T., 798*t*, 801–805, 801*t*
TEI (Tangible, Embedded, and Embodied Interaction), 741
The Telecommunications-Transportation Tradeoff (Nilles),
  755–756
telecommuting, 755–756
teleological ethical approaches, 53–54
telework, 986–989. *See also* remote work; virtual teams
  autonomy paradox and, 764
  challenges measuring, 717
  commuting impacts of, 770
  company benefits of, 771
  consequences of, 754
  costs and savings of, 770
  COVID-19 pandemic impact on, 719, 762, 771–773
  coworkers and, 768–769

cyberslacking and, 765–766
definitions of, 755–759, 755t
digital online, 755t, 758–762, 759f, 769
drivers of, 754, 762–763
in Europe, 718–720
gender and, 765
home-based, 755t, 756, 764–766
impacts of, 769–771
individual and organizational performance and,
770–771
leadership, managers and, 765, 772–773
mobile, 756–757, 766–769
motivation for, 762
prevalence of, 761–762
qualities of effective, 772
resilience and future of, 773–775
team members in, 758–759
technology enabling, 772
telecommuting and, 755–756
Toffler's vision of, 753–754, 757, 770
in United States and Canada, 719–720
Tellegen, A., 448
temporal design, 213–214, 222
temporal dynamics in organizational psychology.
See time in organizational psychology
temporal footprint of work, 280
temporal precedence, 213
temporarily switching rhythms, planned organizational
change and, 1564
temporary employment, 786, 1129. *See also* informal work
temptation, 59–61t
Tepper, Bennett, 920–922
Terman, Lewis, 8
terror management theory (TMT), 637
Tesser, A., 813
Tetlock, P. E., 798t
Tett, R. P., 212, 1146
T-groups (training groups), 12, 1623, 1632–1633
Thaler, R. H., 401–402
Thayer, P. W., 691, 693–694
theoretical description, analysis and, 319–320
theory-induced blindness, 111
Theory of Activity, 673–674
Theory of Planned Behavior (TPB), 218, 244–245,
1373–1374
Theory of Reasoned Action (TRA), 218
theory of work adjustment (TWA), 466–467
Theory X, 686
thermodynamics, generative emergence and, 1574–1575
Thibaut, J., 1065–1066
Thinking, Fast and Slow (Kahneman), 398
The Third Wave (Toffler), 753–754

third workplaces, 757, 768
Thomas, K. W., 1031
Thompson, R. A., 452–453
Thorndike, E. L., 8
Thorsrud, E., 80–81, 84, 86, 92
threatening situations, organizational responses to, 1558
threat-rigidity theory, organizational change and, 1558
three-way interaction models, 239–240
thriving
in PWO studies, 163
at work, positive psychology and, 1355
tidiness, conscientiousness and, 560
time, mobile workers and, 757
time-conscientiousness, 1368
time in organizational psychology
as construct or variable, 286–287, 287f
elapsed, 286
future of, 292–294
as future prediction, 284–288
importance of, 280
individual perceptions of, 284–285
leadership and, 285–286
management techniques for, 285–286
measurement of, 289
in methodology, 291–292
negative time aspects and, 284–285
objective, 281, 285–286, 293
organizational behavior theory and, 288–289
overview of, 280–281
research approaches to, 282–292, 283f
research shortcomings on, 280–281, 289–291
subjective, 281, 284–285, 293
synchrony preference and, 289–291
temporal change and issues of, 281–282
in theory, 288–291
working-time arrangements and restrictions and,
285–286
timeliness, 289–291
time management, 1403–1404
time-specific indirect effects, 213
timing, planned organizational change and, 1564
Tims, M., 709–710, 712t, 1233
TMS (transactive memory system), 844, 870
TMT (terror management theory), 637
TNA (training needs assessment), 1183–1185
TNDE (total natural direct effect), 221
TNIE (total natural indirect effect), 221
Tobin, R., 558
Toffler, Alvin, 753–754, 757, 770
Tofighi, D., 258
Tomprou, M., 289–291
top-down job redesign, 1358

1718 • INDEX

Tornow, W. W., 818
Tosti-Kharas, J., 1238
total indirect effects, 213
total natural direct effect (TNDE), 221
total natural indirect effect (TNIE), 221
Total Quality Management (TQM), 354
Total Worker Health™ (TWH™), 1384–1385,
  1533–1534
touching, unsolicited, 808
"tough love" leadership, 921
Toulouse, E., 19
Towne, Henry R., 5–6
TPB (Theory of Planned Behavior), 218, 244–245,
  1373–1374
TQM (Total Quality Management), 354
TRA (Theory of Reasoned Action), 218
training
  action regulation for, 105
  active learning in, 1179–1180
  adaptation, 1179
  age discrimination and, 641
  for autonomy, 1600
  behavioral objectives of, 1178
  challenges of, 1189
  characteristics of effective, 1179–1182
  core instructional processes in, 1182
  cross-cultural, 335
  definition of, 1177–1178
  diversity, 540–541
  effort in, 1181
  evaluation, 1188–1189
  evidence of effective, 1179
  feedback in, 1182
  HRM, globalization and, 334–335
  HRM and, 334–335, 1109
  interpersonal skill, 1454
  job skill, 1454
  learning and, 1177–1179
  managerial, 1179
  motivation for, 1184–1185
  opportunity to perform and, 1186
  overqualification and performance in, 1207
  overview of, 1177–1178
  in political skill, 497
  posttraining influences on, 1185–1188
  pretraining influences on, 1183–1185
  resilience, 186
  safety, 1490
  science of, 1178
  self-management, 422–423
  self-regulation in, 1180
  sensitivity, 1623, 1632–1633

  social support for, 1184–1187
  structure, 1180–1181
  systems for, 1182–1189
  team, 847–848, 1179
  transfer of, 1185–1188
training groups (T-groups), 12, 1623, 1632–1633
Training magazine, 1184
training motivation, older workers and, 618–619
training needs assessment (TNA), 1183–1185
Training Needs Assessment Phase, in TNA, 1183–1184
trait affectivity, 452
trajectory growth curve mediation models, 219
transactional framework, on stress, 1401–1402
transactional leadership, 126, 580, 1485–1486
transactional model of stress, 1343–1344
transactional psychological contracts, 627–628,
  1128–1129
transactional stress theory, 1162–1163
transaction cost economies, 996
transactive memory system (TMS), 844, 870
transferability, qualitative research standards for, 321t
transfer of training, 1185–1188
transformational leadership, 126, 580, 1485–1486
transgender workers. *See* sexual and gender minorities
transition, retirement, 1254–1255, 1263–1265
transition processes, in teamwork, 841–842
translation, in qualitative research, 302, 320
Treaty of Rome, 10–11
triangulating multiple sources of evidence, 27–28, 30
triggering events, sense-making and, 1002–1003
Trist, Eric L., 12, 78–80, 83, 1503–1504, 1623–1624
Troth, A. C., 452–453
troublesome peers, 985–986
trust
  conflict management and development of, 1033–1034
  KSAOs related to, 866–867
  mutual, 1033
  in OD consultation, 1626–1627
  social exchange theory and, 1034
  teamwork and, 843
  virtual teams and, 869
trust-worthiness, 38–39
  cross-cultural IWOP, globalization and, 360–362
  qualitative research standards for, 321t
The Truth about Burnout (Maslach & Leiter), 1292–1293,
  1451
Tsoukas, H., 1002
Tukey corrections, 233
Turing, Alan, 744
turnover
  downward communication and, 979–980
  job insecurity and, 1167

overqualification and, 1209
  well-being and, 1531
Tversky, Amos, 14, 392–396, 399
TWA (theory of work adjustment), 466–467
TWH™ (Total Worker Health™), 1384–1385,
  1533–1534
2-1-1 multilevel mediation model, 265*f*, 266–268, 267*t*
2-2-1 multilevel mediation model, 265*f*, 266, 267*t*
two-factor theory of motivation, 686–687, 961
"tyranny of negativity," 160

Uber, 1556
UBI (universal basic income), 196
ubiquitous computing, 730, 739
Ulrich, D., 1117
uncertainty
  in environments, 997–998
  generative emergence and, 1580
  justice perceptions and, 1069–1070
  justice reducing, 1072
  resilience and, 1488
  social comparison and, 814–816
  teamwork and, 847
unconditional model, 256–258
unconventional alternatives, in generative emergence,
  1581
underemployment
  in humanitarian work and organizational psychology,
    194
  overqualification as, 1195–1196
  of young workers, 603
under-investment, 1136
unemployment, 184
  in humanitarian work and organizational
    psychology, 194
  overqualification and history of, 1203
  young workers and, 595–596
unemployment-to-work transitions, 1235–1236
unethical behavior, 57
  intentional, 57
  rudeness, incivility compared to, 57–58
unethical leadership, 943–944
unethical pro-organizational behaviors (UPBs), 436
"unfreezing" organizations, 1635–1636
unilateral adaptation, 1130
uninformative priors, 216
unintentional organizational learning, 1560–1561
United Nations
  Convention on the Rights of Persons with a Disability,
    668
  Global Compact, 189
  Human Rights Council, 659–660

millennium development goals of, 185, 187
  Sustainable Development Goals of, 185, 188,
    363–364, 787
  WCED, 1082–1083
United States
  QWL studies in, 1504–1505
  telework/remote work in, 719–720
  work and family and laws of, 1369–1370
universal basic income (UBI), 196
Universal Declaration of Ethical Principles for
  Psychologists (Universal Declaration), 50
  specificity in, 56
universalism, 51
  in ethics, 51–52
  nonmaleficence and, 51–52
universalizability, in ethics, 52
universities, authority for change in, 1555
University of Michigan, 1624–1625
unlearning, intentional, 1561
unsolicited touching, 808
unstructured interviews, 1148
UPBs (unethical pro-organizational behaviors), 436
upward-and-downward comparisons, 818–819
upward communication
  concept of, 982–984
  dissent and, 984
  distortion and, 983–984
  equivocation and, 983–984
  organizational silence and, 983
  telework and, 988
upward mobility, overqualification and, 1208
usability, in HCI, 739
user experience, in HCI, 739–740
US Society for Occupational Health Psychology
  (SOHP), 1339–1340
USSR, OP in, 17–18
utilitarianism, 53–54
Utrecht Work Engagement Scale (UWES), 1293
  detractors of, 1293–1294
  introduction of, 1294
  job demands-resources model using, 1297
  subscales of, 1295, 1298
  wide-spread use of, 1293–1295

valence-expectancy theory, 280–281
value chain, 1556
value-focused thinking, 403–404
value in diversity, 538–539
values
  conflict, 59–61*t*
  congruence and CSR, 1088–1089
  core, generative emergence and, 1582

values (*continued*)
  in decision-making, 14
  definition of, 74 n.2
  educators and, 63
  ethics and, 55–56
  importance of, 55
  new order linked to, in generative emergence, 1583
  organizational behavior and employee, 957–958
  organizational change and, 1561
  well-being and priorities of, 149
values-driven, 1219–1221
"value the feminine" strategy, 584
Van der Heijde, C. M., 1230–1231
Van der Heijden, B. I. J. M., 1225–1226, 1230–1231
Van der Laan, V., 815–816
Vantilborgh, T., 289–291
Van Vianen, A. E., 469–471
Van Yperen, N. W., 1344–1345
variability, in learning, 1181
variance-covariance components, of multilevel
      models, 256
variation, in population-level learning, 1559
variety, diversity and, 537–538
Vella-Brodrick, D. A., 712*t*
vicarious learning, 422–423
victim precipitation theory, 1435
video games, in HCI, 742
Vietnam War, 14
Vinchur, A. J., 1140
virtual organization, 969
virtual teams
  defining and measuring, 861–863
  definition of, 755*t*
  effectiveness of, 871–872
  emergent states in, 869–871
  feedback and, 868–869
  future research on, 873–874
  geographic dispersion of, 861–862
  HATs and, 872–873
  ICTs in, 863–866, 864*f*
  IMOI framework for effectiveness of, 863–871, 864*f*
  leadership and, 868–869
  learning and adaptation on, 868
  members of, 758–759
  mobile, 758–759
  motivation and, 871
  practical implications of, 873
  relevance of, 860–861
  shared mental models and, 870–871
  situational demands in, 867
  team members' KSAOs in, 866–867
  team perceived virtuality and, 862

team processes in, 868–869
team tasks in, 866
transactive memory system and, 870
trust and, 869
virtue (aretaic) theory, 54
virtuous approach to ethical dilemmas, 67
virtuous universal values, 910
Vitamin Model of well-being, 673–674
  additional decrement (AD) in, 143*f*, 144
  affective disposition and, 148
  age and, 148
  attention deployment in, 151–152
  constant effect (CE) in, 143*f*, 144
  degree of adaptation and, 150–151
  emotion regulation and, 151–153
  environmental sources of well-being in, 142–147,
      142*t*, 143*f*
  gender and, 148
  inherited differences in, 147–148
  job design and, 689–690
  personal differences in, 147–153, 147*f*
  personality traits and, 149–150
  personal resources in, 698
  positive and negative perspectives in, 140
  reappraisal in, 153
  scope of, 140
  situation selection and modification in, 151
  stimulus-outcome relationships in, 141
  subsequent behavior in, 153
  value priorities and, 149
vocational development theory, 1218, 1228
vocational fit theory, 466–467
Vogtenhuber, S., 1200–1201
volatility, uncertainty, complexity, and ambiguity
      (VUCA), 333
Volvo case, sociotechnical approach and, 90–91, 1503
voting behavior, job insecurity and, 1169
Vroom, Victor, 15
VUCA (volatility, uncertainty, complexity, and
      ambiguity), 333
vulnerable narcissism, 509, 517–518
vulnerable victim, 1435

wage intervals, in humanitarian work and organizational
      psychology, 191–193
wage precarity, informal work and, 782–783
wages, overqualification and, 1206–1207. *See also*
      compensation
Wagner, J. A., III, 115
Walden Two (Skinner), 14–15
Walker, L., 1065–1066
Wall, T., 89

Walsh, J. P., 167
Walton, R., 1499, 1509
Wang, M., 341, 1261, 1264–1265
warmth
    in SCM, 574, 621–622
    in stereotype content model, 621–622
Warner, William Lloyd, 9–10
Warr, P. B., 673–674, 690–691, 693–695. *See also* Vitamin
    Model of well-being
Washington Post, 1274
Waterman, R. H., 996
Watson, D., 448
Watson, J. B., 8
Wayne, S. J., 801*t*, 802–803, 1300
WCED (World Commission on Environment and
    Development), 1082–1083
weak invariance, 243–244
The Wealth of Nations (Smith, A.), 684–685
Weber, Max, 6–7
Weick, K. E., 14, 996, 1001, 1004–1005, 1008
Welch, C., 93–94
welfare, definition of, 50
welfare state, 10
well-being, 140. *See also* Vitamin Model of well-being
    Adaptation-Level Theory and, 1523
    AET and, 1523–1524
    affective disposition and, 148, 1517–1518
    age and, 148
    ambivalence and, 141
    antecedents of, 1525–1528
    attention deployment in, 151–152
    broaden-and-build theory and, 1522–1523
    collective, 1524–1525
    context-free, 143, 143*f*, 145–146
    cross-level and multilevel antecedents of, 1528–1530
    cross-level and multilevel outcomes of, 1531–1532
    definition of, 1505–1506
    degree of adaptation and, 150–151
    domain-specific, 141–142, 145
    emotion regulation and, 151–153
    environmental sources of, 142–147, 142*t*, 143*f*, 689
    eudaimonic, 141, 1519–1520, 1527–1528
    feature-specific, 145
    financial, 1261
    flourishing, 141
    flow and, 1519–1520
    future research on, 1535–1536
    gender and, 148
    happiness compared to, 141
    happy-productive worker thesis on, 1521–1522
    health and, 1531
    hedonic, 141, 1517–1518, 1526–1529

    home-based telework/remote work and, 766
    individual strategies for, 1535–1536
    inherited differences in, 147–148
    intervention to improve, 1535–1536
    in JD-R model, 690
    job characteristics and, 1525–1528
    job design and, 695–696
    job performance and, 1521–1522, 1528–1531
    leadership and, 1526–1528
    life satisfaction and, 1517
    need satisfaction and, 131–132
    occupational stress impact on, 1340–1343, 1341*t*
    organizational climate and, 1529–1530
    organizational dehumanization's impact on,
        1466–1467
    organizational strategies for, 1535–1536
    outputs and consequences of, 1531–1532
    overqualification and, 1205–1206
    overview of, 1515, 1516*f*
    personal differences in, 147–153, 147*f*
    personality and individual, 1526–1528
    personality traits and, 149–150
    physical, 1261
    physical-oriented strategies for, 1532–1533
    promotion strategies, 1534–1535
    protection strategies, 1534–1535
    psychosocial, 1261
    psychosocial-oriented strategies for, 1532–1534
    psychosocial safety climate and, 1530
    purpose and meaning at work and, 1518–1519
    quality of working life and, 1505–1507
    reappraisal in, 153
    during retirement, 1261
    rewarding activities and, 1519–1520
    SDT research outcomes on, 131–132
    self-determination theory and, 1524
    situation selection and modification in, 151
    subjective, 1516
    subsequent behavior in, 153
    team affective climate and, 1524–1525
    team stress climate and, 1529–1530
    theories on work and, 1520–1524
    turnover and, 1531
    value priorities and, 149
    withdrawal behavior and, 1531
    at work, 1515–1516
    working conditions and, 1525–1526
    worthwhile activities and, 1519
Well-Being Game, 1535
wellness programs, 1417–1418, 1534
Weseler, D., 712*t*
West, C., 535

1722 • INDEX

WFC. *See* work-family conflict

WFH (working from home), 773. *See also* remote work; telework

Whatever Happened to Shell's New Philosophy of Management? (Blackler and Brown, C.), 1503–1504

Wheeler, L., 813

White, R. K., 11

Whitman, D. S., 885–888

WHO (World Health Organization), 1505–1506

Whyte, W. H., Jr., 14–15

Whyte, William F., 12

WIF (work-family interference), 1355–1356, 1398–1399

Wiley, N., 1000

Williams Institute, 649

Wilpert, Bernhard, 18

W-I-O psychology. *See* organizational psychology

withdrawal behavior, well-being and, 1531

witnesses, abusive supervision effects on, 927

Wittenberg-Cox, A., 583–584

Wizard of Oz technique, HCI and, 738

women. *See* gender in organizations

Wood, D. J., 1082

Woodworth, Robert S., 8

WOP. *See* work and organizational psychology

WOP-P (work, organizational and personnel psychology), 187

Work, Family, and Health Network (WFHN), 1384

work, organizational and personnel psychology (WOP-P), 187

workaholism, work engagement and, 1295–1296, 1300

work alienation
    organizational dehumanization and, 1465–1466
    QWL and, 1502

work and family
    adaptation theory and, 1373–1374
    affective events theory on, 1373–1374
    antecedents related to, 1378–1379
    balance, 1376–1377
    border theory on, 1372
    boundary theory on, 1372
    conservation of resources theory on, 1371
    constructs related to, 1376–1377
    effort-recovery theory on, 1373
    flextime and, 1383
    formal support for, 1382
    future directions in, 1384–1386
    gender and, 1368–1369, 1377
    history and current state of, 1368–1370
    informal support for, 1382–1383
    integration/segmentation preferences for, 1372–1373
    integrative work-family systems model, 1371
    interventions, 1383–1384

    older workers and issues in, 1369
    organizational support for needs of, 1382–1385
    outcomes related to, 1381–1382
    overview of, 1368
    PE fit and, 1373
    personnel selection and issues of, 1385–1386
    role theory on, 1370–1371
    social exchange theory on, 1373
    systems theory on, 1371
    technology and, 1369
    theories related to, 1372–1374
    theory of planned behavior and, 1373–1374
    United States laws and, 1369–1370
    work-family conflict, 1355–1356, 1374–1381, 1398–1399
    work-family enrichment, 1356, 1374–1376, 1378–1379, 1381–1382
    work-family interference, 1355–1356
    work-home resources model and, 1371–1372

work and organizational psychology (WOP). *See also* humanitarian work and organizational psychology; positive work and organization studies
    administrators of, 66
    definition of, 49
    educators and, 62–63
    employee assistance programs and, 187
    ethics in, 49–70
    ethics survey data from, 58–62
    HRM and, 1105–1107
    multiple work roles in, 62
    practitioners of, 64–66
    researchers and, 63–64

work attitudes. *See* job attitudes

"work centers," 671–672

work design. *See also* job crafting; job design
    in action regulation, 104–105
    definition of, 683–684, 708
    IWD model and, 692–695, 693*f*
    sociotechnical approach to work organization and, 80–82

work efficiency studies, 9

work engagement, 166. *See also* Maslach Burnout Inventory; Utrecht Work Engagement Scale
    burnout and, 1293
    concept of, 1293–1294
    dark side of, 1300–1301
    interventions to improve, 1298–1300
    job crafting and, 1299–1300
    job demands-resources model and, 1297–1298, 1527–1528
    measuring, 1294–1296
    organizational behavior and, 956–957

overview of, 1292–1293
psychological connections with, 1295–1296
workaholism and, 1295–1296, 1300
workers, employees compared to, 781. *See also* informal work
work-family conflict (WFC), 1355–1356
   antecedents to, 1377–1379
   boundary management and, 1378
   outcomes related to, 1380–1381
   safety and, 1380–1381
   stressors and, 1398–1399
   work-family enrichment compared to, 1374–1376
work-family enrichment, 1356
   antecedents of, 1378–1379
   outcomes related to, 1381–1382
   work-family conflict compared to, 1374–1376
work-family interference (WIF), 1355–1356, 1398–1399
Workforce (Johnston and Packer), 541
work groups, 80–82
work-home resources model, 1371–1372, 1385
work hours, 1368–1369
work-industrial-organizational psychology.
   See organizational psychology
working conditions
   hedonic well-being and, 1525–1526
   organizational interventions for, 1596–1597
working from home (WFH), 773. *See also* remote work; telework
working objectification, 1464–1465
working-time arrangements and restrictions, 285–286
work in the informal economy, 786–787
worklife profiles, 1449–1451
workload, as stressor, 1398
work motivation. *See* motivation
work-nonwork conflict
   cross-cultural IWOP and, 359
   home-based telework/remote work and, 765
work-nonwork interface, 1237–1238
work performance. *See* job performance
workplace. See also *specific topics*
   age diversity in, 624
   diversity in, 537–538, 545
   intelligence in, 552–553
   Machiavellianism in, 510–513
   narcissism in, 508–510
   physical environment of, 969
   political skill and outcomes in, 490–495
   psychopathy in, 513–516
   SDT on motivation at, 123–125, 124f
   SDT research in, 134–135
workplace bullying, 920. *See also* abusive supervision; workplace harassment

antecedents and risk factors for, 1431–1433
behavioral experience approach to, 1430
bystanders and observers of, 1437
concept of, 1426–1427
consequences and outcomes of, 1431
definition of, 1427
dispute-related bullying, 1432
future research on, 1436–1438
as gradually escalating process, 1428
individual risk factors for, 1435–1436
intent in, 1428–1429
interpersonal conflict and, 1432–1433
leader bullying and, 921
leadership, managers and, 1434–1435
measuring, 1429–1430
mental health and, 1431
overview of, 1426
personality and, 1435–1436
power imbalance in, 1428
predatory bullying, 1432
prevalence of, 1426
provocative victim and, 1435
role ambiguity, role conflict and, 1433–1434
self-labeling approach to, 1429–1430
target or perpetrator focus of, 1427–1428
vulnerable victim and, 1435
work pressure and, 1434
work-related risk factors for, 1434–1435
Workplace Bullying Institute, 920
workplace harassment. *See also* workplace bullying
   concept of, 1426–1427
   future research on, 1436–1438
   as gradually escalating process, 1428
   intent in, 1428–1429
   measuring, 1429–1430
   occupational stress and, 1349–1350
   overview of, 1426
   power imbalance in, 1428
   prevalence of, 1426
   target or perpetrator focus of, 1427–1428
   types of, 1426
workplace health promotion programs, 1534
workplace mistreatment, 1397–1398
workplace safety
   overview of, 1351–1353, 1480–1482
   physical hazards and, 1351
   psychological research framework for, 1481, 1481f
   safety climate and, 1352–1353
   safety leadership and, 1353
work precariousness. *See* precarious work
work pressure, 966, 1426
   workplace bullying and, 1434

work psychology. *See* organizational psychology
work rationalization, 10
work-related stress. *See* occupational stress; stress
work sample tests, 1149
work stress. *See* occupational stress
work-to-family conflict (WTFC), 1377–1381, 1383
work-to-family enrichment (WTFE), 1379, 1381–1382
work-to-retirement transitions, 1236–1237
work-to-work transitions, 1235–1236
World Commission on Environment and Development (WCED), 1082–1083
World Employment and Social Outlook Trends, 779
World Health Organization (WHO), 1505–1506
World Report on Disability, 667
World War I, 8–9
World War II, 10
worthwhile activities, well-being and, 1519
Wright, Sewall, 208
Wrzesniewski, A., 709–713, 715
WTFC (work-to-family conflict), 1377–1381, 1383
WTFE (work-to-family enrichment), 1379, 1381–1382
Wundt, Wilhelm, 4, 18–19, 353

X-Y theory of motivation, 961

Yacht Club simulation, 379–382
Yahiaoui, D., 336
Yanar, B., 115–116
Yao, X., 1252–1253
Ybema, J. F., 820–821, 823–824
Yela, M., 19
Yerkes, Robert M., 8, 353
yielding behavior, 1029
yoga, 1454

Yom Kippur War, 14
young workers
   age stereotypes of, 598, 636
   automation and, 603
   career competencies and, 597–601
   career identity and, 600
   digital literacy of, 598, 603
   discrimination against, 642
   education level of, 598
   future research directions on, 603–604
   generational differences and, 601–603
   global importance of, 595
   human capital and, 597–598
   indecision of, 600–601
   know-how and, 597–598
   know-whom and, 598–600
   know-why and, 600–601
   life-span developmental theories and, 597
   motivations of, 601–603
   nonstandard employment of, 596
   overqualification and, 1202
   school-to-work transitions for, 596
   self-efficacy and, 599
   social capital and, 598–599
   trends of, 595–596
   underemployment of, 603
   unemployment and, 595–596
yo-yos, 757

Zacher, H., 293
Zhang, F., 710–711, 714–716
Zhou, J., 1305–1306
Zijlstra, F. R. H., 673–674
Zimmerman, D. H., 535
Zurriaga, R., 823–824